SECONDARY ION MASS SPECTROMETRY

SIMS XII

SECONDARY ION MASS SPECTROMETRY SIMS XII

Proceedings of the Twelfth International Conference on
Secondary Ion Mass Spectrometry (SIMS XII),
Université Catholique de Louvain, Brussels, Belgium,
September 5-10, 1999

Editors

A. BENNINGHOVEN, P. BERTRAND, H-N. MIGEON and H.W. WERNER

2000

ELSEVIER
Amsterdam - Lausanne - New York - Oxford - Shannon - Singapore - Tokyo

ELSEVIER SCIENCE B.V.
Sara Burgerhartstraat 25
P.O. Box 211, 1000 AE Amsterdam, The Netherlands

First edition 2000

Library of Congress Cataloging in Publication Data
A catalog record from the Library of Congress has been applied for.

ISBN: 0-444-50323-4

Foreword

This volume contains 242 papers presented as plenary, invited keynotes and contributed oral and posters presentations at the Twelfth International Conference on Secondary Ion Mass Spectrometry (SIMS XII) held on the Brussels' campus of the Université Catholique de Louvain, September 5-10th, 1999.

The Université Catholique de Louvain is one of the oldest universities in Europe. It was founded in 1425 and can boast a number of famous names among its past students: the philosopher Erasmus, the anatomist Vesalius, the geographer Mercator and the physicist Lemaître. The University nowadays counts more than 20,000 students and 5,000 staff members. Its main location is in Louvain-la-neuve, 25 km south of Brussels.

This biennal conference series is the first international forum covering the recent developments in Secondary Ion Mass Spectrometry. All aspects of the most recent developments in SIMS were covered by the scientific program: fundamentals, instrumentation, methodology, and analytical applications in different fields (semiconductor, polymer and organic materials, life sciences, environmental sciences, earth sciences, materials science). Related techniques and topics were also included.

Over 400 hundred participants from 32 different countries attended the conference. The scientific program included two plenary lectures, 10 invited keynote lectures, 330 contributions shared between oral and poster presentations and one workshop. The two plenary lectures opened up the field in two new and challenging directions. J. S. Murday introduced us to "Nanostructures - an exciting journey from science to technology" and M. C. Davies gave a talk on "Understanding the interfacial chemistry of surface engineered biomaterials". The workshop, followed by a panel discussion, addressed the future key issue in SIMS instrumentation for microelectronics: Whole-wafer and in-line-SIMS. An exhibition of SIMS instrumentation, components, data systems, analytical services and library gathered 15 exhibitors.

A number of people contributed a lot to the organization of SIMS XII in order to make this conference a real success. We would like to give special thanks to the local organizing committee and our local colleagues: Brigitte Bertau, Jean-Michel Beuken and Sadia Benyoub for all their time to organize the conference secretariat and to prepare all the documents; Chantal De Laey, for taking charge of all the local arrangements and the social program; Claude Poleunis, for organizing the conference exhibition; Xavier Vanden Eynde, for taking charge, with the help of Michel Lefèvre and Bahia Arezki, of all the technical details during the conference; and Laurent Houssiau, for organizing the poster sessions. We are especially indebted to Prof. Helmut Werner, who took upon himself the huge job of organizing the preparation of these proceedings.

vi

We would like to acknowledge Prof. Alfred Benninghoven and the other members of the International SIMS committee for giving us the opportunity to organize and host this conference.

We would like to thank also the SIMS Scientific Committee and the International Advisory Board for helping us in preparing this first class scientific program. We would like also to acknowledge the agencies, organizations and companies who contributed financially to support the SIMS XII conference.

We would like also to thank the chairpersons of the oral sessions and the workshop, the invited speakers, the contributors of scientific papers, the reviewers of the manuscripts and, finally, all the participants who helped to make this conference so memorable and so successful.

Patrick Bertrand and Henri-Noël Migeon,
SIMS XII Local Chairmen

INTERNATIONAL ORGANIZING COMMITTEE

A. Benninghoven (Chairman)	Münster, Germany
V. T. Cherepin	Kiev, Ukraine
C. A. Evans	Redwood City, CA, USA
Y. Nihei	Tokyo, Japan
G. Slodzian	Paris, France
H. W. Werner	Vienna, Austria
P. Williams	Tempe, AZ, USA

LOCAL ORGANIZING COMMITTEE

B. Bertau (Conference Secretariat)	UCL Louvain-la-Neuve, Belgium
P. Bertrand (Co-Chairman)	UCL Louvain-la-Neuve, Belgium
J.-M. Beuken (Data Processing)	UCL Louvain-la-Neuve, Belgium
Ch. De Laey (Local Arrangements)	UCL Brussels, Belgium
H.- N. Migeon (Co-Chairman)	CRP-CU Luxembourg
C. Poleunis (Exhibition)	UCL Louvain-la-Neuve, Belgium
W. Vandervorst	IMEC Leuven, Belgium
H. W. Werner (Proceedings Manager)	TU Vienna, Austria

SCIENTIFIC COMMITTEE

A. Benninghoven (Chairman)	Münster, Germany
P. Bertrand	Louvain-la-Neuve, Belgium
S. Corcoran	Hillsboro OR, USA
H.- N. Migeon	Luxembourg
Y. Nihei	Tokyo, Japan
J. Vickerman	Manchester, United Kingdom
W. Vandervorst	IMEC Leuven, Belgium

INTERNATIONAL ADVISORY BOARD

Cha Liangzhen (China)	S. Pignataro (Italy)
M. Chaussidon (France)	B. Ratner (USA)
R. von Criegern (Germany)	F. G. Rüdenauer (Austria)
M. Dowsett (United Kingdom)	D. Simons (USA)
R. Gijbels (Belgium)	N. Winograd (USA)
M. Kudo (Japan)	K. Wittmaack (Germany)
H.–J. Mathieu, (Switzerland)	P. C. Zalm (The Netherlands)
Ming L. Yu (China)	

CONTENTS

Section 2:   SECONDARY ION FORMATION

Section 3: CLUSTER FORMATION

Section 4: MOLECULAR FRAGMENT EMISSION

Section 5: FOCUSED ION BEAMS

Section 6: CLUSTER/MOLECULAR ION BEAMS

Section 7:
POST-IONIZATION, SPUTTERED NEUTRAL MASS SPECTROMETRY

Section 8: DATA PROCESSING

xiv

Section 9: QUANTIFICATION

Section 10 : SURFACE ANALYSIS

Section 11: DEPTH PROFILING

Section 12 : SEMICONDUCTORS / MICROELECTRONICS

Section 13 : ORGANIC MATERIALS / POLYMERS

Section 14 : MATERIALS SCIENCE

Section 15 : LIFE SCIENCES

Section 18 : COMBINATION WITH OTHER TECHNIQUES

PLENARY LECTURE

A. Benninghoven, P. Bertrand, H.-N. Migeon and H.W. Werner (Editors).
Proceedings of the 12th International Conference on Secondary Ion Mass Spectrometry,
Brussels, Belgium, 5-11 September 1999

NANOTECHNOLOGY: OPPORTUNITY AND CHALLENGE

J.S.Murday

Code 6100, Naval Research Laboratory, Washington DC 20375.
murday@ccf.nrl.navy.mil

1. Introduction

Nanotechnology is not a new phenomenon. A glaze used by ancient Grecian potters derived its color from nanometer-sized particles; the chemical industry has devoted considerable resources in the development of nanometer- sized catalysts; photographic film relies on the nucleation and growth of Ag nanocrystals.

Why then the current enthusiasm over the science and technology of nanostructures? [1-3]. In the past, technological uses of nanostructures relied heavily on empiricism for their development. The ability to measure and manipulate nanostructures - a prerequisite for detailed scientific understanding - is a recent and rapidly developing capability.

One might argue that the surface and thin film sciences, with their reduction of one dimension to the nanometer scale, were the first major step in the development of nanoscience. Surface/thin film sciences burgeoned in the 1960s and 70s. Those fields were enabled by the developments in ultra-high vacuum (UHV) that preserved carefully prepared surface states. UHV also enabled the panoply of surface spectroscopies / microscopies that measured the composition, structure and properties of the surface and changed empiricism into fundamental understanding. Those surface analytical tools required vacuum so that the mean free path of electrons, ions and atoms is sufficiently long to enable various energy/momentum analyzers.

As surface science matured, it began to look for ways to analyze smaller areas; Auger electron spectroscopy, secondary ion mass spectrometry, scanning electron microscopy and other techniques evolved into microanalytical tools. With 10-1000 nm lateral resolution, these tools were the first nanostructure probes. But it was the development of the proximal probes – such as STM and AFM, analytical tools that derive their capability to analyze nanometer-sized features by virtue of proximity between a tip and feature -– that stimulated the current emphasis on science of nanostructures. The proximal probes provide the fingers and eyes to manipulate and measure nanostructures all the way down to the atomic scale and do so in vacuum, liquid or ambient conditions.

While analytical capability is a necessary component, the drive toward nano-technology must be stimulated by additional reasons. First, the science community is ready.

Solid state physics and chemistry are more than 50 years old and have been addressing the one-dimensional case (surfaces/interfaces) for thirty years. From clean, flat and cold in the late 1960s, by the late 80s surface science was addressing the nucleation/growth of adsorbate multilayers on vicinal surfaces. Second, the rapid evolution of computational power has made possible the first principles calculations of nanometer-sized structures. Third, the models developed to understand many bulk material properties have critical scale lengths in the nanometer range. This means that nanostructures will not behave according to the model predictions; scientific opportunities abound. Fourth, economic incentives are high, the microelectronics industry is miniaturizing into nanometer-sized devices [4]. To continue the phenomenal improvements in information technology (and the economic consequences) experienced in the last twenty years through miniaturization, it will be necessary to harness nanostructures. Equally compelling, another economic engine – biotechnology – depends on nanometer structures [5,6].

2. R&D Recommendations from the Workshop on Nano-Science, Engineering and Technology

The U.S. Interagency Working Group on Nano-Science, Engineering and Technology hosted a study [1] and a workshop to examine the status and likely impact of "nanotechnology". One result of the workshop was identification of fundamental research opportunities and the several "Grand Challenges" listed in Table 1.

Table 1
Nano-Science, Engineering and Technology Grand Challenges

Nanostructured materials "by-design"
Nano-electronics, optoelectronics and magnetics
Healthcare
Bio-nanodevices for detection and mitigation of threats to humans
Nanoscale processes for energy and environment
Microspacecraft

The fundamental research opportunities emphasize the multidisciplinary aspects of nanostructures. They include: discovering and eventually tailoring the novel phenomena of individual and ensembled nanostructures; creating new instruments to measure/manipulate; synthesis/processing of nanostructure building blocks and their potential for self-organization; complement (and supplant) molecular-ensemble averages with single molecule measurements; link physics, chemistry and biology to accelerate progress in understanding living systems; and exploit the capability for both modeling/simulation and experiment to simultaneously address nanostructures quantitatively.

The nanostructured material "grand challenge" research opportunities begin with the need to fabricate quality, individual nanostructures, including techniques to scale-up the fabrication to commercially-viable quantities. Characterization of properties must begin with the individual particle, but then progress to nanostructure networks and matrix isolated nanostructures where near-neighbor interactions modify the properties. Both composites (matrix filled with nanostructure) and compacts (compacted nanostructures with interfacial composition/structure playing a major role) offer macroscopic manifestations of nanostructured materials with innovative properties. Composites and compacts offer enhanced possibility for mixed materials tailored to meet multifunctional demands. High surface area materials provide another perspective—they are thin (nanometer) layers separated by open space. Zeolites and zerogels are examples.

The Semiconductor Industry Association road-map projects the advent of nanoelectronics in 2010-2015. The shift from microelectronics to nanoelectronics, if it is possible, is likely to be as revolutionary as the shift from vacuum tube to transistor. Major problems must be solved. Innovations in manufacture must be found to make nanofabrication affordable. The magnetic, electronic, optic and other properties of nanostructures must be established; their properties will likely be very different than in microstructures. Those new properties must then be incorporated into devices that can serve a useful role in information processing. Finally, it is likely that new system architectures will be necessary, to solve the growing device interconnect problem, if for no other reason.

Concern for the environment may be addressed through new high surface area materials for separation and complexation. New manufacturing techniques, such as self-assembly or compaction, may produce less waste than our present approaches to hacking away material to reach a desired shape. Energy is a related challenge, with the projections for diminishing petroleum resources in 2010-2020 providing additional incentive. Nanostructures should impact solar energy conversion, fuel cell efficiency (catalyst, membrane), and reduction in materials friction/wear/corrosion/fatigue (failure mechanisms generally initiate at the nanoscale).

Microspacecraft provides an imaginative focus for innovations emanating from the above challenges. Spacecraft demands on materials are extreme - radiation resistant, light yet strong, capable of large temperature extremes, etc. The volume limitations and need for on-board intelligence compel miniaturization of electronics simultaneously with power reduction. Solar conversion as a prime energy source will be stretched on missions away from the sun. Chemical energy need be expended with greatest efficiency and might be provided by consumption of material from multifunctional structures (strength for lift-off, fuel for space).

The final challenges – medicine and human performance - focus on living systems. Living systems originate in the chemistry/physics of nanometer sized biomolecules. The polynucleic acids (DNA), polypeptides (proteins), and polysaccharides governing living systems derive their properties from topologies and dynamics on nanometer scales. The ability to manipulate and measure individual molecules will accelerate the already phenomenal advances in molecular biology. For instance, protein folding is considered a "grand challenge" of molecular biology; the tools of nanoscience are up to that challenge. The evolution of MicroElectroMechanical Systems (MEMS) into NanoElectroMechanical Systems (NEMS) will provide sense/dispense capabilities in a size compatible with in-vivo applications. Techniques for rapid DNA sequencing will provide individualized drug therapies and eventual DNA repair.

6

3. Chemical Spectroscopy of Nanostructures

Since their genesis in the early 1980's, the progress in proximal probes has been impressive. There are three generally recognized classes [7] Scanning Tunneling Microscopy/Spectroscopy (STM/S) that depends on electron tunneling from tip to structure, Force Microscopy/Spectroscopy that depends on the displacement of a small cantilever by forces between a tip and structure, and Near Field Microscopy/Spectroscopy that exploits the absence of diffraction limits constraining far-field electromagnetic imaging. The proximal probe capabilities are extensive and well covered in the literature [8 –14]. However, one of their main deficiencies is the paucity of chemical information. Much of nanometer science is done under carefully controlled conditions where the elemental composition of a structure is limited. Under these conditions, it is frequently possible to differentiate between the elements. However, presented a totally unknown nanostructure, the analytical chemist has few tools capable of identifying composition.

The workhorse tools of analytical chemistry – mass spectrometry for mass; UV/vis, Ultraviolet Photoelectron Spectroscopy for valence electron density-of-states; X-ray Photoelectron Spectroscopy, Auger Electron Spectroscopy, Electron Loss Spectroscopy, X-ray Emission Spectroscopy for core electronic states; IR/Raman for vibrational states; and Magnetic Resonance for spin states – have microprobe capability. They have analogues in the proximal probes but with significant limitations, as might be expected as the number of atoms being analyzed gets small. A delineation of microprobe and proximal probe chemical analysis tools is in Table 2.

Table 2

Chemical Microprobes and *Nanoprobes*

Technique	Instrument	SOA resolution
Mass	TOF-SIMS*	0.1 μm
	Scanning Tunneling Atom Probe	1 nm
Vibration	micro-FTIR*	5 μm
	Scanning Tunneling Spectroscopy	1 nm
	Tip-induced Sum Frequency Generation	1 nm
Magnetic resonance	Magnetic Resonance Imaging	0.1 mm
	Magnetic Force	0.1 μm
Valence electron	UV/vis	1 μm
	Scanning Tunneling Spectroscopy	1 nm
	Near-Field Scanning Optical	10 nm
Core electron	Field Emission Auger*	<15 nm
	Photoelectron Emission Microscope	20 nm
	SEM/Energy Dispersive Spectroscopy*	1 μm
	Field Emission Scanning Auger	10 nm
Force	*Chemical Force Microscopy*	10 nm

* Data from Charles Evans & Associates home page: http://www.cea.com.table.htm
Italicized techniques are based on proximal probe technology.

For the measurement of mass, a scanning tunneling atom probe (STAP) time-of-flight spectrometer has been developed by Weierstall and Spence [15]. The STAP is an STM that allows atomic clusters of interest to be relayed from surface to tip to time-of-flight spectrometer for species identification. The technique has successfully detected Ge clusters on Si. Nishikawa [16,17] has developed a scanning atom probe (SAP) that utilizes special extraction optics to mass analyze the apex of microprotrusions on a surface. The experiments with both the SAP and STAP yield counts in multiple tens of ions; single atom/molecule sensitivity has not been demonstrated. A third approach to mass measurement, thus far successful only with much larger structures, has been to measure a mass by its effect on the resonant frequency of a microfabricated cantilever. As cantilevers are made smaller [18], one of the goals set out for NanoElectroMechanical Systems (NEMS), cantilever resonant frequencies of GHz with Q's of 10^4 may enable measurements of $<10^5$ atom clusters.

Since mass spectrometry is generally the instrument of choice for trace analysis, it is interesting to analyze the requirements for mass analyzing a single nanostructure. First, the structure must be extracted with unit efficiency. This requirement is ameliorated when the extraction tool (tip) can be used to image the surface and confirm successful extraction. Second, the nanostructure must be injected as an ion into the mass analyzer. Field ionization from a tip will yield ions with high probability, but the nanoparticle must be at the apex of the tip. Migration away from the apex has been postulated as one explanation for STAP failure to observe Ag on Si [15]. Third, the analyzer and detector must have unit efficiency. Both these conditions are possible but not easy. The initial efforts (STAP and SAP) are a giant step forward, but much work remains to meet this challenge.

The measurement of highly localized valence electron density of states is possible by scanning tunneling spectroscopy. Scanning tunneling spectroscopy with spatial resolution <1nm is widely practiced; it measures the valence electron density of states approximately ±5 volts to either side of the Fermi level. Its chief limitation is the lack of atom/molecule specific information in the broad emission spectrum, a problem common to all valence electron analytical tools. It is most useful when the elemental/molecular constituency is controlled and one seeks to differentiate between known elements or molecules [19-21]. Electroluminescence is also observed; the photon emission has a few nanometer spatial resolution because the excitation does not necessarily occur right under the tunneling tip [22]. The valence electron density of states can also be probed by fluorescence stimulated by Near-Field Optical Microscopy / Spectroscopy. NSOM/S has spatial resolution of approximately 10 nm. However the sensitivity is adequate to detect the fluorescence of single molecules [23] and the technique is useful for locating tagged materials [24-26].

Core electron spectroscopy requires sufficient energy in the excitation probe to excite electrons from the atomic core levels – approximately 50ev and greater. Photon sources with this energy are in the X-ray part of the spectra; focussing X-ray photons can be done with capillary optics, but micron resolution is the state of art [27]. Electron beams with energies >50ev can be readily focussed to nanometer dimension, either through focussing optics (high voltage and microfabricated lower voltage sources [28]) or proximal tips [29, 30]. Excessive current makes it necessary to retract a proximal tunneling tip from the surface [31] and the resulting resolution approaches that of current Scanning Auger Nanoprobe and Photoelectron Emission Microscope instruments.

Vibrational information with atomic resolution is possible from scanning tunneling spectroscopy. Ho and coworkers [32, 33] have recently successfully demonstrated this measurement after careful attention to stability and noise. There is hope for extending the range of conditions where vibrational measurements will be successful. An alternative approach utilizes the tunneling tip as an antenna to localize electromagnetic irradiation; spectroscopic information comes from coupling variable frequency light with non-linear characteristics of the proximal tip [34]. This approach has been demonstrated with microwave and infrared irradiation, but IR chemical fingerprints have not yet been accomplished. The problem is low signal to noise, coupled with heating effects when larger laser intensities are employed to raise the signal. To the extent that heating is the limiting feature, it might be possible to couple the tips with femtosecond light pulses for nanostructure resolution of vibrational modes. Near-field Surface-Enhanced Raman imaging has been demonstrated with 100 nm resolution [35-38] in cases where small particles can be exploited.

Force microscopy has provided an innovative approach to magnetic resonance spectroscopy. Rugar et al [39, 40] and more recently Markert [41] have shown that the force microscope can detect forces as low as $10^{-15} - 10^{-18}$ N. With special cantilevers and low temperatures, the forces associated with nuclear and electron spins can be detected. This technique will likely need ultra-low temperatures for adequate signal-to-noise and won't become a routine approach to the identification of an unknown nanostructure. Earlier work by Manassen et al [42] reported that the precessing spin induced field modulation might be detected in the current of a tunneling tip.

The ability of the force microscope to measure forces on the scale of chemical bonding between individual atoms provides a new approach to chemical identification. The possibilities here have been shown by work of Lee [43, 44] and Gaub [45, 46] who have shown that forces associated with molecular recognition and chain folding could be measured. Lieber [47] has demonstrated that specially prepared carbon nanotube probe tips can discriminate between different surface chemistries.

This paucity of chemical analytical tools is clearly a challenge to the world's scientific communities. It is worth noting that the references in this assessment are quite recent. If past practice is an indicator, European response to this challenge is most likely.

4. Conclusion

The opportunities inherent in nanotechnology [48] are increasingly being recognized by companies and government funding sources. Japan was an early participant with the Atom Technology Project sponsored by MITI beginning in 1992. The growing European interest has been summarized by Malsch [49]. The United States has formed an Interagency Working Group on Science, Engineering and Technology of Nanostructures (IWGN).

A report on an IWGN sponsored workshop entitled "Vision of Nanotechnology R&D for the Next Decade" will be available late in 1999; it will call for a significant increase in funding for research and development in nanoscience/nanoengineering. It is clear that the transition from nanoscience to nanotechnology is beginning in earnest. It is also clear that significant advances in the chemical analysis of nanostructures are critically needed to accelerate the rate of progress.

References

[1]   Nanostructure Science and Technology: R&D Status and Trends in Nanoparticles, Nanostructured Materials, and Nanodevices, R.W. Siegel, E. Hu, D.M. Cox, H. Gorokin, L. Jelinski, C.C. Koch, J. Mendel, M.C. Roco and D.T. Shaw (Baltimore: Loyola College, International Technology Research Institute, ISBN #1-883712, 1998).

[2]   Analyse und Bewertung Zukuenftiger Technologien: Innovationsschub aus dem Nanokosmos, G. Bachmann (VDI Technologiezentrum, Duesseldorf, Germany, ISSN 1436-5928, 1998).

[3]   Nanomaterials: Synthesis, Properties and Applications, Eds A.S. Edelstein and R.C. Cammarata (Institute of Physics, Bristol, 1996).

[4]   The National Technology Roadmap for Semiconductors: Technology Needs, Semiconductor Industry Association, San Jose, CA, 1997.

[5]   "Thinking Small on a Global Scale: The International Outlook for Nanobiotechnology", Report of the US-EC Workshop on Nanobiotechnology, September 23-24, 1997, Arlington, VA, USA

[6]   "Bioengineering: Building the Future of Biology and Medicine", National Institutes of Health Bioengineering Symposium Report, 6/4/98, page 38, http://www.nih.gov/grants/becon/report_19980228.pdf

[7]   J.S. Murday and R.J. Colton, in Chemistry and Physics of Solid Surfaces VIII, eds. R. Vanselow and R. Howe, Springer Series in Surface Sciences 22 (Springer-Verlag, New York, 1990), Chap. 15.

[8]   J.S. Murday, R.J. Colton and B.B. Rath, Key Engineering Materials **77-78**, 149 (1993).

[9]   R. Wiesendanger (Cambridge University Press, Cambridge, 1994).

[10]   R.J. Hamers, J. Phys. Chem. **100**, 13103 (1996).

[11]   R.J. Colton, D.R. Baselt, Y.F. Dufrene, J-B.D. Green and G.U. Lee, Current Opinion in Chemical Biology **1**, 370 (1977).

[12]   L.A. Bottomley, Anal. Chem. 70(12), 425 (1998).

[13]   G.E. McGuire, J. Fuchs, P. Han, J.G. Kushmerick, P.S. Weiss, S.J. Simko, R.J. Nemanich, and D.R. Chopra, Anal. Chem. **71**, 3737R (1999).

[14]   J.K. Gimzewski and C. Joachim, Science 283 (12 March), 1683 (1999).

[15]   U. Weierstall and J.C.H. Spence, Surface Science **398**, 267 (1998).

[16]   O. Nishikawa, M. Watanabe, Y. Ohtani, K. Maeda, K. Tanaka, T. Sekine and J. Itoh, J. Vac. Sci. Technol. B17(2), 608 (1999).

[17]   O. Nishikawa, K. Maeda, Y. Ohtani, M. Watanabe, K. Tanaka, T. Sekine, M. Iwatsuki, S. Aoki, J. Itoh, and K. Yamanaka, Appl Surf. Sci. **146**, 398 (1999).

[18]   A.N. Cleland and M.L. Roukes, Appl. Phys. Lett. **69**(18), 2653 (1996).

[19]   J.K. Gimzewski, T.A. Jung, M.T. Cuberes, R.R. Schlittler, Surf. Sci. **386**, 101 (1997).
[20]   C.L. Claypool, F. Faglioni, W.A. Goddard III, H.B. Gray, N.S. Lewis and R.A. Marcus, J. Phys. Chem. B **101**(31), 5978 (1997).
[21]   D.N. Fataba and S. Chiang, J. Vac. Sci. Technol. A15(3), 1295 (1997).
[22]   A. Downes and M.E. Welland, Phys. Rev. Lett **81**(9), 1857 (1998).
[23]   J.K. Trautman, J.J. Macklin, L.E. Brus, and E. Betzig, Nature (London) **369**, 40 (1994).
[24]   C.E. Talley, M. A. Lee and R.C. Dunn, Appl. Phys. Lett. **27**(23) 2954 (1998).
[25]   J. Kerimo, D.M. Adams, P.F. Barbara, D. M. Kaschak and T.E. Mallouk, J. Phys. Chem. **B 102**, 9451 (1998).
[26]   E. Tamiya, S. Iwabuchi, N. Nagatani, Y. Murakami, T. Sakaguchi and K. Yokoyama, Anal. Chem. **69**(18), 3697 (1997).
[27]   C.A. MacDonald, S.M. Owens and W.M. Gibson, J. Appl. Cryst. **32**, 160-167 (1999).
[28]   T.H.P. Chang, M.G.R. Thomson, E. Kratschmer, H.S. Kim, M.L. Yu, K.Y. Lee, S.A. Rishton, B.W. Hussey and S. Zolgharnain, J. Vac. Sci. Technol. **B14**(6), 3774 (1996).
[29]   M. L. Yu and T.H.P. Chang, Appl. Surf. Sci. **146**, 334 (1999).
[30]   H.-W. Fink, Physica Scripta **38**, 260 (1988).
[31]   B. Reihl and J.K. Gimzewski, Surf. Sci. **189/190**, 36 (1987).
[32]   B.C. Stipe, M.A. Rezaei, and W. Ho, Science **280** (12 June) 1732 (1998).
[33]   B.C. Stipe, M.A. Rezaei, and W. Ho, Phys. Rev. Lett. **82**(8), 1724 (1999).
[34]   Th. Gutjahr-L ser, A. Hornsteiner, W. Krieger, and H. Walther, J. Appl. Phys. **85**(9), 6331 (1999).
[36]   V. Deckert, D. Zeisel, R. Zenobi and T. Vo-Dinh, Anal. Chem. **70**(13), 2646 (1998).
[37]   B. Knoll and F. Keilmann, Nature **399** (13 May), 134 (1999).
[38]   S. Nie and S.R. Emory, Science 275 (21 February), 1102 (1997).
[39]   K. Kneipp, Y. Wang, H. Kneipp, L.T. Perelman, I. Itzkan, R. R. Dasari and M.S. Feld, Phys. Rev. Lett. **78**(9), 1667 (1997).
[40]   J. A. Sidles, J.L. Garbini, K.J. Bruland, D. Rugar, O. Zueger, S. Hoen and C.S. Yannoni, Rev. Mod. Phys. **67**, 249 (1995).
[41]   K. Wago, D. Botkin, C.S. Yannoni and R. Rugar, Appl. Phys. Lett. **72**(21), 2757 (1998).
[42]   T.A. Barrett, C.R. Miers, H.A. Sommer, K. Mochizuki, and J.T. Markert, J Appl. Phys. **83**(11), 6235 (1998).
[43]   Y. Manassen, R.J. Hamers, J.E. Demuth, et al., Phys. Rev. Lett. **62**(21), 2531 (1989).
[44]   G.U. Lee, D.A. Kidwell and R.J. Colton, Langmuir **10**, 354 (1994); G.U. Lee, L.A. Chrisey and R.J. Colton, Science **266**, 771 (1994).
[45]   G.U. Lee, L.A. Chrisey, C.E. O'Ferrall, D.E. Pilloff, N.H. Turner and R.J. Colton, Israeli Journal of Chemistry **36**, 81 (1996).
[46]   M. Ludwig, M. Rief, L. Schmidt, H. Li, F. Oesterhelt, M. Gautel and H.E. Gaub, Appl Phys A: Materials Science and Processing 68(2), 173 (1999).
[47]   M. Grandbois, M. Beyer, M. Rief, H. Clausen-Schaumann and H.E. Gaub, Science **283**(12 March), 1727 (1999).
[48]   S.S. Wong, A.T. Woolley, E. Joselevich, C.L. Cheung, and C.M. Lieber, J. Am. Chem. Soc. **120**, 8557 (1998).
[49]   D. Rotman, Technology Review (March/April), 44 (1999).
[50]   I. Malsch, Nanotechnology **10**, 1 (1999).

INVITED LECTURES

A. Benninghoven, P. Bertrand, H.-N. Migeon and H.W. Werner (Editors).
Proceedings of the 12th International Conference on Secondary Ion Mass Spectrometry,
Brussels, Belgium, 5-11 September 1999

MODELLING OF CLUSTER EMISSION FROM METAL SURFACES DUE TO ION IMPACT

G. Betz*, and W. Husinsky

Inst. f. Allgemeine Physik, Technische Universität Wien,

Wiedner Hauptstr. 8-10, A-1040 Wien, Austria

*) E-mail: betz@iap.tuwien.ac.at

1. Introduction

It is well known from experimental investigations that the flux of particles sputtered from a metal surface under keV ion bombardment may contain large clusters that consist of up to several tens of atoms [1,2]. Those clusters, which are emitted in an ionised state or are post-ionised, are observed in Secondary Ion Mass Spectrometry (SIMS) and related techniques. The molecular dynamics technique (MD) is ideally suited to study the fundamental processes of ion bombardment during the time of a few ps, in which the impinging particle transfers its energy to the target atoms leading to disorder (mixing) at and near the surface and to particle emission (sputtering). Many features of the sputtering process, like energy distributions, angular distributions, depth of origin of sputtered particles, cluster emission or mixing inside the crystal can be investigated with such MD calculations. In addition, this technique offers the possibility of visualisation of these processes or even by producing videos to show the dynamic evolution of a sputter event.

The emission of clusters, especially of large ones (cluster sizes of 10 and more atoms) as observed experimentally, is a puzzling phenomenon and we will discuss it as an example what information MD calculations can give us on the basic processes. The typical time scale during which particle emission (sputtering) takes place is in the order of 1 ps or less. After 1 ps the average energy of the atoms in the collision cascade is below the surface binding energy, preventing further emission of atoms, as can be clearly seen in MD simulations of the sputtering process [3]. However, we have found that large clusters are emitted much later than the main part of sputtered particles and small clusters - typically after 5 ps and later - due to thermal processes. The main focus of this contribution is concerned with the emission of large clusters (n > 10), but for completeness results for small clusters will also be discussed. We will distinguish between emission of small (n < 10) and large clusters (n > 10) to elaborate the two processes, which lead to cluster emission from metal targets under energetic ion bombardment.

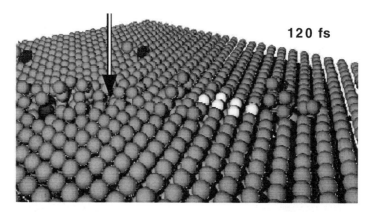

Fig. 1a: Emission of a small cluster:

The 5 keV Ar ion impact point on the Cu (111) surface is indicated by the arrow. The six white surface atoms, which are neighbouring atoms (connected group of atoms) will be sputtered together forming a cluster of size 6. Figure 1a shows the situation 120 fs after ion impact. As can be seen there are two distinct surface regions, where sputtering has started. One area is near the ion impact point, the other is near the six white atoms. Analysis of the cascade shows that it develops underneath the impact point, but in addition a subcascade is forming below the surface, where the six white atoms are located. This subcascade is responsible for the second group of sputtered atoms.

Fig. 1b: Emission of a small cluster:

The close - up after 150 fs shows, that the subcascade causes the surface to bulge upward. The six white surface atoms receive similar momenta from this process and are uplifted from the surface.

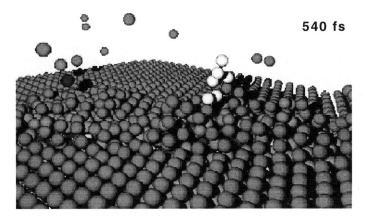

540 fs

Fig. 1c: Emission of a small cluster:
After 540 fs these six atoms have formed a cluster of size 6 no longer interacting with the surface. Nearby surface atoms, which have received more energy have already left the surface. The cluster did not decay, at least up to the end of our post-evaluation (100 ps). It should be noted, that in most cases of cluster emission, the originally emitted group of connected atoms, will reduce in size due to unimolecular decomposition.

2. Small Clusters (n < 10)

Using molecular dynamics simulations cluster emission under 5 keV Ar bombardment of a Cu (111) surface has been investigated using a many body (tight binding) potential for the Cu - Cu interaction [3]. References to similar investigations are given in [3, 4, 5]. The details of the code and the potentials used have been described in detail in Reference [3]. Results presented here are from additional calculations, where instead of a Born - Mayer a Ziegler - Biersack - Littmark (ZBL) - potential [6] was used for the repulsive potential in the Ar-Cu as well as Cu-Cu interactions. All the qualitative conclusions presented in Reference [3] have been verified also with this more realistic potential combination. The development of the collision cascade and the emission of sputtered atoms was followed up to 1 ps. Emitted clusters might be highly excited and decay into smaller subunits by unimolecular decomposition (even the total energy of the original cluster is negative in the centre of mass system). Therefore all emitted particles were followed in a separate calculation for an additional 100 ps to take into account their decay.

It was found that emission of small clusters occurs essentially due to correlated motion in the collision cascade, resulting in the emission of a group of neighbouring atoms located at the surface. Thus correlated processes not considered in any statistical model account for the high yields of small clusters and also correctly predict their energy distribution [3]. Such a process can be envisioned, if for example a few layers below the surface an energetic recoil causes the development of a subcascade, as demonstrated in Fig. 1 for the emission of a cluster of size 6. Energy transferred by this event towards the surface is strongly directional and can lead to the simultaneous emission of a group of neighbouring surface atoms, which in some cases will remain bonded and form a cluster after emission, if the conditions of simultaneous emission and nearly parallel momenta are fulfilled. We assume that at least for larger clusters (n > 3) the outward expansion of the target surface due to the internally deposited energy in the cascade is responsible for the highly correlated momentum transfer causing cluster emission.

The main features characteristic for the emission of small clusters are:

- Sputtering occurs essentially during the first ps after ion impact. This is also true for the emission of small clusters, however it is found the average emission time for a cluster of size n increases with n and approaches 1 ps for large clusters of size n > 6.

- About 92% of the sputtered flux is from the surface layer. For clusters, the contribution of surface atoms is even more pronounced. In addition, in most cases cluster atoms belong to a connected group of atoms, i.e. form a group of next neighbour atoms (see Fig. 1). This suggests a high correlation in the emission process, where a group of atoms receive similar momenta leading to their emission as a cluster.

- Uplifting of the surface due to internally deposited energy (for example in a subcascade) is responsible for the correlated motion of atoms toward the surface.

- From such calculations, in agreement with experimental findings, yields and energy distributions of small emitted clusters (cluster size up to n=6) have been obtained [3].

3. Large clusters (n > 10)

Emission of large clusters (cluster sizes of 10 to 100 atoms and more) as observed experimentally is an even more puzzling phenomenon. From our calculations we conclude, that the emission of such large clusters does not occur during the collisional phase of sputtering but much later (5 - 10 ps after particle impact). Emission can occur for spike events, where all the energy of the impinging ion is locally deposited into a small volume near the surface. These are typically high sputter yield events, where the yield is 3-5 times the average yield. Such events are rare events, but we have found a few cases in the calculations, where stable clusters consisting of more than 20 atoms were emitted. Melting of the spike volume occurs and the high temperatures and pressures produced can cause emission of large fragments during the thermal phase.

A typical event leading to the emission of a large cluster is described: It is a high sputter yield impact, where a spike is formed near and intersecting the surface. Temperature of target atoms is calculated in the usual manner by assuming equipartition between potential and kinetic energy [7]. To check the validity of the temperature concept we analysed the velocity distribution of the atoms in the centre of the spike after 1ps. It agrees well with a Maxwell-Boltzmann distribution with an equivalent temperature of about twice the melting temperature of Cu (compare also Fig. 2a). Thus the spike region is a molten zone, which starts to shrink after about 2 ps due to heat conduction to the surrounding crystal. At the surface protrusions are

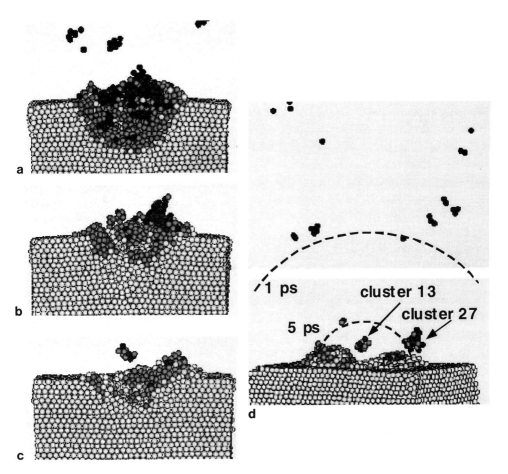

Fig. 2: Emission of large clusters for a 5 keV Ar ion impact on a Cu (111) surface. The different graylevels of the atoms indicate their temperature (white: $T < T_{melt}$ (1300K); light gray: $T_{melt} < T < 2 T_{melt}$; dark gray: $2 T_{melt} < T < 3 T_{melt}$; black: $T > 3 T_{melt}$). Figures a) - c) are cross-sections through the crystal. a) After 1 ps, cascade sputtering is terminated. Most sputtered atoms are far away from the target and are no longer visible in the Figure. Sputtered atoms are all very "hot" (black: $T > 3 T_{melt}$) as can be seen for those still visible. A molten spike region has formed below the ion impact point. b) After 4ps the spike region has strongly decreased in size due to cooling. Only asperities at the surface remain hot, due to the limited heat transfer to the bulk of the crystal. c) After 6 ps a cluster of size 13 is emitted from such an asperity. Actually 2 clusters of size 13 and 27 are leaving the surface after 5-6 ps. After 10 ps the temperature of the crystal has decreased below the melting point everywhere. d) View of the crystal after 5 ps: the circles indicate typical distances of sputtered surface atoms, which have been sputtered 1 ps or 5 ps after ion impact, respectively. Note that the area between the 1 ps and 5 ps circles is empty, indicating no sputtering

between 1 and 5 ps. formed (Fig. 2b). Only after 5 ps, when most of the spike region has re - solidified, except for the still hot asperities, two clusters are leaving the surface from such protrusions. For the event shown, the clusters consist of 13 and 27 atoms, respectively. Analysis shows for all such large clusters emitted after a few ps, that the atoms forming the cluster are no longer dominantly surface atoms, but come from different layers of the target. Indeed only 11 atoms of the cluster 27 are surface atoms and atoms from up to the sixth layer are contained in the cluster. After 100 ps the cluster 13 has lost 2 atoms and the cluster 27 has lost a dimer and 2 atoms forming now a stable cluster of size 23.

A typical event leading to the emission of a large cluster is described: It is a high sputter yield impact, where a spike is formed near and intersecting the surface. Temperature of target atoms are calculated in the usual manner by assuming equipartition between potential and kinetic energy [7]. To check the validity of the temperature concept we analysed the velocity distribution of the atoms in the centre of the spike after 1ps. It agrees well with a Maxwell-Boltzmann distribution with an equivalent temperature of about twice the melting temperature of Cu (compare also Fig. 2a). Thus the spike region is a molten zone, which starts to shrink after about 2 ps due to heat conduction to the surrounding crystal. At the surface protrusions are formed (Fig. 2b). Only after 5 ps, when most of the spike region has re-solidified, except for the still hot asperities, two clusters are leaving the surface from such protrusions. For the event shown, the clusters consist of 13 and 27 atoms, respectively. Analysis shows for all such large clusters emitted after a few ps, that the atoms forming the cluster are no longer dominantly surface atoms, but come from different layers of the target. Indeed only 11 atoms of the cluster 27 are surface atoms and atoms from up to the sixth layer are contained in the cluster. After 100 ps the cluster 13 has lost 2 atoms and the cluster 27 has lost a dimer and 2 atoms forming now a stable cluster of size 23.

Thus the composition of such large clusters is quite different from the one of small clusters. They consist of atoms from different layers and the constituents are also generally not next neighbour atoms, but generally from the same neighbourhood. This changed origin of the cluster atoms reflects the mixing and diffusion processes occurring in the molten zone before emission. The calculations indicate that thermal phenomena might play a role in the emission of large fragments.

Thus emission of large clusters can be summarised as follows:
-    Large clusters are emitted after a few (5) ps during the thermal part of the cascade evolution, much later than the majority of sputtered atoms and small clusters.
-    Large clusters are formed from atoms of the same neighbourhood, but no longer from surface atoms.
-    Thermal processes in the molten zone of the spike are responsible for cluster emission.

While for typical metals cluster emission is a rare process, in computations we can perform calculations for a "weak" pseudo - Cu, in which the cohesive energy has been halved. Such a weak pseudo-Cu has about twice the sputtering yield of Cu, a lower melting point; for such a material the emission of large clusters becomes quite a frequent event indeed [5]. An example for the emission of such large clusters occurring again after 5 ps is given in Reference [5].

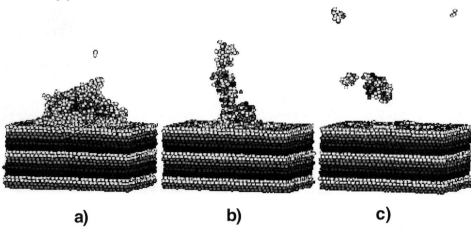

a)   **b)**   **c)**

Fig. 3: An amount of 4 keV of energy is assumed to have been deposited as thermal energy within 500 fs in a Cu (111) crystal in a cylindrical volume (radius = 2nm, depth = 2nm) bordering the surface. The maximum temperature in the heated volume was 5000K at the end of thermal energy deposition. Typically in such calculations, emission of one or two large clusters is observed. Different layers of the crystal are drawn in different graylevels, to indicate that clusters are composed of atoms from different layers. The time scale is: a) view of the crystal after 3 ps; b) after 8 ps; c) after 15 ps.

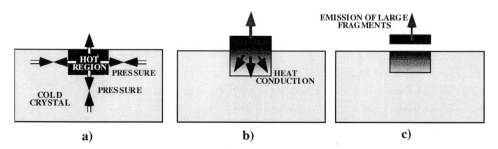

a)   **b)**   **c)**

Fig.4: Model for the emission of large clusters. a) The bombarding ion creates a dense cascade (spike) near the surface. A hot molten region is formed (after 1 ps). This hot region (a few 1000K) exerts pressure to all sides as it tries to expand. At all sides except the surface this pressure is counteracted by the crystal. b) This leads to a collective motion of the hot surface parts away from the surface. At the same time heat conduction towards the cold bulk leads to cooling of those parts of the molten zone in contact with the crystal. The surface area and especially asperities formed remain hottest and maintain their momentum away from the surface. c) Due to the imparted collective motion large clusters are emitted after a few ps. As shown in Fig. 3 the impinging ion serves only as the provider of sufficient energy to create a hot molten volume intersecting the surface.

4. Model

To test the influence of the collisional part of the cascade we have performed additional MD simulations, where the "kinetic energy of a bombarding ion" was distributed "thermally" in a 3D volume under the surface. Therefore, in this case, no impinging ion was present, and no collision cascades could have been formed. This addition of thermal energy was done during 0.5 ps, which is the typical time scale of a collision cascade. The size of the cylindrical volume, where the thermal energy has been added, was of the order of the dimension of a dense collision cascade. It was 2 nm in any lateral radial direction around the centre of the crystal surface and 2 nm deep and contained about 2000 atoms. In these calculations the crystal was coupled to a heat bath at 300K and periodic boundary conditions were used as in [8].

While for energy depositions below 3 keV no emission at all was observed, for higher energies (4 keV and above) the emission of one or two large clusters always was found to take place, as shown in Fig. 3, even when the collisional part of the cascade was absent. Also typically much larger clusters are emitted than under ion bombardment at the same deposited energy.

From these considerations, we propose the model for the emission of large clusters, as outlined in Fig. 4; it assumes that the process is essentially of a thermal and hydrodynamical nature. A rapidly heated volume intersecting the surface will start to expand in the direction towards the surface and can lead to the emission of large fragments. Such processes are also most likely responsible for the extreme sputtering yields observed experimentally for keV Au cluster bombardment of Au [9], as under cluster bombardment very dense cascades due to cascade overlapping are obtained.

References

[1]   A.Wucher and M.Wahl, Nucl. Instr. and Meth. B, **115** (1996) 581

[2]   H.M.Urbassek and W.O.Hofer, Det kongelige Danske Vid. Selsk. Mat. Fys. Medd., **43** (1993) 97

[3]   G.Betz and W.Husinsky, Nucl. Instr. and Meth. B, **102** (1995) 281

[4]   A.Wucher and B.Garrison, J. Chem. Phys, **105** (1996) 5999

[5]   T.J.Colla, H.M.Urbassek, A.Wucher, C.Staudt, R.Heinrich, B.J.Garrison, C. Dandachi and G.Betz, Nucl. Instr. and Meth. B, **143** (1998) 284

[6]   J.F.Ziegler, J.P.Biersack and U.Littmark, Stopping Powers and Ranges of Ions in Matter, vol. 1, Pergamon, New York, 1985

[7]   H.M.Urbassek, Nucl. Instr. and Meth. B, **122** (1997) 427

[8]   G.Betz and W.Husinsky, Nucl. Instr. and Meth. B, **102** (1995) 311

[9]   H.H.Andersen, A.Brunelle, S.Della-Negra, J.Depauw, D.Jacquet, Y.Le Beyec, J.Chaumont and H.Bernas, Phys. Rev. Lett., **80** (1998) 5433

A. Benninghoven, P. Bertrand, H.-N. Migeon and H.W. Werner (Editors).
Proceedings of the 12th International Conference on Secondary Ion Mass Spectrometry,
Brussels, Belgium, 5-11 September 1999
© 2000 Elsevier Science B.V. All rights reserved.

OPTIMIZATION OF A TIME-OF-FLIGHT SECONDARY ION MASS SPECTROMETER FOR SHALLOW JUNCTION PROFILING

S. Corcoran, P. Zimmerman, Intel Corporation, 5000 W. Chandler Blvd, Chandler, AZ, 85244, USA <paul.zimmerman@intel.com>

E. Niehuis, ION-TOF GmbH Mendelstr 11, D-48149 Münster, Germany

1. Introduction

Increasingly, the semiconductor industry is making use of low energy ion implants for shallow junction formation. These implants, which are often accomplished at between a few hundred to a few thousand electron volts, require an analysis capability that will allow depth resolutions $\leq$ 1nm to be obtained. Certain tools have had limited success due to instrumental limitations, while other tools have been particularly suited to a specific shallow implant. For example, the quad-SIMS has historically given outstanding results for shallow B or As implants, but reliable P profiles are difficult to obtain due to the restricted mass resolution of the technique. Recently, an upgraded CAMECA IMS-6f has demonstrated acceptable depth profiling performance for low energy boron and phosphorous. The IMS 6f can be upgraded to allow sub-keV bombardment energies with excellent sensitivity.

While there can be no argument to the capability of many tools presently in the field to successfully meet the needs of high depth resolution analyses, there is now a requirement from the industrial sector for tools to be more flexible and cost effective. This trend has motivated a combined effort between Intel and an original equipment manufacturer (OEM) of TOF-SIMS instrumentation. The goal of the project was to incorporate the necessary modifications into the TOF-SIMS to make the shallow-junction profiling tool (SJP) feasible. This had to be done without degrading the performance of the system in the area of surface analysis. The TOF-SIMS was a favo-rable candidate for this effort because of the predisposed technical aspects of the tool. Parallel detection coupled with high mass resolution and high secondary ion trans-mission, combine to make TOF-SIMS an obvious choice for a SJP. Additional details of the profiling capabilities of TOF-SIMS have been described elsewhere [1 - 3].

2. Experimental

A SJP tool has requirements beyond that of a standard TOF-SIMS instrument, consequently the instrumentation used in this study was a modified version of the Cameca TOF-SIMS IV. Depth profiles were acquired in the dual beam interlaced mode [3]. A three-lens Ga ion gun was used for the sample analysis, operated at 15 keV in a high current bunched mode [4]. A dual source sputter gun [2] was used for Cs^+ and O_2^+ sputtering in the energy range from 400 eV up to 1 keV at an impact angle of 45°.

Several modifications to the standard TOF-SIMS IV were implemented in order to improve the analysis of shallow junction profiles. First of all, a major concern for good reproducibility and accuracy is the current stability of the sputter gun. In the dual beam mode, a change of the sputter current leads to an error in the depth scale, but has no influence on the secondary ion signals. By introducing new high precision electronics, we were able to reduce the drift of the sputtering current at very low energies to < 1 % during a 60 minute period after a 45 minute warm up period. A drift of the analysis current is less critical and can be eliminated by point-to-point normalization of the profiles. The drift of the pulsed analysis current was below 1 % over a 20 minute period. The raster of the sputter gun was modified to improve the flatness of the crater bottom and to make use of a larger area in the crater bottom for the analysis. The reduction of the current density of the analysis gun ensures that its contribution to the atomic mixing can be neglected. In order to reduce the background and improve the dynamic range, a secondary beam blanker and a blanking aperture was implemented in front of the detection system.

The other SIMS instruments used in this work include an Atomika 4100 quadrupole and a Cameca IMS 6f.

The samples analyzed include a 2.3 keV $^{11}BF_2$ implant, a 4 keV As implant with 1.6E15 at/cm^2 and a 2 keV P implant with 1E15at/cm^2. Additionally, a dose skew of ± 10% was analyzed for a 1 keV P implant. The depth of all sputter craters was measured using a Tencor Alpha step 500 or a Tencor P-11.

3. Results and discussion

3.1. Boron

The goal of this portion of the study was to optimize the TOF configuration for the analysis of B and then to compare the data with another accepted SIMS-technique such as normal incidence O_2^+ bombardment in a quadrupole SIMS.

In the TOF-SIMS, O_2^+ sputtering at 550 eV was used with an incidence angle of 45°, combined with oxygen flooding. These bombardment conditions have been shown to give good depth resolution and a short transient regime [5, 6] and avoid sample

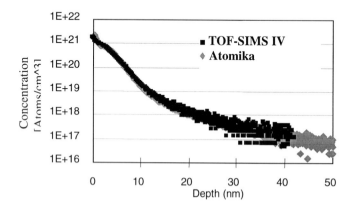

Figure 1: Comparison of the TOF-SIMS and quad-SIMS data for the analysis of B implants.

roughening often observed with oxygen flooding and oblique incidence under non-ideal analysis conditions [7 - 12]. In the quadrupole SIMS, normal incidence oxygen sputtering was applied. Figure 1 shows a data overlay of B profiles for the quad-SIMS and the TOF-SIMS for a 2.3 keV BF_2 implant. Note the close agreement in the data in spite of the differing analytical conditions. The near surface spike is more pronounced in the quad-SIMS profile, which is known to be an artifact of the normal incidence oxygen sputtering. The detection limit of the quad-SIMS is lower by about a factor of 3 compared to the TOF-SIMS profile.

The reproducibility of the dose measurement was tested for the TOF-SIMS. For the same B implant multiple profiles were run and the crater depth was measured with the profiler. The spread in the measured dose is less that 1.5 % max-min. This spread may be partly due to the error introduced by the limited accuracy of the crater depth measurement. This data is typical for what can be obtained for this dose.

It has been clear in the past that the low duty cycle of the TOF has impaired its sensitivity. Now however, after a recent modification, the capability to increase the repetition rate to 50 kHz has allowed a factor of 5 of increase in dynamic range to be realized. The result obtained for the same BF_2 implant is shown in figure 2. This new capability provides five decades of dynamic range bringing the detection limit down to the 1E16 at/cm^3 range.

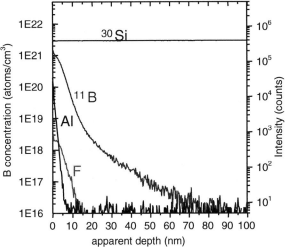

Figure 2: Profile of a 2.3 keV BF_2 implant obtained wiht 50 kHz repetition rate.

Additionally, the parallel mass detection of all elements allows the analysis of metal contaminants like Al from the implanter and of F from the implantation of BF_2 in the same run (figure 2). Evaluating the decay length for the Al ($\lambda_d = 0.68$ nm) it becomes clear, that the depth resolution obtained with a 500 eV O_2 sputtering beam is sufficient to probe the 2.3 keV BF_2 implant.

3.2 Phosphorous

The analysis of shallow phosphorous implants offers unique challenges compared to other implants. First of all, the interference of the P with ^{30}SiH requires high mass resolution to achieve reasonable detection limits. Therefore, attempts to use quadrupole SIMS for P shallow implants have not been successful [13]. Magnetic sector SIMS offers the high mass resolution and the sensitivity is very good with Cs in negative SIMS mode. However, the high negative target potential makes it rather difficult to use low energy Cs sputtering to improve depth resolution. By reducing the secondary ion acceleration voltage to only 0.6 keV, Cs impact energies down to 1.6 keV at impact angles of about 23° have been used [14]. These conditions lead to a significant loss in sensitivity and are still not adequate for very low energy implants. Alternatively, O_2^+

profiling with oxygen flooding has been used to improve the depth resolution [13], but the ion yield and sensitivity for P is not very good in positive SIMS.

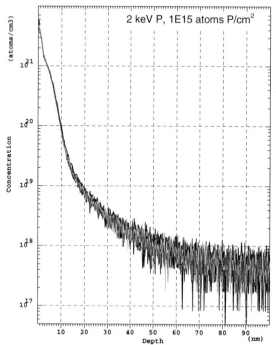

TOF-SIMS allows to com-bine very low energy Cs sput-tering in negative SIMS mode with high mass resolution. The performance and reprodu-cibility has been tested for 2 keV P implants with a dose of 1E15 at/cm^2. Ten different pieces of silicon with the same dose have been analyzed with 400 eV Cs at 45° impact angle and each data set con-sists of three runs. The data were collected in the batch job mode with automated sample positioning, z adjustment and data acquisition. For each sample, the current of the two ion guns was checked and adjusted if needed. The data shown in figure 3 are typical for all the data collected under identical instrumental condi-tions. The profiles show a very high P concentration in the first few nm. The shape near the surface is affected by the presence of an oxide layer and transient corrections are required to get an accurate dose. The data shown indicate that the reproducibility necessary for dose matching exists using TOF-SIMS. The data provide a max to min spread of about 2 %, which must be considered to be partly caused by the individual crater depth measurement.

Figure 3: Data showing the reproducibility for the analysis of 2 keV P implants with TOF-SIMS

To illustrate the sensitivity to concentration variation, a sample set consisting of a 1.10E14 at/cm^2, 1.05E14 at/cm^2, 1.00E14 at/cm^2, 0.95E14 at/cm^2 and 0.90E14 at/cm^2 implant has been analysed. The sample was implanted with 1 keV P at the appropriate dose directly from as-received material from a wafer vendor.

Figure 4 shows the normalized SIMS dose vs. the implanted dose for the dose skew analysis. The data for this plot was obtained by averaging over five runs for each sample. The clear indication from this data is that TOF-SIMS possesses the necessary sensitivity required to accurately complete dose matching for a shallow junction profile. It is likely that most of the observed error comes from the lack of processing of these wafers prior to implantation. Because of the high concentration region of the implant located directly beneath the surface, even slight differences in the native oxide thickness and the presence of surface contaminants can have a strong effect on the accuracy of the dose measurement .

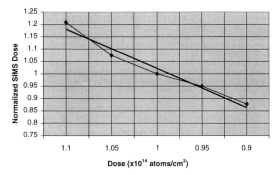

Figure 4: Response curve for P dose skew

3.3 Arsenic

The final dopant analyzed for comparison is arsenic. As profiles were attempted some time ago with TOF-SIMS but due to several factors, satisfactory results were not possible. With the advent of the 3-lens Ga ion gun and a blanking plate in the analyzer the As analysis in now easily accomplished.

A comparison of the profiles obtained for the TOF-SIMS and the Cameca 6f is shown in Figure 5. In the TOF-SIMS 400 eV Cs sputtering with As⁻ monitoring was used while in the Cameca low energy Cs sputtering (1.9 keV, 56°) with AsCs⁺ analysis was applied. Low energy Cs sputtering in negative SIMS mode is difficult in the Cameca due to the high positive target potential (cf. 3.2). The data indicates a very similar trend except in the very near surface region. Both, the AsCs⁺ and the As⁻ show a matrix effect at the SiO_2/Si interface. The surface spike is more pronounced for the As⁻ signal because of a significantly higher As⁻ secondary ion yield

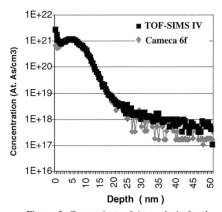

Figure 5: Comparison of As analysis for the TOF and the Cameca 6f, showing the As⁻ and the AsCs⁺ signal, respectively.

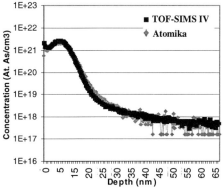

Figure 6: Comparison of TOF-SIMS and quad-SIMS performance for a 4 keV As implant. Here, the AsSi⁻ signal is shown.

in the oxide, while the AsCs⁺ yield may be diminished in the transient region. In contrast to the As⁻, the AsSi⁻ signal (figure 6) does not show such a strong matrix effect and is rather insensitive to the oxygen concentration.

The comparison of the TOF profile (400 eV Cs, 45°) with that of the Atomika (750 eV Cs, 60°) uses the AsSi⁻ species for both instruments. Figure 6 shows the data overlay. Note the similarity in all aspects of the profile. The intensities, dynamic ranges and depth resolutions are all comparable. The performance here shows that the measurement of shallow As can be accomplished successfully with a variety of tools including the

TOF-SIMS. It should be noted that all of the As and P data was collected with a repetition rate of 10 kHz indicating that a further improvement in the data obtained thus far can be expected if a repetition rate of 50 kHz is used.

4. Conclusions

Combining all of the advances presently available within the TOF-SIMS instrumentation allows the accurate analysis of shallow junction profiles to be accom-plished. Comparative analysis of B, As and P implants on state of the art SJP systems shows that the results obtained from the TOF-SIMS IV are essentially equivalent to those of existing and accepted techniques.

The coordinated effort between Intel and ION-TOF provides a business model by which development of new capabilities can be accomplished while providing an overall cost savings to both parties. Additionally, such cooperative arrangements can speed up the overall development process, thus reducing the analytical gaps that presently exist.

Acknowledgements

The authors would like to thank David Hercules and John Mehl for providing help with some of the initial work on this project.

References

[1] K. Iltgen, C. Bendel, E. Niehuis, A. Benninghoven, Proc. of SIMS X, Wiley (1997), New York, p. 375.
[2] M. Terhorst, H-G. Cramer, E. Niehuis, Proc. of SIMS X, Wiley (1997), p. 427.
[3] H.-G. Cramer, U. Jürgens, E. Niehuis, M. Terhorst, Z. Zhang, A. Benninghoven, Proc. of SIMS IX, Wiley (1994), p. 449.
[4] E. Niehuis, T. Heller, C. Bendel, J. Zehnpfenning, Proc. of SIMS XI, Wiley (1998), p. 779.
[5] K. Iltgen, C. Bendel, A. Benninghoven, E. Niehuis, J. Vac. Sci. Technol. A15(3) (1997) 460.
[6] K. Iltgen, O. Brox, A. Benninghoven, E. Niehuis, Proc. SIMS XI, Wiley (1998), p. 305.
[7] Z. X. Jiang, P. F. A. Alkemade, E. Algra, S Radelaar, Surf. And Interface Anal. 25 (1997) 285.
[8] K. Wittmaack, S.F. Corcoran, J. Vac. Sci. Technol B16 (1998) 272.
[9] D. P. Chu, M. G. Dowsett, T. J. Ormsby, G. A. Cooke Presented ULSI '98, Gaithersburg, March 1998, to appear in the Proceedings.
[10] Z. X. Jiang, P. F. A. Alkemade, J. Vac. Sci. Technol. B16 (1998) 1971.
[11] B. W. Schueler, D. F. Reich, Fifth International Workshop on Ultra-shallow junctions, Research Triangle Park, NC, March 1999, in conference proceeding and to be published in JVST.
[12] Z. X. Jiang, P. F. A. Alkemade, Appl. Phys. Lett. 73 (1998) 315.
[13] S. P. Smith, C. J. Hitzman, C. W. Magee, Proc. of SIMS XI, Wiley (1998), p. 277.
[14] R. Loesing, G. M. Guryanov, D. P. Griffis, Fifth International Workshop on Ultra-shallow junctions, Research Triangle Park, NC, March 1999, in conference proceeding and to be published in JVST.

A. Benninghoven, P. Bertrand, H.-N. Migeon and H.W. Werner (Editors).
Proceedings of the 12th International Conference on Secondary Ion Mass Spectrometry,
Brussels, Belgium, 5-11 September 1999

HOW DO LARGE ORGANIC MOLECULES SPUTTER ?
INSIGHTS FROM TOF-SIMS AND MOLECULAR DYNAMICS SIMULATIONS.

A. Delcorte,[1+] P. Bertrand,[2] J. C. Vickerman[3] and B. J. Garrison[1]

[1]Department of Chemistry, The Pennsylvania State University, 152 Davey Lab, University Park, PA 16802,USA

[2]PCPM, Universite catholique de Louvain, 1 Croix du Sud, B1348, Louvain-la-Neuve, Belgium

[3]Surface Analysis Research Centre, Department of Chemistry, UMIST, PO Box 88, Manchester, M60 1QD, UK

[+]phone: 1-(814)-863-2108; fax: 1-(814)-863-5319; e-mail: delcorte@chem.psu.edu

1. Introduction

The bombardment of organic solids by keV ions induces the emission of molecular species, including characteristic fragments and large parent-like ions, which form the useful secondary ion signal. Unfortunately, it also produces small, uncharacteristic or considerably rearranged fragments, constituting an additional 'noise' that gives rise to amazingly complex spectra. Although several important advances arise from empiricism (heavy metal substrates, ionic salt matrices or polyatomic projectiles), as scientists, we would like to base future improvements on a fundamental understanding of the molecular ion emission mechanisms. From an experimental study based on the interpretation of kinetic energy distributions (KED) of molecular ions, new insight was gained into the energy transfer process and reaction channels involved in the formation of the observed ejected species [1]. To complement this work, molecular dynamics simulations have been initiated recently, with polystyrene (PS) tetramers and dibenzanthracene (DBA) molecules adsorbed on Ag{111} as the model systems for the investigation of the mechanisms of polyatomic fragment ejection. In this review, the good match often found between simulation and experiment will be highlighted, as well as the results that are more challenging to model.

2. Methods

2.1. ToF-SIMS experiments. Thin organic layers were formed by solution casting onto a clean polycrystalline silver support [2]. The organic molecules were sec-butyl ended polystyrene tetramers ($C_4H_9(C_8H_8)_4H$) and dibenzanthracene ($C_{22}H_{14}$). The samples were bombarded with a (5 kHz) pulsed Ga^+ beam (15 keV) and the secondary ions were mass- and energy- analyzed in a Phi-Evans TRIFT1 Time-of-Flight SIMS [3]. The angle between the ion gun and the normal to the sample surface was 35°. In this system, the accelerated secondary ions are energy-selected by an energy slit (1.5 eV passband) inserted at the crossover following the first hemispherical electrostatic analyzer. The detailed procedure to measure KEDs has been described in Ref. [4].

2.2. MD simulations. In the model, the silver substrate is approximated by a finite microcrystallite containing 1404 Ag atoms arranged in 9 layers of 156 atoms each. Either five

PS tetramers or six DBA molecules were placed on the Ag surface. Ar atoms (500 eV) were directed parallel to the surface normal. Four thousand trajectories were calculated for the PS/Ag system, and one thousand trajectories with the DBA/Ag system. A fresh undamaged sample was used for each trajectory. The integration scheme as well as the many-body and pairwise potentials used in the simulation have been described elsewhere [5]. The hydrocarbon interactions were described by the Brenner hydrocarbon potential function [6,7] thus allowing us to model chemical reactions.

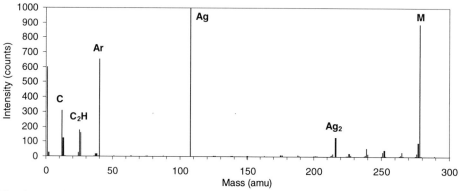

Fig. 1. Calculated neutral mass spectrum obtained after the bombardment of DBA/Ag{111} by 500 eV Ar atoms at 6 ps.

3. Experimental and calculated mass spectra

In SIMS analysis, the information is typically provided by the mass spectrum. It is the result of the combined action of several processes, including collision cascades, fragmentation in the surface region, ionization and metastable decay in the vacuum. Obviously, current MD simulations cannot account for ionization processes and long-lifetime metastable decay. Nevertheless, it will be shown in the following discussion that the comparison between the results from experiment and simulation yields insight into these processes also. In particular, the similarities and differences between the calculated and experimental mass spectra may be used as a key to start the analysis of the emission mechanisms in SIMS. The calculated mass spectrum of DBA on silver is shown in Fig. 1. The main peaks in the low-mass region (below 100 amu) correspond to small hydrocarbon fragments with one to three carbon atoms. In the high-mass region (beyond 100 amu), beside the entire molecule, there is a less intense series of fragments with more than ten carbon atoms. The main hydrocarbons of the high-mass region, including the entire molecule, correspond to the formula C_xH_{x-8}. For comparison purpose, the partial SIMS spectrum of DBA (region between 200 and 300 amu) can be found in Ref. 8. The main peaks are the same C_xH_{x-8} (252, 265, 278 amu) but beside these species, the spectrum also exhibits intense hydrogen-deficient fragments that are not found in the calculated spectrum (250, 263, 276 amu). The calculated spectrum of DBA will serve as an example to guide us into the fundamentals of the emission mechanisms.

4. Kinetic energy distributions: a means to elucidate fragmentation and metastable decay processes

A striking difference between the high-mass range of the DBA spectra is the quasi-absence of $C_{22}H_{12}$ in the simulation versus its high intensity in the experiment. To understand this difference, it is helpful to look at the experimental KED of $C_{22}H_{12}^+$ (Fig. 2). Beside the narrow peak in the positive range of the KED (peak I), a large fraction of the intensity is observed at 'negative energies' (peaks II and III). The two peaks and their oblique baseline correspond to $C_{22}H_{12}^+$ with a significant energy deficit with respect to the full acceleration energy. In fact, all these ions have been formed by metastable decay of larger parent ions either in the acceleration or in the field-free drift section of the spectrometer, transferring a part of their energy to the undetected neutral product [8]. Peak III corresponds to H_2 loss from $C_{22}H_{14}^+$, peak II to a single H loss from $C_{22}H_{13}^+$, and the baseline to unidentified reactions in the acceleration section. For this ion, the overall intensity fraction corresponding to metastable reactions occurring *after* 10^{-9} s is more than 75 % of the total intensity. Unimolecular dissociation happening *before* 10^{-9} s will lead to energies included in peak I and, therefore, cannot be distinguished from direct emission of the fragment. Thus, Fig. 2 shows that the major part of the peak $C_{22}H_{12}^+$ in the experimental spectrum of DBA is due to late metastable decay reactions in the vacuum. This is also true for most of the other hydrogen-deficient fragments observed in the spectrum of DBA and for the polycyclic aromatic ions in the spectrum of PS [8].

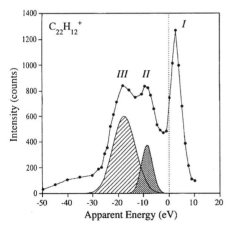

Fig. 2. Kinetic energy distribution of $C_{22}H_{12}^+$ (276 amu) sputtered from DBA on Ag. The Gaussian curves (hatched areas) indicate the calculated area of the identified H (II) and H_2 loss peaks (III). From Ref. [8].

Such late metastable decay events will not be observed in MD simulations where the timescale is limited to a few picoseconds. Moreover, it is not clear whether the Brenner hydrocarbon potential is appropriate to model elimination reactions such as H_2 loss. Nevertheless, the metastable decay rate depends directly on the internal energy of the fragments, which is accessible from MD. Thus, it is possible to define an internal energy threshold beyond which the sputtered particle will not be stable enough to be detected and to filter the 'stable' fragments in the MD results. Examples of adequate internal energy thresholds can be found in the literature. For instance, the naphthalene and phenanthrene cations will not be detected if they have more than 7 and 7.5 eV of internal energy, respectively [9]. The mass spectra and other properties like the KEDs and the angular distributions can be corrected using this internal energy threshold [5]. To illustrate this feature, PS is more appropriate as an example than DBA because it produces a whole range of characteristic fragments with a significant intensity between 0 and 100 amu. In Fig. 3a, the correction has been implemented for two characteristic fragments of PS with markedly different sizes, C_2H_2 and C_7H_7, using a 7.5 eV threshold for both species. The calculated KEDs were also corrected to mirror the 2 eV energy resolution of the experiment. The high energy tail of the KED of C_7H_7 (dots) is depleted when excited particles are excluded (dashed line), and the agreement with the experimental KED (Fig. 3b) becomes much better. Fig. 3 compares the experimental KED of $C_2H_3^+$ to the calculated KED of C_2H_2. Indeed, the intensity of C_2H_3 is weak in the simulation and the KED of the intense C_2H_2 averages the noisy distribution of C_2H_3. In contrast with C_7H_7, the KED of C_2H_2 does not change after correction, and remains very similar to the experimental KED of $C_2H_3^+$.

Fig. 3. Kinetic energy distributions of fragments sputtered from PS oligomers. (a) Simulation: C_7H_7 with (---) and without (•••) a 7.5 eV internal energy filter. (b) Experiment (2 eV passband).

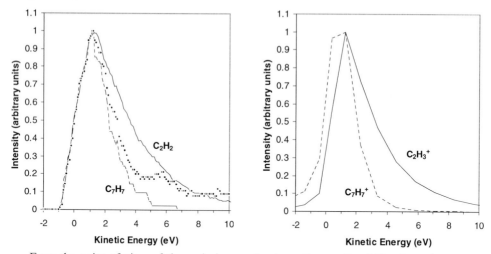

From the point of view of the emission mechanisms, the results of Fig. 3 are important because they show that characteristic fragments of PS like C_7H_7 can be sputtered by collisional mechanisms. In addition, the reduction of the mean kinetic energy with increasing fragment size [1] can be explained partly by the nature of the collisional interaction (non-corrected distribution of C_7H_7 versus C_2H_2) and partly by the internal energy-dependent dissociation of excited fragments (corrected distribution of C_7H_7). On the other hand, the fact that the experimental KED of $C_7H_7^+$ is shifted towards negative energies suggests that a significant fraction of the 'positive energy' peak of $C_7H_7^+$ can be attributed to unimolecular dissociation, too (Fig. 3b).

In the experiments, the average kinetic energy of DBA parent ions and Ag-cationized PS oligomers is unexpectedly high, as indicated by the width and high-energy tail of the KEDs [2]. Although the uncorrected KEDs calculated by MD are close to that obtained in the experiment, the internal-energy filtered KEDs of entire molecules are significantly thinner when a 7.5 eV stability threshold is used. To explain this disagreement, we propose that the value of the stability threshold might significantly depend on the fragment size. The implementation of a more realistic, size-dependent stability threshold based on the RRK theory is one of our major priorities.

5. Emission mechanisms as revealed by the MD simulation

To understand the emission mechanisms of fragments and parent molecules, a representative set of trajectories has been analyzed in detail. A major ejection scenario emerges from the MD simulation to explain the ejection of molecular fragments from flat molecules like DBA and PS tetramers (as opposed to vertical alkyl [10] and alkanethiol chains [11]). It appears indeed that the early and direct collision between the primary particle and a carbon atom of the molecule is the most efficient way to produce fragments. For PS tetramers, the implantation of one backbone atom in the substrate, followed by a second bond-breaking due to another moving carbon atom (or a small hydrocarbon) resulting from the primary particle impact, is an efficient way to release characteristic fragments with a low internal energy from inside the chain. This mechanism will be described at length in Ref.12. Instead, collision cascades developing in the silver substrate mainly lead to the ejection of entire molecules.

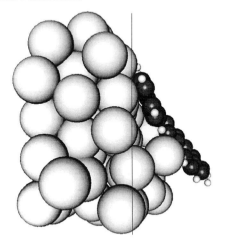

Fig. 4. Side view of an event showing the uplifting of a DBA molecule by several silver atoms. Silver is light grey and carbon is dark grey. The plane of the original silver surface, perpendicular to the page, is indicated by the full line. The molecule is pushed upwards by three silver atoms.

For entire PS and DBA molecules, MD simulations indicate two possible emission scenarios. First, the ejection can be induced by a single, energetic silver atom. Second, the molecule liftoff may be the result of the interaction with two, or more, moving silver atoms (cooperative uplifting). The first scenario is likely to produce molecules with a large amount of vibrational motion, as well as the interaction with several silver atoms having completely uncorrelated velocity vectors. For the flexible PS tetramers (and to a lesser extent for the stiff and lighter DBA molecules), the uplifting by several substrate atoms with quite similar velocity vectors will be the most efficient way to desorb 'cool' molecules with the high kinetic energy indicated by the experiments. This 'soft' uplifting mechanism is illustrated in Fig. 4 for DBA.

6. Conclusion

The combined approach including experimental measurements and MD simulations appears promising to elucidate the emission and fragmentation of organic molecules in SIMS. The MD simulation allows us to isolate collisionally-induced processes, excluding electronic and ionization effects as well as late metastable decay mechanisms. The influence of late metastable decay may be estimated using an internal energy filter for the sputtered fragments. As the introduction of ionization mechanisms in the MD code is not straightforward, the easiest way to overcome this limitation would be to postionize neutral fragments and molecules in the experiment. Concerning mechanisms, the detailed analysis of calculated trajectories showed that the direct interaction with the primary particle is very efficient to generate characteristic fragments, whereas collision cascades tend to eject entire molecules. The ejection of stable PS tetramers with more than 1-2 eV of kinetic energy and, furthermore, of larger organic molecules, is most likely to occur via a soft uplifting mechanism induced by several substrate atoms with similar momenta.

Acknowledgements. The authors (AD and BJG) would like to acknowledge the support from the National Science Foundation. Additional computational resources were provided by the Center for Academic Computing. AD and PB are grateful to the *Communaute Francaise de Belgique* which supported this work through its *Action de Recherche Concertee* (94/99-173). The ToF-SIMS equipment was acquired with the support of the *Region Wallonne* and *FRFC-Loterie Nationale* of Belgium.

References

[1] P.Bertrand and A.Delcorte, SIMS XI Proceedings; G.Gillen, R.Lareau, J.Bennett and F.Stevie (Eds.), Wiley, New York, (1998), p 437, and references therein.
[2] A.Delcorte and P.Bertrand, Surf.Sci.J. 412/413 (1998) 97-124.
[3] B.W.Schueler, Microsc.Microanal.Microstruct. 3 (1992) 119.
[4] A.Delcorte and P.Bertrand,.Nucl. Instr. And Meth. B 115 (1996) 246.
[5] R.Chatterjee, Z.Postawa, N.Winograd, B.J.Garrison, J. Phys. Chem. B 103 (1999) 151.
[6] D.W.Brenner, Phys.Rev. B 42 (1990) 9458.
[7] W.Brenner, J.A.Harrison, C.T.White, R.J.Colton, Thin Solid Films 206 (1991) 220.
[8] A.Delcorte, B.G.Segda and P.Bertrand, Surf.Sci.381 (1997) 18.
[9] Y.Gotkis, M.Oleinikova, M.Naor and C.Lifshitz, J. Phys. Chem. 97 (1993) 12282.
[10] R.S.Taylor and B.J.Garrison, Langmuir 11 (1995) 1220.
[11] K.S.S.Liu, C.W.Yong, B.J.Garrison, J.C.Vickerman, J. Phys. Chem. B 103 (1999) 3195.
[12] A.Delcorte, X.Vanden Eynde, P.Bertrand, J.C.Vickerman, B.J.Garrison, unpublished.

A. Benninghoven, P. Bertrand, H.-N. Migeon and H.W. Werner (Editors).
Proceedings of the 12th International Conference on Secondary Ion Mass Spectrometry,
Brussels, Belgium, 5-11 September 1999
© 2000 Elsevier Science B.V. All rights reserved.

33

STANDARDIZATION OF SIMS

Y. Homma

NTT Basic Research Laboratories, Atsugi, Kanagawa 243-0198, Japan
Homma@will.brl.ntt.co.jp

1. Introduction

The standardization of analytical methods provides means to ensure the reliability and efficiency of analyses. It primarily aims at the methods for industrial use, thus the objective fields of standardization are technologically mature rather than state of the art. However, because the recent rapid progress of advanced technologies reduces the turn-around time of standard preparation, interaction between standardization and the most advanced scientific fields becomes increasingly important.

The standardization of SIMS is proceeding as part of the activities of Technical Committee 201 (TC 201) [1] of the International Organization for Standardization (ISO). Subcommittee Six (SC6) is focusing on SIMS and related techniques. This paper reviews SIMS standardization in TC 201 and reports its current status.

2. Standardization in ISO

2.1 ISO Standards

According to the Directives of ISO, an international standard is a *"standard that is adopted by an international standardizing/standards organization and made available to the public"*[2]. For materials analysis, the international standards organization is ISO. ISO is supported by voluntary activities. All national standards organizations have the right to participate in the work of ISO technical committees and subcommittees. In making ISO standards, reaching a consensus is the crucial process. The ISO Directives read [3]: *"Consensus, which requires the resolution of substantial objections, is an essential procedural principle and a necessary condition for the preparation of International Standards that will be accepted and widely used. Although it is necessary for the technical work to progress speedily, sufficient time must be allowed before the approval stage for the discussion, negotiation and resolution of significant technical disagreements."*

For this purpose, the experts from each national standards organization or liaison organization hold meetings and discuss disagreements as they move through the various stages of the standardization procedure. The technical work is developed through these stages and associated documents are prepared. The stages are the preliminary stage (preliminary work item: PWI), proposal stage (new work item proposal: NP), preparatory stage (working draft: WD), committee stage (committee draft: CD), enquiry stage (draft international standard: DIS), approval stage (final draft international standard: FDIS), and publication stage (international standard: ISO). A project should advance to the enquiry stage within three years. Every ISO standard is reviewed at least every five years.

Table 1 Subcommittees and working group of ISO/TC 201

SC1	Terminology
SC2	General Procedures
SC3	Data management and Treatment
SC4	Depth Profiling
SC5	Auger Electron Spectroscopy
SC6	Secondary Ion Mass Spectrometry
SC7	X-ray Photoelectron Spectroscopy
SC8	Glow Discharge Spectrometry
WG2	Total Reflection X-ray Fluorescence Spectroscopy

2.2 TC201

TC201 was established in 1991 and is concerned with the standardization of surface chemical analysis [1]. It consists of eight subcommittees (SC) and one working group (WG). Table 1 list the fields that each SC or the WG covers. The analytical techniques considered for standardization are Auger electron spectroscopy, X-ray photoelectron spectroscopy, secondary ion mass spectrometry, grow discharge spectroscopy, and total reflection X-ray fluorescence spectroscopy. Common topics among the different analytical techniques, such as specimen handling and reference materials, are handled in General Procedures (SC2). SC6 focuses on SIMS and related techniques.

3. Activities of SC6

3.1 Policy of SC6

Although the scope of SC6 includes dynamic SIMS, static SIMS, and sputtered neutral mass spectrometry, standardization has proceeded from dynamic SIMS because it is the technique most widely used in industries. Since the most important application of dynamic SIMS is the determination of dopants or impurities, the focus has been on quantification. This requires a separate standard for each combination of matrix and dopant because of the large matrix effect of SIMS. Thus, the main policy has been to put priority on the material systems of industrial significance. Currently SC6 has two working groups and one study group (pre-working group) proceeding with the standardization of different aspects of dynamic SIMS.

3.2 WG1: Quantification of boron in silicon

Based on the above policy, the combination of the silicon matrix and boron as a dopant was chosen for consideration first. It utilizes the certified reference material of boron implants in silicon, NIST SRM 2137 [4]. One standard, ISO/FDIS 14237: "Determination of boron atomic concentration in silicon using uniformly doped materials", has almost been completed. In this standard, boron-doped bulk silicon specimens are calibrated using NIST SRM 2137 and are used as secondary reference materials for daily analysis. Two major issues have surfaced in the course of the standard's development. One is the mass discrimination between ^{10}B and ^{11}B. The NIST SRM 2137 is implanted with the minor isotope, ^{10}B, but most cases require determination of the major isotope, ^{11}B. The SIMS sensitivity to ^{10}B and ^{11}B was found to vary depending on the adjustment conditions of the spectrometer and detector because of the large relative mass difference between ^{10}B and ^{11}B ($\Delta M/M = 0.1$) [5, 6]. However, correction for the mass discrimination effect is difficult because the natural isotopic abundance of boron fluctuates and calibration standards for SIMS are not available. As a temporary method of correction, the ratio of $^{10}B^{28}Si^-$ to $^{11}B^{28}Si^-$ is used in order to evaluate the isotope abundance of bulk boron-doped silicon specimens. The other issue is the linearity evaluation of the detector. Initially, a linearity checking method was proposed that uses a calibration curve based on three levels of boron doping in bulk specimens. However, consensus on the use of three doping levels could not be reached. In the end, this method was adopted as an option instead of a normative procedure.

The ISO/FDIS 14237 is in the final stage and will soon be published. Currently, depth profiling procedures are being discussed for boron in silicon (ISO/WD 17560: "Method for depth profiling of boron in silicon"). In this standard, the calibration of boron concentration follows the procedure in ISO/FDIS 14237. Thus, the central concern is depth calibration. ISO/WD 17560 describes two procedures for sputter crater depth measurements: stylus profilometry and optical interferometry. Although this standard is for boron in silicon, the depth calibration procedure can be extended to crater-depth measurement in general. Therefore, it will serve as a prototype for quantitative SIMS depth profiling.

3.3 WG2: Documentary standards

In this working group, international standards are being developed based on local documents. Local SIMS standards that are currently available are those of the American Society for Testing and Materials (ASTM). Accordingly, two standards are being developed based on the ASTM standards: "Determining relative sensitivity factors from ion-implanted reference materials" (ISO/NP 18114) and "Reporting SIMS data". ISO/NP 18114 is based on ASTM†E1505-92 "Standard guide for determining SIMS relative sensitivity factors from ion implanted external standards" and describes the procedure for determining relative sensitivity factors (RSF) by using the formula

$$RSF_{A,M} = \frac{\Phi \cdot n}{\sum_{i=0}^{n}\left[(I_{A,i} - I_{BG})/I_{R,i}\right]z},$$

where, Φ is the implanted fluence of species A, n is the number of cycles over which the depth profile is integrated, $I_{A,i}$ and $I_{R,i}$ are the count rates of the analyte and reference species, at measurement cycle i, I_{BG} is the mean background count rate of species A, and z is the depth over which the depth profile is integrated.

The standard for reporting data is supposed to be based on ASTM E1162-87 "Standard practice for reporting sputter depth profile data in secondary ion mass spectrometry (SIMS)" and ASTM E1504-92 "Standard practice for reporting mass spectral data in secondary ion mass spectrometry (SIMS)".

3.4 Study group: Evaluation of depth resolution

A new approach under discussion is the development of procedures for depth resolution evaluation. In SC4, a standard is being developed for the use of hetero layers (see next section). This can be applied to SIMS, but for depth profiling of dopants, it is preferable to evaluate the depth resolution in a single matrix. Thus a delta-doped material is useful for the SIMS depth profiling. Multi-delta-doped materials are proposed as the reference materials for depth resolution and sputter rate evaluation. They can also be used for the optimization of ion beam irradiation (i.e., the energy, shape, and scanning condition of the primary ion beam). GaAs-delta-doped silicon is being examined in an international round robin study in order to establish measurement and data-analysis procedures. Critical issues would be the certification of delta-doped materials and definitions of parameters describing depth resolution.

4. Other ISO standards relevant to SIMS
SC1 has developed a vocabulary document (ISO/CD 18115: Vocabulary) that provides the definitions of terms useful for surface chemical analysis. This standard defines 14 surface analysis methods and more than 300 terms.

A reference-material document under development in SC2 is ISO/NP 16268 "Ion-implanted surface-analytical reference materials: Procedure for standardizing the retained areic dose in a working reference material". The document is grounded on theVAMAS project on ion-implanted materials [7], and describes the procedure for the certification of retained dose densities in wafer-type host materials using X-ray fluorescence spectroscopy or electron microbeam analysis.

For sputter depth profiling (SC4), two standards are being developed. One is ISO/DIS 14606: "Optimization using layered systems as reference materials", which describes the optimization of sputter depth profiling parameters using single-layer materials or multilayered materials in order to achieve optimum depth resolution. The other is ISO/CD 15969: "Guidelines to the measurement of sputtered depth". This gives information of various methods of sputter depth measurement, and will be published as an ISO technical report.

5. Summary
International standards relevant to SIMS are being developed in ISO/TC 201. The subcommittee for SIMS, SC6, is working on the quantification of boron in silicon, documentary standards, and the evaluation of depth resolution. Three official documents are under development, and one will soon be published as ISO 14237. For the future extension of standardization, such as to shallow depth profiling, development of reliable reference materials is increasingly important.

References
[1] C. J. Powell and R. Shimizu, Surf. Interface Anal. **20** (1993) 322; *ibid* **25** (1997) 860.
[2] *ISO/IEC Directives, Part 3 Rules for the structure and drafting of International Standards* 3rd edition, 1997.
[3] *ISO/IEC Directives, Part 1 Procedures for the technical work* 3rd edition, 1995.
[4] D. S. Simons, *Secondary Ion Mass Spectrometry SIMS IX*, ed. by A. Benninghoven, Y. Nihei, R. Shimizu and H. W. Werner, Wiley, Chichester, 1994, p.140.
[5] S. Hayashi *et al.*, *Secondary Ion Mass Spectrometry SIMS X*, ed. by A. Benninghoven, B. Hagenhoff and H. W. Werner, Wiley, Chichester, 1997, p.661.
[6] Y. Homma *et al.*, *Secondary Ion Mass Spectrometry SIMS X*, ed. by A. Benninghoven, B. Hagenhoff and H. W. Werner, Wiley, Chichester, 1997, p.681.
[7] D.W. Moon in these proceedings.
[8] W. H. Gries, Surf. Int. Anal. **24** (1996) 431.

A. Benninghoven, P. Bertrand, H.-N. Migeon and H.W. Werner (Editors).
Proceedings of the 12th International Conference on Secondary Ion Mass Spectrometry,
Brussels, Belgium, 5-11 September 1999

37

APPLICATIONS OF LOW TEMPERATURE SIMS IN CRYOBIOLOGICAL AND ECOLOGICAL STUDIES

M.V. Kosevich*, V.S. Shelkovsky, O.A. Boryak

B.Verkin Institute for Low Temperature Physics and Engineering of the National Academy of Sciences of Ukraine, 47, Lenin Ave., Kharkov, 310164, Ukraine, mvkosevich@ilt.kharkov.ua

1. Introduction

The multitude of objects and processes of physical, chemical, biological interest are successfully studied by various mass spectrometric techniques in the ambient or elevated temperatures range. There are, however, several specific branches of science dealing with phenomena proceeding at the low (subzero in the centigrade scale) temperatures, which necessitates the devise of adequate methods of investigation. Possibilities of application of low temperature (LT) secondary ion mass spectrometry (SIMS) and fast atom bombardment (FAB) techniques to the cryobiology and ecology comprise the subject of the present overview.

The main process which affects living organisms and their environment on temperature reduction is freezing of water and water solutions [1], and its study is a main challenge of cryobiology and related branch of physical chemistry. The most important feature of freezing of water is that at the practically achievable rates of freezing of macroscopic volumes (hundreds of degrees centigrade per minute) crystallization occurs. Amorphous state of water can be obtained only at the rates of cooling higher than $10^{5\circ}C \cdot s^{-1}$ and is produced experimentally by deposition of water vapour on surfaces cooled below about -140°C. Water ice does not co-crystallize with the majority of compounds (although water molecules are included in the crystalline hydrates lattice) and phase separation takes place on cooling of water solutions. A practical implementation of an attractive idea of deep freezing of biological objects to provide their prolonged storage with subsequent thawing is significantly hampered by damaging factors caused by water crystallization [1, 2]. Along with purely mechanical damage by sharp ice crystallites, more complicated molecular mechanisms of biomolecules damage are operative, such as increase of concentration and change of pH of solution which remains between the growing ice crystallites during freezing To reduce these negative effects special compounds called cryoprotectors are developed [2].

The parameters of freezing of water solutions and the composition of the samples formed are described by phase diagrams. Examples for two-component water-organic (glycerol) and water-inorganic compound (HNO_3) systems are presented in Fig. 1 and Fig. 2 respectively. Equilibrium (water+glycerol) phase diagram is of the simplest type with one eutectic point and, in ideal case, complete phase separation. The peculiarity of this system is that glycerol, in contrast to water, is strongly prone to amorphysation (vitrification) under comparable moderate rates of cooling, as indicated by the right wing of the diagram in Fig. 1, achieved only at very special conditions, marked by a dotted line. This property of glycerol predestines its use as an efficient cryoprotector to which, in practice, non-equilibrium phase diagrams (not shown here) are to be applied.

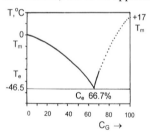

Fig. 1. Equilibrium phase diagram of water-glycerol system, based on data from [2]. Dotted line indicates that vitrification rather than crystallization occurs in practice for glycerol.

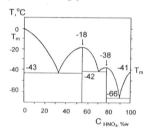

Fig. 2. Phase diagram of water-HNO₃ system based on data from [3]. Two types of crystalline hydrates HNO₃•3H₂O and HNO₃•H₂O are formed at -18 and -38°C.

In the case of (water + HNO_3) system, in dependence on the initial concentration of solution, two types of new compounds, the crystalline hydrates $HNO_3 \cdot 3H_2O$ and $HNO_3 \cdot H_2O$ are formed. This system is of particular interest for ecology and atmospheric chemistry [4], since nitric acid trihydrate was discovered in the composition of polar stratospheric clouds.

A number of possible applications of LT SIMS/FAB in the studies of the above objects and phenomena, poorly accessible to other experimental techniques, are as follows.

- Determination of the chemical and phase composition of the frozen multy-component mixtures, identification of new compounds formed on freezing.
- Investigation of changes in intermolecular interactions in the condensed samples in comparison with those in ambient liquid solutions of biologically active molecules.
- Investigation of peculiarities of real (non-ideal) non-equilibrium processes, monitoring of phase transitions in about 200°C temperature range available.
- Study of condensation of various ecological pollutants on ices on the Earth's surface and in the atmosphere and the effects of collisions of accelerated particles with such ices.

2. Experimental

First we shall stop not so much on a definite instrument design as on distinctive features of the LT SIMS technique. In earlier LT SIMS experiments aimed at the study of condensed gases [5] rather stringent requirements for ultra high vacuum (better than 10^{-7}Pa [6]) were imposed and rather complicated cryostats with liquid helium cooling were necessary. In the case of water solutions the temperature range provided by liquid nitrogen as a cooling agent (down to -196°C) is quite sufficient. The temperatures of condensation of practically all inorganic components of the residual gas are lower than the liquid nitrogen temperature, so that they do not affect the frozen sample and the use of normal commercial instruments (at pressures of about 10^{-6} Pa) becomes possible. As to the organic traces, vacuum pump fluids and water can be efficiently removed by cryogenic shields (traps) around the working area of the LT ion source. The decrease of saturated vapour pressure over the surface of condensed samples with temperature decrease permits to preserve in the intact state some objects which undergo rapid dehydration, sublimation or evaporation under ambient mass spectrometric conditions. Along with these advantages, the main limitations of the LT experiments are connected with the necessity to work at low pressures, which does not permit to make direct correlations with the phase diagrams of water solutions determined, usually, at atmospheric pressure. Sublimation of ice, which is completed for small samples of several micrograms weight under pressure of 10^{-5}-10^{-6}

Pa at about -55±5°C [7, 8], distorts the composition of the sample and, in principle, does not allow to observe melting of water solutions, since the eutectic temperature of many of such systems occurs above this value [3].

Since highly heterogeneous samples are formed due to phase separation on freezing of water solutions, the proper account of the sample morphology and estimate (or prescription) of its composition using the phase diagrams of the system under study is a crucial point for interpretation of the LT SIMS/FAB spectra, described in detail in [9].

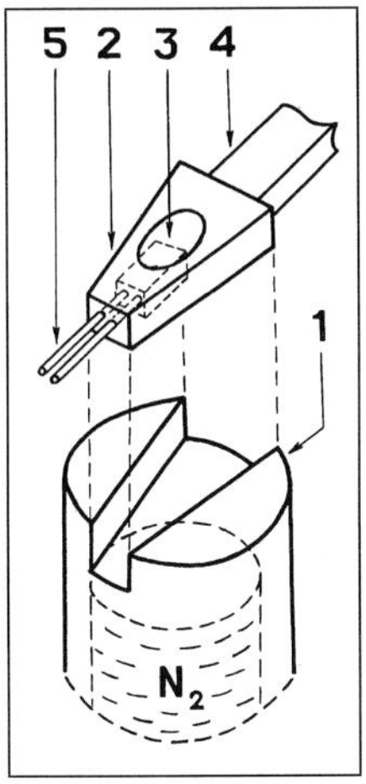

Fig. 3. Cryogenic block of the LT SIMS/FAB ion source (see text for details).

The results described in the present overview were obtained using a sector magnetic MI-1201E mass spectrometer (Ukraine), equipped with a dedicated cryogenic secondary ion source [10], (Fig. 3), the design of which allows one to study cooled and frozen solutions under controlled temperature conditions in the range of -196° to 0°C. The cryogenic block consists of a hollow copper cylinder (1) cooled by liquid nitrogen. A copper sample holder (2) with a grove for a sample (3) is fixed on a rod (4) of the sample direct inlet system. The temperature is controlled by a change of flow of liquid nitrogen or its vapors and measured by a thermistor (5). Samples of 5-10 µL volume were frozen in vapours of liquid nitrogen on a copper or aluminum sample holder with the rate of cooling of 200°C•min^{-1} and rapidly inserted into the cryogenic block through a vacuum lock. Neutral argon atoms of 4.5keV primary beam energy were used as a bombarding agent. Vacuum prior the bombarding gas inlet was usually about 10^{-5} - 10^{-6} Pa. The selection of the objects for these studies has been limited by mass range of 1500 a.u. of the instrument used.

Some experiments were performed on VG-ZAB (Micromass, UK) double-focusing mass spectrometer [11, 12]. In this case no special temperature stabilization system was used: the sample was frozen directly on the sample inlet rod and thawed in the ion source due to thermal leak. High speed of spectra recording permitted to obtain a number of spectra during the frozen sample lifetime (usually 5-10 minutes).

3. Results and discussion

A systematic study of objects and phenomena of cryobiological interest by means of LT SISM/FAB technique has been conducted recently [7-13]. At first a number of cryoprotectors and water-cryprotector mixtures were studied [7, 11, 12]. Correlations between the dependencies of LT SIMS spectral patterns on temperature of the sample with phase transitions in the systems were established for water mixtures with glycerol [7] and primary alcohols ethanol and methanol [11-13] (the latter posses excellent cryoprotector properties but cannot be used in practice due to high toxicity). No mixed water-solute clusters were observed for glycerol, which agrees with complete phase separation in the system, while in the case of ethanol and methanol sets of $M_n \bullet (H_2O)_m \bullet H^+$ hydrate clusters were recorded, which correlates with the existence of stable hydrates for these compounds in the liquid. Hydrate clusters, reflecting presence of water which remains bound with biomolecules in the solid state after freezing have been recorded by now for oligomers of polymethyleneglycol.

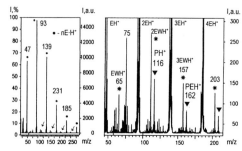

Fig. 4. LT SIMS mass spectrum of the frozen saturated solution of amino acid proline (P) in distilled 95.5% ethanol (E). T = -120°C.

Next, solutions of small biomolecules in alcohos were tested. In Fig. 4 a part of the LT spectrum of solution of amino acid proline (P) in ethanol, which is liquid in -130°C to -100°C range [13], is presented. The intensity of the peaks of the protonated proline PH^+ and its clusters with ethanol $P \cdot E_n \cdot H^+$ (n=1-5) is much smaller as com-pared with the intensity of the pure ethanol clusters, which reflects the solubility of the amino acid or its content in the liquid eutectic phase at such low temperatures. Solutions of some other amino acids and of a salt NaCl showed similar behavior.

As a next step, frozen solutions of a mixture of small biomolecules, pyrimidine nitrogen bases, with salts of mono- and divalent metals in water and cryoprotector glycerol were compared with the aim to reveal differences in parameters of biomolecule-metal ion binding in two solvents at the reduced temperatures [8]. It appeared that certain parameters of LT SIMS spectra reflect the damaging factors on molecular level for the frozen water solutions and, by contrast, positive role of a cryoprotector media. Significant increase of binding of alkali metal ions with nitrogen bases (which is rather small at the ambient conditions [14]) in the frozen water solutions was detected on the basis of relatively high intensity of biomole-cule-metal ion clusters MNa^+, MK^+, which can be explained by a noticeable concentration of the solutes in the channels between growing ice crystallites during freezing. Hydrate clusters of the nitrogen bases were not observed, which points to their dehydration in the condensed state. Both the phenomena observed affect normal media for functioning of biomolecules and can cause conformational changes and denaturation in the case of large biopolymers. In contrast, in the LT SIMS spectra of glycerol solutions, which solidify amorphously (see Fig. 1) with rough preservation of the even distribution of the solute characteristic of liquid solutions, no nitrogen base-metal ion clusters were observed. At the same time, glycerol-base clusters were recorded, which points to preservation of interactions of the solute with the solvent molecules in the condensed state. Both factors are positive in relation to cryoprotection.

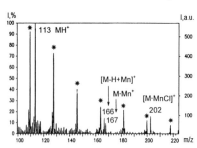

Fig. 5. LT FAB mass spectrum of the frozen 10^{-3} M water solution of a nitrogen base Uracil (M) and $MnCl_2$ salt. T = -60°C. (*) - $(H_2O)_n \cdot H^+$.

Certain correlations between binding of divalent metal ions with the nitrogen bases in the ambient and frozen water solutions were observed. An example for (uracil+$MnCl_2$+water) frozen system is presented in Fig. 5. Along with singly charged clusters $M \cdot Mn^+$ and $[M \cdot MnCl]^+$, a peculiar ion $[M-H+Mn]^+$ was recorded, which corresponds to substitution of one hydrogen of the base by the divalent metal. The same mechanism of divalent metals binding with substitution of the hydrogen is characteristic of the liquid water solution [14], and it may be concluded that its products are preserved under freezing.

For deeper insight into properties of water-salt media, frozen water solutions of chlorides of some divalent metals (Mg, Mn, Ca, Cu, Zn, Ba) were analyzed. Crystalline hydrates are formed in these systems under freezing and hydrate clusters are expected to be present in the spectra. Indeed, LT FAB mass spectra of all salts solutions contained Me^+ and $(H_2O)_n \cdot Me^+$, $(H_2O)_n \cdot (MeX)_m \cdot Me^+$ cluster ions. Along with these, OH-containing ions $[MeOH]^+$, $[(H_2O)_n \cdot MeOH]^+$ were recorded, and $[MeOH]^+$ species remained after the dehydration of the sample. It was suggested to explain this observation by separation of a phase of a basic salt $Me(OH)Cl$ as a product of the salts hydrolysis under non-equilibrium conditions of freezing [15]. Melting of the corresponding crystallites on thawing can cause local change of pH [15], which may damage biomolecules [2] occurring in such spatial region of the cryo-treated object.

As to ecological problems, an obvious application of the LT SIMS is in analysis of ecological pollutants adsorbed in the surfaces of snow and ices of different origin. An effect of expelling of the solutes to the surface of the growing ice crystallites enhances dramatically the sensitivity of LT SIMS to traces of metal ions present in water [16].

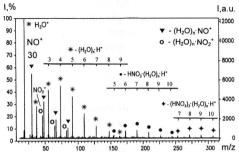

Fig. 6. LT FAB mass spectrum of the 67.4% frozen water solution of HNO_3. The sample consists mainly of $HNO_3 \cdot 3H_2O$. T = -80°C.

Modeling of heterogeneous reactions on surfaces of solid particles and ice grains present in the atmosphere is presently a challenge in atmospheric research, in particular, in connection with the ozone hole problem [4]. Using the phase diagram for (water+HNO_3) system, Fig. 2, samples of the nitric acid trihydrate $HNO_3 \cdot 3H_2O$, present in the polar strato-spheric clouds, were prepared. The LT FAB mass spectra, Fig. 6, contained sets of cluster ions, corresponding to hydrates of NO, NO_2, HNO_3, and water clusters. It should be marked that, while gas-phase mechanisms of ion formation are well studied within the framework of the atmospheric chemistry [17], a possibility of ion production due to collisions of accelerated particles of cosmic rays with the frozen grains has not been considered in full measure. The present results show, that a variety of cluster ions can be produced with a rather high efficiency under the particles impact on the nitric acid-containing ice, which may contribute to the ion population of the related region of the stratosphere.

4. Conclusion

The presented overview of the results obtained by now by means of LT SIMS demonstrate its potentialities in the studies of various objects in the subzero temperature range. These types of investigations may be further extended to the systems containing large biopolymers and natural biological fluids. Elaboration of a mapping technique for frozen tissues, well developed in inorganic SIMS, seems promising as well.

Acknowledgments: The authors are grateful to Dr. K. Vekey for his kind help with high performance mass spectrometric facilities and to Prof. P.J. Derrick for fruitful discussion of some results.

42

References
[1]   F. Franks, Water - A Comprehensive Treatise, Vol. 7. Water and aqueous solutions at subzero temperatures, Plenum Press, New York, London, 1982.
[2]   A.M. Belous and V.I. Grishenko, Cryobiology, Naukova Dumka, Kiev, 1994.
[3]   A.A. Revdel and A.M. Ponomareva (eds.), Short Reference Book on Physico-Chemical Data, Khimiya, Leningrad, 1983.
[4]   P. Hamill, O.B. Toon, Phys. Today, 44 (1991) 34.
[5]   J. Michl, Int. J. Mass Spectrom. Ion Phys., 53 (1983) 255.
[6]   V. Cherepin, Secondary Ion Mass Spectroscopy of Solid Surfaces, Utrecht Science Press, Utrecht, 1987.
[7]   O.A. Boryak, M.V. Kosevich, V.S. Shelkovsky and Yu.P.Blagoy, Rapid Commun. in Mass Spectrom., 9 (1995) 978.
[8]   O.A. Boryak, M.V. Kosevich, V.S. Shelkovsky and Yu.P.Blagoy, Ibid., 10 (1996) 197.
[9]   M.V. Kosevich, Eur. Mass Spectrom., 4 (1998) 251.
[10] O.A. Boryak, M.V. Kosevich and V.S. Shelkovskii, Instrum. and Experim. Techniques, 6 (1993) 935.
[11] M.V. Kosevich, G. Czira, O.A. Boryak, V.S. Shelkovsky and K. Vekey, Rapid Commun. in Mass Spectrom., 11 (1997) 1411.
[12] M.V. Kosevich, G. Czira, O.A. Boryak, V.S. Shelkovsky and K. Vekey, J. Mass Spectrom., 33 (1998) 843.
[13] M.V. Kosevich, Eur. Mass Spectrom., 3 (1997) 320.
[14] Yu. P. Blagoy (ed.), Metal Complexes of Nucleic Acids in Solutions, Naukova Dumka, Kiev, 1991.
[15] M.V. Kosevich, Problems of Cryobiology, 2 (1999) 54.
[16] M.V. Kosevich, O.A. Boryak, I.O.Stepanov and V.S.Shelkovsky, Eur. Mass Spectrom., 3 (1997) 11.
[17] D. Smith and P. Spanel, Mass Spectrom. Rev., 14 (1995) 255.

A. Benninghoven, P. Bertrand, H.-N. Migeon and H.W. Werner (Editors).
Proceedings of the 12th International Conference on Secondary Ion Mass Spectrometry,
Brussels, Belgium, 5-11 September 1999

NONDESTRUCTIVE DEPTH PROFILING WITH ATOMIC DEPTH RESOLUTION WITH MEDIUM ENERGY ION SCATTERING SPECTROSCOPY

D. W. Moon[*1], H.K.Kim[1], H.J.Kang[2]

[1]Surface Analysis Group, Korea Research Institute of Standards and Science, Yusung P.O.102, Taejon 305-600, Korea, [2]Department of Physics, Chungbuk University, Cheongju 360-763, Korea,

1. Introduction

Distortion of original profiles due to ion beam bombardment requires further development for minimizing sputter induced surface damage. Widely investigated approaches are based on using low energy ions, glancing incidence angles, and cluster ions.[1] In this report, Medium Energy Ion Scattering Spectroscopy (MEIS) depth profiling based on precise determination of electronic energy loss of 100 keV ions in solids is described. MEIS itself provides composition profile information with atomic layer depth resolution, which can be used to understand the sputter damage process in detail. The understanding can help us to minimize the sputter damage or deconvolute the original undistorted profiles from measured profiles.

2. The Role of MEIS for Nondestructive Depth Profiling with Atomic Layer Depth Resolution for Ultrathin Films

The most important feature of MEIS is its quantification capability with atomic layer depth resolution. MEIS analysis is based on binary scattering of 100keV H^+ ions with target atoms with accurately predictable scattering cross sections[2]. Therefore, after calibration of a MEIS analysis system with a known standard such as single crystals or ion implanted samples, MEIS intensities of any elements can be quantitatively converted into areal atom densities. The electronic stopping powers of projectiles are maximum around 100 keV and the use of an electrostatic energy analyzer improve the depth resolution of MEIS down to .5nm, which is about 10 times better than that of RBS. The analysis depth range is around several 10nm.

Even though a prolonged exposure to projectile ions damages an surface layer, most of MEIS analyses can be finished below the ion dose of 10^{13} ions/cm^2. The movement of samples during MEIS analysis further minimizes the damage problem. Therefore MEIS results can be regarded to be nondestructive. Nondestructive nature of MEIS analysis with atomic depth resolution make it very useful to understand the ion-surface interactions such as radiation damage profiles and the change of surface and near-surface layer composition change due to sputtering[3]. It also suggest that MEIS is an excellent choice for compositional profiling analysis of ultrathin films, while sputtering based profiles are subject to profile distortion problems.

Channeling and blocking analysis of crystalline substrates and epitaxial layers provide very local structural information such as strain and radiation damage. The minimum in the angular distribution of scattered ions corresponds to the bond angle with neighbor atoms due to the blocking mechanism. Combined with the atomic layer depth resolution, blocking analysis can give strain profiling and damage profiling. [4-6]

With these special features, MEIS has been successfully used to study radiation damage profiles, surface and interface structural analysis, and strain profiles of ultrathin film interfaces.

3. Instumentation of MEIS

Details of the MEIS system at Korea Research Institute of Standards and Science is given elsewhere [3] and a brief description will be given here. In this experiment, 100 keV, 10 nA H$^+$ ion beams were used and the energy of the scattered H$^+$ ions were analyzed by a toroidal electrostatic energy analyzer with a two-dimensional position sensitive detector. The base pressure of the MEIS chamber was 10×10^{-10} torr but during MEIS analyses, the operating pressure was 10×10^{-9} torr. To measure crystalline substrates or epitaxial thin films, the combined channeling and blocking technique was employed. Most of the MEIS spectra for (100) surfaces were taken in the double alignment condition with the channeling and the blocking along the [111] axial directions corresponding to the incidence angle of 35.3^0 from the surface normal and the scattering angle of $70.5°$.

4. Depth Profiling of nm Gate Oxides

To demonstrate the MEIS capabilities of compositional and structural profiling analysis of ultrathin films, the MEIS spectrum for ultrathin 3-5 nm SiO$_2$ gate oxide on Si(001) is given in Fig.1. The energy spectrum were fitted by simulations that calculate the energy and intensities of the back-scattered particles scattered from thin slabs in the specimen. For the 3.0 nm gate oxide, the thickness of the stoichiometric SiO$_2$ layer is 1.2 nm.

The thickness of the interface is $(4.8 \pm 1.0) \times 10^{15}$ Si atoms/cm^2, which corresponds to (1.2 ± 0.3) nm considering the volume expansion due to Si oxidation. According to the detailed simulation [4], there is a transition region with continuously decreasing O density and continuously increasing Si density from the thermal oxide to the Si substrate. The existence of the Si crystalline and its distribution in the transition region could be seen clearly in the presence and the change of the blocking dips in the angular profiles of the Si peak near the [111] direction[4]. The most interesting and important observation in this experiment is the shifts of the [111] blocking dips to a higher scattering angle in the interface with respect to the dips at the bulk silicon.

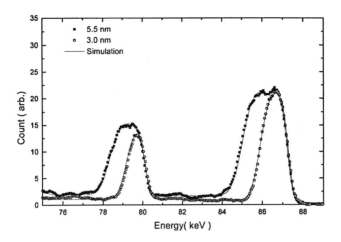

Fig.1: MEIS spectrum for ultrathin 5.5 nm and 3.0 nm SiO_2 gate oxides on Si(001)

From the shift of the blocking dip position, the strain of the crystalline Si lattices could be estimated. The blocking dip shift of the thermal oxide shows the compressive strain distribution of the Si lattice in the interface transition layer. Details of the strain profiling is described elsewhere [4-6].

Recently it has been reviewed regarding to preferential sputtering of Ta_2O_5, sputter damage of Si and Pt and Cu single crystals, depth profiling and interface analysis of ultrathin 3-5 nm SiO_2 on Si(001), ultrathin film growth with 10 monolayer epitaxial Ge on Si(001) with H surfactant.[7]

5. Ultimate Single Atomic Layer Depth Resolution of MEIS

Ultimate single atomic layer depth resolution was demonstrated with a Cu_3Au (100) surface with 100 keV N^+ ions as shown in Fig. 2. For Cu_3Au (100), the 1st surface atomic layer is a Cu-Au layer and the 2nd layer is pure Cu layer. The use of N^+ ions increases the electronic stopping power so that the depth resolution improved to differentiate the 3rd Au layer from the 1st layer. Under the double aligned condition, subsurface atoms are completely shadowed by the 1st layer atoms. With 9.75^0 off from the channeled direction, the 3rd layer Au atoms could be separated. Heavier N^+ ions may cause the damage problem but for single crystalline metals, the damage problem is generally not significant. [8] Unfortunately, the use of N^+ ions for analyses of Si surfaces is not possible due to ion beam damage problem. However, with H^+ ions, the beam damage problem is negligible under normal analysis conditions.

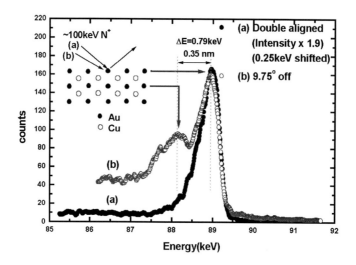

Fig 2: The 100 keV N⁺ MEIS spectrum for a Cu₃Au(100) surface.

6. Sputter Damage Profiles with MEIS

Out recent studies on sputter damage profiles with MEIS were introduced briefly here. To study the damage profile development due to ion bombardment as a function of the ion dose and the ion incidence angle effect on the damage profiles, MEIS spectra were taken from a clean Si(100) surface and ion beam sputtered Si(100) surfaces. [9] MEIS analysis shows that the Si(100) surface layer becomes amorphous initially and the amorphous surface layer gets thicker for a Si(100) surface bombarded with 3 keV Ar^+ ions. The damage profile of the Si(100) saturated at the ion dose of $3x10^{16}$ ions/cm² at the incidence angle of 35° from the surface normal. At the saturation ion dose, the depth of the damaged layer was 9.6 nm.

The depth of the damaged layer was significantly reduced from 14.2 nm at the surface normal to 4.8 nm at the incidence angle of 80°. Though the depth of the damaged layer was minimized for the sputtering at the extremely glancing angle of 80°, the damaged layer did not disappear but remained as a very shallow surface layer. Similar studies on Pt(111), Cu(111) metallic single crystals showed little radiation damage compared to Si crystals.[8]

To understand the surface oxidation due to the primary oxygen ions commonly used in SIMS analysis, ion beam oxidation of Si(100) was studied with 3 keV O_2^+ ions at room temperature.[10] At the ion dose of $5x10^{15}$ /cm² range, the Si surface becomes amorphous without any formation of an oxidized Si layer. Above $1x10^{17}$/cm² ion dose, the MEIS spectrum clearly showed the formation of a SiO_2 layer with a Si suboxide layer and a disordered Si layer in the interface, of which the thickness is 6.7nm, 2.5nm and 3.3 nm, respectively.

7. Preferential Sputtering Studied with MEIS

Changes of surface composition due to preferential sputtering have been studied with MEIS as summarized here. For a WSi_2 sample sputtered with 3 keV Ar^+ ions in the incidence angle of 50^0 from the surface normal up to 10^{17} ions/cm^2, the MEIS spectra showed a very clear W enriched surface layer as in Fig. 3.

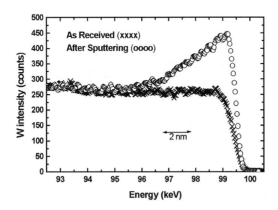

Fig 3: The W MEIS spectrum of WSi_2 after sputtering with 3 keV Ar^+ ions in the incidence angle of 50^0 from the surface normal up to 10^{17} ions/cm^2.

The composition of the WSi_2 was $W_{0.33}Si_{0.67}$ from ICP-OES analysis. Using the unmodified bulk composition as an internal standard, the peak intensity of W in the modified surface layer corresponds to 56.7 atomic % of W. The increase of W concentration in the surface altered layer is more than 75%, which is higher than the change of 45% for Ta_2O_5.[3] The half-width of the altered surface layer is 3.1±0.5nm but the modified layer extends up to 8nm as shown in Fig. 3. As a comparison, the half-width of the altered surface layer due to the preferential sputtering of oxygen atoms from Ta_2O_5 was 2.6±0.8nm [3], which is similar to the value observed for WSi_2. It has been shown that preferential sputtering is minimized at glancing incidence angle with Ta_2O_5.[3]

8. Conclusions

The special features of MEIS were described in terms of nondestructive compositional and structural depth profiling with atomic layer depth resolution. It was shown that MEIS is very useful to analyze ultrathin films and understand the sputter damages with examples with 3-5nm SiO_2 gate oxides, WSi_2 and Ta_2O_5 thin films films.

References

[1] M.G.Dowsett, Secondary Ion Mass Spectrometry SIMS XI, eds. A.Benninghoven et al (J.Wiley and Sons 1997), 259

[2] J.F. van der Veen, Surf. Sci. Rep. **5**, 199 (1985).

[3] J.C. Lee, C.S. Chung, H.J. Kang, Y.P. Kim, H.K. Kim and D.W. Moon, J. Vac. Sci. Technol. A **13**, 1325 (1995).

[4] Y. P. Kim, S. K. Choi, H. K. Kim and D. W. Moon, Appl. Phys. Lett., 71,3504, (1997)

[5] Y.H.Ha, S.-H. Kim, S.Y.Lee, J.H. Kim, D.H. Baek, H.K. Kim and D.W.Moon, Appl. Phys. Lett., in press(1999).

[6] S.-J.Kahng, Y.H.Ha, J.-Y.park, S.Kim, D.W.Moon, Y.Kuk, Phys. Rev. Let., 80,4931 (1998)

[7] D. W. Moon, H. K. Kim, and H. J. Kang, J. Surf. Anal. in press(1999).

[8] D.W. Moon, Y.Ha, H.K.Kim, K.J.Kim, H.S.Kim, J.Y.Lee, S.-H. Kim, Appl. Surf. Sci. in press (1999).

[9] J.S.Lee, S.C.Jeong, H.J.Kang, H.K.Kim, and D.W.Moon, Applied. Surf. Sci. 100/101. 97- 101 (1996).

[10] Y.P.Kim, S.K.Choi, Y.H.Ha, S.-H.Kim, H.K.Kim, D.W.Moon, Appl. Surf. Sci., 117/118, 207-201 (1997)

A. Benninghoven, P. Bertrand, H.-N. Migeon and H.W. Werner (Editors).
Proceedings of the 12th International Conference on Secondary Ion Mass Spectrometry,
Brussels, Belgium, 5-11 September 1999

DUAL BEAM SIMS DEPTH PROFILING

E. Niehuis, T. Grehl
ION-TOF GmbH, Mendelstr. 11, D-48149 Muenster, Germany
e-mail: ewald.niehuis@ion-tof.com

1. Introduction

In standard SIMS depth profiling instruments (quadrupole, magnetic sector), a single primary ion gun generates the secondary ions used to characterise the surface composition and at the same time, erodes the sample with a sufficiently high current density to get in-depth information. In Time-of-Flight SIMS (TOF-SIMS), the primary ion gun is operated in a pulsed mode with nanosecond ion pulses. The current densities are reduced by about 4 – 5 orders of magnitude compared to a DC operation. For this reason, TOF-SIMS was originally considered as a powerful surface analysis tool with very good sensitivity, parallel detection of all masses and high mass resolution, but not considered as a tool for in-depth analysis. In order to overcome this limitation, a dual beam approach has been introduced [1]. The high energy pulsed analysis gun is combined with a low energy sputter gun for the erosion. This dual beam approach offers a unique flexibility and allows to optimise the parameters for analysis and erosion independently. It is applied successfully in basic research, depth profiling of ultra-thin layers, interface analysis and micro area depth profiling.

2. Principle of dual beam TOF-SIMS depth profiling

The average analysis current of the pulsed beam in TOF-SIMS is rather low, typically in the range of a few pA, not sufficient for a reasonable erosion speed. A simple way to increase the erosion speed would be to alternate an acquisition phase of a few seconds with pulsed gun operation and a sputter phase of a similar duration with a DC operation of the gun. Such a mode has been used for single gun depth profiling in TOF-SIMS [2]. The major disadvantages of this approach are the interruption of the analysis during the sputter phase, which leads to a significant reduction in the average data rates, and the high beam energy needed to generate short pulses with high intensity, which gives poor depth resolution.

Both problems can be overcome in the dual beam interlaced mode [1]. Two separate pulsed guns are used for analysis and erosion. The timing diagram of the interlaced mode is shown in figure 1. A short pulse of the analysis gun with a duration T_p of 0.5 – 50 ns generates secondary ions, which are then accelerated by the extraction field and travel through the TOF analyser. This is repeated with a cycle time T_C which is equivalent to the flight time of the highest mass to be recorded. At a repetition rate of 10 kHz ($T_C = 100$ µs) the mass range is about 1000 u and it decreases rather rapidly with the increase in repetition rate. The highest useful repetition rate is about 50 kHz ($T_C = 20$ µs) which gives a mass range of about 50 u. During the travel time of the secondary ions, the extraction field is switched off and a pulsed sputter gun with very long pulses erodes the surface. The extraction period of the secondary ions is rather short (5 - 10 us) compared to T_C, which leads to a rather high duty cycle of the sputter gun of 80 – 90 % at 10 kHz. For each data point of a depth profile, the secondary ions are counted for some $10^4 - 10^5$ cycles. Crater edge effects are minimised by rastering the analysis beam over a small area (typically 50x50 µm²) in the centre of a sputter crater with an area about 3 to 4 times larger (typically 200x200 µm²).

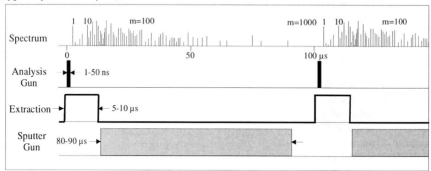

Fig.1 Timing diagram for TOF-SIMS dual beam profiling

Usually, the analysis gun is operated at rather high energies of 10 keV and above to generate very intense, sub-ns pulses with a small spot size. The sputter gun is operated at very low energies ≤ 1 keV and appropriate impact angles to achieve good depth resolution. As the extraction field is switched off during the sputtering, any sputter energy and angle is possible in contrast to conventional instruments with DC extraction fields. Reactive species are used for sputtering to optimise the secondary ion yields in positive or negative SIMS mode. The species of the analysis gun reach only very low concentrations in the steady state and do not influence the ion yields.

The contribution of the analysis and sputter beam to the sample consumption in the analysed area is given by the ratio R_E of the erosion rates of the two beams (js, jA - current density of sputter and analysis beam; Ys, YA - sputter yield of sputter ions and analysis ions):

$$R_E = \frac{j_S}{j_A} \cdot \frac{Y_S}{Y_A}$$

R_E can be used to distinguish three interesting regimes for dual beam depth profiling. In ultra-shallow depth profiling the depth resolution is of major importance. With $R_E = 100 - 1000$ the contribution of the analysis beam to the atomic mixing can be neglected. The depth resolution depends only on the parameters of the sputter beam. In micro area depth profiling the decrease in the analysis area leads to an increase in the current density of the analysis beam. In the range $R_E = 10 - 100$ the depth resolution is already degraded (see 4.). Most of the material is still removed by the sputter beam and not used for analysis. If the analytical volume becomes extremely small, a large fraction of the material needs to be removed by the analysis beam to get good detection limits. With $R_E = 0.1 - 1$, the low energy sputter beam is only used to generate a high surface concentration of reactive species for optimum SIMS yields. The depth resolution is determined by the parameters of the analysis beam.

In view of the various types of applications, a comparison of the TOF-SIMS dual beam profiling technique to other types of instruments like quadrupole and magnetic sector is rather complex and beyond the scope of this paper. The reader is referred to other papers in this volume and to the results of a recent round robin for Boron ultra-shallow profiling [3]. It can be stated, that TOF-SIMS profiling is attractive for the analysis of very thin layers of a few nm up to some 10 nm, for the detailed analysis of interfaces and for applications in which many different elements need to be profiled. Especially, the capability of a complete retrospective analysis makes it ideally suited for the profiling of samples with unknown composition. High resolution spectra can be reconstructed for any depth interval, profiles can be reconstructed for every mass of interest as well as images for any mass at any depth.

3. Ultra-shallow depth profiling

The dual beam technique for TOF-SIMS has been introduced about 6 years ago [1], but the number of papers published on this subject is still very limited. In early studies the technique has been used for depth profiling of shallow implants and delta dopant layers as well as for the analysis of gate oxides [4, 5]. A pulsed Ar gun at 11 keV was used for the analysis and the erosion was performed using either 1 keV Ar sputtering in combination with oxygen flooding for electropositive elements or 1 keV Cs sputtering for electronegative elements. The impact angle was $45°$- $52°$. Iltgen [6] has studied the depth resolution for B delta doped samples for a variety of primary ion species like noble gases, O_2^+ and SF_5^+ in the energy range between 500 eV and 2 keV. The impact angle of the sputter gun was varied between $42°$ and $63°$. The low energy sputtering was combined with oxygen flooding to fully oxidised the Si surface. A decay length well below 1 nm has been achieved for molecular primary ions like O_2^+ and SF_5^+ at sub-keV energies.

A serious problem in ultra-shallow depth profiling are erosion rate changes and changes of the relative sensitivity factors (RSF) in the transient regime. It has been shown for O_2 depth profiling of Si that this can lead to errors in the depth scale (surface shift) and to significant errors in the measured total dose for low energy implants [7, 8]. The width of the transient regime is decreasing approximately proportional to the sputter energy and is smaller for molecular primary ions like O_2^+ and SF_5^+ than for atomic species like Ar^+ under oxygen flooding conditions [9]. With the decreasing width of the transient regime, the surface shift is also decreasing [10]. Sputter angles around $45°$ are favourable to minimise sample roughening under oxygen flooding [10, 11].

The parallel detection of all masses in TOF-SIMS offers the capability to profile all matrix species and detect matrix changes in the transient regime. Iltgen [9] applied the valency model to determine the Si oxidation state at each point of the profile. By measuring the sputter rates and RSF as a function of the lattice valency, profiles can be corrected for erosion rate and RSF changes in the transient regime.

Oxygen depth profiling at sub-keV energies has been investigated in detail by a number of research groups. However, for a number of important sample systems Cs depth profiling is preferred. Examples are ultra-shallow As and P implants, dielectric layers with a thickness of only a few nm and III/V heterostructures in optoelectronic devices. Cs depth profiling is used for the enhancement of negative SIMS yields, but

52

also in the MCs$^+$ mode for quantitative or semi-quantitative profiling [12, 13]. Dual beam TOF-SIMS profiling has been used for the analysis of gate oxides [4, 14] and Ge and Sb delta layers [5, 15].

Compared to O$_2$ profiling, the reduction of the Cs beam energy well below 1 keV is rather problematic. The reduction in sputter yield leads to a fast rise of the Cs surface concentration θ_{Cs}. Using flux considerations under steady state conditions, θ_{Cs} can be calculated from the sputtering yield of the target species and the backscattering coefficient [16]. The increase in Cs concentration in the transient regime and the related sputter rate changes result in depth scale distortions and surface shifts. The emission of negative secondary ions and MCs$^+$ ions in the regime of high Cs concentrations needs to be studied in detail.

Different methods have been applied in the past to get more insight in ion formation as a function of Cs concentration like Cs adsorption [17], high dose Cs implantation [18 - 20], and the investigation in the transient regime in Cs profiling [21, 22]. We have adapted TOF-SIMS dual beam profiling for fundamental studies of SIMS emission from Cs enriched surfaces [23]. A dual source sputter column [5] is used to generate a coaxial Xe and Cs beam. For the Xe-Cs cosputtering, the sputter phase is separated into a time fraction for Xe and for Cs sputtering. Both beams have the same mass, energy, angle and spot size. Via a single timing parameter, the Cs surface concentration under steady state conditions can be varied in a simple and linear way according to the Cs current fraction I_{Cs} of the total sputter current I_P:

$$\Theta_{Cs} = \Theta_{Cs,\max} \cdot \frac{I_{Cs}}{I_P}$$

The maximum Cs concentration $\Theta_{Cs,\max}$ for 100% Cs sputtering ($I_P = I_{Cs}$) can be made very high by using beam energies below 500 eV at an angle of 45°. The surface under steady state conditions is probed with a pulsed Ga gun at 15 keV.

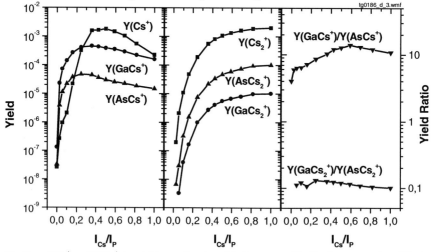

Fig. 2:   *MCs$^+$ and MCs$_2$$^+$ ion yields as a function of I_{Cs}/I_P measured by Xe-Cs cosputtering of GaAs Analysis conditions: sputter energy Xe/Cs 350 eV, 45°; analysis Ga 15 keV, 45°*

As an example, fig. 2 shows the results for the MCs$^+$ and MCs$_2$$^+$ ion yields of GaAs as a function of Cs concentration. The MCs$^+$ yields rise very rapidly at low Cs concentration and go through a maximum at a Cs fraction of about 25 %. At higher Cs concentrations the MCs$^+$ yields as well as the Cs$^+$ yield drop due to the strong decrease of the work function of the surface. The MCs$_2$$^+$ as well as the Cs$_2$$^+$ yield rises much slower and reach a plateau at the highest Cs concentration. In spite of the large variation of the Cs concentration and the change of the ion yields over more than 4 order of magnitude, the GaCs$^+$/AsCs$^+$ ratio varies only by a factor of 2.5 and the GaCs$_2$$^+$/AsCs$_2$$^+$ ratio as little as by a factor of 1.25. Electropositive elements like Ga are emitted mostly as MCs$^+$ whereas electronegative elements like As show stronger emission of MCs$_2$$^+$. The delayed rise of the Cs$^+$ leads to strong variations of the MCs$^+$/Cs$^+$ ratio which is not in agreement with the recombination model [12, 13, 24]. In contrast to this, the MCs$_2$$^+$/Cs$_2$$^+$ shows only little variations.

The technique of Xe/Cs cosputtering in dual beam profiling allows to reduce the sputter energy to a few hundred eV and to adjust the Cs surface concentration for optimum yields in negative SIMS or MCs$^+$ SIMS independant of energy and type of sample. Due to the reduction in Cs surface concentration the changes of the erosion rate and the related surface shifts can be reduced.

4. Micro area depth profiling

Low energy sputter guns have spot sizes typically in the range of 10 - 100 μm diameter. Hence, a combination of high depth resolution and high lateral resolution is not possible in conventional SIMS instruments. Magnetic sector SIMS instruments allow direct imaging in the microscope mode, but for a reduced extraction field the lateral resolution would be in the order of a few micron only. In the dual beam mode the combination of low energy sputtering with high lateral resolution analysis can overcome this limitation. Modern TOF-SIMS instruments with a Ga microprobe can image a small area with a lateral resolution in the range of 0.2 μm while sputtering with sub-keV energies. A 4-dimensional data file (raw data) with cycle number N_i, coordinates X_i Y_i and flight time T_i can be accumulated and later, by mass and depth calibration be converted to a data file with (Z_i, X_i, Y_i, M_i) for every detected secondary ion i. This enables full retrospective 3D analysis with high lateral resolution and high depth resolution simultaneously. If a depth profile is reconstructed from a small area, it is obvious that the count rates are proportional to the area and that the detection limits are inversely proportional to the area.

The capabilities of dual beam depth profiling for micro analysis have been investigated by van Berkum [25]. The test sample has been a SiGe diode with 20 nm p$^+$-SiGe on n$^-$-Si. The sample has been sputtered with 900 eV O$_2$$^+$ in an area 200 x 200 μm² and analysed with a pulsed Ga gun at 25 keV in an area of 20 x 20 μm². The decay length for B and Ge was measured as a function of the Ga gun current. The results are shown in Fig. 3. It is seen in Fig. 3a) that the decay length increases significantly above a current density ratio j_{Ga}/j_{O2} of some 1E-3, which corresponds approximately to an erosion rate ratio $R_E = 100$. An increase in the current density of the analysis gun by a factor of 10 increases the decay length by about a factor of 4. As the detection limits are also related to the current density ratio for a given area, this leads to a trade-off between depth resolution and detection limit for small areas.

54

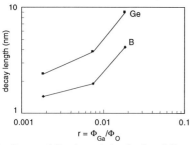 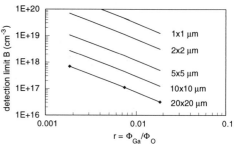

Fig. 3:   a) Depth resolution for B and Ge   b) detection limits for B and Ge
            vs. current density ratio Φ_{Ga}/Φ_{O2} of the analysis and sputter gun, courtesy van Berkum [25]

5. Conclusion

Dual beam depth profiling in TOF-SIMS allows an independent optimisation of the sputter parameters and the analysis parameters. In addition, TOF-SIMS offers high transmission, parallel detection of all masses, high mass resolution and full retrospective analysis. This makes the approach not only attractive for fundamental studies on sputtering and secondary ion formation, but it has also proven to be rather powerful for important applications like ultra-shallow depth profiling and micro area depth profiling.

References

[1] H.-G. Cramer, U, Jürgens, E. Niehuis, M. Terhorst, Z. Zhang and A. Benninghoven, Proceedings SIMS IX, Wiley, Chichester (1994), 449
[2] B. Schueler, R.W. Odom, J.A. Chakel, Proceedings SIMS VIII, Wiley, Chichester (1992), 281
[3] J. Bennett, A. Diebold, these proceedings
[4] K. Iltgen, C. Bendel, E. Niehuis, A. Benninghoven, Proc. SIMS X, Wiley Chichester (1997), 375
[5] M. Terhorst, H.-G. Cramer, E. Niehuis, , Proceedings SIMS X, Wiley Chichester (1997), 427
[6] K. Iltgen, C. Bendel, A. Benninghoven, E. Niehuis, J.Vac.Sci.Technol. A15(3) (1997) 460
[7] K. Wittmaack, Surf. Interface Anal. 24 (1996), 389
[8] K. Wittmaack, S.F. Corcoran, J.Vac.Sci.Techn. B16(1) (1998), 272
[9] K. Iltgen, O. Brox, A. Benninghoven, E. Niehuis, Proc. SIMS XI, Wiley, Chichester (1998), 305
[10] B.W. Schueler and D.F. Reich, Proc. of the 5th International Workshop USJ-99, Research Triangle Park, NC USA, March 1999, 120
[11] C.W. Magee, G.R. Mount, S.P. Smith, B. Herner, H.-J. Gossmann, J.Vac.Sci.Technol. B16(6) (1998), 3099
[12] Y. Gao, J.Appl.Phys., 64(7) (1988), 3760
[13] C.W. Magee, W.L. Harrington, E.M. Botnick, Int.J.Mass Spectrom.Ion Proc. 103 (1990), 45
[14] T. Hoshi, L. Zhanping, M. Tozu, R. Oiwa, Proceedings SIMS XI, Wiley, Chichester (1998), 269
[15] K. Iltgen, A. Benninghoven, E. Niehuis, Proceedings SIMS XI, Wiley, Chichester (1998), 367
[16] G.S. Tompa, W.E. Carr and M. Seidl, Appl.Phys.Lett. 49(22) (1986), 1511
[17] M.L. Yu, Phys.Rev. B26(8) (1982), 4731
[18] H. Gnaser, Surf. Sci. 342 (1995), 319
[19] M. Ferring, T. Mootz, F. Saldi, H.N. Migeon, Proc. SIMS XI, Wiley, Chichester (1998), 911
[20] T. Mootz, W. Bieck, H.N. Migeon, Proceedings SIMS XI, Wiley, Chichester (1998), 953
[21] H. Gnaser, Phys. Rev. B54(23) (1996), 17141
[22] H. Gnaser, Phys.Rev. B54(23) (1996), 16456
[23] E. Niehuis, T. Grehl, to be published
[24] Y. Gao, Y. Marie, F.Saldi, H.N. Migeon, Proceedings SIMS IX, Wiley, Chichester (1994), 382
[25] J. van Berkum, presented at AVS meeting in Baltimore (1998), private communications

A. Benninghoven, P. Bertrand, H.-N. Migeon and H.W. Werner (Editors).
Proceedings of the 12th International Conference on Secondary Ion Mass Spectrometry,
Brussels, Belgium, 5-11 September 1999
© 2000 Elsevier Science B.V. All rights reserved.

IMPROVING SIMS DEPTH PROFILING BY SAMPLE ROTATION

J.G.M. van Berkum

Philips CFT, Prof. Holstlaan 4 (WY42), 5656 AA Eindhoven, The Netherlands

j.g.m.van.berkum@philips.com

1. Introduction

Depth profiling by means of sputter erosion always involves the risk of roughening the surface being eroded (see e.g. [1] and references therein). Poly-crystalline, non-amorphizing materials like metals become rough because the different crystallographic orientations of the grains have different sputter yields. Amorphous or amorphizing materials like semiconductors and most oxides are insensitive to this mechanism of roughening. However, semiconductors like Si or (Al)GaAs exhibit ripple formation under oblique-incidence ion bombardment, in particular when using oxygen ions [1-3]. Ripple formation starts when a critical fluence, that depends on energy and angle-of-incidence, is reached. In the past two years, ripple formation in Si was found already at very shallow depth in case of low-energy O_2^+ bombardment [4,5]. Also, the effects with low-energy ions appear to be more serious than with high-energy.

The primary adverse effect of roughnening is degradation of depth resolution. Secondary effects of roughening, in particular in the case of ripple formation, are alterations of the (partial) sputter yields and, as a consequence, of the erosion rate (for Si, changes by 12% are reported [2]), and alterations of the ionization probabilities of sputtered particles (changes by 10% up to a factor 6 [1]). If a constant erosion rate and constant sensitivity factors are applied, this results in an erroneous depth scale and erroneous concentration scales.

Sometimes, the problem of roughening can be avoided by choosing analytical conditions that do not cause roughening, e.g. normal-incidence or Cs bombardment for semiconductors, or profiling from the backside for a metal layer on a non-metal substrate. If this is impossible, e.g. because the available instrumentation does not allow it, or undesirable, e.g. because the erosion rate with normal incidence bombardment is too low, alternative solutions must be found. Oxygen flooding up to 'full' oxidation often suppresses roughening in the case of semiconductors and also for e.g. aluminium layers, but it also decreases the erosion rate by typically a factor of two and in many cases the suppression is only partial. Sample rotation suppresses roughening in almost all cases. Especially for metal layers and (Al)GaAs multilayers, enormous depth resolution improvements have been reported [6-10]. This paper aims to review the practical use and the clear benefits of sample rotation to SIMS depth profiling, with some particular attention to the case of ultra-shallow profiles in Si.

2. Experimental

All experimental results of this paper have been acquired using a Cameca ims 4f. The sample bias voltage V_s, i.e. the secondary ion extraction voltage, equals ±4500, ±2250 or ±1125 V. The impact energy $E = e_0 \left| V_p - V_s \right|$, where e_0 is the elementary charge and V_p is the primary ion source terminal voltage, is limited by V_s: $E > e_0 \left| V_s \right| /3$ if primary and secondary ions have the same polarity and $E > e_0 |V_s|$ if they are opposite. The (approximate) angle of incidence θ is given by $\sin\theta = 0.5(1 - V_s/V_p)^{-1/2}$.

The Cameca is equipped with a two-axis rotation stage from Kore Technology Ltd., Cambridge, UK (first described in [9]). The stage allows for two independent xy (i.e. parallel to the sample surface) positionings: one positions the rotation axis to bring it in-line with the ion-optical axis of the mass spectrometer, the other one allows to bring any part of the sample surface in-line with the rotation axis. Thus, small-area or multiple analyses do not require careful pre- or re-positioning of the sample in the sample holder. The rotation axis has to be re-aligned only when the optical axis has been re-aligned, e.g. after changing from positive to negative mode or vice versa or after changing between the three sample voltages.

The alignment of the rotation axis[1] is most conveniently performed on a piece of blanket Si: (i) position the beam on the optical axis of the mass spectrometer, (ii) produce a visible impression on the sample surface with an unrastered, well-focussed beam and mark this position in the sample viewing microscope, (iii) start rotation and wait until the circular track of the beam is visible, and finally (iv) stop rotation at the original azimuthal angle and translate the rotation axis until the centre of the circle is at the marked position in the microscope. The procedure can be repeated once or twice for further fine tuning.

The use of the Kore Stage has a few limitations. Due to (i) play in the mechanical construction, (ii) small differences between the orientations of the rotation axis, the ion-optical axis and the surface normal (the latter should be adjusted very carefully before mounting the stage), and (iii) small inhomogeneities of the secondary extraction field causing a non-constant primary ion deflection during rotation, it is impossible to keep the position of an unrastered beam perfectly still during rotation. The typical movement with the best possible alignment is 20-40 μm, which limits the smallest analysable area. Further, because of the same reasons (in particular the inhomogeneous extraction field causing non-constant lateral secondary ion deflection), the ion yields and especially the transmission of the Cameca change during rotation. This causes an undesirable modulation of the measured intensities with the rotation period.

Apart from careful alignment, the modulation can be minimized by consideration of the sample holder geometry: the sample holder should be either close to rotationally symmetric, so that very close to the centre the extraction field distortions are almost rotationally symmetric, or as flat as possible (i.e. thin front plate with large windows), so that the distortions are small. For the experiments described in this paper, the first strategy is followed: the sample holder has a front plate of 375 μm with one hole of 8 mm diameter in the middle and all measurements have been done less than 0.5 mm off-centre. The amplitude of the modulation also depends on the species monitored and on the analytical conditions in a complex way. A general rule-of-thumb is: the wider the emission-angle distribution of the detected ions, the larger the amplitude. Thus, cluster ions have smaller amplitude than single-atom ions, smaller contrast apertures generally decrease the amplitude and energy-filtering to select high kinetic energies, which in Cameca instruments implies close-to-normal emission, always decreases the amplitude.

For accurate concentration calibration, the modulation can be averaged out by choosing an integration time per species equal to (a multiple of) the rotation period. Since the KORE stage has a maximum speed of 10 rpm, i.e. 6 s period, this strategy implies a compromise between erosion rate (i.e. analysis time) and sampling distance, especially if multiple species are monitored simultaneously. With multiple species, a smaller sampling distance can be obtained in principle by choosing the full measurement cycle (sum of integration times of all species and

---

[1] Special thanks to A. Chew (Loveborough) for guidelines when I started to use the Kore stage in 1995.

the waiting times) equal to the rotation period, but this is a dangerous procedure. A small difference between the measurement cycle and the rotation period will cause relatively large long-term signal variations, that are not easily recognized. In addition, the variations of the impurity and matrix signal will be shifted in phase, so that point-to-point ratioing will result in unreliable concentration profiles. With the integration time equal to the rotation period, a small difference between mismatch leads to relatively small long-term variations and the variations of different species are almost in phase.

3. Results

3.1 Metal layers

A typical illustration of the importance of sample rotation to profiling metal layers concerns the interdiffusion of Au and Pt in a Au/Pt/Ti metal stack on Si after 3000 s at 425° C. The SIMS depth profiles obtained without and with sample rotation (see Fig. 1) agree very well on the Pt signals in the Au layer, but the Au signal in the Pt layer of the measurement without rotation is completely determined by the roughening. The Pt signal in the Pt layer does not even show a real plateau, indicating that the roughness after sputtering the Au layer is already close to the Pt layer thickness (0.2 μm). In the measurement with sample rotation, the Pt signal is constant throughout most of the layer. Measurements on a sample without heat treatment (not shown)

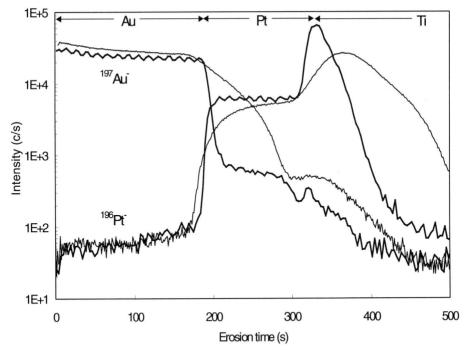

Fig. 1: $^{196}Pt^-$ and $^{197}Au^-$ depth profiles through a Au/Pt/Ti metal stack (nominal thicknesses 0.65/0.2/0.25 μm) on Si acquired using ~100 nA 14.5 keV Cs^+ primary ions (V_p = 10 kV, V_s = −4500 V), raster 250×250 μm² and an analysed area Ø30 μm. Thin lines: without rotation, thick: with rotation (2 rpm, integration time 2 s, so modulation not averaged out).

have a Pt signal in the Au layer that is 20 times less and Au in Pt that is 4 times less than in Fig. 1. Therefore, it is concluded that significant interdiffusion does take place during the heat treatment.

3.2 Deep B profiles in Si

With high-energy (3-10 keV) oblique-incidence O_2^+ primary ions, commonly used for deep B profiles in Si, the ripple formation usually starts after eroding 2 to 4 μm. With sample rotation, the usual degradation of the depth resolution does not occur [6], which proves the absence of roughening. To illustrate the effect of rotation on the secondary ion yields, we have recorded the intensities of B^+, Si_2^+ and SiO_2^+ (the two matrix species that exhibit the largest decrease and increase, respectively, of the species mentioned in Table 2.7A of ref. [1]) from a p-type Si-substrate (see Fig. 2). The change in the intensities after ~2.5 μm indicates the onset of ripple formation. After ~4.5 μm, the SiO_2^+ intensity has risen by more than a factor 4. Switching on sample rotation at this point leads to large instantaneous intensity changes. Apparently, after ripple formation, the intensity strongly depends on the azimuthal angle and the average over all angles differs greatly from the value for the fixed original azimuth. While eroding with sample rotation, the intensities gradually approach the values measured before ripple formation, indicated by the horizontal dashed lines (without ripples, the intensities without and with rotation are not exactly equal because of the modulation mentioned in Sec. II). Very likely, this means that the ripples are being removed. When rotation is switched off, the intensities are quickly drifting away again, which means that the ripple history has not been removed completely in the period of rotation. With rotation, the intensities recover again.

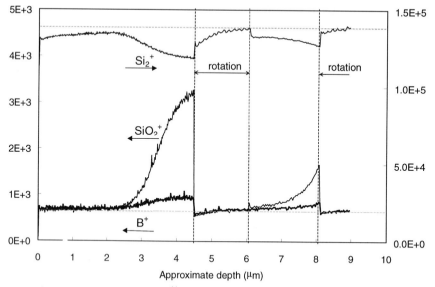

Fig. 2: Secondary ion intensities of $^{11}B^+$, Si_2^+ (mass 56) and SiO_2^+ (mass 60) from a p-type (100) Si-wafer ($5.3e18$ cm^{-3} ^{11}B) recorded using 5.5 keV O_2^+ primary ions ($V_p = 10$ kV, $V_s = 4500$ V), raster 250×250 μm^2 and an analysed area Ø30 μm. Sample rotation is switched on in the indicated regions (10 rpm, integration time 6 s per species). The depth scale is merely indicative, because it is based on the incorrect assumption of a constant erosion rate.

3.3 Ultra-shallow profiles in Si

With oblique-incidence, low-energy O_2^+ beams, ripple formation start already between 10 and 100 nm or even from the very beginning. Very significant depth scale errors [11,12], errors in the concentration calibration [4] and degradation of the depth resolution [11,12] have been reported. At present, ultra-shallow profiling with oxygen beams is performed only with normal-incidence (no ripple formation), with a very confined set of energy/angle-combinations where ripple formation is minimal [5] or with not too large angles (θ<50°) in combination with oxygen flooding to suppress roughening [13].

With sample rotation, the freedom in choosing optimum analytical conditions is much larger: conditions that yield poor results without rotation can give excellent profiles with rotation (see Fig. 3). The sample is a Si-layer with B-spikes, distributed for the Sematech-sponsored round robin [14] as '21/D'. To quantify the effects of the possible changes in erosion rate, the depth scale calibration is based on the region where there is probably the least change: the distance between the 5th and 6th spike is set to 15 nm This procedure yields an erosion rate between the 5th and 6th spike without rotation only 61% of the erosion rate with rotation. This already indicates strong effects of roughening. If the MBE growth rate has been really constant, the deviations of the measured peak distances to the nominal ones yield the relative erosion rates in the different intervals (see also Fig. 3, right axis). Without rotation the peak positions are 1.7, 5.7, 10.4, 15.2, 20.1 and 35.1 nm, implying measurable erosion rate change at least up to 25 nm (the true depth of the 5th peak). The cumulative offset is almost 5 nm after 25 nm erosion.

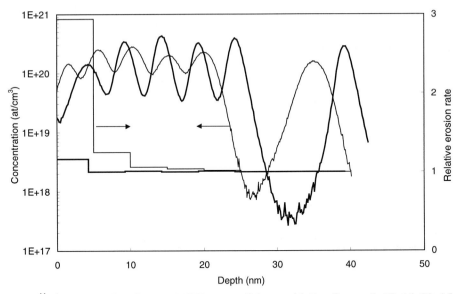

Fig. 3: $^{11}B^+$ depth profiles from an MBE-grown Si-layer with B-spikes at 5, 10, 15, 20, 25, 40, 55, ... nm [14] and the relative erosion rate (erosion rate between 25 and 40 nm set to unity) as a function of eroded depth, obtained using 500 eV O_2^+ primary ions (V_p = 1625 V, V_s = 1125 V), raster 250×250 μm^2, analysed area Ø30 μm and O_2-flooding, without rotation (thin lines) and with (thick lines, rotation with 10 rpm, integration time 6 s per species). Depth scale obtained by setting the distance between the 5th and 6th spike equal to 15 nm.

With rotation, the peak positions are 4.3, 9.3, 14.3, 19.3, 24.2 and 39.2 nm, implying only a slight erosion rate change in the beginning and a total offset less than 1 nm.

The loss in depth resolution due to roughening shows clearly in the high-concentration parts: the full width at half maximum of the 6th spike is 3.7 nm without and 1.9 nm with rotation. The difference of 1.8 nm must be the order of magnitude of a roughness parameter like R_q (root mean square deviation) or R_a (absolute mean deviation). The total influence of roughening ultimately extends up to the peak-to-valley distance in the crater bottom. Since the depression between the 5th and 6th spike is changed by the roughening, this distance must be at least ~6 nm (the distance between depression and nearest spike). Note that the measurement without rotation still has very steep downslopes: $\lambda_d = 0.78$ nm versus $\lambda_d = 0.69$ nm with rotation. This is because the downslope is determined by a topographic subset of the crater bottom with much less roughness: only the upward protrusions contribute.

Sample rotation does not suppress roughening completely in all cases. With intermediate flooding (not full oxidation), the worst case for roughening [11], the typical intensity changes were observed with rotation, but they occurred a few times later than without rotation.

4. Conclusions

The adverse effects of roughening of the crater bottom can often be eliminated by sample rotation. In case of metal layers, the depth resolution degrades so fast without rotation, that it is almost an indispensable tool. In case of high-energy oblique-incidence oxygen beams, the strong changes in secondary ion yields caused by ripple formation are absent with sample rotation. This allows accurate concentration calibration up to any practical depth. For low-energy oblique-incidence oxygen beams, the effects of ripple formation on depth resolution, erosion rate and secondary ion yields (latter not shown here) are often very significant, but they can be avoided by the use of sample rotation.

References

[1] R.G. Wilson, F.A. Stevie and C.W. Magee, Wiley, New York, 1989, p. 2.7-1, p. 4.2-1.
[2] K. Wittmaack, J. Vac. Sci. Technol. A 8 (1990) 2246.
[3] K. Elst and W. Vandervorst, J. Vac. Sci. Technol. A 12 (1994) 3205.
[4] K. Wittmaack and S.F. Corcoran, J. Vac. Sci. Technol. B 16 (1998) 272.
[5] Z.X. Jiang and P.F.A. Alkemade, Appl. Phys. Lett. 73 (1998) 315.
[6] E.-H. Cirlin, J.J. Vajo, T.C. Hasenberg and R.J. Hauenstein, J. Vac. Sci. Technol. A 8 (1990) 4101.
[7] E.-H. Cirlin, J.J. Vajo, R.E. Doty and T.C. Hasenberg, J. Vac. Sci. Technol. A 9 (1991) 1395
[8] F.A. Stevie and J.L. Moore, Surf. Interf. Anal. 18 (1992) 147.
[9] D.E. Sykes and A. Chew, Surf. Interf. Anal. 21 (1994) 231.
[10] F.A. Stevie, J.L. Moore, S.M. Merchant, C.A. Bollinger and E.A. Dein, J. Vac. Sci. Technol. A 12 (1994) 2363.
[11] Z.X. Jiang and P.F.A. Alkemade, J. Vac. Sci. Technol. A 16 (1998) 1971.
[12] K. Wittmaack, J. Vac. Sci. Technol. A 16 (1998) 2776.
[13] Promoted by C.W. Magee, B.W. Schueler, M. Schuhmacher and others, e.g. at the SIMS Europe workshop, October 1-2, 1998, Muenster, Germany.
[14] J. Bennett, A. Diebold and S. Corcoran, in these Proceedings.

WORKSHOP

A. Benninghoven, P. Bertrand, H.-N. Migeon and H.W. Werner (Editors).
Proceedings of the 12th International Conference on Secondary Ion Mass Spectrometry,
Brussels, Belgium, 5-11 September 1999
© 2000 Elsevier Science B.V. All rights reserved.

WORKSHOP
ON WHOLE-WAFER- AND IN-LINE-SIMS

Organized, chaired and reported by
Rolf von Criegern,
Siemens AG, Corporate Technology, Otto-Hahn-Ring 6, D- 81730 Munich, Germany
rolf .criegern@mchp.siemens.de

1. Introduction

In recent years SIMS manufacturers have devoted remarkable efforts to the development of instruments that are able to measure whole (i. e. unbroken) wafers of 200 mm or, more recently, 300 mm diameter (whole-wafer instruments), and even of instruments that additionally fulfill the requirements of a clean room production line (in-line SIMS instruments). On the other hand, considerable uncertainty is prevalent regarding the market chances of such instruments: Is such instrumentation really needed now or in the future? Who would buy and apply it? Which tasks would it have to undertake? What are the requirements that need to be fulfilled by such instruments?
This workshop had the aim of bringing together representatives of the leading SIMS manufacturers, representatives of (some major) microelectronics manufacturers, plus additional experts in the audience, in order to try to get some of these questions answered.

The workshop was divided into an instrumentation session and a panel discussion. This paper reports the essential facts and statements that were presented in the course of the workshop, and shortly summarizes its results.

2. Instrumentation session (Manufacturer presentations)

2.1 "THE WHOLE-WAFER DYNAMIC SIMS ATOMIKA 4600"

presented by **Hans Maul**,   ATOMIKA Instruments GmbH, Bruckmannring 40,
D-85764 Oberschleissheim, Germany,
JLMaul.@atomika.com

Key features of the Atomika 4600 quadrupole instrument are:

- 200 mm or 300 mm wafers as well as sample pieces
- two Floating Low Energy Ion Guns (FLIG™):
  Cs^+ (60° fixed) and O_2^+ (0° fixed) for 150 eV to 5 keV
- position-tolerant secondary ion transfer field
- preprogrammed multi-spot analyses over whole wafer area

The instrument is aimed at obtaining a high dose precision, and it has been suggested for use as a monitor for dose depth profiling, dopant profile shape, and junction depth. Multi-spot-measurements of a 5×10^{14} cm^{-2} boron dose have achieved a relative standard deviation of 0.41 %. Further informations on this instrument can be found in a dedicated paper in these proceedings [1].

2.2 "THE DYNAMIC IN-LINE SIMS INSTRUMENT CAMECA Wf"

presented by **Michel Schuhmacher**, CAMECA Instruments, 103 Bvd. Saint-Denis/ BP 6,
F-92403 Courbevoie Cedex, France,
schuhmac@cameca.fr

The Cameca Wf is a magnetic sector field instrument designed for near-the-line and in-line use. Its main features are:

- 300 mm wafer compatible
- Cs^+ (60°) and O_2^+ (60° or 45°) ion beams at 250 eV - 10 keV
- Z auto-positioning for high measurement repeatability
- X, Y: 300 mm positioning with 2 μm reproducibility
- in-situ crater depth measurements by interferometry
- fully automated analyses, also on patterned wafers (pattern recogn. system)

Potential applications in the silicon technology are dose matching and junction monitoring, and dopant concentration and layer thickness monitoring in the epitaxial growth of III-V-compound structures. A throughput of between two and four wafers per hour has been estimated (1 to 2 craters per wafer).

The prototype instrument is planned to be delivered to a customer in December 1999. Additional information on the instrument can be found in these proceedings [2].

2.3 "THE CAMECA TOF-SIMS IV WHOLE WAFER INSTRUMENT "

presented by **Ewald Niehuis**, ION-TOF GmbH, Mendelstr. 11,
D - 48149 Münster, ewald.niehuis@ion-tof.com

The TOF-SIMS IV is a time-of-flight mass spectrometer system with the following main features:

- 200 mm and 300 mm versions
- 5-axes manipulator (X, Y, Z, 360° rotation, tilt -15°/+45°); access to the whole wafer surface
- positioning reproducibility: < 5 μm (200 mm version), < 1 μm (300 mm), the latter by interferometric control
- KLA / Tencor navigation
- highly automated operation (automated Z adjustment; batch job capability)
- ion gun options (all guns at 45° to the non-tilted wafer): for analysis: liquid metal ion gun 12-25 keV, electron impact gas ion gun 5-10 keV for sputtering: dual source sputter gun with oxygen, noble gases, and cesium, 0.5-3 keV

        - electron gun for charge compensation
        - imaging either by raster scanning the beam or the sample (macro-raster)

Not only can TOF-SIMS be used for surface analyses but also, thanks to the "dual beam mode" (combination of a sputter ion beam and an analysis ion beam), for depth profiling. Since the focal quality of the sputter beam is not of great influence in the dual beam mode, sputtering is mostly done at low energies (0.5 to 1 keV).

The following main applications of TOF-SIMS are seen for off-line and near-line laboratories:
        - Trace metal detection (detection limits: 1×10^8 to 1×10^{10} cm^{-2})
        - Screening for organic contaminants
        - ulta-shallow depth profiling
        - defect review

The 200 mm version of the TOF-SIMS IV instrument has been evaluated under near-the-line conditions in a project of the European Community (SEA "FABTOF") (results to be published). 24 instruments of this type and one 300 mm-instrument have been intalled at customers' sites (not in-line) so far.

2.4 "THE WHOLE-WAFER TOF-SIMS INSTRUMENT OF PHI"

presented by **Bruno W. Schueler**,   Physical Electronics, Inc., 575 Chesapeake Drive,
                               Redwood City, CA 94063 USA
                               bschueler@phi.com

The main features of the PHI TRIFT II time-of-flight SIMS instrument are:

        - 200 mm and 300 mm versions
        - manipulation: X, Y and rotation (360°), sensed by precision optical encoders
        - access to the whole wafer surface
        - positioning reproducibility: < 2.4 µm standard deviation (200 mm stage)
        - imaging: either stigmatic imaging or by raster scanning
        - KLA / Tencor navigation
        - Ion gun options: Liquid Metal Ion Gun (Ga or In), < 25 keV, 35°
        Dual source column at 42°: Duoplasmatron, 250 eV - 8 keV,
                              and Cs source, 250 eV - 11 keV
        (for low-energy sputtering or high-energy pulsed for mass analysis)
        - high operational availability: Uptime guarantees up to 90 % are offered, up to
        98% demonstrated.

Sixteen 200 mm-instruments and one 300 mm-instrument supporting the microelectronics technology are installed near-the-line and off-line, and one 200 mm instrument is installed "in-line", i.e. in the cleanroom of a microelectronics production line [3]. The attractive features of the TOF-SIMS method, including the dual beam mode, and its potential applications for the production support, as listed in the previous section, apply for this type of instrument as well.

3. Panel discussion: "IN-LINE-SIMS: NECESSITY OR ILLUSION?"

Figure 1: The discussion panel: From left to right: Hans Maul, Michel Schuhmacher, Ewald Niehuis, Bruno Schueler, Joe Bennett, Wim Claassen, Sean Corcoran, Yuji Kataoka [Photo: Courtesy Xavier Vanden Eynde, Local Organizing Committee SIMS 12]

The panel members:

Joe Bennett,	SEMATECH, 2706 Montopolis Drive, Austin, TX 78741 USA joe.bennett@sematech.org
Wim Claassen,	Philips Semiconductors, PMO, Gerstweg 2, 6534 AE Nijmegen, The Netherlands w.a.p.claassen@philips.com
Sean F. Corcoran,	INTEL Corporation, MS: RA1-329, 5200 NE Elam Young Parkway, Hillsboro, OR 97124 USA sean.corcoran@intel.com
Yuji Kataoka,	Fujitsu Labs. Ltd., 10-1 Morinosato-Wakamiya, 243-0197 Atsugi, Kanagawa, Japan kataoka@ana.flab.fujitsu.co.jp

and the **representatives of SIMS vendors** (introduced above). In addition, colleagues from the **audience** provided valuable input to the discussion.

To start with, the session chair recalled the role of the optional analytical sections dealing with microelectronics process support, i.e. *in-line* process monitoring and analysis, *near-line* failure analysis lab, and external, i.e. *off-line* analytical lab (**Figure 2**). By asking the auditory it was found that about half of the industrial SIMS colleagues who support microelectronics plants come from near-line labs, and the other half from off-line labs. Unfortunately, it had not been possible to motivate a production line engineer to take part in the workshop. In order to compensate this lack, the panel members were encouraged to contribute informations derived from their cooperation with production line engineers, the prospective users of in-line instruments.

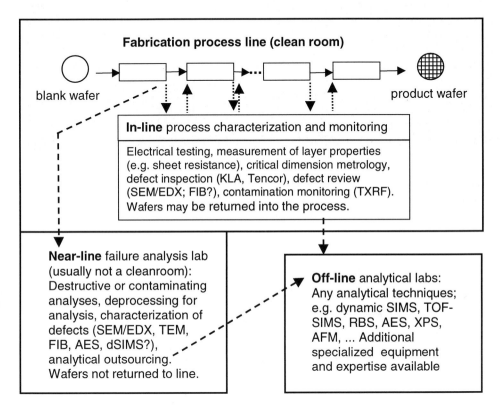

Figure 2: Schematic of analytical facilities involved in the support of microelectronics manufacturing [RvC]

Following are the statements of the SIMS colleagues representing the microelectronics industry.

Joe Bennett: As an international consortium representing the world's leading semiconductor device manufacturers, SEMATECH responds to the needs of their member companies. What are the member companies saying about whole-wafer and in-line SIMS? Very little ...! Whole-wafer SIMS metrology does not appear to be a concern. The cost and the inconvenience of breaking wafers for off-line analysis are not yet prohibitive. Potential problem: Could whole wafers that were analyzed outside the line be returned into the line (Ga, Cs contamination, particles added)? The current dopant metrology methods that are available in-line appear still sufficient (thermal wave, 4-point-probe/ sheet resistance measurement); they are cheaper, faster, and easier to operate than SIMS. Also, fab floor space (in the production line cleanroom) is expensive, a consideration against in-line SIMS. On the other hand, doping technologies will soon exceed the capabilities of the mentioned in-line metrology tools, and (some) process monitoring will have to be done by SIMS. Therefore, the industry needs a new type of SIMS instrument: a whole-wafer dynamic SIMS capable of unattended overnight operation *off-line* and with auto-loading from cassettes to minimize handling and contamination. As this type of instrument remains under the control of the analytical lab (outside the process line), the requirements for automation can be relaxed as compared to potential in-line instruments.

Wim Claassen: The PMO (Proces en Materiaal Onderzoek) laboratory is a near-line lab for the support of five production units in Nijmegen. Recently we have been participating in the European Semiconductor Assessment project "FABTOF" (mentioned above). Its aim was to assess a specific instrument (the Cameca/IONTOF "TOF-SIMS IV") for the use in a microelectronics' fabrication environment. Most of the study was done on an instrument at ST Agrate / Italy (Dr. G. Queirolo), also involving MEMC and Siemens as partners. In our opinion the most valuable merit of such an instrument is its ability of analyzing surface contamination, be it inorganic or organic. In comparison to other techniques (SEM/EDX, AES, XPS) the detection limits (for metallic surface contamination) are much lower. Even in comparison with TXRF, TOF-SIMS achieves lower detection limits in most cases, especially for low Z elements (Al, Na, ..), and its small size of the analyzed area ($< 50 \mu$m) permits even local analyses on patterned wafers (e.g. Cu). Therefore, we see a potential for a dedicated TOF-SIMS to be applied as an *in-line* monitor for surface cleanliness after cleaning, etching, implantation, lithography, etc., perhaps in part even replacing TXRF. Besides this, *off-line* TOF-SIMS may be applied to defect reviewing and to the support of process characterization and optimization.

Sean Corcoran: All semiconductor manufacturers would like to get rid of all metrology equipment, as metrology is (seen as) a 'non-value-adding' tool. Therefore, there is a huge barrier to be overcome to get equipment into a fab line. Generally, stringent new metrology requirements or even 'killer-applications'must provide the 'force of gravity' to *pull* SIMS into a line. "If you try to *push* SIMS into the lines, you better have strong economic or metrology improvements. At the present time there is no compelling reason to implement an in-line SIMS tool." At present routine sampling on product wafers does not appear necessary. Near-line SIMS is fully adequate, even though product wafers will not be returned to the line. Near-fab tools with full-wafer capabilities and a higher level of automation are needed. They need to be easy to use (recipe-driven), but still flexible enough for the use of experts in 'forensic' cases. Looking into applications, dynamic SIMS is important for the ion implant support (dose matching, high energy implant angle verification, uniformity) and may gain increasing importance for selective doped epi deposition, including bulk contamination analysis. At present, these tasks do not require in-line instrumentation. In contrast, much better chances are seen for TOF-SIMS "to go in-line": Supporting yield improvement activities (reduction of defect density) may justify or even require in-line instrumentation. Organic and metallic contamination analyses on patterned or unpatterned wafers, and some particle analysis may become the main field of application. Whether in or out of clean-room, whether dynamic

SIMS or TOF-SIMS, the instrumentation needs to be highly automated, recipe-driven, and highly repeatable for statistical process control.

Yuji Kataoka: Our off-line laboratory cooperates closely with Fujitsu's in-line sections in developing processes and devices based upon the CMOS ULSI technology. One recently identified analytical difficulty is the monitoring of junction depths in the process line. So far, after ion implantation and annealing, only the sheet resistance is monitored in-line. But, generally, the sheet resistance is sensitive to the impurity concentration distribution rather than the junction depth. With implantation energies becoming smaller and with the junction depths becoming smaller than 40 nm, the sheet-resistance is no longer an unambigous indicator for the correctness of a dopant profile, i.e. especially for its junction depth. **Figure 3** shows a case where a junction depth at around 30 nm (wafer A) is related to a high sheet resistance, whereas on the wafer related to process option C, the sheet resistance is conventionally considered "good" (below 600 Ω/square), but the junction depth is considered not good (above 40 nm). Therefore, in the mass production of ULSI devices we need to know both, the sheet resistances *and* the impurity depth profiles over the whole wafers. In order to be able to check our results immediately, we intend to apply SIMS *in* the line.

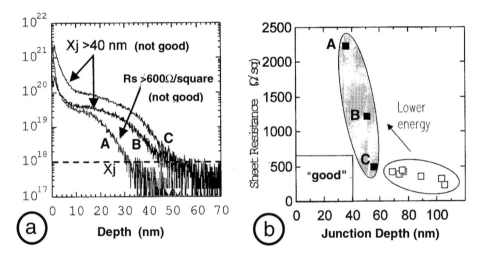

Figure 3: (a) Boron concentration (atoms/cm^3) versus depth. The junction depth Xj (nm) is defined as the depth at which the Boron concentration is equal to the donor concentration (here: 1×10^{18} atoms/cm^3) **(b)** Sheet resistance Rs versus junction depth. The same three implantation conditions (A, B, C) apply to both graphs, (a) and (b). [Yuji Kataoka]

4. Results of workshop (including contributions from the audience)

1. All the major SIMS vendors offer instruments for whole-wafer analysis, both for 200 mm and 300 mm wafers, and they are prepared to deliver in-line versions.

2. Whereas several whole-wafer TOF-SIMS instruments have been installed at customer sites off-line and near-line, only one instrument is known to have been installed in a class 1 cleanroom of a microelectronics production line so far ("in-line") [3].

3. Pro's and Con's of *in-line* SIMS instrumentation:

Pro:
- Immediate availability and fast access for in-line tasks
- Replacement or extension of conventional monitoring techniques by more sensitive or more conclusive SIMS method(s): Two cases could be identified:
- Metal trace surface analysis with TOF-SIMS in a range below 1×10^{10} cm^{-2} (complementing in-line-TXRF)
- Shallow junction monitoring (complementing in-line sheet resistance measurements)

Contra:
- The cost of an in-line instrument (price, floor space, and maintenance in the cleanroom) is much higher than the one of a near-line or off-line instrument
- Instruments outside the line may also be used for broken and contaminated samples; not so the in-line instruments.
- The often quoted argument the wafers were too valuable to be discarded for outside-the-line analyses was not supported by the representatives of the microelectronics manufacturers (i. e. for the silicon technology!). Other cost considerations are predominant.

4. Requirements of manufacturing engineers regarding (any) in-line instrumentation:
High operational availability (90 to 95%) within specs: Vendors held responsible!
Fast service response (24 hours around the clock), at least if backup instrument not available
Ease of operation (by trained technicians, not by academic staff)
Highly automated operation and data evaluation, recipe-driven.

5. Generally, the production line engineers do not appear to be concerned about SIMS and do not really ask for in-line SIMS. In most cases they appear to be satisfied with SIMS support from outside the line (so far).

6. The prevalent conclusion was therefore that in the near future whole-wafer SIMS instruments shall in most cases be used *near-line and off-line* rather than *in-line*. The SIMS instrumentation needs first to be perfected towards a near-line metrology tool (precision!) and further-on towards an on-line metrology tool (precision, time, and automation!) [S.C.].

7. It was also concluded that the situation may immediately change if and as soon as some crucial in-line monitoring tasks can no longer be done with the already existing in-line methods and may need to be done by a SIMS method. A tendency towards this need was postulated by several participants.

5. References

[1] J.L. Maul, S.B. Patel, A. Scars, N. Loibl, L. Bögl, M.G. Dowsett: in this volume
[2] T. Bitner, E. De Chambost, P. Monsallut, B. Rasser, M. Schuhmacher: in this volume
[3] P. Fiorani, G. Margutti, G. Mariani, S. Matarazzo, G. Moccia, SPIE Conference, Santa Clara, California, Sept. 1998, SPIE Vol. 3509, p. 221 - 227

SECTION 1 :
SPUTTERING

A. Benninghoven, P. Bertrand, H.-N. Migeon and H.W. Werner (Editors).
Proceedings of the 12th International Conference on Secondary Ion Mass Spectrometry,
Brussels, Belgium, 5-11 September 1999
© 2000 Elsevier Science B.V. All rights reserved.

XPS STUDY OF ION INDUCED OXIDATION OF SILICON
WITH AND WITHOUT OXYGEN FLOODING

H. De Witte[1,2], T. Conard [1], R. Sporken [3], R. Gouttebaron [3], R. Magnée [3],
W. Vandervorst [1,4], R. Caudano [3], R. Gijbels [2]

[1] IMEC, Kapeldreef 75, B-3001 Heverlee, Belgium
[2] MiTAC, University of Antwerp, Universiteitsplein 1, B-2610 Wilrijk, Belgium
[3] LISE, University of Namur, Rue de Bruxelles 61, B-5000 Namur, Belgium
[4] INSYS, University of Leuven, Kard. Mercierlaan 92, B-3001 Heverlee, Belgium
e-mail: dewitte@imec.be

1. Introduction

Insight in the artifacts of SIMS requires an understanding of the ion-solid interaction occurring during the analysis. In this work these interactions are studied for low energy O_2^+ and Ar^+ primary ion bombardment on a Si substrate at different angles of incidence and with or without additional oxygen bleed-in. The surface stoichiometry of the build-up oxides, the dynamics of the oxide growth, and the stoichiometry of the underlying layers are investigated with XPS (X-ray Photo-electron Spectroscopy).

2. Experimental

Immediately before introduction in the preparation chamber of the instrument, the pure Si samples received a HF dip to remove the native oxide layer. In the preparation chamber, they were bombarded with a 2.75 keV O_2^+ or Ar^+ ion beam and at different angles of incidence, ranging from 0° to 75°. For flooding an oxygen pressure of 5.10^{-6} Torr is created in the preparation chamber. A large spot ion beam (spot size diameter ≈ 1.5 cm) was needed in order to bombard the whole sample area. XPS analysis was performed in situ on the bombarded area at steady state conditions.

3. XPS Si 2p and valence band fitting procedure

The ion-beam oxidation of Si targets leads to the formation of several mixed chemical bonds of Si atoms with other Si and O atoms, i.e. pure silicon, suboxides and stoichiometric silicon dioxide. Quantification of the different oxidation states can be derived by performing a detailed deconvolution of the Si 2p photoelectron peak in the binding energy region from 99.0 to 105.0 eV [1].

Studying the ion-beam induced oxidation of Si by primary oxygen bombardment, Alay [2] observed that the valence band for the altered layers experiences a strong increase in total width from 11 eV (crystalline Si) or 10 eV (SiO_2) to 15 eV. This effect arises primarily from the merging of the valence bands of Si and SiO_2 to one wider single band for these altered layers. The new altered valence band can be divided in two different regions, a Si-like (ca.0-7 eV) and SiO_2-like (ca.7-16 eV) valence subband. His model will also be applied here.

74

4. Oxygen angle dependent bombardment measurements

The aim of these measurements is the determination of the critical angle for full oxide formation under O_2^+ bombardment with O_2 flooding compared to without flooding. This angle is determined according to three different methods: 1) from the deconvolution of the different suboxides in the XPS Si 2p region, 2) from the angle dependence of the sputter yield, 3) by comparing the valence band spectra with those of pure Si and SiO_2.

4.1 Si suboxide concentration
In Figure 1 the Si suboxide chemical relative concentrations observed at steady state for 2.75 keV O_2^+ with O_2 flooding at different incidence angles are shown. Up to about 45° almost full oxidation is reached. For larger incidence angles no full oxidation can be obtained anymore, which can be derived from the large increase in the suboxide concentrations. Compared to a similar series of experiments and results without flooding [2] the full oxidation regime is shifted from about 35° to 45° (the threshold is set at 90 % of the Si^{4+} concentration).

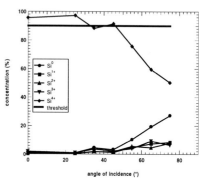

Figure 1: Angle dependence of Si suboxide concentrations for O_2 bombardment with oxygen flooding

4.2 Si sputter yield
The critical angle also corresponds to the point where the partial sputter yield of Si reaches 0.5 Si atoms/O atom [3] (critical point in Figure 2). TRIMCSR [4] calculates the stationary values of Y(Si) for O bombardment on Si (initial state) and on SiO_2 (ideal final state). ISRD [5] calculates the dynamic evolution of the substrate under O bombardment: from the initial pure Si substrate to the final (partially) oxidized steady state. Combining the oxygen content determined by XPS with Y(Si) TRIMCSR calculations on SiO_x substrates, yields the XPS experimental-TRIMCSR curve.

Without additional oxygen flooding ISRD calculates a critical value of 37° for 2.75 keV O_2^+ (1.375 keV O), which is only slightly higher than the experimental values obtained under similar conditions (33° for 1 keV O [6] and 35° for 2.5 keV O [2]).

With oxygen flooding the ISRD calculated critical angle is 42°. Up to about 45° the ISRD results

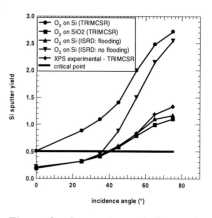

Figure 2: Comparison of the angle dependence of the Si partial sputter yield, as calculated by TRIMCSR, ISRD and experimentally determined

coincide with the TRIMCSR values on SiO_2. However for higher incidence angles ISRD produces higher sputter yields indicating that no full oxidation is reached anymore. The XPS experimental-TRIMCSR curve deviates from the ISRD curve for angles higher than about 55°. However for these large incidence angles the measured oxide thickness becomes close to the projected range of the primary bombarding ions. Therefore the sputtered atoms determining Y(Si) are escaping not only from the ion beam induced oxide layer, but also from the underlying Si substrate. The latter is not included in the XPS-TRIMCSR calculation. Comparison between the critical angle with and without oxygen flooding as determined from the Si partial sputter yield leads to the same conclusion, namely a shift of roughly 10°.

4.3 Valence Band

Plotting the valence band spectra obtained under oxygen bombardment with oxygen flooding at incidence angles ranging from 0° to 75°, shows that the first spectra are comparable to the SiO_2 spectrum and the last are similar to Si. In between a mixture of both extremes is found. Fitting the (background-subtracted) spectra obtained at the different incidence angles as a linear combination of pure Si and SiO_2 valence band spectra leads to a critical angle of 45°, in good agreement with the XPS Si 2p spectra.

5. Comparison of steady state conditions at normal incidence

This section compares the final steady states obtained by bombardment of pure Si at normal incidence using O_2^+ primary ions, O_2^+ with additional oxygen bleed-in and Ar^+ with oxygen flooding. First, we discuss the distribution of the Si suboxide peaks as fitted on the Si 2p XPS spectrum. Secondly, we give an overlay of the XPS valence band spectra. Third, we compare the final oxide thickness.

5.1 Suboxide distribution

Both cases of oxygen primary ion bombardment are well comparable. The dominant contribution is certainly the Si^{4+} peak confirming the formation of a SiO_2 layer. The contribution of the suboxide peaks is very small. In case of additional oxygen flooding, a slightly higher contribution of the Si^{4+} peak is observed, which might suggest a small difference in final full oxidation state. A change from the reactive and oxidizing O_2 primary beam to neutral Ar ions in combination with a reactive O_2 ambient doesn't lead to the same effects. The Si suboxide distribution is still dominated by the Si^{4+} peak, but the contribution of the other suboxide peaks is no longer negligible.
Comparing the steady states for these three frequently used conditions shows that the use of Ar leads to a target which is far less, and thus not completely, oxidized.

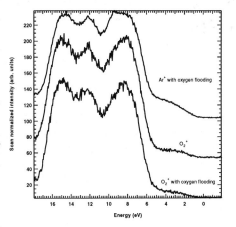

5.2 XPS valence band spectra

Figure 3 gives an overlay of the XPS valence band spectra. Also here the spectra obtained under primary oxygen bombardment are very comparable. Comparing the valence band spectra obtained under Ar^+ and O_2^+ primary ion

Figure 3: XPS valence band spectra at steady state for bombardment of pure Si at normal incidence by O_2^+, O_2^+ with oxygen flooding and Ar^+ with oxygen bleed-in

bombardment with oxygen flooding shows a higher density of the electronic states in the Si like sub-region in the case of Ar^+ bombardment. These electrons are available for neutralization of an ion escaping from the sample surface (tunneling effect). This explains why the SIMS fractional ion yields under Ar^+ with flooding are lower than under oxygen bombardment [7].

5.3 Oxide thickness
The final oxide thickness for O_2^+ bombardment when using additional oxygen flooding is only slightly different from the one without flooding. Both indicate a thickness of about 10 nm. The oxide layer obtained under Ar^+ bombardment with oxygen flooding is far thinner (ca. 7 nm) than with O_2^+ bombardment. So not only surface oxidation is operative, but also recoil mixing and defect enhanced diffusion must be included to explain its extent. The latter is in line with previous observations of Holmen [8].

6. Conclusions

The study on the angular dependence of the ion beam induced oxidation of Si by oxygen bombardment in the presence of an additional oxygen atmosphere shows that up to about 45° almost full oxidation is reached at steady state conditions. Compared to similar results without flooding the full oxidation regime is shifted from about 35° to a higher incidence angle of 45°, extending the useful impact angle range for SIMS experiments by about 10°.
The final oxide thickness for O_2^+ bombardment is about 10 nm. Use of additional oxygen flooding doesn't lead to significant differences. The oxide layer obtained under Ar^+ bombardment with oxygen flooding is far thinner (7 nm) than with O_2^+ bombardment. The thickness extends beyond a simple surface oxidation model and requires a concept based on recoil mixing and defect-enhanced diffusion to explain the results.

Acknowledgement

H. De Witte is Aspirant of the Fund for Scientific Research – Flanders (Belgium) (FWO). R. Sporken acknowledges support from the Belgian Fund for Scientific Research (FNRS). This work was supported in part by the Belgian Office for Scientific, Technical and Cultural Affairs (IUAP/PAI program).

References

[1] P.J. Grunthaner, M.H. Hecht, F.J. Grunthaner, N.M. Johnson, J. Appl. Phys. 61 (2), 629 (1987)
[2] J. Alay, W. Vandervorst, Phys. Review, 50 (20), 15015 (1994)
[3] K. Wittmaack, Surface Science, 419 (2-3), 249 (1999)
[4] J.F. Ziegler, J.P. Biersack and U. Littmark, The Stopping and Range of Ions in Solids, Vol. 1. Pergamon Press, New York (1985)
[5] H. De Witte, W. Vandervorst, R. Gijbels, in SIMS XI proceedings, 327 (1997)
[6] K. Wittmaack, private communication (1997)
[7] C. Tian, W. Vandervorst, J. Vac. Sci. Technol. A 15 (3), 452 (1997)
[8] G. Holmen, H. Jacobsson, Appl. Phys. Lett. 53 (19), 1838 (1988)

A. Benninghoven, P. Bertrand, H.-N. Migeon and H.W. Werner (Editors).
Proceedings of the 12th International Conference on Secondary Ion Mass Spectrometry,
Brussels, Belgium, 5-11 September 1999
© 2000 Elsevier Science B.V. All rights reserved.

MICROSTRUCTURAL EVALUATION OF SIMS CRATER ROUGHENING

B.I. Prenitzer[1], L.A. Giannuzzi[1,2], B.W Kempshall[1,2], J.M. McKinley[3], F. A. Stevie[3]

[1] Advanced Materials and Processing and Analysis Center, 12443 Research Parkway, Suite 305, Orlando, FL 32826 bsp35905@pegasus.cc.ucf.edu
[2] Department of Mechanical, Materials, and Aerospace Engineering, University of Central Florida, PO Box 162450, 4000 Central Florida Blvd., Orlando, FL 32816-2450.
[3] Cirent Semiconductor, (Lucent Technologies) 9333 S. John Young Parkway, Orlando, FL 32819

1. Introduction

It is well known that sputter-induced surface roughening degrades depth resolution during analyses performed by secondary ion mass spectrometry (SIMS) [1], x-ray photoelectron spectroscopy (XPS), and Auger electron spectroscopy (AES). The characteristics of the topographical irregularities that form during ion bombardment have been previously shown to be dependent on accelerating voltage, ion dose, incident angle, target material, reactive gas pressure, and incident ion species [1-6, 10]. The search to uncover the mechanism of ion-beam sputter induced ripple formation has been somewhat intense within the SIMS community. A parallel race to achieve polished surfaces by ion-beam erosion has been undertaken among transmission electron microscopists. The mechanisms that have been proposed to explain the observed phenomena are numerous and varied. It should be noted however that the existing mechanisms are not necessarily mutually exclusive. The effect of incident angle on sputter induced topography seems to be pervasive and is addressed in many forms in the existing literature. In a systematic investigation by Wittmaack [2], it was shown that erosion rate and ripple formation are inherently linked to incident angle. A subsequent study of low energy O_2^+ bombardment by Jiang et al. [3] showed similar results. Work done by Karen et al. [4] addressed the effect of localized incident angle on the chemical aspects of sputtering. Stevie and Moore [5] investigated the effect of sample rotation during O_2^+ bombardment on several materials (e.g. GaAs, Al, Si). They showed that roughening could be largely suppressed by rotating the sample, in essence partially randomizing the incident angle with respect to the target surface. Similarly, sample rotation during ion milling has been applied in the preparation of thin polished specimens for transmission electron microscopy (TEM). The development of the current low angle rotating ion mills as well as the Zalar rotation stage (a trademark of Perkin Elmer) were at least in part based on the accomplishments of Barna, Barna and Zalar [6].

To reiterate, much of the existing work addressing sputter induced topography seems to involve the incident milling angle. The physical effect that incident angle exerts on sputtering rates has been thoroughly investigated; however, if the incident angle is considered in terms of the orientation that the beam makes with respect to specific crystallographic directions within the target material, a more comprehensive vista of the roughening phenomena may be elucidated. As such, this systematic investigation is intended to link angularly dependent surface roughening specifically to the microstructural properties of target materials.

2. Experimental methods

Multiple sites were analyzed by SIMS in both (100) Si and (111) Si wafers. SIMS analyses were made with a Cameca IMS 6f using an O_2^+ beam at a primary acceleration voltage of 10 keV and a sample voltage of 4.5 keV. The net impact energy was 5.5 keV and the normal impact energy was 4.06 keV at an incident angle of 42.39° from normal. The 0.3 μA beam was rastered over an area of 130 μm x 130 μm. The analysis area was circular, 60 μm in diameter, and at the center of the raster. The crater depths were measured with a Tencor P10 profilometer. The depth of the (100) Si craters varied from 0.282 μm to 7.92 μm and the depth of the (111) Si craters varied from 2.04 μm to 5.96 μm. Cross section TEM specimens of the roughened surfaces were prepared from the centers of the crater bottoms using the focused ion beam lift-out technique (FIB LO) [7]. TEM analyses of the specimens were performed with a Phillips EM 430 operating at 300 keV.

3. Results and discussion

The craters formed in the (100) and (111) Si wafers were used to study the relationship between the crystallography and the surface roughening that occurs as a secondary effect of energetic ion bombardment. As a result of the SIMS analysis, the crater bottoms roughened in a manner that resembled terrace like ledges which formed in a direction perpendicular to the incident beam. The cross section TEM images in figures 1a and 1b clearly show evidence that this roughening is due to the development of discrete facets along specific crystallographic planes. Figure 1a shows a cross section TEM image and superimposed selected area diffraction pattern (SADP) for the 7.92 μm deep crater in (100) Si. As revealed by the TEM micrograph in figure 1a, the (100) Si exhibited a distinct tendency to facet on the {111} family of planes. Figure 1b shows a cross section TEM image and superimposed SADP for the 5.96 μm deep crater in (111) Si. Facetting on the {100} type planes is shown in figure 1b. Although {100} type facets are present, it should be noted that planar facets of other crystallographic orientations can also observed in figure 1b. The propensity of the (100) Si to facet on the {111} planes may be explained by the fact that the {111} planes are the most densely packed planes in the diamond cubic structure; hence, they represent the most resistant surfaces to erosion. In addition, Auciello and Kelly explained observed facetting with evidence that suggests the {100} and the {111} planes are the most stable under ion bombardment in the closely related fcc crystal structure.[8] The observation of the {111} facetting on the (100) Si surface and the {100} facetting on the (111) Si surface (as shown in figures 1a and 1b) is thus consistent with Auciello and Kelly [8].

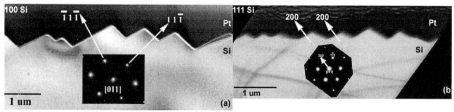

Figures 1a and 1b. SADPs superimposed on cross section TEM images showing (a) the {111} facetting of the 7.92 μm deep crater in (100) Si and (b) some {100} and other arbitrary facetting of the 5.96 μm deep crater in (111) Si.

Figure 2 consists of a series of bright field TEM images of the (100) and (111) Si samples superimposed on their corresponding SIMS depth profiles. Figure 2 correlates the morphological development of roughening with the variation in erosion rate. Furthermore, figure 2 shows how the sputtering transition characteristics vary as a function of crystallographic orientation with respect to the incident beam direction. As a note, the transition region is accentuated by intentionally plotting the graphs on a linear scale. Figure 2 shows that the onset of the transition occurs earlier in the (100) Si sample than in the (111) Si sample. Similar transition depths were reported by Stevie et al. [1]. By examining the corresponding micrographs, it can be seen that as sputtering progresses, the physical characteristics of the asperities change from what appears to be arbitrary ripples into larger crystallographically distinct facets. The apparent lateral motion and coalescence of the features are in accordance with the geometrical models suggested by Townsend et al. [9] and Barna et al.[6].

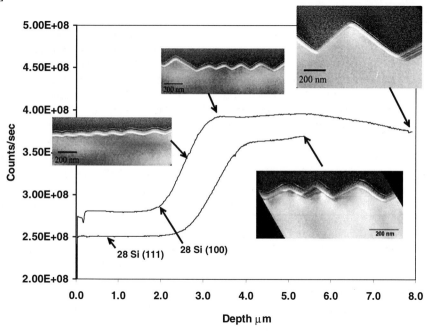

Figure 2. Cross-section TEM images of facetted crater bottoms in (100) Si and (111) Si superimposed at the corresponding location on their respective SIMS depth profiles.

Further comparison between the TEM images of the (100) and (111) samples reveal that in the early stages of the transition the characteristics of the crater bottoms are virtually indistinguishable. In these monocrystalline materials we have observed facetting to progress from random planes to preferred crystallographic orientations. It is believed that the seemingly arbitrary ripples in the shallow (100) craters (as shown in figure 2) may be considered as distinct facets occurring on random and multiple crystallographic planes. Inspection of the micrograph shown in figure 1b reveals that not all of the planar facets in the 5.96 μm deep

(111) Si crater may be identified as a single family of planes. In accordance with observations of the 2.64 μm and 3.40 μm deep (100) Si craters (as seen figure 2), it is believed that the crater shown in figure 1b was not sputtered extensively enough to allow the preferred crystallographic facets to fully evolve. Elst et al. proposed a two step model that separates the nucleation and growth of milling induced topography into distinct processes.[10] The data presented in this work suggests that the growth of crystallographically distinct facets is simply an extension of the nucleation process of roughening in crystalline materials. Furthermore, this model may also explain the occurrence of roughening in polycrystalline or amorphous materials. Roughening is inevitably initiated by the arbitrary ejection of the first atom. As ion bombardment continues, this model suggests that subsequent atomic ejections in a polycrystalline specimen will cause each grain to preferentially erode along unique sets of crystallographic planes as governed by the surface binding energies. The formation of specific crystallographic facets will vary from grain to grain and will depend on the angular relationship between the incident beam and the individual grains. As the grain size of a polycrystalline surface is reduced to the limit of that of an amorphous material, atom ejection from that surface will occur in a seemingly more statistical and random fashion. Therefore, due to the lack of long range atomic order in an amorphous material, any and all atomic ejections would be expected to be dictated solely by the probability predicted by the collision cascade.

4. Conclusion

The development of surface topography as a function of crystallographic orientation and ion dose was investigated in a series of craters milled in (100) and (111) Si using a Cameca IMS-6f. SIMS analysis shows how erosion rates and transition characteristics vary based on the direction of the incident beam with respect to the crystal planes of the target. The rate of roughening as well as the sputtering rate is observed to be greater in the (100) Si than in the (111) Si. Milling induced topographical features were identified by TEM analyses as facets on distinct crystallographic planes. Based on experimental observations, a model was developed suggesting that the atomic arrangements of the target material will ultimately determine the nature of the sputter induced roughened surface.

Acknowledgements

Funding for this work was provided by the I4/UCF/Cirent Semiconductor partnership and NSF award DMR # 9703281.

References

[1]   F. A. Stevie et al., J. Vac. Sci. Technol. A 6(1), (1988) 76
[2]   K. Wittmaack, J. Vac. Sci. Technol. A 8(3), May/Jun (1990) 2246
[3]   Z. X. Jiang and P. F. A. Alkemade, Appl. Phys. Let., Vol.73, No. 3 (1998) 315
[4]   A. Karen et al., J. Vac. Sci. Technol. A 9(4), Jul/Aug (1991) 2247
[5]   F. A. Stevie and J. L. Moore, Surf. Interface Anal., Vol.18 (1992) 147
[6]   A. Barna, P. B. Barna and A. Zalar, Surf. Interface Anal., Vol. 12 (1988) 144
[7]   L. A. Giannuzzi et al., Mater. Res. Soc. Symp. Proc., Vol. 480 (1997) 19
[8]   O. Auciello and R. Kelly ed., Elsevier, Amsterdam, 1984, 9
[9]   P. D. Townsend et al., Academic Press, London, 1976, 131
[10]   K. Elst et al., J. Vac. Sci. Technol. B 11(6), Nov/Dec (1993) 1968

A. Benninghoven, P. Bertrand, H.-N. Migeon and H.W. Werner (Editors).
Proceedings of the 12th International Conference on Secondary Ion Mass Spectrometry,
Brussels, Belgium, 5-11 September 1999

DETECTION OF HIGH-ENERGY IONS EJECTED FROM GALENA (PbS) DUE TO keV OXYGEN OR CESIUM ION SURFACE BOMBARDMENT

K. Franzreb[1*], D. Karpuzov[2$], A. R. Pratt[3#], and N. S. McIntyre[1]

[1] Surface Science Western, University of Western Ontario, London, Ont. N6A 5B7, Canada
[2] Institute of Electronics, Bulgarian Academy of Sciences, Sofia 1784, Bulgaria
[3] Earth Sciences, University of Western Ontario, London, Ontario N6A 5B7, Canada
* Corresponding author, E-mail: franzreb@surf.ssw.uwo.ca

1. Introduction

Several studies on the ejection of high-energy particles during keV ion surface bombardment [1-7] have recently been made. This renewed interest was partly triggered by a controversy [3] with respect to surprisingly high emission energies reported for negatively charged particles [2], where negative ions might have been confused with electrons, according to ref.[5]. The present combined SIMS/LEIS study has been made in order to provide kinetic energy distribution raw data on both sputtered secondary ions as well as backscattered primary ions. Such experimental information is important for comparison with computer simulations [7,8]. Our results of a corresponding MARLOWE-type calculation, made for PbS as well as FeS$_2$, will be given in refs. [8,13]. The study of galena (PbS) under oxygen or Cs$^+$ bombardment is of particular interest due to the mass differences for both projectile (m_1=16 (O$^{+,-}$) or 133 (Cs$^+$)) and target (m_2=32 (S$^{+,-}$) and 208 (Pb$^+$)).

2. Experimental and Data Evaluation

Measurements of kinetic ion energy distributions were made on a modified Cameca IMS-3f magnetic sector SIMS instrument. The sample potential U$_S$ was scanned over a maximum range of ±5 kV to 0 kV, and the electrostatic analyzer was used as an energy filter with a constant pass energy of 4500 eV (energy window ≈ 10 eV) [1,9]. Because of the variation of the electrostatic secondary ion extraction field, the initial kinetic ion emission energy E is given by: E=|q$_2$| · 4500 eV - q$_2$ · e · U$_s$. Unfortunately, the primary ion bombarding energy E$_i$ and the bombarding angle θ$_i$ (defined with respect to the sample normal) depend both on the potential U$_i$ of the primary ion source as well as on U$_s$ according to: E$_i$=q$_1$ · e · (U$_i$ - U$_s$) and sin(θ$_i$)=sin(θ$_g$)/(1-U$_s$/U$_i$)$^{1/2}$ with θ$_g$≈30° [1,9,10]. The ion energy distribution raw data are therefore distorted, since the bombarding energy, the bombarding angle as well as the collection efficiency [11,12] for ion extraction along the sample normal vary during such sample potential scans. Polished cross sections of galena (PbS) were analyzed with mass-filtered primary ion beams of ^{16}O$_2^+$, ^{16}O$^-$ or ^{133}Cs$^+$ under steady state bombarding conditions. Secondary ions of ^{32,34}S$^+$, ^{208}Pb$^+$ and ^{32,34}S$^-$ as well as backscattered (and re-sputtered) ions of ^{16}O$^+$, ^{133}Cs$^+$ and ^{16}O$^-$ were detected using a post-acceleration voltage of ± 6 kV (10.5 keV ion impact) at the first dynode of the single ion counting system.

$ Dimitre Karpuzov thanks the Centre for Chemical Physics, UWO for financial support.
# Present address: CANMET, Natural Resources Canada, Ottawa, Ont., Canada K1A 061.

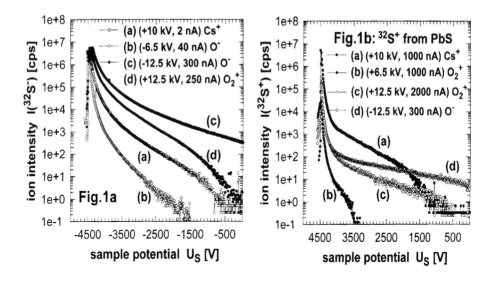

Fig. 1: Secondary ion emission from PbS.   (Fig. 1a: 32 S-; Fig.1b: 32S+).

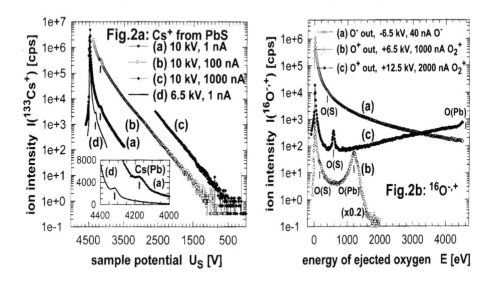

Fig.2: Primary ion backscattering [9] from PbS. (Fig.2a: Cs+ ; Fig.2b: O-,+).

3. Results and Discussion

Raw kinetic energy distributions of sputtered secondary ions as well as backscattered primary ions are displayed in Figs. 1a,1b and Figs. 2a,2b, respectively. The corresponding results on the maximum emission energies E_{max} observed (the values of E_{max} represent lower limits) are summarized in Table 1. Secondary ion ejection in 'backwards direction' ($\theta_i/\theta_e \approx 35°/0°$; change of momentum by $\approx 145°$) is found to extend to emission energies as high as several keV, with ratios of E_{max}/E_i of well above 10% and even as high as about 60% for $^{32}S^{+\cdot}$. Computer simulations may reveal in some detail if or how much the latter surprisingly large value for sulfur may be affected by energy transfer in subsequent S→Pb (scattering) collisions [8,13]. The intensity ratio of S^-/S^+ at E=4500 eV (U_S=0 V) is roughly 60 (Figs.1a,1b) for 12.5 keV O⁻. A comparison of E_{max}/E_i with T_{max} (energy transfer in the first projectile → target 'head-on' collision) supports the relation of $E_{max}/E_i \leq T_{max}$, while a straightforward direct correlation is not apparent. With respect to primary ion backscattering, a large ratio of E_{max}/E_i of roughly 80% is observed for oxygen. While this is expected for O→Pb backscattering because of the large mass difference, the corresponding result of 40% for Cs^+ is surprisingly high (i.e. well above the elastic Cs(Pb) backscattering peak [9] (Fig.2a)). The latter result for cesium is therefore believed to be attributed to sequences of multiple scattering collisions. Further details on the dynamics are expected from the results of a computer simulation [8,13], since multiple scattering of the cesium projectile may then be distinguished from re-sputtering of previously incorporated cesium [13].

4. Summary

Raw kinetic energy distributions of sputtered secondary ions (S^+, Pb^+, S^-), as well as of backscattered primary ions (O^+, O^-, Cs^+), have been measured for keV oxygen (O_2^+, O^-) or cesium (Cs^+) bombardment of galena (PbS). Ejection of high-energy (several keV) ions, with emission energies of up to ~ 60% of the bombarding energy for sputtering of the lighter target component ($S^{+\cdot}$), and of up to ~ 80% ($O^{+\cdot}$) or ~ 40% (Cs^+) for primary ion backscattering, has been observed.

References

[1]   S. N. Schauer and P. Williams, Int. J. Mass Spectrom. Ion Processes 103, 21 (1990) ;
      S. N. Schauer and P. Williams, Phys. Rev. B46, 15452 (1992).
[2]   R. A. Baragiola et al., Phys. Rev. A45, 5286 (1992).
[3]   K. Yasui, Phys. Rev. A48, 1711 (1993);
      R. A. Baragiola et al., Phys. Rev. A48, 1714 (1993).
[4]   J. Fine et al., Nucl. Instrum. Methods B122, 199 (1997).
[5]   B. van Someren et al., Surf. Sci. 391, L1194 (1997).
[6]   T. Mousel, W. Eckstein, and H. Gnaser, Nucl. Instrum. Methods B152, 36 (1999).
[7]   B. van Someren et al., Surf. Sci. 423, 276 (1999).
[8]   D. Karpuzov, K. Franzreb, A. R. Pratt, and N. S. McIntyre, SIMS XII (these proceedings).
[9]   K. Franzreb et al., Surf. Interface Anal. 26, 597 (1998).
[10] Z.-X. Jiang and P. F. A. Alkemade, Surf. Interface Anal. 25, 817 (1997).
[11] K. Wittmaack, Surf. Sci. 429, 84 (1999).
[12] D. Karpuzov, K. Franzreb, and N. S. McIntyre, SIMS XII (these proceedings).
[13] D. Karpuzov, K. Franzreb, A. R. Pratt, and N. S. McIntyre, to be published.

Table 1: Maximum [a] kinetic emission energy E_{max} of ions sputtered or backscattered from galena (PbS) under various ion surface bombardment conditions. Energies [b] E in eV ; potentials [c] U in Volts (vs. ground) ; angles [d] θ in ° (with respect to surface normal). See notes [a] to [e] below for definitions.

ion	E_{max}	projectile	U_i	U_s	E_i	θ_i/θ_e	T_{max} [e]	E_{max}/E_i
$^{32}S^+$	3500	$^{16}O_2^+$	+12500	+1000	5750	31/0	0.888	0.60
$^{208}Pb^+$	880	$^{16}O_2^+$	+12500	+3620	4440	36/0	0.265	0.20
$^{16}O^+$	»4500	$^{16}O_2^+$	+12500	0	6250	30/0	-------	>0.72
$^{32}S^+$	950	$^{16}O_2^+$	+6500	+3550	1475	48/0	0.888	0.64
$^{208}Pb^+$	280	$^{16}O_2^+$	+6500	+4220	1140	58/0	0.265	0.24
$^{16}O^+$	1550	$^{16}O_2^+$	+6500	+2950	1775	43/0	------	0.87
$^{32}S^+$	>4500	$^{16}O^-$	-12500	0	12500	30/0	0.888	>0.36
$^{208}Pb^+$	2500	$^{16}O^-$	-12500	+2000	14500	28/0	0.265	0.17
$^{32}S^+$	3200	$^{133}Cs^+$	+10000	+1300	8700	32/0	0.625	0.37
$^{208}Pb^+$	1000	$^{133}Cs^+$	+10000	+3500	6500	38/0	0.952	0.15
$^{133}Cs^+$	3700	$^{133}Cs^+$	+10000	+800	9200	31/0	-------	0.40
$^{133}Cs^+$	»500	$^{133}Cs^+$	+6500	+4000	2500	54/0	-------	»0.20
$^{32}S^-$	4100	$^{16}O_2^+$	+1250	-400	6450	29/0	0.888	0.63
$^{32}S^-$	»4500	$^{16}O^-$	-12500	0	12500	30/0	0.888	»0.36
$^{32}S^-$	2500	$^{16}O^-$	-6500	-2000	4500	37/0	0.888	0.55
$^{16}O^-$	»4500	$^{16}O^-$	-6500	0	6500	30/0	------	>0.69
$^{32}S^-$	3700	$^{133}Cs^+$	+10000	-800	10800	29/0	0.625	0.34

[a]   The values of E_{max} are lower limits that depend on the ion detection sensitivity.

[b] $E = = |q_2| \cdot 4500 \text{ eV} - q_2 \cdot e \cdot U_s$; kinetic emission energy as a function of sample potential.
$E_i = q_1 \cdot e \cdot (U_i - U_s)$; bombarding energy as a function of source and sample potential.
The values of E_i refer to the impact energy per atom (i.e. $E_i(O_2^+)$ is divided by 2).

[c]   The error ΔU_i of the source potential is thought to be less than 50 V.
The sample potential U_s was scanned in 10 V steps (for energy window of ≈10 eV).

[d] $\sin(\theta_i) = \sin(\theta_g)/(1 - U_s/U_i)^{1/2}$ with $\theta_g \approx 30°$; calculated bombarding angle θ_i.
The actual bombarding angle may deviate by roughly 5° from the calculated value because of the alignment of the primary ion beam.

[e] $T_{max} = 4 \cdot m_1 \cdot m_2/(m_1 + m_2)^2$; maximum energy transfer in first 'head-on' collision.
m_1, m_2, q_1, q_2 are primary and secondary mass and charge state, respectively.

A. Benninghoven, P. Bertrand, H.-N. Migeon and H.W. Werner (Editors).
Proceedings of the 12th International Conference on Secondary Ion Mass Spectrometry,
Brussels, Belgium, 5-11 September 1999

THE ALTERED LAYER CREATED BY ULTRA LOW ENERGY OXYGEN BOMBARDMENT AT NORMAL INCIDENCE

M.G.Dowsett[a], S.B.Patel[b] and G.A.Cooke[a]

[a]Department of Physics, University of Warwick, Coventry CV47AL, UK

[b]Atomika Instruments GmbH, Bruckmannring 40, D-85764 Oberschleißheim, München

1.Introduction

The incorporation of impurity distributions in the altered layer involves ballistic and chemically-related effects which redistribute the atoms and determine the depth resolution which can be achieved. A knowledge of the thickness, and internal structure of the altered layer, and internal profiles of redistributed material is important to understanding the limitations of SIMS. In the past, altered layers for normal incidence oxygen bombardment of silicon down to energies of 2 keV/O_2^+ have been extensively studied, for example by Kilner et al. [1], Vandervorst et al. [2], Dowsett et al. [3], leading to widely accepted thickness versus energy behaviour. In addition, in the early 90's, altered layer characteristics for beam energies down to 40 eV were studied by Vancauwenberghe et al. [4,5], and Todorov et al. [6] from the point of view of ion beam synthesis of oxides. These two groups found surprisingly large ion beam oxide (IBO) thickness T, with only a small change in T for beam energy E below 1 keV/ O_2^+. In particular, Vancauwenberghe's work shows a variation in thickness from 4 - 6 nm over the range 0.1-1 keV, with an approximate power law behaviour $T = 6.9E^{0.25}$ (T/nm, E/keV) compared to the higher energy behaviour reported by Kilner [1], approximately described by $T = 4.6E^{0.73}$. The two characteristics join with a sharp knee in the range 2-4 keV. Recently, Wittmaack has examined the use of MCs^+ ions (2 keV Cs^+ primary ions) for the characterization of IBO's and shown that thicknesses may be considerably underestimated using the OCs^+ signal [7]. Nevertheless, we use this method for the time being, and note significant differences between both erosion rates and $SiCs^+$ behaviour between our bombardment conditions and his.

The large thickness of the sub-keV altered layer, and its rather small variation with energy has important implications for ultra-low energy SIMS for two reasons. Firstly, the thickness of the altered layer is far larger than either the decay length or the overall depth resolution for B, Ge or Sb in silicon. This means that for a buried structure to remain resolvable, it must be incorporated into the altered layer and reach the surface relatively unperturbed. For 300 eV O_2^+ at normal incidence the intrinsic resolution of SIMS for boron (50% valley criterion, corrected for the finite width of a real delta layer) is 1.4 nm (decay length 0.7 nm), and 2 or 3 periods of such a structure will fit into the altered layer predicted by Vancauwenberghe's data. Secondly, the retained dose is determined by the thickness. Fig.1 shows retained dose calculated from the low energy thicknesses and assuming a density for the altered layer of 2.2 g cm^{-3} (dashed line) compared with measured transient dose (solid line) [8]. Given that some of the low energy beam is scattered, and some probe material is resputtered, one would

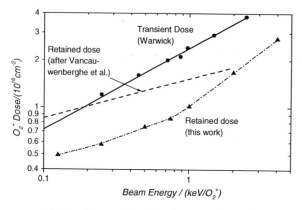

expect the latter curve to lie significantly above the former over the whole range. Taken at face value, the data suggest that all the 250 eV transient dose is retained in the sample - which seems unlikely. Alternatively, either the surface is oxidising before the bulk, stabilizing the degree of ionization rapidly, but leaving the sputter yield to vary over a longer period of time - the transient doses are underestimated, or the thicknesses measured by Vancauwenberghe do not correspond to the SIMS conditions and are overestimated.

Fig.1   Comparison between transient dose and retained dose implied by oxide thickness

The first possibility would lead to short and long term variations in ion and sputter yields, and corresponding difficulties in accurate quantification whilst the second might help to explain the high depth resolution achievable. Note that any analytical condition which aims to achieve full oxidation, for example bombardment at oblique incidence with flooding, will suffer from a similar problem. In this work, therefore, we report *in-situ* measurements of O_2^+ altered layer thicknesses made using a method similar to Kilner's [1].

2.Experimental

Normal incidence altered layers 1 mm square covering the energy range 0.1-4 keV were made and analysed in an Atomika 4500 instrument. The transient behaviour of several species was monitored, and the doses applied were well into the steady-state region. Each layer was profiled immediately after its creation using 23 nA, 0.5 keV Cs^+ ions at 60° to normal with a 275 μm raster. Positive ions OCs^+ and $SiCs^+$ were recorded amongst others. No charge compensation was used. For beam energies up to 1keV the OCs^+ signal was used to characterize the layer. For the 2 keV and 4 keV data, the ratio $OCs^+/SiCs^+$ ratio was used because charging affected the near surface regions of the profile. The experiment was repeated on 0.5 keV altered layers made exactly to the transient dose ($\Phi_{tr}=1.7\times10^{16}$ O_2^+ cm^{-2}). Following ref. [1], the 50% intensity level was used as a measure of the thickness (whether the profiles were ratioed or not made no significant difference to the Cs dose at which this level occurred), but it was not practical to use profilometry to measure craters accurately. Instead, in order to convert the Cs dose to depth, we initially attempted to use a 24.5 nm thick (ellipsometry and step etching) thermal oxide as a reference (profiled with charge compensation). This produced a significant underestimate in the thickness of the 4 keV and 2 keV layers which were already known, and the erosion rate of the 4 keV layer was found to be 1.33 times that of the thermal oxide. (Different from ref. [7]) Therefore the 4 keV layer itself was used as the reference, and its 50% level assigned a depth of 12.5 nm from previous work.

In ancillary experiments, the sensitivity of the 1 keV and 0.5 keV altered layer profile to laboratory exposure and boron concentration was tested. Neither two days air exposure, nor fabrication in (100) Si with B doping ranging from 0 to 10^{20} cm^{-3} had a measurable effect on the oxygen profiles or other signals, with the exception that some of the laboratory exposed

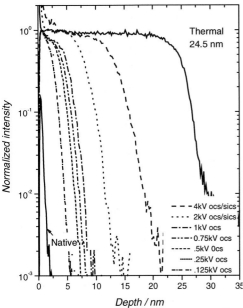

Fig.2　Altered layers created with normally incident $^{16}O_2^+$ between 0.125 and 4 keV / O_2^+ compared with native and thermal oxides

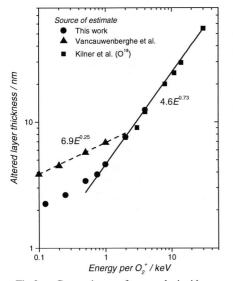

Fig.3　Comparison of normal incidence altered layer thicknesses.

samples acquired high surface levels of B. A 0.5 keV altered layer was characterized *ex-situ* using medium energy ion scattering (MEIS) as an independent check on the data.

3.Results and Discussion

The erosion rate differences between thermally grown oxide and altered layers show that, although the altered layers have SiO_2 stoichiometry, their physical structure is different. (Note that this was not apparent under the higher Cs energy conditions in ref. [7]). The fact that a 12 nm altered layer can be profiled without serious charging whereas a thermal oxide of similar thickness cannot, also points to structural differences. Another difference between this work and that of ref [7] was that the $SiCs^+$ signal was decreased in the Si rather than increased.

Fig.2 shows normalized, depth calibrated profiles for the altered layers with thermal oxide and native oxides for comparison. The $OCs^+/SiCs^+$ ratio is used for the thermal oxide and the native oxide data are plotted at the measured relative intensity. The near-surface intensity in the raw data for O_2^+ energies up to 1 keV varied by less than 12% and was not systematically lower at low energies. The depth calibration from the 4 keV layer produces a thickness for the 2 keV layer of 7.6 nm, in good agreement with Kilner's work. The thickness at 0.5 keV is found to be 3.4 nm, compared to 3.5 nm from the MEIS measurement on a similar layer. Fig.3 shows a compilation of data from this work (filled circles), ref. [1] (filled squares) and ref. [4] (filled triangles). Our measurements lie significantly below the latter values and on the same trend as Kilner's down to 0.75 keV. However, at lower energies they too show a smaller energy dependence. The 0.1 keV thickness is about half that quoted in ref. [4]. Returning to Fig. 1, the dotted line shows the retained dose calculated from our thickness estimates which lies below the transient dose as expected.

However, these data on their own do not show that the altered layer is fully formed for a dose Φ_{tr}. Fig.4 deals with this crucial point. The solid and dashed lines show layers created with

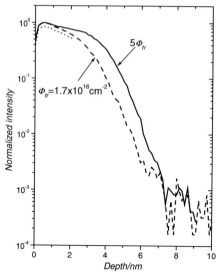

Fig.4   Altered layer profiles (OCs⁺) from 1 and 5 transient doses.

5Φ_{tr} and Φ_{tr} respectively. The dotted line shows the actual relative intensity for the Φ_{tr} data. It is clear that, whereas the surface is at or close to full oxidation in both cases, the Φ_{tr} altered layer is only 70% of the final thickness.

One might expect the thinner altered layers to be increasingly distorted by the obliquely incident Cs⁺ beam. Examination of the decay lengths for the altered layers in the 0.01-0.1 intensity range shows that they vary monotonically from 0.43 nm to 1.16 nm and do not apparently reach a lower limit imposed by the 500 eV Cs⁺. Either the 0.125 keV layer is still within the resolution limit of the beam, or the decays are being artificially sharpened at the low energy end because the profiles lie within the transient region of the Cs⁺. The transient behaviour of signals such as Cs⁺ and SiCs⁺ appears to be over well within the apparent thickness of the 0.125 keV altered layer, at an apparent depth of ≤ 1 nm, so this seems unlikely. Layers which are thinner still, such as native oxides, do not reach the same signal intensity as the altered layers and certainly lie within the transient region of the Cs⁺ beam.

4. Conclusions

Ultra low energy Cs⁺ profiles of normal incidence altered layers formed in (100) Si by $^{16}O_2^+$ at energies of 0.125 keV to 1 keV suggest that the layers are significantly thinner than has previously been reported, although the reasons for the differences in thickness estimate are not clear at present. Given reservations on the use of MCs⁺ ions for oxide thickness measurements [7] the results presented here, whilst in agreement with a MEIS measurement, require further confirmation. If correct, the layers retained doses are comfortably lower than previously measured transient doses. Nevertheless, we find that at the transient dose, the 0.5 keV altered layer has only reached 70% of its final thickness.

M.G.D. and G.A.C. would like to thank EPSRC and Atomika Instruments GmbH for their support of this work.

References

[1] J.A.Kilner, G.P.Beyer and R.J.Chater, Nucl.Instrum.Meth.in Phys.Res. B84 (1994) 176
[2] J.L.Alay and W.Vandervorst, Surf. Interface Anal. 19 (1992) 313
[3] M.G.Dowsett, Fres.Z.Anal.Chem. 341 (1991) 224
[4] O.Vancauwenberghe, N.Herbots and O.C.Hellman, J.Vac.Sci.Technol. A10 (1992) 713
[5] N.Herbots, O.Hellman, P. Ye, X.Wang and O.Vancauwenberghe, in Low Energy Ion-Surface Interactions, ed. J.W.Rabalais, J.Wiley and Sons (1994) Ch.8
[6] S.S.Todorov and E.R.Fossum, Appl.Phys.Lett 52 (1988) 48
[7] K.Wittmaack, SIMS IX, eds. Benninghoven et al., J.Wiley and Sons Ltd. (1994) 394
[8] M.G.Dowsett, T.J.Ormsby, D.I.Elliner and G.A.Cooke, SIMS XI, eds. G.Gillen et al., J.Wiley and Sons (1998) 371

A. Benninghoven, P. Bertrand, H.-N. Migeon and H.W. Werner (Editors).
Proceedings of the 12th International Conference on Secondary Ion Mass Spectrometry,
Brussels, Belgium, 5-11 September 1999

SURFACE MORPHOLOGY DEVELOPMENT DURING ION SPUTTERING. A^{III}B^{V} CASE

A. Merkulov[a], O. Merkulova[b]

[a]Cameca Instruments Inc., 204 Spring Hill Rd., Trumbull, CT 06611 USA
[b]Radiophysical Dep., St-Petersburg Technical University, 29 Politechnicheskaya St.,
St-Petersburg, Russia

1. Introduction

For the past two decades, secondary ion mass spectrometry (SIMS) has been one of the most commonly used techniques for dopant profiling and structural characterization of semiconductor materials and devices. However, there are problems inherent in sputter depth profiling that can cause broadening of the measured interfaces. Of the many factors that contribute to the beam induced profile broadening in sputter depth profiling considerable attention has been recently given to surface morphology development during sputtering. It has been observed that the surface topography that develops during sputter depth profiling plays a very important role in degradation of depth resolution. However, the understanding of the surface roughening process due to ion beam bombardment is still incomplete, even though the surface roughening problem could be minimized (but not excluded) by rotation of the sample.

2. Experimental results and discussion

In this work fractal theory is applied, to investigate the possibility of characterization of the surface roughness using the fractal dimension. Mandelbrot [1] introduced fractal geometry, which is an extension of Euclidean geometry and allows for the existence of geometrical objects with non-integer dimension. This dimension, referred to as the fractal dimension D, is limited by upper and lower bonds (for surfaces 2<D<3), and depending on how much volume it occupies. The fractal dimension introduces a new notion of roughness, the fractal roughness that can be used to characterize the irregularity of a surface as well as to compare the complexity of two surfaces in a quantitative way. The roughness of surfaces formed by random processes is usually scale-invariant, at least over some range of the scale. The mathematical description of a surface should mirror this feature, and also be compatible with theoretical models of its structure, such as kinetic growth models. The fractal description fulfills these conditions and is used for a quantitative evaluation of the surface roughness. Commonly used models for calculating D assume the scaling to be equal in the lateral directions on the surface but not necessary the same as in the normal direction. Such surfaces are called self-affine and differ from self-similar surfaces with equal scaling in all three directions. The fractal analysis from AFM images may be used to develop methods for extrapolating results from the other methods.

However, the estimation of D from an AFM image depends on the way D is calculated. Earlier, several algorithms have been used to calculate D, the most popular ones being the integrated Fourier-spectra method [2,3], the area-perimeter [1,4-6] method, the structure function [2-5] and the variational [2-5] methods. We use the structure function method, because it gives us statistical parameters, which have a clear physical means. If $z(i,j)$ is the measured height in pixel (i,j) of an image, the two-dimensional discrete structure function in pixel (k,m) is calculated as:

$$Str(k,m) = Str(\tau) = \frac{1}{(N-k)(N-m)} \sum_{i}^{N-k} \sum_{j}^{N-m} [z(i,j) - z(i+k,j+m)]^2$$

Here N is the number of pixels in each direction and τ is a lag vector or a distance $\tau=|\tau|$.

The sum is evaluated, giving a two-dimensional map of the structure function. Any anisotropy's is revealed in this map. Then $Str(\tau)$, for each τ, is averaged over different direction in the map. This algorithm is denoted the two-dimensional structure function method. We have examined the surface isotropy by computation of a two-dimensional structure function in two perpendicular directions, to insure that ripples are not formed. The structure function of the fractal surface, plotted in double logarithmic

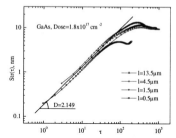

Fig.1 The structure function obtained for different scan length

coordinates, should be linear and its slope should be proportional to the fractal dimension of the surface. That is demonstrated on **Fig1**, which shows the structure functions, calculated for different scan-length and instrumental resolution. We have investigated the change of the fractal dimension during ion sputtering in our samples. In **Fig.2** we show that there is an increase of the fractal dimension during sputtering for all investigated samples, in the lateral scale 1-100 nanometers. That is, in this scale the surface roughness increases during bombardment by Cs^+ ions. This increase of roughness leads to the development at the surface of

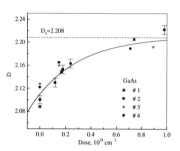

Fig.2 Behavior of the fractal dimension D as a function of the dose of ion irradiation for GaAs samples.

cone-like features with a characteristic diameter up to 100 nanometers, which are visible on AFM-images. The measured values of RMS characterize the roughness on a greater scale. We observed (see **Fig.3**) that for some samples RMS increases while for another samples it decreases, corresponding to processes that result in roughening or smoothing of the surface. From **Fig.3** it is possible to mark the presence of some steady-state RMS value for large enough doses of ion irradiation. It is safe to assume that there is some σ_0 characterizing of the equilibrium state of some process 'roughening-smoothing' for specific pairs of primary ion-substrate, when ripple is not formed. In the $Cs^+ \rightarrow A^{III}B^V$ case, we think that the asymptotic behavior of RMS can be explained because the process of formation of cone-like features and their overlapping attains the steady-state, as demonstrated by the saturation in the evolution of D, the fractal dimension. In order to confirm the results of the statistical analysis by using the fractal approach, a direct measurement from AFM images of the dimensions of the features, arising

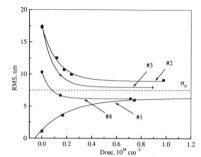

Fig.3 . Dependence of RMS as a function of Cs^+ dose irradiation for GaAs samples

on the initial smooth surfaces, as well as on the rough surfaces was made. The algorithm includes an off-line calculation of the dimensions of the surface features, such as effective diameters, heights, volumes and surface coverage. On the **Fig.4** the correlation between diameters and heights of cone-like (semi-spheres) features on the surfaces is shown. The horizontal dash line shows the assumed detection limit of cone-like features on the surface. Its absolute value is well correlated with the top limit of the linear region of the structure function, plotted in the log-log coordinates, or in other words it is the area of definition of D- the fractal dimension. The presence of this limit indicates the overlapping and merging of big size features, and that forms the larger scale surface structure. It

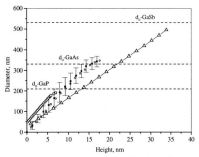

Fig.4 Correlation between diameters and heights of cone-like features

may be suggested that this process for some experimental conditions (T, E_p, and oxygen concentration) may result in ripple formation, as well as in the smoothing of the surface on the micron scale.

3. Computer modeling of surface during sputtering

The evolution of surface morphology during deposition or sputtering is the result of balance between multiple roughening and smoothing processes, or in other words, is a result of the microscopic dynamics of growth and removal. Stochastic addition or removal of material tends to roughen the surface while transport driven by surface energy minimization tends to smooth the surface. Enhanced mobility of adatoms and defects during deposition can result in smoother films and more uniform coverage of steps. Determining the dynamic response of the surface can provide important insight into the interaction of these various surface processes. Conversely, understanding the interaction among these various processes is essential to the atomic level control of surface morphology. The sub-micron topology of a surface produced by ion bombardment or erosion has received far less theoretical attention than that of deposited film. It is possible, however, that the scaling theories applicable to non-equilibrium film growth may also be applicable to ion bombardment, so long as no eroded material is re-deposited onto the surface. If so, the topography of a film deposited onto an initially smooth substrate should be quite similar to that of an initially smooth surface which is subjected to ion bombardment: a self-affine fractal surface is expected to develop, and its RMS roughness should increase with time. At sub-micron level, ion-bombarded surfaces have in fact been reported to be similar to those of vapor deposited films, and initially flat surfaces have been observed to roughen upon exposure to ion bombardment. Nucleation kinetics and film growth can be influenced by ion bombardment in epitaxial growth. Kinetics of surface chemical process can be enhanced by energetic ion bombardment. However, kinetic studies of the roughening

Fig.5 Determination of coordinate system M' for computer modeling

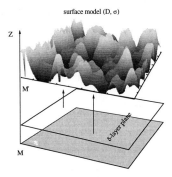

processes with the above approach are very difficult. First, it is important to understand the nature of ion bombardment, the dynamic surface processes that occur as a result, and then, the evolution of surface structure during sputtering can be predicted. Thus, in this work only one aspect of surface topography evolution during ion beam erosion is discussed. A simplified statistical model of surface development under sputtering for compositional SIMS depth profiling is used to show that bombardment induced topography determines the depth resolution of such analysis. In the model, an initially plane surface of a semi-infinite solid (in the z direction) of atomic density N is exposed to a uniform flux density J of ions incident to the surface, and where each ion sputters Y surface plane atoms. If this surface changes with time due to some physical processes then most generally it can be presented by the equation: $\varphi(x,y,z,t)=0$. The problem consists in finding φ as a function of the spatial coordinates and time knowing the physical processes. However, for our purpose it is sufficient to apply the computer-generated surfaces with known statistical characteristics, which are adequately described by a fractal dimension. The resulting surface of III-V binary compounds under Cs^+ bombardment can be represented by a random set of cone-like features [7]. This successive addition point was used to generate self-affine fractal

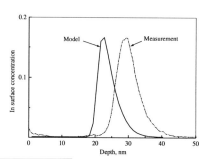

Fig.6 The calculated kinetics of surface composition during depth profiling of GaAs structure with $In_xGa_{1-x}As$ 4 nm barrier.

surfaces with fractal dimension D. This surfaces are processed then as a surface function φ, determined in the coordinate system M' moving with respect of laboratory system M, as it is shown in **Fig.5**. In **Fig.6** the calculated kinetic of the surface composition is presented for a GaAs multilayer structure containing the $In_xGa_{1-x}As$ 40Å barrier.

4. Conclusions

The surface modification of GaAs, GaP, GaSb and GaN during irradiation by heavy Cs^+ ions was investigated, by measurement of the height distribution of features at the surface by means of AFM, with their subsequent statistical processing. It was shown that the digitized AFM data could be used to accurately measure the fractal dimension of the surface. The two-dimensional structure function method was demonstrated to be suitable for the characterization of surfaces arising during ion irradiation. In summary, the fractal analysis provides an outstanding way to describe rough surfaces from AFM images. The analysis of the structure function and the statistical analysis of spatial characteristics of cone-like features allow estimating the characteristic parameters of the processes, accompanying ion sputtering for subsequent modeling.

References
[1] B.B. Mandelbrot, The fractal Geometry of Nature, Freeman, New York, 1982.
[2] A.-L Barabasi., H.E. Stanley, Fractal concepts in surface growth, Cambrige, University Press, 1995.
[3] J.Krim, I.Heyvaert, C.Van Haesendock, Y.Bruynseraede, Phys. Rev. Let., 70 (1993) 57.
[4] N.Almqvist, Surface Science, 355 (1996) 221.
[5] A.I. Olemskoi, Soviet Scientific Reviews, Section A, Physics Reviews 18 (1995).
[6] J.M.Gomez-Rodriguez, M.Baro, J. Vac. Sci. Technol. B, 9(2) (1991) 495.
[7] A.Merkulov, O.Merkulova, R.Asomoza, App. Surface Science, (126)3-4 (1998) 205.

A. Benninghoven, P. Bertrand, H.-N. Migeon and H.W. Werner (Editors).
Proceedings of the 12th International Conference on Secondary Ion Mass Spectrometry,
Brussels, Belgium, 5-11 September 1999

EFFECT OF OXYGEN FLOODING ON CRATER SURFACE COMPOSITION AND SURFACE ROUGHENING IN ULTRA SHALLOW DEPTH PROFILING

C.M. Ng[1], A.T.S. Wee[1]*, C.H.A. Huan[1], A. See[2]

[1]Department of Physics, National University of Singapore, Lower Kent Ridge Road,
Singapore 119260 *Corresponding e-mail: phyweets@nus.edu.sg
[2]Chartered Semiconductor Manufacturing Ltd., 60 Woodland Industrial Park D, Street 2,
Singapore 738406

1. Introduction

Oxygen flooding is now regularly used in SIMS analysis particularly for ultra shallow depth profiling of the near surface region. Despite its advantages in enhancing positive ion sputter yield and minimizing matrix effect, many works have reported a possible resultant profile distortion that may cause misinterpretation [1,2]. One of the causes that lead to profile distortion has been identified as the onset of surface roughness in the crater during sputtering [3]. The aim of this work is to study the nature of oxide formed during 1 keV O_2^+ sputtering under oxygen flooding, to explore any correlation with the resulting surface roughening.

2. Experimental

The sample used in this experiment was a 2 keV B^+ implanted (1E15 B/cm^2) silicon wafer, preamorphized with 1E15 Ge/cm^2 implanted at 5 keV to reduce the channeled implant distribution. All SIMS depth profiles in this experiment were performed in a CAMECA IMS6f instrument with O_2 inlet using a 1 keV O_2^+ beam (50 nA) at an incident angle of 60° to the surface normal, and rastered over an area of $500 \times 500~\mu m^2$. In addition to the SIMS sputtering performed using essentially the same conditions as that used in the work of Jiang et al [3], the profiles were terminated at different depths at varying O_2 partial pressure and the evolution of the crater bottom studied using XPS and AFM. Oxygen inlet was done with O_2 jet through a movable capillary tube directed towards the sample and the oxygen partial pressure was measured with an ion gauge located about 10 cm from the sample holder in the analysis chamber. Sputtering under oxygen flooding were performed at pressures between 3.1E-8 and 1.9E-7 mbar. The crater depths were measured with a Tencor Alpha 500 series stylus profilometer and the depth scale was established by assuming constant erosion rate.

XPS spectra for the crater surfaces were obtained using a high resolution VG Scientific ESCALAB 220I-XL system equipped with a monochromatic Al Kα x-ray source and a concentric hemispherical analyzer that is capable to achieve an energy resolution of 0.4 eV on clean Si surface. The electron take-off angle was 90°. The system was set at constant analyzer pass energy of 20 eV for the data collection yielding an energy resolution of 0.7 eV. The analyzed area of XPS analysis was set to be $150 \times 150~\mu m^2$ and the x-ray beam was directed to the central region of the crater bottoms. The transfer of each sample from CAMECA to VG took only less than 5 minutes and no significant change in the sample surface conditions were expected. The various experimental Si^0 and Si^{n+} (n = 1, 2, 3, 4) intensities were determined by curve fitting the Si 2p spectra into component peaks. We used the binding energies (BE) as given by Niwano et al (Si^0: 99.2 eV, Si^{1+}: 100.2 eV, Si^{2+}: 101.0 eV, Si^{3+}: 101.7 eV, Si^{4+}: 103.2 eV) [4]. A spin-orbit splitting of 0.61 eV and a Si $2p_{3/2}$: Si $2p_{1/2}$ spin-orbit intensity ratio of 2:1 was assumed. The surface roughness at the centre of the crater was measured *ex-situ* using a Digital Instruments Nanoscope Multimode TM D3000 series AFM. All AFM images were collected in tapping mode with autoslope correction and scan sizes of $2 \times 2 \ \mu m^2$.

3. Results and Discussion

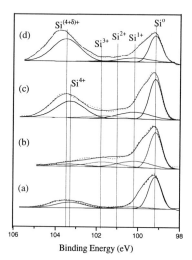

Fig.1: Curve fitting for the XPS spectra obtained for (a) virgin sample (b) no oxygen inlet (3.5E-9 mbar) (c) intermediate pressure (6.5E-8 mbar) and (d) saturated pressure (1.9E-7 mbar). (b), (c) and (d) were obtained a sputtered depth of about 100nm. The dots represent the raw XPS spectra. The $2p_{1/2}$ spectra are not shown now.

Figure 1 shows peak-fitted XPS spectra at three different oxygen partial pressures at a depth of about 100 nm after the oxidation states of the altered layer achieved equilibrium together with the spectrum obtained from a virgin sample. It can be clearly seen that the relative intensities of the different Si oxidation states, namely Si_2O (Si^{1+}), SiO (Si^{2+}), Si_2O_3 (Si^{3+}) and SiO_2 (Si^{4+}) change significantly with oxygen partial pressure. With no oxygen inlet (3.5E-9 mbar), the final oxidation states were essentially dominated by Si_2O (Si^{1+}) and Si_2O_3 (Si^{3+}) with relatively little contribution from SiO_2 (Si^{4+}). The SiO (Si^{2+}) state was almost negligible. The dominance of the sub-oxides (Si_2O (Si^{1+}) and Si_2O_3 (Si^{3+})) reduced with increasing oxygen partial pressure as shown by the spectrum for pressure of 6.5E-8 mbar. With high oxygen flooding pressure (1.9E-7 mbar) the oxide formed was predominantly stoichiometric SiO_2, which is consistent with the results of Elst *et al* [5] where an 8 keV O_2^+ primary beam was used. In additional, the SiO_2 component intensity was higher at higher flooding pressures which indicates that the oxide thickness increased with higher oxygen partial pressure. Comparison between spectra of the virgin sample with that of no flooding suggests the removal of the native oxide in the initial stage.

At 1.9E-7 mbar oxygen inlet pressure, an additional binding energy shift of +0.2 eV in the SiO_2 component was observed. This behaviour was not observed for all lower oxygen inlet pressures. This positive BE shift is attributed to the presence of oxygen interstitial defects resulting in an effectively increased Si oxidation state which we label $Si^{(4+\delta)+}$. The high oxygen partial pressure is believed to have provided an oxygen supersaturation environment in the near surface region favouring the formation of these oxygen interstitials.

The variation of the ratios of the the intensity of the dioxide to the sum of the intensities of elemental silicon and dioxide, $I(Si^{4+})/[I(Si^0)+I(Si^{4+})]$ is displayed in Figure 2 at different oxygen inlet pressures as a function of depth. The three lines that appear in Figure 2, and the following Figure 3 and Figure 4 merely serve as a guide to highlight the general trends in three pressure regimes observed. Figure 2 is indicative of the thickness of the oxide formed on the crater surface during sputtering [6]. The three pressure regimes display different characteristics in the sputtering transient region. The first is with no oxygen flooding where the ratio, and hence the oxide thickness, remained relatively low (~0.16) throughout. At intermediate pressures (approx. 5E-8 to 1E-7 mbar), the ratios rose gradually and saturated at about 0.55 after a depth of 50 nm. Finally, when the flooding pressure was 1.9E-7 mbar, the oxide:Si ratio dropped from an initial value (~0.7) and saturated at a slightly lower value of about 0.65 after a depth of 30 nm. The equilibrium ratios were generally higher at higher oxygen partial pressures indicating that a thicker oxide forms at higher pressures.

Figure 3 illustrates the contribution of the sub-oxide states (Si_2O (Si^{1+}), SiO (Si^{2+}) and Si_2O_3 (Si^{3+})) on the crater bottom. This was done by including the relative intensities of all sub-oxide states into both numerator and denominator of the ratio introduced above. For the ease of discussion, we shall refer the previous ratio as R1 and the new as R2. Any appreciable difference between the values of R1 and R2 would indicate a significant contribution from the sub-oxides. R2 for the sputtering with no oxygen flooding was significantly higher than the corresponding R1 and this clearly indicates that the sub-oxides form a large proportion of the

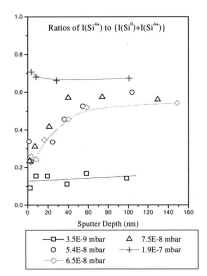
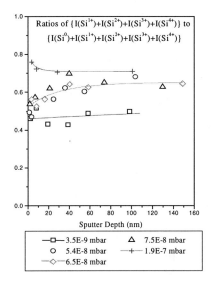

Fig.2: Ratios of intensities of Si^{4+} to the sum of intensities for (Si^0 and Si^{4+}).

Fig.3: Ratios of sum of intensities for all sub-oxide states (Si^{1+}, Si^{2+}, Si^{2+} and Si^{4+}) to intensities for (Si^0, Si^{1+}, Si^{2+}, Si^{2+} and Si^{4+})

oxidised species throughout. This dominance was in general reduced when the oxygen partial pressure was increased. The difference between R1 and R2 fraction of sub-oxides reduced gradually from the surface and R2 gradually settled down at a ratio difference of 0.05 after 50 nm at an oxygen inlet of 6.5E-9 mbar. This may suggest a transition from sub-oxides to stoichiometric SiO_2 states during the transition region since the corresponding thickness was not increased much. At high oxygen partial pressures (1.9E-7 mbar), the oxide was essentially SiO_2 and equilibrium is attained quickly.

Figure 4 displays the variation of crater surface roughness as function of depth. Both sputtering with no oxygen flooding and at high oxygen partial gas pressure (1.9E-7 mbar) did not result in significant changes in crater surface roughness. However, crater surface roughness during sputtering at intermediate pressures developed rapidly over the depth range of 20 to 40 nm and continued at a slower rate beyond the depth of about 60 nm. The AFM roughness evolution with depth shows a similar saturation behaviour at about the same depth where the oxidation saturation was achieved within the second regime in Fig. 3. The same result was first reported by Jiang *et al* [3]. In addition, we observe in our present work a direct correlation between oxidation states and crater surface roughness when oxygen flooding is incorporated in SIMS.

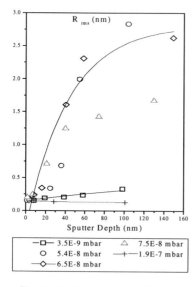

Fig. 4: Surface roughness of crater surface as function of depth.

Figures 1 and 4 show that when the sputtered oxide surface has either a low (in case of no oxygen flooding) or high SiO_2 fraction (in case of high oxygen partial pressures) the resultant surface roughening will be insignificant. On the other hand, when oxygen flooding of immediate pressure is used, an oxide layer of comparable SiO_2 and sub-oxide fraction is formed with high surface roughness. This is consistent with the work of Elst *et al* [5] who hypothesized that the presence of a heterogeneous layer is indispensable for the seeding and subsequent growth of ripple structures. Figure 4 shows the suppression of ripple growth by the increasing SiO_2 fraction in the altered layer after sputtering beyond the transient region. This may be attributed to the reduction of heterogeneity in the oxidation layer that consequently leads to the suppression of ripple growth.

4. Conclusion

Concerning incorporation of oxygen flooding in SIMS analysis, this work shows explicitly the evolution of the oxidation states on the crater bottom and proposes a direct correlation between the oxidation states of the crater surface and the corresponding surface roughening. The onset of the surface roughening, commencing typical at depths ranging from 20 to 60 nm, occurs when the crater oxide layer is inhomogeneous comprising comparable fractions of SiO_2 and sub-oxide states. The formation of homogeneous stoichiometric SiO_2 (Si^{4+}), on the other hand, suppresses further surface roughening. In addition, sputtering at high oxygen partial pressure results in the oversaturation of oxygen incorporation into the sample.

References:
[1]   K. Wittmaack and S.F. Corcoran, J. Vac. Sci. Technol. B 16 (1998) 272
[2]   K. Wittmaack, J. Vac. Sci. Technol. B 16 (1998) 2776
[3]   Z.X. Jiang and P.F.A. Alkemade, J. Vac. Sci. Technol. B 16 (1998) 1971
[4]   M.Niwano, H. Katakura, Y. Takakuwa and N. Miyamoto, J. Appl. Phys. 68 (1990) 5576
[5]   K. Elst and W. Vandervorst, J. Vac. Sci. Technol. A 12 (1994) 3205
[6]   D.F. Mitchell, K.B. Clark, J.A. Bardwell, W.N. Leonard, G.R. Massoumi and I.V. Mitchell, Surf. Interface Anal. 21 (1994) 44

A. Benninghoven, P. Bertrand, H.-N. Migeon and H.W. Werner (Editors).
Proceedings of the 12th International Conference on Secondary Ion Mass Spectrometry,
Brussels, Belgium, 5-11 September 1999

THE MODEL OF A WAVE-ORDERED STRUCTURES FORMED ON AMORPHOUS MATERIALS DURING ION SPUTTERING

A.S.Rudy[a] and V.K.Smirnov[b]

[a]Microelectronics Department, Yaroslavl State University, Sovetskaya St., 14,
Yaroslavl,150000, Russian Federation rudy@univ.uniyar.ac.ru
[b]Institute for Microelectronics of Russian Academy of Sciences, Universitetskaya St., 21,
150007, Russian Federation

1. Introduction

Elaboration of the methods to control spontaneous formation of a wave-ordered structures (WOS) during ion sputtering of solids is one of the most important problems of ultrashallow SIMS. Solution of this important practical problem was complicated by the fact that mechanism of WOS formation remained unclear. All of known models, from earliest [1] to recent [2], either did not consider a mechanism of embryonic WOS generation, or failed to predict its regularities (e.g. wavelength dependence on an angle of bombardment and a lack of wavelength-intensity correlation, angular range of WOS existence, etc.) as well as a wavelength proper. In present paper the hydrodynamic model of embryonic WOS, enabling an explanation of above regularities and resulting in correct values of a wave periods and angular range of WOS existence is set forth.

2. Hydrodynamic Model of Amorphous Layer

The model is based on the approach to amorphous layer as a high-viscosity fluid [3] which flow within a small shear stress is purely Newtonian [4]. Within this approach fluid dynamics is defined by kinematic viscosity ν, surface tension α and volume force $\boldsymbol{F}$. The mathematical model of an amorphized layer is formulated as a boundary value problem for Navier-Stokes and continuity equations for a layer h of incompressible fluid on a rigid bottom

$$\frac{\partial \bar{v}}{\partial t} + (\bar{v}, \nabla)\bar{v} = \frac{\bar{F}}{\rho} - \frac{\nabla P}{\rho} + \nu(\nabla, \nabla)\bar{v},$$

$$\frac{\partial \zeta}{\partial t} = \int_{\zeta}^{-h} \frac{\partial v_x}{\partial x} dz, \quad \bar{v}(-h) = 0,$$

$$\left(\frac{\partial v_x}{\partial x} - \frac{\alpha}{2\eta}\frac{\partial^2 \varsigma}{\partial x^2}\right)\left(\frac{\partial \varsigma}{\partial x}\right)^2_{z=0} = \left(\frac{\partial v_z}{\partial z} - \frac{\alpha}{2\eta}\frac{\partial^2 \varsigma}{\partial x^2}\right). \tag{1}$$

In Eq. (1) ρ is density, $\bar{v}$ is fluid velocity, ζ is a local deviation of a free surface from its zero level. The volume force in the r.h.s. of Eq. (1) is treated as the average of the momentum transmitted by slowing down ions to a unit volume in a unit time, thus its components can be expressed through ion current $I / cos\Theta$, modulus of momentum of incident ion $p = \sqrt{2m_N E_0}$ and their stopping range l as follows

$$F_x = \frac{I \, sin\,\Theta}{I \, cos^2\,\Theta} \sqrt{2m_N E_0} \, ,$$

$$F_z = \frac{I}{I \, cos\Theta} \sqrt{2m_N E_0} \, . \tag{2}$$

Periodic solutions of the boundary value problem (1) linearized in a vicinity of its stationary solution

$$v_x(z) = \frac{F_x}{\eta}(h^2 - z^2),$$

$$P(z) = -F_z z \tag{3}$$

are sought for in a form of travelling waves $v_x(x, z, t) = u_x(z) \, exp(i\theta)$, $v_z(x, z, t) = u_z(z) \, exp(i\theta)$, $P(x, z, t) = F_z \varsigma(x, t)$, where $\theta = \omega t - kx$. The analysis of the problem (1) yields two spatial-periodic solutions

$$\frac{\varsigma_n(x, t)}{h} = \pm\varsigma_{0n} \, exp\left(\pm\frac{t}{\tau_n}\right) sin \, k_n x, \, n = 1,2 \tag{4}$$

with amplitudes

$$\varsigma_{0n} = \frac{\sqrt{cosh\mu_n(cosh\,\mu_n - 1)}}{\sqrt{3}\mu_n \, sinh\,\mu_n} . \tag{5}$$

Though solutions (4) are unstable, their increment as well as damping decrement

$$\frac{1}{\tau_n} = \frac{3}{2}\frac{\alpha}{\eta} k_n \tag{6}$$

turns out to be so small that there is no point to attribute factors (6) to solutions (4) but both should be considered as quasi-stationary states.

The wave numbers k_n in above expressions are obtained as the roots of equation

$$a^2 = 4\,cosh\mu \, (\mu \, sinh\,\mu - 2\,cosh\mu + 2)/ \, \mu^2(cosh^2\,\mu - cosh\mu + 3\,sinh^2\,\mu), \tag{7}$$

where $a = \sqrt{2\alpha/ \, F_z}/ \, h$ is a normalized capillary constant, $\mu = 2\pi h/ \, \lambda$. Dependence of WOS period λ on capillary constant is shown in Fig. 1.

3. Dependence of WOS Period on an Angle of Bombardment

The parameters a and μ contain an amorphous layer thickness, which can be replaced by a polynomial $h(\Theta)$, approximating experimental dependence of a thickness on the angle of bombardment. Taking into consideration this dependence one may treat a in Eq. (7) as a critical surface $a_c(\Theta, L)$ in a phase space a, Θ, L, where $L = \lambda / h(0)$, below which WOS may exist. The cross-sections of this surface by planes $a = const$ define the regions of WOS existence in the phase plane Θ, L. In Fig.2 this result is matched with our experimental data on Si sputtering by N_2^+ ions with energies $5\ keV$ and $9\ keV$ within the angular range $45° \div 70°$.

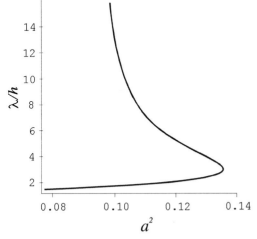

Fig.1. Dependence of normalized WOS period on capillary constant.

From this plots and assumption that capillary constant diminishes through ion bombardment appears that WOS formation starts in a small vicinity of a global maximum of a function $a_c(\Theta, L)$ marked by cross in Fig. 2. With a diminution below this maximum the range of WOS existence extends until capillary constant reaches its limit value. To all appearances WOS formation demands a certain supercriticality of control parameter $a < a_{bf}$, where a_{bf} is its bifurcational value determined as a maximum in the cross-section of $a_c(\Theta, L)$ by the plane $\Theta = const$.

As WOS formation occurs in a supercritical region while theory predicts critical values of capillary constant, only a lower estimate of a WOS period is possible. The most precise such evaluation will be for the angle $\Theta = 55°$ corresponding to the minimum supercriticallity. In this case the model yields a critical value of WOS period $\lambda = 48.5nm$ while that of experimentally observed for $E_0 = 5keV$ is $\lambda \approx 65nm$, thereby the inaccuracy in using lower evaluation of the period is 26%.

According to above results with $E_0 = 5keV$ the maximum value of capillary constant falls at the angle $\Theta = 55°$ (Fig. 2 a). In the case of $E_0 = 9keV$ this maximum is already local (Fig. 2 b), hence with energy reduction this maximum probably becomes more convex. This means that with ion energy diminution, provided that supercriticallity remains constant or also reduces, the angular range should contract into a point at $\Theta = 55°$. Experimental data on critical angles in the range of energy variation $1 \div 12keV$ completely confirm this conclusion

100

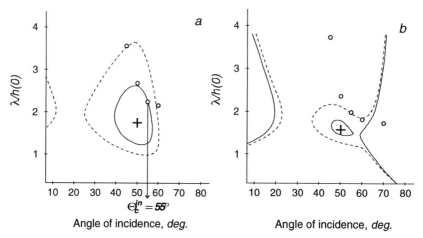

Angle of incidence, *deg.*   Angle of incidence, *deg.*

Fig. 2. Comparison of calculated and experimental angular dependences of a normalized WOS period obtained for $N_2^+ - Si$ with ion beam energies **5keV** and **9keV** : (a) E_0 = **5keV**, the solid and dashed curves are the contours of $a_c(\Theta, L)$ cross-sections by the planes **a** = **0.367** (corresponding the maximum of observed capillary constant value) and **a** = **0.353**, (b) E_0 = **9kEV**, solid and dashed contours correspond **a** = **0.345** and **a** = **0.342** respectively. The circles present the experimental points, the cross marks the top of a surface $a_c(\Theta, L)$.

4. Summary

The results of a hydrodynamic model analysis satisfactory agree with most of known experimental facts. The disadvantage of the model is the extremely small flow velocities meaning a long time of WOS formation. As this value is of the same order as the time of sputtering to the depth of evolved WOS amplitude, a better agreement may be reached if a problem is formulated as a moving boundary problem, e.g. Eqs. (1) in combination with Kuramoto-Sivashinsky equation. It is also necessary to stress, that the above results being obtained within the framework of hydrodynamic model describe only embryonic structure. Their comparison to experimental data was carried out in supposition that the sputtering only evolves WOS relief without substantial changing its wavelength. Furthermore these results do not provide direct relations of WOS parameters and chemical composition of a modified layer and ion beam. The chemical factor in this model affects WOS parameters mediately through rheological properties of a simulated fluid (viscosity and surface-tension).

References
[1] R.M.Bradley and J.M.E.Harper, J. Vac. Technol. A 6 (1988) 2390.
[2] G.Carter, Nucl. Instr. and Meth. B 115 (1996) 473.
[3] G.Carter, Surf. and Interf. Anal. 25 (1997) 36.
[4] C.A.Volkert, J. Appl. Phys. 70 (1991) 3521.

A. Benninghoven, P. Bertrand, H.-N. Migeon and H.W. Werner (Editors).
Proceedings of the 12th International Conference on Secondary Ion Mass Spectrometry,
Brussels, Belgium, 5-11 September 1999
© 2000 Elsevier Science B.V. All rights reserved.

SIMS ROUND-ROBIN STUDY OF DEPTH PROFILING OF BORON IMPLANTS IN SILICON [II]
—Problems of quantification in high concentration B profiles—

F.Toujou[a,b], M.Tomita[b], A.Takano[b], Y.Okamoto[b], S.Hayashi[b], A.Yamamoto[b], and Y.Homma[b]

[a] Matsushita Technoresearch, Inc., Characterization Technology Group
3-1-1, Yagumo-Nakamachi, Moriguchi, Osaka 570-8501, JAPAN
[b] Members of SIMS-Depth Profiling WG, JSPS-141 Committee
toujou@mtr.mei.co.jp

1. Introduction

In recent high performance ULSI devices, the doping region becomes shallower, and the dopant concentration of shallow implants is much higher than a normal doping level. It is thus important to quantify the high concentration of dopant profiles. We have performed round robin studies to evaluate the reproducibility of depth profiles and the linearity of the ion intensity using boron-implanted silicon specimens with high ion doses ($>1 \times 10^{16}$ ions/cm^2).

In the previous studies, we reported the results of the reproducibility of depth profiles and the linearity of the ion intensity [1][2]. In these results, quantitative analysis with relative standard deviation (RSD) of 11% could be performed in the dose range from 3×10^{14} to 3×10^{16} ions/cm^2 (for B$^+$, BSi$^-$ ions). However, for the 1×10^{17} ions/cm^2 specimen, the relative sensitivity factor for B$^+$ was smaller than the others, and its RSD was much larger than the others. For higher B doses (over 1×10^{16} ions/cm^2), the peak concentration of implanted B is over 1×10^{21} atoms/cm^3. The SIMS profiles of B and Si were distorted due to the matrix effect of boron. These distortions affected the quantification of higher dose specimens.

In this paper we focus on the behaviors of Si and B ions for the boron concentration of $\geq 10^{21}$ atoms/cm^3, and discuss the primary-ion species and impact-angle dependence of the matrix effect due to boron.

2. Experimental

Specimens were cut from three Si wafers implanted with ^{11}B$^+$ at 50 keV using AMT PI-9500 (xR) ion implanter (Applied Materials Inc.). The B doses were 1×10^{16} (Sp3), 3×10^{16} (Sp4) and 1×10^{17} (Sp5) ions/cm^2. The SIMS instruments used were ATOMIKA SIMS 4000 and 4500.

B profiles were acquired using a 4 keV O$_2^+$ primary ion beam for ^{11}B$^+$, ^{39}BSi$^+$, and ^{27}BO$^+$, and using a 4 keV Cs$^+$ beam for ^{39}BSi$^-$ and ^{11}B$^-$. The matrix ions (^{30}Si, ^{56}Si$_2$, etc.) were alternately monitored with those boron-related ions (since the ion intensities of B$^-$ and BO$^+$ were low, these species were excluded from the analysis). The impact angles were 0, 15, 30, 45, and 60° from surface normal. The crater depth eroded by SIMS primary ion beam were measured by using stylus profilometers in order to convert the sputtering time into the real depth scale.

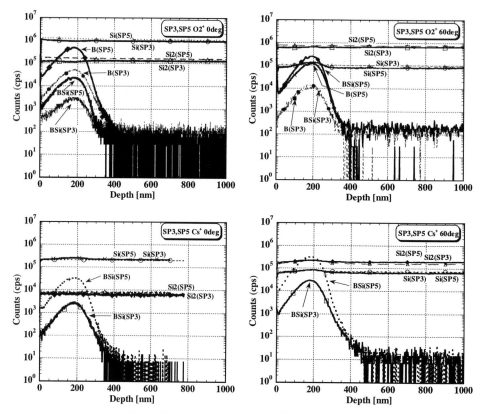

Fig.1 Typical depth profiles of boron and sillicon.

3. Results & discussion

Figure 1 shows typical depth profiles of B and Si for Sp3 and Sp5 under 0- and 60°-O_2^+ and Cs^+ bombardment. The Si profiles exhibit no particular features up to 1×10^{16} ions/cm^2 (Sp3). However, a Si intensity change appears at around the B peak concentration in the 1×10^{17} ions/cm^2 profile (Sp5). Obviously, the Si-ion signal suffers yield change from the matrix effect of the high boron concentration. The degree of Si-ion intensity change as a function of the primary-ion impact angle is shown in Figure 2. For O_2^+ bombardment, the Si$^+$ intensity change becomes small as the impact angle decreases, indicating that the matrix effect due to boron is masked by the surface oxygen supplied from the primary ion beam. On the other hand, the influence of the matrix effect is smaller for Si_2^+ under O_2^+ bombardment, and both for Si$^-$ and Si_2^- under Cs^+ bombardment. These yield changes of matrix ions can affect the results of quantification and their accuracy [2].

To extract the angular dependence of matrix effect, we need to cancel out the transmission change for different impact angles. This was performed by normalizing the integrated ion intensities of Sp4 and Sp5 to that of Sp3.

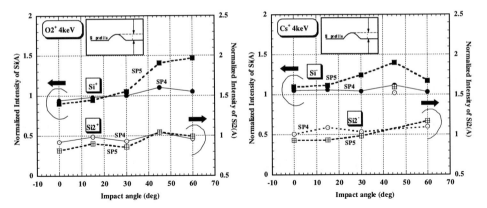

Fig.2 Si ion intensity change.

The ion intensity of analyte X at impact angle θ is given by

$$I^X(\theta) = \eta^X(\theta) \cdot \gamma^{X\pm}(\theta) \cdot S(\theta) \cdot C^X \cdot I_P \tag{1}$$

where η^X is the transmission of the instrument, $\gamma^{X\pm}$ is the ion yield of X, S is the sputtering yield, C^X is the concentration of X, and I_P is the primary ion intensity. Measured depth profiles are integrated up to an appropriate depth, and resulted quantities of Sp4 and Sp5 are normalized to that of Sp3 at each impact angle. Then, the ion yield ratio of analyte X is obtained:

$$\frac{\gamma^{X\pm}_{(Sp\alpha)}(\theta)}{\gamma^{X\pm}_{(Sp3)}(\theta)} = \frac{\sum_{k=1}^{M} C^X_{k\,(Sp3)} \Delta Z_M}{\sum_{k=1}^{N} C^X_{k\,(Sp\alpha)} \Delta Z_N} \cdot \frac{\sum_{k=1}^{N} I^X_{k\,(Sp\alpha)}(\theta) \Delta Z_N}{\sum_{k=1}^{M} I^X_{k\,(Sp3)}(\theta) \Delta Z_M} \tag{2}$$

where, Sp$\alpha\alpha$Sp4 or Sp5, $\Delta Z_N = Z/N$, and $\Delta Z_M = Z/M$. For boron, the integration of C^X gives the implanted dose, i.e., $\sum_{k=1}^{M} C^X_{k\,(Sp3)} \Delta Z_M = \Phi_{(Sp3)}$, and $\sum_{k=1}^{N} C^X_{k\,(Sp\alpha)} \Delta Z_N = \Phi_{(Sp\alpha)}$. Therefore, the first term of the right-hand side of Eq. 2 is the dose ratio. For silicon, it gives unity.

Using Eq. 2, the impact angle dependence of ion yield ratio is calculated for Si$^\pm$, Si$_2^\pm$, B$^+$, and BSi$^-$, and shown in Figure 3. Under O$_2^+$ bombardment, the ion yield ratios of Si$^+$, B$^+$, and BSi$^+$ increase with an increase of impact angle. The increment depends on the ion species: that of B$^+$ for Sp5 amounts to 2 at 60° with respect to 0°, while that of Si$^+$ is only 1.2. When the surface oxygen concentration is high enough at near normal incidence, the ion yields are almost saturated, thus, the matrix effect due to boron does not appear. The oxygen effect is overwhelming compared to the boron effect up to 30°. For larger angles, the boron effect becomes dominant. As is the oxygen case, the boron-matrix effect affects differently for different ion species. For Si$_2^+$ the ion yield ratio shows no angle dependence, i.e., no boron-matrix effect. This is also similar to the Si$_2^+$ behavior under the presence of oxygen [3].

Surprisingly, negative ions, both atomic and molecular ions, under Cs$^+$ bombardment exhibit very small angle dependence. There are two possible interpretations for this result. One is that the high concentration of boron does not affect negative ion formation. The other is that since the surface cesium concentration is high enough even for 60° [4], the ion yields are saturated throughout the impact angle range measured.

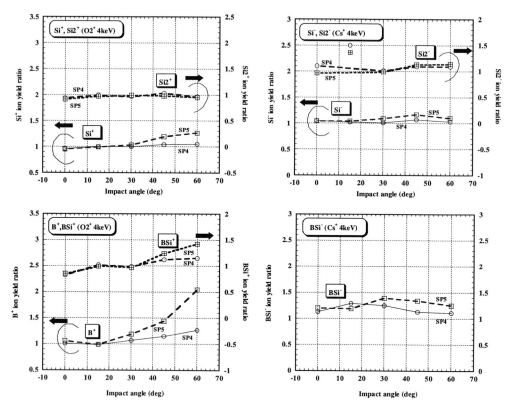

Fig.3 Impact angle dependence of ion yield ratio.

4. Conclusion

We have investigated the influence of the high concentration of boron, on the order of 10^{21} atoms/cm^3 or higher, on quantitative analysis. Under O_2^+ bombardment at the impact angle of > 30°, B- and Si-ion yields increased due to the boron-matrix effect for the boron concentration of > 10^{21} atoms/cm^3. The boron-matrix effect becomes dominant when the surface oxygen concentration decreases. Under Cs^+ bombardment, no boron-matrix effect was found for negative ions up to the impact angle of 60°. These results can be applicable to the quantification of shallow depth profiling, where the near surface concentration of dopant can be very high.

References

[1] Y.Okamoto et.al., in Secondary Ion Mass Spectrometry SIMS XI,
      ed. by G. Gillen, R. Lareau, J. Bennett and F. Stevie, Wiley, Chichester, 1998, p.1047.
[2] F.Toujou, et al, J. Surf. Anal. 5 (1999) 30.
[3] J.Maul et.al., Surf. Sci.,47,(1975)363.
[4] K.Wittmaack, in Secondary Ion Mass Spectrometry SIMS X
      ed. by A.Benninghoven, B.Hagenhoff and H.W.Werner, John Wiley&Sons, 1996, p.39.

A. Benninghoven, P. Bertrand, H.-N. Migeon and H.W. Werner (Editors).
Proceedings of the 12th International Conference on Secondary Ion Mass Spectrometry,
Brussels, Belgium, 5-11 September 1999

A MARLOWE COMPUTER SIMULATION OF HIGH-ENERGY PARTICLE EMISSION DURING keV SPUTTERING OF PbS AND FeS$_2$

D. Karpuzov[2][*][$], K. Franzreb[1], A. R. Pratt[3][#], and N. S. McIntyre[1]

[1] Surface Science Western, Univ. of Western Ontario, London, Ontario N6A 5B7, Canada
[2] Institute of Electronics, Bulgarian Academy of Sciences, Sofia 1784, Bulgaria
[3] Earth Sciences, The University of Western Ontario, London, Ontario N6A 5B7, Canada
*Corresponding author, E-mail: karpuzov@surf.ssw.uwo.ca

1. Introduction

During the last decades several computer simulation codes have been developed to calculate the emission characteristics of particles ejected from ion-bombarded surfaces [1-3]. This has now become an important tool to provide some microscopic insight into the fundamental mechanisms relevant for surface analytical techniques such as SNMS, SIMS and ISS [4]. The present study applies a dynamic version of the MARLOWE computer code [5-8] for an attempt to predict the energy- and angular distributions of both energetic sputtered secondary as well as backscattered primary particles for binary compounds under ion bombardment [8]. Since such an ambitious simulation is complex [8-11], it is important to compare the results with experimental SIMS/LEIS data obtained for the same systems under similar bombarding conditions [12]. Of interest in this study is the question on how high-energy particle ejection may be affected by the differences in mass between projectile and the target constituents.

2. Dynamic MARLOWE Simulation for Sputtering or Backscattering

Standard assumptions of the MARLOWE computer code [5,6] were applied to model the atomic collision cascades in the ion-beam irradiated target. These include Moliere interatomic potential to describe the elastic part of the interaction between the atomic particles as well as equipartitioned local and non-local inelastic losses for the primary ions. We usually follow and record more parameters of the outcoming particles then original MARLOWE codes do, incl. details on the collision of origin, hard collision sequences etc. Novel here is the surface enrichment of the metallic component of the target included. In addition, in the case of Cs bombardment its incorporation in the target was taken into account. The surface binding energies were taken corresponding to the cohesion energy for the metal component and the enthalpy of the compound formation for the non-metallic one. After each small dose increment
the dynamic change of the target composition was determined by the mass balance expected for saturation conditions to occur, i.e. the sputter ratio of the species to match their bulk ratio. Several steps were usually enough to have sputter yields matching the bulk composition ratio within 10%, and when this condition was met the collection of the data was started. Simulated cases include 4 and 8 keV bombardment of PbS and FeS$_2$ by oxygen and 8 and 12 keV bombardment of PbS by Cs ion beam. The angle of incidence was 35° for the 4 and 8

[#] Present address: CANMET, Natural Resources Canada, Ottawa, Ont., Canada K1A 0G1
[$]Financial support of the Centre for Chemical Physics, UWO is gratefully acknowledged

keV beams and 30° for 12 keV. In each case the simulations were performed both for stoichiometric (constant) and for modified (dynamic) composition of the target. The number of ion trajectories and the induced collision cascades followed was between 5 and 10·10^4.

3. Results and Discussion

Fig.1 shows the calculated energy spectra of particles sputtered by 8 keV oxygen bombardment of PbS, both for constant (50:50) and modified target composition. The depth profile of the altered layer (as a result of saturation at the end of the simulations) is shown in the inset. It depends on the system chosen and the incident beam energy E_i. Saturation ratio decreases with E_i, being 72:28 for Pb:S at the surface of PbS and 52:48 at FeS$_2$ surface under bombardment of 4 keV O. In the case of Cs bombardment the target was allowed to incorporate also primary particles which resulted in about 10% Cs accumulated at the surface.

Despite the difference in the partial sputter yields with changing composition, the modified stoichiometry in the case shown in Fig.1 (unlike the Cs-PbS case) doesn't affect much the energy spectra of the secondary particles. If one compare the distributions for Pb and S, they look however quite different. Maximum energies of sputtered Pb fall off at about 1000 eV, while the spectra for sulfur extends to energies of 3 keV and higher. A Sigmund-Thompson (S-T) distribution [3] on the energy is shown for comparison, $A \cdot E_s/(E_s+E_{sb})^3$, with E_{sb} being the (average) surface binding energy (its value is not important for the high energy range considered here) and A constant, fitted to match the simulated yield in the range of 50 to 200 eV. It is not expected to approximate the spectra at high energies (where the particles are sputtered within a few collisions only) and certainly not with a single curve for light (S) and heavy (Pb) sputtered particles. In addition, S-T approach doesn't address the anisotropy resulting from the oblique incidence.

The results for 4 keV O bombardment of PbS are compared to the experimental data in Fig. 2. It has to be noted that:(a) no fitting was applied other than scaling the intensities at 250 eV of simulated data to that of the experimental intensity; (b) simulations refer to a constant primary energy, E_i=4 keV, while in the experiment the target bias voltage changes with E_s (see the related paper of the authors in this proceedings for details) , so that E_i changes along the E-spectra from 4 to 5.5 keV; (c) presented simulated data are full (all angles) energy spectra; (d) computer simulations don't take into account any charge effects, actually they may apply to neutral atomic species only. In view of these differences the agreement is rather good. Similar fit is found for the case of Cs bombardment which may indicate that the energy dependence of the transmission and ionization may compensate to some extent.

The difference between the sulfur spectra taken from matrices of the galena and the pyrite, is illustrated in Fig. 3. The ratio of the intensity of S sputtered from FeS$_2$ and PbS is evaluated for various emission energies, and it is compared to three sets of experimental data (normalized at 200 eV). With changing the emission energy E_s the primary energy in the measurements ranges from 8 to 11 keV for S$^-$/O$^-$ case, from 8.5 to 7 for S$^-$/O$_2^+$ and 17 to 14 for S$^+$/ O$^-$. The simulated data refer to constant (8 keV) primary energy. The data are rather scattered but the trend is the same, and in view of the differences the correlation between the measured and the simulated data is quite reasonable. Since energetic S, that is put into motion during the collision cascade, can easily bounce back outwards (i.e. without losing most of its kinetic energy) in collisions with heavy lead underneath because of their large mass difference, this observation of more high-energy S ejected from PbS than from pyrite is not surprising.

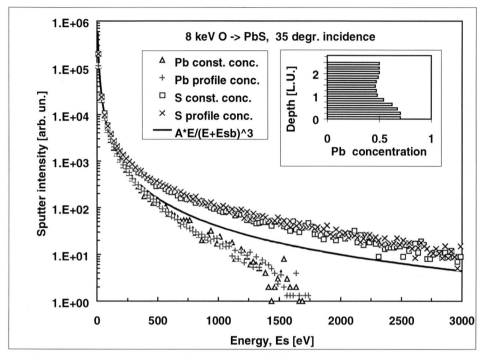

Fig 1. Simulated spectra for 8 keV bombardment of PbS assuming constant stoichiometric or profile concentration. In the inset the resulting steady state Pb-profile is shown

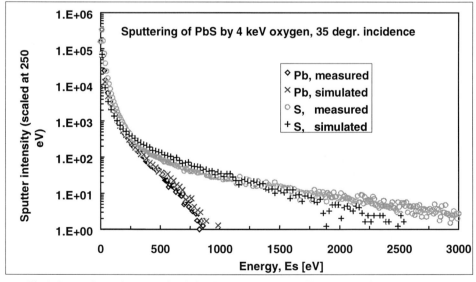

Fig.2 Comparison of measured and simulated (assuming profile concentration) energy spectra for 4 keV oxygen bombardment of PbS

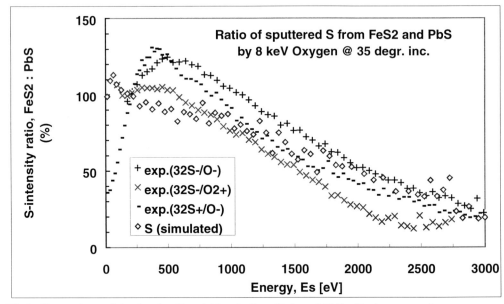

Fig.3. Comparison of simulated sulfur yield ratio from FeS₂ and PbS with three sets of experimental data (normalized at 200 eV). See text for details

4.Summary

The calculated energy distribution of the lighter component, sulfur, is found to extend up to emission energies of several keV (about half of the bombarding energy) in the case of PbS under oxygen bombardment, while this high-energy tail was less pronounced for FeS₂. This different behavior, observed also in a corresponding SIMS experiment, is attributed to the mass dependence of the kinetic energy that is transferred during elastic collision sequences.

References

[1] M. T. Robinson, in: Sputtering by Particle Bombardment I, Ed. R. Behrisch (Springer, Berlin, 1981), p.114.

[2] W. Eckstein and J. P. Biersack, Appl. Phys. **A37** (1985) 95 .

[3] P. Sigmund et al., Nucl. Instrum. Methods **B36** (1989) 110.

[4] Secondary Ion Mass Spectrometry, Ed. A. Benninghoven, F. G. Rüdenauer, and H. W. Werner (Wiley, New York, 1987).

[5] M. T. Robinson and I.M.Torrens, Phys.Rev. **B9** (1974) 5008.

[6] M. Hou and M.T.Robinson, Appl. Phys. **17** (1978) 371.

[7] B. van Someren et al, Surf. Sci. **423** (1999) 276.

[8] D. Karpuzov, K. Franzreb, A. R. Pratt, and N. S. McIntyre, to be published.

[9] H. J. Kang and R. Shimizu, Surf. Sci. **169** (1986) 337.

[10] W. Eckstein et al, Nucl.Instr.Methods **B153** (1999) 345.

[11] T. J. Colla and H. M. Urbassek, Nucl. Instrum. Methods **B152** (1999) 459.

[12] K. Franzreb, D. Karpuzov, A. R. Pratt, and N. S. McIntyre, SIMS12 (these proceedings).

SECTION 2 :
SECONDARY ION FORMATION

A. Benninghoven, P. Bertrand, H.-N. Migeon and H.W. Werner (Editors).
Proceedings of the 12th International Conference on Secondary Ion Mass Spectrometry,
Brussels, Belgium, 5-11 September 1999
© 2000 Elsevier Science B.V. All rights reserved.

IONIZATION PROBABILITY OF SPUTTERED CLUSTERS

R. Heinrich, C. Staudt, M. Wahl and A. Wucher

Institute of Laser and Plasma Physics, University of Essen, 45117 Essen, Germany
wucher@uni-essen.de

1. Introduction

It is well known that the flux of secondary ions sputtered from a solid surface generally contains clusters of several atoms as well as purely atomic ions. The formation of these cluster ions during the sputtering process represents one of the most interesting but still unresolved questions regarding the fundamental processes of SIMS. As a general practice, the yield of a specific secondary ion $X^{+,-}$ is factorized according to

$$Y(X^{+,-}) = Y_X \cdot \alpha_X^{+,-} \tag{1}$$

where Y_X denotes the partial sputtering yield of the species X (regardless of its charge state) and $\alpha^{+,-}$ defines the ionization probability of the sputtered particle. This treatment divides the formation of a secondary cluster ion into two steps, namely i) the formation of a sputtered cluster and ii) its ionization during its ejection from the surface. While the first process can be reasonably well described - for instance by molecular dynamics computer simulations of the collision cascade initiated by the impinging primary ion [1] - the mechanisms leading to the ionization of a sputtered cluster are still largely unresolved. One of the major reasons for this state of affairs is given by the apparent lack of experimental data characterizing $\alpha^{+,-}$ for the particular case of sputtered clusters. This, on the other hand, is due to the fact that an experimental determination of $\alpha^{+,-}$ requires the detection of sputtered neutral species, which must be post-ionized in order to be detectable in a mass resolved manner. Moreover, in order to be quantitative the post-ionization efficiency must be known and secondary ions and neutrals must be detected under otherwise identical experimental conditions. We have recently developed a method which fulfils these requirements and is based on the in-situ determination of secondary ion and neutral particle densities above an ion bombarded surface. The present work describes an application of this method to determine the ionization probability of clusters sputtered from the respective clean surfaces as a function of the cluster size.

2. Experimental

The experimental procedure used in the present work is described in detail elsewhere in this volume [2], and the description will therefore not be repeated here. Briefly, polycrystalline samples are bombarded under UHV conditions with rare gas ions of 15 keV extracted from an ion gun which is used either in dc mode (for sputter cleaning the surface) or in pulsed mode (during data acquisition) with a pulse duration of several microseconds. The number densities of sputtered neutral particles and positively charged secondary ions are detected in situ at a distance of about 1 mm above the surface, the neutrals being post-ionized by a VUV laser operated at 157 nm. As an essential part of the method, all atoms and clusters are ionized by single photon absorption and the available laser intensity is high enough to drive the post-ionization efficiency into saturation, thus eliminating the influence of the *a priori* unknown photoionization cross sections of the clusters [3,4]. The ionization probability is then directly determined from the ratio between the mass spectrometric signals of secondary ions (measured without the ionizing laser) and the saturated secondary neutral signals without any further correction.

3. Results and Discussion

Figures 1 - 4 show the resulting values of the ionization probability for the formation of singly positively charged ions measured for Ag_n, Ge_n, Ta_n and Nb_n clusters sputtered from the respective clean surfaces. In Figure 1, three different sets of data have been included which cover partly overlapping cluster size ranges. The deviation between the different α^+-values measured for the same cluster size within these ranges may therefore regarded as a measure of the reproducublity of the experiment.

As a first obervation, low α^+-values below 10^{-3} are found for sputtered Ag, Nb and Ge atoms. This finding is in good agreement with the common sense that the formation probability for atomic ions ejected from the respective sputter cleaned surfaces is generally low [5]. In particular, the absolute values determined here agree within a factor of two with data published by *Benninghoven* [6], which was obtained by comparing measured total secondary ion currents with tabulated data of total sputtering yields. In view of the fact that our data has been evaluated without the application of any correction factors regarding, for instance, postionization efficiency, instrument transmission etc., we consider this an impressive agreement. The second important observation concerns the cluster size dependence of α^+. For small clusters containing less than approximately 10 atoms, the ionization probability is found to increase strongly with increasing nuclearity of the sputtered cluster. This is observed in all cases studied so far and must therefore be regarded as a general trend.

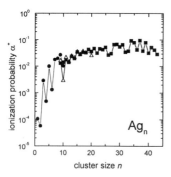

Figure 1. Ionization probability of sputtered silver clusters vs. cluster size.

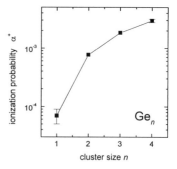

Figure 2. Ionization probability of sputtered germanium clusters vs. cluster size.

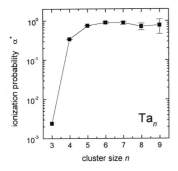

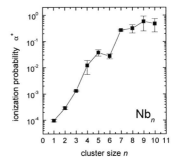

Figure 3. Ionization probability of sputtered tantalum clusters vs. cluster size.

Figure 4. Ionization probability of sputtered niobium clusters vs. cluster size.

For larger clusters containing more than 10 atoms, the ionization probability seems to saturate. Unfortunately, only for the case of silver the cluster sputtering yields are large enough to access this range of cluster sizes within the sensitivity of our experiment. For this system, a tendency towards saturation had already been observed in our previous work [4], the value of α^+ in the saturation regime being of the order of several percent. However, from the limited range of cluster sizes accessible at that time (less than 15 atoms), the possibility of a gradual increase towards unity for larger clusters could not be safely ruled out. From the results presented in Figure 1, it is now clear the the ionization probability of sputtered silver clusters actually saturates at a value below ten percent. As a consequence, we must conclude that the vast majority of all sputtered silver clusters is emitted in the neutral state. The same seems to be true for germanium clusters (Figure 2), although in this case the accessible size range is clearly not large enough to decide on the saturation behaviour with increasing cluster size.

The low values of α^+ observed for silver and germanium clusters are in marked contrast to the data measured on Ta_n and Nb_n clusters (Figure 3 and Figure 4), which show that for these systems the ionization probability may be non negligible even for small clusters containing as few as only 4 (Ta) or 7 (Nb) atoms, respectively. Although also in these cases the accessible size range is small and, hence, an assessment of the saturation behaviour is difficult, it is evident that all detected Ta_n clusters containing more than 5 atoms are predominantly emitted in the *ionic* state. In the case of niobium, it is found that the yields of charged Nb_n clusters become comparable to those of the neutral counterparts for cluster sizes above 7 atoms. The physical reasons for these findings and, in particular, for the discrepancy between the silver / germanium data on one hand and the tantalum / niobium data on the other hand are unclear at the present time.

Interestingly, the ionization probabilities measured for the tantalum and niobium *trimers* are comparable to those of the silver and germanium trimer, thus indicating that the difference between the two sets of data are presumably not caused by any systematic error of the experiment. On the other hand, it is known that transition metals like Ta and Nb may exhibit dramatic increases of the ionization probability upon surface reactions with residual gas contaminants (mostly oxygen) [5]. Although the sample surface was carefully sputter cleaned prior to each experiment, the pulsed nature of the ion bombardment during data acquisition may in principle lead to a gradual buildup of surface contamination during the acquisition of a mass spectrum (which is averaged over several thousand laser shots). We have, however, not detected any significant amounts of mixed neutral clusters containing reactive atoms like oxygen, nitrogen etc., which have been shown to be a good indicator of the contaminant surface concentration [7]. Moreover, the ionization probability measured for the Nb atoms is very low, thus indicating a relatively clean surface. We therefore feel that it is not surface contamination which leads to the large ionization probabilities observed for Ta_n and Nb_n clusters. In addition, we would expect the magnitude of such an effect to be largest for sputtered atoms and decrease with increasing cluster size.

4. Conclusion

The theoretical interpretation of the data presented in Figures 1-4 is difficult. To the best of our knowledge, only one theoretical model describing the ionization probability of sputtered clusters has appeared in the literature [8]. The results of this calculation, which is based upon the assumption that sputtered clusters are ejected with large internal energies and may therefore exhibit thermionic emission of electrons in order to form a positive ion, qualitatively reproduce the tendency of increasing ionization probability with increasing cluster size. The order of magnitude of the α^+-values calculated for larger silver clusters, however, is significantly higher than the data presented in Figure 1. More theoretical work is therefore needed in order to gain a better understanding of the fundamental mechanisms leading to the ionization of a sputtered cluster.

References

[1]   A. Wucher and B. J. Garrison, J. Chem. Phys. 105 (1996) 5999.
[2]   A. Wucher, R. Heinrich, and C. Staudt, these proceedings
[3]   A. Wucher and M. Wahl, Nucl. Instr. Meth. B 115 (1996) 581.
[4]   M. Wahl and A. Wucher, Nucl. Instr. Meth. B 94 (1994) 36.
[5]   A. Benninghoven, F. G. Rüdenauer, and H. W. Werner (1987)
[6]   A. Benninghoven, Surf. Sci. 53 (1975) 596.
[7]   A. Wucher and H. Oechsner, Nucl. Instr. Meth. B 18 (1987) 458.
[8]   V. K. Ferleger, M. B. Medvedeva, and I. A. Wojciechowski, Nucl. Instr. Meth. B 125 (1997) 214.

A. Benninghoven, P. Bertrand, H.-N. Migeon and H.W. Werner (Editors).
Proceedings of the 12th International Conference on Secondary Ion Mass Spectrometry,
Brussels, Belgium, 5-11 September 1999

TOF-SIMS ANALYSIS OF CARBOCYANINE DYES
ADSORBED ON SILVER SUBSTRATES

J. Lenaerts[(1)]*, G. Verlinden[(1)], L. Van Vaeck[(1)], R. Gijbels[(1)] and I. Geuens[(2)]

[(1)] University of Antwerp, Department of Chemistry, Antwerp, Belgium

[(2)] Agfa-Gevaert N.V., Mortsel, Belgium

*corresponding author: lenaerts@uia.ua.ac.be

1. Introduction

Carbocyanine dyes are used in the photographic industry as spectral sensitizer for silver halide materials. Silver halide microcrystals are intrinsically sensitive only to blue light in the visible region. To extend the spectral region of photographic response it is necessary to use sensitizing dyes.

Time of flight secondary ion mass spectrometry (TOF-SIMS) was used to investigate thin films of organic carbocyanine dyes on a silver substrate. The purpose of the present study was to gain insight in the secondary ion formation process of organic dye films through the combined use of specific features in the survey spectra, the damage cross sections (σ) and concentration dependent signal intensities. Special attention is paid to the formation of specific interaction products (e.g. Ag – adducts).

2. Experimental

Measurements were performed on a TOF SIMS IV Cameca instrument [1,2], equipped with a gallium liquid metal ion gun (LMIG) operating at 25 keV. Analysis conditions were maintained within the static regime, with a primary ion dose of approximately 5.10^{12} ion/cm^2.

The organic dyes were dissolved in methanol with different concentrations ranging from 10^{-2} M to 10^{-5} M. Aliquots of 10μl of the solution were spincoated (5000 e/min, 20 sec) on the silver substrate. The silver was etched in nitric acid (20%) and rinsed afterwards with methanol for 15 min in an ultrasone bath to remove nitric acid from the surface.

3. Results and Discussion

The positive ion mass spectrum (between m/z = 500 and m/z = 850) of a benzoxazole carbocyanine dye (conc. 10^{-3} M) adsorbed on an etched silver substrate is shown in figure 1. The most important features at high m/z values for this spectrum are the high intensity of the adduct ions [M+H]$^+$, [M+Ag]$^+$ and [M–H+2Ag]$^+$ and the presence of structural fragment ions such as [M-HSO$_3$]$^+$. These results show that TOF-SIMS analysis of organic dye layers adsorbed on solid silver substrates yields a significant amount of molecular information.

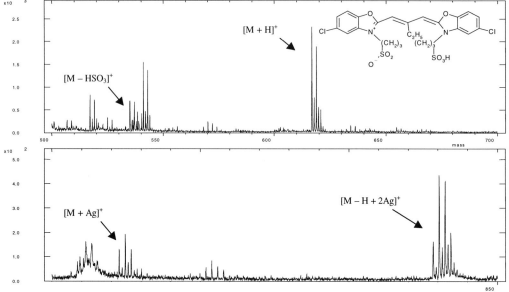

Figure 1: Secondary positive ion mass spectra from a carbocyanine dye spincoated on an etched silver surface (conc. 10^{-3} M)

The intensity of the adduct ions as well as the fragment ions was studied as a function of the surface coverage on the etched silver substrate. Different degrees of surface coverage were achieved by spincoating solutions with different dye concentration under identical conditions. The evolution of the Ag^+ ion intensity is consistent with the surface coverage: the intensity of the Ag^+ signal decreases as the dye concentration in the spincoated solution increases (figure 2).

The purpose of spincoating was to create homogeneous layers with a random orientation of the dye molecules. Spincoating should prevent molecules to order themselves on the surface[3]. Different measurements on the same sample gave almost identical spectra, indicating that the dye deposition occurred rather homogeneously (table 1).

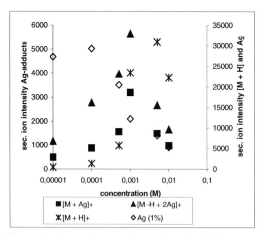

Figure 2: Secondary ion intensities for different adduct ions from carbocyanine dye as function of concentration and 1% of the intensity of Ag^+ as function of the concentration

concentration	Absolute ion intensity (cts) of			
	$[M-HSO_3]^+$	$[M+H]^+$	$[M+Ag]^+$	$[M-H+2Ag]^+$
10^{-2} M	1. 7033 2. 6284 3. 8199	1. 23146 2. 20562 3. 22952	1. 948 2. 800 3. 1151	1. 1591 2. 1406 3. 1944
5.10^{-3} M	1. 9021 2. 9784 3. 11743	1. 31690 2. 28530 3. 32492	1. 1406 2. 1283 3. 1748	1. 2585 2. 2290 3. 3096
10^{-4} M	1. 4317 2. 3612 3. 4097	1. 1425 2. 1285 3. 1250	1. 899 2. 847 3. 861	1. 2867 2. 2633 3. 2814

Table 1: Secondary ion intensities for 3 different measurements (different locations) on the same sample for 3 different concentrations

Figure 2 shows that absolute intensity of adduct ions and fragment ions as a function of the surface coverage yields a prominent maximum for a dye solution concentration between 5.10^{-3} M and 10^{-3} M. The interpretation of these data is based on the monolayer information depth. The decreasing yield at low concentrations ($\leq 5.10^{-4}$ M) is associated with low secondary ion intensities due to incomplete surface coverage or, in other words, submonolayer coverage. The low secondary ion intensities for higher concentration ($\geq 10^{-2}$ M) on the other hand are related to multilayer coverage. Further study has to be done to investigate whether the multilayer is a regular 2D structure or rather a 3D structure composed of islands on the surface. Meanwhile assuming that the maximum in fig 2 corresponds to monolayer coverage, this data suggests that the interaction between the dye molecules and the silver substrate decreases upon multilayer formation. The dye molecules are no longer adsorbed on a noble metal surface but on a layer of organic molecules. The decrease can be explained because noble metals offer distinctly higher sputter yields in comparison to organic surfaces[4].

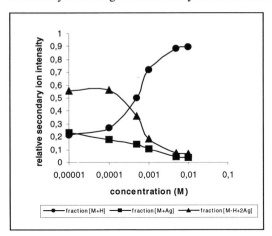

Figure 3: Adduct ion intensities of a carbo-cyanine dye normalised on the sum of $[M+H]^+$, $[M+Ag]^+$, $[M-H+2Ag]^+$ as a function of the concentration in solution

In figure 2 it can also be seen that the optimal concentration for silver cationized molecules is shifted towards lower concentrations compared to the optimum for protonated molecules. Moreover figure 3 shows that the relative contribution of the Ag-cationized dyes increases as the concentration of the deposited dye solution decreases. These two observations indicate that the formation of Ag-cationized molecules is promoted compared to the formation $[M+H]^+$ as the surface coverage decreases or, in other words, as the silver - dye interaction increases (according to the assumptions explained above).

118

Besides the survey of mass spectra and the study of the influence of surface coverage on the secondary ion formation, special attention was paid to the calculation of damage cross sections (σ) of different adduct ions and a characteristic fragment ion. The damage cross section is determined by the average surface area damaged by a single ion impact[5]. To study the influence of multilayer coverage on σ, we prepared samples with dye solution concentrations of 10^{-3} M (monolayer coverage) and 10^{-2} M (multilayer coverage). Table 2 shows the results for these measurements for different secondary ions.

Secondary ion	Damage cross section in 10^{-14} cm^2 at different concentrations	
	10^{-3} M	10^{-2} M
$[M + H]^+$	5.7	5.4
$[M + Ag]^+$	3.6	3.8
$[M - H + 2Ag]^+$	5.5	4.3
$[M - HSO_3]^+$	1.8	1.8

Table 2: Damage cross sections for different secondary ions from spincoated carbocyanine dye layers (concentration 10^{-3} and 10^{-2} M) under 25 keV Ga$^+$ bombardment

Table 2 shows that damage cross sections are comparable for different types of secondary adduct ions. For fragment ions of the same sample the σ is lower by a factor 3 - 4. This decrease indicates that surface areas that are damaged by primary ion bombardment so that they can no longer yield molecular adducts may still be able to yield some fragments. Changing the surface coverage of the sample from monolayer to multilayer coverage has no effect on the damage cross sections of the different secondary ions. This indicates that the sample depth is restricted to the outer most surface layer, even for large fragment ions ($[M- HSO_3]^+$). Primary ion bombardment on a surface layer totally destroys the underlying organic layers so they can no longer yield any significant molecular information.

4. Conclusion

The most important features of TOF-SIMS analysis of spincoated carbocyanine dye layers on a silver plate can be summarized as follows. The carbocyanine dye layers yield a significant amount of molecular information. Different types of adduct ions and fragment ions can be detected. The formation of Ag-cationized molecules indicates that there is a specific interaction between the dye and the silver surface. The concentration experiment illustrates that this interaction becomes more important as the surface coverage decreases. Calculation of damage cross sections indicates that there is no significant difference in the damage cross sections of different type of adduct ions; for fragment ions on the other hand the damage cross section is lower. Damage cross sections of different secondary ions are not significantly influenced by the thickness of the adsorbed dye layer.

References

[1] E. Niehuis, T. Heller, H. Feld and A. Benninghoven, J. Vac. Sci. Technol., 1987, 5,

[2] A. Benninghoven, B. Hagenhoff and E. Niehuis, Anal. Chem., 1993, 65, 630A-640A

[3] S. Hiroshi and S. Makoto, Microscopy Research and Technique, 1998, 42, 123-138

[4] A. Benninghoven, F.G. Rüdenauer and H.W. Werner, Secondary Ion Mass Spectrometry, John Wiley and Sons, 1987, p724

[5] D. Stapel, O. Brox, A. Benninghoven, Applied Surface Science, 140 (1999), 156-167

A. Benninghoven, P. Bertrand, H.-N. Migeon and H.W. Werner (Editors).
Proceedings of the 12th International Conference on Secondary Ion Mass Spectrometry,
Brussels, Belgium, 5-11 September 1999
© 2000 Elsevier Science B.V. All rights reserved.

MCs$_n^+$ (*n*=1, 2, 3) MOLECULAR ION EMISSION FROM THE Si/SiO$_2$ SYSTEM

W. Bieck[1], H. Gnaser[2], H.N. Migeon[1]

[1]CRP-Gabriel Lippmann / Laboratoire d'Analyse des Matériaux (LAM),
162a, av. de la Faïencerie, L-1511 Luxembourg

[2]Institut für Oberflächen- und Schichtanalytik (IFOS) and Fachbereich Physik,
Universität Kaiserslautern, D-67663 Kaiserslautern, Germany

1. Introduction

A quantitative evaluation of SIMS data is facilitated by monitoring MCs$^+$ (or MCs$_n^+$) molecular ions [1] emitted, from samples under Cs$^+$ ion bombardment. Matrix effects have been reported also for this detection scheme [2]. In particular, a varying oxygen content apparently may change the formation probability of MCs$^+$ ions, an observation reported for SiO$_x$ [3], and other oxides [4,5]. Very often, also strong variations of the Cs$^+$ intensity in different matrices are observed [6]. To a large extent these might be due to different stationary surface concentrations of Cs which change, via the surface work function, the ionization probability of Cs$^+$ ions, P_{Cs}^+. It has been demonstrated repeatedly that the surface concentration (and hence P) can be varied by a variation of the sputtering yield (this is accomplished, e.g., using different ion-impact angles or energies [7,8]). Generally, changes of the Cs$^+$ intensity are accompanied by corresponding changes of the intensities of MCs$^+$ ions [9]. These variations would be of little concern if they were equal for all MCs$^+$ species emitted from a given system because for analytical purposes most often intensity ratios are employed for the quantification. Only a few investigations of MCs$^+$ ion yields changes due to a Cs$^+$ intensity variation have been done so far. In the present work we examined the intensities of Cs$_n^+$ and MCs$_n^+$ ions ($n = 1, 2, 3$) in Si and SiO$_2$ utilizing different impact energies and angles of the Cs$^+$ primary beam.

2. Experiments

Two different Cameca IMS instruments were used. The one at Luxembourg is a modified IMS-6f (IMS-LAM) whereas the instrument at Kaiserslautern is a standard IMS-4f. For given bombarding conditions (impact energy and angle), they were operated using similar experimental settings. Typically primary ions currents were 1–10 nA and the raster-scanned area was in the range (125 µm)^2 to (250 µm)^2. Positive secondary ions were accepted from circular areas with diameters between 33 µm and 60 µm. With the exception of a specific study into possible charging at the interface Si/SiO$_2$ (with narrow energy slit $\Delta E \sim 2$ eV), all measurements were done at low mass resolution ($M/\Delta M \sim 300$) and with a broad energy window ($\Delta E \sim 100$ eV). For this work we used polycrystalline Si (100 nm) on a SiO$_2$ (30 nm) on top of a crystalline Si substrate.

3. Results

Fig. 1 depicts the variation of the Cs$^+$ and Cs$_2^+$ intensities when sputtering through the two interfaces. These data are for 5 different impact energies ranging from 1.8 keV to 7 keV (note that this energy variation is accompanied by a variation of the impact angle which decreases from about 65° to 39° [11]). While for the lowest energies the transition of the signals between the two layers is fairly smooth, for the higher energies very drastic variations are observed, which are particularly pronounced for 5.5 and 7 keV. (The intensity evolution of Cs_3^+ is comparable to that of Cs_2^+ but the changes are even more drastic; for example, the dip at a depth of about 100 nm amounts then to more than two orders of magnitude.) A comparison of the two data sets indicates that the intensities of the two ion species are largely anti-correlated. An increase of Cs^+ is accompanied by a decrease of Cs_2^+. Again this is most distinct for the highest energies.

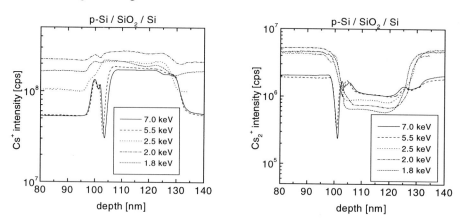

Fig. 1. Intensities of Cs^+ and Cs_2^+ ions during sputtering through the two interfaces with the primary ion energy as parameter.

4. Discussion: probable origin of the pronounced variations of the Cs^+ intensity (cf. Fig. 1). First it is noted that with decreasing Cs^+ impact energy the incidence angle and the sputtering yield Y increase. On the other hand, the intensity ratios Cs_2^+/Cs^+ and Cs_3^+/Cs^+ in the Si-layer decrease with increasing sputtering yield. Since the former ratio was considered [7] to be proportional to the Cs surface concentration, c_{Cs}, these data indicate that c_{Cs} is considerably lower at 1.8 keV than at 5.5 and 7 keV impact. Because a high Cs concentration lowers the work function and the ionization probability [10], this finding agrees with the much higher Cs^+ intensity in the Si at 1.8 keV than for the 7 keV bombardment (Fig. 1). These differences are less pronounced in the SiO_2 layer, probably because the variations of Y (and hence of c_{Cs}) are more moderate.

More difficult to understand is the oscillatory behavior of the Cs^+ signal under 5.5 and 7 keV bombardment when the eroded surface reaches the Si/SiO_2 interface. We have carried out dynamic TRIM calculations for both 2 and 7 keV Cs impact in order to elucidate the evolution of the partial sputtering yields and the surface concentrations at this interface. The outcome from these simulations does not exhibit any features comparable to those seen in the experiment; rather, the surface concentrations and the yields vary monotonously across the boundary. From this we conclude that ballistic processes (like recoil implantation and mixing), which the program can only monitor, are not responsible for the observed results. Other processes must, therefore, be operative. Two possible ones are identified presently. One would involve a rapid segregation of Cs atoms from the instantaneous surface towards the oxide as soon as the former has approached the latter within a distance comparable with the range of defects created by the ion beam (roughly one to two times the ion's range). The driving force might be found in the affinity for oxygen. The depletion of Cs at the surface is reflected in the rapid drop of the Cs_2^+ intensity and causes an enhancement of P_{Cs}^+ (in analogy to what has been discussed above in the context of the yield change). With the eroded surface moving into the actual oxide, this segregation ceases but the instantaneous value of c_{Cs} is high and causes ion yield changes which are opposite to the ones just discussed, i.e., the high c_{Cs} *lowers* P_{Cs}^+ and the Cs^+ intensity (cf. Fig. 1). When the eroded surface moves from the oxide into the underlying Si substrate, these mechanisms do not occur as there is no segregation of Cs atoms possible.

A second possible process which may induce migration of Cs is due to a surplus of surface charge as the oxide interface is reached. In a separate depth profile the instantaneous surface potential was determined by monitoring the energy distribution of sputtered Cs^+ ions. At the interface between the Si top layer and SiO_2 the surface potential rises rapidly (by about 12 V) and, during further erosion, drops to the initial value roughly at the midpoint of the oxide. It is conceivable that this positive surface charge is a sufficiently strong driving force, in particular in the presence of a large number of irradiation-induced defects in the near-surface region of the specimen. The mechanisms of ion yield enhancement (or depletion) might then be similar to those discussed in the foregoing paragraph.

Not surprisingly, these strong variations of Cs^+ and Cs_2^+ ions are also seen in the respective MCs^+ and MCs_n^+ signals. They are, however, largely removed by forming the ratios of the O⁻ and Si-specific intensities. Fig. 2 shows the signal ratios of $OCs^+/SiCs^+$ and $OCs_2^+/SiCs_2^+$ across the two interfaces. Two features are immediately noted: First, for both molecular ion species the intensity ratio in the SiO_2 depends on the bombarding energy/angle, being higher (by about a factor of two) for the low energies. Second, the apparent width of the

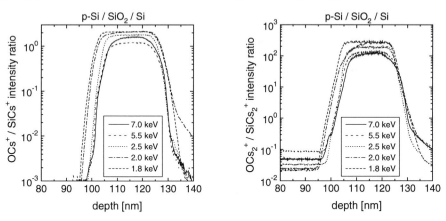

Fig. 2. Intensity ratios $OCs^+/SiCs^+$ and $OCs_2^+/SiCs_2^+$ in the SiO_2 layer for the different primary-ion energies.

oxide layer also varies with the energy; it comes close to the nominal value of 30 nm for the two lowest impact energies, but is distinctly smaller for the higher energies. Both observations indicate that even the ratios of the formation probabilities of two MCs^+ (or MCs_n^+) species are dependent on the respective Cs^+ (or Cs_2^+) intensities. It was shown by Homma et al. [3] that the formation of OCs^+ ions sputtered from SiO_x samples (by 5.5 keV Cs^+ ions) increases with increasing oxygen content by about a factor of 20, whereas the corresponding $SiCs^+$ signal remains essentially unchanged. The delayed rise of the $OCs^+/SiCs^+$ ratio in Fig. 2 for the highest energies might therefore be related to that variation of the OCs^+ formation with the oxygen concentration. On the other hand, this would imply that such an effect is not operative under low-energy irradiation conditions. Similar arguments may then be applied to the Cs_2-carrying molecular ions; unfortunately, no data as to their oxygen-dependent formation do exist. We have, however, compared the $OCs_2^+/SiCs_2^+$ ratio from the SiO_2 specimen with the corresponding ratio obtained from an oxygen implantation profile and observed that also this ratio (corrected by the respective concentration values) increases with increasing oxygen content, by a factor (~ 20) which is comparable to the one observed for $OCs^+/SiCs^+$ [3].

5. Conclusion

In summary, the results presented show that drastic variations of MCs_n^+ yields are encountered even in a fairly simple system like Si/SiO_2. Apart from distinctly different intensity levels in these two matrices, a very pronounced variation of the signals at the interface between the Si- and the SiO_2-layer was noted; the data indicate that these are due to strong variations of the near-surface concentration of Cs which appears to depend on the bombarding conditions. From an analytical point of view, increasing the sputtering yield and thereby lowering c_{Cs} may constitute a suitable remedy for those yield changes.

Financial support of the Fondation pour le Développement de la Coopération Allemagne-Luxembourg dans le Domaine des Sciences is gratefully acknowledged.

References

[1] See, e.g., *Secondary Ion Mass Spectrometry SIMS IX*, eds., A.Benninghoven et al., Wiley, Chichester (1994), p.375-425

[2] K.Wittmaack, in *Secondary Ion Mass Spectrometry SIMS X*, eds., A.Benninghoven et al., Wiley, Chichester (1997), p.39

[3] Y. Homma, Y. Higashi, T. Maruo, C. Maekawa, S. Ochiai, in *Secondary Ion Mass Spectrometry SIMS IX*, eds., A. Benninghoven et al., Wiley, Chichester (1994), p. 398

[4] P. Willich, R. Bethke, in *Secondary Ion Mass Spectrometry SIMS XI*, eds., G. Gillen et al., Wiley, Chichester (1998), p. 991

[5] W. Bieck, T. Mootz, F. Saldi, in *Secondary Ion Mass Spectrometry SIMS XI*, eds., G. Gillen et al., Wiley, Chichester (1998), p. 907

[6] W. Bock, H. Gnaser, H. Oechsner, Anal. Chim. Acta **297**, 277 (1994)

[7] K. Wittmaack, Nucl. Instrum. Methods B **85**, 374 (1994)

[8] Y. Marie, Y. Gao, F. Saldi, H.N. Migeon, Surf. Interf. Anal. **23**, 38 (1995)

[9] H. Gnaser, Surf. Sci. **342**, 319 (1995)

[10] H. Gnaser, Phys. Rev. B **54**, 17141 (1996)

[11] R.G. Wilson, F.A. Stevie, C.W. Magee, *Secondary Ion Mass Spectrometry*, Wiley&Sons, New York (1989), pp. 1.3.1-4

A. Benninghoven, P. Bertrand, H.-N. Migeon and H.W. Werner (Editors).
Proceedings of the 12th International Conference on Secondary Ion Mass Spectrometry,
Brussels, Belgium, 5-11 September 1999

123

RESONANCE CHARGE EXCHANGE PROCESSES IN HYPERTHERMAL FULLERENE - SURFACE COLLISIONS.

E. Kolodney , A. Bekkerman and B. Tsipinyuk

Department of Chemistry, Technion - Israel Institute of Technology ,
Haifa 32000, Israel, e-mail: eliko@tx.technion.ac.il

1. Introduction

Negative ion formation during low energy surface scattering or sputtering is of fundamental physical and practical importance. The charge transfer processes studied in the past are mainly neutralization and negative ion formation during grazing incidence collisions of positive atomic ions with metal surfaces at high impact energies [1]. Although there is an increasing interest in recent years in surface scattering of large polyatomic species (molecules and clusters) at hyperthermal energies (10 -200 eV) the associated processes of neutralization or negative ion formation were not studied beyond the tetra-atomic species [2,3]. Inherent complication with the hyperthermal scattering of large polyatomic ions and molecules is collision induced dissociation which is strongly promoted by the impact kinetic energy. In this respect, C_{60} , which retains its structural integrity during hyperthermal surface collisions, constitutes an excellent model system for studies of electron transfer processes between a large polyatomic collider and a surface.

Gaining deeper understanding of the charge transfer dynamics during a collision between a large polyatomic species and a surface is also important in relation with cluster/SIMS mechanisms. The first step along the incoming trajectory is neutralisation of the polyatomic ion followed by impulsive interaction leading to strong distorsion and heating of both the collider and surface (sub-unit) and eventually complete fragmentation of the collider. Besides using C_{60} as a model system we are also exploring the potential use of C_{60}^- and C_{60}^o as projectiles for SIMS analysis. Neutral C_{60}^o at the energy range of 10 – 100 eV can be generated by the supersonic seeded beam technique and at higher energies (100 eV – 10 keV) by delayed electron emission from electrostatically accelerated C_{60}^- [4]. In the following, we will describe recent experiments of scattering and charge exchange using both neutral and negatively charged C_{60} projectiles.

2. Experimental

The molecular beam-surface scattering apparatus is show in Fig.1. Neutral C_{60}^o molecules are accelerated to hyperthermal energies ($E_o = 4 – 50$ eV) using seeded beam expansion from a high temperature nozzle. The kinetic energy is controlled by varying the nozzle backing

124

pressure while keeping the nozzle temperature nearly constant. The beam is then scattered from a fully carbonized polycrystalline nickel target (Ni/C) in a UHV chamber. All experimental evidence point out that the carbonaceous film is a graphite monolayer. Surface temperature is maintained constant at 950 K. The scattering configuration is that of a rotating surface and fixed detector with a scattering angle $\psi = 180 - (\theta_i + \theta_r)$ where θ_i is the incidence angle and θ_r is the reflection angle, both measured from the surface normal. The measurements reported here were taken for both near-normal ($\psi = 135°$) and near grazing ($\psi = 45°$) impact. Primary beam normal energies are $E_{o\perp} = 3.7 - 39$ eV and $E_{o\perp} = 2.3 - 9.4$ eV for $\psi = 135°$ and $\psi = 45°$ respectively. Signal intensities of surface scattered C_{60}^- and C_{60}^0 were measured by a quadrupole mass spectrometer (QMS) equipped with a retarding field energy analyzer (RFA). For each impact energy value signal intensities of both charge states (neutral and negative) and the corresponding energy and angle distributions were measured by switching polarities and grounding the ionizer as needed. The neutral C_{60}^0 was electron impact ionized and detected as C_{60}^+. The C_{60}^- flight path from surface to RFA was completely field free. Relative yield of C_{60}^- was obtained by dividing signal intensities of scattered C_{60}^- by scattered C_{60}^0, both measured at the peak of the corresponding incidence angle dependencies. Primary beam energies were measured on-line using 90° electrostatic analyzer.

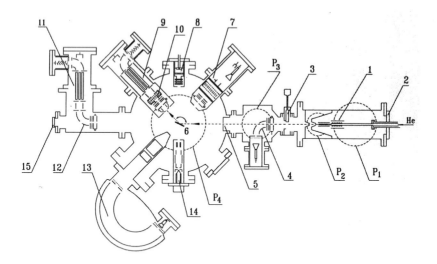

Fig. 1. The experimental set-up: (1) Two stage all ceramic nozzle. (2) Nozzle base plate. (3) Beam flag (gate). (4) 90° energy analyzer. (5) Collimator. (6) Rotatable surface. (7) Retarding field energy analyzer. (8) Ion gun. (9) Mass filter / Retarding field analyser. (11,12) Mass filter / 90° energy analyzer.

3. Impact of hyperthermal neutral C_{60}^0

Hyperthermal C_{60}^0 beam was collided with the Ni/C surface. Due to efficient surface - C_{60}^0 electron transfer the scattered particles included both neutral (C_{60}^0) and negative fullerene ions (C_{60}^-). Negative ions mass spectrum of the scattered particles showed a single C_{60}^- peak (relative abundance higher than 10^4 over the 1–1000 amu mass range). No negative C_n^- fragments (n =1 – 59) were observed in spite

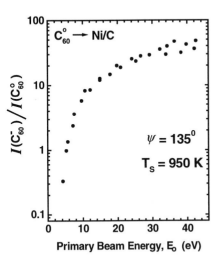

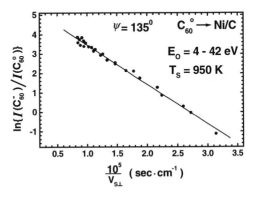

Fig. 2 Relative C_{60}^- yield following impact hyperthermal C_{60} (E_o = 4 - 42 eV) on the Ni/C surface for near normal incidence angle (ψ=135°, θ_i = 16.5°).

Fig. 3 Logarithmic plot of relative C_{60}^- yield (taken from Fig.2) as a function of reciprocal normal velocity (peak values) of the scattered C_{60}^-. The straight line (best fit) gives a slope of 2.24×10^5 cm.• sec.$^{-1}$.

of the fact that most of them have higher electron affinity values than C_{60} (EA(C_{60}) =2.65 eV). Energy and angle distributions of both C_{60}^0 and C_{60}^- were measured for the two different scattering angles (ψ = 45° and ψ = 135°). For near grazing incidence (ψ = 45°) a gradually developing energy dependent shift was observed between the angular distributions of C_{60}^0 and C_{60}^-. A constant small shift between maxima of the corresponding energy distributions was also observed. These shifts were analyzed and explained in terms of image charge effects on the outgoing trajectory (deflection) and exit energy (retardation) of the C_{60}^- [5]. Here we will focus an the dependence of the C_{60}^- anion yield on the C_{60}^0 impact energy. As is shown in Fig.2, an increase of nearly two orders of magnitudes is observed for the relative C_{60}^- yield starting from an apparent threshold at 3 – 4 eV.

The conventional picture regarding charge transfer in atom-surface collisions assumes a full memory loss of the initial charge state along the incoming trajectory. The final charge populations are therefore being determined along with a gradual distance dependent evolution of a fast resonant charge exchange between the approaching particle and the surface electrons.

At some distance from the surface a complete mixing between the incident particle and the surface electrons sets in and the particle loose track of its initial charge state. Under certain limiting conditions (low normal velocity $V_{S_\perp}$ of the scattered ion and low surface temperature) it could be theoretically shown [1] that the ion yield should follow an exponential dependence of the form $\exp[- B/V_{S_\perp}]$ where B is a constant (the characteristic velocity). Under well defined collision conditions this expression was verified experimentally before only for medium energy Li$^-$ scattering from cesiated tungsten [6]. In Fig. 3 we show that this relation is obeyed also for a large polyatomic particle at hyperthermal impact energies. A detailed analysis of the slope B can give information about the so called critical distance (Z_C) for ion formation. the exit path. This memory loss is related

4. Impact of hyperthermal C_{60}^- anions

As was mentioned above, a basic assumption (experimentally verified) in the collisional charge transfer models for atomic ions is that the final charge fraction is independent of the incoming charge state. Here we would like to give an experimental evidence that this assumption is valid also with regards to different charge states of C_{60}. The independence of the scattering dynamics and negative ion yield on the incoming charge state is demonstrated by using incident C_{60}^- on Ni/C surface at the impact energy range of 40 – 100 eV. The primary ion beam was generated as described before [5]. The same relative energy losses were measured for incident C_{60}^- ions as for neutral C_{60}^o. The scattered C_{60}^- ion yield was found to be practically the same (to within a factor of two) for both incident C_{60}^o and C_{60}^- at impact energy 40 eV. In addition to the scattering off Ni/C surface we have also scattered C_{60}^o and C_{60}^- off a clean gold surface (no carbon layer growth). It was found that the scattered C_{60}^- yield in both cases is below 10^{-4} irrespective of the initial charge state. The C_{60}^o beam is not being ionized while the C_{60}^- beam undergoes highly effective neutralization without reionization.

References

[1] J.Los and J.J.C Geerlings. Physics reports 190 (1990) 133.
[2] W. Heiland in: Low Energy Ion-Surface Interactions. Edited by J.W.Rabalais, Chichser 1994, p. 313 and references therein.
[3] W.R. Koppers, K. Tsumori, J.H.M. Bejersbergen, T.L. Weeding , P.G. Kistemaker and A.W. Kleyn, Int. J. Mass. Spectrom. and Ion Proc. 174 (1998) 11.
[4] A. Bekkerman, B. Tsipinyuk and E. Kolodney, Int. J. of Mass Spect. and Ion Proc. 185/186/187 (1999) 773.
[5] A. Bekkerman, B. Tsipinyuk, S. Verkhoturov and E. Kolodney J.Chem.Phys. 109 (1998) 8652.
[6] J.J.C. Geerlings, R. Rodink, J. Los and J.P. Gauyacq , Surf.Sci. 186 (1987) 15.

A. Benninghoven, P. Bertrand, H.-N. Migeon and H.W. Werner (Editors).
Proceedings of the 12th International Conference on Secondary Ion Mass Spectrometry,
Brussels, Belgium, 5-11 September 1999

TOWARDS AN IMPROVED UNDERSTANDING OF MCs+- AND MK+-SIMS DATA WITH COMPUTATIONALLY DETERMINED MOLECULAR PROPERTIES

P. Ecker[a*], W. Bieck[b], M. F. Ruiz-López[c]

[a]Cinvestav-IPN (Ing. Eléctrica - SEES), av. IPN #2508, Col. Zacatenco, Apdo. Postal 14-740, 07300 México D.F. (México), e-mail:pecker@mail.cinvestav.mx

[b]CRP-Gabriel Lippmann / Laboratoire d'Analyse des Matériaux (LAM), 162a, av. de la Faïencerie, L-1511 Luxembourg (G.D. Luxembourg)

[c]Laboratoire de Chimie Théorique, Université Henri Poincaré, Nancy I, Domaine Scientifique Victor Grignard, bd. des Aiguillettes BP 239, F-54506 Vandoeuvre-lès-Nancy Cedex (France)

1. Introduction

For quantitative SIMS of major sample constituents the specimen is sputtered using Cs^+ primary ions and elements M are commonly detected as MCs^+ in order to reduce well known matrix effects. There is however only little information available about the molecular properties and the formation processes of the monitored molecular gas-phase ions. Such knowledge could indeed be very helpful for the interpretation of the SIMS data. The aim of the present study is to investigate the correlation of computationally determined molecular properties and the relative ion yields of MA^+ and MA_2^+ (A = Cs, K) species. First numerical results obtained for oxygen (M = O) are compared with a formation model previously proposed by H. Gnaser [1].

2. Experimental

All MCs_x^+ and MK_x^+ yield measurements have been performed with an improved Cameca IMS 6f mass spectrometer (IMS LAM) described elsewhere [2]. Various oxides of known stoichiometry were sputtered with 5.5 keV Cs^+ and K^+ primary ions at an impact angle of about 42° with respect to the surface normal. The raster size was 200×200 μm^2 and positive secondary ions were accepted from an area 60 μm in diameter centred on the scanning area. A thin (≈ 50 nm) Au layer has been deposited on top of each specimen and an additional electron beam was used for charge compensation.

The *ab initio* calculations [3] were performed using the GAMESS software [4]. The energies and geometries were first computed at Hartree-Fock level [5,6,7] and than refined using the configuration interaction method [8,9]. For all the species considered only the ground state and equilibrium geometry have been taken into account.

3. Results and discussion

The atomic combination model (ACM) [10] has been successfully employed to describe the origin of sputtered molecules. Following this model, MCs^+ diatomics are formed by combination of a neutral M^0 and a Cs^+ sputtered independently, i.e. $M^0 + Cs^+ \rightarrow MCs^+$, first proposed by Ray et al. [11].

H. Gnaser [1] considered this reaction in terms of the dipole momentum of M induced by the electrical field of the alkali ion. The resulting interaction potential can be written in the following form (atomic units [12], energies in eV): $V(d) = (R/d^{12}) - (\propto_M.e^2)/d^4$

$$V(d) = \frac{R}{d^{12}} - \frac{\alpha_M \cdot e^2}{d^4} \tag{1}$$

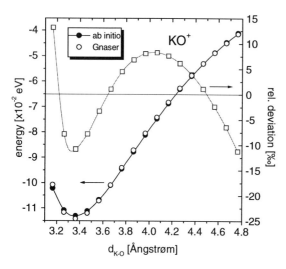

Fig. 1: Interaction potential of KO$^+$: Comparison of the *ab initio* calculation with the classical model of Gnaser (dipole-monopole interaction) and the relative deviation (E$_{abinitio}$-E$_{model}$)/E$_{abinitio}$ of the calculated potential energy versus interatomic distance.

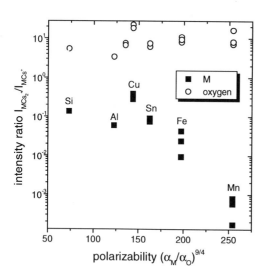

Fig. 2: MCs$_2^+$/MCs$^+$ intensity ratios versus polarisability obtained from oxides of the type M$_x$O$_y$

where d (in Å) stands for the internuclear distance and α_M (in Å^3) for the volume polarisability of M. The parameters R and α_M determine the depth of the potential well (or binding energy) which is supposed to govern the formation and survival probability of MCs$^+$ molecules. The yield of MCs$^+$ should thus depend on α_M. Taking into account the angular and energy dependence of $\gamma_{M^0-Cs^+}$ [13] finally leads to I$_{MCs}$ $\propto$ $\alpha^{9/4}$ [1]. Previous experiments [14,15] performed on the same instrument showed already that independent of the matrix and the primary beam alkali ion, all MCs$^+$ (MK$^+$) yields follow the same trend when plotted against a parameter sensitive to the position of M in the periodic table (e.g. ionization potential, electronegativity or polarisability). High values of α_M are observed for instance in the case of Gr.I and Gr.II elements (e.g. alkalis) and comparatively low values can be found in the case of halogens (Gr.VII). These experimental results confirm so far the hypothesis of Gnaser and justify also to focus numerical considerations on MK$^+$ diatomics to check whether eq. (1) can reproduce the calculated potential curve. So *ab initio* calculations have been performed for the case of KO$^+$. Fig.1 compares the model of Gnaser with the *ab initio* result using as fit parameters in eq. (1) R = (117866 ± 1004) eV·Å^{12} and α_O = (1.52 ± 0.01) Å^3.

The corresponding relative difference $(E_{abinitio}-E_{Gnaser})/E_{abinitio}$ plotted in fig.1 is small. The (theoretical) polarisability value of oxygen from literature is $\alpha_O = 0.80$ Å^3 [16,17] with an estimated error of about 10%. The classical approximation describes well the interaction potential calculated with sophisticated computer simulation, thus finally confirming the applicability of the classical approach in the case of MK$^+$ (MCs$^+$) molecule formation.

Analysing oxide samples of the type M$_x$O$_y$ employing the MCs$^+$-technique and plotting the data MCs$_2$$^+$/MCs$^+$ versus the polarisability of M shows another typical result: in the case of large α_M values (electropositive elements) the MCs$^+$ emission channel dominates whereas for low values (electronegative elements, here oxygen) the MCs$_2$$^+$ channel is dominating (cf. fig. 2). For oxygen the emission of OCs$_2$$^+$ is about a factor of 5-20 more intense than the one of OCs$^+$. This type of result is even more striking if one takes into account that generally the corresponding intensity ratio Cs$_2$$^+$/Cs$^+$ is in general less than 0.01. Similar observations have recently been made by Hongo [18] including other electronegative entities like CN or SiN and by Gao [19] (with fluorine). These findings comply to basic chemical rules, i.e. ions that one expects to be chemically stable are more readily observed than ions that do not have a favourable chemical and electronic structure. FCs$_2$$^+$ has a more stable electronic structure (closed shell) than FCs$^+$ and, of course, F$^+$ and the yields of these ions follow this order. Also OCs$_3$$^+$ is expected to be the most stable molecule of the series OCs$_x$$^+$ (x = 1 to 3).

molecule	fragments	energy ΔE
OK$_2$$^+$	KO + K$^+$	0.163 eV
	KO$^+$ + K	0.144 eV
	K$_2$$^+$ + O	0.820 eV
	2K$^+$ + O$^-$	2.593 eV
OK$^+$	K$^+$ + O	0.173 eV

Tab. 1: Dissociation energies for various fragmentation channels of K$_2$O$^+$ molecules.

Table 1 summarises the calculated dissociation energies of various fragmentation channels of the K$_2$O$^+$ molecule. Because of the symmetry of the molecule, the extraction of oxygen is energetically expensive. Thus the molecule can store much more energy in the symmetric vibration mode than is required for a dissociation in the case of an antisymmetric stretch. This might explain the high stability of K$_2$O$^+$ compared to KO$^+$. Determining the charge distribution of these molecules gives K$^{0.995+}$O$^{0.991-}$K$^{0.995+}$ for K$_2$O$^+$ and K$^{0.995+}$O$^{0.005+}$ for KO$^+$. This supports the idea that basic chemical knowledge is applicable even to uncommon species like MK$_2$$^+$, i.e. the positive charge is essentially concentrated on the potassium whereas the oxygen is neutral or even negative. It also comforts the hypothesis that the more electronegative an element M, the more ionic (i.e. stronger) is the bonding in a (K–M–K)$^+$ molecule.

4. Conclusions

The present work investigated the formation and stability of MCs$^+$ (MK$^+$) molecular ions. A formation model based on the polarisbility of M proposed by Gnaser has been confirmed by new experimental data. In addition, to prove its general applicability to stable molecules, the interaction potential of OK$^+$ was calculated and shows a good agreement with the proposed model. Further theoretical results are the strong molecular stabilities of OK$_2$$^+$ and OK$_3$$^+$ because of favourable electronic structures.

5. Acknowledgements

This work contains results from the PhD thesis of P. Ecker (University of Metz, 1998) directed by J.F. Muller and H.N. Migeon. Financial support by the Ministère de l'Education Nationale of Luxembourg is gratefully acknowledged. We are indebted to H. Gnaser and J.F.

Muller for their stimulating interest and useful comments and discussions. We also would like to thank H.N. Migeon for providing the possibility to carry out a part of this study using the LAM facilities.

References

[1]   H. Gnaser, H. Oechsner, Surf. Sci. Lett. 302 (1994) L289

[2]   W. Bieck, B. Rasser, M. Schumacher, P. Sudraud, H.N. Migeon, Proceedings SIMS X, Wiley, Chichester, 1997, p. 975

[3]   J.A. Pople, R.K. Nesbet, J. Chem. Phys. 22 (1954) 571

[4]   M.W.Schmidt, K.K.Baldridge, J.A. Boatz, S.T.Elbert, M.S.Gordon, J.J.Jensen, S.Koseki, N.Matsunaga, K.A.Nguyen, S.Su, T.L.Windus, M.Dupuis, J.A.Montgomery, J. Comput. Chem. 14 (1993) 1437

[5]   D.R. Hartree, Proc. Cambr. Phil. Soc. 24 (1927) 89

[6]   V. Fock Z. Phys. 61 (1930) 126

[7]   C.C.J. Roothaan, Rev. Mod. Phys. 23 (1951) 69

[8]   B. Brooks, H. F. Schäfer, J. Chem. Phys. 70 (1979) 5092

[9]   B. Brooks, W. Laidig, P. Saxe, N. Handy, H.F. Schäfer, Physica Scripta 21 (1980) 312

[10] W. Gerhard, H. Oechsner, Z. Phys. B22 (1975) 41

[11] M.A. Ray, J.E. Baker, C. M. Loxton, J. E. Greene, J. Vac. Sci. Technol., A6 (1988), 44

[12] R. McWeeny K, Nature 243 (1973) 196

[13] G.P. Können, A. Tip, A.E. de Vries, Rad. Effects 21 (1974) 269

[14] Y. Marie, W. Bieck, H.N. Migeon, Proceedings SIMS X, Wiley, Chichester, 1995, p 685

[15] Y. Marie, W. Bieck, H.N. Migeon, Proceedings SIMS X, Wiley, Chichester, 1995, p 211

[16] T.M. Miller, B. Bederson, Advances in Atomic and Molecular Physics 13 (1977) 1

[17] D.R. Lide (ed.), CRC Handbook of Chemistry and Physics, 73rd ed., CRC Press Inc., 1992/93

[18] C. Hongo, M. Tomita, M. Suzuki, Appl. Surf. Sci., 144-145 (1999) 306

[19] Y. Gao, Y. Marie, F. Saldi, H.N. Migeon, Proceedings SIMS IX, Wiley, Chichester, (1993) p. 406

[20] Y. Homma Y. Higashi, T. Maruo, C. Maekawa, S. Ochiai, Proceedings SIMS IX, Wiley, Chichester, 1993, p. 398

* Present address: Cinvestav-IPN (Ing.Eléctrica – SEES), av. IPN #2508, Col. Zacatenco, Apdo.postal 14-740, 07300 México D.F. (México)

A. Benninghoven, P. Bertrand, H.-N. Migeon and H.W. Werner (Editors).
Proceedings of the 12th International Conference on Secondary Ion Mass Spectrometry,
Brussels, Belgium, 5-11 September 1999
© 2000 Elsevier Science B.V. All rights reserved.

TRACE ANALYSIS OF Pt AND Au USING PRIMARY ION BEAMS OF CS+ AND K+ - A COMPARATIVE STUDY

G.McMahon[a], L.J. Cabri[b], A. Hamed[c], R.L. Hervig[d], and P. Williams[c]

[a]CANMET, MTL, 568 Booth Street, Ottawa Canada K1A OG1
gmcmahon@NRCan.gc.ca
[b]CANMET, MMSL, 555 Booth Street, Ottawa Canada K1A OG1
[c]Dept. of Chemistry, Arizona State University, Tempe, AZ, USA 85287-1704
[d]Center for Solid State Science, Arizona State University, Tempe, AZ, USA 85287-1704

1. Introduction

The application of SIMS in the mining industry has enjoyed increasing popularity over the last number of years as the advantages of the technique become more widely known to scientists working directly in the industry or in related analytical laboratories. One implication of this phenomenon is the demand by these organizations to have their own, less experienced operators, operate the SIMS instrumentation by themselves. Unfortunately, analysis of Au and Pt in sulfide minerals requires the use of high mass resolution in order to eliminate the CsS_2 and CsS_2H interferences at masses 197 and 198 amu, respectively. Operating the SIMS in this mode can pose quite a challenge to the novice operator, and as a result the validity of the data may suffer. Therefore, a means of analyzing these types of samples without recourse to high mass resolution mode was sought. Since the main interferences encountered are molecular ions containing Cs, it seemed logical to try to find an alternative primary ion beam, which would eliminate the mass interference problem, and hopefully still yield detection levels equivalent or better than those obtained with the Cs^+ beam. A primary beam of K^+ had been successfully used previously (1,2), and so it was believed that it would be a potential candidate to help solve the present dilemma.

2. Analytical Methodology

All work using the K^+ primary ion beam was performed at the Center for Solid State Science at Arizona State University using a Cameca ims3f with a self-designed thermally ionized K ion source described at this conference. For these studies, a 60 μm diameter analyzed area was used, a 400 μm contrast diaphragm, and a 200 nA $^{39}K^+$ ion beam. The accelerating voltage used was 10 kV, and a 50V offset was employed to eliminate any other mass interferences, as this amount of voltage offset was found to yield the best compromise between peak intensity and background counts (Figure 1). The energy bandpass was 40 eV.

Experiments using the Cs^+ primary ion beam were conducted at the Materials Technology Laboratory/CANMET using a Cameca ims4f instrument with a commercial microbeam Cs source. Similar experimental parameters were used, that is, a 60 μm analytical area, a 10 kV accelerating voltage, a 400 μm contrast aperture, and beam currents ranging from 150 to 550 nA. However, in this set of studies, a mass resolving power of about 2000 was employed by closing both the entrance and exit slits, while the energy slit remained wide open.

132

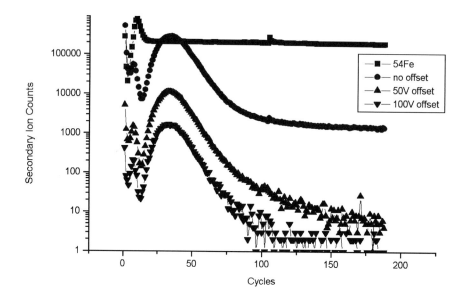

Figure 1: Depth profiles of a chalcopyrite ^{198}Pt standard using a primary K$^+$ ion beam with various degrees of energy discrimination. Use of a 50V offset was found to give the best results.

The minerals selected for producing the ion implant standards were from a variety of sources, and ideally had low concentrations of the element to be implanted and consisted of monomineralic crystalline masses larger than the 1-cm diameter ion implantation beam. The minerals were sectioned and mounted in carbon-loaded 2.5 cm diameter mounts and subsequently polished.

Ion implantation of ^{197}Au to a dose of 2.5 x 10^{13} atoms/cm^2 was carried out AECL Chalk River Laboratories at an energy of 1 MeV. The accuracy of these implant fluences was determined using RBS on a series of five implanted silicon standards with doses ranging from 1 x 10^{14} to 1 x 10^{15} atoms/cm^2. The RBS measurements indicated the fit between the RBS and measured dose of current to be accurate to within about 5 %.

The implantation of ^{198}Pt was carried out at Interface Science Western at the University of Western Ontario also at an energy of 1 MeV to a dose of 1 x 10^{13} atoms/cm^2. These implant standards were similarly verified for accuracy using RBS on equivalently implanted Si wafers. The results from these experiments confirmed that the implant fluences were accurate again to approximately 5%. However, subsequent SIMS analyses of the ^{194}Pt, ^{195}Pt, and ^{196}Pt showed a significant co-implantation of these isotopes (Figure 2). In fact, of the total dose, only about 79% could be attributed to ^{198}Pt. Interestingly, the percentages of the co-implanted species behaved opposite to that expected, with the most significant contribution coming from the ^{194}Pt isotope (13%), followed by the ^{195}Pt isotope (5%) and finally by the ^{196}Pt isotope (3%). The actual dose of ^{198}Pt for the determination of relative sensitivity factors and minimum detection limits was therefore adjusted accordingly.

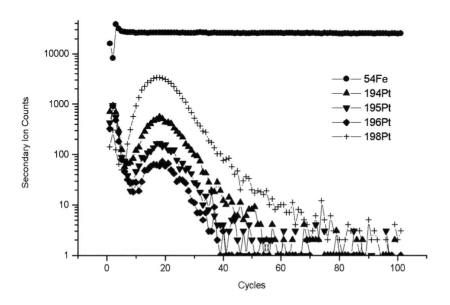

Figure 2: Depth profile of a pyrite ^{198}Pt standard using a K$^+$ primary ion beam showing significant co-implantation of ^{194}Pt, ^{195}Pt and ^{196}Pt.

3. Results and Discussion

The results of this study in the form of the minimum detection limits obtained from the background count rate on the ion implant standards depth profile are shown in Table 1. The data indicates that the use of a K$^+$ primary ion beam in conjunction with a modest degree (50V offset) of energy discrimination can yield Au detection limits equivalent if not better than those obtained using a Cs$^+$ primary ion beam in high mass resolution mode. Since the former technique is much more user-friendly for the novice operator, it would be the analytical method of choice. It could be further argued that even for experienced operators who have no difficulty coping with high mass resolving powers, there are certain advantages to using a K$^+$ primary ion beam with energy discrimination. For example, extensive use of high mass resolving powers will cause a non-uniform wear of the entrance slits. As a result, the slits must often be closed more than would normally be the case in order to eliminate the signal from the interfering masses entering the spectrometer through the worn regions of the slits. The result of this is a loss in the dynamic range of the depth profile, and a resultant increase in the detection limits. The spread in the values for the detection limits using the Cs^+ beam is to some extent a result of this phenomenon.

Although more data needs to be acquired using the K^+ primary ion beam on the Pt standards, initial results indicate that better detection limits are still obtained using high mass resolution and a Cs^+ primary beam. This suggests that the interfering mass (potentially $^{56}Fe_2\,^{54}Fe^{32}S$) is still not completely eliminated using the energy discrimination technique. Nevertheless, the detection limits obtained for Pt using this method are still 20-100 times better than what might be expected using proton induced X-ray emission (PIXE), for example (5).

The use of a K^+ primary ion beam therefore seems very promising, and may very well be the future primary beam of choice for laboratories doing extensive work in the mineralogical and geological sciences, particularly if these labs have a large number or a high turnover of inexperienced users.

| | Cs^+ primary ion beam | | K^+ primary ion beam | |
	Au MDL (ppmw)	Pt MDL (ppmw)	Au MDL (ppmw)	Pt MDL (ppmw)
Pyrite	0.223	0.225-0.300	0.049	0.378
Chalcopyrite	0.130	0.181	0.027	
	0.020*	0.117-0.175		
	0.047*			
Pyrrhotite	0.065	0.278	0.022	1.270
	0.025*	0.136-0.300		
Pentlandite	-	0.361	-	
		0.200-0.500		
Arsenopyrite	0.059*	-	0.053	

Table 1: Summary of minimum detection limits derived from the background counts of the ion implant standards using primary ion beams of Cs^+ and K^+. Values marked with an asterisk represent minimum detection limits found using other ^{197}Au implant standards with a dose of 5.5×10^{13} atoms/cm^2 from unpublished proprietary studies.

References
[1] R.T. Lareau and P. Williams, SIMS V, A. Benninghoven, R.J. Colton, D.S. Simons and H.W. Werner eds. (Springer New York 1986) p. 149
[2] Y. Marie, W. Bieck and H.-N. Migeon, SIMS X, A. Benninghoven, B. Hagenhoff and H.W. Werner eds. (John Wiley & Sons 1996) p. 211
[3] L.J. Cabri and G. McMahon, Can. Mineral. 33 (1995) 349
[4] T. Oberthur et al, Can. Mineral. 35 (1997) 597
[5] L.J. Cabri, Trans. Instn Min. Metall. (Sect. B: Appl. Earth sci.) 103 (1994) B3

A. Benninghoven, P. Bertrand, H.-N. Migeon and H.W. Werner (Editors).
Proceedings of the 12th International Conference on Secondary Ion Mass Spectrometry,
Brussels, Belgium, 5-11 September 1999

SYNTHESIZING A SECONDARY IONIZATION MODEL FOR MATRIX ELEMENTS SPUTTERED FROM SiO$_x$: FINDINGS AND TRENDS.

J. J. Serrano[*†], H. De Witte[+1], B. Guzmán[*], J.M. Blanco[*], W. Vandervorst[+⊥].

[*] Electronic Technology Dept. at the Polytechnical University of Madrid, E.T.S.I.T. Ciudad Universitaria, 28040 Madrid, Spain

[+] IMEC (Interuniversity Microelectronics Center), Kapeldreef 75, B-3001 Leuven, Belgium

[⊥] INSYS, KULeuven, Belgium

[†] E-mail: jjserran@etsit.upm.es

1. Introduction

The present work is devoted to the modeling of the secondary ionization probability of atoms emitted by sputtering of silicon by oxygen primary ions. It focuses on the Si$^+$ and O$^+$ SIMS signals during the initial transient. The probability for a given sputtered species to reach the detector as an ion, is described in our model[1] by two consecutive phenomena of electronic interchange. The initial ionization of a given departing atom depends on the electronic interchange between the escaping atom and the atoms forming the emission site, when the bonds are broken. So, on the average, the probability to depart as a positive ion, P$_b$, depends on the distribution of possible emission sites because each type has its own initial ionization probability. This is proportional to the emission site electronegativy[2] through an exponential function. Afterwards, the escaping ion can interchange one or more electrons with the remaining surface. These electrons must jump through an energy barrier (tunnel effect[3]), built-up by the electric forces between the ion and the surface. Hence, the ion has a non-unity probability, P$_t$, to survive on its way to the detector. Since both phenomena are independent, the ionization probability, P$^+$, is the product of both probabilities:

$$P_t \sim exp \{ K_t (\Phi\text{-}I) \} \tag{1.1}$$

$$\Phi(SiO_x) = 4.8 + (0.15 + 4C_\Phi)x^2 - (0.05 + C_\Phi) x^3 + C_\Phi x^4 \tag{1.2}$$

$$P_b \sim \Sigma_n (X_n exp\{ K_b(E_O n + E_{Si} (4 - n))\}) \tag{2}$$

$$P^+ \sim P_t P_b \tag{3}$$

In the tunnel effect probability, P$_t$, K$_t$ is a constant inversely proportional to the ion escape velocity, I the ionization potential and Φ is the surface's work function where C$_M$ is a fitting parameter. In a given SIMS measurement, the detector energy window is usually held constant and narrow when changing the mass/charge ratio. Therefore, for any couple of ionic species (i, j) the relation m$_i$v$_i^2$ = m$_j$v$_j^2$ holds, where m$_i$ and m$_j$ are the respective masses and v$_i$ and v$_j$ their corresponding escape velocities. Taking into account the relation between the escape velocity and the tunnel constant[3], for two given ions in the same ionization state, their tunnel constants should follow the ratio: K$_{tj}$ / K$_{ti}$ = (m$_j$ / m$_i$)$^{1/2}$. The bond-breaking probability, P$_b$, is calculated based on the emission site electronegativity. In eq. (2) K$_b$ is a unknown normalizing constant, E$_{Si}$ and E$_O$ are respectively the silicon and oxygen electronegativities and

---

[1] H. De Witte thanks the Fund for Scientific Research (Flanders, Belgium) for supporting this research work.

X_n is the fraction of emission sites of type n formed by n oxygen atoms and 4-n silicon atoms (silicon atoms in the oxidation state n before being sputtered).

The model needs the surface matrix composition in the first few monolayers, as these determine the ionization phenomena. The lack of data for this region can be overcome using the ISRD[4] (Implantation, Sputtering, Relocation/Replacement and Diffusion) simulation code. This program provides surface atomic concentrations and neutral sputtering yields as a function of primary ion dose, which are used as input data for the secondary ionization model[5]. Finally, since we can not calculate absolute probabilities, the simulation of the initial transients in the SIMS signal, where the sputtering yields as well as the surface composition dynamically change, offers a nice opportunity to verify the model while using the steady state signal as a reference for normalization.

2. The model

To set up the emission site distribution for silicon one could use a pure statistical approach[6] without any chemical consideration, the Random Bonding Model (RBM). Simulations based on the RBM approach are presented elsewhere[5]. A comparison with experimental data on oxidation states (fig. 1), obtained by XPS[7], shows that RBM approach does not fit the measurements very well, probably because chemical driving forces lead to a non-random distribution. An approach based solely on the experimental data is not feasible as at low oxygen concentrations no experimental results are available. To overcome this limitation we have used a combination of experimental data[7] in the high oxygen concentration range and RBM for low oxygen concentrations. This mixed model (MIX) is based on the assumption that for low oxygen concentrations, where data are not available, the RBM could apply since the oxygen atoms are well separated from each other and the chemical forces should be less important. However, in our simulations the very low oxygen concentration range is never achieved. For oxygen the problem is simpler as there is only one type of emission site because most of the oxygen atoms are attached only to silicon atoms[8]. Therefore, the bond-breaking contribution does not depend on the surface oxygen concentration and the oxygen ionization probability is only proportional to the tunnel effect contribution, P_t.

Based on the ISRD-output and the resulting distribution functions, eq.(1) and (2) can be calculated and the simulated SIMS signal as a function of ion dose can be obtained. In fig.2 the profiles correspond to a 15 keV/O beam at different angles whereas in fig.3 the energy varies from 7.5 to 12.5 keV at normal incidence. Whereas the agreement with the Si-data is already quite good, large discrepancies can be seen for oxygen, in particular at higher oxygen concentrations. The model parameters take the following values: $K_b = 0.75$ eV^{-1}, $K_{t\,Si} = 12$ eV^{-1}, $K_{t\,O} = 9.09$ eV^{-1}, $C_\Phi = 0.04$. Since the detected ions were ^{30}Si and ^{16}O, the tunnel effect constant is verified using the ratio $K_{t\,Si} / K_{t\,O} = (m_{Si} / m_O)^{1/2} = 1.32$.

3. Fitting functions

We have therefore also extracted a fitting function for the ionization probabilities by matching the experimental data with the simulations (still using the ISRD-output). For silicon the function fitting the ionization probability F_{Si}^+ is $(10,700(1-x_{Si})^{3.7} + 10(1-x_{Si}))(1+1.9\exp[-5.5(x_{Si} -1/3)]) + d$. This function follows the tendencies published by Wittmaack[9] (linear variation with the surface oxygen concentration for silicon weakly oxidized and variation proportional to the power 3.7 of the oxygen concentration for more oxidized samples) except for the ionization in pure silicon (the fitting parameter d) and by Alay[10] (exponential growing near full oxidation). For oxygen, the fitting function, F_O^+, is $\exp(K_t \Phi)$, where Φ is shown in eq.(1.2). Therefore, F_O^+ has two parameters (formally they are the same as for P_O^+) the fourth order coefficient, C_Φ, and a constant multiplying Φ, K_t, but taking different values. The optimized fitting parameter values are: d = 10 for the Si-fit and for the O-fit: K_t = 18.5, C_Φ = -0.014 (15 keV/O); K_t = 19.5, C_Φ = -0.014 (12.5 keV/O); K_t = 20.5, C_Φ = 0 (10 keV/O); K_t = 24.5, C_Φ = 0 (7.5 keV/O). Note that the fitting function for Si, without changing the parameter value, is applicable for all energies and all angles, whereas for oxygen one fit covers the entire angular range but needs to be adapted for different energies.

4. Discussion

For the Si-signals the model and the fitting function are very close to each other, with a slightly better agreement for the fitting function at low oxygen concentrations. Both approaches fit the experimental signals, see figs. 2a and 3a, except at the beginning, in the native oxide region, where they give a value about a factor of 2 too high. The latter might suggest that the sputter process reduces the native oxide so rapidly that ionization in this region is less than expected based on the oxygen concentration. For oxygen, at the highest energy and any incidence angle (see fig. 2b), the model fits the data in the native oxide and deeper in the sample until a high surface oxygen concentration (about 50%) is achieved. Contrarily, the fitting function overestimates the signal in the native oxide. With decreasing angle, i.e. higher oxygen content, a serious discrepancy can be observed. The latter becomes even more pronounced when the energy is reduced (see fig. 3b). Moreover, with decreasing energy the separation point between measurement and model appears sooner, i.e. at lower surface oxygen concentrations. In all those cases the calculations with the fitting functions overestimate the native oxide signal. The latter is in line with our concept of a reduced native oxide. Since the fitting function optimizes the ionization yield in the (fully oxidized) substrate, its overestimation in the native oxide implies that the latter is not so oxygen rich or that it behaves as a more poorly oxidized layer.

5. Conclusions

We have combined the ISRD code and two quantitative approaches to the secondary ionization probability to simulate SIMS signal initial transients of matrix ions from silicon when using oxygen as primary species in certain sputtering conditions. Where the present model description works reasonable well for Si, the discrepancies seen for high concentrations of oxygen imply that an additional mechanism (only operative for oxygen) needs to be considered. In addition the overestimate in the native oxide region, may imply that the ion beam mixing effects reduces this very rapidly or that it behaves (electronically) not as a thick oxide layer.

References

[1]   J.J. Serrano, J.M. Blanco, B. Guzmán, M. Aguilar and O. Ameziane, SIMS XI, (1998), p. 363.
[2]   M. L. Yu in Topics in Applied Physics Vol. 64: Sputtering by Particle Bombardment III, p. 107, Editors R. Behrisch and K. Wittmaack, Ed. Spring Verlag, Berlin Heidelberg 1991.
[3]   J. K. Norskov and B. I. Lundqvist, Physical Review B19(11), p. 5661 (1979)
[4]   O. Vancauwenberghe, N. Herbots and O.D. Hellman, J. Vac. Sci. Technol. A 10(4), p. 713 (1992).
[5]   J. J. Serrano, H. De Witte, W. Vandervorst, B. Guzmán, J.M. Blanco, to be published.

138

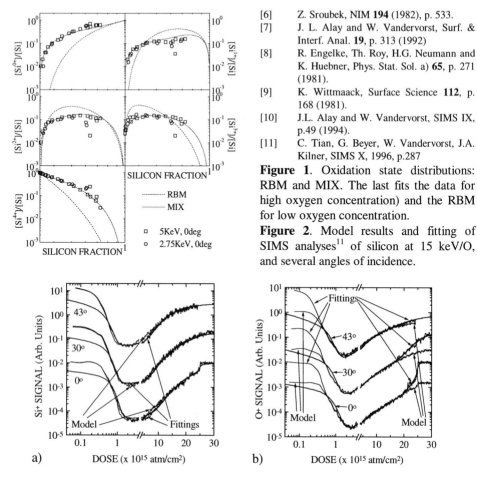

[6]   Z. Sroubek, NIM **194** (1982), p. 533.

[7]   J. L. Alay and W. Vandervorst, Surf. & Interf. Anal. **19**, p. 313 (1992)

[8]   R. Engelke, Th. Roy, H.G. Neumann and K. Huebner, Phys. Stat. Sol. a) **65**, p. 271 (1981).

[9]   K. Wittmaack, Surface Science **112**, p. 168 (1981).

[10]   J.L. Alay and W. Vandervorst, SIMS IX, p.49 (1994).

[11]   C. Tian, G. Beyer, W. Vandervorst, J.A. Kilner, SIMS X, 1996, p.287

Figure 1. Oxidation state distributions: RBM and MIX. The last fits the data for high oxygen concentration) and the RBM for low oxygen concentration.

Figure 2. Model results and fitting of SIMS analyses[11] of silicon at 15 keV/O, and several angles of incidence.

Figure 3. Some SIMS analyses made at normal incidence and at several energies: 10 keV/O, 12.5 keV/O, 10 keV/O and 7.5 keV/O. For 15 keV/O see Fig. 2.

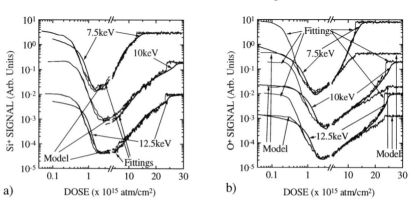

A. Benninghoven, P. Bertrand, H.-N. Migeon and H.W. Werner (Editors).
Proceedings of the 12th International Conference on Secondary Ion Mass Spectrometry,
Brussels, Belgium, 5-11 September 1999

ASSOCIATIVE DETACHMENT REACTIONS IN OXYGEN-SPUTTERED URANIUM

Peter Williams[1,2] and Richard L. Hervig[2]
[1]Department of Chemistry and Biochemistry
[2]Center for Solid State Science
Arizona State University
Tempe, AZ 85287
PW@ASU.EDU

1. Introduction

A number of metals, most notably uranium, but also including Mo, Nb, Zr and the lanthanides, produce very intense fluxes of MO^+ and higher oxides when sputtered in the presence of oxygen (introduced from the primary ion beam, from the gas phase, or as the metal oxide). Often it appears that the oxide ion channels compete with the atomic ion channel, so that the atomic ion signal is typically lower than might be expected from the ionization systematics (inverse exponential scaling of ion yields with ionization potential). In the case of uranium, the low-energy U^+ signal from a fully oxidized surface is actually lower than from the clean metal [1]. To examine the mechanism of this phenomenon, we have determined, in a Cameca IMS 3f ion microscope, initial energy distributions of the range of species sputtered from a uranium target by an Ar^+ primary beam as the oxygen partial pressure is varied.

2. Results and Discussion

Fig. 1 shows the dramatic change in the shape of the U^+ energy spectra as the oxygen partial pressure is increased. At the lowest pressure, the energy spectrum is normal. But as the oxygen pressure increases, although there is a significant enhancement of the high-energy ion signal, the low-energy signal is only slightly enhanced and actually drops significantly at the highest pressure. The spectra strongly suggest that the normal oxygen enhancement of the U^+ signal is counteracted by some process which depletes the low-energy ion flux. The low-energy U^+

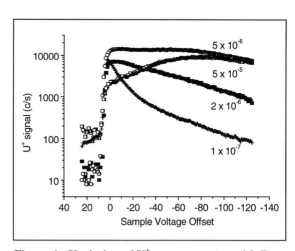

Figure 1. Variation of U^+ energy spectra with P_{O2}

140

signal drops by a factor of ~ 7, but in fact, given that oxygen enhances the high-energy U^+ signal ~ 100-fold, the actual depletion of low-energy U^+ is probably closer to a factor of ~ 700. Accompanying the U^+ depletion is a strong increase in the UO^+ signal over this pressure range.

What sort of process could produce this effect? Oxidation of the uranium surface very probably produces an oxide surface with an increased surface binding energy which should reduce the sputter yield, but although such changes could shift the position of the energy maximum by a few eV, they should not significantly alter the shape of the curves. The chemical bond in the UO molecule is extremely strong, and energy transfer between U and O in collisions is inefficient, so that adjacent U and O atoms in the surface can be sputtered as UO species with high efficiency. But this does not seem sufficient to account for the exceptional depletion of low-energy U^+.

We suggest that an additional process, specific to uranium and similar oxide-formers, allows sputtered U and O species to react to form UO^+ even if they are sputtered from quite widely separated locations in the sputtering site. Fite *et al* [2] in 1974 showed that the reaction:

$$U + O \rightarrow UO^+ + e^- \qquad (1)$$

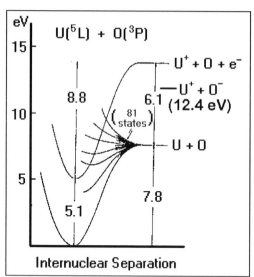

Figure 2. U + O potential curves. From Fite
et al. **[1]**

has an extremely high cross-section, ~4 x 10^{-15} cm^2, and explained this in terms of the potential energy diagram shown in Fig. 2. The bond energy of UO is high, 7.8 eV, and the ionization potential is quite low, 5.1 eV. Also the ground state of the U+O system is 81-fold degenerate, so that a dense array of potential curves exists between the ground state bonding and the antibonding curve. Roughly half of these curves cross the UO^+ curve, and a transition to the ion curve, ejecting an electron, locks the system into the ion channel. Such a reaction can occur between U and O atoms sputtered from an oxygenated uranium surface, but this does not yet explain depletion of the U^+ signal. For that we look to another reaction not examined by Fite *et al*, namely:

$$U^+ + O^- \rightarrow UO^+ + e^- \qquad (2)$$

Only the ion-pair dissociation limit for UO $\rightarrow U^+ + O^-$ is shown on the figure, but we note that the potential well is considerably deeper and wider than the neutral dissociation curve –

the ion-pair dissociation energy is 12.4 eV and the two ions interact via the long-range Coulomb force. The $U^+ + O^-$ curve also has a high degeneracy, and an even greater fraction of these curves cross the UO^+ curve, so that almost all U^+ and O^- ions sputtered in the same event, even 10 Å or more apart, have a very significant probability of reacting to form UO^+ as indicated in equation (2).

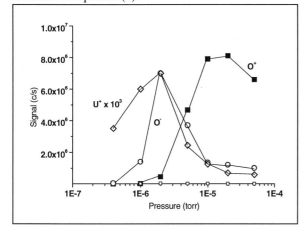

Figure 3. Variation of low-energy U^+, O^- and O^+ signals with increasing oxygen pressure

If indeed U^+ and O^- ions are mutually scavenged by reaction (2), their signals should respond similarly to surface oxygenation. Figure 3 shows that indeed the U^+ and O^- signals at first increase then reach a maximum near a pressure of 2×10^{-6} torr then both decrease by a factor of ~ 7, while the O^+ signal by comparison continues to increase strongly through this pressure range (the O^+ signal increases by a factor of $>10^3$ between 1×10^{-6} and 1×10^{-5} torr). Note that there is no corresponding reaction process to scavenge the O^+ flux.

Reaction (2) could be rewritten:

$$U^- + O^+ \rightarrow UO^+ + e^- \tag{3}$$

and indeed the potential well here is even deeper. However, the sputtered U^- flux is several orders of magnitude smaller than the O^+ signal, so reaction (3) should not appreciably deplete the O^+ signal. However, U^- should be depleted and indeed this does occur as shown in Fig. 4, the low-energy U^- signal behavior mirroring the response of U^+ to increasing oxygen pressure.

The fact that the O^+ signal shows no sign of depletion other than a small drop at the highest pressure where gas phase scattering and charge exchange begin to affect ion signals is an indication that direct sputtering of UO species tightly bound in the surface is not a major cause of the U^+, U^- and O^- depletions.

We should note two *caveats*. First, the oxygen pressure is not necessarily a good measure of oxygen surface coverage, by which the various plots should ideally be compared, because primary ion current density and sputter yields can change slightly when switching secondary ion polarity. Thus the good correspondence between the maxima of the U^+ and O^- signals in Fig. 3 may be partly coincidental. However, the fact remains that the two data sets are similar in shape, and are qualitatively different from the O^+ data. Second, the O^- energy spectra do not change shape like those of U^+ and U^- but continue to exhibit a low-energy peak as the overall intensity falls by a factor of 7. The reason for this is not yet understood. Finally, it might be argued that oxygen should suppress negative ion emission as it acts to enhance positive ion emission, so that the drop in the O^- signal might not be related to the reactions proposed here. However it has long been known that oxygen quite generally enhances sputtered negative ion yields [3], and the author has determined more recently that on a more "normal" substrate such as silicon, the ionization efficiency of O^- is also enhanced by increasing the oxygen surface coverage [4].

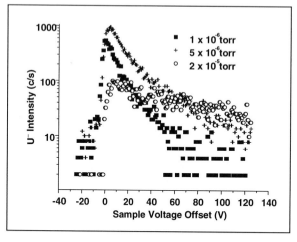

Figure 4. Variation of U^- energy spectra with P_{O2}

3. Conclusion

These results show yet again the rich field of ionization phenomena to be encountered in SIMS, and the potential complications that can impede quantitative analysis. Understanding the ionization behavior of uranium is important in order to have confidence in the quantification of uranium and lead in zircons for dating purposes, using the SIMS signals alone. Because zirconium probably undergoes a similar associative detachment reaction, and so could compete with uranium for the available O^- while lead almost certainly does not, ionization behavior in these samples could be remarkably complex.

References

[1] A.E. Morgan, H.W. Werner, *Surface Science* **65** (1977) 687
[2] W.L. Fite, H.H. Lo, P. Irving, *J. Chem. Phys.* **60** (1974) 1236
[3] P. Williams, C.A. Evans, Jr., *Surface Science* **78** (1978) 324
[4] P. Williams, unpublished.

A. Benninghoven, P. Bertrand, H.-N. Migeon and H.W. Werner (Editors).
Proceedings of the 12th International Conference on Secondary Ion Mass Spectrometry,
Brussels, Belgium, 5-11 September 1999
143

A METHOD FOR QUANTITATIVE DETERMINATION OF SECONDARY ION FORMATION PROBABILITIES

A. Wucher, R. Heinrich and C. Staudt

Institute of Laser and Plasma Physics, University of Essen, 45117 Essen, Germany

wucher@uni-essen.de

1. Introduction

One of the key parameters characterizing the ion formation process in SIMS is the ionization probability $\alpha^{+,-}$, i. e. the probability that a sputtered particle leaves the surface in a positively or negatively charged state. Numerous theoretical models have been published describing $\alpha^{+,-}$, a fairly recent review of which can be found in [1]. An experimental determination of this quantity requires the detection of sputtered neutral species (besides the corresponding secondary ions), a task which adds complexity due to the fact that these particles must be post-ionized prior to mass and energy spectrometric detection. In order to permit a quantitative evaluation of $\alpha^{+,-}$, it is essential that i) the post-ionization probability must be precisely known and, even more importantly, ii) related neutral and ionic sputtering yields must be determined under otherwise identical experimental conditions. Particularly the latter condition is generally hard to fulfil, since most experiments employ post-ionization schemes which are sensitive to the *number density* of sputtered neutrals at a point located relatively far away from the surface, while the detection of secondary ions usually involves a direct measurement of the *flux* of charged particles leaving the surface, often even assisted by an accelerating electrostatic field. As a consequence, ion optical conditions and therefore the instrumental detection efficiency for secondary ions and post-ionized neutrals will in general be different.

2. Method

In this paper, we describe an experimental method which avoids these problems. The technique is based on the *in situ* detection of sputtered secondary ions and the respective sputtered neutral species within the ionization region of a reflectron Time-of-Flight (ToF) mass spectrometer, which has been described in great detail earlier [2,3]. A schematic view of the setup is shown in Fig. 1. The sample is bombarded with a pulsed ion beam. During the primary ion pulse, the sample is held at ground potential in order to ensure that the spatial region between the surface and the extraction electrode E_1 is field-free. The sputtered neutral particles are ionized by an excimer laser operated at wavelengths of 248, 193 or 157 nm which is fired immediately

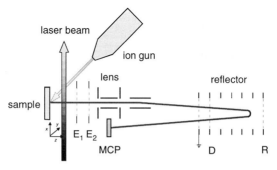

Fig. 1 Schematic setup of time-of-flight mass spectrometer

144

after the primary ion pulse. The resulting
photoions are extracted by an electric field
which is switched on shortly (about 20 ns)
after the ionizing laser pulse with a rise time
short enough (< 10 ns) to ensure that motion
of the ions during the slope of the extraction
field is negligible. As a consequence, it is the
the leading edge of the field pulse (and not
the exact firing time of the ionization laser)
which determines the zero of the flight time
measurement in the reflectron ToF mass
spectrometer. Moreover, the use of this
timing sequence ensures that the temporal
width and shape of the flight time peak
recorded for particles of a particular mass are exclusively determined by the time
refocusing properties of the reflectron ToF spectrometer and, in particular, do not depend
on either the timing jitter or the temporal width of the ionization laser pulse.

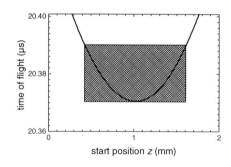

Fig. 3 Calculated flight time vs. starting
coordinate z along the surface normal

An important aspect of the technique concerns the ionization volume V_{ion} , i. e. the
spatial volume within the extraction region from which ions are accepted and detected by
the mass spectrometer. In the direction parallel to the sample surface, both the location as
well as the extension of V_{ion} are simply determined by ion optical conditions. In the
direction along the surface normal, however, the situation is slightly more complicated.
Here, both the exact location of the center of V_{ion} as well as its spatial extension are
determined by the time refocusing properties of the reflectron ToF spectrometer. In order
to illustrate this, Fig. 3 shows the calculated flight time of ions as a function of their

starting coordinate z at the time
when the extraction field is
switched on for a typical set of
experimental parameters. The
shape of the measured ToF peak is
to first order determined by the
inverse derivative of the depicted
curve, the peak will therefore be
centered around a flight time
corresponding to the local minimum in Fig. 3. The corresponding
z-value determines the center of
the ionization volume. The experimentally observed half width
of the peaks is about 20 ns
corresponding to a z- interval of
about 1 mm (indicated by the
shaded area in Fig. 3), ions starting
farther away from the center are
quickly dispersed in flight time and
are therefore not detected in the

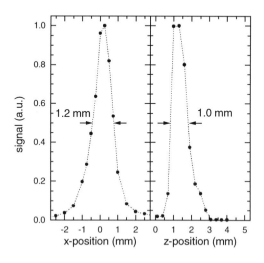

Fig. 2 ToF signal of post-ionized sputtered neutrals
vs. position of the ionizing laser beam

peak, but rather contribute to a structureless background in the ToF spectrum. The shape of curves like that displayed in Fig. 3 therefore acts as an effective restriction of the sensitive volume of the mass spectrometer along the z-direction. In order to demonstrate this, Fig. 2 shows the measured ToF signal of post-ionized sputtered neutral particles vs. the position of a tightly focused ionization laser beam which was translated in directions parallel and perpendicular to the sample surface. It is clearly seen that the effective diameter of V_{ion} is about 1 mm in both directions.

For the quantitative detection of sputtered neutrals, it is essential to eliminate the influence of the generally unknown post-ionization cross sections. In our approach, this is accomplished by saturating the photoabsorption process, thus leading to a complete photoionization of all neutral particles within the ionization volume. In order to achieve and identify this condition, it is essential that i) photoionization is accomplished by absorption of only one single photon, since only in this case the laser intensity dependence of the measured photoion signals is easily understood and ii) the ioinizing laser beam is defocused to the dimension of V_{ion}. A typical laser intensity dependence measured under these conditions is depicted in Fig. 4, which clearly shows the saturation behaviour expected for a single photon absorption process (dotted line fitted to the data). In the present context, it is important to note that the saturated signal is representative of the *number density* of sputtered neutral particles present within V_{ion} at the firing time of the laser.

For the detection of secondary ions, the ionization laser is simply switched off, while all other parameters of the experiment remain unchanged. Under these conditions, all of the above arguments with respect to the extension of V_{ion} and the generation of a ToF spectrum remain valid, and the instrument therefore detects sharp flight time peaks of secondary ions which are present within V_{ion} at the switching time of the extraction field. Fig. 5 shows an example which was obtained on sputtered neutral Ge atoms. For comparison, a spectrum taken with the ionization laser switched on is included, which clearly shows that the mass spectral characteristics of secondary ions and post-ionized neutrals are identical. It should be explicitly noted at this point that this way of generating a secondary ion mass spectrum is fundamentally different from the usual way ToF-SIMS spectra are acquired. In particular, the width of the flight time peaks is independent of the primary ion pulse length and, hence, long pulses (several μs) can be employed which ensure that the ionization volume is completely filled with sputtered particles (ions and neutrals) of all emission velocities. Under these conditions, the measured ion signals are representative of the *number*

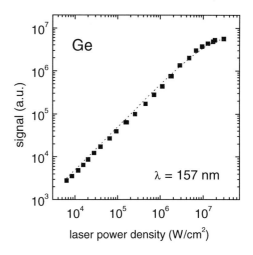

Fig. 4 ToF signal of post-ionized sputtered neutral Al atoms vs. peak power density of the ionizing laser

146

density of secondary ions within the ionization volume (instead of the flux as in usual ToF-SIMS spectra) and, as such, are directly comparable to the respective post-ionized neutral signals. Moreover, since the instrument cannot distinguish between post-ionized neutrals and secondary ions present within V_{ion}, the transmission and detection efficiency for both species are identical. As a consequence, the method presented here allows the detection of secondary neutrals and ions of the same mass under exactly the same experimental conditions, and the ionization probability for the formation of positively charged secondary ions can therefore be directly determined as

$$\alpha^+ = \frac{S(X^+)}{S_{sat}(X^0) + S(X^+)}$$

without any further corrections.

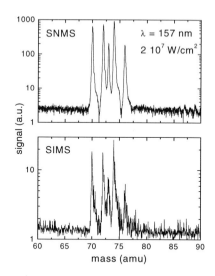

Fig. 5 ToF-mass spectrum of sputtered atoms recorded a) with and b) without ionization laser)

3. Example and conclusion

As an example, Table 1 shows the resulting ionization probability of Ge and Ag atoms sputtered from the respective clean surfaces under UHV conditions. It should be stressed again that the absolute magnitude of α^+ is a direct outcome of the experiment and contains no further correction for instrument transmission, post-ionization efficiency etc. For comparison, data taken from ref [4] is included which was obtained in a non mass resolved manner by comparing absolute secondary ion yields with known total sputtering yields. Further examples in which the method is used to

	α^+	Ref.
Ge	7 ($\pm$ 2) $\cdot 10^{-4}$	4.4 $\cdot 10^{-3}$
Nb	10 ($\pm$ 5) $\cdot 10^{-5}$	6 $\cdot 10^{-4}$
Ag	6 ($\pm$ 3) $\cdot 10^{-5}$	--

Table 1 Ionization probability of atoms sputtered from the respective clean surfaces

determine the ionization probability of sputtered clusters are presented elsewhere in this volume [5].

References

[1] M. L. Yu in Sputtering by Particle Bombardment III, ed. R. Behrisch and K. Wittmaack (Springer Verlag 1991) 91.
[2] M. Wahl and A. Wucher, Nucl. Instr. Meth. B 94 (1994) 36.
[3] R. Heinrich and A. Wucher, Nucl. Instr. Meth. B 140 (1998) 27.
[4] A. Benninghoven, Surf. Sci. 53 (1975) 596.
[5] R. Heinrich, C. Staudt, M. Wahl, and A. Wucher, these proceedings.

A. Benninghoven, P. Bertrand, H.-N. Migeon and H.W. Werner (Editors).
Proceedings of the 12th International Conference on Secondary Ion Mass Spectrometry,
Brussels, Belgium, 5-11 September 1999

147

VELOCITY DISTRIBUTIONS OF THE MONOATOMIC SECONDARY IONS OF COPPER

P.A.W. van der Heide and D. Karpuzov
[1]Materials Research Science and Engineering Centre (MRSEC), Chemistry Department,
University of Houston, Houston, Texas 77204-5500, U.S.A.
[2]Institute of Electronics, Bulgarian Academy of Science, Sofia 1784, Bulgaria

1. Introduction

The electronic interaction of an atom, or ion, close to a metal surface is dictated by the overlap of the respective wave functions[1]. This electronic interaction may take the form of a resonance or Auger charge transfer process, which will result in the ionisation, and/or neutralisation of the departing species. One or the other of these are assumed in the electron tunnelling, bond breaking and surface excitation models[2, 3].

The rate at which these processes occur depends on, among other things, the velocity, v, the atom/ion departs from the surface. This stems from (a) wave functions of the substrate and a departing atom/ion decay in an exponential like fashion with distance from the respective nuclei (valence electrons only are considered as their wave functions extend out the greatest distance) and (b) that distance, time and velocity are implicitly related. Note; any subsequent processes, for example de-excitation, may overshadow or even hide the velocity dependence of the original electronic interaction.

Since the emission velocity is a function of emission energy, E, secondary ion velocity distributions (commonly plotted in $1/v$ units) can be defined from raw intensity data collected as a function of emission energy once the instrument transmission function, T(E), and the secondary neutral yield, S(E), are accounted for. This gives a value of the number of ions produced per sputtered neutral. Typically the neutral yield is represented by the Sigmund Thompson relation since these are difficult to measure.

This study reports on the collection of velocity distributions for various positive and negative secondary ion populations of Cu emanating from a Cu surface under O^-, O_2^+, Ar^+ and Cs^+ primary ion impact.

2. Experimental

Data from a 99.9999% Cu foil was collected on a Cameca IMS-3f using 17 keV (impact energy) O^-, O_2^+, Ar^+ and Cs^+ primary ion sources incident at ~20° with respect to the sample normal. Since the 17keV impact energy represents the sum of the accelerating voltage plus the secondary ion extraction voltage, Cu^- data was collected under O_2^+, Ar^+ and Cs^+ primary ion impact and Cu^+ was collected under O^- primary ion impact only. Due to the fixed geometry of this instrument any other combination will result in a variation in the impact energy and angle.

Surface oxides were removed via Ar^+ primary ion bombardment prior to data collection. The ^{63}Cu and ^{65}Cu secondary ions were collected along the normal axis and only once steady state signals prevailed. These were collected over the –25 to 250 eV, or greater E, range. This was accomplished by scanning the sample bias (set at 4500 V) over the appropriate range. Crater edge

148

effects were avoided by collecting secondary ions from a circular region, 60 um in diameter, in the middle of the 500x500 μm raster pattern, (the primary ion beam drift is less than 10 μm per 100 V variation of the sample bias). Velocity distributions were derived by converting E into 1/v and dividing the recorded intensities by T(E).S(E) to give corrected intensities, I_{corr}, as illustrated in Fig. 1. Further details can be found elsewhere[4].

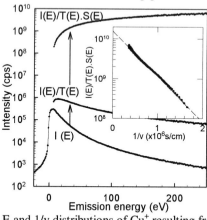

Fig. 1 E and 1/v distributions of Cu^+ resulting from O^- ion bombardment.

Computer simulations of sputtered neutral distributions resulting from 17 keV Ar^+ and Cs^+ primary ion impact at 20° were carried out using the MARLOWE code. Polycrystalline surfaces were modeled by rotating the single crystal between successive trajectory calculations. Following an appropriate testing procedure, a target 20 atomic layers thick was used and 200,000 trajectories were calculated.

3. Results and discussion

As indicated in Fig. 1, velocity distributions are derived by assuming the Sigmund Thompson distribution effectively describes the secondary neutral populations of Cu, and that the instrument transmission function is of the correct form. Though there exists experimental and simulated data showing the effectiveness of the Sigmund Thompson relation (see [5] for example), simulations for a polycrystalline surface were calculated for the conditions used in the Cameca IMS-3f to 6f group of instruments. Results for Ar^+ and Cs^+ primary ion impact are shown in Figure 2 by the hollow and filled symbols respectively. The solid line represents a best fit of the Sigmund Thomspon relation ($E/(E+E_b)^n$) to the data. The fit was derived by varying the exponent, n, and the binding energy, E_b, in an interactive manner. Since these values are consistent with that expected and describe both data sets, they were used in the calculations.

To ascertain the effect of variations in either n or E_b, corrected intensity versus inverse velocity plots of Cu^+ were derived from the same data set used in Fig. 1, by altering these values over the 2.8-3.2 and 3-8eV range. The results shown in Figure 3, and in the inset, reveal that variations in E_b has little effect, particularly at higher E (>50eV). Variation in the value of n however has a greater effect, i.e., slope and I_{corr} data are altered in a progressive manner. The general shape however, remains unchanged.

In all cases the expected exponential trend is noted which is consistent with:

$$Y(Cu^+) \propto I_{corr} \propto \exp(-v_o/v) \tag{1}$$

Where Y is secondary ion yield, I_{corr} is the corrected intensity and v_o, is the characteristic velocity (this is a parameter containing all the factors that dictate the probability that a secondary ion will be formed and survive neutralisation).

The transmission function used was derived from Slodzian's equations[6]. This does not contain any variable parameters apart from the instrument settings i.e., contrast aperture, etc. These parameters only have the effect of re-scaling the data along the I_{corr} axis, i.e., do not alter the shape. The strong extraction field used in these instruments also serves to significantly reduce any angular distribution anisotropies that may be present in the sputtered population (a cosine dependence centred around the sample normal was assumed). This high extraction field, count rate, primary ion energy, and close to normal primary ion beam incidence angle all serve to improve data accuracy.

Analysis of the negative secondary ions of Cu show somewhat different velocity distributions than that seen of the positive secondary ions, i.e. a simple exponential dependence no longer holds. Furthermore, these vary in shape according to the primary ion used as can be seen in Fig. 4. This shape variation will stem, to some degree, from the modification of the electronic structure of the surface by the implantation of the chemically active O and Cs into the sample. Sputter yield variations known to occur for these primary ions were removed by arbitaraly normalising the data to unity at $1/v=0$.

These distributions can be modelled via the use of two exponential functions (the thin solid and dashed lines) as shown in Fig. 5 for the Ar^+ impact. This indicates:

$$I_{corr} \propto a \exp(-v_{o1}/v) + b \exp(-v_{o2}/v) \tag{2}$$

Here the two exponential functions represent two separate ionisation/neutralisation processes with different velocity dependencies expressed by the differing v_o terms. The sum of these is represented by the thick solid line in the inset of Fig 5. The thick solid line was fitted to the experimental data (symbols) by adjusting v_{o1} and v_{o2} (represented by the thin solid and dashed lines) in an iterative manner, and then scaling this along the y axis, via the a and b variables, to fit the experimental data as discussed elsewhere[7].

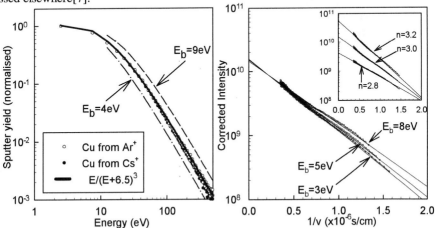

Fig. 2 E distributions for Cu^o resulting from Ar^+ and Cs^+ impact.

Fig. 3 1/v distributions for Cu^+ with various E_b and n values.

150

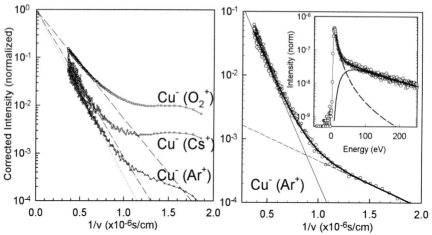

Fig. 4 1/v distributions for Cu⁻ resulting from Ar⁺, O₂⁺ and Cs⁺ impact.

Fig. 5 Reconstructed 1/v and E (inset) distributions for Cu⁻ from Ar⁺ impact.

In the inset of Fig. 5 is shown the reconstructed E distribution on the basis of Equation 2. Of particular interest is the fact that the E distribution from the higher energy function (solid line) peaks at ~60eV. This effect is generally hidden in raw E distributions since the E dependent transmission function of the instrument preferentially enhances the intensity of secondary ions emitted at lower E (higher 1/v).

These results are consistent with previous experimental and theoretical velocity distribution studies [3,7-9], which have suggested that the higher E process is due to a resonance charge transfer process and the lower E process is due to an excitation type process (one possibility may be in the filling of a core hole in the departing atom by an electron from the substrate, and the simultaneous emission of a second electron from the substrate to remove the excess energy).

4. Conclusions

Velocity distributions of Cu⁺ are found to exhibit a single exponential dependence on emission velocity while those of Cu⁻ reveal two separate exponential trends. This indicates that two competing processes are active over the E range studied. The relative efficiency of these processes also depends on the primary ion species used.

References

[1] H.J. Andra, *Fundamental processes of atomic dynamics*, Plenum Press, New York, 631, (1988).
[2] M.L.Yu. *Nucl. Instr. Meth. Phys, Res.* B14, (1986), 403.
[3] Z. Sroubek, *Spectrochimica Acta.* 44(3), (1989), 317.
[4] P.A.W. van der Heide, *Surf. Sci. Lett.,* 302, (1993), L312.
[5] J. Dembowski, H. Oechsner, Y. Yamamura, M. Urbassek, *Nucl. Instr. Meth. Phys, Res.* B18, (1987), 464.
[6] R. Castaing, G. Slodzian, *J. Microsc.* 1, (1962), 395.
[7] P.A.W. van der Heide, *Surf. Sci.,* 341, (1995), 150.
[8] D.V. Klushin, M.Yu. Gusev, S.A. Lysenko, I.F. Urazgilden. *Phys. Rev. B.,* 54(10), (1996), 7062.
[9] M.H.S Low, C.H.A. Huan, A.T.S. Lee, K.L. Tan, *J. Condens. Matter,* 9, (1997), 9427.

A. Benninghoven, P. Bertrand, H.-N. Migeon and H.W. Werner (Editors).
Proceedings of the 12th International Conference on Secondary Ion Mass Spectrometry,
Brussels, Belgium, 5-11 September 1999

OXYGEN ENHANCEMENT OF IONIZATION PROBABILITIES IN SI

T. Janssens, W. Vandervorst[1]

IMEC, Kapeldreef 75, B-3001 Leuven, Belgium
[1] also : KULeuven, INSYS, Kard. Mercierlaan 92, B-3100 Leuven, Belgium
email: Janssent@imec.be

1. Introduction

The exact chemical composition of the sputter surface has a major influence on the number of emitted secondary ions. The presence of oxygen enhances the probability of positive ion emission from Si for all elements, but the amount of enhancement is very element dependent. In order to investigate the influence of elemental properties on the ionization processes during oxygen bombardment, the ions studied here have a mass ranging from 7(Li) to 195(Pt) amu and an ionization potential between 3.89(Cs) and 17.42(F). The relation between the oxidation degree of matrix surface and the ionization probability is investigated in detail for different elements sputtered from Si by O_2^+ bombardment.

2. Experimental

The experiments are performed in a magnetic sector SIMS Cameca 4f with a primary ion beam of 3 keV O_2^+ and an impact angle of 52°. The diameter of the imaged field is 60μm; that of the contrast aperture used is 60μm. A primary ion current of 100nA and a scan length between 175μm and 400μm are used. The collection efficiency of an electron multiplier (EM) is lower for heavier masses than for light masses. To correct for the mass dependency of a Balzers EM the relation efficiency = $3.1755 *mass^{-0.4596}$ [1] is used for masses heavier than 20 amu. The useful yield of an element M, $\tau_M^+ = \alpha_M^+ \eta_M$ (with α_M^+ the ionization probability and η_M the transmission efficiency), is determined by measuring reference material. This reference material is an ion implantation of a known amount of element M in Si. When the ionization probability of the alkali metal Cs (Ionization Potential IP(Cs) = 3.89) is considered to be unity, the useful yield of Cs is equal to the transmission efficiency of the instrument. This assumption enables us to calculate absolute ionization degrees.

The ionization degrees of elements sputtered from Si are followed as a function of the oxidation degree of the sample surface. In order to keep the angle of incidence of the primary ions fixed, the oxidation of the sample surface is changed using oxygen flooding. The pressure above the reference material is varied between 1e-9 Torr and 2e-5 Torr. The oxidation of the sample surface is monitored by the matrix ion species ratio Si_2^+/SiO_2^+. XPS measurements of crater bottoms after O_2^+ bombardment [2] made it possible to relate the Si_2^+/SiO_2^+ ratio to the real oxygen concentration in Si [3]. The use of a grazing angle of incidence (52°) combined with intermediate flooding conditions enhances the formation of ripples on the crater bottom. The surface roughness makes it impossible to determine ionization degrees in an oxygen concentration range between 57 and 64.5 at.% oxygen for

3keV O_2^+ and 52°. In order to prevent fast ripple formation in this region an angle of incidence of 35° is used, the primary ion energy is 10.5 keV.

3. Results and discussion

The ionization degrees of elements sputtered from Si are plotted against their ionization potential (IP) for two different experimental conditions (Fig.1). First, 3 keV O_2^+ bombardment at 52° under vacuum conditions, resulting in 40 at.% oxygen concentration at the Si surface[3]. Second, flooding conditions inducing a surface oxidation of nearly 66 at.%. This condition induces the same surface configuration, as the surface of thermal SiO_2 would have after 3 keV O_2^+ bombardment at 52° under vacuum conditions [3]. The ionization degrees do not reach their maximum at these flooding conditions. A significant additional enhancement is possible by using higher oxygen flooding pressures (e.g. 24.5% for Si and 41% for Ga) [3].

For a fixed experimental condition the dependency of the ionization probabilities on the ionization potential is roughly exponential, for an IP between 5 and 10. The slope of the exponential dependency lowers as the oxidation of the Si surface increases. From the results in Fig.1.(a) it is obvious that the enhancement of the ionization probability by oxygen for elements with a high IP (Sb, Zn, Cu...) will be much larger than that for low IP elements (K, Al, In...).A more detailed picture of the evolution of ionization degrees of elements sputtered from Si as a function of the oxygen concentration is shown in Fig.1(b). For all elements it is possible to make a distinction between two completely different regimes. First the "low" oxygen coverage (40 at.%<C_{ox}<63.5 at.%), where all ionization degrees have a power dependency on the oxygen content, with a power between 1and 6. Second, at high oxygen coverage (C_{ox}>63.5 at.%) the ionization degrees are enhanced much faster.

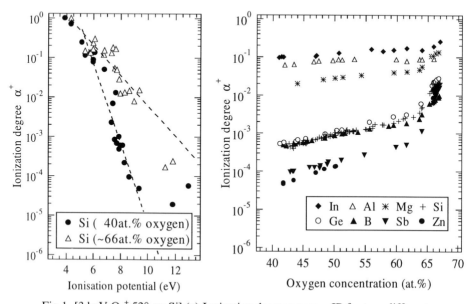

Fig.1. [3 keV O_2^+ 52° on Si] (a) Ionization degrees versus IP for two different oxidizing conditions. (b) Ionization degrees as a function of oxygen content in Si.

In the two regimes a totally different mechanism seems to be responsible for the enhancement of ionization degrees. Though the oxygen concentration stays almost constant, the ionization degrees increase very fast at high oxygen coverage (Fig.1(b)). A model for the ionization probability enhancement, which is only based on the increasing number of oxygen neighbours, will fail in this regime. The formation of a band gap lowers the probability of an electron transfer between the leaving positive ion and the sample surface. This enhances the ion yield drastically near complete oxidizing conditions. The formation of a band gap in this high oxygen content region is confirmed with XPS [2]. The contribution of the ionization probability enhancement at high oxygen concentrations,

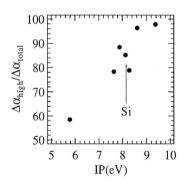

Fig.2: ratio of the ionization degree enhancement, due to the formation of a bandgap at high C_{ox}, to the enhancement over the total studied oxygen region

$\Delta\alpha_{high}=\alpha^+(66$ at.%O)- $\alpha^+(63.5$ at.%O), to the enhancement over the whole studied oxygen concentration range, $\Delta\alpha_{total}=\alpha^+(66$ at.%O)- $\alpha^+(40$ at.%O), increases as the ionization potential increases (Fig.2). This indicates that in this high oxygen coverage regime the enhancement rate of the ionization degrees increases as their ionization potential increases.

In the "low" oxygen coverage regime the ionization probability has a power dependency on the number of oxygen atoms $\alpha^+\propto C_{ox}^p$. In Fig.3 the evolution of the power p is shown as a function of the ionization potential of the sputtered element. The magnitude of this power increases steeply around an ionization potential of 8eV. The relation $\alpha_{Si}^+ \propto C_{ox}^{4.74}$ describes the variation of the Si ionization degree when the oxygen concentration at the Si surface is altered between 40 and 63.5 atomic percent.

A power dependency on the oxygen content was observed for the Si$^+$ ion yield by Wittmaack

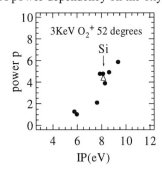

Fig.3 : oxygen dependency of the ionisation degrees $\alpha \sim C_{ox}^p$
(△ power $\alpha_{Si}(Ar^+)$[4,5])

[4], when a Si sample with varying oxygen content is bombarded with 3 keV Ar$^+$. The author reports the relation $\Delta I(Si^+) = I(Si)-I_{clean}(Si) \propto C_{ox}^{3.7}$, with $I_{clean}(Si)$ the ion intensity of Si$^+$ sputtered with Ar$^+$ from an oxygen free Si surface. The data in the article are restricted to the oxygen concentration range between 1 and 33 at.%. Additional measurements at higher oxidation levels were done by Tian [5] to cover the whole range between 1 and 66 atomic percent. Here we convert the $\Delta I(Si^+)$ data, collected under Ar$^+$ bombardment, into ionization degrees $\alpha_{Si}^+(Ar)$, to be able to compare them with $\alpha_{Si}^+(O_2^+)$: the ionization degrees of Si sputtered with 3 keV O$_2^+$ bombardment under 52°(Fig.1(b)). The result of this conversion is shown in Fig.4. The evolution of the ionisation degree of Si under Ar$^+$ bombardment, $\alpha_{Si}^+(Ar^+)$, on the oxidation of Si can be

154

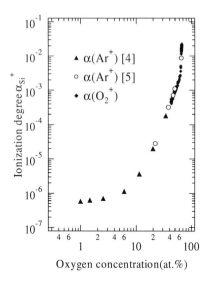

Fig.4: comparison between
$\alpha_{Si}^+(Ar^+)$ and $\alpha_{Si}^+(O_2^+)$

described by a power dependence $C_{ox}^{4.381}$ (triangle in Fig.3) for oxidation states between 10 and 65 atomic percent.

The change in $\alpha_{Si}^+(Ar^+)$ saturates to a minimal value for concentrations lower than 10 at.%. At the highest oxygen concentrations the formation of a bandgap will be responsible for a faster yield enhancement. These results for Ar^+ bombardment are now compared to our results for O_2^+ bombardment. The implantation of oxygen during O_2^+ bombardment (even at grazing angles) reduces the studied oxidation degree interval for $\alpha_{Si}^+(O_2^+)$ with respect to that of $\alpha_{Si}^+(Ar^+)$. At "low" oxygen concentrations the ionization degree $\alpha_{Si}^+(O_2^+)$ is enhanced slightly faster (p=4.74) than $\alpha_{Si}^+(Ar^+)$ (p=4.38). Notice that most of the data points used to determine the power dependency of $\alpha_{Si}(O_2^+)$ and $\alpha_{Si}(Ar^+)$ are not located in the same oxygen concentration interval. It is possible that data points for $\alpha_{Si}(Ar^+)$ in the region 40-63 at.% would reveal that the enhancement of $\alpha_{Si}(Ar^+)$ can also be described by $C_{ox}^{4.74}$ in this region. At full oxidising conditions the magnitude of the ionization degree of Si $\alpha_{Si}(Ar^+)$ under Ar^+ bombardment is lower then the one under O_2^+ bombardment $\alpha_{Si}^+(O_2^+)$. This difference does not only occur for α_{Si}^+ but is seen for all elements when ionization degree data, collected for O_2^+ + flooding and Ar^+ + flooding, are compared [5]. Fig.4 shows that the largest difference occurs near complete oxidation of the Si surface.

4. Conclusion

Ionization degrees of all elements are enhanced by the presence of oxygen on the Si surface. The enhancement process can be divided in two different regimes. At low oxygen coverage (<63.5 at.%) the ionization degree has a power dependence on the oxidation degree: $\alpha^+ \propto C_{ox}^p$. The power p increases steeply around the ionization potential 8. At oxygen concentrations above 63.5 at.%, the enhancement rate increases steeply due to the formation of a band gap. These results are compared to the dependency of ionization degrees on the oxygen content at the surface during Ar^+ bombardment. A good similarity is seen for low oxygen coverage, but near full oxidation the ionization degrees under O_2^+ bombardment exceed these under Ar^+ bombardment.

References
[1] P.A.W van der Heide, D.A.Fichter, I.Bello, S.Ramamurthy, Proc Sims XI (1997) 995
[2] J.L.Alay,W.Vandervorst,Phys.Rev.B,vol50,20(1994)15015
[3] T.Janssens and W.Vandervorst these proceedings
[4] K.Wittmaack, Surf.Sci. 112 (1981) 168-180
[5] C.Tian and W.Vandervorst unpublished data

SECTION 3 :
CLUSTER FORMATION

A. Benninghoven, P. Bertrand, H.-N. Migeon and H.W. Werner (Editors).
Proceedings of the 12th International Conference on Secondary Ion Mass Spectrometry,
Brussels, Belgium, 5-11 September 1999

FORMATION OF SPUTTERED CLUSTERS: A MULTISTEP MODEL

N. Kh. Dzhemilev* and A. Wucher[#]

*Cluster Physics Lab, Arifov Institute of Electronics, 700125 Tashkent, Uzbekistan
root@ariel.tashkent.su
[#]Institute of Laser and Plasma Physics, University of Essen, 45117 Essen, Germany

1. Introduction

The formation of clusters among the particles leaving the surface in a sputtering event represents a fascinating phenomenon which is still not satisfactorily understood in terms of a simple analytical model description. Analysis of the experimental data available on neutral and charged clusters sputtered from various clean metallic surfaces under bombardment with hydrogen or rare gas ions shows that the measured data do not agree with theoretical models describing cluster formation in sputtering which have been published to date (for a fairly recent review see [1] and references therein). This holds true for the mass distribution describing the abundance of sputtered clusters as a function of their size as well as for their kinetic energy distribution. Therefore, in the present paper we propose a new multistep model of cluster formation and emission in sputtering which is based upon the following idea. In the first step, recoil atoms may be lifted above the surface during the collision cascade, but may not receive enough energy to overcome the surface barrier and, hence, fall back onto the surface. Atoms, falling onto the surface, have considerable kinetic energy, so after a collision with the surface they do not accommodate with it at once, i.e. stay "hot". If two such atoms meet within the range of interatomic attraction forces, they can associate into a dimer. Further, the dimers grow by successive addition of atoms arriving at the surface, similar to the concept of nucleation during thin film growth by means of atoms deposited onto a surface [2]. During the growth process, cluster-precursors may thus be formed with an initial internal energy which depends on the number of "hot" atoms forming the precursor and will be rapidly distributed among the cluster's internal degrees of freedom. "Hot" atoms, undergoing such a recombination, could be apparently considered as particles of a two-dimensional gas with the dissociation energies being characteristic for the stationary gas-phase value in the ground state. It has been shown in a number of experiments that such clusters of adatoms may exist on the respective surface and move around as an entity rather than as individual atoms [3]. As a central assumption behind the proposed model, we therefore postulate the precursor clusters to be in a relatively loosely bound state, because the interaction of atoms with each other compensate the loosening of each of them with the lattice. In the second step, the cluster precursor "prepared" at the surface during the early stage of a collision cascade may be sputtered as a whole by quasisymmetrical knockon of a cascade atom during the later stage of the same cascade. When the energy of the knocking atom is sufficiently small, the collision time increases and transmission of equal momentum to few cluster atoms is possible before the colliding particles will move apart. Such suggestion gives rise to consider the pre-cluster as a hard particle with an effective mass $M_{eff} = M_n$. This idea is not new. Similar arguments were used for the explanation of energy transfer in gas phase molecular collisions [4], scattering of relatively slow ions from metal surfaces [5], sputtering of metallic targets with polyatomic ions in the near threshold range of sputtering energies [6]. In the following, we will present a simple formulation of this model using a statistical description of the precursor formation and a single collision mechanism describing the desorption of the precursor into vacuum. Due to the assumptions involved both in the formation and emission of the precursor clusters, we would like to note that the present model is primarily suited to describe the sputter generation of small clusters.

2. Formation of the cluster precursor on the surface during ion bombardment.

The derivation will be based on the following general assumptions:

- The formation (and emission) of a precursor takes place within an area F around the impact point of the primary ion with a typical diameter of 2-3 nm.
- The mean number of atoms Y_R which is originally set in motion towards the vacuum but is then reflected at the surface barrier and returned to the surface within the area F is approximately equal to the total sputter yield Y_{tot}. [7].
- n atoms falling back onto the surface within an area f are associated into one n-atomic pre-cluster. The dimension of f is estimated on the basis of an experimental investigation of the mobility of rhodium atoms and clusters being adsorbed on their own lattice [3].

Under these assumptions, the probability of generating an n-atom precursor cluster reduces to the probability of finding n adatoms within f among a total of Y_R adatoms being statistically distributed over F. This is described by the Poisson distribution

$$W_n = \frac{C^n f^n e^{-cf}}{n!} \qquad (1)$$

with the surface concentration of adatoms being determined by

$$C = \frac{Y_R}{F} \approx \frac{Y_{tot}}{F} \qquad (2)$$

Eq. (1) describes the average size distribution of precursor clusters which develops at the surface in the course of a collision cascade.

Assuming the partial sputtering yield of clusters to be proportional to the concentration of the respective precursors on the surface, the prediction of eq. (1) can be compared with experimental data collected for silver clusters sputtered from a silver surface under bombardment with 5-keV Ne$^+$, Ar$^+$ and Xe$^+$ ions [8]. The calculations were performed using the data depicted in Table 1. The essential parameter entering eq. (1) is the total sputter yield Y_{tot}, which for the specific bombardment conditions was taken from the

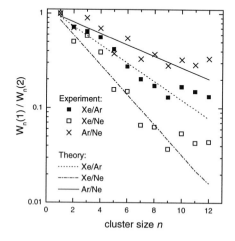

Fig.1 Experimental and calculated ratio W_n/W_1 (see text) vs. cluster size.

literature [9]. The results show satisfactory agreement between the model calculation and the experimental data for small cluster sizes ($n \leq 5$), whereas for larger clusters, the abundance predicted by eq. (1) decreases much faster with increasing n than measured. In principle, this could be due to the fact that a fixed value of f was assumed for all cluster sizes, whereas in a more realistic treatment one would expect f to increase with increasing n. Moreover, one might expect the sputtering cross section for the emission of a precursor to increase with increasing cluster size. Finally, precursor clusters can in principle move and merge forming larger entities.

Table 1

	Xe	Ar	Ne
Y_{tot}	15	8.5	6.5
Y_R	15	8.5	6.5
F (nm^2)	15.1	10.7	9.4
f (nm^2)	2	2	2

It should further be noted that the model calculation does not account for the transformation of the abundance distribution which is due to unimolecular fragmentation of the emitted clusters. In order to exclude these influences, it is advantageous to look at ratios of the type $W_n(1)/W_n(2)$ - where 1 and 2 refer to two different bombarding conditions – since in this case f as well as the sputtering cross section remains the same. The resulting ratio values, which are shown in Fig.1, are found to reproduce the trends observed in the experiment very well.

3. Emission of precursor clusters

As already outlined above, we suppose the collision between a recoil atom and an excited cluster to be equivalent to a collision between an atom and a hard particle with the effective mass M_n. This assumption certainly constitutes an oversimplification, but it permits us to calculate the maximum energy transmitted to a cluster with mass M_n in the approach of a binary elastic collision with a recoil target atom with mass m_1 and the energy E_1 as :

$$T_n = \frac{4 m_1 M_n}{(m_1 + M_n)^2} \cdot E_1 = \lambda_n \cdot E_1 \qquad (3)$$

If $\phi_l(E_l)$ denotes the energy distribution of recoil atoms, we thus arrive at a modified kinetic energy distribution of the emitted clusters which is given by

$$\phi_n(E) \propto \phi_1(\lambda_n E) \qquad (4)$$

Moreover, we assume that the the internal energy of a cluster which has been accumulated during the formation process is preserved during its emission. If this internal energy exceeds the dissociation threshold, the cluster will undergo fragmentation reactions which reduce its size, thus leading to an apparent reduction of the kinetic energy of the resulting fragments. If a detected n-atom cluster (fragment) originates from a nascent $(n+m)$-atom precursor, its kinetic energy distribution should therefore be described by

$$\phi^{(m)}{}_n(E) \propto \phi_1\left(\frac{n}{n+m} \lambda_{n+m} E\right). \qquad (5)$$

In order to demonstrate the role of such processes, Fig. 2 shows normalized kinetic energy distributions measured for neutral clusters [8] as well as secondary cluster ions [10] sputtered from clean silver and gold surfaces. Using the measured $\phi_l(E)$, we can calculate the direct distribution $\phi_n(E)$ (dotted lines in Fig. 2), which in all displayed cases clearly fails to describe the

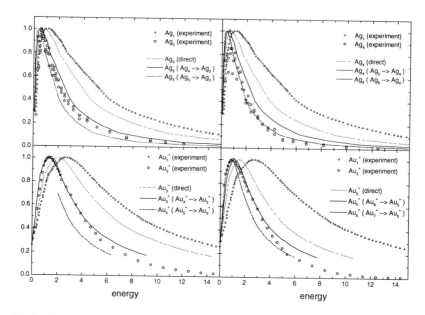

Fig. 2 Kinetic energy distributions of sputtered silver clusters. Symbols: experimental data; Solid lines: theoretical distributions calculated from eqs. (4) and 5), respectively.

measured distributions. However, if we assume the detected X_n to originate from fragmentation of X_{n+1}- or X_{n+2}-precursors and compute the corresponding energy distribution according to eq. (5) using $m = 1$ or 2, repectively (solid and dashed lines in Fig. 2), we arrive at a much better description of the experimental curve. This indicates that practically all detected clusters containing more than 2 atoms are produced by fragmentation of larger precursors. As a consequence, we conclude that the unimolecular decomposition of sputtered nascent clusters represents a very important step in determining the measured kinetic energy spectra of the detected final species.

References
[1]   H.M. Urbassek and W.O. Hofer, Mat. Fys. Medd. Dan. Vidensk. Selsk. 43 (1993) 97.
[2]   D. Walton, J. Chem. Phys. 37 (1962) 2182.
[3]   T.T. Tsong, Phys. Rev. B 6 (1972) 417.
[4]   L.D. Landau and E. Teller, Phys. Z. Sowjetunion 10 (1936) 34.
[5]   V.I. Veksler, Izv. Akad. Nauk Ser.Fiz. 30 (1966) 857 (in Russian).
[6]   Y. Yao, Z. Hargitai, M. Albert, R.G. Albridge, A.V. Barnes, J.M. Gilligan, B. Pratt Ferguson, G. Luepke, V.D. Gordon, N.H. Tolk, J.T. Tully, G. Betz and W. Husinsky, Phys. Rev. Lett. 81 (1998) 550.
[7]   P. Sigmund, Phys. Rev. 184 (1969) 383.
[8]   M. Wahl and A. Wucher, Nucl. Instr. Meth. B 94 (1994) 36.
[9]   H.H. Andersen and H.L. Bay in Sputtering by Particle Bombardment I, ed. R. Behrisch (Springer 1981) 145.
[10] N.Kh. Dzhemilev, S.V. Verkhoturov, and I.V. Veryovkin, Nucl. Instr. Meth. B 51 (1990) 219.

A. Benninghoven, P. Bertrand, H.-N. Migeon and H.W. Werner (Editors).
Proceedings of the 12th International Conference on Secondary Ion Mass Spectrometry,
Brussels, Belgium, 5-11 September 1999

PECULIARITIES OF CLUSTER PRODUCTION FROM CRYSTALLINE HYDRATES UNDER LOW TEMPERATURE SIMS CONDITIONS

V.A. Pashinskaya, M.V. Kosevich[*], O.A. Boryak, V.S. Shelkovsky, V.V. Orlov

B.Verkin Institute for Low Temperature Physics and Engineering of the National Academy of Sciences of Ukraine, 47, Lenin Ave., Kharkov, 310164, Ukraine, mvkosevich@ilt.kharkov.ua

1. Introduction

Cooling of the samples just to keep them in condensed state suitable for secondary ion mass spectrometric (SIMS) or fast atom bombardment (FAB) studies at low pressure conditions is only one straightforward utilization of low temperature (LT) technique in mass spectrometry. More sophisticated task for LT SIMS/FAB (or any other desorption technique) is to study objects which can exist only at the reduced or subzero temperatures. Some types of crystalline hydrates of salts, alkali, acids fall in this category.

Each type of crystalline hydrates exists in a certain concentration-temperature-pressure range, described by a phase diagram for a given system. Equilibrium saturated vapour pressure over the surface of some crystalline hydrates, which are stable at the ambient conditions (e.g. $CuSO_4 \cdot 5H_2O$), appeared to be high enough to cause their rapid dehydration under low pressure conditions, which does not permit their investigation by «room-temperature» mass spectrometry. Since the saturated vapour pressure decreases with temperature, cooling of the sample can stabilize these hydrates structure in vacuum. Some other crystalline hydrates, in particular those of inorganic acids HCl, HNO_3, are formed at the subzero temperatures only. Crystalline hydrates are characterized by a variety of the components arrangements in their crystalline lattices [1], in which connection information on possible correlations between the structural peculiarities of the solid sample and its SIMS mass spectrometric pattern can be expected from the crystalline hydrates study.

2. Experimental

LT FAB/SIMS measurements were performed using a magnetic sector mass spectrometer equipped with LT secondary ion source described elsewhere [2, 3]. Temperature control of the sample was provided by a copper cryogenic block cooled by flow of liquid nitrogen. Samples of 5-10 μL volume were frozen in vapours of liquid nitrogen on a copper or aluminum sample holder with the rate of cooling of 200°C • min^{-1} and rapidly inserted into the cryogenic block through a vacuum lock. The temperature was measured by a thermistor.

Neutral argon atoms (of 4.5 keV primary beam energy) were used as a bombarding agent, since ionic bombardment leads to charging of a dielectric sample surface and impairs the quality of the spectra. Vacuum prior the bombarding gas inlet was usually about 10^{-5} - 10^{-6} Pa. Aqueous solutions of chlorides of alkali (Na) and some divalent (Mg, Ca, Mn, Co, Cu, Zn, Ba) metals were prepared using deionized water. Commercially available acids HCl,

HNO₃ and alkali NaOH were used without purification. Concentrations were chosen using phase diagrams of each water-solute system to produce samples of desirable morphology.

3. Results and discussion

On the basis of the results of our previous works [3-5] the main points which are to be taken into account during interpretation of LT FAB/SIMS mass spectra of frozen water solutions can be summarized as follows. Phase separation takes place during cooling of water solutions in accordance with the phase diagrams of a given water-solute system. As a result, heterogeneous polycrystalline samples are formed (homogeneous amorphyzation is not achievable under the rates of freezing applied). LT FAB/SIMS spectrum is a super-position of the spectra characteristic of individual components present in the heterogeneous system, and it is usually characterized by sets of cluster ions. A set of clusters $(H_2O)_n \cdot H^+$ originates usually from water ice crystallites; Me^+, $(H_2O)_n \cdot (MeX)_m \cdot Me^+$ clusters (where n and m are in various combinations, Me - metal, X - cation) originate from the crystalline hydrates. Phase transitions in the sample are responsible for temperature changes of the LT spectrum pattern (in fact, about 200°C temperature range is available for monitoring), the main of which are sublimation of water ice and dehydration of the crystalline hydrate [3, 4].

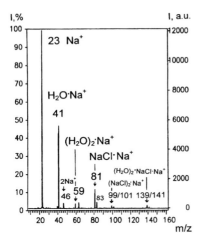

Fig. 1. LT FAB of mass spectrum of 1 M solution of NaCl at T = -55°C.

Above listed points can be illustrated by an example of a simple system (NaCl +H₂O) [3], Fig. 1. A new compound, a crystalline hydrate NaCl•2H₂O, starts to form in this system in a peritectic reaction at T_p = +0.15°C and C_p = 26.3% [3]. At C < C_p a frozen sample contains ice crystallites and ice-NaCl•2H₂O eutectic. After sublimation of ice (which occurs under the conditions used at about -55°C [4]) pure crystalline hydrate remains in the sample. Its spectrum, Fig. 1, contains characteristic ions Na⁺, $(H_2O)_n \cdot Na^+$ (n = 1-4), $(NaCl)_m \cdot Na^+$ (m = 1-3), $(H_2O)_n \cdot (NaCl)_m \cdot Na^+$. Hydrate clusters are present in the absence of ice and thus originate from the crystalline hydrate.

In Fig. 2 LT FAB spectrum of frozen aqueous solution of alkali of the same metal (NaOH+H₂O) is presented.

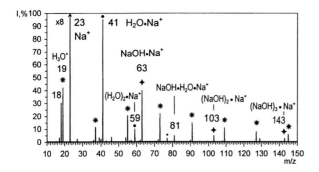

Fig. 2. LT FAB mass spectrum of (NaOH+water) system.

Ice sublimation is not completed here at T = -70°C and a set of water clusters (*) is present. Ions characteristic of the crystalline hydrate of alkali are: Na^+, $(NaOH)_m \cdot Na^+$ (m = 1-3), $(H_2O)_n \cdot Na^+$ (n = 1-3), $H_2O \cdot NaOH \cdot Na^+$.

A series of crystalline hydrates of chlorides of divalent metals: Mg, Ca (Fig. 3), Mn (Fig. 4), Co, Cu, Zn, Ba was analyzed. The same rules as above were applicable to these samples, although practically each compound showed its own peculiarities. It could be predicted that the spectra would contain $(H_2O)_n \cdot Me^+$, $(H_2O)_n \cdot (MeX)_m \cdot Me^+$, Me^+ singly charged ions, since efficient recombination of dications usually takes place under sputtering. The exceptions were crystalline hydrates of $CaCl_2$ (Fig. 3) and $BaCl_2$, in which case Me^{2+} and $(H_2O)_n \cdot Me^{2+}$ were recorded. An explanation of this fact was suggested based on the lowest value of the second ionization potential (energy) of these metals among the above row, which hampers recombination [6].

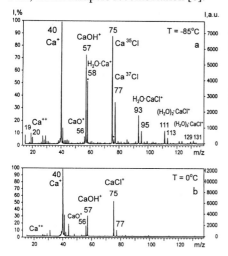

Fig. 3. LT FAB mass spectrum of the frozen 10% aqueous solution of $CaCl_2$.

A rather unexpected finding consisted in the observation of OH-containing ions in the spectra of Mg, Ca, Mn, Ba salts. Although there is a mass overlap of $[(H_2O)_n \cdot MeOH]^+$ and $[(H_2O)_{n-1} \cdot MeCl]^+$ ions, the yield of the latter can be separated using 3:1 ratio of the ^{35}Cl:^{37}Cl isotopes, as shown in Fig. 4. While, on the basis of some literature data, a suggestion can be made that in the presence of $(H_2O)_n \cdot Me^+$ hydrate clusters OH-containing ions may be their fragments, the persistence of $MeOH^+$ at higher temperatures at which dehydration is completed and water-solute clusters disappear, points to relation of these ions to a new individual compound(s). Such OH-containing compounds, namely basic salt $Me(OH)Cl$ and, with much smaller probability, hydroxide, are formed as products of hydrolysis in reaction of water with salts upon their dissolution. The reaction is reversible under equilibrium conditions. A suggestion was made, however, that at the rates of cooling applied in the present work equilibrium is not achieved and some share of hydrolysis products can be separated into individual phases [7]. This observation may be of practical value for freeze-drying technology. The hydrolysis products also form crystalline hydrates, which is evident from $[(H_2O)_n \cdot MeOH]^+$ clusters, with exception of Ca (Fig. 3), since Ca hydroxide is anhydrous.

164

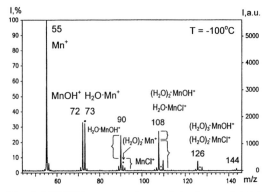

Fig. 4. LT FAB mass spectrum of the frozen 0.1 M solution of MnCl₂

As to acids, LT FAB mass spectrum of nitric acid trihydrate $HNO_3 \cdot 3H_2O$ has a rather complicated character and contains sets of hydrates of oxides $(H_2O)_n \cdot NO^+$, $(H_2O)_n \cdot NO_2^+$ and protonated nitric acid $(H_2O)_n \cdot (HNO_3)_m \cdot H^+$, as well as abundant water clusters. In the case of $HCl \cdot 3H_2O$ [8] there is a set of $(H_2O)_n \cdot H^+$ clusters only in the spectra, in which the proton originates from the H^+ cation of the acid.

4. Conclusion

A number of interesting peculiarities of cluster production from the crystalline hydrates were revealed which point to the existence of certain correlations of the LT SIMS mass spectra and the structure of the sample [6-8]. Absolute abundance of all types of ions produced from the crystalline hydrates is about an order of magnitude higher as compared with that characteristic of anhydrous salts or pure water ice. Obviously, the mixed type of ionic and H-bond interactions in the crystalline hydrate lattice facilitates in some way the ion sputtering as opposed to solids with a single type of interactions. Pure water clusters $(H_2O)_n \cdot H^+$ were not produced from the crystalline hydrates of salts, but were present in the LT SIMS spectra of the hydrates of acids, in particular $HCl \cdot 3H_2O$ [8] and $HNO_3 \cdot 3H_2O$. Correlations with the structure are obvious here as relatively long H-bonded chains of water molecules are present in the crystalline lattice of these compounds.

It can be concluded that LT SIMS/FAB technique allows to obtain a versatile information on the crystalline hydrates properties.

Acknowledgment: This investigation was supported by INTAS-96-0865 grant.

References

[1] J.D.Bernal, J. Chim. Phys. Phys.-Chim. Biol. 50 (1953) C1.
[2] O.A.Boryak, M.V.Kosevich and V.S.Shelkovskii, Instrum. Experim. Techn. 6 (1993) 935
[3] M.V. Kosevich, Eur. Mass Spectrom. 4 (1998) 251.
[4] O.A.Boryak, I.O.Stepanov, M.V.Kosevich, V.S.Shelkovsky, V.V.Orlov and Yu.P.Blagoy, Eur. Mass Spectrom. 2 (1996) 329.
[5] O.A. Boryak, M.V. Kosevich, V.S. Shelkovsky and Yu.P.Blagoy, Rapid Commun. in Mass Spectrom. 9 (1995) 978.
[6] O.A. Boryak, M.V. Kosevich, V.S. Shelkovsky and V.V.Orlov, Int. J. Mass Spectrom., 193 (1999) in press.
[7] M.V.Kosevich, Problems of Cryobiology, 2 (1999) 54.
[8] O.A. Boryak, M.V. Kosevich, I.O.Stepanov and V.S. Shelkovsky, Int. J. Mass Spectrom. 189 (1999) L1.

A. Benninghoven, P. Bertrand, H.-N. Migeon and H.W. Werner (Editors).
Proceedings of the 12th International Conference on Secondary Ion Mass Spectrometry,
Brussels, Belgium, 5-11 September 1999

THE FORMATION MECHANISM OF M^+, M_2^+ AND M_3^+ SPECIES – A CASE STUDY

S.L. Lim*, A.T.S. Wee, R. Liu and L.C.M. Kiong
Department of Physics, National University of Singapore
Lower Kent Ridge Road, Singapore 119260 *Email: phylimsl@nus.edu.sg

1. Introduction

Secondary ion mass spectrometry (SIMS) as an analytical tool has the advantage of high detection sensitivity and good depth resolution. However, due to the strong dependence of ionization probability on the chemical environment of the analyzed species (the so-called matrix effect), the relationship between the intensity of an ion signal and the corresponding elemental concentration is often nonlinear and rather complicated [1]. Consequently, quantitative analysis using SIMS is only well developed for minor impurity concentration where a constant ionization probability results in a linear relationship between the ion signal and the concentration of the corresponding species. However, quantification of matrix elements has been particularly difficult. To date, common ways to overcome the matrix effect include the post-ionization and MCs^+ techniques. The post-ionization technique involves analyzing the sputtered neutral atoms and hence decouples the ionization process from the sputtering process [2]. The MCs^+ technique assumes that the ionic clusters are formed between the individually sputtered Cs^+ ions and the neutral M (matrix) atoms above the surface: $M + Cs^+ \rightarrow MCs^+$ [3].

Recently, a new M_2M_3 technique has been proposed and used for the quantitative analysis of matrix elements [4, 5]. It is suggested that the formation of M_2^+ ions is similar to that of MCs^+, i.e. by a recombination process taking place above the surface [4]. It has also been argued that the M_2M_3 technique analyzes the quadratic and cubic responses of elemental concentration to SIMS [5]. In this work, using a multilayer chromium/chromium-oxide standard sample, we study the signals of various ionic clusters at different experimental conditions, with the hope of understanding the formation mechanisms of such species.

2. Experimental

The multilayer chromium/chromium-oxide standard sample (NIST SRM 2136) consists of eight chromium thin-film layers (with thickness between 28 to 32 nm) on a polished Si(100) substrate, and each interface between these chromium layers is composed of a thin chromium-oxide layer (2 to 3 monolayers). The SIMS experiments were carried out on a Cameca IMS6f instrument, using O_2^+ and Cs^+ primary ions of 1 keV impact energy. All results reported were acquired in the positive SIMS mode. Incident angles are calculated based on primary and secondary HV, and are with respect to the surface normal.

3. Results and discussion

Fig. 1 shows the secondary ion intensities of Cr^+, Cr_2^+ and Cr_3^+ from bombardment of 1 keV primary Cs^+ and O_2^+ ions at different incident angles. However, only the results acquired under Cs^+ bombardment are discussed in detail, since the results are less complex for the study of oxygen matrix effect induced by the transition from a metallic to an oxide matrix. Furthermore, it presents stronger changes in response to matrix transition compared to those under O_2^+ ion bombardment.

The Cr^+ signals for both Cs^+ and O_2^+ primary ions are enhanced, although to different extents, at the oxide layers due to matrix effect. With Cs^+ primary ions, the Cr_2^+ signal also increases at the oxide layers, clearly indicating that the formation of Cr_2^+ clusters is still affected by matrix effect. On the other hand, the Cr_3^+ signal dips at the oxide layers, in agreement with the drop in chromium concentration in these layers.

There are mainly two possible candidate mechanisms for the formation such ionic clusters, namely one in which the clusters are formed by recombination of individually sputtered M and M^+ species, and another in which the clusters are sputtered as an entity before being ionized subsequently. In the recombination model, the signal intensities of M^+ and M_2^+ can be written as

$$M^+ \propto c\alpha^+$$

and $M_2^+ \propto c^2\alpha^+$

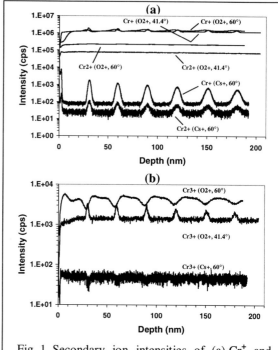

Fig. 1 Secondary ion intensities of (a) Cr^+ and Cr_2^+, and (b) Cr_3^+, under bombardment of 1 keV Cs^+ and O_2^+ primary ions at different incident angles.

where c is the relative concentration of element M in the matrix ($c \leq 1$), and α^+ the ionization probability of element M. We assume that the recombination process is independent of the matrix. Hence, the signal ratio should obey

$$R \equiv \frac{M^+}{M_2^+} \propto \frac{1}{c} \qquad (1)$$

In the transition from the metal layer (denoted with a subscript m) to the oxide layer (denoted with a subscript o), we have

$$\frac{R_m}{R_o} = \frac{c_o}{c_m} \qquad (2)$$

assuming that sputtering yield does not depend significantly on matrix density. Taking a stoichiometry of Cr_2O_3 for the oxide layers, eq. 2 predicts $R_m/R_o = 2/5$. A calculation of Cr^+/Cr_2^+ from Fig. 1, with R_m normalized to unity in the metal matrix, shows that R_o (at the center of the oxide layers) is ~5 in the first oxide layer and decreases to ~3 in the fifth layer. The decrease in signal ratio could be related to sputter-induced roughening that increases with depth [6]. Another possibility is that the sputtering has induced changes in the stoichiometry of the oxide layers through mixing. Although these values do not agree exactly with the prediction of 2.5 (under the assumption of perfect stoichiometry), the magnitude of the discrepancy does not allow the recombination mechanism to be ruled out.

On the other hand, for the sequential mechanism, the signal intensity of M_2^+ can be written as

$$M_2^+ \propto c^2 \beta^+$$

where β^+ denotes the ionization probability of M_2 cluster. Here, we assume the relative concentration of M_2 being equal to c^2. Hence the signal ratio

$$R' \equiv \frac{M^+}{M_2^+} \propto \frac{\alpha^+}{c\beta^+} \tag{3}$$

and

$$\frac{R'_m}{R'_o} = \frac{c_o \alpha_m^+ \beta_o^+}{c_m \alpha_o^+ \beta_m^+} \tag{4}$$

Assuming a perfect stoichiometry of Cr_2O_3 for the oxide layers, and using the deduced value of R'_m / R'_o from Fig. 1, we obtain

$$\frac{\alpha_m^+}{\beta_m^+} \leq \frac{\alpha_o^+}{\beta_o^+} \tag{5}$$

If the concentration of Cr in the oxide layers is sub-stoichiometric, eq. 5 would indicate that α^+/β^+ is essentially constant. In other words, within the sequential model, our result seems to indicate that the ionization probabilities of Cr^+ and Cr_2^+ remain proportionally constant in both matrices. Experimental measurement of neutral M and M_2 must be conducted to examine the validity of eq. 5.

Extending the discussion to the formation of M_3^+, we have the signal ratio, for the recombination mechanism,

$$Q \equiv \frac{M_2^+}{M_3^+} \propto \frac{1}{c} \tag{6}$$

and, for the sequential model,

$$Q' \equiv \frac{M_2^+}{M_3^+} \propto \frac{\beta^+}{c\gamma^+} \tag{7}$$

where γ^+ denotes the ionization probability of M_3 cluster.

Comparing eq. 1 and 6, the recombination model implies that

$$\frac{R_m}{R_o} = \frac{Q_m}{Q_o} \tag{8}$$

We have checked this relation by computing the ratio

$$\lambda \equiv \frac{Q_m}{Q_o} \bigg/ \frac{R_m}{R_o}$$

for all data points of Fig. 1, and found that λ has a statistical mean of 0.96, a median of 0.87 and a standard deviation of 0.45. That is, λ is statistically ~1. Hence, the data are reasonably accountable by the recombination mechanism. On the other hand, from eq. 3 and 7, the sequential mechanism predicts

$$\lambda' \equiv \frac{Q'_m}{Q'_o} \bigg/ \frac{R'_m}{R'_o} = \frac{\alpha_o^+ \left(\beta_m^+\right)^2 \gamma_o^+}{\alpha_m^+ \left(\beta_o^+\right)^2 \gamma_m^+} \tag{9}$$

Since the LHS is ~1 for our sample, we obtain

$$\frac{\alpha_m^+ \gamma_m^+}{\alpha_o^+ \gamma_o^+} \approx \left(\frac{\beta_m^+}{\beta_o^+}\right)^2 \tag{10}$$

By substituting eq. 5, we deduce

$$\frac{\beta_m^+}{\gamma_m^+} \leq \frac{\beta_o^+}{\gamma_o^+}$$

In other words, the sequential mechanism predicts that in the case of our sample, the ionization probabilities of Cr_2^+ and Cr_3^+ are systematically proportional. Again, measurement of neutral M_2 and M_3 species is needed to examine the prediction of the sequential model.

4. Summary

We have analyzed our SIMS signals of Cr^+, and Cr_2^+ and Cr_3^+ clusters under Cs^+ bombardment within the framework of two possible formation mechanisms. Our results seem to agree reasonably well with the predictions of the recombination model for sub-stoichiometric Cr oxide. The sequential model has predicted a few expressions on the relationship between ionization probabilities of the ion and clusters. Further experiments on the measurement of neutral M, M_2 and M_3 species need to be conducted to determine the contribution of this mechanism in cluster formation.

References

[1] A. Benninghoven, F.G. Rüdenauer, and H.W. Werner, Secondary Ion Mass Spectrometry (Wiley, 1987).
[2] A. Benninghoven, R.J. Colton, and D.S. Simons, Eds., Secondary Ion Mass Spectrometry SIMS V (Springer, 1986).
[3] Y. Gao, J. Appl. Phys. 64 (1988) 3760.
[4] J. Vlekken, T.-D. Wu, M. D'Olieslaeger, G. Knuyt, W. Vandervorst, and L. De Schepper, J. Am. Soc. Mass Spectrom. 9 (1998) 638.
[5] J.W. Erickson, J. Sheng, Y. Gao, H. Pham, and I.L. Singer, J. Vac. Sci. Technol. A 16 (1998) 1750.
[6] L. Kiong, A.T.S. Wee, R. Liu, and S.L. Lim, "An Investigation on the Effects of Surface Topography on Depth Resolution in Secondary Ion Mass Spectrometry", SIMS XII (this proceedings).

A. Benninghoven, P. Bertrand, H.-N. Migeon and H.W. Werner (Editors).
Proceedings of the 12th International Conference on Secondary Ion Mass Spectrometry,
Brussels, Belgium, 5-11 September 1999
© 2000 Elsevier Science B.V. All rights reserved.

TEMPERATURE DEPENDENCE OF SPUTTERED CLUSTER YIELDS

C. Staudt[a], R. Heinrich[a], P. Mazarov[a], A. Wucher[a], V. I. Tugushev[b], N. Kh. Dzhemilev[b]

[a]Institute of Laser and Plasma Physics, University of Essen, 45117 Essen, Germany
wucher@uni-essen.de
[b]Cluster Physics Lab, Arifov Institute of Electronics, 700143 Tashkent, Uzbekistan

1. Introduction

It is well known that the flux of particles released from a solid surface under bombardment with energetic ions contains clusters as well as atomic species. The formation of these clusters during a sputtering event represents one of the most interesting phenomena in sputtering physics. In general, sputtering is believed to be a strongly non thermal process dominated by relatively violent elastic collisions, which is only weakly influenced by thermal excitations within the bombarded solid. Strongly averaging observables like the total sputtering yield of polycrystalline or amorphous surfaces have therefore revealed only weak dependences on the target temperature [1], provided the temperature remains significantly below the melting point. More subtle characteristics like the energy and angular distributions of atoms sputtered from single crystal surfaces, on the other hand, have shown to depend on the target temperature in a much more pronounced fashion [2,3]. In view of these results, the interesting question arises as to which extent the formation of sputtered clusters (and cluster ions) is influenced by the target temperature. In this work, we therefore investigate the temperature dependence of secondary cluster ion formation processes during sputtering. In order to distinguish between the collisional emission of a cluster on one hand and its ionization on the other hand, it is essential to detect both neutral and ionic species leaving the surface. For that purpose, the neutral species must be post-ionized, which in the present work is done by photoionization from a pulsed UV-laser.

2. Experimental

Part of the experiments were performed with an experimental setup (setup 1) which has been described in detail elsewhere [4]. In short, a double focusing mass spectrometer consisting of a magnetic sector and an electrostatic prism is used to detect positive ionic clusters which are sputtered from a clean silver sample by 8.5 keV Ar^+ ions. The ion current density was about 3 mA/cm^2 with an incident angle of 45°. The base pressure in the chamber was about 10^{-10} mbar.

The second part of the experiments was performed with a reflectron time-of-flight mass spectrometer (setup 2, base pressure 10^{-9} mbar) which has also been previously described [5]. Here, the bombarding energy was 12.6 keV with an ion current density of about 30 $\mu A/cm^2$. During data acquisition, the primary ion-gun was used in a pulsed mode with a pulse length of 10 μs at a repetition rate of 10 Hz. In order to reduce the effect of surface contamination due to residual gas adsorbates during the acquisition of a mass spectrum, a cw sputter cleaning cycle of 10 sec was performed after every 500 shots. The technique employed for the detection of positive secondary ions and neutrals with this instrument is described elsewhere in this volume [6]. The excimer laser used for post-ionization was operated at $\lambda = 193$ nm and focused to dimensions of about 1.2 x 2.2 mm in directions perpendicular and parallel to the surface, respectively. Note that in this particular experiment the photoionization efficiency is not saturated, and the measured signals of post-ionized neutrals therefore depend on the laser power density. In order to eliminate the influence of this dependence, the pulse energy of the laser was kept constant within a few percent.

3. Results and Discussion

Fig. 1 a) and b) show the secondary ion signals measured with both experimental setups as a function of the target temperature for selected cluster sizes. In order to demonstrate the temperature dependent variation, the data for a specific cluster size was normalized to the respective signal obtained at the lowest temperature. First, it is seen that the signals tend to increase with increasing temperature, the effect being more pronounced for larger cluster sizes. Although details of the curves show slight differences, this qualitative trend as well as the overall magnitude of the effect (a factor of two for Ag_7) is comparable in both figures. In view of the large difference between the two experimental setups we consider this a reassuring agreement. The only exception is given by the monomer ions, which appear to increase in Fig. 1a but slightly decrease in Fig. 1b. The reason for this difference is unclear at the present time. Fig. 2 shows the relative yields (i. e. the yield normalized to that of the monomer ions) of cluster ions as a function of the cluster size for two values of the target temperature. In order to compare the data taken with the two setups, it is important to note that setup 1 detects the flux, whereas setup 2 detects the number density of secondary ions within a volume located approximately 1 mm above the surface [6]. In order to convert to flux, the data obtained with setup 2 must therefore be corrected for the average inverse velocity $\left\langle v^{-1} \right\rangle$ of the sputtered particles. From our previous measurements of the velocity distribution of sputtered silver clusters, we assume that $\left\langle v^{-1} \right\rangle$ varies with cluster size as $n^{0.8}$. and corrected the signals measured with setup 2 accordingly. It is seen that the resulting yield distribution measured at a

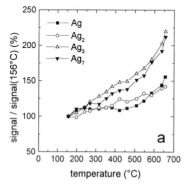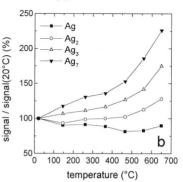

Fig. 1. Yield variation of secondary cluster ions vs. target temperature measured with a) setup 1 and b) setup 2 (see text)

temperature of about 650 °C shows a good agreement between both setups.

The important observation made in Fig. 2 concerns the difference between the cluster yield distributions measured for high and low temperature, respectively. From the presented data, it is apparent that the relative contribution of larger cluster ions becomes more abundant at higher temperature. Note that this trend is reproduced in both setups and should therefore be regarded as independent of the particular experimental details. In principle, two possible causes may lead to an increased abundance of larger cluster ions from the heated surface, namely either i) an enhanced formation

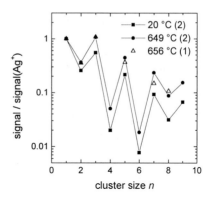

Fig. 2. Relative yields of secondary cluster ions vs. cluster size measured with (1) setup 1 and (2) setup 2.

probability or ii) an increased ionization probability of larger sputtered species. In order to distinguish between these possibilities, it is necessary to compare the mass spectra measured for secondary cluster ions with those of the respective sputtered neutral species. As explained above, we have done this by post-ionizing the neutral clusters using an intense pulsed UV laser. The resulting temperature dependence of the corresponding signals of post-ionized sputtered neutral clusters are shown in Fig. 3. It is immediately seen that the yields of sputtered neutrals do not increase with increasing temperature, but instead exhibit a small decrease, which is most pronounced for Ag atoms and Ag_2 dimers. Practically no temperature dependent variation is observed for larger clusters. From our previous work, we know that the ionization probability of silver clusters sputtered from a clean silver surface under conditions comparable to those applied here is small (below 10 % for all clusters). This means that the neutral yields reflect the partial sputtering yields of the clusters (regardless of their charge state). As a consequence, we conclude that the collisional processes leading to the formation of a sputtered cluster do not depend on the temperature of the bombarded surface. The temperature effect observed in Fig. 1 and Fig. 2 must therefore be attributed to an enhanced ionization of larger clusters at elevated temperatures. In order to illustrate this, we plot in Fig. 4 the ratio between the signals of secondary ions and post-ionized neutrals as a function of the target temperature. Since the post-ionization efficiency can be regarded as constant and, in particular, independent of the surface temperature, the resulting values are proportional to the ionization probability α^+ of the sputtered clusters. The data in

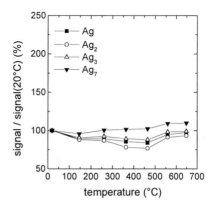

Fig. 3.Yield variation of sputtered neutral clusters vs. target temperature

Fig. 4 show that the values of α^+ increase with increasing temperature, the effect being the more pronounced the larger the cluster.

The physical origin of the increased ionization probability with increasing target temperature cannot unambiguously be identified at the present time. One possible explanation involves the residual gas contamination of the surface. It is known that already small amounts of electronegative species present at a metallic surface may lead to a drastic enhancement of the formation probability of positive ions [7]. If the residual gas pressure in the vacuum chamber rises with increasing temperature, one might

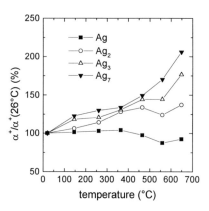

Fig. 4. Relative ionization probability of sputtered clusters vs. target temperature

therefore expect an increase of the measured ionization probabilities. Indeed, we find a relatively strong increase of mass spectrometric signals detected, for instance, for oxygen containing mixed clusters like Ag_3O_2 both in the secondary ion and the neutral spectrum above a temperature of 300 °C. However, we would intuitively expect the effect of an oxygen contamination to be largest for the monomers and dimers, since these species exhibit the lowest ionization probabilities ($< 10^{-4}$ [5,8]) when emitted from the sputter cleaned surface. Interestingly, practically no temperature dependence is observed for the ionization probability of the monomers. A second cause of surface contamination is given by the segregation of impurities within the silver target itself. Inspection of the mass spectra shows a signal of indium which strongly increases with increasing temperature. Due to the apparent lack of theoretical models describing the ionization mechanism of a sputtered cluster, it is not clear at the present time how such an indium coverage would influence the ionization probability of silver atoms and clusters of different sizes.

References

[1] H. E. Roosendaal in Sputtering by Particle Bombardment I, ed. R. Behrisch (Springer 1981) 219.
[2] W. Szymczak and K. Wittmaack, Nucl. Instr. Meth. B 82 (1993) 220.
[3] S. W. Rosencrance, N. Winograd, B. J. Garrison, and Z. Postawa, Phys. Rev. B 53 (1996) 2378.
[4] N. Kh. Dzhemilev, U. K. Rasulev, and S. V. Verkhoturov, Nucl. Instr. Meth. B 29 (1987) 531.
[5] M. Wahl and A. Wucher, Nucl. Instr. Meth. B 94 (1994) 36.
[6] A. Wucher, R. Heinrich, and C. Staudt, these proceedings.
[7] A. Benninghoven, F. G. Rüdenauer, and H. W. Werner (1987), secondary Ion Mars spectrometry, Wiley & sons, Chichester, U.K.
[8] R. Heinrich, C. Staudt, M. Wahl, and A. Wucher, these proceedings.

SECTION 4 :
MOLECULAR FRAGMENT EMISSION

A. Benninghoven, P. Bertrand, H.-N. Migeon and H.W. Werner (Editors).
Proceedings of the 12th International Conference on Secondary Ion Mass Spectrometry,
Brussels, Belgium, 5-11 September 1999

INTERNAL EXCITATION OF SPUTTERED NITRIC OXIDE

A. Schnieders, R. Kamischke, M. Schröder, H. F. Arlinghaus, A. Benninghoven

Physikalisches Institut der Universität, Wilhelm-Klemm-Str. 10,
D-48149 Münster, Germany

1. Introduction

TOF-SIMS and, in favourable cases, Laser-SNMS with resonantly enhanced multiphoton ionization (REMPI) are powerful tools for molecular surface analysis. However, despite the wide use of both techniques, the process of ion-induced desorption of molecular particles is hardly understood. Sputtered molecular species are not only characterized by their yield, their electronic excitation, their kinetic energy distribution, and their angular distribution, as are sputtered atomic particles, but also by their rotational and vibrational energy distributions. By means of REMPI it is possible to determine the internal energy distributions of sputtered molecules [1, 2, 3]. In this work a systematic investigation of the internal excitation of nitric oxide sputtered from adsorption layers on different solid surfaces (Au, Cu, Ni, and Si) is presented.

2. Experimental

The experiments were performed in a reflectron-type time-of-flight mass spectrometer equipped with an electron impact gas ion source. As primary ion species Ar^+, Xe^+, and SF_5^+ were used. The primary ion energy was varied between 4 and 10 keV.

NO was adsorbed as a monolayer on liquid nitrogen cooled substrates ($T = 100$ K). As substrates pure Si wafers and Ni, Cu and Au surfaces were used. For cleaning purposes, the substrates were heated up to 470 K in vacuum before cooling down to 100 K. Then the area of interest was sputter cleaned (primary ion fluence $F_{Pl} > 1 \cdot 10^{15}$ cm^{-2}). NO was adsorbed on the substrates by introducing gaseous NO with a partial pressure of $p = 1 \cdot 10^{-5}$ Pa for 10 s into the chamber

For resonantly enhanced multiphoton ionization an excimer laser ($\lambda = 308$ nm) pumped dye laser with a spectral range from 220 nm to 330 nm (after frequency doubling) was available. The internal energy distributions of sputtered NO molecules were determined by $(1 + 1)$ REMPI via the $A\ ^2\Sigma^+$—$X\ ^2\Pi_{1/2,\ 3/2}$ transition. Hönl-London factors and Franck-Condon-factors, which are generally used for unsaturated lines, must not be applied, due to the saturation of the A — X transition.

3. Results and discussion

Figure 1 shows a REMPI-excitation spectrum of sputtered NO from an adsorption layer on a cooled Si wafer. The data are acquired in the spectral range of the (0 - 0) band and in parts of the (1 - 1) band of the $A\ ^2\Sigma^+$—$X\ ^2\Pi_{1/2,\ 3/2}$ transition. The spectrum displays features from

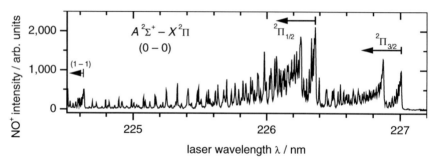

Fig. 1: *REMPI-excitation spectrum of sputtered NO from an adsorption layer on a cooled Si wafer (static sputtering: 10 keV Ar⁺). Intensities are corrected for variations in the laser pulse energy and sputter-induced removal.*

vibrational and rotational states of the $^2\Pi_{1/2}$ and $^2\Pi_{3/2}$ ground electronic states of NO. The lines could be assigned to the corresponding transitions. Molecular constants were taken from the paper of Engleman and Rouse [4].

To determine the distribution law of the rotational excitation, the NO⁺ intensity as a function of the rotational state is plotted in Figure 2 versus the state energy E_{rot} in a double logarithmic plot. Also, the theoretical rotational energy distribution in the vibrational ground state according to Sigmund et al. [5, 6] is given in Figure 2. This distribution was calculated on the basis of the linear collision cascade model. It was assumed that the collision starting the molecular motion is entirely between the cascade recoil and one atom of the molecule, whereas the other atom of the molecule simply acts as a spectator under the collision. Only for rotational energies E_{rot} of the order of the vibrational quantum $hc\omega_e$ the predicted behaviour is reflected. For lower rotational energies, there is a pronounced deviation from the theoretical distribution law. In this range the experimental data level off as is expected for the rotational energy distribution in vibrationally excited states. It was not possible to determine experimental values for states with a rotational energy higher than the vibrational quantum, because in this range most of the respective lines are overlapped by more intense lines of the (1 - 1) band.

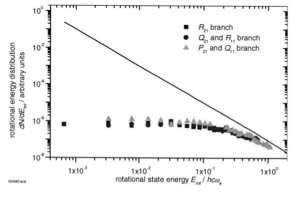

Fig. 2:
Rotational energy distribution of the vibrational ground state of sputtered NO from an adsorption layer on a cooled Si wafer derived from the REMPI-excitation spectrum in Figure 1. The rotational energy is given in units of the vibrational quantum $hc\omega_e$. The solid line corresponds to the theoretical distribution according Sigmund et al [5].

From the experimental data, it cannot be decided whether the distribution of the rotational energy is according to the model of Sigmund and Urbassek. This is mainly due to the missing data in the higher energy range. The mismatch between model and experiment in the low energy range could be explained by the disregard of surface binding energies on the excitation of sputtered particles in the model. Urbassek stated in a further development of the model [7] that rotation is strongly affected by the torques exerted by the surface binding potential on the ejected molecule. He predicted a change of the rotational distribution function of the molecule after passage through the surface barrier.

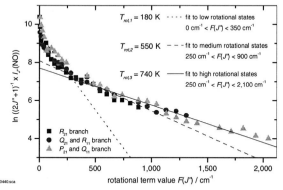

Fig. 3:
Boltzmann plot of the rotational energy distribution in the vibrational ground state of sputtered NO *from an adsorption layer on a cooled* Si *wafer derived from the REMPI-excitation spectrum in Figure 1.*

In Figure 3, the same data are plotted in a Boltzmann plot. It can be seen that the rotational energy distribution of sputtered NO has a distinct non-Boltzmann character and therefore is non-thermal. Different energy regions can be distinguished: beginning with a very steep decrease in the low rotational levels and resulting in a relatively flat dependence in the higher range of levels. The dependence in the different regions can be approximated by straight lines, the slopes of which correspond to different "rotational temperatures". The data in the high energy part of the distribution could be fitted by a temperature $T_{rot,3} = 750$ K $\pm$ 50 K, and the data in the medium energy part could be fitted by a temperature $T_{rot,2} = 550$ K $\pm$ 40 K. For the low energy range the distribution runs against a Boltzmann distribution with the target temperature as parameter $T_{rot,1} = 180$ K $\pm$ 20 K $\rightarrow T_{target} = 100$ K.

The use of temperatures to describe the rotational excitation of sputtered NO does not imply that the rotational energy distribution is a superposition of different Boltzmann distributions. The temperatures are only used as parameters to describe the distribution function and to compare the rotational excitation of sputtered particles under different conditions.

The integral intensity ratio of the (1 - 1) ($\lambda = 224.5275 \ldots 224.64$ nm) and the (0 - 0) band heads ($\lambda = 226.91 \ldots 227.025$ nm) is 0.48 ± 0.03. It has to be weighted by correction factors $f_{v'}$ concerning the different ionization probabilities in dependence on the vibrational quantum number v' of the excited state during the REMPI process. [8] The ratio corresponds to a vibrational temperature of $T_{vib} = 2,950$ K $\pm$ 200 K. Similar to the evaluation of the rotational excitation, the use of a temperature does not imply a thermal vibrational energy distribution.

The degree of internal excitation of sputtered NO is of the same order as that of other sputtered, covalently bound molecules as shown for sputtered sulphur dimers [9, 10] and sputtered, electronically excited MgO [11]. In all these systems a higher vibrational excitation is found compared to the rotational excitation. These molecules are all sputtered by direct emission of pre-formed molecules initially located on the surface. The situation is different for sputtered metal clusters [2, 3], since in that case no pre-formed molecules exist on the surface. By comparing REMPI-excitation spectra of NO sputtered (10 keV Ar$^+$) from adsorption layers on different substrates, the influence of the substrate on the rotational excitation is visible. The Boltzmann plots deliver again "rotational temperatures" $T_{rot,2}$ and $T_{rot,3}$ for the medium and high energy range. The values are given in Table 1. The differences may be due to different masses of the substrate (recoil) atoms or due to different surface binding energies of NO to the substrates. The measurements to determine the dependence

substrate	$T_{rot,2}$ / K	$T_{rot,3}$ / K
Au	590 ± 40	1,000 ± 100
Cu	380 ± 25	650 ± 50
Ni	440 ± 55	670 ± 50
Si	550 ± 40	750 ± 50

Table 1: Distribution parameters $T_{rot,2}$ and $T_{rot,3}$ of the rotational energy distribution of NO sputtered (10 keV Ar$^+$) from an adsorption layer on different substrates

of the internal excitation on the primary ion species and the primary ion energy require accurate timing and positioning of the laser focus. Especially, the delay between the primary ion pulse and the laser pulse is an important parameter. This is due to a correlation of the internal energy and the kinetic energy of the sputtered particles. [9, 10] First measurements have shown for some sputter conditions a trend of increasing distribution parameter $T_{rot,2}$ with increasing primary ion energy. Sputtering with Ar$^+$ generally results in lower excitation than sputtering with Xe$^+$ and SF$_5^+$. Further measurements with accurate control of the timing are necessary to get reliable results. Especially, the determination of the kinetic energy distributions seems to be necessary.

References

[1] A. Schnieders, R. Möllers, A. Benninghoven, K. Reihs, in *Secondary Ion Mass Spectrometry SIMS X*, John Wiley & Sons, Chichester, 1997, p 775

[2] P. Fayet, J. P. Wolf, L. Wöste, Physical Review **B33**, 6792 (1986)

[3] A. Wucher, Physical Review **B49**, 2012 (1994)

[4] R. Engleman, Jr. P. E. Rouse, Journal of Molecular Spectroscopy **37**, 240 (1971)

[5] P. Sigmund, H. M. Urbassek, D. Matragrano, Nuclear Instruments and Methods in Physics Research **B14**, 495 (1986)

[6] H. M. Urbassek, Nuclear Instruments and Methods in Physics Research **B18**, 587 (1987)

[7] H. M. Urbassek, Journal of Physics: Condensed Matter **4**, 4871 (1992)

[8] H. Zacharias, F. de Rougemont, T. F. Heinz, M. M. T. Loy, Journal of Chemical Physics **105**, 111 (1996)

[9] R. de Jonge, T. Baller, M. G. Tenner, A. E. de Vries, K. J. Snowdon, Nuclear Instruments and Methods in Physics Research **B17**, 213 (1986)

[10] R. de Jonge, K. W. Benoist, J. W. F. Majoor, A. E. de Vries, K. J. Snowdon, Nuclear Instruments and Methods in Physics Research **B28**, 214 (1987)

[11] P. G. Fournier, J. Fournier, B. Bellaoui, O. Benoist d'Azy, G. Taieb, Nuclear Instruments and Methods in Physics Research **B78**, 144 (1993)

A. Benninghoven, P. Bertrand, H.-N. Migeon and H.W. Werner (Editors).
Proceedings of the 12th International Conference on Secondary Ion Mass Spectrometry,
Brussels, Belgium, 5-11 September 1999
© 2000 Elsevier Science B.V. All rights reserved.

CHARGE REMOTE FRAGMENTATION OF ORGANIC MOLECULES EXCHANGED ON AN AMINOETHANE THIOLATE SELF-ASSEMBLED MONOLAYER

C.W. Diehnelt, M.J. Van Stipdonk, R.D. English, and E.A. Schweikert

Department of Chemistry, Texas A&M University, PO Box 30012, College Station, TX, 77843-3144, U.S.A., diehnelt@mail.chem.tamu.edu

1. Introduction

Charge remote fragmentation (CRF) is a well known gas-phase decomposition that occurs for organic ions with a stable, fixed charge-site [1]. These cleavages are typically observed when the molecular ion, produced by fast atom bombardment (FAB), from a fatty acid, an alkyl sulfate or sulfonate, a bile acid, a steroid conjugate, or a peptide, is collisionally activated and the mass spectrum recorded [2]. Charge remote fragmentation has proven beneficial in determining the location of double bonds in unsaturated fatty acids [1].

Energetically, CRFs are thought to be relatively high energy reactions that are analogous to the gas-phase thermal decompositions of neutral molecules [2]. Hence, little or no CRF was seen in the FAB analysis of alkyl sulfates [1]. In a few limited cases, prompt charge remote fragmentation, without collisional activation, has been observed in plasma desorption mass spectrometry (PDMS) of bradykinin [3], atomic SIMS of zwitterionic compounds [4], and liquid-SIMS of cationic organic dyes [5].

Here we report evidence of prompt CRF occurring for several organic species exchanged on an aminoethane thiolate self-assembled monolayer under atomic and polyatomic primary ion bombardment. The intensity of CRF increases when going from atomic to polyatomic primary ions, indicating the energetic nature of secondary ions sputtered by cluster impact.

2. Experimental

The experiments were performed on a dual Time-of-Flight (TOF) mass spectrometer built in house [6]. Atomic and polyatomic primary ions were produced by ^{252}Cf fission fragment impacts on a Mylar foil coated with source material. Cesium iodide was used as a source material to produce $(CsI)_nCs^+$ (n=0,1,2) primary ions. Primary ions were accelerated to a particular kinetic energy (10-30 keV) and impacted the sample with an incident angle of $\sim 27^0$. Samples studied include: octyl sulfate (OS) (MW = 209), tetradecyl sulfate (TDS) (MW = 293), and taurocholic acid (TCA) (MW = 515). Samples were prepared by depositing a solution of the sample onto a protonated aminoethane thiolate (AET) monolayer. The sample molecules all exist as preformed negative ions and will be immobilized on the monolayer surface through ion pair or ion exchange interactions. AET monolayers ready for ion exchange were prepared according to a procedure outlined in reference 7. All experiments were performed using a coincidence counting data collection approach [8] at the

180

limit of single ion impacts. The relative yield (%) of each SI was calculated by integrating the area of the SI peak and dividing this number by the number of incident primary ions.

3. Results

The CRF scheme for OS is shown below. As can be seen, the process consists of a series of alkyl chain cleavages producing peaks 14 mass units apart. The relative yields of the charge remote fragments produced by 15 keV Cs^+ and $(CsI)Cs^+$ are shown in Figure 1.

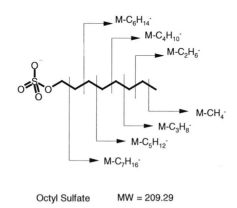

Octyl Sulfate   MW = 209.29

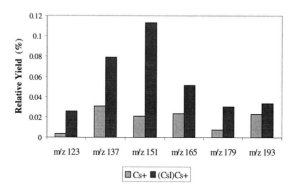

Fig. 1. CRF yields from octyl sulfate.

The total yield of charge remote fragments, defined as the sum of the relative yield of each charge remote fragment, is shown in Figure 2 for OS. The yield of CRF from $(CsI)Cs^+$ primary ions produce roughly three times more charge remote fragmentation than do Cs^+ primary ions at the same impact energy.

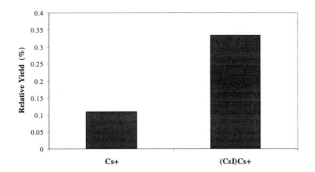

Fig. 2. Total CRF yields from OS produced by 15 keV Cs$^+$ and (CsI)Cs$^+$ primary ions.

Bile salts are also known to undergo CRF under FAB-CAD analysis [9]. Taurocholic acid was analyzed on an AET monolayer, and charge remote fragments at m/z 288, 358, and 442 were observed. When (CsI)Cs$^+$ projectiles were used, it was found that a greater extent of CRF occurred for TCA, as seen in Figure 3.

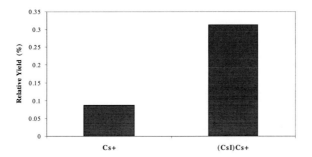

Fig. 3. Total CRF yields from TCA produced by 20 keV Cs$^+$ and (CsI)Cs$^+$.

4. Conclusion

We have shown here that polyatomic primary ions can increase the extent of charge remote fragmentation that certain organic ions undergo. This result is consistent with many reports of increased fragmentation caused by polyatomic ion impact. Rather than view the increase in prompt fragmentation as a detrimental side effect, it was thought that this effect could be utilized as a probe to provide additional information to the analyst. Specifically, a structurally specific fragmentation reaction was examined. It was found that a polyatomic primary ion produces a greater abundance of the structurally specific charge remote fragments than an atomic primary ion. In this way, a polyatomic primary ion could be used to increase the information content of the mass spectrum by providing structural information in addition to molecular weight information.

References

[1] K.B. Tomer, F.W. Crow, and M.L. Gross, J. Am. Chem. Soc. 105 (1983) 5487.

[2] J. Adams, Mass Spectrom. Reviews 9 (1990) 141.

[3] D.M. Bunk and R.D. Macfarlane, J. Am. Soc. Mass Spectrom. 2 (1991) 379.

[4] O.W. Hand, and R.G. Cooks, Int. J. Mass Spectrom. Ion Processes 88 (1989) 113.

[5] R.E. Carlson and K.L Busch, Org. Mass Spectrom. 29 (1994) 632.

[6] M.J. Van Stipdonk, R.D. Harris, and E.A. Schweikert, Rapid Commun. Mass Spectrom. 10 (1996) 1987.

[7] R.D. English, M.J. Van Stipdonk, and E.A. Schweikert, SIMS XII Proceedings.

[8] M.A. Park, B.D. Cox, and E.A. Schweikert, J. Chem. Phys. 96 (1992) 8171.

[9] K.B. Tomer, N.J. Jensen, M.L. Gross, and J. Whitney, Biomed. Mass Spectrom. 13 (1986) 265.

[10] C.W. Diehnelt, M.J. Van Stipdonk, and E.A. Schweikert, SIMS XII Proceedings.

A. Benninghoven, P. Bertrand, H.-N. Migeon and H.W. Werner (Editors).
Proceedings of the 12th International Conference on Secondary Ion Mass Spectrometry,
Brussels, Belgium, 5-11 September 1999

A COMPARISON OF THE ENERGY DENSITY DISTRIBUTION WITH ATOMIC AND POLYATOMIC PROJECTILES IN ORGANIC SIMS

David W. Ward[a], T. C. Nguyen[a], Kristin D. Krantzman[a]
and Barbara J. Garrison[b]

[a]Department of Chemistry and Biochemistry, College of Charleston
Charleston, SC 29424, USA

[b]Department of Chemistry, The Pennsylvania State University
University Park, Pennsylvania 16802

1. Introduction

Numerous organic SIMS experiments have demonstrated that polyatomic projectiles enhance the yield of secondary ions compared to monoatomic projectiles [1-4]. Recently, experiments have compared the secondary ion yield with Xe and SF_5 projectiles [5-6]. Although Xe and SF_5 have approximately the same mass, there is a significant enhancement in the yield with the polyatomic projectile. We have performed molecular dynamics simulations of the bombardment of a monolayer of biphenyl molecules on Cu(100) and Si(100)-(2x1) substrates with 0.6 keV SF_5 and Xe projectiles [7], which have shown that SF_5 produces more yield than Xe. It is hypothesized that the secondary ion yield is greater with polyatomic projectiles because the energy deposited is spread out over a larger surface area, leading to more ejected molecules from the surface. In this paper, we examine the energy density distribution with Xe and SF_5 projectiles.

2. Method

The classical method of molecular dynamics simulations is used to study the systems of interest and the details of this method are described extensively elsewhere [8]. Details of the calculations have been described previously [9] and will be described in more detail elsewhere [10]. The model systems consist of a monolayer of biphenyl molecules adsorbed on copper and silicon substrates, where the positions of the biphenyl molecules are determined by allowing the adsorbates to equilibrate at 0 K on the substrate using an algorithm based on the generalized Langevin equation (GLE). The forces among the atoms are described by the best currently available potential energy functions, the majority of which are multi-body in nature. The Xe and SF_5 projectiles are brought in at normal incidence with 0.6 keV of energy, and the orientation of the SF_5 projectile with respect to the surface is selected randomly. The results are calculated with each projectile for 150 trajectories, where each trajectory has a different aiming point on the surface.

3. Results
a. Yield and Mechanisms

Our simulations have demonstrated that SF_5 enhances the yield compared to Xe, and that the degree of enhancement depends on the nature of the substrate [7]. On the silicon substrate, the yield with SF_5 is 2.1 times greater than with Xe. On the copper substrate, the yield with SF_5 is only 1.2 times greater than with Xe. The differences in the enhancement between the two substrates can be explained by the differences in their lattice structure. With the more open lattice structure of silicon, the SF_5 is able to penetrate the lattice and break up within the substrate underneath the monolayer of biphenyl molecules. With the more closely packed copper substrate, on the other hand, the SF_5 cluster breaks up on the surface rather than within it. The break up of SF_5 within the lattice leads to upward motion of the silicon substrate atoms, causing a greater number of ejected biphenyl molecules from the surface.

b. Energy Density

Only the energy density from the upward moving substrate atoms are considered because these are the atoms that cause ejection of whole biphenyl molecules. Contributions to the energy density from the primary particle are not included because collisions with the primary particle lead to fragmentation of the biphenyl molecules. In order to calculate the energy density distribution, the surface area is divided up into thirty by thirty bins, each with an area of four Å^2. For each time step, the energy within each bin is calculated by summing over the kinetic energy of the substrate atoms in the volume of the bin that have an upward momentum and are within two Å above the substrate surface. The energy density is calculated by dividing the total energy by the volume of the bin and the maximum kinetic energy density over time in each bin is recorded for the trajectory.

Figures 1a and 1b show plots of the maximum energy density within each bin for a typical trajectory on the Si(100)-(2x1) substrate with the SF_5 and Xe projectiles. Both projectiles have the same impact point on the surface. SF_5 produces a yield of five ejected biphenyl molecules and one fragmented molecule and Xe produces a yield of two ejected biphenyl molecules. The plus signs on the plots represent the positions of the center of mass of the ejected biphenyl molecules and the asterisk in Figure 1a represents the position of the biphenyl molecule fragmented by the impact of the SF_5 projectile. In general, positions of high energy density correlate with the positions of biphenyl molecules that are ejected. The SF_5 projectile produces a larger area of energy density on the silicon surface compared to Xe, which distributes its energy in a smaller region, and consequently, more biphenyl molecules are ejected with the SF_5 projectile.

Figures 2a and 2b show plots of the energy density with the SF_5 and Xe projectiles on the Cu(001) substrate. With this impact point, SF_5 has a yield of three biphenyl molecules and Xe has a yield of two biphenyl molecules. The magnitude of the energy density is greater on the copper substrate than the silicon substrate because of the greater mass of its substrate atoms. As in the case with the silicon substrate, SF_5 distributes the energy over a larger area than Xe. However, the increase in area is not as great as on the silicon substrate because SF_5 breaks up on the copper surface rather than within it.

185

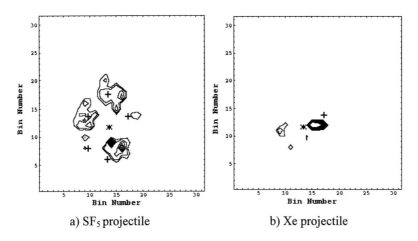

a) SF₅ projectile　　　　　　b) Xe projectile

Figure 1: Energy density distribution on the Si(100)-(2x1) substrate. Contour lines are drawn to represent positions of energy density at values of 0.5 eV/8 Å^3, 1.0 eV/ 8 Å^3, 2.0 eV/8 Å^3, 3.0 eV/8 Å^3, and ... 10.0 eV/8 Å^3.

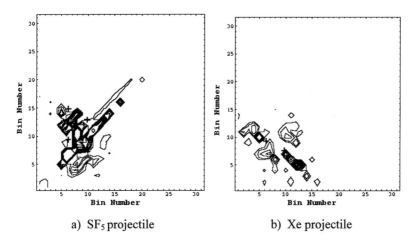

a) SF₅ projectile　　　　　　b) Xe projectile

Figure 2: Energy density distribution on the Cu(001) substrate. Contour lines are drawn to represent positions of energy density at values of 0.5 eV/8 Å^3, 1.0 eV/ 8 Å^3, 2.0 eV/8 Å^3, 3.0 eV/8 Å^3, and ... 10.0 eV/8 Å^3.

4. Summary

Plots of the distribution of the maximum energy density with the Xe and SF_5 projectiles on the Si(100)-(2x1) and Cu(001) substrates are presented for typical trajectories. Our simulations show that only substrate atoms with upward momentum cause ejection of whole biphenyl molecules, and therefore, only these atoms are included in the calculation of the energy density. In general, positions of high energy density correlate with the positions of ejected biphenyl molecules. SF_5 produces a larger area of energy density than Xe, and this is especially true on the silicon substrate. The larger area of energy density leads to a greater yield of biphenyl molecules ejected from the surface.

5. Acknowledgments

The financial support of the National Science Foundation, the Petroleum Research Fund and the Research Corporation is gratefully acknowledged. Computing facilities were provided by grants from the National Science Foundation and the IBM Selected University Research Program at the Center for Academic Computing of The Pennsylvania State University. In addition, we thank Anthony Appelhans and Michael Van Stipdonk for insightful discussions about this work and Jeff Nucciarone for assistance with the computations.

References

[1]   A. D. Appelhans and J. E. Delmore, Anal. Chem. 61 (1989) 1087.
[2]   M. G. Blain, S. Della-Negra, H. Joret, Y. LeBeyec, E. A. Schweikert, Phys. Rev. Lett., 63 (1989) 1625
[3]   J. F. Mahoney, J. Perel, S. A. Ruatta, P. A. Martino, S. Husain, T. D. Lee, Rapid Commun. Mass. Spectrom., 5 (1991) 551.
[4]   O. W. Hand, T. K. Majumdar, R. G. Cooks, Int. J. Mass Spectrom. Ion Processes, 97 (1990) 34.
[5]   F. Kötter and A. Benninghoven, Appl. Surf. Sci., 133 (1998) 47-57.
[6]   E. T. Ada and L. Hanley, Int. J. Mass Spectrom. Ion Processes, 174 (1998) 231.
[7]   J. A. Townes, A. K. White, E. N. Wiggins, K. D. Krantzman, B. J. Garrison and N. Winograd, J. Phys. Chem. A, 103 (1999) 4587.
[8]   J. Garrison and N. Winograd, *Science*, 216 (1982) 806; B. J. Garrison, Chem. Soc. Rev., 21 (1992) 155; D. N. Bernardo, R. Bhatia and B. J. Garrison, Comp. Phys. Comm., 80 (1994) 259-273.
[9]   R. Zaric, B. Pearson, K. D. Krantzman and B. J. Garrison, Int. J. Mass Spectrom. Ion Processes, 174 (1998) 155; R. Zaric, B. Pearson, K. D. Krantzman and B. J. Garrison in *Secondary Ion Mass Spectrometry, SIMS XI*; eds. G. Gillen, R. Lareau, J. Bennett and F. Stevie (Wiley, 1998), p. 601; J. A. Townes, A. K. White, K. D. Krantzman and B. J. Garrison in *Applications of Accelerators in Research and Industry*, eds. J. L. Duggan and I. L. Morgan (The American Institute of Physics, 1999), p. 401.
[10] T. Nguyen, D. Ward, J. A. Townes, A. K. White, K. D. Krantzman and B. J. Garrison, manuscript in preparation.

A. Benninghoven, P. Bertrand, H.-N. Migeon and H.W. Werner (Editors).
Proceedings of the 12th International Conference on Secondary Ion Mass Spectrometry,
Brussels, Belgium, 5-11 September 1999

FUNDAMENTAL ASPECTS OF MOLECULAR DESORPTION IN SIMS

Nicholas Winograd

Department of Chemistry, Penn State University
184 MRI Building, University Park, PA 16802 USA, nxw@psu.edu

1. Introduction

Mechanisms of molecular desorption from ion-bombarded surfaces are still not well-understood. Elucidation of these mechanisms is, of course, essential to maximizing the information content of the SIMS signal. To determine the important physical and chemical processes that lead to desorption, our laboratory has concentrated on measuring the energy and angle-distributions of ejected neutral molecules[1]. This information is then compared when possible to molecular dynamics computer simulations of the ion-bombardment event[2]. The comparison is important since these types of calculations provide a molecular-level view of the atomic motion in the solid that leads to the ejection process, and if the calculated trajectories agree with the measured trajectories, then we feel confident that the picture presented by the computer is a realistic one. In this report, results from several different systems are examined. The results yield a rather confusing picture associated with a variety of desorption mechanisms that yield diagnostic trajectory information. These include sputtering by collision cascades and momentum transfer, various thermal desorption mechanisms and mechanisms involving electronic processes. Moreover, the type of bonding between the adsorbate and the substrate strongly influences the nature of the fragmentation pattern associated with the SIMS spectra. Although complex, these factors contribute to a framework about which a more general understanding can emerge.

2. Results and discussion

The first example is the case of a fraction of a monolayer of benzene adsorbed onto Ag{111}. For this situation, we have already shown that the kinetic energy (KE) distribution of benzene molecules peaks at a value of about 1 eV and is similar in appearance to the Ag KE distribution[1]. Molecular dynamics calculations match up very well with the experimental ones if molecules calculated to contain more than 5 eV are removed from consideration[2]. These molecules, it is assumed, would undergo unimolecular decay on the way to the detector. For this situation, the desorption mechanism is clearly initiated by a collision cascade of Ag atoms, and the theory works very well.

For multilayers of benzene on Ag, the situation changes dramatically. The KE distribution peaks at 0.04 eV, and takes on a Maxwell-Boltzmann appearance with a fit temperature that is much greater than the substrate temperature (500K vs 120K). Bombardment with H_2^+ projectile ions does not result in the ejection of molecules, indicating that momentum transfer is a critical part of the process. At present, these data support the notion that there is a molecular collision cascade in the multilayer film which involves

188

vibrational and rotational excitation of the molecules and exothermic reactions of fragments formed in the cascade. These events can cause local heating of the substrate and emission of molecules with effective temperatures higher than the macroscopic surface temperature. Molecular dynamics calculations are not yet available to test these ideas, although our formalism is presently being adapted to allow this type of modeling.

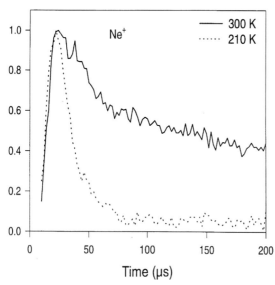

Fig. 1. TOF distribution of the neutral tryptophan fragment at m/z 130 using 8 keV Ne$^+$ projectiles as a function of surface temperatures.

A third type of molecular desorption is represented by a sample made of pellets of tryptophan[3]. In this case, we monitor a neutral tryptophan fragment at m/z 130 after bombardment with 8 keV Ne$^+$ ions at 300 K and 210 K surface temperatures. As seen in Figure 1, the TOF distributions at both surface temperatures have a well-defined peak close to 20 μs. This value corresponds to a KE of about 0.1 eV , a value similar to that seen for benzene ice. At 300 K, however, the TOF distribution exhibits a continuous emission of molecular fragments that persists for longer than 200 μs after bombardment. Note that this emission is not observed when the sample is cooled to 210 K. A possible explanation of this effect is that energy is stored in some kind of electronically excited state for a time after excitation. Deexcitation may involve a radiationless decay transferring KE to the solid matrix. Tryptophan is known to have a long-lived triplet state, which would be quenched at lower temperatures. It will be interesting to see if other systems exhibit such unusual effects, or if there is simultaneous light emission associated with these materials.

For all of the above cases, the molecules are only weakly bonded to their substrates. In many cases, there are strong covalent bonds between the adsorbate and the substrate that can dramatically alter the energy dissipation pathways. A prototypical example involves the desorption of organic molecules covalently attached to polystyrene spheres. This is a very important practical situation since these spheres are used to create large combinatorial libraries associated with drug discovery research. As shown in Figure 2, we find that the TOF-SIMS spectra of stearic acid attached to a polystyrene surface using the chemical linker shown in the figure exhibits only fragment ions associated with the bead itself. After a brief exposure to a vapor of trifluoroacetic acid (TFA) and chloromethane, however, the molecular ion at M+H$^+$ and the fragment at M-OH$^+$ are clearly visible. This treatment cleaves the covalent bond, allowing the stearic acid molecule to rest comfortably on the polystyrene surface. This type of result was also predicted by early MD simulations where it was reported that molecules strongly chemisorbed on Pt surfaces were more readily fragmented than were

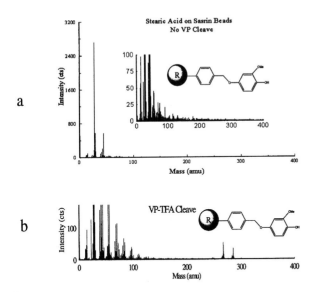

Fig. 2. TOF-SIMS spectra of stearic acid attached to a polystyrene resin (R) by a sasrin linker as shown. The beads in (a) are untreated and in (b) are exposed to TFA vapor for five minutes.

physisorbed molecules[4]. The principle obviously imparts broad implications to TOF-SIMS measurements including detec-tion of small bio-molecules bound to receptor sites, antibody-antigen inter-actions as well as surface adsorption studies in general.

Finally, we consider how the orientation of the molecule influences the mechanism of desorption. The initial mole-cular dynamics simulations of organic molecule desorption predicted that the tops of long chain molecules would be preferentially removed from the surface[4]. To test this prediction, we constructed oriented Langmuir-Blodgett films of phosphatidylcholine dipalmitoyl (DPPC) such that either a headgroup or a tailgroup is forced toward the air-film interface[5].

To prepare a film with the tailgroup pointing away from the surface, a SiO_2/Si substrate was pulled through a layer of DPPC on a water subphase. This substrate presents a polar surface that preferentially binds the lipid headgroup. To prepare a film with the headgroup pointing away from the surface, a C_{16} alkane thiol monolayer on gold was inserted through a layer of DPPC on the same water subphase. The TOF-SIMS results illustrated in Figure 3 provide a clear verification of this principle. In fact, the main headgroup fragment ion at m/z 184 and the tailgroup hydrocarbon fragment ion at m/z 311 provide enough contrast such that imaging phospholipid domains becomes feasible.

3. Conclusions

Here we have compared the sputtering behavior of a variety of classes of molecules to attempt to identify the key physical and chemical properties that influence the mechanism of desorption. Perhaps the important point at this stage of understanding is that we have identified many factors that can be involved, and that as much as possible needs to be known about the system before predictions of SIMS spectra can be made. Our efforts have focused on the role of the nuclear motion, leaving ionization effects for future studies. However, it is clear that a better understanding of the events associated with the molecular collision cascade will offer a better chance at predicting *a priori* how a system will respond to ion bombardment.

190

Financial support of the National Science Foundation, the National Institutes of Health, and the Office of Naval Research are gratefully acknowledged.

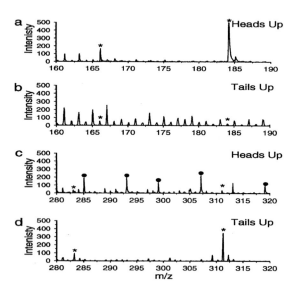

Fig. 3. TOF-SIMS spectra of DPPC LB film prepared with the headgroup exposed to the beam (a and c) and the tailgroup exposed to the beam (b and d). The labeled peaks (•) refer to mass peaks from the substrate or peaks which change with orientation (*).

References

[1] R. Chatterjee, D. E. Riederer, Z. Postawa and N. Winograd, J. Phys. Chem. **102** (1998) 4176-4182.
[2] R. Chatterjee, Z. Postawa, N. Winograd, and B. J. Garrison, J. Phys. Chem. **B103** (1999) 151-163.
[3] R. Chatterjee, D. E .Riederer, Z Postawa and N. Winograd, Rapid Comm. Mass Spec. (1998) 1226-1231.
[4] R. S. Taylor and B. J. Garrison, J. Am. Chem. Soc. **116** (1994) 4465.
[5] M. L. Pacholski, D. M. Cannon, Jr., A. G. Ewing, and N. Winograd, J. Am. Chem. Soc. **121** (1999) 4716-4717.

A. Benninghoven, P. Bertrand, H.-N. Migeon and H.W. Werner (Editors).
Proceedings of the 12th International Conference on Secondary Ion Mass Spectrometry,
Brussels, Belgium, 5-11 September 1999

TOF-SIMS STUDY OF THE ADSORPTION OF BENZOTRIAZOLE ON COPPER AND SILVER SURFACES : KINETIC ENERGIES DISTRIBUTIONS OF ORGANIC AND ORGANOMETALLIC MOLECULAR IONS

G. Dauchot, R. Combarieu, M. Repoux and F. Delamare

Ecole des Mines de Paris, CEMEF, URA CNRS 7635, BP 207, 06904 Sophia-Antipolis Cedex France
email adress: combarieu@cemef.cma.fr

1.Introduction

Many investigations have been conducted on the chemical nature, composition, thickness and structure of the protective layer formed on copper by the benzotriazole molecules but the real nature of this film is still the object of controversy in the literature [1,2]. ToF-SIMS analyses on such films [3,4] show the presence of organocuprous ions which can also be interpreted as copper-cationized adducts of the benzotriazole molecule. It will be interesting to compare their kinetic energy distributions (KEDs) to those of real cationized adducts. Adsorption of benzotriazole ($C_6H_5N_3$) on Si, Fe, Ag , Cu and brass substrates has been compared using XPS and Tof-SIMS techniques.

2.Experimental

Studied samples were : silicon wafer, steel IF-Ti low carbon, silver 99, copper 999 and brass 65/35. Samples were successively cleaned in ultrasonic baths with 4 solvents (dichloromethane, hexane, acetone and methanol), then they were dipped in a solution of benzotriazole in methanol (3%wt) during 15 minutes at room temperature and allowed to dry before XPS and ToF-SIMS investigations.

XPS analyses were performed in an ISA Riber MAC II spectrometer using Al K$\square$X-ray (10kV, 25mA). The secondary ion mass spectra were obtained in a ToF-SIMS TRIFT I (Charles Evans & assoc.) using a 10 kHz pulsed Ga+ beam (15kV, 500pA.DC) [5]. The primary beam was rastered onto a (83x83 $\square m^2$) area, keeping the primary ion dose below 10^{12} ions/cm^2 for 5 min acquisition.

KED measurements on ToF-SIMS TRIFT I have already been described by Delcorte [6]. Secondary ions are usually first accelerated by a 3kV potential directly applied on the sample. They are then energy-analysed by a slit of 100 $\square$m width located at the crossover following the first electrostatic analyser, corresponding to a passband of 1.5 eV. The different energy windows are selected by varying the sample voltage by 1.2 eV step around the 3kV nominal value. The acquisition of mass spectra for each sample voltage allowed us to obtain simultaneously the KEDs for the different secondary ions. In order to ensure quite static conditions during a full KED measurement, that is to say near 20 acquisitions, the primary ion dose is kept below 5×10^{11} ion/cm^2 for each spectrum, corresponding to an acquisition time of 30 sec. The zero of the energy scale is determined from the intersection between the tangent to the increasing part of the KED of atomic ions and the energy axis: Me$^+$ in positive mode and Me$^-$, Cl$^-$ in negative mode.

3.Results

XPS analyses confirm previous results in literature. With Si, Fe and Ag substrates treated with benzotriazole, the most intense peaks are the metallic ones and the atomic concentrations in nitrogen are rather low. In the case of copper surfaces, nitrogen concentrations are higher (Table. 1) and all the copper atoms have an oxidation degree of +1 different from the one of the copper surface before dipping. Ratio Cu/N/C are close to 1/3/6 as for an organic cuprous polymer in agreement with Cotton model [7]. The same observations can be obtained with brass surfaces due to the quasi-absence of Zn atoms in the first layers of the surface.

Table 1. XPS atomic compositions (%) of copper and silver surfaces after dipping in benzotriazole (C* : contamination carbon)

Atomic %	Metal		O	N	C (C*)	N/Me
Copper	Cu (I)	5.9	15	16.5	62 (29)	2,8
Silver	Ag	41.6	9.5	5.7	43.2 (40)	0.14

Tof-SIMS analyses show also particularities of copper and its alloys versus other surfaces. Spectra show not only molecular ions $(M+H)^+$ and $(M-H)^-$ of benzotriazole but also intense ions identificated as series $Cu_xM_{x-1}^+$ (up to x=5) in positive mode and $Cu_{x-1}M_x^-$ (up to x=3) in negative mode. Other series can also be observed with substitution of $(M-H)^-$ by CN^- (Fig.1).

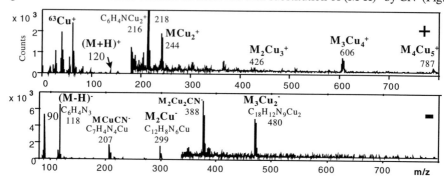

Fig.1 . Positive and negative ion mass spectra of benzotriazole on a copper surface.

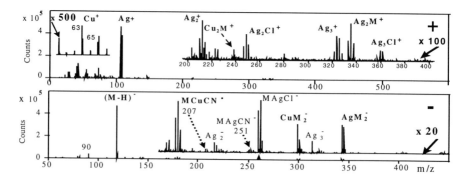

Fig.2. Ion mass spectra of benzotriazole on a silver surface (with 3 ppm Cu in bulk).

Similar ions series (Me$_x$ M$_{x-1}^+$ et Me$_{x-1}$ M$_x^-$ in positive and negative mode for silver up for x=1) can also be observed on silver surfaces but with lower intensities. In contrast, such ions have never been detected on Si and Fe surfaces.

Fig. 2 represents Tof-SIMS spectra obtained on a silver surface containing only 3 ppm of copper in bulk. Ratio I Cu$^+$/ I Ag$^+$ is largely increased (nearly one percent) in the first monolayers. Moreover, we observe that the organocopper peak CuM$_2^-$ at m/z=299 is as intense as the organosilver one AgM$_2^-$ at m/z=343, probably due to the competition between M$^-$, CN$^-$ and Cl$^-$ to form adducts with Ag or Cu ions. As silver and copper are considered as amongst the best cationizing metals, the observation of such ions can be associated either to a cationization process or to the ionization of a real compound present on the metal surface. How to discriminate these two kinds of ions ? Generally, metal cationized molecules can be differentiated by the broadening of their kinetic energy distributions compared to that of the parents-ions [5]. So the kinetic energies distributions of molecular ions (M+H)$^+$, (M-H)$^-$ and of the organometallic ions (Me$_x$M$_{x-1}^+$ and Me$_{x-1}$M$_x^-$) were established for both metals. FWHMs are always slightly higher for negative organo-silver ions than for copper ones (Fig.3) but such differences cannot be really significant considering the limiting factor due to the width of the energy slit. Moreover a part of the organo-copper ions KEDs has an negative relative energy characterizing the fact that a part of these ions are produced by decomposition of larger clusters in contrast to the silver ions.

	Cu$^-$	(M-H)$^-$	CuM$_2^-$	MCuCN$^-$	Ag$^-$	(M-H)$^-$	AgM$_2^-$	MAgCN$^-$
FWHM(eV)	12	3.1	3.8	3.6	10.9	4.7	4.8	4.2
Shifts (eV)	6.5	2.5	2.6	1.7	10.9	2.8	2.6	4.2

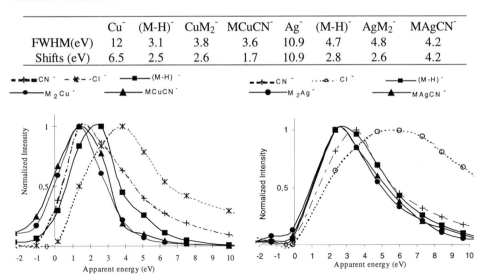

Fig.3. KEDs of negative organometallic ions on Cu (left) and Ag (right) surfaces.

In positive mode, we observe as expected, the decreasing with x of FWHMs and shifts of KEDs for Ag$_x^+$ clusters. More interesting seem to be the differences in the KE distributions of organometallic ions: the broadening of KEDs is observed (Fig.4) for Ag$_y$M$^+$ ions with increasing y and their energy maxima are also shifted at higher apparent energy (M$^+$ < AgM$^+$ <Ag$_2$M$^+$). These KEDs look really like those of cationised ions (same FWHMs and shifts as for Ag$_y$X$^+$ with X= CN, Cl and Br).

194

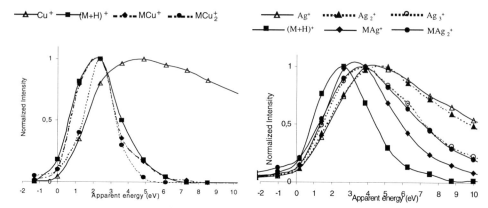

Fig.4. KEDs of positive organometallic ions on Cu (left) and Ag (right) surfaces.

No such observations can be made for the organo-copper ions: the FWHM of $(M+H)^+$ and M_x Cu_y^+ distributions were largely smaller than the FWHM of atomic and other metallic clusters Cu_x^+ and cationised ions $Cu_xCl_y^+$, or $Cu_xCN_y^+$. Moreover, their FWHMs seem to slightly decrease with y and are always smaller than the molecular ion one : $(M+H)^+ > MCu^+ > MCu_2^+$

	$(M+H)^+$	CuM^+	Cu_2M^+	$(M+H)^+$	AgM^+	Ag_2M^+
FWHMs (eV)	3.5	2.7	2	2	4.8	5.9
Shifts (eV)	2.1	2.7	2	2.5	3.2	4.8

4. Conclusion

Comparison of the kinetic energy distributions of organo-metallic ions allowed us to isolate different emission processes for copper and silver surfaces treated with benzotriazole. The broadening of KEDs observed for Ag_yM^+ is quite similar to that observed during a cationization process like Ag_yX^+ clusters. As no such broadening can be observed with positive organo-copper ions and as their KEDs have the same width than molecular ions, we assume that the emission of organo-cuprous ions does not occur by the same process but rather by a soft emission process of intact precursor-like ions species. However, even with Ag surfaces, no such broadening can be observed for negative organo-copper or -silver ions, probably due to different ionization processes in positive and negative mode.

References

[1] D. Kuron, H-J. Rother, R. Holm and S. Storp, Werstoffe und Korrosion, 37 (1986) 83.
[2] J-O. Nilsson, C. Törnkvist and B. Liedberg, Applied Surface Science, 37 (1989) 306.
[3] M. Oertel, P. Klüsener, M. Kempken, A.Benninghoven, H-J. Rother and R. Holm, Applied Surface Science, 37 (1989) 135.
[4] R. Combarieu, G. Dauchot and F. Delamare, in Metal 98, ed. by W. Mourey, James and James, London (1998) 223.
[5] B.W. Schueler, Microsc. Microanal. Microstruc. 3 (1992) 119.
[6] A. Delcorte and P. Bertrand Surf. Sci. 412/413 (1998) 97.
[7] J.B Cotton, I.R.Scholes, Brit. Corrosion J., 2 (1967) 1.

A. Benninghoven, P. Bertrand, H.-N. Migeon and H.W. Werner (Editors).
Proceedings of the 12th International Conference on Secondary Ion Mass Spectrometry,
Brussels, Belgium, 5-11 September 1999

TOF-SSIMS STUDIES OF SELF-ASSEMBLED MULTILAYERS

S.C.C. Wong, J.-C. Canry, N.P. Lockyer, and J.C. Vickerman

Surface Analysis Research Centre, Department of Chemistry,
UMIST, PO Box 88, Manchester M60 1QD, UK.
Corresponding author, e-mail: Stephen.Wong@stud.umist.ac.uk

1. Introduction

Static SIMS is developing into a powerful technique for the characterisation and analysis of more complex organic surfaces. However, the secondary ion generation processes from such surfaces are yet to be fully understood. This would seem essential to the utilisation of all the information potentially available and the proper understanding and interpretation of data acquired. To tackle this issue, well defined 'idealised' model organic systems can be applied to investigate the effects of ion bombardment and the mechanisms of secondary ion formation and emission.

Self-assembled monolayers (SAMs) have been successfully studied by, and applied to the study of the SIMS process[1-5]. Because the monolayers are highly ordered and oriented, a wide range of chemical surfaces can be created. Further monolayers may then be chemisorbed onto this layer, either directly or following further chemical modification[6]. Films can then be made to defined thicknesses, and individual layers labelled, so that the information depth can be probed. An additional advantage of self-assembled systems is that they are very well characterised due the intense interest in SAMs over the past decade.

2. Experimental

Acid-terminated monolayers were formed by immersion of thermally evaporated gold films in 1 mM ethanoic solution of mercaptoundecanoic acid (MUA) solution overnight. The acid surface was converted to a metal-salt, on exposure to 1 mM $Cu(ClO_4)_2$ ethanoic solution for approximately 5 minutes. The second and subsequent layers were formed by re-immersion in thiol solution for a further 10 hours, repeated an appropriate number of times, and then 'capped' with dodecanethiol (DDT). The samples were finally thoroughly rinsed in copious amounts of absolute ethanol, blown dry in a nitrogen stream, and immediately inserted into the instrument for analysis.

The samples were sputtered by a 25 keV Ga^+ primary beam using doses of 10^{12} ions/cm^2, and secondary ions extracted into a reflectron ToF mass analyser by pulsing the sample stage to 2.5 kV.

3. Results & discussion

For simplicity, the 'quasimolecular' species corresponding to MUA (m/z = 217), and DDT (201) have been labelled M and M' respectively. The values plotted represent the absolute integrated intensities for identical primary ion doses and experimental conditions. Under these conditions, the absolute yields of CH⁻ and S(H)⁻ remained constant throughout the entire range of samples. The SSIMS spectra from the multilayer films are similar to those reported for single layer SAMs[1].

The negative ion spectra contain the most important and informative peaks. Apart from M⁻, the other intact molecular peaks of MUA are Au[M-COOH]⁻ and Au_2M^-. On formation of the copper salt surface on the MUA monolayer, the gold containing ions are greatly reduced, resulting in the attenuation of high mass peaks (m/z > 200) relative to the low mass, including Au[M-COOH]⁻ and the complete loss of the Au_2M^- peak.

Adsorption of DDT onto this layer restores the gold related yields, and the resultant spectrum appears at first glance to be a superposition of both Au/MUA and Au/DDT spectra. The AuMM'⁻ molecular cluster ion is only observed for the bilayer, and not witnessed on adsorption of further layers. The Au_2M^- cluster also disappears beyond three monolayers, and may both be due to the yields decreasing below the noise level.

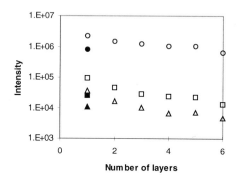

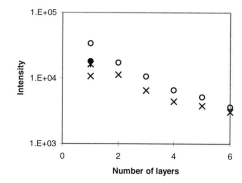

Fig. 1 Variation of (O) Au⁻, (□) Au_2^- and (Δ) Au_3^- integrated intensities with number of layers (multilayer thickness). ●, ■ and ▲ denote the signals following exposure of the MUA monolayer to $Cu(ClO_4)_2$ solution.

Fig. 2 Variation of (×) M⁻ and (O) Au[M-COOH]⁻ signal with multilayer thickness. ✻ and ● denote the corresponding signal for Cu⁺ on MUA. The first layer values are taken for Au/MUA, whilst subsequent layers are capped with DDT.

As the number of layers increases, the Au_n^- yields steadily decay (as shown in Figure 1), indicative of growing film thickness. The Au[M-COOH]⁻ intensities closely shadow this downward trend, as does M⁻ (Figure 2), reflecting an increasingly 'spongy' base with increasing numbers of layers similar to Langmuir-Blodgett films[7]. The stopping power of the gold surface is much greater than that of the organic film, and so the primary particle energy is deposited deeper in the multilayer film. Within the multilayers, the MUA is chemically bound both above and below as well as experiencing intralayer H-bonding and weaker van der Waals forces, so the probability of breaking free and escaping through the DDT layer diminishes. The escape depth of the Au[M-COOH]$^-$ species can be determined by labelling underlying acid layers using mercaptopropionic acid (MPA), for example, and monitoring the loss of Au[M-COOH]$^-$.

The Au$_n$:Au$_n$S$_m^-$ peak ratios remain similar to that of the Au/MUA monolayer, which could suggest Au escaping from the multilayer carrying S from below the surface. This though, can only be confirmed by isotopically-labelling the S- head group.

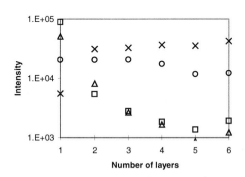

Fig. 3 Variation of ($\times$) M$'^-$, ($\bigcirc$) AuM$'^-$, ($\triangle$) Au$_2$M$'^-$, and ($\square$) AuM$'_2^-$ signals with multilayer thickness. *Note:* Here, the monolayer is Au/DDT, whereas Au/MUA was used as the monolayer in Figures 1 and 2, above.

For a Au/DDT monolayer, the M$'$ are detected predominantly in AuM$'_2^-$ and Au$_2$M$'^-$ molecular clusters, with relatively little M$'^-$, reflecting the affinity and strength of the covalent M$'$ bond to Au. In the multilayer systems, the DDT are adsorbed on Cu$^+$, where the S-Cu interaction is ionic. The yields of M$'^-$ are therefore expected to be greater than the molecular clusters, as is seen in SSIMS studies of SAMs on Ag substrates[8]. With the DDT making up the surface layer, M$'^-$ can be desorbed intact and unobstructed, so the intensities can be expected to remain relatively constant. Over the first few layers though, the yields of M$'^-$ actually increases, as can be seen in Figure 3. This may be due to an initial reduction in fragmentation with decreasing energy density, as the primary ion energy is deposited further from the surface.

It is possible that Au atoms and clusters continuously 'pick up' and are 'stripped' of molecules and fragments associated with the SAMs as they progress up through the layers. On passing through the final layer and leaving the surface, the Au and any molecules attached, escape comparatively unhindered, and intact. This is suggested by the presence of molecular clusters of Au$_n$M$'_m^-$, even though there are several MUA layers between the Au substrate and the DDT overlayer. Although the Au$_2$M$'^-$, and AuM$'_2^-$ both decrease rapidly with decreasing Au yield, the AuM$'^-$ intensity remains relatively constant for the first few monolayers, with increasing Au escape depth. It may be that stable AuM$'$ only forms within a certain energy window. With lower numbers of layers (higher energies), AuM$'$ fragments, forming predominantly neutral AuS(CH$_2$)$_{n'}$, or bond with further Au$_n$M$'_m$ species, where the energy can be more easily dissipated. As the film thickness increases, the escaping Au will reach the surface with lower energy, causing less fragmentation to the molecules that attach to it as it is ejected from the surface. It is expected however, that the intensity will start to drop as the Au yield continues to decline. Different mechanisms could also be responsible for the Au$_2$M$'$/AuM$'_2$ and AuM$'$ species.

198

The corresponding positive SSIMS spectra are generally less informative. At low mass, the spectrum is dominated by Cu^+, whose intensity remains relatively constant, even up to 18 layers[5]. This could suggest that the Cu^+ signal mainly originate from immediately below the DDT capping layer (which is also stable, as already shown above). In contrast to the negative ion spectra, the only positively charged molecular clusters are low intensities of $Au[M-H]^+$ and AuM'^+. $Au[M-H]^+$ appears more intense than AuM'^+, and appears to increase in yield relative to the Au_2^+ ion with increasing number of layers, for the number of layers studied.

4. Conclusion

The SSIMS spectra of long chained organosulphur SAMs on gold are rich in characteristic molecular clusters, allowing for easy identification. Multilayers can be self-assembled, a monolayer at a time, and by labelling the topmost layers of a multilayer system, the origins of the sputtered particles can be investigated. These results confirms the depth and chemical sensitivity of SSIMS for surface analysis, but suggest that some of the secondary ions generated in SIMS could be result of chemical association at the surface. The sputtered neutral species from self-assembled multilayers are currently under investigation by single-photon laser post-ionisation.

Acknowledgements

The financial support of EPSRC and helpful discussions with Graham Leggett and Nick Brewer are gratefully acknowledged.

References

[1] Tarlov and J.G. Newman, Langmuir 8 (1992) 1398.
[2] B. Hagenhoff, A. Benninghoven, J. Spinke, M. Liley, and W. Knoll, Langmuir 9 (1993) 1622.
[3] D. Rading, R. Kersting and A. Benninghoven in *Secondary Ion Mass Spectrometry SSIMS XI*, ed. G. Gillen, R. Lareau, J. Bennet, and F. Stevie, J. Wiley & Sons, Chichester, 1998, p 455.
[4] J.-C. Canry and J.C. Vickerman in *Secondary Ion Mass Spectrometry SSIMS X*, ed. A. Benninghoven, B. Hagenhoff, and H.W. Werner, J. Wiley & Sons, Chichester, 1997, p 623.
[5] J.-C. Canry, PhD Thesis, UMIST 1999.
[6] (a.) S.D. Evans, A. Ulman, K.E. Gobbert-Berarducci, and L.J. Gerenser, J. Am. Chem. Soc. 113 (1991) 5866. (b.) T.L. Freeman, S.D. Evans and A. Ulman; Thin Solid Films 224 (1994) 784. (c.) T.L. Freeman, S.D. Evans, and A. Ulman, Langmuir 11 (1995) 4411.
[7] G. Bolbach, A. Viari, R. Galera, A. Brunot, J.C. Blais, Int. J. Mass Spectrom. Ion Processes 112 (1992) 93.
[8] D.A. Hutt, E. Cooper, and G.J. Leggett, J. Phys. Chem. 102 (1998) 174.

A. Benninghoven, P. Bertrand, H.-N. Migeon and H.W. Werner (Editors).
Proceedings of the 12th International Conference on Secondary Ion Mass Spectrometry,
Brussels, Belgium, 5-11 September 1999
199

INFLUENCE OF THE SUBSTRATE ON THE KINETIC ENERGY OF MOLECULAR FRAGMENTS IN SIMS OF POLYMER OVERLAYERS

B. Arezki, A. Delcorte and P. Bertrand
Unité de physico-chimie et de physique des matériaux, Université Catholique de Louvain,
1 pl.Croix du sud, B-1348 Louvain-la-Neuve, Belgium

1. Introduction

Static secondary ion mass spectrometry (SSIMS) is known as a very sensitive technique for the analysis of thin polymer layers [1] and their chemical characterisation. However, our understanding of the physics underlying organic molecule sputtering is still incomplete. To improve this knowledge, Tof-SIMS may also provide fundamental insights into the mechanisms involved in organic secondary molecular ion formation, via the interpretation of the kinetic energy distribution (KED) of the ejected species. The shape of these distributions, directly related to the mechanisms at play, provide information about both sputtering and ionisation processes. In this work, in order to contribute to the understanding of the emission processes in molecular ToF-SIMS, we focus on the influence of the substrate on the KEDs of molecular fragments sputtered from polystyrene films spin-coated onto Si and Ag, respectively. It is found that the distributions are significantly steeper for the Si substrate than for the Ag substrate, showing that not only the yields, but also the energies of the sputtered ions, are influenced by the nature of the substrate.

2. Experimental

2.1 Sample preparation.

A solution of the polymer sample, monodisperse tert-butyl ended polystyrene (PS) (M_n=2000), has been spin coated onto Si and Ag substrates cleaned in isopropanol and hexane. The Ag substrates were formed by evaporation of a silver polycrystal film onto silicon wafers under vacuum. Prior to spin coating, PS was dissolved in toluene with a concentration equal to 3 mg/ml. With this concentration, the spin-coating technique produces very thin films, appropriate to study the influence of the substrate. In all the samples investigated, a significant and reproducible secondary ion signal corresponding to the substrate was indeed detected. In addition, charging effects may be avoided using such films, as required for the KED measurements.

2.2 KED measurements.

The experimental setup and the KED measurements have already been described in detail elsewhere [1,2]. The main features can be summarized as follows. The KED measurements were performed by means of a time of flight secondary ion mass spectrometer TOF-SIMS microscope microprobe (Charles Evans & assoc.) using a (5 kHz) pulsed Ga+ beam (15 keV, 400-800 pA DC current; 2 ns pulse width) [3]. The primary current was focused (0.2 μm) and rastered onto a (130 μm ×130 μm) area. The secondary ions were accelerated by a 3 kV potential directly applied on the sample and then they were energy-analyzed by a slit (1.5 eV passband) placed at the crossover preceding the second hemispherical electrostatic analyser (ESA). For each KED measurement, ~15 positive mass spectra (~10^{12} ions/cm^2 per acquisition) in the range 0-300 amu were recorded with different sample voltages (different energy windows). Finally, the zero of energy scale was estimated from the intersection between the tangent to the increasing part of the KED of the atomic substrate ions and the voltage axis.

3. Results and Discussion

3.1 Degradation of the bombarded area

To scan the energy range of interest, about fifteen mass spectra are recorded on the same sample area. Due to the high primary ion fluence required to obtain a good signal/noise ratio using the energy slit, these repeated bombardment sequences induced a significant degradation of the sample surface. In order to correct the effects of the degradation on the KEDs, we first determined the evolution of the secondary ion yields in this range of fluence.

The degradation laws for some of the most characteristic ions of PS spin-coated onto Si and Ag respectively, are plotted in Fig. 1. It is important to note that both the $C_7H_7^+$ (m/z=91) and the $C_4H_9^+$ (m/z=57) ions, characteristic of the benzyl endgroup and of the t-butyl endgroup of the polymer respectively, are very sensitive to the surface degradation. In contrast, the intensity of the less characteristic $C_2H_3^+$ ion (m/z=27) does not vary much during the acquisitions. This suggests that the latter could be formed as a result of degradation whereas the others originate essentially from the unbombarded PS chains. In addition, this comparison shows a non negligible influence of the substrate on the degradation of $C_2H_3^+$ and $C_4H_9^+$, whereas it does not influence the $C_7H_7^+$ ion. In the following KED measurements, the intensities will be divided by the normalized intensities reported in Fig. 1.

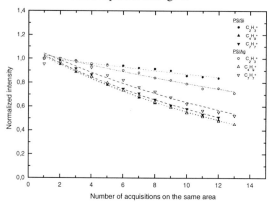

Fig. 1. Degradation laws of several characteristic ions sputtered from PS spin-coated on Si and Ag

3.2. Kinetic energy distributions

Fig. 2 shows the KEDs of several characteristic ions of t-butyl ended polystyrene oligomers for the two substrates Si and Ag. For all the investigated molecular ions, there is a significant difference in the shape of the curves. In general, the high energy tail of the KEDs is steeper for the Si substrate than for the Ag substrate. In contrast, in the studied energy range, no substrate effect is observed in the 'negative' energy tail corresponding to ions formed by unimolecular dissociation reactions in the vacuum. The only noticeable exception is $C_4H_9^+$ which exhibits a steeper 'negative' energy tail for PS deposited on Si.

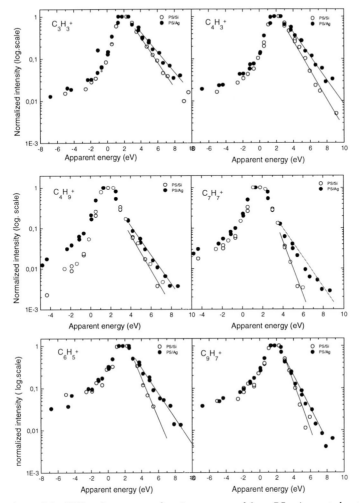

Fig. 2. *Comparison of the KEDs of some secondary ions sputtered from PS spin-coated onto Si (°) and Ag (•).*

Although the energy resolution of our instrument is limited to 1.5 eV, preventing any interpretation of the low energy part of the KEDs (0-2 eV), the divergence of the high energy tails is significant (beyond 2 eV in Fig. 2). As indicated by previous measurements [2] and by the agreement between ion KEDs measured by ToF-SIMS and neutral distributions calculated via MD simulation [4], the influence of ionization on the kinetic energy of sputtered organic fragments appears negligible. Therefore, the differences reported in Fig. 2 are most likely related to the mechanistic details of the ejection process. In addition, the fact that the same behavior is observed for the vast majority of the fragment ions shows that it is not due the organization of the PS chains on the surface, that might differ with Ag and Si substrates, but rather to the very nature of the substrate. From the mechanistic viewpoint, Ag and Si differ by their atomic mass and by the structure of the lattice they constitute. Both factors influence the penetration depth of the impinging particle and the development of the collision cascades in the solid. Although the detailed role of the substrate in the formation of fragments is still unknown, it is probable that Ag atoms, heavier and larger than Si, interact with several carbon atoms simultaneously, while the interaction with Si should be more local. The different substrate atoms might then induce the emission of fragments with significantly different amounts of kinetic and internal energy. It is interesting to note that a reduction of the kinetic energy of benzene molecules has been also observed when going from benzene monolayers (Ag substrate) to benzene multilayers (benzene substrate) [5]. In that case, the different binding energies with the two substrate might constitute an important part of the explanation. In our samples, the energy required to eject the fragments should not change, because the same covalent bonds must be broken irrelevant of the nature of the substrate. Nevertheless, the different binding energies of the PS molecules to the two substrates might still play a minor role.

4. Conclusion

In this preliminary work, we have shown, owing to the ToF-SIMS analysis, a significant influence of the substrate on the energy distribution of fragment ions sputtered from PS films. In general, the KEDs are narrower and have steeper high energy tails with the Si substrate than with the Ag substrate. Although uncompletely understood, the reason of this behavior resides most likely in the ejection step, rather than the ionization step of the secondary ion formation. Experimentally, additional substrates such as graphite, copper and gold could be used to check if there is a correlation between the mass of the substrate atoms or the lattice structure and the kinetic energy of the sputtered fragments. From the theoretical viewpoint, molecular dynamics simulations might be performed to check the validity of the proposed explanation. As the sputtered yield is also strongly influenced by the substrate, a better understanding of the most relevant parameters should lead to a more systematic design of the samples in order to achieve high yields of sputtered molecular species.

5. Acknowledgements

B. Arezki gratefully acknowledges Pr. W. Bruyneel and the 'AGCD-UCL' for supporting her participation in this work. A. Delcorte was supported by the 'Action de Recherche' (94/99-173) of the 'Communauté Francaise de Belgique'. The TOF-SIMS equipment was acquired with the support of the FRFC and the 'Région Wallonne' of Belgium.

References

[1]   P. Bertrand and L.-T. Weng, Mikrochim. Acta [Suppl] 13 (1996) 167
[2]   A. Delcorte and P. Bertrand, Nucl. Instr. and Meth. B 115 (1996) 246
[3]   B.W.Schueler, Microsc. Microanal. Microstruct. 3 (1992) 119
[4]   A. Delcorte, X. Vanden Eynde, P. Bertrand, J. C. Vickerman and B. J. Garrison, unpublished results
[5]   R. Chatterjee, D. E. Riederer, Z. Postawa and N. Winograd, J. Phys. Chem. B (1998) 4176

SECTION 5 :
FOCUSED ION BEAMS

A. Benninghoven, P. Bertrand, H.-N. Migeon and H.W. Werner (Editors).
Proceedings of the 12th International Conference on Secondary Ion Mass Spectrometry,
Brussels, Belgium, 5-11 September 1999

USEFUL ION YIELD ENHANCEMENT FOR LMIS-SIMS BY OXYGEN ION IMPLANTATION : A SYSTEMATIC STUDY

M Hughes[1], DS McPhail[1], RJ Chater[1] and J Walker[2]

[1]Materials Dept., Imperial College of Science, Technology and Medicine, London SW7 2BP UK
[2]FEI Europe Ltd., Cottenham, Cambridge CB4 4PS UK

1. Introduction

The development of the Gallium liquid metal ion source (LMIS) facilitates SIMS analyses to be conducted with a very high lateral resolution, in the order of tens of nanometres [1,2]. The major difficulty over the more conventional oxygen or cesium ion source systems is in the reduced secondary ion yield revealed as an undesirably low sensitivity [3]. The limited amount of research into increasing the secondary ion yield of LMIS SIMS that has been carried out [3-5] agrees, not unexpectedly, that the introduction of surface oxygen enhances positive secondary ion emission. In this investigation, oxygen for positive ion yield enhancement with Ga^+ sputtering is introduced into silicon by O_2^+ ion beam implantation.

The altered layer produced by high dose oxygen ion implantation in silicon and surface silica layers has been studied in depth and modelled for high O_2^+ ion energies [6,7]. Similar studies have characterised the layer at O_2^+ ion implant energies appropriate to SIMS analysis [8]. Vandervorst [9] has recently reviewed all aspects of oxygen incorporation in a SIMS context with an emphasis on the initial build-up period prior to a steady state, set thickness.

The goals of this work were to explore how the Si^+ secondary ion yield enhancement for Ga^+ LMIS sputtering varied with the depth distribution of the implanted oxygen. The O_2^+ oxygen implantation was carried out using an Atomika 6500 microprobe and the Ga^+ LMIS depth profiling and imaging of the samples using an FEI FIB200 instrument equipped with a quadrupole mass spectrometer [10].

2. Experimental Method

2.1 Oxygen implantation into Silicon

Oxygen was implanted into silicon using the Atomika 6500 SIMS instrument to form thin crater base oxide layers at $^{16}O_2^+$ beam energies of between 3keV and 15keV at normal incidence. The oxygen build up in the 250 x 250 μm^2 crater base of the sample was monitored using secondary ion detection for steady state sputtering conditions. A set of samples was similarly produced at incidence angles of between 5° and 35° at a fixed incident beam energy of 15keV.

2.2 Oxide layer characterisation with Ga^+ LMIS and Xe^+ primary ion beams

Ga^+ primary ion depth profiles of the crater base oxide layer were obtained by raster scanning over an area of 50 x 50 μm^2 inside the original 250 x 250 μm^2 crater in the FEI FIB200 instrument. The Ga^+ primary beam energy was fixed at 30keV and 5.7nA with a pixel width of 150nm and pixel separation of 150nm. Si^+ (28amu) and O^+(16 amu) secondary ions were recorded from an area of 25 x 25 μm^2 (25% gate) at the centre of the Ga^+ beam scanned area. This electronic gating ensures that the recorded depth profile is free of crater edge effects. The depth profiling was continued until the secondary ion signals indicated that the steady state sputtering conditions in the substrate silicon had been achieved.

Xe^+ primary ion depth profiling was performed under similar conditions in the Atomika 6500 SIMS instrument. The Xe^+ beam energy was 3keV with a beam focus of ~50μm into a crater size of area 150 x 150 μm^2 . Ions were collected from a 3.5% gate at the centre of the Xe^+ beam scanned area. Electrons at 2keV from a flood gun source were used to reduce charging effects occurring during the profiling.

Two reference samples were used to interpret the secondary ion signals and calibrate the beam sputterate for steady state sputtering conditions; unprocessed silicon and a 200μm thick thermal oxide layer. Analysis of the thermal oxide layer required a compensating electron gun. The depth of the craters formed after analysis were measured using a microscope-based interferometric optical surface profiler (ZYGO NewView 200).

3. Results and discussion

The typical depth profile result shown schematically in Fig. 1 is used to define a number of symbols and regions of the profile for the following discussion. The secondary ion intensity at the turning point where the plateau region intersects the signal decay region is I_{TP} . The position on the depth profile when the intensity has reduced to $0.5I_{TP}$ defines the yield enhancement depth, D. This point is the demarcation between surface oxide and substrate silicon for which slightly different sputterates apply. For example, 1.08 for Ga^+ LMIS sputtering from the reference samples which compares with 1.09 from SRIM-2000. The intensity of the secondary ion signal decays to a value I_{BULK} once the implanted oxygen of the surface layer has been removed. The enhancement associated with this oxygen is

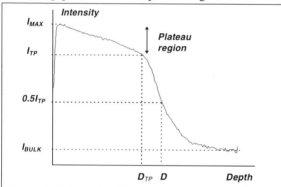

Figure 1 Schematic diagram of a typical Si^+ depth profile obtained using either the Xe^+ or Ga^+ LMIS primary ion sputtering beams

characterised by I/I_{BULK} and this has a maximum value for both Ga^+ LMIS and Xe^+ primary ion sputtering near the start of the profile, I_{MAX}/I_{BULK}.

Results derived from the SIMS depth profiles for oxide layers implanted by normal incidence oxygen implantation are summarised in Fig. 2 on the basis of the Fig. 1. terminology. The yield enhancement depth, D for Ga^+ LMIS sputtering shows a linear dependence on energy. The values found for Xe^+ sputtering agree with previous SIMS studies in this laboratory (Beyer[11], data plotted as symbols in Fig. 2) and published SIMS, AES, RBS and TEM measurements [9]. Compared to Xe+ sputtering, the intercept is the same (3.5+/-0.5nm) but the slope is down by a factor (0.4+/-0.04). Thus in this set of experiments a major fraction of the oxide layer was not participating in Si^+ yield enhancement. The maximum yield enhancement, I_{MAX}/I_{BULK} is consistently down by a factor of 3 to 4 on the values recorded for Xe^+ ion sputtering. (The yield enhancement for native oxide on silicon was about 22, a further factor of 8 down). Since the sputterate for SiO_2 by Xe^+ compared with the bulk silicon is 1.06

cf. 1.08 for Ga⁺, the factor of 3 or 4 is mainly associated with the ratio of the ionization coefficients in the two cases.

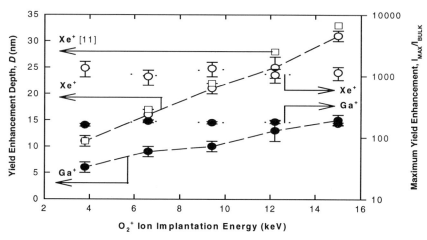

Fig. 2. Silicon implanted with O_2^+ ions at normal incidence.

The results for non-normally incident O_2^+ ions are shown in Fig. 3 and present a similar, but more complicated picture, compared with the results for normally incident O_2^+ ions. The yield enhancement depth, D for Ga⁺ LMIS sputtering shows the same trends compared with Xe⁺ sputtering. The agreement with Beyers results [11] is not as good as for the normal case. The maximum yield enhancement, I_{MAX}/I_{BULK} is similarly down by approximately the same factor for angles up to 25°. This incidence angle corresponds to the limit for the formation of a continuous stoichiometric oxide layer [8].

The yield enhancement shows a pronounced negative slope of about 12 per nm in the plateau region for all of the different O_2^+ ion implant energies and angles up to 20° where little variation was expected. The oxygen concentration in the altered layer is known to be constant, corresponding closely to SiO_2 [8]. The slope in the decay region is approximately 10 times larger. Charging during the SIMS analysis was not implicated either as electron compensation was not required and the gallium ion range exceeded the oxide thickness in all the O_2^+ ion implant samples, see below.

The two important differences between SIMS depth profile analyses with Xe⁺ and Ga⁺ LMIS sputtering are the widths of the mixed layer (Rp+ΔRp) and the reactive nature of the gallium ions. As the mixed layer for 3keV Xe⁺ in SiO_2 is 7.3nm, so the build-up and establishment of steady state sputtering conditions is entirely contained within the ion-implanted SiO_2 layer. In contrast the mixed layer for 30keV Ga LMIS sputtering is 36nm which is larger than the thickest ion implanted SiO_2 layer. In this case the depth profiles recorded are those of the build-up region in a matrix whose composition is changing. However the immediate domination of gallium in the near surface layers is reflected in the almost constant (I_{MAX}/I_{BULK}) level recorded for all energies and angles up to 20°. Ga-O bonds will form in preference to Si O bonds because of thermo-dynamic considerations (Heat of Formation). Also the surface

208

composition of the crater base will be changing from (Si, O) to (Si, O, Ga). If Ga-O bonds increasingly dominate the surface of the altered layer during the build-up period for Ga⁺ LMIS sputtering then Si⁺ ion emission will decrease as the crater base receeds into the bulk silicon. This trend follows that predicted by the bond-breaking model usually invoked to explain positive secondary ion production from metal surfaces with oxygen beams.

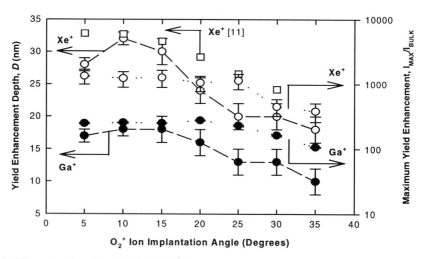

Fig. 3. Silicon implanted with 15keV O_2^+ ions at incidence angles between 5 and 35degrees.

4. Conclusions

The yield enhancement for positive silicon ions is dominated by the presence of gallium at the crater base surface in contrast to SIMS analysis with xenon ions. The initial yield enhancement maximum is followed by a negative slope in the plateau region corresponding to the mixing of gallium and dilution of oxygen in the initially stoichiometric SiO_2 layer.

References

[1] J. Orloff Rev. Sci. Instrum. **64** (1993) 1105
[2] L. W Swanson Applied Surface Science **76** (1994) 80
[3] M. Schumacher, H.N. Migeon, B. Rasser in *Proc. 8th Int. Conf. On Secondary Ion Mass Spectrometry, SIMS VIII*, John Wiley & Sons (1991), pp.49-53
[4] G.A. Crow, L. Christman, M. Utlaut J. Vac. Sci. Technol. **B13** (1995) 2607
[5] J. Kinoshita, K. Shiozawa, T. Yamasaki in *Proc. 9th Int. Conf. On Secondary Ion Mass Spectrometry SIMS IX*, John Wiley & Sons (1993), pp.569-572
[6] R.J. Chater et al. Nucl. Instr. & Methods in Phys. Res. **B55** (1991) p686-690
[7] H.U. Jager et al. Thin Solid Films, 161 (1988) 333-342
[8] S. Littlewood and J.A. Kilner J. Appl. Physics **63** (1988) 2173
[9] W.Vandervorst et al. in *Proc. 9th Int. Conf. On Secondary Ion Mass Spectrometry SIMS IX*, John Wiley & Sons (1993), pp.599-608
[10] T. Dingle et al. in *Proc. 10th Int. Conf. On Secondary Ion Mass Spectrometry SIMS X*, John Wiley & Sons (1995), pp.517-520
[11] G.P. Beyer PhD Thesis, University of London (Imperial College of Science, Technology and Medicine), London SW7 2BP UK

A. Benninghoven, P. Bertrand, H.-N. Migeon and H.W. Werner (Editors).
Proceedings of the 12th International Conference on Secondary Ion Mass Spectrometry,
Brussels, Belgium, 5-11 September 1999
© 2000 Elsevier Science B.V. All rights reserved.

RECENT RESULTS AND DEVELOPMENTS ON THE CAMECA NANOSIMS 50

F.Hillion[a], F. Horreard[a] and F. J. Stadermann[b]

[a] CAMECA, 103 Boulevard Saint Denis, 92400 Courbevoie, France. E-mail: hillion@cameca.fr
[b] Mc Donell Center for Space Sciences and Physics Department Washington University, 1
Brookings Drive, St Louis, MO 63130, USA. E-mail: fjs@ howdy.wustl.edu

1. Introduction

Based on Pr. Slodzian and al. [1, 2] original design, the commercial version of the NANOSIMS 50 incorporates several new developments in order to improve performances:
- The magnet radius has been increased up to 550 mm.
- Seven detector are now available in the multicollection system.
- A mechanical switch is installed, allowing use of both Cs and Duoplasmatron source.
- A Wien filter allows mass filtering of the duoplasmatron ion beam.

2. Description of the instrument

It includes a normal primary ion incidence and a normal co-axial secondary ion extraction, to optimize simultaneously the objective lens performance and the ion collection. This design allows to reduce the final objective/sample distance (0.4 mm), leading to very low aberration coefficients and thus to a smaller spot size for a given probe current.

As the polarity of primary ion and secondary ion must of opposite sign, the ion sources are the duoplasmatron, used in O^- mode for electro-positive elements, and the Cesium micro-beam surface ionization source, for electro-negative elements. A mechanical switch under vacuum permits to rapidly change of primary ions. As shown on figure 1 the cesium source can be moved under vacuum from position A where the duoplasmatron is used to position B where the cesium ion beam is sent into the primary column. In order to mass-filter the ions coming out of the duoplasmatron, a Wien filter is available.

Beam sizes of 50 nm (16-84 %) Cs^+ and 150 nm (16-84 %) O^- are obtained together with high mass resolution and high transmission.

The mass spectrometer is based on a double focusing magnetic sector of Mattauch-Herzog-like geometry. The magnet radius has been increased to 550 mm in order to allow simultaneous collection of ^{12}C, ^{13}C, ^{28}Si, ^{29}Si and ^{30}Si. The minimum radius is 130 mm leading to a mass range of more than 17 which permits to collect for example mass 10 and 170 simultaneously. Maximum mass is 400 at 8 keV energy for the secondary ion beam.

Seven detectors are now available (Figure 1):
- four moveable miniature electron multiplier (EM) with moveable slits of predefined width (three different values),
- one Faraday cup attached to the first moveable EM,
- one fixed miniature EM at a radius of 528 mm, with 3 slits of predefined width,
- one large EM at a radius of 550 mm equipped with a continuously adjustable slit and a cylindrical electrostatic sector between the slit and the EM to improve the abundance sensitivity.

In addition, each detector is equipped with a pair of parallel plates allowing to scan the secondary ion beam on the first EM's dynode, record a HMR mass spectrum around the current mass, and allow a precise positioning of mass line in the detector slit.

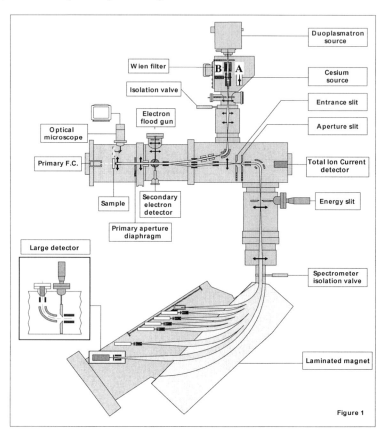

Figure 1

3. Applications to Space Sciences

The first NANOSIMS 50 instrument will be installed at the Laboratory for Space Science of Washington University in St. Louis MO, USA, by the end of 1999. One important focus of the work there is the chemical and isotopic characterization of sub-micron particles from meteorite residues [3]. The isotopic compositions of these particles vary significantly and give clues about their origin. Because of the experimental difficulties, most of the work so far has concentrated on the larger size fraction of these presolar grains. We performed several tests [4] with the NANOSIMS prototype to evaluate whether such measurements can be extended to smaller presolar dust grains, which are more abundant in the existing meteoritic separates and whose size is more typical of grains in the interstellar medium [5].

Several 300 nm Al_2O_3 standard particles have been deposited on a Au foil. These small dust grains can easily be identified by raster imaging and individually measured in multidetection mode without affecting other particles less than one micron away.

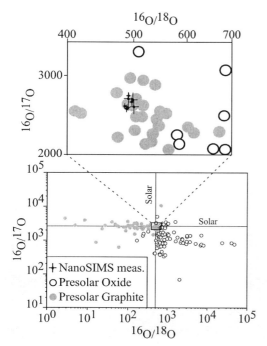

Figure 2: Comparison of the achievable precision in oxygen isotopic measurements.

The results of these measurement of the Al_2O_3 standard particles are shown in Figure 2 in comparison with the compositions of larger presolar dust grains ($\rangle 1\mu m$) that have been measured with Washington University's IMS 3f instrument [6].

The circles show the compositions of micron-sized (i.e. "large") presolar grains as measured with the IMS 3f. The black crosses (with error bars) indicate the results of NANOSIMS 50 measurements on individual 300 nm Al_2O_3 standards.

The capability of the NANOSIMS 50 to measure all three oxygen isotopes in particles this small with such a high precision means that measurements of even smaller presolar grains will yield meaningful results.

4. Applications to Biology

Tissue sections (0.5 micron thick) of a culture of melanoma cells incubated 24 hours with two labeled molecules ^{14}C-Uridine (1 μM) and ^{15}N-Arginine (1mM), were analysed. The preparation was fixed with glutaraldehyde and embedded in epoxy resin.

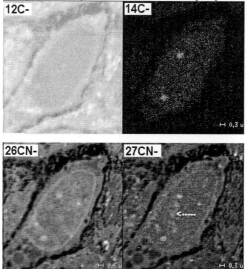

Figure 3: Four simultaneous images of a melanoma cell. Field of view: 10x10 μm^2. Acq. time 30 mn, lin scale.

212

One set of four simultaneous images (Figure 3, courtesy of Elif Hindié, Laboratoire de Biophysique, Faculté de Médecine, Université Paris-XII, Créteil France) was obtained by recording respectively $^{12}C^-$, $^{14}C^-$, $^{12}C^{14}N^-$ and $^{12}C^{15}N^-$ ions with a mass resolving power of 5000. The different cell constituents are seen on the $^{12}C^{14}N^-$ image (lower-left). The nuclear membrane is clearly visible. The $^{14}C^-$ image (upper-right) shows the distribution of ^{14}C-Uridine which is present in the cytoplasm and in the nucleus, with a higher concentration in the nucleoli (two bright dots) as expected. Distribution of ^{15}N (both natural and linked with Arginine) is shown on the $^{12}C^{15}N^-$ image (lower-right). Differences between ^{14}N image and ^{15}N image would correspond to incorporated ^{15}N-Arginine: higher incorporation seems to occur in some nuclear structures (white arrows) which could correspond to newly-formed nuclear proteins (Histones). At the opposite the nuclear membrane is less visible than in the ^{14}N image indicating a lower rate of incorporation of 15N-Arginine.

Simultaneous acquisitions allow to estimate (i) the concentration of ^{14}C-U by calculating the isotopic ratio $^{14}C/^{12}C$, (ii) the renewal rate of ^{15}N-A by calculating the increase of the isotopic ratio $^{15}N/^{14}N$ above the natural occurrence (0.367%).

5. Applications to Material Sciences

Two different types of ceramic materials (YAG) have been analyzed. Figure 4 shows Silicon maps on this insulating material obtained by recording Si⁻ ions using a cesium beam size of 100 nm (16-84%), without using any charge compensation. Silicon, one of the additives, has been found segregated either at grain boundaries or at triple points of grains. On the left image, Si concentration can be estimated around 0.1 %.

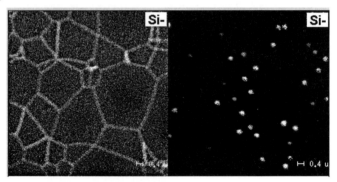

Figure 4: Si-maps of two different YAG samples, left : YAG with stoichiometric composition (Y/Al= 3/5), right: YAG with Y/Al= 3.015/5. Field of view 10x10 μm², Acquisition time 30 mn, linear scale. (Courtesy of Haneda Hajime, National Institute for Research in Inorganic Materials, Tsukuba, Ibaraki JAPAN.)

References
[1] G. Slodzian, B. Daigne, F. Girard, F. Boust, High Sensitivity and High Spatial Resolution Ion Probe Instrument, Proceedings of the 6th SIMS Conference, Versailles, Sept. 87.
[2] F.Hillion, B. Daigne, F. Girard, G. Slodzian, A new high performance instrument : The Cameca Nanosims 50, Proceedings of the 9th SIMS Conference, Yokohama, Nov. 93.
[3] Bernatowicz T. and Walker R. M. (1997) Physics Today, Dec., 26-32.
[4] Stadermann F. J. et al. (1999) Lunar Planet. Sci. Conf. XXX, #1407.
[5] Mathis J. S. (1990) Ann. Rev. Astron. Astrophys., 28, 37.
[6] Zinner E. (1998) Ann. Rev. Earth Planet. Sci., 26, 147.

A. Benninghoven, P. Bertrand, H.-N. Migeon and H.W. Werner (Editors).
Proceedings of the 12th International Conference on Secondary Ion Mass Spectrometry,
Brussels, Belgium, 5-11 September 1999

CHEMICAL SURFACE CHARACTERIZATION OF COMPLEX AGX MICRO-CRYSTALS BY IMAGING TOF-SIMS AND DUAL BEAM DEPTH PROFILING

G. Verlinden[a], R. Gijbels[a], I. Geuens[b], R. De Keyzer[b]

[a]University of Antwerp, Department of Chemistry, Universiteitsplein 1,
2610 Wilrijk, Belgium, e-mail: verlinde@uia.ua.ac.be
[b]Agfa-Gevaert N.V., R&D Laboratories, Mortsel, Belgium

1. Introduction

The increasing demand for more environment friendly, light sensitive materials with higher efficiency, better image quality and stability has resulted in significant changes in the different synthesis procedures. As a result, the nanostructural design of silver halide microcrystals has gradually changed during the last five years. The newly designed crystals are characterized by thin conversion layers, shallower halide gradients, lower concentrations of particular halides and adsorbed organic layers.

In previous work [1,2], we have presented a method based on imaging TOF-SIMS and local image depth profiling for the analysis of silver halide microcrystals with subpercent global iodide concentrations confined in surface layers with a thickness well below 5nm. The lateral resolution of the Ga LMIS of the TOF-SIMS IV instrument (ca. 65 nm, calculated with computer generated line profiles) allows the analysis of individual microcrystals with a size well below 1 μm in a given emulsion. In this paper, it is shown that TOF-SIMS analysis can also be employed for the molecular imaging of thiocyanate adsorbed layers (SCN) at crystal surfaces and for the differentiation of iodide conversion layers synthesized under different conditions.

2. Experimental

All experiments were performed on a TOF SIMS IV instrument. A Ga$^+$ LMIS operating at an energy of 25 keV is used as the analysis ion source. The primary ion dose densities used for the acquisition of secondary ion mass spectra and scanning ion images are respectively 7.4 E12 PI/cm^2 per spectrum and 5.5 E13 PI/cm^2 per image. The acquisition time for one image is 82 s. For the dual beam depth profiling experiments, a 1 keV Cs$^+$ sputter ion beam with a current density of 3.5 E13 PI/(cm^2·s) was used for the sputtering of the surface layer.

The photographic emulsion is diluted with water and degelled by ultracentrifugation or by the addition of trypsine for enzymatic degradation. After centrifugation the crystals are redispersed in water. A drop of the dispersion is placed onto a piece of silicon and dried to the air.

3. Results and discussion

Molecular imaging of thiocyanate adsorbed layers (SCN) at the surface of tabular Ag(Br,I) microcrystals

An emulsion of Ag(Br,I) tabular microcrystals with a mean diameter of 1.1 μm and a mean thickness of 230nm, containing 99 mole % AgBr and 1 mole % AgI was treated with different concentrations of KSCN (ranging from 1.4 mmole SCN/mole Ag to 14 mmole SCN/mole Ag) to study the adsorption of the SCN at the microcrystal surface. The adsorbed SCN plays an important part in the chemical sensitization of the material to increase the efficiency of latent image formation and thus improves the sensitivity of the photographic material [1]. If we calculate the total number of silver ions present at the surface for a symmetrical hexagonal crystal with dimensions described above (1.6 E7 atoms/crystal) and compare this with the number of SCN⁻ ions added per crystal for the various concentrations (5.2 E6-5.2 E7 SCN⁻/crystal), we obtain a sub-monolayer surface coverage for the

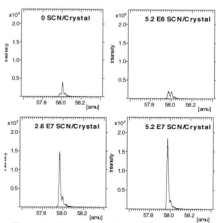

Figure 1: Increase of the SCN⁻ secondary ion intensity (left peak) in the TOF-SIMS spectrum

lowest concentration and multilayer coverage for the highest concentration added (assuming 100 % efficiency of the adsorption).

Figure 1 shows clearly the difference in the SCN⁻ ion intensity in the mass spectrum when various KSCN concentrations are added to the emulsion. A significant difference is already detected between the lowest concentration and the blank emulsion. The other two signals ($SiH_2N_2^-$ and $SiCH_4N^-$ (middle peak and right peak respectively in figure 1, top left corner)) measured at mass 58 originate from the substrate material and are more or less constant for the four samples. The SCN⁻/Br⁻ was calculated for each analysis to correct for the number of crystals present in the analyzed field. The results (see table 1) still show small but significant differences in the SCN-/Br- ratio for the lowest concentration.

	KSCN concentration (molecules/crystal)	Mean SCN⁻/Br⁻ ratio (5 measurements)
Sample 1	0	2.15 E-2 ± 1.1 E-3
Sample 2	5.2 E6	2.53 E-2 ± 1.2 E-3
Sample 3	2.6 E7	2.54 E-1 ± 1.4 E-2
Sample 4	5.2 E7	2.47 E-1 ± 1.2 E-2

Table 1: Measured SCN⁻/Br⁻ secondary ion intensity ratios for four samples with different KSCN concentrations added

For the two highest concentrations of KSCN added, the SCN⁻/Br⁻ ratio increases approximately with a factor 10. If we take into account the standard deviation on the mean value, it is not possible to distinguish between the two samples. This observation indicates that for both KSCN concentrations added, the surface coverage of the microcrystal is complete, which is in agreement with our calculation. A different thickness in adsorbed layer is still expected and was verified with secondary ion imaging.

The Br⁻ and SCN⁻ distribution at the surface of a group of tabular microcrystals for the different concentrations is shown in figure 2. Some correlation between the two distributions is already obtained for the lowest concentration. The two highest concentrations reveal crystal surfaces covered with a homogenous SCN⁻ layer. Subsequent scans of same analyzed field with a primary ion dose of 5.3 E13/cm² per scan result in the significant erosion of the surface layer at a rate of 1-1.5 monolayers/image [1]. Local image depth profiling was performed to calculate the different SCN⁻/Br⁻ ratios in individual microcrystals (figure 3). It is indeed found that the adsorbed SCN layer is thicker for the highest KSCN concentration added. The thickness of the layer is estimated to be a few monolayers. It is possible that the SCN adsorbed layer is thicker but that due to the primary ion bombardment emission of intact SCN molecules is hampered.

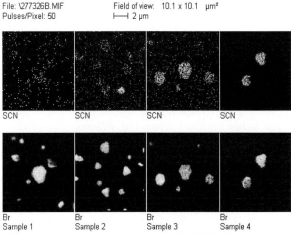

File: \277326B.MIF   Field of view: 10.1 x 10.1 µm²
Pulses/Pixel: 50   ⊢—⊣ 2 µm

Figure 2: Secondary ion images of the SCN⁻ (top row) and corresponding Br⁻ distribution (bottom row) for sample 1 (blank emulsion) to sample 4 (5.2 E7 SCN molecules/crystal)

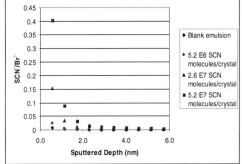

Figure 3: SCN⁻/Br⁻ secondary ion intensity ratios based on local image depth profiling of individual micocrystals

Analysis of iodide enriched surface layers synthesized with different methods on tabular Ag(Br,I) microcrystals

The creation of an iodide enriched surface layer at the surface of silver halide microcrystal is advantageous for the extension of the light absorption region of the material, the increase of the intrinsic sensitivity and the aggregation of organic molecules at the surface [1]. From an ecological viewpoint, it is important to keep the iodide concentration as low as possible.

The layers were created using two different methods. For one emulsion KI was used as the iodide source. In a second emulsion, AgI nano-particles with a mean size of 30 nm were added. Other experimental parameters like temperature, pH, reaction time and flow rate of the reagentia were kept constant. The layers were grown on tabular AgBr microcrystals with the same dimensions as described above. We analyzed two sets of two samples with a global iodide concentration of 0.7 and 0.14 mole % (referenced to the total halide concentration in the microcrystal). This corresponds even for the highest concentration with a submonolayer surface coverage of iodide. The resulting iodide concentration distributions based on the dual beam TOF-SIMS depth profiles are shown in figure 4. The iodide concentration estimate is based on the secondary ion intensity ratio of I⁻/Br⁻ [1]. The depth scale is based on sputter rate experiments on pure silver halides under 14.5 and 5.5 keV Cs^+ ion bombardment [1,5] in combination with TRIM simulations [1]. The synthesis of iodide enriched layers with KI results in a significantly higher iodide concentration at the surface of the tabular AgBr microcrystals in comparison with the AgI nanoparticles method. There is only a small difference in iodide concentration at the surface for the two samples with the KI method but the highest concentration results in a thicker iodide enriched layer. The different results of the two methods can be explained by the different kinetics of the two methods. When KI is added to the emulsion, the iodide is present in the solution in its ionic state and can be readily incorporated in the crystal surface. An iodide layer created with AgI nanoparticles demands the dissolution of the nanoparticle in the vicinity of the mi-

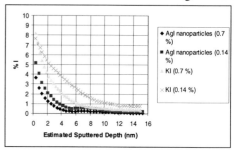

Figure 4: Iodide distribution in the iodide enriched surface layer synthesized with two different methods

crocrystal to release the iodide prior to the reaction with the microcrystal surface. This is of course a much slower process. The advantage of the AgI nanoparticle method is that it creates thinner, more homogeneous iodide layers through the better control over the reaction (figure 4).

4. Summary

TOF-SIMS analysis was used to study the distribution of adsorbed SCN at the surface of individual tabular microcrystals. The secondary ion distribution of the SCN^- reveals a homogeneous surface coverage of the microcrystal. The thickness of the adsorbed layer corresponds with the expected values based on the number of atoms present at the crystal surface and the added KSCN concentration. Iodide enriched surface layers created with two different methods were analyzed using dual beam TOF-SIMS analysis. Global iodide concentrations of 0.14 % resulting in a submonolayer surface coverage of the crystal can still be detected. The kinetic differences in both methods are reflected in the iodide concentration incorporated at the surface and the thickness of the iodide enriched layer. Both effects are clearly visible in the depth profiles.

References

[1] G. Verlinden, R. Gijbels, I. Geuens, A. Benninghoven, SIMS XI, Eds. G. Gillen et al., (1998) 871-874
[2] G. Verlinden, R. Gijbels, I. Geuens, R. De Keyzer, J. Anal. At. Spectrom. 14 (1999) 429-434
[3] M. Kawasaki, Y. Oku, J. Phot. Sci. 43 (1995) 122
[4] T. James, The theory of the photographic process, MacMillan Press, New York, 1977
[5] G. Verlinden, R. Gijbels, I. Geuens, accepted by the Journal of the American Society of Mass Spectrometry
[6] J. Ziegler, J. Biersack, U. Littmark, The stopping and range of ions in solids, Pergamon Press, New York, 1996

A. Benninghoven, P. Bertrand, H.-N. Migeon and H.W. Werner (Editors).
Proceedings of the 12th International Conference on Secondary Ion Mass Spectrometry,
Brussels, Belgium, 5-11 September 1999

THREE-DIMENSIONAL CHEMICAL SPECIES ANALYSIS
USING A Ga FIB FOR MICRO-CROSS-SECTIONING AND TOF-SIMS MAPPING

T. Sakamoto[1*], Y. Kuramoto[2], Zh. H. Cheng[2], K. Takanashi[2], H. Wu[2,3], M. Owari[1,2] and Y. Nihei[2]

[1]Environmental Sc. Ctr, Univ. of Tokyo, 7-3-1 Hongo, Bunkyo-ku, Tokyo 113-0033, Japan
[2]Instit. of Industrial Sc., The Univ. of Tokyo, 7-22-1 Roppongi, Minato-ku, Tokyo 106-8558, Japan
[3]Sumitomo Metal Mining Co. Ltd., 5-11-3 Shimbashi, Minato-ku, Tokyo 105-8716, Japan
*E-mail: sakamoto@esc.u-tokyo.ac.jp

1. Introduction

We previously developed a novel three-dimensional (3D) microanalysis apparatus based on successive cross-sectional Auger mapping technique using a Ga focused ion beam (FIB) and a focused electron beam [1]. The apparatus named «ion and electron dual focused beam apparatus» aims at the 3D elemental microanalysis of particles and industrial solid materials, e.g., suspended particulate matters and ICs. Recently, both environmental science and solid materials industry face the analytical requirement of higher sensitivity and chemical species identification which are not obtainable with Auger mapping.

Time-of-Flight Secondary Ion Mass Spectrometry (TOF-SIMS) is recognized as a unique method for obtaining information on chemical species and their distribution with high sensitivity. Therefore, if we replace the Auger mapping with the TOF-SIMS mapping of successive cross sections, 3D chemical species mapping with high sensitivity will be realized.

In this paper, we describe the first report on the development of the 3D mapping method and instrumentation of a 3D TOF-SIMS apparatus. An application of this method to the analysis of a buried region of an IC bonding pad is also described.

2. Conception and Instrumentation of the 3D Mapping Apparatus

There are two ways for realizing 3D TOF-SIMS mapping. One is to use a single FIB alternatively operated in direct current (DC) for cross-sectioning and pulse mode for mapping. Since the cross section is created nearly parallel to the FIB axis, the sample should be tilted for TOF-SIMS mapping of the cross section. The other way is realized by using dual FIBs (a DC-FIB and a pulsed FIB). This dual FIBs method will obtain precisely-coordinated 3D maps, while the single FIB method can be realized with a simple instrumental setup. In this article, we describe the single FIB method as the first step of the development.

The 3D mapping apparatus shown in Fig. 1 was constructed based on the ion and electron dual focused beam apparatus [1]. The apparatus was newly equipped with a TOF mass spectrometer (TOF-MS) system, and the control electronics of the FIB was modified for this study.

The single FIB method requires alternative operation of the FIB for DC and pulse mode. The FIB we used was originally designed only for DC operation. We realized such alternative operation by making a high-speed voltage amplifier consisting of four operational amplifier ICs. The amplifier-outputs are connected to two sets of bipole blanker located between the condenser lens and objective lens as shown in Fig. 2. These two blankers are arranged to have a right angle and a space of 56 mm between them. Beam chopping is performed with blanker 2 and aperture 2. It is known that the crossover made with the condenser lens shifts

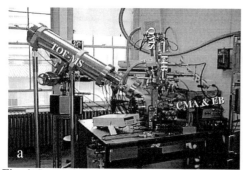

Fig. 1: Ion and electron dual focused beam apparatus for 3D microanalysis (**a**: entire of the vacuum chamber, **b**: interior of the chamber viewed after the specimen stage was removed.)

towards the deflection direction in case of high speed deflection. Therefore, we must use the chopped beam made with not reciprocal deflection but one-way deflection to avoid the formation of two beam spots on the sample surface. Blanker 1 is used so that the beam moves across the aperture from the one direction. Consequently, the beam spot movement draws a rectangle on the aperture plane. In this pulsing method, a pulsed FIB with 40 ns width at FWHM, 0.8 µm in diameter and 800 pA current (observed under DC operation) is obtained. Smaller beam diameter and lower beam current are also obtained by using smaller selectable aperture 1. Mass separation of $^{69}Ga^+$ and $^{71}Ga^+$ is not performed in this study.

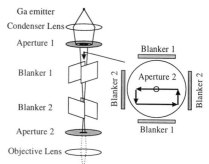

Fig. 2: Diagrams of the FIB column (aligner, stigmator and deflector electrodes are not shown), and top-view of beam spot movement on aperture 2.

A TOF-MS used here was constructed with a secondary ion extraction optics (homemade) and a dual-slope reflectron TOF-MS components (R. M. Jordan). Data registration is performed with a Time-to-Digital Converter (KORE technology) connected with a personal computer. From preliminary experiments, the useful yield of $^{27}Al^+$ and mass resolution at $^{27}Al^+$ peak were estimated to be 3.1×10^{-5} and 220, respectively.

In this stage of the development, «3D» means not the complete three-dimensional distribution analysis, but the cross-sectional TOF-SIMS mapping at aimed position. The first step of the analysis is micro-cross-sectioning using the Ga FIB in DC mode. A special beam scanning technique named «shave-off» is used for obtaining a flat cross section at any part of a sample [2]. The positioning accuracy of the shave-off cross-sectioning is around 10 nm when the spot diameter is 100 nm [3]. This is because that a cross section is created with not the whole of the FIB spot, but an edge part [4].

3. Experimental

The cross-sectional TOF-SIMS mapping was applied to the analysis of an IC bonding pad manufactured by Sumitomo Metal Mining Co. Ltd. A contact region consisting of a Au wire and an Al pad (nominal thickness: 0.8 µm) was the analysis target. This contact region is known to be degraded both electrically and mechanically after preheat tests. Conventional method for the analysis of such buried region uses mechanical polishing to expose the region of interest. However, mechanical polishing induces destruction and large roughness of the analysis surface.

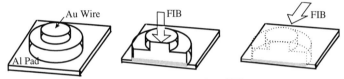

Fig. 3: Procedure of micro-cross-sectioning using a FIB to expose the wire-pad contract region.

The procedure of our preparation using the FIB cross-sectioning technique is illustrated in Fig. 3. The sample was introduced into the apparatus after the removal of the mold resin with chemical etching. The first cross-sectioning of the wire-pad was performed vertically with respect to the pad. This enabled us to observe the position of the wire-pad contact region. Then the sample was tilted to make the FIB and bonding pad parallel. The cross-sectioning was performed for thinning until the contact region was exposed.

Mass spectrum and mapping measurements were performed with the same FIB after switched it to the pulse mode. The pulse frequency and width were 20 kHz and about 40 ns, respectively. The FIB was used with an acceleration energy of 20 keV and a current of 1 nA (measured in DC mode). A mass spectrum (m/z: 27~71) was acquired with 4096 pulses at each pixel. Total time required for mapping was about 4 hrs including the data recording time.

4. Results and Discussion

4.1 Micro-Cross-Sectioning to Expose the Contact Region

The micro-cross-sectioning process for thinning the bonding wire-pad is shown in Fig. 4. In these images, clear grain contrasts are found in the Au wire. The observation of grain contrasts means that the crystalline structure was not

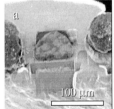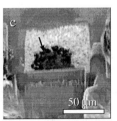

Fig. 4: FIB-induced sample current images showing the thinning process with shave-off cross-sectioning parallel to the bonding pad.

heavily destructed with the cross-sectioning, while such contrasts cannot be observed after mechanical polishing. Another remarkable observation is dark parts found in the Au wire cross sections in images b and c. The dark parts were distributed like a ring within the contact region. The image c shows the cross section after the cross-sectioning process was finished.

4.2 TOF-SIMS Analysis of the Contact Region

A TOF mass spectrum of the cross-sectioned sample is shown in Fig. 5. Secondary ion peaks of $^{27}Al^+$, $^{28}Si^+$ and $^{197}Au^+$ were originated in the Al pad, Si substrate and SiO_2 layer, and Au bonding wire, respectively. Since the $^{27}Al^+$ and $^{28}Si^+$ secondary ion signals showed sufficient count rate to be mapped, TOF-SIMS mapping was performed for these two signals. Obtained maps are shown in Fig. 6. In the $^{27}Al^+$ map, the contact region, particularly outer part (a) was bright. This higher yield of $^{27}Al^+$ ions means that this part of the Al pad was oxidized. Another bright part (b) in the $^{27}Al^+$ map was also due to oxidation, because it was vicinity to the SiO_2 layer which was found as a bright part in the $^{28}Si^+$ map. The secondary ion signal of $^{28}Si^+$ from the elemental Si part around the Al pad was weak.

220

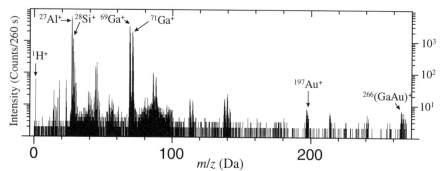

Fig. 5: Time-of-flight secondary ion mass spectrum of the cross-sectioned sample.

Summarizing this result, we can expect the structure of the contact region of the wire-pad as illustrated in Fig. 7. The cross section was not parallel to the Al pad but slightly slanted to the FIB incident direction (left-side in Fig. 7). Therefore, the cross section involved the SiO_2 layer, Al pad and contact region from left to right in Fig. 7. The oxidation of Al occurred particularly around the outer part of the contact region. Further improvement of the apparatus and experiments will reveal more detailed 3D structure and intermetallic compounds in the contact region by employing the analytical features of TOF-SIMS.

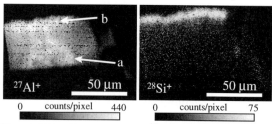

Fig. 6: TOF-SIMS maps of $^{27}Al^+$ and $^{28}Si^+$ obtained from the cross-sectioned bonding pad.

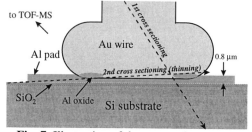

Fig. 7: Illustration of the expected structure.

5. Conclusion

A 3D (cross-sectional) TOF-SIMS mapping method and apparatus were described. The application of this method to a buried contact region revealed its structure. In future, full 3D mapping will be realized by adding a pulsed FIB at right angles to the existing FIB.

This study was supported by a Grant-in-Aid for Scientific Research of the Ministry of Education, Science, Sports and Culture, project number 09450308.

References
[1] T. Sakamoto, Zh. H. Cheng, M. Takahashi, Y. Kuramoto, M. Owari and Y. Nihei, Jpn. J. Appl. Phys., 37, Part 1, No.4A (1998) 2051.
[2] H. Satoh, M. Owari and Y. Nihei, J. Vac. Sci. & Technol., B6 (1988) 915.
[3] B. Tomiyasu, H. Komatsubara, M. Satoh, S. Sakasegawa, M. Owari and Y. Nihei, *Secondary ion mass spectrometry SIMS XI*, eds. G. Gillen, R. Lareau, J. Bennett and F. Stevie, John Wiley & Sons, Chichester (1998) p383.
[4] T. Sakamoto, B. Tomiyasu, M. Owari and Y. Nihei, *ECASIA '95*, eds. H. J. Mathieu, B. Reihl and D. Briggs, John Wiley & Sons, Chichester (1996) p.639.

A. Benninghoven, P. Bertrand, H.-N. Migeon and H.W. Werner (Editors).
Proceedings of the 12th International Conference on Secondary Ion Mass Spectrometry,
Brussels, Belgium, 5-11 September 1999
© 2000 Elsevier Science B.V. All rights reserved.

SIMS THREE-DIMENSIONAL DEPTH PROFILING OF GRAIN BOUNDARY SEGREGANTS IN NICKEL ALLOYS

N.S. McIntyre,[1†] C.M. Huctwith,[1] K.F. Taylor[1], E. Keating,[2] N.O. Petersen,[2] and A.M. Brennenstühl[3] ; [1] Surface Science Western, Western Science Centre, University Western Ontario, London, Ontario N6A 5B7 CANADA, smcintyr@uwo.ca ; [2] Department of Chemistry, Chemistry Building, University Western Ontario, London, Ontario N6A 5B7 CANADA ; [3] Ontario Power Technologies, 800 Kipling Avenue, Toronto, Ontario M8Z 5S4 CANADA

1. Introduction

The corrosion degradation of nickel alloys used for heat exchange between primary and secondary sides of nuclear boilers frequently involves the boundaries between the metal grains. Such boundaries are the preferred pathways for stress corrosion cracking (SCC) because of the many chemical and mechanical inhomogeneities which reside there. The SCC failure process has been studied extensively, and at first was attributed primarily to grain boundary chemistry; for example, the existence of chromium carbides in the grain was shown to reduce the chemical susceptibility to SCC [1]. Other elemental impurities (particularly boron) have been shown to have a possible deleterious effect if not combined with chromium carbides [2]. More recently, an abundance of low sigma "special" grain boundaries has also been shown to be important in "breaking" the connectivity between boundaries with random sigma values and thus terminating crack propagation [3,4].

Most experimental studies of the structure of grain boundaries have used high resolution transmission electron microscopy (HRTEM) to detect elemental concentration gradients. However, the areas of measurements are very limited, as is the sensitivity to minor and trace elements which have undergone segregation. Imaging SIMS presents an alternative method of measuring the distributions of grain boundary segregants. It is now possible to produce images with micron scale resolution showing elemental quantities in the picogram range [5]. The benefits are considerably greater if one acquires the information in 3-D form [6], such that all relational aspects of the grains may be observed. By acquiring a sequence of up to 200 images of the same secondary ion through a depth of 20 microns, a "pseudo" 3-D volume representation of the grain boundary directions can be plotted (see Figure 1(a)). The effects of sputter-induced topographic changes may be accounted for, approximately, from mechanical profilometry after the SIMS profile [7]. Such images may be volume rendered to give a better understanding of the segregant distribution in 3-D (see Figures 1(b) and (c)).

SIMS 3-D imaging has been used to examine the grain boundary compositions of nickel-based boiler alloys which had experienced some measure of crack growth during service. Of particular interest was the relationship of boron and carbon distributions in the boundaries. If most of the boron intensity detected came from microregions (spots) within a few pixels of those for carbon, it could be argued that two elements were associated chemically; conversely, boron not in this category can be assumed to be "free" and could possibly contribute to SCC events. The sheer number density of spots and the difficulty in achieving a quantitative

222

visualisation precluded the possibility of a visual correlation of carbon and boron distributions. Thus, image cross-correlation spectroscopy (ICCS) [8,9] was used to identify the statistical significance of the relationship between elemental distributions acquired in the 3-D depth profiles. Cross-correlation functions provide a mathematical means of expressing how closely two variables are related over distance.

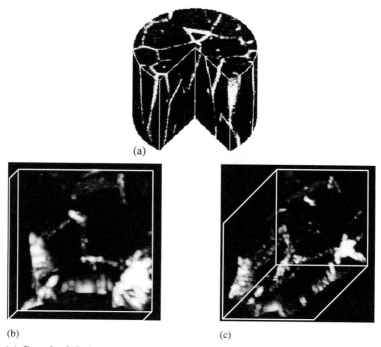

Figure 1. (a) Pseudo 3-D image of C_2^- image for specimen R26C36. The vertical height is ~ 20 μm and the diameter is ~ 100 μm. (b) and (c) Volume rendered 3-D images of a section of the image shown in (a) from two different angles 30 apart.

2. Experimental

Polished cross-sections from three separate UNS N06600 boiler tubes were prepared. They had been removed from service at Pickering Nuclear Generating Station when they were found to have cracks which partly penetrated the wall thickness. One tube, R35C57, had a crack whose length (800 μm) exceeded that predicted on the basis of special boundary fraction [4], while the other two, R26C36 and R19C31, had crack lengths which were able to be predicted from the special boundary fraction. Thus, possible additional contributions from grain boundary chemistry were sought as an explanation for the extended crack length.

Each section was studied in a Cameca IMS 3f ion microscope using a 600 - 1000 nA Cs$^+$ primary beam and negative secondaries. Analysis regions were chosen so as to be close to, but not on, a crack tip. About 75 sequential images of ^{11}B$^-$ and ^{24}C$_2^-$ were acquired in each location; this produced an information volume that was ~ 20 μm in depth and 100 μm in diameter for each secondary ion.

The acquisition of the 3-D images has been described previously [7]. The ICCS calculations were performed on a massively parallel processor. In ICCS, the fast Fourier transforms of each 2-D image of the two elements are multiplied. The product is inversely transformed and divided by the product of the average of the intensities from each original image and unity is subtracted [8]. The result is a properly normalised cross-correlation function which is a function of the lag-distances 'ξ' and 'η'.

3. Results and discussion

For any particular image "slice" the value of the cross-element cross-correlation function for $^{24}C_2^{-}$ and $^{11}B^{-}$, $g(\xi,\eta)$ [8], can be plotted as a function of the lag distances (in microns). Such plots are shown in Figures 2(a) - 2(c) for representative image slices for each of the three specimens. It can be seen that, not unreasonably, the maximum cross-correlation occurs for each of these at zero-lag (coordinate (0,0)), the point where the two signals overlap if the elements are colocalised on the surface. We can measure the relative amount of cross-element cross-correlation at this coordinate with the function $g(0,0)$. The cross-correlation function can be normalised by dividing it by the autocorrelation function for each element. Effectively, this provides the fraction which measures the extent of colocalisation of the two elements. If boron and carbon always co-exist, this fraction will be unity. If boron and carbon co-exist only by random chance across the surface, this fraction will be zero [10]. The fraction allows one to measure the degree of correlation within those features which dominate the images (the grain boundaries), while minimising the contributions from boron and carbon in other regions (the bulk material).

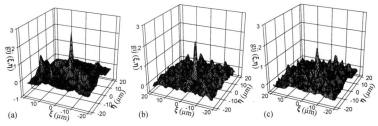

Figure 2.   Plots of $g(\xi,\eta)$ for samples: (a) R26C36, (b) R19C31, and (c) R35C57. The absolute scale of the distances in microns is approximate, but the scales are identical for each sample.

In Table 1 the correlation value, $g(0,0)$ and fraction, F, are given for every fifth image slice in descending order for specimen R26C36. An average and standard deviation of the mean are also given for the entire 70 images from which five images had been eliminated as outliers. Inspection of the complete table of F values shows a slow, but minor, undulation in the values over the volume surveyed. Based on the standard deviations shown in Table 2, the F values for all three samples R26C36, R19C31, and R35C37 are believed to be statistically unique.

An average fraction value is given for each of three specimens in Table 2. It can be seen that the relative amount of uncorrelated or "free" boron in the grain boundaries is least in the specimen which has the shortest average crack length, and greatest for the specimen which has the longest cracks. From these measurements, it is suggested that the statistically higher ratio of free boron in the boundaries of this latter specimen may be a contributing factor to its unusually high rate of crack propagation.

Table 1. ICCS correlation values (g(0,0)) and fractions (F) for representative image slices for sample R26C36.

Image Slice	g(0,0)	F	Image Slice	g(0,0)	F	Image Slice	g(0,0)	F
1	2.13	1.26	25	1.79	1.06	50	2.14	0.86
5	1.97	0.72	30	1.16	0.42	55	2.01	0.65
10	2.51	1.46	35	0.92	0.84	60	5.53	1.15
15	2.28	1.04	40	2.16	1.00	65	0.73	0.79
20	3.02	0.99	45	1.69	0.83	Average for 66 Slices	2.10	0.90
						Standard Deviation	0.88	0.04

Table 2. B/C ICCS fraction compared to crack length.

Sample	Crack Length	Average Fraction (F)
R26C36	350 μm	0.90 ± 0.04 †
R19C31	575 μm	0.49 ± 0.02 †
R35C57	800 μm	0.25 ± 0.03 †

† One standard deviation of the mean.

Statistically, the ICCS procedure can be regarded as a more valid indicator of interelemental effects than any individual microscopic analysis carried out by TEM or other techniques.

References

[1] G.S. Was and V.B. Rajan, Met Trans., **18A**, 1313 (1987).
[2] Y. Yamanaka, in Sixth Int. Symp. Environ. Degradation in Nuclear Power Systems Water Reactions, Eds, R.E. Gold and E.P. Simonen, (Minerals, Metals and Materials Society, Metals Park, OH, 1994) p.105.
[3] G. Palumbo, P.J. King, P. Lichtenburger, K.T. Aust and U. Erb, Proc. Mat. Res. Soc., **238**, 311 (1992).
[4] E. Lehockey, Ontario Power Technologies, private communication.
[5] N.S. McIntyre, R.D. Davidson, C.M. Huctwith, A.M. Brennenstühl, O. Lepik and M. Clark, Corrosion Science, **40**, 1799 (1998).
[6] S.F. Lu, G.R. Mount, N.S. McIntyre and A. Fenster, Surf. Interface Anal., **21** 177 (1994).
[7] M.L. Wagter, A.H. Clarke, K.F. Taylor, P.A.W. van der Heide and N.S.McIntyre, Surf. Interface Anal., **25**, 788 (1997).
[8] M. Srivastava, N.O. Petersen, G.R. Mount, D.M. Kingston, and N.S. McIntyre, Surf. Interface Anal., **26**, 188 (1988).
[9] M. Srivastava and N.O. Petersen, Methods Cell Sci., **18**, 47 (1996).
[10] N.O. Petersen, C. Brown, A. Kaminski, J. Rocheleau, M. Srivastava and P.W. Wiseman, Faraday Discuss., **111**, 289 (1998).

A. Benninghoven, P. Bertrand, H.-N. Migeon and H.W. Werner (Editors).
Proceedings of the 12th International Conference on Secondary Ion Mass Spectrometry,
Brussels, Belgium, 5-11 September 1999
© 2000 Elsevier Science B.V. All rights reserved.

CROSS-SECTIONAL SIMS IMAGING OF FUEL CHANNEL I.D. SURFACES

M.C. Biesinger and N.S. McIntyre

Surface Science Western, The University of Western Ontario
London, Ontario, Canada N6A 5B7
e-mail: biesingr@julian.uwo.ca

1. Introduction

SIMS has an important role in the assessment of oxide integrity in the presence of corrosive liquids. This is certainly the case where water is the corrosive liquid. Many of the corrosion processes involve hydrogen which can appear in such corrosion products as hydroxides, hydrates and hydrides. SIMS is one of the few surface and microanalytical techniques sensitive to hydrogen and it is therefore a key technique for understanding corrosion processes.

In some nuclear reactor systems, particularly the CANDU series, the form of aqueous coolant used is D_2O, instead of H_2O. SIMS investigation of material corroded in the presence of D_2O can be particularly revealing. The detection of the deuterium isotope is much easier than for protium due to the background of spurious protium, both in the SIMS instrument and in the environment. Thus, it has been possible to detect deuterium reaction products in nuclear materials at concentrations as low as 1×10^{17} at. cm^{-3} [1].

The ZAB-2F SIMS[2] at SSW has several capabilities which render it particularly useful for such studies. The relatively good vacuum conditions, the electronic and mechanical stability of the entire detection system, and the use of a non-pulsed primary beam all contribute to the quality of the images achieved with this instrument. The sensitivity of this particular instrument to the local detection of hydrogen and its isotopes appears to be better than commercial static and dynamic SIMS systems.

The development of the procedures for preparing the surface of the cross-section prior to imaging were refined during some initial studies of a cross-section of an out-reactor specimen which had been exposed to D_2O in an autoclave[3]. That work showed that localised deuterium ingress could be detected in such specimens, even though image acquisition times usually extended to several hours. In this present study, a section from a fuel channel from a nuclear generating station operated by Ontario Hydro was examined. The section originated from a channel which had been found to have low concentrations of deuterium. Some evidence of localised inner oxide breakdown is observed with the ingress of deuterium into the region of the alloy immediately beneath. In one instance, the breakdown of the oxide appears to be coincident with localised alloy impurities such as chlorine.

226

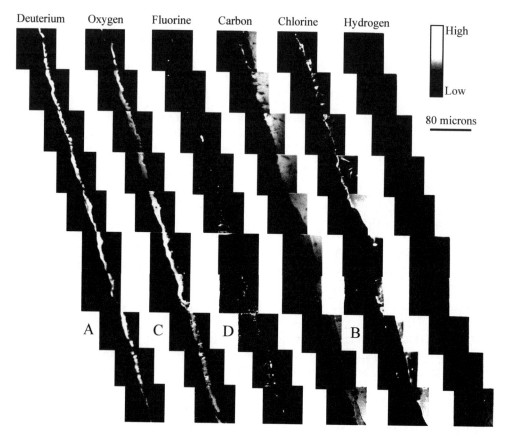

Deuterium   Oxygen   Fluorine   Carbon   Chlorine   Hydrogen

High

Low

80 microns

A   C   D   B

Figure 1. Montage of SIMS images. The metal substrate is to the left of the oxide (mounting resin is on the right).

2. Experimental

The cross-section was prepared at Ontario Hydro Technologies. It was a straight cut across the tube; the exact position of the cut on the channel is not known. The section had been exposed to a brief HF etch and this was evident in some of the SIMS images. A gallium primary beam with a current of 0.1 nA and a 25 kV accelerating voltage was used, in an 80 μm x 80 μm raster pattern. Previous work had shown that pre-sputtering of the area for two to three hours was necessary to create adequate conductivity of the oxide portion of the section, as well as to provide adequate removal of the native oxide film covering the metallic portion of the section[3]. Images were taken in overlapping regions along one part of the cross-section. This allowed these individual sections to be later presented as a montage of images. The lateral resolution of the images produced is usually less than 1 μm; this depends, of course, upon S/N. All images acquired were of negative ions, which are more sensitive for critical species such as deuterium.

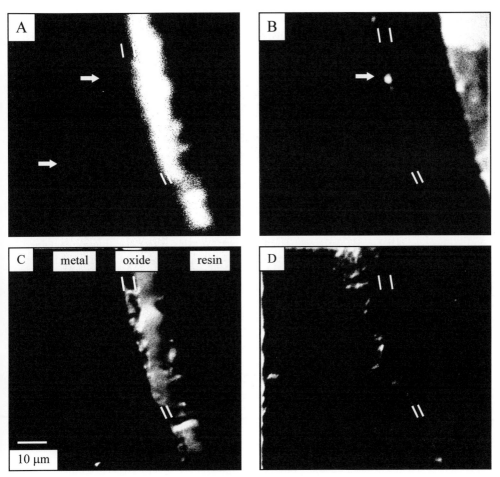

Figure 2. Deuterium (A) ion image showing possible areas of ingress into the metal. (B) Chlorine, Oxygen (C) and Fluorine (D) ion images. Areas shown are enlargements of areas A through D from Figure 1. The white lines denote the dense inner oxide.

3. Results and Discussion

Figure 1 shows a montage of various secondary ion images for ten overlapping regions of the oxide/metal interface. The field of each image is 80 μm; thus, the length of interface surveyed would represent about 0.8 mm.

Of primary interest is the area of deuterium ingress through the oxide indicated by the arrow in Figure 2(A). Close examination reveals that the deuterium "breakthrough"cuts across the area of recently formed oxide; the region of oxide breakdown is estimated to be less than 1 μm in diameter. It is believed that deuterium is deposited at the metal side of the oxide as a result of reduction of D_2O or OD^- groups which have migrated through the oxide breakdown region.

Beneath the breakthrough area in the metal, there is a local deuterium "cell" of about 5 to7 μm in diameter. This represents deuterium which had moved through the breakdown area, but had been immobilised, probably by subsurface defects. Figure 2(B) shows the Cl image. Of primary interest is the localised chlorine (see arrow) which is found exactly at the point where deuterium "breakthrough" was detected. The chlorine is concentrated in the alloy. While some chlorine is obviously present in the mounting material for the cross-section, the very localised distribution of chlorine in the alloy suggests that there was little evidence of cross-contamination.

Coincidental examination of C, O, and Cl images allowed the inner oxide region to be fairly well defined. The inner oxide was seen to be a region approximately 2 to 4 μm across, in which these elements (as well as deuterium) are largely absent. By contrast, the porous outer oxide, which is several times thicker (approximately 10 μm), has copious concentrations of all these elements.

The structure of the subsurface alloy is well outlined by the F⁻ images shown in Figures 1 and 2(D). The processes used in polishing the cross-sections involved fluorinated agents; thus, the fluorine observed is believed to originate, at least in part, from this, rather than fluoride contained in the original reactor material. However, the selective etching of regions of localised oxidation and high dislocation density help to outline many features, particularly in the metallic region immediately below the interface with the oxide. Intersections of the grain boundary with the oxide interfaces are particularly well outlined here, although they can also be observed in the oxygen images.

The SIMS imaging study shows that deuteride migration from outer oxide to the underlying metal is very localised; only one site was identified along a 0.8 mm section. This particular site is associated with a high localized concentration of chloride - a well-known initiator of oxide breakdown. One other incidence of localised deuterium migration through the oxide was found in another part of the section not shown here. However, no localised chlorine was detected in this instance. Thus, other chemical or mechanical effects may also lead to localised migration of deuterium.

The authors would like to thank Ontario Hydro Technologies for the samples prepared for this study.

4. References

[1]   N.S. McIntyre, C.G. Weisener, R.D. Davidson, A. Brennenstuhl and B. Warr, J. Nucl. Mat. **178**, (1991) 80.

[2]   D. Schuetzle, T.J. Prater, S. Kaberline, J.E. deVries, A. Bayly and P. Vohralik, Rev.Sci. Intrum. **60 (1)**, (1989) 53.

[3]   M.C. Biesinger, P.A.W. van der Heide and N.S. McIntyre, in Secondary Ion Mass Spectrometry, SIMS XI, Eds. G. Gillen, R. Lareau, J. Bennett and F. Stevie, Wiley, Chichester, (1998) 859.

A. Benninghoven, P. Bertrand, H.-N. Migeon and H.W. Werner (Editors).
Proceedings of the 12th International Conference on Secondary Ion Mass Spectrometry,
Brussels, Belgium, 5-11 September 1999
© 2000 Elsevier Science B.V. All rights reserved.

RECENT DEVELOPMENT OF THE CHEMICAL MICROSCOPE - A LOW-COST AUTOMATED IMAGING SIMS INSTRUMENT

A.J. Eccles* and T.A. Steele

Millbrook Instruments Limited, Blackburn Technology Centre, Blackburn, BB1 5QB, UK
* corresponding author. e-mail millbrook@compuserve.com

1. Introduction

The Millbrook Chemical Microscope is a unique low cost, self contained benchtop imaging SIMS instrument designed for running rapid, routine repetitive analyses of surfaces. It is designed to be easy to use, with high reliability and fast sample loading to maximise analysis throughput. Since its launch last year, the instrument has achieved its objective of reducing the entry-level cost for a SIMS analysis, making the technique available to a much wider user base.

Figure 1. The Millbrook Chemical Microscope, an automated benchtop instrument for Imaging SIMS analysis.

Obviously a low cost automated instrument cannot offer the same ultimate performance and flexibility in surface analysis as a conventional SIMS system. However, by exploiting the strengths of the SIMS technique (in particular the surface specificity and the ability to determine molecular structure), the instrument is often able to provide the key information needed to solve a particular problem [1]. The instrument has been used in an industrial environment for quality control, failure analysis and new product development. It is equally well suited to a university environment for both undergraduate teaching and research, often complementing other surface analytical instrumentation [2].

This short paper describes the recent additional features that have been incorporated into the design of the instrument, both to extend the range of samples that can be analysed and to assist the inexperienced operator with data interpretation. Reference is made to examples of applied surface analysis that can now be addressed as a result of the enhanced capability.

2. Instrument Design

The fundamental design of the Chemical Microscope (Figure 1) remains unchanged [3], using a 6 kV liquid metal primary ion gun with raster scanning for full imaging capability and a

230

300 daltons quadrupole mass spectrometer for analysis of both positive and negative secondary ions. Secondary electrons are also collected, generating a real time topographical image of the sample to allow the selection of physical features for subsequent analysis. The operator controls the system through a dedicated personal computer, which also continually monitors the performance of the instrument. The Windows™ based software makes the system exceptionally easy to use even for an inexperienced operator.

A modem link has now been implemented to allow remote operation of the instrument; as well as routine use by the customer, this link is used to assist with servicing and maintenance, and to improve the training available to a new operator.

Figure 2.   O⁻ image of a test grid. The smallest bars are 10 μm in width.

2.1 Dynamic Emittance Matching

The secondary ion collection efficiency has been improved by a dynamic emittance matching system, whereby secondary ion collection is optimised for a small area and scanned in tandem with the focused primary ion beam. As well as a x3 improvement in overall transmission, this change now gives uniform image intensity (Figure 2) right up to the full 20 mm² maximum field of view.

2.2 Defocused Primary Beam (static SIMS)

For the analysis of organic samples, it is often necessary to irradiate a large area of the sample to maintain primary beam doses within the Static SIMS limit of $<10^{13}$ ions cm^{-2}. Initially this was achieved by giving the operator the option to raster the focused primary beam over several mm² during collection of a mass spectrum. However, the operator now has the additional option of defocusing the primary beam during spectral acquisition, thus avoiding any possibility of localised bombardment induced damage from the high current density of a focused beam.

As would be expected, this defocused mode produces higher quality spectra with more intense molecular secondary ion peaks in the upper mass range. Typical results are presented elsewhere in these proceedings [4], and the availability of both positive and negative spectra allows a detailed interpretation of molecular structure (see below). Once the molecular structure has been established in this way, an image of one of the more stable (lower mass) characteristic ions can be acquired with the focused beam to show the lateral distribution of the species.

2.3 Charge Compensation

The most important change to the instrument design has been the incorporation of an auxiliary electron gun to extend the analysis capability to semiconducting and insulating samples. The system (based on the design of Gilmore & Seah [5]) utilises an indirect primary electron beam to generate the low energy (secondary) electrons required for efficient neutralization. In addition, the sample bias oscillates, which makes exact balancing of the primary ion and electron beam fluxes unnecessary.

This sophisticated system therefore has the advantage of extreme simplicity of operation. Using the defocused primary beam, spectra can be obtained immediately from all samples without any set-up by the operator (Figure 3). The system automatically adjusts to allow for a change to negative secondary ion analysis or to a focused primary ion beam for imaging. Full optimisation for an individual sample (Figure 4) can then be achieved by the adjustment of just one parameter which controls the intensity of the primary electron beam.

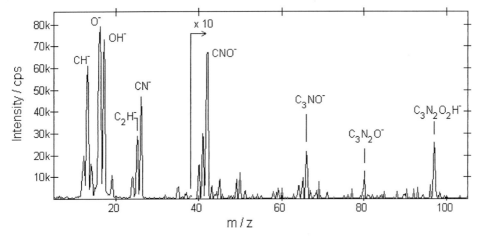

Figure 3.   Negative Mass Spectrum from an N-doped insulating diamond like carbon film using a defocused primary beam for large area survey analysis.

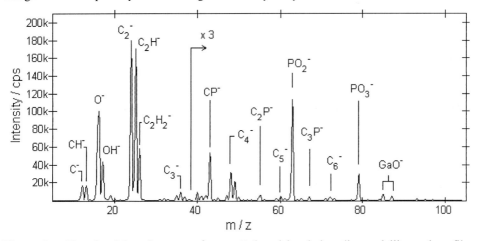

Figure 4.   Negative Mass Spectrum from a P-doped insulating diamond like carbon film using a focused primary beam for localised point analysis.

2.4 Data Interpretation

As data collection has become straightforward using the Chemical Microscope, interpretation of the data has been highlighted as a further barrier to wider use of the SIMS technique. In a quality control or other repetitive analysis situation, comparison of two samples is often all that is necessary, and in such applications full data interpretation is not required.

However, for use in a wider analysis role, the software suite for the instrument can now be extended to assist the operator with data interpretation. An optional software module suggests assignments for individual peaks in the mass spectrum. If there are two or more interferences at a given mass, it also helps the operator to make the correct selection by indicating the other mass peaks that should be present in the spectrum for each possible assignment. The operator can choose to view the corresponding formulae of the secondary ions, and this has been found to be an excellent way for a student or novice operator to learn the type of secondary ions to be expected from a given class of materials.

For organic molecules, individual peak assignments in the mass range below m/z = 100 daltons have usually been sufficiently informative to identify the generic molecular structure present. However, a mass spectrometry based technique such as SIMS has the power to identify a compound more precisely, and it is this additional information which is so valuable in unambiguously pinpointing the origin of e.g. a contaminant on a defective surface. This is best achieved by "fingerprint" matching of the full spectra (positive and negative) using the characteristic peaks above m/z = 100 daltons. For this reason, a version of the SurfaceSpectra Library [6] containing several hundred common compounds (mainly organics) is also provided with the instrument. The Library spectra are displayed in modified format to simulate acquisition by the Chemical Microscope, allowing the operator to make a direct comparison of relative peak intensities. The earlier Reference [4] again provides an example of this approach.

3. Conclusion

The availability of the Chemical Microscope has reinforced the view that there are many times when SIMS is the quickest and the most direct analysis technique capable of solving a problem or monitoring a process. The Chemical Microscope means that this analysis can now be performed in the same time and for the same overall cost as other more common analysis techniques. The examples above prove that, given a modified analytical approach to utilise fully the unique configuration of the instrument and work within its technical specification, the Chemical Microscope provides valuable information in a wide range of application areas.

References

[1] A.J. Eccles, T.A. Steele & A.W. Robinson, Appl. Surf. Science 144 (1999) 106
[2] D.J. Wilson et al., Surface and Interface Analysis, in press
[3] A.J. Eccles & T.A. Steele in Proc. SIMS XI, G. Gillen et al (Eds.), Wiley, 1998, 775-8
[4] A.J. Eccles, T.A. Steele & D. Briggs, these proceedings
[5] I.S. Gilmore & M.P. Seah, Surface and Interface Analysis 23 (1995) 191
[6] The Static SIMS Library, J.C. Vickerman et al (Eds.), SurfaceSpectra, Manchester, 1999

A. Benninghoven, P. Bertrand, H.-N. Migeon and H.W. Werner (Editors).
Proceedings of the 12th International Conference on Secondary Ion Mass Spectrometry,
Brussels, Belgium, 5-11 September 1999

CATION MASS SPECTROMETER: AN INSTRUMENT DEDICATED TO THE ANALYSIS OF MCsx+ CLUSTERS.
DESCRIPTION OF THE INSTRUMENT AND PRELIMINARY RESULTS

Th. Mootz[1], B. Rasser[2], P. Sudraud[3], E. Niehuis[4], T. Wirtz[1], W. Bieck[1], H.-N. Migeon[1]

[1] Laboratoire d'Analyse des Matériaux, CRP- Gabriel Lippmann, 162a, av. de la Faïencerie,
L-1511 Luxembourg (migeon@crpgl.lu)

[2] Cameca, 103 bd St Denis. F-92400 Courbevoie

[3] ORSAY PHYSICS, Z.A. St Charles, F-13710 Fuveau

[4] ION-TOF GmbH, Mendelstr. 11, D-48149 Münster

1. Introduction

It has previously been demonstrated that the measurement of MCs^+ (and MCs_2^+) ions, with M being the species of interest, greatly minimizes the matrix effect which is observed on standard SIMS ions [1-3]. This is understood assuming that the MCs^+ ions are generated by the combination of a secondary neutral M^0 with a resputtered Cs^+ ion in the near surface region of the surface. Consequently, the emission process for the species M is decoupled from the subsequent MCs^+ ion formation process in analogy to the ion formation in secondary neutral mass spectrometry resulting in a drastic decrease of the matrix effect.

The efficiency of MCs^+ formation is determined on one hand by the recombination probability of M^0 with Cs^+. This has been shown to depend on the polarizability of the neutral M^0 [4] and the energy distribution of M^0 which is dominated by the surface binding energy [5]. On the other hand, the MCs^+ formation depends strongly on the numbers of M^0 and Cs^+ available for the combination process. Especially the Cs^+ ion emission can depend very critically on the surface concentration of cesium. An increasing Cs surface concentration can lower the electron work function below a critical value, situated slightly below the ionization energy of Cs. If this occurs the probability of secondary Cs^+ formation and consequently also the formation of the MCs^+ ions are strongly decreased in accordance with the electron tunneling model for secondary ion formation [6].

In commonly used dynamic SIMS instruments, the Cs surface concentration in the sample is determined by the primary bombarding conditions (energy, angle, primary ion density) which yield a distinct total sputter yield Y and consequently determine the cesium surface concentration C_{cs} according to

$$C_{cs} = 1/(1+Y)$$

It is not likely that this, bombarding determined, Cs surface concentration is equal to the optimum concentration for highest MCs^+ yields. Indeed experiments have shown [7] that the variation of the Cs surface concentration obtained by changing the bombarding angle under constant bombarding energy changes the total sputter yield and subsequently the Cs surface concentration, which again influences the MCs^+ yields. Further experiments varying the Cs surface concentration by profiling a high energy preimplanted sample give evidence for the above mentioned correlation between the Cs surface concentration, the electron work function, the probability of Cs^+ formation and consequently the efficiency of MCs^+ formation [8-10].

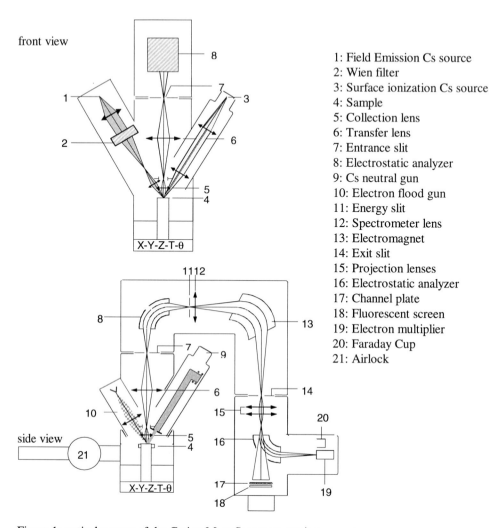

front view

side view

1: Field Emission Cs source
2: Wien filter
3: Surface ionization Cs source
4: Sample
5: Collection lens
6: Transfer lens
7: Entrance slit
8: Electrostatic analyzer
9: Cs neutral gun
10: Electron flood gun
11: Energy slit
12: Spectrometer lens
13: Electromagnet
14: Exit slit
15: Projection lenses
16: Electrostatic analyzer
17: Channel plate
18: Fluorescent screen
19: Electron multiplier
20: Faraday Cup
21: Airlock

Figure 1: optical system of the Cation Mass Spectrometer instrument

2. Description of the Cation Mass Spectrometer (CMS) instrument:

The analysis of MCs_x^+ clusters is currently performed using SIMS instruments equipped with a primary ion column delivering Cs^+ ions in order to incorporate Cs into the specimen. This technique has been successfully applied to the analysis of a wide variety of materials but faces limitations when using such instruments:

- Magnetic Sector SIMS do not allow a tilt of the specimen nor provide an adjustable distance "sample-extraction lens" which permit to vary the sputtering yield of the specimen (at constant primary ion energy) .

- Quadrupole SIMS provide low transmission which, together with the low ionization efficiencies of MCs_x^+ clusters, affects the sensitivity of this technique.

- Tof -SIMS require pulsed interlaced steps of sputtering and analyzing which restricts the maximum dynamic range of secondary ion intensities.

In order to optimize the analysis of these clusters, the Cation Mass Spectrometer (CMS) incorporates the following features (figure 1):

- two cesium ion guns: one with a surface ionization Cs source as in conventional SIMS instruments and one gun equipped with a field emission Cs source in order to allow small beam operation with high densities for sub-micron analysis
- a column delivering a neutral flux of Cs at the sample surface with a deposition rate adjustable from 0 to 1 monolayer per second
- a sample stage and a dedicated collection optics providing tilt capabilities
- a secondary column with microscope imaging, presently equipped with a magnetic sector but which can be fitted with a ToF spectrometer.

3. Preliminary results

3.1 Performance of the CMS instrument

The following performances have been obtained up to now:

- Surface ionization Cs column: the beam diameter is adjustable from 20 to 100 microns at 5 KeV impact energy, the primary intensity ranges from 0 to 50 nA
- Field emission Cs source: testing on an SEM showed a beam diameter better than 100 nm, but a life time of 20 hours. Presently operated with a Ga beam on the CMS instrument
- Cs neutral gun: on a separate test bench a flux from 0 to 1 monolayer of Cs per second has been measured. This flux is continuously adjustable within less than 100 msec.
- Secondary column:
    . lateral resolution of the ion microscope: better than 1 micron
    . mass resolution: from 300 to 10 000
    . Transmission : based on Cs+ secondary intensity/Cs+ primary intensity in InP : better than 17%

3.2 Variation of the Cs concentration implanted by ion bombardment under variable angle of incidence

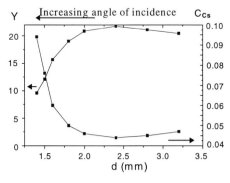

Fig: 2: Variation of the sputter yield (Y)and the Cs concentration derived from $C_{cs} = 1/(1+Y)$ against the distance sample-extraction lens (d) in InP

In order to vary the sputtering yield, and consequently the Cs concentration, measurements have been performed using the z motion of the sample stage. Under constant primary ion source voltage and sample voltage, the lowering of the sample-extraction distance allows to increase the impact angle. As shown in Fig. 2 the maximum yield is obtained for d=2.5mm using +8.5 kV and +4.5 kV for the source and sample voltages respectively (a simulation using SIMION allows one to estimate an impact angle of 80° for d=2 mm).

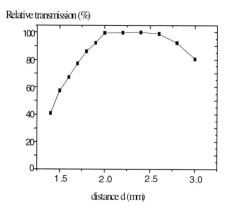

Fig 3: Transmission against the distance d

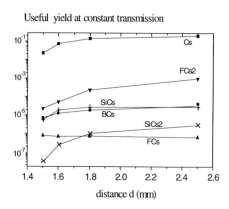

Fig 4: Changes of useful yields against d

In order to estimate the changes in transmission induced by the variation of d, measurements of the ratio "secondary intensity of Cs^+ under steady state conditions/primary intensity of the Cs beam" were performed on InP. Contrary to the conditions used in fig.2, the use of +10 and +4.5 kV for the primary and secondary voltages allowed to operate with impact angles slightly below the angle providing maximum sputtering yield. Under those conditions, the slight changes of the sputtering yield do not induce significant changes in the ionization of Cs. A maximum transmission is observed for d = 2-2.5 mm, in good agreement with the calculations of the secondary column (fig.3).

To study the effect of the surface Cs concentration changes, the behavior of the useful yield of different species was analyzed during a variation of the distance d, using the same primary and secondary voltages as in fig.2. For these experiments, a Si target implanted with ^{11}B at 10^{16} cm^{-2} and ^{19}F at 10^{17} cm^{-2} at 300 keV has been investigated. The useful yields shown on fig. 4 have been corrected for the changes of the transmission of the secondary column. All species indicated the highest yield for d=2.5 mm which is the distance corresponding to the lowest Cs concentration achievable at the sample surface, thus indicating sufficient lowering of the work function to affect the ionization efficiency of Cs^+. Under these conditions a useful yield of 10^{-3} is achieved for FCs_2 whereas the yield of BCs is approximately $3x10^{-5}$.

[1]. Gao Y (1988) J Appl Phys 64: 3760-3762
[2]. Gnaser H, Oechsner H (1991) Fresenius J Anal Chem 341: 54-56
[3]. Wittmaack K(1992) Nucl Instrum Methods B64: 621-625
[4]. Gnaser H, Oechsner H (1994) Surface Science Letters 302: L289-292
[5]. Mootz Th, Adams F (1996) Int J Mass Spectrom Ion Processes 152: 209-216
[6]. Yu M L, Lang N D (1983) Phys Rev Lett 50(2): 127-130
[7]. Wittmaack K (1994) Nucl Instrum Methods B85: 374-378
[8]. Gnaser H (1996) Physical Review B54, 23: 17141-17146
[9]. Mootz Th, Bieck W, Migeon H N (1997) in SIMS XI, John Wiley: 953-956
[10]. Ferring M, Mootz Th, Saldi F, Migeon H N (1997) in SIMS XI, John Wiley: 911-914.

A. Benninghoven, P. Bertrand, H.-N. Migeon and H.W. Werner (Editors).
Proceedings of the 12th International Conference on Secondary Ion Mass Spectrometry,
Brussels, Belgium, 5-11 September 1999

THE NEW ATOMIKA SIMS 4600 FOR FULL 200/300 mm WAFERS

J.L. Maul[a], S.B. Patel[a], A. Sears[a], N. Loibl[a], L. Bögl[a], M.G. Dowsett[b]

[a] ATOMIKA Instruments GmbH, Bruckmannring 40, 85764 Oberschleissheim, Germany

[b] Department of Physics, University of Warwick, Coventry CV47AL, UK

e-mail: JLMaul@atomika.com

1. Introduction

There are two major trends in SIMS performance and instrumentation requirements: the depth profiling of ultra shallow junctions and the analysis of full wafers without breaking them into small pieces. The reduction of implant energies to low and sub-keV implantation energies is due to the progress of the semiconductor industry towards the nm design rule era. This requirement has generated the need to reduce the energy of the SIMS analysis beams to below 1 keV. One of the challenges related to this task has been to maintain acceptable depth profiling speeds whilst maintaining adequate dynamic range.

SIMS analysis of full wafers is motivated by two main reasons: the recent importance of using SIMS for dose monitoring and cost issues. The traditional methods of dose monitoring, based on ion implantation induced damage, does not work well with high dose ultra shallow implants. There are cost savings by performing SIMS on full wafers rather than on cut pieces. For example, savings can be made by reclaiming of expensive 300 mm wafers, and the same monitor wafer could be used for analysis by a range of techniques. With the increasing value of processed 300 mm wafers, preventive monitoring instead of failure analysis is a matter of serious consideration. SIMS tools for this task also need to have large degree of automation and simplified operation.

Two years ago, ATOMIKA introduced the model 4500 [1] with the new Floating Low Energy Ion Gun (FLIG™) technology [2] to depth profile with primary ion energies as low as 150 eV (75 eV per oxygen atom). ATOMIKA is now introducing the 4600 model full wafer SIMS for 200/300 mm wafers for at-fab SIMS requirements and a technology basis for future in-fab requirements.

238

2. Instrument Description

The 4600 is equipped with FLIG's to cover the entire range from MeV implants to ultra shallow junctions by a primary ion energy range of 5 keV to 150 eV. The primary ion beam angles are fixed. The oxygen beam is at normal incidence to the surface, while the cesium beam is at 60 degree to the normal. An automated z alignment procedure ensures that the analysis surface is at a fixed distance from primary ion guns and secondary ion optics respectively. The extraction fields transferring the secondary ions to the quadrupole mass spectrometer are kept below 10 Volts/mm to assure effects on the low energy primary ions being negligible. Each analysis site can be programmed either by using x/y co-ordinates or by moving to the spot of interest and storing its position. Analysis sites across an entire wafer can be accessed by the combination of rotation and translation movement, thereby considerably reducing the diameter of the vacuum chamber.

In addition to 300 and 200 mm wafers, smaller diameter wafers and small cut pieces (up to 49 at a time) can be loaded. 300 and 200 mm wafer cassette loading is available as an option. Here, multiple wafers can be analysed in an automated queue with automatic loading and unloading of wafers by a robotic arm. Wafers are transferred automatically to the wafer stage inside the analysis chamber with a transfer time of less then 15 minutes from atmosphere to 10^{-9} torr operation pressure. The base pressure is in the low 10^{-10} torr range. Custom designs can be made for integration with other systems (and SEC's[*] and GEM[*]). Data processing includes recipes for batch quantifying any desired number of depth profiles for useful quantities such as dose statistics or dose mapping.

3. Results

The results shown here are concentrating on precision ion dosimetry. These measurements have been carried out in an automated queue followed by recipes to carry out data evaluation in a batch process. The relative dose values have been obtained directly from the raw data without a need for depth or concentration calibration of the individual profiles.

Figure 1 shows an example of dose statistics with an RSD of 0.41% measured at 20 different sites across a 300 mm boron implanted wafer using 1 keV O2 primary ions at normal (0°) incidence. Figure 2 shows depth profile shape overlay of another set of 9 B profiles taken from a 2 x 2 mm area. The RSD value of 0.09 % is reflected by the perfect overlay in the linear scale. To illustrate junction depth repeatability the log scale overlay is shown as well. Figure 3 shows relative As dose measured across a 300 mm wafer with Cs primary ions at 60° incidence.

---

[*] SEC: SEMI Equipment Communications Standard
GEM: Generic Equipment Model

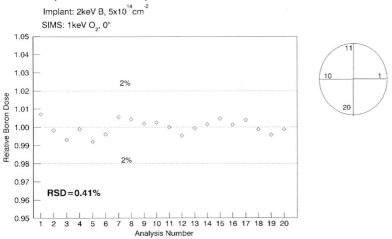

Fig. 1: Relative B dose of 20 measurements with an RSD of 0.41% obtained from 20 measurements across a 300 mm wafer (the individual sites are indicated in the graph).

Implant: 2keV B, $5x10^{14}$ cm^{-2}

SIMS: 1keV O_2'$0°$

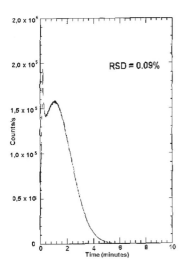 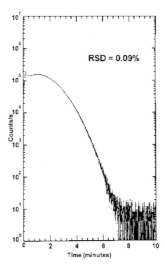

Fig. 2: Linear and log scale overlay of 9 boron profiles measurements with an RSD of 0.09 % obtained from an 2 x 2 mm area on a 300 mm wafer. The wafer and the SIMS conditions have been the same as in fig.1.

240

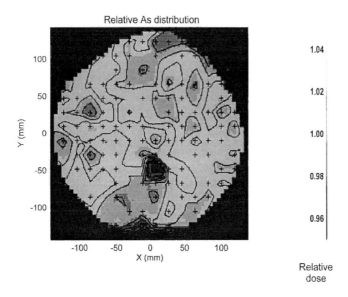

Fig. 3: Arsenic dose map with an RSD of 0.77% obtained from 140 depth profiles across a 300 mm wafer (the individual sites are marked by +). Note that this grey scale image has been reduced from a colour image for this presentation.

4. Conclusions

The ATOMIKA 4600 excells in depth profiling of shallow and ultra shallow implants and very thin layers without sacrificing efficient depth profiling deep into the samples. This full wafer SIMS provides rather simple operation by increased automation and stability of the tool to bring routine SIMS depth profiling capability closer to the fab. A large number of profiles can be measured in unattended run sequencies, such considerably reducing the cost per depth profile and likewise for dosimetry with an RSD of better than 1%. This holds true for measurement of a large number of samples as well as for full wafer mapping.

References

[1]   J. L. Maul and S. B. Patel, Secondary Ion Mass Spectrometry, SIMS XI, Eds. G. Gillen et al., John Wiley and Sons (1997), p707

[2]   M.G. Dowsett et al., Secondary Ion Mass Spectrometry, SIMS X, Eds. A. Benninghoven et al., John Wiley and Sons (1996), p367

A. Benninghoven, P. Bertrand, H.-N. Migeon and H.W. Werner (Editors).
Proceedings of the 12th International Conference on Secondary Ion Mass Spectrometry,
Brussels, Belgium, 5-11 September 1999

BREAKING THE RULES OF ION SOURCE DESIGN: ON-AXIS NEGATIVE ION EXTRACTION AND ION SOURCES FABRICATED FROM INSULATORS

Peter Williams,[1,2] Hamed Abdulkawi[1] and Richard L. Hervig[2]
[1]Department of Chemistry and Biochemistry
[2]Center for Solid State Science
Arizona State University
Tempe, AZ 85287
PW@ASU.EDU

1. Introduction

Apart from the introduction of liquid metal ion sources, there has been little innovation in ion source design for SIMS instruments for a number of years. Duoplasmatron designs have barely evolved over the past 30 years, while thermal cesium ion source designs date back over 10 years (Cameca design [1]) and over 20 years (tungsten frit design [2]). We report here some novel developments in duoplasmatron and cesium ion source design. Our duoplasmatron source has been modified to incorporate an asymmetric magnetic field which allows negative ion operation with an on-axis intermediate electrode. A new type of thermal cesium ion source has been constructed, in which cesium vapor is ionized on effusion through a heated aperture; a novel feature of this source is that the ion-optical components are constructed from insulating material.

2. Duoplasmatron with semimagnetic anode

To produce negative ion currents, typically O⁻, duoplasmatrons are operated with the aperture in the intermediate (or Z-) electrode offset from the central axis of the source. The edge of the Z-electrode aperture is roughly aligned with the center of the anode aperture, and ions are sampled from the fringe of the discharge plasma issuing from the Z-electrode aperture. The reason for this is not widely understood: it is *not* the case that negative ions are more abundant at the fringe of the plasma. Rather, the offset produces an asymmetric magnetic field necessary to suppress the intense electron current that would otherwise be extracted from the on-axis configuration. This electron current otherwise places an unacceptably high current drain on the ion accelerating voltage supply. Offsetting the Z-electrode displaces the magnetic axis of the source relative to the axis defined by the anode aperture so that electrons exiting the anode aperture follow the off-axis field lines and return to the anode.

We have tested an alternative approach to obtaining an asymmetric magnetic field for electron suppression while maintaining a coaxial alignment of anode aperture and Z-electrode. This is achieved by using a split anode fabricated from magnetic and non-magnetic metals.

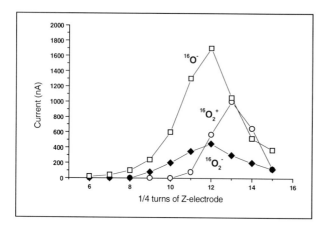

Figure 1. Positive and negative ion current variation with Z-electrode position

The 2.5 cm diameter screw-in anode insert for the Cameca duoplasmatron was machined from a bimetallic bar fabricated by brazing together soft iron (magnetic) and 304 stainless steel (non-magnetic).The magnetic/non-magnetic join is aligned with the on-axis anode aperture which was drilled in a tungsten insert. With this design, O^- ion currents are substantially the same as with the offset Z-electrode design. However, it is pos-sible now to operate with the Z-electrode almost on-axis. With the split-anode design, exact alignment of the Z-electrode is not required; negative ions can be extracted across the entire range of motion of the Z-electrode without loading down the accelerating voltage supply. As shown in Fig. 1, very minor readjustment of the Z-electrode position (about 1/4 turn) is required to optimize the current when switching between positive and negative ion operation, and it appears possible to dispense completely with Z-electrode motion in future duoplasmatron designs. The remaining slight offset between negative and positive ion current maxima may indicate that the magnetic/non-magnetic join should be offset somewhat from the center of the anode aperture.

To further improve performance of our duoplasmatron, we have added a lens, vacuum isolation (5/8" diameter gate valve), a 60 L/s turbomolecular pump, vacuum gauge and N_2 venting capability upstream of the primary magnet. The results of this modification are: 1) decreased time for maintenance because of the small volume vented, 2) no or minor interruption of cesium source use during duoplasmatron maintenance, 3) higher intensities for O^- (typically 700 nA through a 400 μm aperture near the sample, with a maximum of >1 μA), 4) slight improvement of minimum beam diameters.

3. New cesium source design

The two types of cesium ion source in common use are the tungsten frit source and the Cameca microbeam source. The performance of the frit source appears to be limited by the slow rate of diffusion of cesium vapor through the frit and by the inherent microroughness of the front surface of the frit. The Cameca source was designed to overcome these difficulties: a higher cesium flow rate is achieved through an annular aperture, and ions are produced at the flat surface of a solid tungsten ionizer. However, reproducible fabrication of the source in tungsten metal appears difficult, and the use of electron beam heating adds another complication because the heater power changes whenever the accelerating voltage is

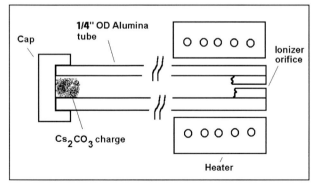

Figure 2. Alumina tube cesium source design

changed. This makes optimization of the accelerating potential for shallow depth profiling inconvenient, as the source must be allowed to restabilize after each vol-tage change.

As an alternative to both these designs, we have developed a novel cesium ion source, fabricated (apart from a heater coil) completely from ceramic materials. The source is a 1/4 inch (6.35 mm) O.D. alumina tube, approximately 8 cm long. The front of the tube is sealed with ceramic cement, the surface of the cement is polished flat, and a small channel, currently 250 μm diameter, is drilled axially through the cement.

Approximately 5 g of cesium carbonate (which decomposes on heating to cesium oxide) is loaded into the tube, and the rear of the tube is capped and sealed with the ceramic cement A resistance heater similar to that used in the tungsten frit source is attached and the assembly is mounted in the housing used for the tungsten frit source. In operation, the aperture end of the tube is heated to about 1200 °C for thermal ionization; conduction heats the rear of the tube and vaporizes and decomposes the cesium oxide.

The source design is intended to optimize cesium vapor flow, through the 250 μm channel, to present a small, well-defined ion optical object to the primary beam ion optics, and to be easy and inexpensive to construct. We chose to fabricate the source from readily-available and inexpensive alumina tubing, avoiding the expense of machining the source structure in a refractory metal. In addition, this offers the option of winding the heater directly on the ionizer if desired. (The more bulky frit source heater was used here simply for convenience in mounting the tube source in the frit source housing). Remarkably, the ion optical properties of the source appear not to be affected by the use of insulators; it appears that ionic conduction maintains an equipotential surface across the heated ceramic cement surface. Tested with the primary column of a Cameca IMS 3f, the source produces a maximum current > 1 μA at the sample, and spot sizes and current densities comparable to our tungsten frit source. Performance on an IMS 6f column and comparison with the Cameca cesium source remain to be evaluated.

With a cesium carbonate charge the source appears to operate quite cleanly. A cesium iodide charge produced some corrosion, presumably due to iodine produced by dissociation, while cesium chromate reacted with the alumina to produce ruby.
The lifetime of the source in current operation is approaching 1000 hours, and short- and long-term stability is acceptable for depth profile and isotope ratio determinations.

As an added benefit, the ceramic cement is a rich source of K^+ ions, and ~ 1 µA of K^+ can also be delivered to the sample, although beam quality is not as good as for Cs^+ because the ions are produced over a wide area.

References

[1]   Slodzian, G., Daigne, B., Girard, F., Boust, F., Hillion, F. in *Proc. 8th Int. Conf on SIMS,* A. Benninghoven, K.T.F. Janssen, J. Tumpner, H.W. Werner, eds, John Wiley & Sons, Chichester, 1992, p. 227

[2]   Williams, P., Lewis, R.K., Evans, C.A., Jr., Hanley, P.R., *Anal. Chem.* **49**,1399, (1977).

SECTION 6 :
CLUSTER/MOLECULAR ION BEAMS

A. Benninghoven, P. Bertrand, H.-N. Migeon and H.W. Werner (Editors).
Proceedings of the 12th International Conference on Secondary Ion Mass Spectrometry,
Brussels, Belgium, 5-11 September 1999

247

STATIC SIMS OF MATRIX ISOLATED MOLECULES UNDER POLYATOMIC PRIMARY ION BOMBARDMENT

C. Crone, R. Ostendorf, M. Thiemann, H.F. Arlinghaus, and A. Benninghoven
Physikalisches Institut, Universität Münster, D-48149 Münster, Germany

1. Introduction

Static SIMS of thermally unstable biomolecules is generally limited to small molecules. To enhance sensitivity and accessible mass range, various methods can be employed. Ag-SIMS is a well established technique for mass spectrometry of all kinds of biomolecules [1]. Analyte molecules are deposited as mono- or submonolayers on an Ag substrate. ME-SIMS (Matrix-Enhanced SIMS) was derived from MALDI-MS [2]. The analyte molecules are incorporated in very low relative concentrations (typically 10^{-4} to 10^{-3}) in a solid matrix, consisting of small organic molecules. Polyatomic primary ion bombardment (e.g. SF_5^+) results in a strong increase of molecular secondary ion yields compared with monoatomic primary ion bombardment [3].

The intention of this investigation was to find out to what degree the change from atomic (Ar^+) to polyatomic (SF_5^+) primary ions results in an increase in the secondary ion yields for ME-SIMS (compared to Ag-SIMS) of selected peptides and pharmaceuticals.

2. Instrumentation

We used a TOF-SIMS III reflectron type instrument for the yield determinations. The instrument is equipped with an electron impact (EI) ion source. Samples were analysed with 11 keV Ar^+ and SF_5^+ mass separated primary ions. The primary ion dose densities were less than 10^{12} primary ions/cm^2, so that all spectra and images were taken under static SIMS conditions. Postacceleration was set to 15 kV. Only positive ion mass spectra were taken.

For TOF-SIMS imaging, a gridless reflectron type TOF-SIMS instrument was used. This instrument provides a liquid metal ion source. The sample was analysed with 30 keV Ga^+. Post acceleration was set to 10 kV.

3. Samples

DHBS was used as the matrix for the ME-SIMS measurements. It is a well known MALDI matrix and consists of a mixture of 2,5-dihydroxybenzoic acid (DHB) with 2-hydroxy-5-methoxy-benzoic acid (9:1 (v:v)), dissolved in 1:1 (v:v) H_2O/Acetonitrile at a concentration of 0.5 mol/l.

We investigated several peptides and pharmaceuticals. The peptides (Insulin (bovine 5732.6 u), Melittin (2847.5 u), Substance P (1347.7 u) and Angiotensin II (1046.2 u)) were dissolved in H_2O at a concentration of 10^{-4} mol/l for the ME-SIMS measurements and in 1:1 H_2O / Acetonitrile at a concentration of 5×10^{-5} mol/l for the Ag-SIMS measurements. Of the pharmaceuticals investigated, two were steroids, two benzodiazepins and one an antidepressant. The steroids (β-Estradiol-17-Cypionate (396.6 u) and Testosterone Acetate (220.5 u)) and the benzodiazepins (Diazepam (284.7 u) and Oxazepam (286.7 u)) were dissolved in Methanol and Acetone respectively at a concentration of 10^{-3} mol/l for both kinds of measurements. The antidepressant (Imipramine (280.4 u)) was dissolved in H_2O at a concentration of 10^{-3} mol/l for the ME-SIMS measurements and in 1:1 H_2O/Acetonitrile at a concentration of 5×10^{-4} mol/l for the Ag-SIMS measurements.

4. Sample Preparation

For the ME-SIMS measurements, equal volumes of analyte and matrix solution ($1 - 2 \mu l$) are mixed on the substrate and left to dry in air at room temperature (dried-droplet preparation). An HF-dipped silicon substrate provides a hydrophobic surface, allowing only minimal spread of the applied matrix/analyte droplet. This results in the development of a matrix/analyte crystal ring with a macroscopic crystal structure forming the ring and microscopic crystals at the center. The best spectra and highest yields could be obtained from the macroscopic crystals of the ring.

For the Ag-SIMS measurements 2 μl of the aqueous solutions (peptides and imipramine) or 1 μl of the organic solutions (steroids and benzodiazepins) are pipetted onto etched silver substrates with drying taking place in air at room temperature. Compared to the ME-SIMS preparation, the sample is relatively homogeneous with no significant spot-to-spot variation in the measured analyte ion yields.

5. Evaluation Procedure

The yields of $(M+H)^+$- signals of the peptides and pharmaceuticals were evaluated. Because of considerable spot-to-spot fluctuations of the analyte ion yields, largely due to taking spectra from spots next to matrix/analyte-crystals instead of directly from matrix/analyte-crystals, several spectra of each sample were taken and the resulting yields were averaged.

6. Results and Discussion

As an example of the structure of the dried-droplet preparation of analyte with matrix (DHBS), static TOF-SIMS images of a ME-SIMS preparation of Oxazepam are shown in figure 1. Although, overall the sample shows substantial inhomogeneity, the analyte signal can be detected quite homogeneously from the analyte/matrix-crystals (except for shadow effects) (figure 1, lower row). The images also show, that the crystals present a thick layer, since no substrate signal can be detected from areas, where the matrix signal is strong (figure1, upper right corner and lower left corner).

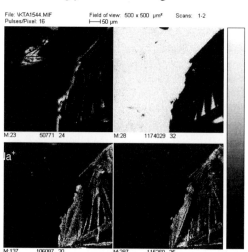

Figure 1: *TOF-SIMS images of a dried-droplet preparation of Oxazepam with DHBS; 500 × 500 μm²*

Figure 2 shows details of TOF-SIMS spectra of Substance P taken with ME-SIMS and Ag-SIMS under mono- and polyatomic primary ion bombardment.

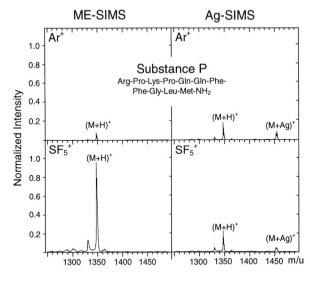

The spectra show a considerable increase in $(M+H)^+$ yields for ME-SIMS with SF_5^+ primary ions instead of Ar^+ primary ions, but hardly any increase for Ag-SIMS with SF_5^+ instead of Ar^+. Also, we found a slightly higher yield for Ag-SIMS compared with ME-SIMS for Ar^+ primary ion bombardment and a significantly higher yield for ME-SIMS compared with Ag-SIMS for SF_5^+ primary ion bombardment.

Figure 2: Sections of TOF-SIMS spectra of Substance P

Table 1 contains the measured yields and yield enhancements for the peptides investigated. With SF_5^+ instead of Ar^+ primary ion bombardment extensive yield enhancements were achieved for ME-SIMS, but only very small yield enhancements for Ag-SIMS.

Peptides:	ME-SIMS			Ag-SIMS		
	Yield/10^{-6}		Yield enhancement	Yield/10^{-6}		Yield enhancement
	Ar^+	SF_5^+	$Y_{SF_5^+}/Y_{Ar^+}$	Ar^+	SF_5^+	$Y_{SF_5^+}/Y_{Ar^+}$
Insulin	0.3	1.9	6.3	-	-	-
Melittin	1.2	21.0	17.5	5.8	13.0	2.2
Substance P	48.9	1595	32.6	154	505	3.3
Angiotensin II	61.0	850	13.9	6.1	7.1	1.2

Table 1: Measured (averaged) yields and yield enhancements for the investigated peptides

Table 2 shows the measured yields and yield enhancements for the pharmaceuticals investigated. The steroids and benzodiazepins show higher yields for ME-SIMS compared to Ag-SIMS for both Ar^+ and SF_5^+ primary ion bombardment. Contrary to this, imipramine shows higher yields for Ag-SIMS compared to ME-SIMS for both Ar^+ and SF_5^+ primary ion bombardment. All pharmaceuticals investigated showed a substantially higher yield enhancement for ME-SIMS compared to barely enhanced yields with Ag-SIMS, when SF_5^+ primary ions were used instead of Ar^+ primary ions.

Pharma-ceuticals:	ME-SIMS			Ag-SIMS		
	Yield/10^{-6}		Yield enhancement $Y_{SF_5^+}/Y_{Ar^+}$	Yield/10^{-6}		Yield enhancement $Y_{SF_5^+}/Y_{Ar^+}$
	Ar^+	SF_5^+		Ar^+	SF_5^+	
Estradiol	96.1	565	5.9	151	187	1.2
Test. Acet.	132	1790	13.6	17.8	38.2	2.1
Diazepam	183	1379	7.5	36.8	67.5	1.8
Oxazepam	334	3070	9.2	54.2	143	2.6
Imipramine	302	3260	10.8	3020	4880	1.6

Table 2: : Measured (averaged) yields and yield enhancements for the investigated pharmaceuticals

7. Summary and conclusion

Employment of Ag-SIMS with polyatomic primary ion bombardment (SF_5^+) results in only an increase in the secondary ion yields by about a factor 2 compared with monoatomic primary ion bombardment (Ar^+).

Employment of ME-SIMS with polyatomic primary ion bombardment (SF_5^+) results in an increase in the secondary ion yields by about one order of magnitude compared with monoatomic primary ion bombardment (Ar^+).

This different behavior of Ag-SIMS and ME-SIMS is in good agreement with more general investigations of SIMS with polyatomic primary ions [3]. Our model, giving an explanation for the different yields of mono- and polyatomic primary ions, is that since both types of primary ions have the same kinetic energy, the energy per atom is significantly lower for the polyatomic primary ion, resulting in an energy deposition closer to the surface. This leads to an extensive yield enhancement especially for sample and substrate materials made up of low-mass elements, explaining the larger yield enhancements for ME-SIMS with polyatomic primary ion bombardment instead of atomic primary ion bombardment compared to the yield enhancements for Ag-SIMS.

Our results show, that ME-SIMS with polyatomic primary ion bombardment is a useful tool for the investigation of thermally unstable biomolecules. By enhancing the yield, an increase of the accessible mass range can be obtained. However, the preparation of matrix and analyte is critical, so that reproducibility is not easily achieved. Thus far, only MALDI-matrices have been used for yield optimization. Aside from influencing the ionization process, these matrices also must absorb light of the (in MALDI) used laser wavelengths. The latter feature is not needed in ME-SIMS, making a new range of materials accessible as possible ME-SIMS matrices.

References

[1] A. Benninghoven, F.G. Rüdenauer, H.W. Werner, Secondary Ion Mass Spectrometry, John Wiley & Sons, New York (1987)

[2] K. J. Wu, R. W. Odom, Anal.Chem **68** (1996) 873

[3] A. Benninghoven, D. Stapel, O. Brox, B. Burkhardt, C. Crone, M. Thiemann and H.F. Arlinghaus, these proceedings

A. Benninghoven, P. Bertrand, H.-N. Migeon and H.W. Werner (Editors).
Proceedings of the 12th International Conference on Secondary Ion Mass Spectrometry,
Brussels, Belgium, 5-11 September 1999

PROSPECTS IN THE DEVELOPMENT AND USE OF SPUTTER CLUSTER ION SOURCES

S.F.Belykh, I.G. Gorelik, A.V.Zinoviev, S.N.Morozov, V.V. Palitsin, U.Kh. Rasulev,
A. Adriaens*),
Arifov Institute of Electronics Acad. of Sci. of Uzbekistan, Tashkent, 700143
*).University of Antwerp, Antwerp, Belgium

1. Introduction

Nowadays neutral and charged clusters are the objects of intensive studies. The clusters, being an intermediate state between atom and condensed matter, are considered as perspective elements. They are connected with the creation of new technological materials. Next to the study of the clusters characteristics and properties is the issue of the development and the practical use of these ion cluster beams with an energy E_0 about several keV. Such beams provide the transportation of the atoms with the energy $E=E_0/n<1$ keV (n-number of the atoms in a cluster) to the samples / targets and can serve as the tool at the solution of a complex research, technological and analytical problems.

For the development of cluster ions, various kinds of sources with different operating principles are used. Our viewpoint is that sputter cluster ion sources are very efficient. Their advantage lies in obtaining stable and rather intensive fluxes for both homogeneous and heterogeneous positive and negative cluster ions. Their principle is based on sputtering solid state materials by atomic or cluster ions.

2. Fundamental bases of cluster ion source designing

It is well known that relative yields of the sputtered neutral M_n^0 and charged clusters M_n^+ correspond to the power function $Y_{m,n} \sim n^{-\delta}$. The exponent δ - depends on the energy E_0 and the mass M_m^+ of a bombarding atomic or cluster ion, the mass M_2 of a target atoms, the binding energy Δ of atoms in a sputtered element of a target and the incidence angle α of projectile [1, 2]. It has been shown that the charge state formation mechanisms of the sputtered atoms and clusters are different. The degree of ionization for M_n clusters (for $n \geq 5$ on 2 - 3 order) exceed those for atoms and does not depend on the number n [3]. The effect of anomalous high non-additive sputtering of metals as large charged cluster ions under polyatomic ion bombardment with an energy $E_0 \sim keV/atom$ has been observed [2]. This effect consists of sharp increase (more than $10^2 - 10^3$ times) of M_n^+ ions yield (n>5) in comparison to that under atomic bombardment. For instance, the yields of Ta^+ and Ta_7^+ ions sputtered from Ta target by polyatomic Au_3^- projectiles with energy $E_0=6$ keV/atom have the same values. The yields of Ta_n^+ ($2 \leq n \leq 6$) ions are higher than for Ta^+ and Ta_7^+ ions. There are arguments that the above mentioned effect is caused by reduction of binding energy Δ in sputtered element of metals volume during polyatomic ion bombardment [4].

3. Analysis of cluster ion source operating principles

The designing of sputter cluster ion sources is limited by the low ionization efficiency of the sputtered particles. The solution of this problem can be found through effect of anomalous high non-additive sputtering of metal as large cluster ions. The scheme of a cluster ion source is given in figure 1.

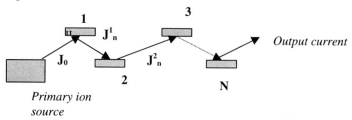

Figure 1

Here 1,2,3... N represent the cascades of targets. A sputtered ion flux from a target 1 (in which already there are clusters), is directed onto the second target 2 and so on.. The efficiency of the cluster ion generation on targt 2 will be much higher because of non-additive effect. Thus the mass spectrum of the sputtered cluster ions from N-th target there should show a shift forwards to the large numbers n (clusters).

The total cluster current with number n generated after N cascades is given by j^N_n:

$$j^N_n = j_0 \sum_m K^N_{m,n} \sum_m K^{N-1}_{m,n} \rightarrow \cdots \rightarrow \sum_m K^1_{m,1} \tag{1}$$

Here j_0 is the primary ion beam current, $K^N_{m,n}$ is the factor describing efficiency of M_n^+ cluster emission at the bombardment of a target by clusters M_m^+: $K^N_{m,\,n} = j_n/j_m$. The superscript N specifies, that the factors $K_{m,n}$ depend on pair «projectile - target» and can be different for each pair.

To analyze the operation of the cascade cluster source when using expression (1) the following approximation was used: it was assumed that cluster ion yield connected with the bombardment current by power function and exponent δ of this function is in range 6 – 9 for atomic, 4 – 5 for diatomic and 3 – 4 for triatomic ion bombardment [2]. Using these data we have calculated the efficiency of cluster ion generation for three targets, using the following sequence of bombarding particles: Au^- - Ta^+_m - Ta^+_m.- Ta^+_m. The calculated results are given in figure 2.

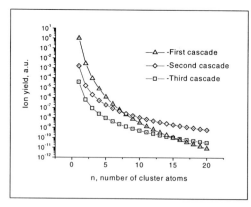

Figure 2

One can see that the second cascade (two-target scheme) demonstrates an increasing of Ta_n^+ cluster generation with n> 7. The third cascade (three-target scheme), due to small value of projectile flux, becomes effective only at n> 15. Nevertheless, for the three-target scheme the enrichment of the sputtered particles spectrum by large clusters takes a place.

4. Experimental results

The sputter cluster ion source with two targets was investigated. The Cs^+ ions bombarded the target 1 with energy 5 kV and their current was 50 μA. The first target was the Au foil. The high sputtering factor of gold, its electron affinity and atomic mass made us chose gold as the first target.

Testing the sputtered flux from the first target of the source has shown that there were the negative ions Au_1^- Au_2^-, Au_3^-, with relative intensities of 1:0.25: 0.08. The sputtered flux from the first target was directed on a tantalum target (target 2). The efficiency of the ion current collection on a target 2 was not less than 90%. The energy of projectile ions was not less than 12 keV.

The essential increase of a Ta_n^+ cluster yield with n> 5 during the bombardment by total ion current, sputtered from the first target was observed. The yield of Ta_5^+ and Ta_7^+ clusters exceeded the yield for Ta^+ ions signal under only atomic bombardment. The relative increase of a Ta_n^+ cluster ion yield with n> 5 exceeded 10 in comparison of monoatomic bombardment.

The preliminary experiments have shown, that the Ta_n^+ cluster ion yield (at least for clusters with n<17) from the sources with number of targets more than 2 are less, than in the case of a source with N=2. Nevertheless, in this case, the center of mass - spectrum of the sputtered particles is shifted to the clusters with large numbers n.

Such sources are apparently not too effective for the analytical purposes, but can be used for problems connected to an irradiation of a surface by fluxes of particles with high mass at the rather low requirements to their mass spectra. The search of suitable pairs «projectile ion - target » will allow to optimize process of generation of clusters and to create three-target sources generating large clusters with n> 20.

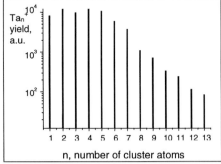

Figure 3 demonstrates the experimental mass-spectrum of designed sputter cluster ion source (three-cascade type).

Thus, in that work the possible direction of sputter large cluster ion sources designing by a cascade principle was demonstrated.

Figure 3

Acknowledgement.
The authors express gratitude to the NATO (Science for Peace Program, Project SfP 97.1929) for financial support.

References

[1] A.Wucher, M.Wahl. Nucl.Instr.Method. **B115**, (1996), 581.
[2] F.Belykh, U.Kh.Rasulev, A.V.Samartsev, I.V.Veryovkin Nucl.Instr.Method. **B136-138**, (1998), 779
[3] M.Wahl, A.Wucher. Nucl.Instr.Method. **B94**, (1994), 36S
[4] V.I.Matveev, S.F.Belykh, V.I.Veryovkin, A.Adriaens, F.Adams. Nucl.Instr.Method. **B155**, (1999), 409

A. Benninghoven, P. Bertrand, H.-N. Migeon and H.W. Werner (Editors).
Proceedings of the 12th International Conference on Secondary Ion Mass Spectrometry,
Brussels, Belgium, 5-11 September 1999

SECONDARY ION EMISSION FROM LB-LAYERS UNDER MOLECULAR PRIMARY ION BOMBARDMENT

D. Stapel[1], M. Thiemann[1], B. Hagenhoff[2], A. Benninghoven[1]

[1]Universität Münster, Physikalisches Institut, D-48149 Münster, Germany
[2]TASCON, Mendelstr. 11, D-48149 Münster, Germany

1. Introduction

Secondary ion yields $Y(X_i^q)$ increase considerably when changing from atomic to molecular primary ions, especially for thick organic layers [1]. This increase may be the result of an increase in sputter yield, transformation probability $P(M \rightarrow (X_i^q))$ or both of them. Determining the yield is not sufficient for deciding whether the observable yield enhancement is just the result of an increase in sputtering or whether it is accompanied by an increased transformation probability. This can be decided by an exact determination of the damage cross section σ. From Y and σ results the ion formation efficiency $E = Y/\sigma$, indicating the total number of secondary ions generated or detected during complete sputtering of a monolayer of surface species M. Only an increase in E results in a corresponding increase in sensitivity and lateral resolution in static SIMS.

We extended our investigations on secondary ion emission from LB-layers and addressed the question if the results on the arachidic acid LB-layers [1] would be validated for another LB system. For a more detailed understanding of the complex sputtering and ion formation processes the influence of primary ion mass, chemical composition, number of constituents and total ion energy on Y, σ and E were investigated.

The earlier results for LB layers were confirmed and we found an increase in Y, σ and E with growing primary ion mass, primary ion energy and an enhancement for molecular primary ions containing up to 6 heavy atoms. For primary ions consisting of 6 to 18 atoms we found an saturation behaviour of Y, σ and E enhancement. Moreover, we found no particular influence of chemical composition of primary ions on secondary ion emission.

2. Experimental

All experiments were carried out with a reflectron time-of-flight instrument, which was equipped with an EI primary ion source and a 90^0 pulsing unit for primary ion mass separation. In order to get a sufficient primary ion flux the applied molecular substances must have a high intensity in EI parent ions as well as a high vapour pressure and a narrow isotopic distribution. We applied Ne^+, Ar^+, Xe^+, O_2^+, CO_2^+, SF_5^+, $C_7H_7^+$, $C_{10}H_8^+$, $C_6F_6^+$ and $C_{10}F_8^+$ primary ions in the energy range from 0.5 to 11 keV.

Comparing secondary ion emission under different primary ion bombardment requires a homogenous coverage of substrate surface. We selected polymethacrylate LB-Layers on Ag. The LB technique produces ordered molecular overlayers of a defined layer thickness (n = 1, 3, 5, 7 and 9 ML) [2]. The mononlayer (n = 1) and multilayer (n = 9) coverage were chosen for our investigations.

3. Results and Discussion

Positive static SIMS spectra were found to be more characteristic than negative spectra. They feature high intensities of metal substrate ions Ag^+ and molecular fragment ions 115, 143 and 185 u of the LB overlayer. Qualitatively similar spectra were obtained by using Ne^+, Ar^+, Xe^+, O_2^+, SF_5^+, $C_7H_7^+$, $C_{10}H_8^+$, $C_6F_6^+$ and $C_{10}F_8^+$ primary ion bombardment. In Fig. 1) Y, σ and E are shown for the characteristic fragment ion 143 u and a coverage of 9 layers, as a function of the number of heavy constituents per primary ion. The total primary ion energy was 11 keV for all applied primary ions. Using atomic primary ion bombardment, Y increases with growing primary ion mass. Increasing the number of constituents from 1 (Ne^+) over 2 (O_2^+) to 6 (SF_5^+) results in a yield enhancement of about two orders of magnitude. A further increase of constituents from 6 (SF_5^+) to 18 ($C_{10}F_8^+$) shows no further increase in yield, indicating a "saturation" effect. For molecular primary ions the total energy can be divided between the constituents in proportion to the masses of the components. Using $C_7H_7^+$ and $C_{10}H_8^+$ primary ions this results in a particularly low energy for H and therefore in a distinctively low sputter yield for H. For that reason $C_7H_7^+$ and $C_{10}H_8^+$ are regarded as molecules with 7 and 10 con-

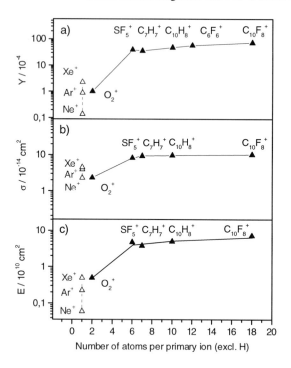

Fig. 1) Y, σ and E as a function of number of constituents per primary ion for fragment 143 u by a coverage of 9 layers

stituents, respectively (Fig. 1 a).

Furthermore, the corresponding damage cross sections were deter-mined. For monoatomic bombar-dment σ increases with growing primary ion mass. Increasing number of components results in an enhancement by a factor of about 4 by changing from 1 (Ne⁺) to 6 (SF₅⁺) atoms. Further increase from 7 to 18 components shows similar cross sections as for 6 (SF₅⁺) constituents (Fig. 1 b).

From Y and σ the secondary ion formation efficiencies E were calculated. The increase in damage cross sections are not as pronounced as the yield enhancement. Using atomic primary ions the ion formation efficiency remains higher for Xe⁺ compared to Ar⁺ and Ne⁺ bombardment. Polyatomic primary ions consisting of more than 6 atoms have a particularly higher efficiency than atomic primary ions (Fig. 1 c).

Other characteristic fragment ions as 115 and 185 u show a similar behaviour in Y, σ and E. For the monolayer coverage the yield and efficiency enhancement is not as pronounced as for the multilayer coverage. This confirms earlier investigations of yield and efficiency under atomic and molecular primary ion bombardment for arachidic acid LB-layers [1]. The saturation behaviour of Y, σ and E under molecular primary ions of different chemical composition indicates no particular chemical influence on the secondary ion emission.

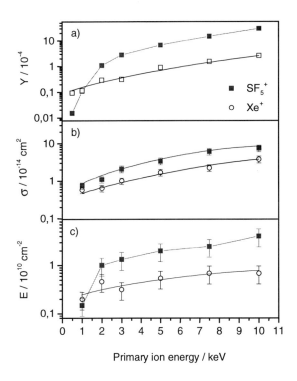

Fig. 2) a) Y, b) σ and c) E as a function of primary ion energy for fragment 143 u by a coverage of 9 layers

Moreover, the influence of primary ion energy on secondary ion emission was investigated. For isobaric primary ions, atomic Xe⁺ (m=129 u) and polyatomic SF₅⁺ (m=127 u), the secondary ion yields were monitored in the energy range from 0.5 to 10 keV. In Fig. 2 a) the values are plotted for the mulitlayer coverage. Primary ion energies over 2 keV show particularly high yields for SF₅⁺ bombardment. The yield ratio of atomic and molecular primary ion bombardment changes for lower energies. Using 1 keV the yields are quite similar, whereas for 0.5 keV the yield for Xe^+ bombardment is even higher than for SF_5^+ bombardment. This holds also for other secondary ions as well as for the monolayer coverage. To decide whether the change in yield ratio is caused by a decrease in sputter yield, transformation probability or both of them, the corresponding damage cross sections were determined. The cross sections in the energy range from 1 to 10 keV are shown in Fig. 2 b). The damage cross section remains higher for SF_5^+ compared to Xe^+ bombardment even in the low energy range. Therefore the removal and/or destruction of surface species is more pronounced for SF_5^+ bombardment and the calculated secondary ion formation efficiency is higher in the energy range from 2 - 10 keV (Fig. 2 b). Using 1 keV results in similar efficiencies for the multilayer coverage, whereas for the monolayer coverage the efficiencies are even lower under SF_5^+ than Xe^+ bombardment.

The pronounced decrease in yield and efficiency for SF_5^+ bombardment in the energy range from 0.5 to 2 keV can be explained with the help of a simple fragmentation model. Distributing the energy between the constituents results in a particularly low energy for F and S. Therefore the desorption as well as ionization probabilities are drastically reduced.

4. Conclusion

Our investigation focused on the influence of number and kinds of constituents of molecular primary ion as well as primary ion energy on secondary ion emission. We found:

- more pronounced increase in Y and E for the multilayer coverage under polyatomic primary ion bombardment (confirming earlier measurements)
- increase in Y, σ and E with growing mass for monoatomic primary ions
- increase in Y, σ and E with growing number of constituents up to 6 atoms
- "saturation" effect of Y, σ and E enhancement for molecular primary ions of constant primary ion energy containing 6 to 18 atoms
- no particular "chemical" influence of the primary ion components on the secondary ion yield under static SIMS conditions
- lower secondary ion yields under SF_5^+ bombardment in the energy range from 0.5 to 1 keV compared to Xe^+ bombardment
- higher damage cross section under SF_5^+ bombardment in the energy range from 1 to 10 keV
- higher efficiencies for SF_5^+ bombardment for energies above 2 keV

References

[1] D. Stapel, O. Brox and A. Benninghoven, Appl. Surf. Sci. 140 (1998) 156

[2] B. Hagenhoff, A. Benninghoven, H. U. Siegmund and D. Holtkamp, Thin Solid Films 210/211 (1992) 601.

A. Benninghoven, P. Bertrand, H.-N. Migeon and H.W. Werner (Editors).
Proceedings of the 12th International Conference on Secondary Ion Mass Spectrometry,
Brussels, Belgium, 5-11 September 1999

STATIC SIMS WITH MOLECULAR PRIMARY IONS

A. Benninghoven, D. Stapel, O. Brox, B. Burkhardt, C. Crone,
M. Thiemann, H. A. Arlinghaus

Physikalisches Institut, Universität Münster, Germany

1. Introduction

The application of molecular primary ions in SIMS is becoming increasingly important, for fundamental research as well as for analytical applications. A variety of polyatomic primary ions in the keV and MeV range have been applied to many different samples [1]. We have reported on results for keV SF_5^+ bombardment of polymers and more recently of LB-layers [2, 3]. We found an increase in both, Y and σ, in such a way that E was higher when changing from atomic to molecular PI-bombardment. Here we want to address a number of open questions, in particular the influence on the secondary ion emission of the chemical nature of the bombarding particle, of sample composition and structure, and the influence of the mass range and the composition of the considered secondary ions.

2. Experimental

We used a time-of-flight SIMS instrument, equipped with a pulsed electron impact primary ion source which allows the generation of mass separated primary ion beams. We studied different groups of samples, mainly polymers with additives, oxide layers on semiconductors and molecular overlayers. We present some selected examples obtained for polyethylene with Irganox, oxidized Si and GaAs surfaces, and pharmaceuticals and peptides embedded in an organic matrix. As primary ions we applied 11 keV O^+, Ne^+, Ar^+, Xe^+, O_2^+, CO_2^+, SF_5^+, $C_7H_7^+$, $C_6F_6^+$ and $C_{10}H_8^+$.

Primary ions were selected in such a way, that we could investigate the influence of primary ion mass by comparing the results for O^+, Ne^+, Ar^+ and Xe^+ bombardment. We checked the effect of atomic against molecular ions of comparable mass by comparing Xe^+ mainly against SF_5^+ and $C_{10}H_8^+$. The influence of the chemical composition of the primary ion species has been studied by comparing SF_5^+ bombardment with $C_7H_7^+$. Finally we checked the influence of the number of atoms in a chemically similar primary ion by looking at the whole series of molecular primary ions mentioned above, changing the total number of atoms in a single ion between 1 and 18.

3. Results and discussion

Polymers and additives

In an earlier investigation we found a pronounced increase in yield and efficiency for quite a number of polymers [2]. For PET, PP, PTFE, PS, PC, PMMA and PEG we found yield enhancements between a factor of 10 and a factor of more than 500 depending on the mass range and sample material. For the additive Irganox in polypropylene we found a very strong yield increase, too. Therefore we selected this additive for further investigation of this effect.

Primary ion bombardment of PE + Irganox 1010 results in the formation of a number of small clusters, starting with a simple ring system up to large fragments and parent ions. The positive spectrum may be divided into two parts : the high mass range and the low mass range. Both

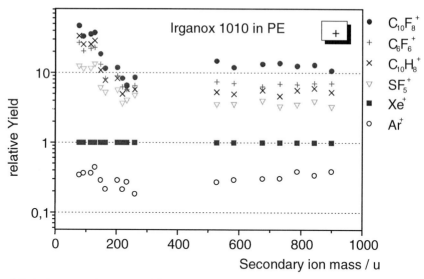

Fig. 1 Relative secondary ion yields Y(X) / Y$_{Xe}$ (X) of Irganox 1010 fragments

show different yield enhancements (Fig. 1). The positive secondary ion yields are normalized to the Xe$^+$ yields. They show a high increase going from Ar$^+$ to Xe$^+$, and an additional increase if we change to molecular primary ions. The highest yields are obtained for these molecular primary particles. In the low mass range the effect is similar, but not so uniform. Yield increases are different for the different groups of secondary ions. The yield enhancement is more pronounced for smaller fragments, indicating an enhanced fragmentation under molecular primary ion bombardment. If we look more carefully in the low mass range we see a structure in the cluster intensities reflecting obviously the stability of the generated secondary ions. Negative secondary ions show a very similar behaviour: a pronounced difference between Ar$^+$ and Xe$^+$ and an additional effect for molecular primary ions. For Ar$^+$ primary ion no secondary signals can be detected in the high mass range, which supplies the analytically most important information on additives in polymers. The comparison of secondary ion yields under SF$_5^+$, C$_7$H$_7^+$ and C$_{10}$H$_8^+$ bombardment of similarly structured positive and negative Irganox fragments indicates no particular chemical influence of fluorine containing SF$_5^+$ primary ions on secondary ion emission under static SIMS conditions.

Oxidized Si and GaAs surfaces

For oxidized Si and GaAs surfaces we found similar increases in secondary ion yields. As an example Fig. 2 shows the negative secondary ion yield of (SiO)$_n$OH$^-$ ions, which are typical secondary ion clusters emitted from oxidized Si surfaces. We found again a very pronounced effect for the two considered molecular primary ions. For Ar$^+$ bombardment the maximum detected cluster size was n = 3. If we switch to Xe$^+$ bombardment we followed up to n = 6. Only for the molecular primary ions, we found larger clusters up to n = 12. We see a large difference between the atomic and the molecular primary ions. Our investigations show a more pronounced cluster ion emission under polyatomic primary ion bombardment, especially for large secondary ion clusters. Again the primary ion with a higher number of atoms results in a higher yield (Fig. 2). For analytical purposes, it is important to note that these $(SiO)_n$ OH⁻ clusters in the high mass range can only be generated by using polyatomic primary ions.

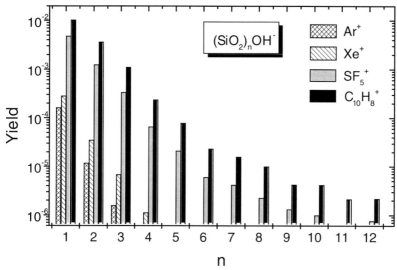

Fig. 2 Yields of negative secondary ion clusters under atomic and molecular ion bombardment

Besides these clusters, in the positive spectrum hydrocarbon ion groups are prominent. We compared yields for these ions too, as a function of primary ion species. We found the same behaviour : Slight differences in yields between Ar^+ and Xe^+ bombardment, and a big difference between atomic and molecular primary ions. These differences are increasing if we go to higher masses. That means, for higher secondary ion masses we get a more efficient secondary ion yield enhancement than for the lower mass range.

This behaviour is very similar for GaAs surface. We found clusters ions of the general composition $Ga_mAs_nO_o^-$. The total number of GaAs units in these ions is k = 3, 5, 7, etc. (k = m+n). If we consider e.g. k = 7, we find a very pronounced structure, supplying plenty of information on the surface oxide. We do not go into details here. This cluster emission behaves very similar to that what we observed for the negative $(SiO_2)OH^-$ ions : an increase for Xe^+ compared with Ar^+, more pronounced in the high m, n, o -range and again a strong increase for molecular primary ions. Indeed for Ar^+ the spectrum reaches only k = 5, whereas for molecular primary ions it goes up to k = 19.

Matrix isolated biomolecules

The sensitivity for the SIMS analysis of molecules can be increased by depositing the analyte as a monolayer on a silver substrate (Ag-SIMS) or by incorporation of these molecules in an appropriate matrix (ME-SIMS, matrix enhanced SIMS). We studies both techniques for a group of peptides and a group of pharmaceuticals. As a matrix we used DHBS, a mixture of 2, 5-dihydroxybenzoic acid with 2-hydroxy-5-methoxy-benzoic acid. The analyte was mixed in the matrix at a ratio of 10^{-4} to 10^{-3} (analyte molecules / matrix molecules). A droplet of this solution was put on a surface so that crystallites were formed. We studied the secondary ion emission for these samples under static Ar^+ and SF_5^+ bombardment. Typical secondary ion yields for peptides are shown in Tab. 1. Under Ar^+ bombardment both preparation techniques result in the emission of $(M+H)^+$. Changing from Ar^+ to SF_5^+ bombardment results in a more pronounced $(M+H)^+$ increase for the matrix isolated analyte than for the Ag preparation. As a general tendency we found for the investigated peptides (mass range 1000 – 6000 u) an average yield increase by a factor of about 2 for Ag-SIMS, and a factor of 6 - 30 for ME-SIMS. For the investigated pharmaceuticals (two steroids, two benzodiazepins and an antidepressant, mass range 220 – 350 u) a similar behaviour was found (yield enhancement factor 6 -14 for ME-SIMS, factor 2 for Ag-SIMS) [5].

Substance (mass)	Y_{Ar} (M+H$^+$) / 10^{-6}	Y_{SF} (M+H$^+$) / 10^{-6}	Relative Yields
Insulin (5733 u)	0.3	1.9	6.3
Melittin (2848 u)	1.2	21.0	17.5
Substance P (1348 u)	48.9	1595.0	32.6
Angiotensin II (1046 u)	61.0	850.0	14.0

Tab. 1 Secondary ion yields of peptides embedded in a DHBS matrix under Ar$^+$ and SF$_5^+$ bombardment

4. Summary

The secondary ion emission behaviour of a wide variety of samples under the bombardment of different atomic and molecular primary ion species has been studied. The experimental results allow a number of general conclusions :

- Y, σ and E increase with an increasing mass of atomic primary ions.
- Y, σ and E are in all studied cases higher for molecular primary ions compared with atomic primary ions of comparable mass.
- Y, σ and E increase with increasing number of heavy atoms (excluding hydrogen) for chemically similar molecular primary ions up to 6 constituents.
- The enhancement effect shows saturation behaviour for molecular primary ions with more than 10 heavy atoms (excluding hydrogen) (see also [4]).
- Damage cross sections σ increase considerably more slowly than the corresponding yields.
- "Chemical effects" could not be detected for different primary ions – as long as static SIMS conditions were met.
- The enhancement effect is higher for thick organic layers and polymers than for metal and semiconductor substrates.
- The enhancement effect depends on the mass and structure of the considered secondary ion species.

The general increase in E for heavy and in particular for molecular primary ions demonstrates clearly that the observed yield enhancement is not only the result of enhanced sputtering, but that in addition the transformation probability of a molecular surface species into a characteristic secondary ion is enhanced. The increase in sputtering efficiency qualitatively follows the prediction of a simple collision model.

The use of molecular primary ions has considerable advantages for spectroscopy as well as imaging. In spectroscopy the increase in Y as well as in E results in shorter acquisition times as well as in an enhanced sensitivities. A similar improvement results for the best lateral resolution, provided fine focussed ion beams for molecular species are available.

References

[1] Y. Le Beyec, Int. J. Mass Spectrom. Ion Proc. 174 (1998) 101
[2] F. Kötter, A. Benninghoven, Appl. Surf. Sci. 133 (1998) 47
[3] D. Stapel, O.Brox, and A. Benninghoven, Appl. Surf. Sci. 140 (1999) 156
[4] D. Stapel, M. Thiemann, B. Hagenhoff, A. Benninghoven, these proceedings
[5] C. Crone, R. Ostendorf, M. Thiemann, H.F. Arlinghaus,A. Benninghoven, these proceedings

A. Benninghoven, P. Bertrand, H.-N. Migeon and H.W. Werner (Editors).
Proceedings of the 12th International Conference on Secondary Ion Mass Spectrometry,
Brussels, Belgium, 5-11 September 1999

263

MOLECULAR SECONDARY PARTICLE EMISSION FROM MOLECULAR OVERLAYERS UNDER SF$_5^+$ -BOMBARDMENT

A. Schnieders, M. Schröder, D. Stapel, H. F. Arlinghaus, A. Benninghoven

Physikalisches Institut der Universität, Wilhelm-Klemm-Str. 10,
D-48149 Münster, Germany

1. Introduction

Ion beam-induced desorption under static sputtering conditions in combination with time-of-flight mass spectrometry has progressed to a sensitive analytical tool, which is widely used for the characterization of organic molecules on solid surfaces. Especially the use of polyatomic primary ions in recent years has shown advantages concerning the sensitivity of static SIMS, since secondary ion yields $Y(X_i^q)$ considerably increase when changing from atomic to molecular primary ions, particularly for thick organic layers. Our present understanding of the yield in dependence on the layer thickness is mainly based on investigations of LB-layers with different numbers of layers, e. g. arachidic acid LB-layers on Au [1].

In this paper we focus on a more accurate investigation of the yield in dependence on the layer thickness. As model systems we used overlayers of adenine and β-alanine on Ag and Si surfaces. The layers were produced by evaporation of the molecules from a Knudsen cell under UHV condition. Because of the high photoion and secondary ion yields it was possible to continuously monitor the secondary particle emission under static sputtering conditions during the layer formation.

2. Experimental

All experiments were performed in a reflectron-type time-of-flight mass spectrometer equipped with a 10 keV electron impact gas ion source for sputtering. We chose Ar$^+$ as one primary ion species, as it is widely used in SIMS and SNMS. For the comparison of atomic and molecular primary ions we applied Xe$^+$ and SF$_5^+$ because of their similar masses. For postionization of adenine a sub-picosecond excimer laser system operating at 248 nm was used, whereas for postionization of β-alanine a standard excimer laser operating at 193 nm was available. The mass spectrometer was equipped with a coolable sample stage.

The molecular overlayers of adenine and β-alanine were produced by Knudsen cell effusion on liquid nitrogen cooled ($T = 100$ K) targets. As substrate material Ag and Si were chosen since sputtering adenine and β-alanine from these substrates results in different molecular yield enhancements under Ar$^+$ bombardment [2]. Starting with a sputter cleaned substrate the flux of photoions and secondary ions (adenine: M$^\oplus$ and (M+H)$^+$, β-alanine: (CNH$_4$)$^\oplus$, which is formed via an α-cleavage process of the molecular radical ion after photoionization, and (M+H)$^+$), which are characteristic for the sputtered molecules, was monitored online under static sputtering conditions until the substrate was covered by several monolayers.

3. Results and discussion

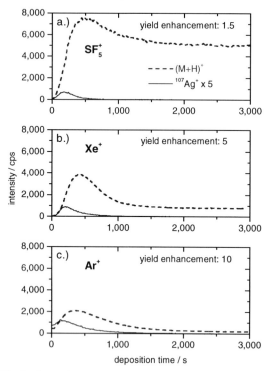

Fig. 1: Secondary ion signal in dependence on the layer deposition time during layer formation of adenine on Ag (primary ion species: a.) SF_5^+, b.) Xe^+, and c.) Ar^+; primary ion flux $1 \cdot 10^6$ s^{-1}).

Figure 1 shows the molecular secondary ion signal $I((M+H)^+)$ in dependence on the layer deposition time during layer formation of adenine on Ag by use of different primary ion species. The protonated molecule shows the same general behaviour under Xe^+ and SF_5^+ bombardment as already demonstrated for sputtering with Ar^+ [2]. The signals linearly increase with increasing surface coverage. After a distinct maximum the signals decrease with further growing layer thickness and reach a plateau after a multilayer of the molecule has been adsorbed on the substrate. The maximum is located at the same deposition time independent from the primary ion species used for sputtering. Differences can be seen in the absolute yields and in the yield enhancement, which is defined as the ratio of the maximum yield to that obtained from a multilayer. The absolute yields clearly increase by changing from Ar^+ to Xe^+ primary ions reflecting the influence of the primary ion mass. A further increase results from changing to the polyatomic primary ion SF_5^+ (see also [3]). The influence of the layer thickness and therefore the influence of the substrate on the desorption process, which is reflected by the yield enhancement, is most pronounced by use of Ar^+ primary ions and is reduced by changing to Xe^+. Using SF_5^+, the layer thickness has almost no influence on the yields. These results are qualitatively in agreement with the results obtained for arachidic acid LB-layer on Au [1]. The minor influence of the substrate on the yields by sputtering with SF_5^+ is also reflected by comparing the results for adenine deposited on Si and on Ag surfaces (see Table 1).

	monolayer yield Y_{mono} / 10^{-4}		multilayer yield Y_{multi} / 10^{-4}					
	yield enhancement							
	adenine				β-alanine			
	Ag		Si		Ag		Si	
SF_5^+	75	50	48	34	23	15	9	7
	x 1.5		x 1.4		x 1.5		x 1.3	
Xe^+	36	8	12	5.6	9	2	2.8	2.3
	4.5		2.2		4.5		1.2	
Ar^+	20	2	3.1	2.4	5.6	0.8	0.8	0.8
	x 10		x 1.3		x 7		x 1	

Table 1: Secondary ion yield of adenine and β-alanine sputtered from (sub-)monolayer and multilayer coverages on Ag and Si. The yield enhancement between multilayer and monolayer sputtering is also given.

Comparing the yields of the characteristic photoion $M^{\oplus}$ and the protonated molecule $(M+H)^+$ in dependence on the layer thickness for Ar^+ sputtering no significant differences can be observed. Both signals show qualitatively the same behaviour with similar values for the yield enhancement. Additionally, the ratio of the disappearance cross sections σ_D measured for sub-monolayer coverages and multilayer coverages coincides with the yield enhancement. [2] Considering these results the dependence of the secondary particle yield of adenine on the layer thickness can be explained by a sputter-induced matrix effect. (Figure 2.a.) The model is based on following equation describing the yield:

$$Y(X_i^q) = \vartheta(M) \cdot \sigma_D \cdot P(M \rightarrow X_i^q) \cdot T \cdot D \qquad (1)$$

with the surface density ϑ, the transformation probability P, the instrument transmission T, and the detection probability D. Assuming a constant disappearance cross section in the sub-monolayer range $\sigma_{D,mono}$, a constant, but lower disappearance cross section in the multilayer

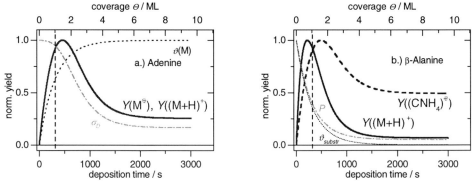

Fig. 2: Calculated yields Y in dependence on the coverage Θ during layer formation for a.) adenine and b.) β-alanine.

range $\sigma_{D,multi}$, and a continuous transition between the two values the dependence of the yield on the layer thickness can be calculated. Considering the same behaviour of neutrals and secondary ions, the transformation probability is assumed to be constant.

The behaviour of β-alanine is different to that of adenine as demonstrated in Figure 3. The secondary ion signal $I((M+H)^+)$ reaches its maximum before the maximum of the photoion intensity $I((CNH_4)^\oplus)$. (The photoion $(CNH_4)^\oplus$ is characteristic for the sputtered neutral molecule, since it is formed via an α-cleavage process of the molecular radical ion after photoionization.) The dependence of the secondary ion yield can be modelled by an additional assumption for the transformation probability $P(M \rightarrow (M+H)^+)$. With the formulation of P as a sum of a constant part P_{multi} and a part

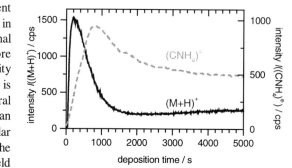

Fig. 3: *Photoion signal and secondary ion signal in dependence on the layer deposition time during layer formation of β-alanine on* Ag *(primary ion species:* Ar⁺; *primary ion flux* 3.5 · 10⁶ s⁻¹).

proportional to the surface density of the substrate ϑ_{substr} the dependence of the secondary ion yield of β-alanine on the layer thickness can be calculated using equation (1). (Figure 2.b.) This ionization matrix effect can also be detected by sputtering of β-alanine on Ag with Xe⁺ and SF₅⁺. For Si as substrate no distinct ionization matrix effect is seen. The yields and the respective values of the yield enhancements for sputtering of β-alanine are also given in Table 1.

4. Conclusion

We have shown that using SF₅⁺ for sputtering of molecular overlayers of adenine and β-alanine on Ag and Si results in higher yields than the use of atomic primary ions like Ar⁺ and Xe⁺. The sputter-induced matrix effect for sputtering adenine is minimized using SF₅⁺ primary ions. Further investigations of the photoion yield of $(CNH_4)^\oplus$ (the characteristic fragment of β-alanine) in dependence on the layer thickness are necessary in order to determine the influence of the additional ionization matrix effect for sputtering of β-alanine under the different sputter conditions.

References

[1] D. Stapel, O. Brox, A. Benninghoven, Applied Surface Science **140**, 156 (1999)
[2] R. Möllers, A. Schnieders, G. Kortenbruck, A. Benninghoven, in *Secondary Ion Mass Spectrometry SIMS X*, John Wiley & Sons, Chichester, 1997, p 943
[3] D. Stapel, M. Thiemann, B. Hagenhoff, A. Benninghoven, this proceedings

A. Benninghoven, P. Bertrand, H.-N. Migeon and H.W. Werner (Editors).
Proceedings of the 12th International Conference on Secondary Ion Mass Spectrometry,
Brussels, Belgium, 5-11 September 1999

ALTERING SECONDARY ION INTERNAL ENERGY BY POLYATOMIC ION IMPACT

C.W. Diehnelt, M.J. Van Stipdonk, and E.A. Schweikert
Department of Chemistry, Texas A&M University, PO Box 30012, College Station, TX,
77843-3144, U.S.A., diehnelt@mail.chem.tamu.edu

1. Introduction

The internal energy of a secondary ion is one of the most important parameters controlling the appearance of a mass spectrum. Rates of ion formation, fragmentation pathways accessed, and the amount of metastable ion dissociation, are all influenced by the internal energy of an ion. Yet, little is understood about the manner by which a primary ion converts its kinetic energy into secondary ion internal energy.

Polyatomic primary ions have been shown to dramatically increase the yield of organic secondary ions (SI) when compared to atomic primary ions of the same energy and velocity [1]. However, polyatomic primary ions have also been shown to increase fragmentation [2] and the yield of non-specific carbon clusters [3,4]. These observations are manifestations of the internal energy content of the sputtered secondary ions. However, little is known about how a polyatomic primary ion transfers its kinetic energy to SI internal energy. Secondary ion internal energy can be qualitatively monitored by examining secondary ion yields, the extent of prompt fragmentation, and the rate of unimolecular dissociation. In this study, we have monitored these parameters for selected organic secondary ions as a function of primary ion type and energy.

2. Experimental

The experiments were performed on a dual Time-of-Flight (TOF) mass spectrometer built in house [5]. Atomic and polyatomic primary ions were produced by ^{252}Cf fission fragment impacts on a Mylar foil coated with source material. Sodium tetrafluoroborate, cesium iodide, ammonium hexafluorosilicate, and C_{60} were used as source materials to produce $(NaF)_nNa^+$ (n=1,2,4), $(CsI)_nCs^+$ (n=0,1,2), SiF_5^-, and C_{60}^+ primary ions, respectively. Primary ions were accelerated to a particular kinetic energy (10-30 keV) and impacted the sample with an incident angle of ~27^0. The sample studied was α-cyano-4-hydroxycinnamic acid. All experiments were performed using a coincidence counting data collection approach [6] at the limit of single ion impacts. The relative yield (%) of each SI was calculated by integrating the area of the SI peak and dividing this number by the number of incident primary ions.

In order to obtain information on the metastable decay of selected secondary ions, an electric field was applied to a grid located ~25 cm down the field free region. This field repels secondary ions, therefore only neutral molecules from metastable decays are collected. The decay fraction is an indicator of the extent of metastable decay in the field free region and is calculated as the ratio of the neutral peak area to the total peak area.

3. Results and Discussion

Earlier work that examined SI internal energy changes with changing polyatomic primary ion [7], focused on the organic acid α-cyano-4-hydroxycinnamic acid. Secondary ions can undergo unimolecular dissociation in the acceleration region of the mass spectrometer, forming "prompt fragments." By comparing the yield of the deprotonated molecular ion, [M-H]⁻, with the fragment at m/z 93, an indication of the amount of energy deposited can be obtained. As can be seen in Figure 1, when the type of primary ion is changed, the extent of fragmentation increases with the complexity of the primary ion.

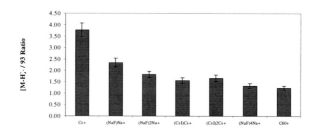

Fig.1. Extent of fragmentation of α-cyano-4-hydroxycinnamic acid.

Some sputtered secondary ions can undergo unimolecular dissociation into ionized and neutral fragments in the field free region of the mass spectrometer. The neutral molecule resulting from this metastable decay will have approximately the same velocity as the precursor ion and will consequently have about the same flight time. By applying an electric field at the end of the field free region, secondary ions are repelled but neutral fragments resulting from metastable fragments will be unaffected. The neutrals are collected at approximately the same flight time as their precursor ion. An indication of the extent of metastable dissociation, and consequently the internal energy content of the selected secondary ion, can be obtained. In Figure 2, the decay fraction of the [M-COOH]⁻ and [M-H]⁻ ions from α-cyano-4-hydroxycinnamic acid are displayed as a function of primary ion type at constant impact energy. The decay fractions of these secondary ions increase when an atomic primary ion is replaced with a polyatomic primary ion.

Next, the impact energy of the primary ion was changed from 10 to 20 keV and the decay fraction of the same secondary ions was monitored. As the impact energy of the primary ion increased, the decay fraction for the selected secondary ions decreased for each primary ion studied. This trend is illustrated in Figure 3, where the decay fractions of the [M-COOH]⁻ and [M-H]⁻ ions produced by (CsI)Cs⁺ primary ions are shown. The data is plotted as function of the square of the projectile velocity.

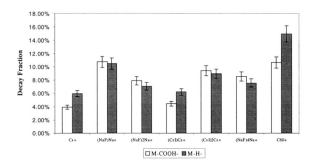

Fig. 2. Decay fractions from α-cyano-4-hydroxycinnamic acid.

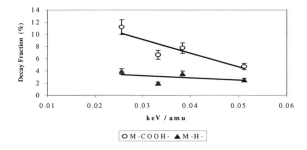

Fig. 3. Decay fractions produced by (CsI)Cs$^+$ primary ions as a function of impact
energy.

This somewhat surprising result can be put into perspective when one considers the
behavior of a primary ion as a function of impact energy. The higher the kinetic energy of
the primary ion, the deeper the primary ion penetrates into the surface. By taking the cube of
the primary ion's penetration depth, the volume affected by a primary ion can be
approximated [2]. In a cluster projectile, the total kinetic energy of the cluster is partitioned
between the cluster constituents, lowering the kinetic energy of each constituent. This leads
a polyatomic primary ion to deposit its kinetic energy into a much smaller volume.
Additionally, the simultaneous impact of several atoms produces collision cascades that can
overlap in both time and space. This leads to a region of high energy density created near the
surface.

In an ion impact, some collision cascades are directed towards the surface. When
several of these cascades strike an analyte molecule, the analyte molecule may be ejected
intact. The translational energy of the substrate atom directed towards the vacuum influences
the amount of energy transferred to vibrational energy of the analyte molecule. The
vibrational energy content of a secondary ion will affect its ability to undergo bond breaking
or rearrangement. The high energy density region produced by a cluster impact could result
in substrate atoms traveling towards the surface with higher kinetic energies. Upon collision
with an analyte molecule, more vibrational energy can be transferred to the analyte molecule,

leading to the increase in both prompt fragmentation and metastable decay observed during polyatomic ion bombardment.

4. Conclusion

We have found that the internal energy of a secondary ion can be increased when a polyatomic primary ion is used instead of an atomic primary ion. This behavior is thought to be caused by the polyatomic primary ion creating higher energy recoiled atoms within the substrate that are more efficient at converting their translational energy to secondary ion vibrational energy. This information is important, as the amount of vibrational energy contained within a secondary ion will control its ability to rearrange and fragment, two processes which contribute to the appearance, and ultimately the analytical utility of the mass spectrum.

References

[1] R.D. Harris, M.J. Van Stipdonk, and E.A. Schweikert, Int. J. Mass Spectrom. Ion Processes 174 (1998) 167, and references therein.
[2] O.W. Hand, T.K Majumdar, and R.G. Cooks, Int. J. Mass Spectrom. Ion Processes 97 (1990) 35.
[3] C.W. Diehnelt, M.J. Van Stipdonk, and E.A. Schweikert, Secondary Ion Mass Spectrometry: SIMS XI, eds. G. Gillen, R. Lareau, J. Bennett, and F. Stevie (Wiley, Chichester, New York, 1998) 593.
[4] C.W. Diehnelt, M.J. Van Stipdonk, and E.A. Schweikert, Phys. Rev. A 59 (1999) 4470.
[5] M.J. Van Stipdonk, R.D. Harris, and E.A. Schweikert, Rapid Commun. Mass Spectrom. 10 (1996) 1987.
[6] M.A. Park, B.D. Cox, and E.A. Schweikert, J. Chem. Phys. 96 (1992) 8171.
[7] C.W. Diehnelt, M.J. Van Stipdonk, and E.A. Schweikert, Proceedings of the 47th ASMS Conference on Mass Spectrometry and Allied Topics, June 1999.

Acknowledgements

This work was supported by the National Science Foundation (CHE-9727474).

A. Benninghoven, P. Bertrand, H.-N. Migeon and H.W. Werner (Editors).
Proceedings of the 12th International Conference on Secondary Ion Mass Spectrometry,
Brussels, Belgium, 5-11 September 1999

SECONDARY ION EMISSION FROM NIOBIUM AND TANTALUM UNDER ATOMIC AND POLYATOMIC ION BOMBARDMENT: 2. KINETIC ENERGY DISTRIBUTIONS OF ATOMIC AND CLUSTER IONS

S.F.Belykh, B.Habets, U.Kh.Rasulev, A.V.Samartsev, L.V.Stroev

Arifov Institute of Electronics, Akademgorodok, 700143 Tashkent, Uzbekistan

1. Introduction

The study of processes of solid sputtering in form of charged and neutral clusters is of great interest [1]. A promising experimental approach to solving this problem is a comparative study of the cluster emission characteristics under bombardment by atomic and polyatomic projectiles. The latter leads to the following features:
1. Each next atom of the projectile interacts with the collision cascade region formed by the previous atom for the time period of 10^{-15} sec. Each next atom of the projectile can therefore be considered as a probe interacting with the near-surface region prior to the relaxation of its vibrational and electronic excitation. 2. A high degree of the collision cascade superposition. These features can form the extreme sputtering conditions resulting in the change of the cluster emission characteristics. In this study, the comparative investigation of the kinetic energy spectra $f(E)$ of Nb_n^+ (n=1-16) and Ta_n^+ (n=1-13) ions sputtered from Nb and Ta - targets by atomic and polyatomic Au_m^- ions (m=1-3) with energy of 6 $keV/atom$ has been completed under identical experimental conditions. The results obtained are discussed.

2. Experimental

The experimental SIMS instrument used has been described in detail in [2]. The kinetic energy spectra $f(E)$ of the secondary ions were measured by variation of the accelerating voltage U_{acc} over the range of ± 300 V relative to $U_{acc} = 2000$ V. The dependencies $f(E)$ for sputtered ions and the cluster fragmentation processes taking place within the accelerating zone of the mass spectrometer between the target and the secondary ion lens could be studied by this procedure. The energy resolution of the SIMS instrument (5.5 eV) was determined from the kinetic energy spectra of alkaline metal ions (Na^+, K^+ and C_s^+) evaporated from the heated Nb and Ta - surfaces without ion bombardment.

3. Results

The kinetic energy spectra $f(E)$ of Nb_n^+ (n=1-16) and Ta_n^+ (n=1-13) ions sputtered by atomic and polyatomic Au_m^- projectiles (m=1-3) with the energy 6 $keV/atom$ have been measured. The typical dependencies $f(E)$ for Nb_n^+ ions (n=1,2,4,7) are shown in Fig.1. For Nb_n^+ ions the extended energy spectra «tails» in the energy range of $-300 \div 0$ eV (relative to

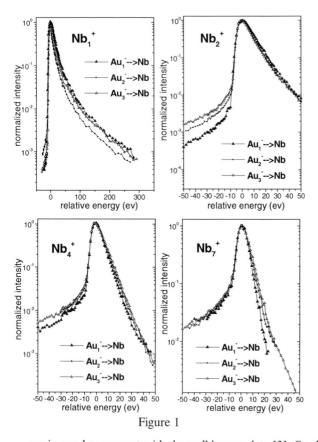

Figure 1

$eU_{acc} = 2000$ eV) correspond to $Nb_{n+1}^n \to Nb_n^+ + Nb$ unimolecular fragmentation and to an additional channel $Nb_4^+ \to Nb_2^+ + Nb_2$ of fragmentation within the acceleration zone of the mass spectrometer. It has been observed that the relative part of the fragmentary ions in the energy spectra is increased with the number n and at the transition from the atomic ion bombardment to polyatomic one: $Au^- \to Au_2^- \to Au_3^-$ at the energy 6 keV/atom. For Ta_n^+ ions the similar results were obtained. **Thus, the higher intensity of the fragment ions was observed under the polyatomic ion bombardment.** The behavior of the dependencies $f(E)$ in the energy range of $+300 \div 0$ eV is very different for $n \le 2$ and $n \ge 3$. In the first case, the relative part of Nb^+ and Nb_2^+ ions in the energy spectra is decreased with the rise of the secondary ion energy E during the change of the bombardment conditions from $Au^- \to Au_2^- \to Au_3^-$ at and these results are in good agreement with the well known data [3]. On the contrary, the relative part of Nb_n^+ ions at $n \ge 3$ decreases with the rise of E during a change of bombardment conditions from $Au_3^- \to Au_2^- \to Au^-$. **Thus, the higher intensity of the energetic large cluster ions was observed under the polyatomic ion bombard-ment.** In order to make a detailed comparison between dependencies $f(E)$, their full widths at half maximum (FWHM) have been determined and the high-energy ranges (>10 eV) have been fitted by a power function $f(E)=\beta E^\alpha$. For Nb_n^+ and Ta_n^+ ions the dependencies $\alpha(n)$ are shown in Fig.2. The area around $n=5$ corresponds to the minimum of all dependencies $\alpha(n)$. In addition, the area around $n=5$ determines the minimum cluster size for which the FWHM values become practically constant and independent of the n variable. A similar behavior of the α exponent under atomic ion bombardment was observed in [4] for kinetic energy spectra of neutral Ag_n clusters: $\alpha(2)=-2.9$, $\alpha(3)=-4.4$, $\alpha(4)=-4.4$, $\alpha(>4)=-4$ and authors [4] considered it as a fact indicating an inaccurate description of the large cluster formation in the framework of the atomic combination model [5] which predicted the monotonous decrease of the α exponent as $\alpha(n)=-2.5n+0.5$. In our opinion, the kinetic energy spectra regularities observed in this study for Nb_n^+ and Ta_n^+ clusters allow us **to distinguish a formation mechanism of large clusters ($n>5$) from that for smaller ones.**

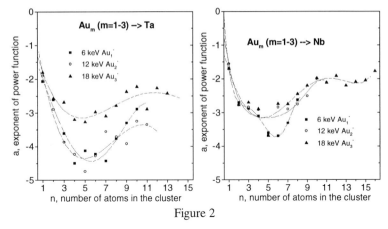

Figure 2

The normalized dependencies $f(E)$ for Nb^+ and Ta^+ and cluster Nb_7^+ and Ta_7^+ ions sputtered under bombardment of Nb and Ta - targets by Au^- and Au_3^- ions with energy of 6 keV/atom are shown in Fig.3. The relative intensities I of atomic ions with the energy E correspond to the following relation: $I(Ta^+) > I(Nb^+)$. This sequence is valid also for cluster ions: $I(Ta_7^+) > I(Nb_7^+)$. For the transition from the atomic ion bombardment to the polyatomic one, the order of the sequence remains the same, but differences in the values of I become more contrast. This shows that the efficiency of the energy transfer from the projectile to a sputtered particle is increased with the rise of the target atom mass. This case corresponds to "the memory" about the first collision in which the energy transfer is defined by the accommodation coefficient $k \sim 4m_1 m_2 / (3m_1 + m_2)^2$ and depends on the ratio of the mass m_1 of the projectile and that m_2 of the target atom. Perhaps, this implies that atomic and cluster ion sputtering occurs during the early stage of the cascade evolution after the small number of collisions between the projectile and target atoms. The mechanism of metal sputtering as large clusters ($n \geq 5$) was proposed [6] for the early stage of the collision cascade evolution ($t < 10^{-13}$ sec). It has been shown [6] that in the collisions with the projectile and recoil atoms

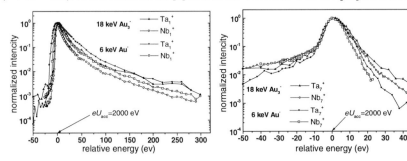

Figure 3

the group of n atoms located near the surface can obtain momentums, correlated in the direction to the surface and close in magnitude, for the time t and leave the metal as a cluster without dissociation. In this approach, the velocity distribution $f(v)$ of sputtered clusters must not depend on the number n, and the increase of the cluster energy E with the rise of n is connected only with the increase of the cluster mass. To verify this statement, the functions $f(E)$ (Fig.1) were converted into the dependencies $f(v)$ $f(v) = nm_2 f(E)$; $v = \sqrt{2E/nm_2}$).

The dependencies $f(v)$ are shown in Fig.4 at $E > 10$ eV for Nb_n^+ ions ($n=1-12$). The differences in the dependencies $f(v)$ decrease rapidly with the rise of n and at $n>5$ the functions $f(v)$ differ weakly.

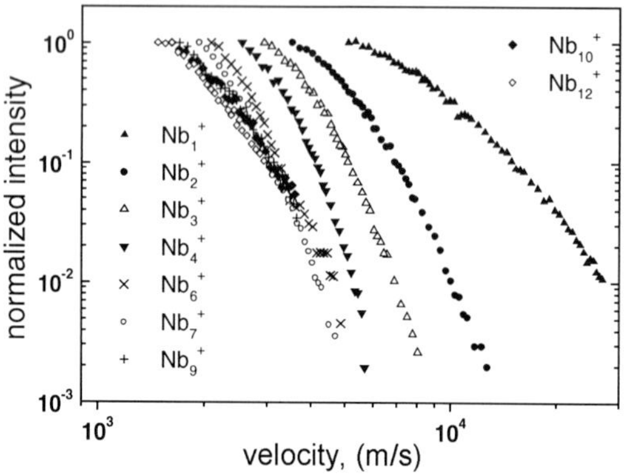

Figure 4

The analysis of the dependencies $f(E)$ (Fig.1, 3) also shows that there are cluster ions of Nb_n^+ and Ta_n^+ ($n>5$) with energy $E > 50$ eV in the flux of sputtered particles. The relative intensities of energetic ions are increased with the rise of n. The fact that energetic large cluster ions appear can be explained by the high degree of correlation (in direction and in magnitude) between the momentums transferred to the group of atoms before this group leaves the surface.

4. Conclusion

The results of the present work allow us to state the following. The large cluster ions sputtered by polyatomic ion bombardment have higher kinetic and vibration energies than those produced by the atomic ion bombardment with the same energy per atom. The kinetic energy spectra regularities indicate the existence of two different cluster ion emission mechanisms for small and large clusters.

Acknowledgements. This study was partially supported by the following organizations: Fundamental Research Support Foundation of the Academy of Sciences of Uzbekistan(Grant 29-96), INTAS (Project 96-0470), and NATO (Science for Peace Program, Project SfP 97.1929).

Reference

[1] Secondary Ion Mass Spectrometry SIMS XI, ed. by G.Gillen, R.Lareau, J.Bennett, F.Stevie, John Wiley&Sons, Orlando, Florida, 1997
[2] S.F. Belykh, U.Kh. Rasulev, A.V. Samartsev, S.V. Verkhoturov and I.V. Veryovkin. Mikrochimica Acta, [Suppl.] V.15, 1998, P.379-385.
[3] D.A. Tompson Rad.Eff. 56 (1981) 105
[4] A.Wucher and M.Wahl, in: Secondary Ion Mass Spectrometry SIMS X, eds. A.Bennighoven, H.W.Werner and B.Hegenhoff (Wiley, 1997), p.65.
[5] G.P.Konnen, A.Tip, A.E. de Vries, Rad. Eff. 21 (1974) 269 and 26(1975)23.
[6] V.I. Matveev, S.F.Belykh, I.V.Veryovkin. J. Tech. Phys. 69 (1999) 64 (in Russian).

A. Benninghoven, P. Bertrand, H.-N. Migeon and H.W. Werner (Editors).
Proceedings of the 12th International Conference on Secondary Ion Mass Spectrometry,
Brussels, Belgium, 5-11 September 1999
© 2000 Elsevier Science B.V. All rights reserved.

SECONDARY ION EMISSION FROM NIOBIUM AND TANTALUM UNDER ATOMIC AND POLYATOMIC ION BOMBARDMENT: 1. MASS SPECTRA OF CLUSTERS

S.F.Belykh, B.Habets, U.Kh.Rasulev, A.V.Samartsev, L.V.Stroev
Arifov Institute of Electronics, Akademgorodok, 700143 Tashkent, Uzbekistan

1. Introduction

The cluster emission is one of the most interesting phenomena in physics of sputtering. The comparative investigation of yields Y_{nm} and mass spectra of secondary Ta_n^+ ions ($n=1\div13$) sputtered from Ta by atomic and polyatomic Au_m^- ions ($m=1\div3$) with the energy of $E_0=6$ $keV/atom$ makes it possible to obtain new results [1-3]. The most important of them is the effect of anomalously high non-additive sputtering of Ta in the form of large positive cluster ions. This effect can be seen in an immediate increase (by two-three orders of magnitude) of the yield Y_{nm} of Ta_n^+ ions ($n>5$) compared to the yield under atomic bombardment. It is very interesting to continue this study for other metals. In this work, the yields Y_{nm} and mass spectra of Nb_n^+ ions ($n=1\div16$) sputtered from the Nb target by atomic and polyatomic ions of Au_m^- ($m=1\div3$) with the energy of $E_0=6$ $keV/atom$ have been studied under identical conditions of experiment. The comparison and discussion of the results obtained for Nb and Ta sputtering are presented.

2. Experimental

The SIMS instrument used was a modified MI-1201 mass spectrometer equipped with a sputtered target assembly, the secondary ion optical system and the primary ion column. The column included the negative Au_m^- ion source ($m=1\div4$) [2], the mass separator and an ion optical system for primary ions. In our experiments, the Au_m^- ions ($n=1\div3$) with the energy of $E_0=6$ $keV/atom$ bombarded the Nb target surface at an incidence angle of $45°$. Nb and Ta were chosen as the target because of their monoisotopic nature and high melting temperature. The target was cleaned by heating for several hours up to temperature of about $2100°C$ and sputterred simultaneously by Au^- ion bombardment. During the experiments, temperature of the Nb target was maintained below $1800°C$ and the residual pressure did not exceed the value of 8.10^{-8} $Torr$. The mass distributions $Y(n)$ of the secondary Nb_n^+ cluster ions were determined from areas under the kinetic energy spectra curve $f(E)$. To make a comparison between relative yields of Nb_n^+ ions ($n=1\div16$), their intensities were normalized according to the ratio between the ion currents of corresponding projectiles. The kinetic energy spectra of the Nb_n^+ ions were measured by variation of the accelerating voltage U_{ac} over the range of ±300 V relative to $U_{ac}=2000$ V. The energy resolution of the SIMS instrument ($5,5$ eV) was determined from the kinetic energy spectra of alkaline metal ions (Na^+, K^+ and Cs^+) evaporated from the heated Nb surface without ion bombardment.

3. Results and Discussion

Normalized to unit current of projectiles, the mass spectra $Y(n)$ of Nb_n^+ ions ($n=1\div16$) and Ta_n^+ ions ($n=1\div13$) measured in sputtering of Nb and Ta targets by atomic and polyatomic Au_m^- ions ($m=1\div3$) with the energy of $E_0=6$ $keV/atom$ and current densities of $j_1 = 1.5.10^{-6}$, $j_2 = 0.17.10^{-6}$ and $j_3 = 0.025.10^{-6}$ A/cm^2, respectively, are shown in Fig.1. These mass spectra differ quantitatively and qualitatively and it is reasonable to compare them for two intervals of n: $n<5$ and $n>5$. For $n<5$ the yield Y_{nm} of sputtered Nb_n^+ ions depends on the projectile species and is increased with the rise of the number m. However, for all cases studied the maximum yield corresponds to Nb_2^+ ions. The yields Y_{nm} of Ta_n^+ ions are also increased with the rise of n, but the dependence $Y(n)$ has a more complicated form. In fact, for Au^-:$Y(Ta^+) > Y(Ta_3^+) > Y(Ta_5^+)$, $Y(Ta_2^+) > Y(Ta_4^+)$ and the maximum yield corresponds to Ta_2^+ ions; for Au_2^-: $Y(Ta^+) < Y(Ta_3^+) < Y(Ta_5^+)$ and $Y(Ta_2^+) \approx Y(Ta_4^+)$; for Au_3^-: $Y(Ta^+) < Y(Ta_3^+) < Y(Ta_5^+)$, $Y(Ta_2^+) < Y(Ta_4^+)$ and the maximum yield corresponds to Ta_4^+ ions. Thus, the redistribution of relative yields of small Ta_n^+ clusters ($n<5$) is observed at the transition from atomic projectiles to polyatomic ones. In contrast to the results of [4] where, under bombardment of Nb and Ta targets by atomic Ar^+ ions with the energy $E_0=5$ keV, the monotonous dependence $Y(n)$ of neutral Nb_n and Ta_n cluster yields was observed, the yields Y_{nm} of Nb_n^+ and Ta_n^+ cluster ions non-monotonously depend on the number n. The non-monotonous character of the dependencies $Y(n)$ measured under atomic bombardment can be due to the influence of several factors: the dependence of the ionization degree on the cluster size [5], the redistribution of the cluster yields owing to the processes of monomolecular fragmentation, these processes occurring for $t<t_0$ ($t_0=10^{-6}$ sec is the time of a particle flight from the target to the detector). It is not excluded that the non-monotonous behavior of the dependencies $Y(n)$ measured under polyatomic bombardment displays the special form of Ta sputtering by polyatomic ions.

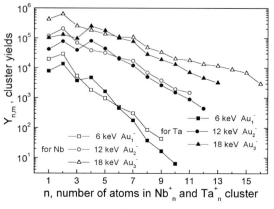

Figure 1

For $n>5$ the mass spectra of sputtered Nb_n^+ and Ta_n^+ ions can be approximated by the power function $Y(n) \propto n^{-\sigma}$, where the exponents σ are equal to: $\sigma(Au^-)= 6.11$; $\sigma(Au_2^-)= 3.45$ and $\sigma(Au_3^-)= 2.79$ for Nb_n^+ ions and, respectively, $\sigma(Au^-)= 8.6$; $\sigma(Au_2^-)= 6.05$ and $\sigma(Au_3^-)= 4.55$ for Ta_n^+ ions. The direct comparison of σ values, obtained in this study for the ion clusters of Nb_n^+ ($\sigma= 6.11$) and Ta_n^+ ($\sigma= 8.6$) sputtered by Au^- ions with the energy $E_0=6$ keV and in [4] for neutral clusters of Nb_n ($\sigma= 8.1$) and Ta_n ($\sigma= 8.5$), is not correct as the value of σ for neutral clusters strongly depends on bombardment conditions, and for the cluster ions on the degree of the cluster ionization. The latter has not been well studied until now [5]. Fig. 1 shows that Y_{nm} emission yields of Nb_n^+ and Ta_n^+ ions caused by the polyatomic ion impact are much higher than those induced by the atomic ion impact. The ratio of these yields increases rapidly with increasing the cluster size n so that for Nb ($n=9$) and for Ta ($n=10$) these ratios reach the following values: $Y_{9,3}:Y_{9,2}:Y_{9,1} = 750: 88: 1$ and $Y_{10,3}:Y_{10,2}:Y_{10,1} = 2170: 201: 1$. By using the data shown in Fig. 1, one can estimate the ratios of the yields of atomic ions and the total yields of cluster

ions. In the case of niobium for the range of $5 \le n \le 9$ these $Y_{1,m}(Nb^+) \Big/ \sum_{n=5}^{9} Y_{n,m}(Nb_n^+)$ ratios

have the following values: 10.41, 1.44 and 1 for Au^-, Au_2^- and Au_3^-, respectively. In the case of tantalum for the range of $5 \le n \le 10$ such ratios have the

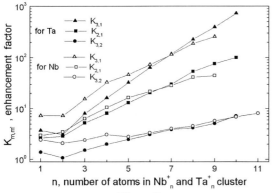

Figure 2

additive effects in sputtering under polyatomic bombardment are usually described by the enhancement factor: $K_{n,m'} = m' \, Y_{n,m} / m \, Y_{n,m'}$, where $Y_{n,m}$ and $Y_{n,m'}$ are yields of n-atomic cluster under m- and m'- atomic ion bombardment, respectively. The dependencies of the $K_{mm'}$ enhancement factor on the n number of atoms in the sputtered cluster are shown in Fig. 2. For Nb_n^+ and Ta_n^+ ions the $\gamma(K_{3,2})$ values are increased with the increase of n values as the $K_{mm'} \propto$

$exp(\gamma n)$ exponential function and the γ exponent factors were of the following magnitudes: $\gamma(K_{3,1})=0.417$, $\gamma(K_{2,1})=0.285$ and $\gamma(K_{3,2})=0.166$ for Nb_n^+ and $\gamma(K_{3,1})=0.834$, $\gamma(K_{2,1})=0.434$ and $\gamma(K_{3,2})=0.198$ for Ta_n^+. The values $K_{mm'}$, obtained for Nb^+ and Ta^+, are several digits and in agreement with the known data [6] while for $n=9$ (Nb) and $n=10$ (Ta) the values $K_{mm'}$ are equal to $(K_{3,1})=255$ and $(K_{3,1})=44$ and, respectively, $K_{3,1}= 723$ and $K_{2,1}=100$. These results demonstrate the effect of the anomalous high non-additivity of sputtering of large cluster ions under the bombardment of niobium and tantalum by polyatomic ions with rather low incident energies of $E_0<10$ $keV/atom$. This effect is increased with increasing the number of atoms n in the sputtered cluster.

The mass spectra shown in Fig.1 make it also possible to study the dependence of the yields Y_{nm} of sputtered ions on their kinetic energy E. For this purpose, it is necessary to transform the "full" mass spectra $Y(n)$ into families of "partial" ones $Y_E(n)$. Each "partial" mass spectrum contains the secondary ions with the energy E_i within the range of E_i, $E_i + \Delta E_i$ ($\Delta E_i =1$ eV). The procedure of obtaining the curves $Y_E(n)$ (see Experimental), instead of measuring the complete area under the curves of the kinetic energy distributions $f(E)$, consists in this case in measuring some part of this area corresponding to the range ΔE_i near some fixed value E_i. For all the spectra measured (Fig.1) the families of the dependencies $Y_E(n)$ were obtained for the following values of E_i: 5, 10, 15, 20, 25, 30, 35, 42, 50 eV.

As an example, the "full" mass spectrum $Y(n)$ and the family of the "partial" ones $Y_E(n)$ measured for the system $Au_3^-(18$ $keV)$-Nb are shown in Fig.3. The shape of curves $Y_E(n)$ for $E_i <15$ eV is in good agreement with the shape of the "full" mass spectrum $Y(n)$. However, while increasing E_i the shape of the curves $Y_E(n)$ is essentially changed. This change is different for small ($n<5$) and large ($n>5$) clusters. In contrast to the dependence

$Y(n)$, at $E_i > 25$ eV the intensity of the Nb_2^+ peak becomes less than that of the Nb^+ peak, and the decreasing rate of $dY_E(n)/dn$ at $n<5$ increases with the rise of energy E_i. On the contrary, at $n>5$ the value of $dY_E(n)/dn$ is slightly decreased with the rise of E_i, vanishing to zero. This behavior of the curves $Y_E(n)$ is observed for all the cases studied and indicates that with the increase of the energy E_i the efficiency of the formation of small clusters $(n<5)$ is immediately decreased with the rise of the number n while the formation of large clusters $(n>5)$ is much less sensitive to the variation of n. In our opinion, the «partial» mass spectra regularities observed in this study for secondary Nb_n^+ and Ta_n^+ ions allow us to separate the large clusters formation mechanism $(n>5)$ from that for smaller ones.

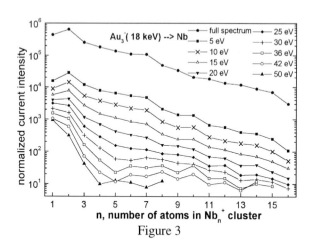

Figure 3

4. Conclusion

The results of this study demonstrate the non-additive effects in the cluster ion emission from niobium and stronger one from tantalum under keV polyatomic ion bombardment. These effects manifest themselves in mass spectra as a dramatic increase in the relative yield of larger clusters $(n>5)$ with increasing the number of atoms, n, in the secondary cluster ion. It is shown, that the efficiency of the formation of large $(n>5)$ and small $(n<5)$ clusters has different sensitivity to the value of kinetic energy of the sputtered particle. It allows to assume two different mechanisms for small and large cluster-ion emissions.

Acknowledgements. This study was partially supported by the following organizations: Fundamental Research Support Foundation of the Academy of Sciences of Uzbekistan(Grant 29-96), INTAS (Project 96-0470), and NATO (Science for Peace Program, Project SfP 97.1929).

References

[1] S.F. Belykh, I.S. Bitensky, D. Mullajanov, U.Kh. Rasulev. Nucl. Instr. Meth., B 129 (1997) 451.
[2] S.F. Belykh, U.Kh. Rasulev, A.V. Samartsev, S.V. Verkhoturov and I.V. Veryovkin. Mikrochimica Acta, [Suppl.] V.15, 1998, P.379-385.
[3] S.F. Belykh, U.Kh. Rasulev, A.V. Samartsev and I.V. Veryovkin. Nucl. Instr. Meth., B 136-138, (1998) 773.
[4] A.Wucher and M.Wahl, Nucl.Instr.Meth. B 115 (1996) 581
[5] M.Wahl and A.Wucher Nucl.Instr.Meth. B 94 (1994) 36
[6] D.A.Tompson, Rad.Eff. 56 (1981) 105

A. Benninghoven, P. Bertrand, H.-N. Migeon and H.W. Werner (Editors).
Proceedings of the 12th International Conference on Secondary Ion Mass Spectrometry,
Brussels, Belgium, 5-11 September 1999

A NEGATIVE CESIUM SPUTTER ION SOURCE FOR GENERATING CLUSTER PRIMARY ION BEAMS FOR SIMS ANALYSIS

Greg Gillen[a], Lance King[a], Brian Freibaum[a], Richard Lareau[b] and Joe Bennett[c]
[a] National Institute of Standards and Technology Gaithersburg, MD 20899-8371
[b] Army Research Laboratory, Adelphi, MD 20783-1197
[c] SEMATECH, Austin, TX 78741

1. Introduction

The use of a cluster (or polyatomic) primary ion projectile for organic secondary ion mass spectrometry (SIMS) has been demonstrated to increase the yield of characteristic molecular secondary ions, more efficiently desorb higher molecular weight species, and reduce the accumulation of primary beam-induced damage [1-3]. For depth profiling of semiconductors, a cluster beam may offer substantial improvements in depth resolution [4]. We have recently begun to explore the use of a commercially available negative cesium sputter ion source for generating cluster ion beams on our Cameca IMS 4F and 6F magnetic sector SIMS instruments*. The principal advantages of using a sputter ion source for cluster generation, as opposed to the SF_5^+ primary ion source [5], are the versatility in target selection and the ability to produce cluster ions from virtually any element in the periodic table. In this paper, we report on the use of the sputter ion source for generating carbon cluster primary ions and the application of these ion beams for organic surface characterization and depth profiling of shallow arsenic implants in silicon.

2. Experimental

We conducted all experiments on a negative cesium sputter source (Peabody Scientific PSX-120*, Peabody, MA) mounted directly on a Cameca IMS 4F microscope in place of the standard duoplasmatron source. The standard Cameca extraction lens was removed and replaced with a circular metal aperture metal plate with a 1 cm diameter hole drilled in the center. The aperture plate helps shield the deflectors and lenses in the primary column from cesium vapor and sputtered material. The sputter ion source is based on the design of Middleton [6] and consists of a sputter target rod and a circular filament enclosed in a common chamber containing cesium vapor. Cesium vapor is introduced into the chamber by heating a cesium reservoir attached to the source body. Cesium is surface-ionized on the filament surface and is attracted to the sputter target by a high negative bias. The sputter target is a water-cooled aluminum rod that has a 1/8" diameter hole drilled into the center. For this work, the hole was packed with spectroscopic-grade graphite (Ernest Fulham, Inc). Typical source operating conditions were a target bias of ¯7 kV, an ionizer bias of ¯3 kV, and a filament current of 20 A. Fig. 1. shows a schematic of the source. To improve the beam quality and output current, an Einzel lens was recently added. The data presented in this paper were acquired before the addition of the Einzel lens. Spectra of the primary ion beam were obtained by using LabView and a digital-to-analog converter board running on a PC to scan the input voltage to the primary beam mass filter. In addition to graphite targets, we also produced small cluster ions from targets of Al, Si, Cu, Au, Ag, B, and NaF.

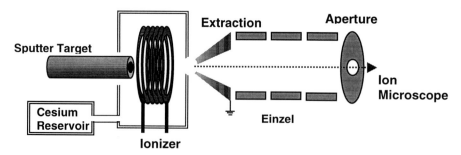

Figure 1. Schematic of the current version of the cesium sputter source.

3. Results and Discussion

Figure 2 shows a mass spectrum of the output from the cesium sputter source running with a graphite target. We typically observe maximum C_2^- beam currents of > 1 μA (as measured on the primary Faraday Cup of the instrument) and several nanoamperes for C_8 - C_{10}^- and CsC_x^- (x = 4,6,8) clusters. The lifetime of the source can be several hundred hours. In initial testing, the source was run for over 1 month on a daily basis without cleaning or recharging of the cesium. Stability is generally a few percent over 20 minutes with a general trend for decreasing primary current and degradation in beam focus over the course of an 8 hour day after installation of a new sputter target. This downward drift is related to the formation of a sputter crater in the target surface that modifies the local extraction field, resulting in an increasing divergence of the sputtered ion beam as the crater gets deeper. Beam diameters of over 1 inch have been observed at the input aperture to the primary beam mass filter of the SIMS instrument. Ion optical modeling of the source indicates that incorporation of the Einzel lens should help compensate for the drift and may significantly increase the beam current delivered to the sample.

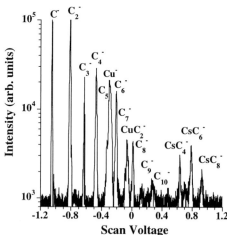

Figure 2 . Primary beam mass spectrum from cesium sputter source using graphite target.

Analytical Examples
Organic Surface Characterization
   For organic SIMS applications, the use of carbon cluster ions greatly increases the yield of molecular secondary ions. Under identical bombardment conditions, the molecular ion yield from amino acid targets was found to increase by as much as a factor of ~800 when comparing C_1^- to C_8^- primary ions. A similar comparison of primary beam-induced damage indicates that the use of the larger carbon cluster ions results in a reduction in the accumulation of beam-induced damage and allows for sustained molecular ion emission at high primary ion doses.

Secondary Ion Imaging
   For imaging applications, the carbon cluster beam from the sputter source can be focused to a spot size of a few micrometers.   Figure 3a is an image of a copper grid sample where we used a C_6^- cluster primary ion and imaged the CN^- secondary ion signal. Figure 3b is a secondary ion image of the parent cation from tetrabutyl ammonium bromide (m/z 242) sputtered from a human hair sample. In this case, the yield of the intact cation was increased by a factor of ~450 when the cluster ion size was increased from C_1^- to C_8^-. The use of the carbon cluster ions for organic imaging is a significant improvement over conventional SIMS imaging of human hair [7].

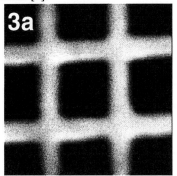 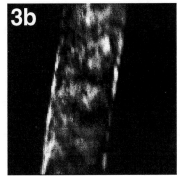

Figure 3a. Secondary ion image of CN^- from a copper grid acquired with a 10 pA, 8 keV C_6^- primary ion. Field-of-view = 70 µm. Figure 3b. Secondary ion image of tetrabutyl ammonium bromide (m/z 242) on human hair acquired with a 10 pA, 17 keV impact energy, C_8^- primary ion. Field-of-view ~ 250 µm. 30 second acquisition time for both images.

Semiconductor Depth Profiling
   Another advantage of using a cluster primary ion beam is enhanced depth resolution for depth profiling of ultra-shallow implants and junctions. We investigated the use of the CsC_6^- cluster ion for depth profiling of low energy arsenic implants. On magnetic sector SIMS instruments, a Cs^+ primary ion beam with negative secondary ion detection is commonly used for the analysis of dopants such as As and P. Due to the high negative extraction field on the sample, this mode of operation gives relatively high bombardment energies and more normal incidence angles. The use of a negatively-charged cesium-containing cluster ion offers two advantages. First, the negative ion is decelerated as it nears the negatively charged sample surface, leading to lower impact energies and more oblique incidence angles. Second, the polyatomic ion dissociates upon impact with the surface further reducing the net impact energy

of the Cs. Figure 4 shows a comparison of two SIMS depth profiles of a 1 keV As implant in silicon acquired with either Cs^+ or CsC_6^- as the bombarding species while monitoring $AsSi^-$. The Cs^+ profile was taken with a cesium source modified for low energy operation and a reduced secondary accelerating voltage (3.6 keV impact, $20°$ incident angle). The CsC_6^- profile was taken under standard conditions with 3.0 keV impact at $47°$. Figure 4 demonstrates that the cluster ion appears to offers a significant improvement in depth resolution. While encouraging, further work is now being conducted to determine if the apparent improvement in depth resolution is a real effect or may be the result of a sputtering artifact such as a transient decrease in sputter rate.

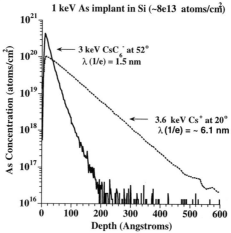

Figure 4. Depth profiles of a 1 keV As implant in silicon.

4. Conclusion

A cesium sputter ion source was used to generate carbon cluster primary ions on a magnetic sector SIMS instrument. The use of these ions appears to offer significant advantages for both organic and semiconductor analyses. Future work is aimed at optimizing the operation and design of this source and pursuing additional analytical applications.

References
[1] A.D. Appelhans and J.Delmore, Anal. Chem., 61 (1989) 1087.
[2] F. Kotter and A. Benninghoven, Appl. Surf. Sci., 133 (1998) 47.
[3] G. Gillen and S. Roberson, Rapid Communications in Mass Spec., 12 (1998) 1303.
[4] K. Iltgen and A. Benninghoven in "Secondary Ion Mass Spectrometry:SIMS XI" G. Gillen et al eds., John Wiley and Sons, Chichester, 1998, p. 367.
[5] G. Gillen, L. King, and F. Chmara, J. Vac. Sci. Technol., 17 (3) (1999) 845.
[6] R. Middleton, Nucl. Instrum. Methods, 214 (1983) 139.
[7] G. Gillen, S. Roberson, C. Ng, and M. Stranick, Scanning, 21 (1999) 173.

*Certain commercial equipment, instruments, or materials are identified in this paper to specify adequately the experimental procedure. Such identification does not imply recommendation or endorsement by the National Institute of Standards and Technology, nor does it imply that the materials or equipment identified are necessarily the best available for the purpose.

A. Benninghoven, P. Bertrand, H.-N. Migeon and H.W. Werner (Editors).
Proceedings of the 12th International Conference on Secondary Ion Mass Spectrometry,
Brussels, Belgium, 5-11 September 1999

A STUDY ON A SURFACE IONIZATION SOURCE FOR MOLECULAR IONS

U.Kh.Rasulev,U. Khasanov, V.V. Palitsin

Arifov Institute of Electronics, 700143, Tashkent, Uzbekistan, e-mail: root@ariel.tashkent.su

1.Introduction

In recent years molecular primary ion beams are of special interest to use them in SIMS. The interaction of polyatomic ions with solid surface creates the conditions to simulate the interaction of atom beams of super-high density with the surface. The simple estimation shows that the equivalent of molecular bombardment can be obtained by atomic one only using the atomic ion beams with $j \sim 10^{10} - 10^{12}$ A/cm^2, that is practically impossible. In fact, atoms of a polyatomic ion practically simultaneously (10^{-14} s) reach the small area of the solid surface. This not simply essentially increases the energy density in the cascade. Each atom of the molecular ion causes the cascade of collisions in the zone of the cascade development caused by other atoms of the same ion; the overlapping of the cascades results in the development, in a solid, of the non-linear cascades or of the high density cascades (spikes), which essentially increases the solid sputtering, especially in the form of polyatomic ions. It is also important that the kinetic energy of each atom in the molecular ion is less than that of the primary molecular ion on the ratio of their masses. Therefore, in this case the cascades is not "deep", they are developed directly near the solid surface. This is very important for obtaining the ultra-high resolution for SIMS. So there is interest in developing the sources of primary polyatomic ion beams to use in SIMS. For these purposes, liquid-metal ion sources, cesium sputtering ion sources to generate negatively charged metal and carbon ions, gas discharge sources e.g. to produce SF_5^+, and others are used now.

It is known that one of the first more effective and widely-used sources of atomic ions is the surface ionization (SI) ion sources [1]. The thermodesorption of multiatomic positive charged ions of specific organic compounds has been found comparatively recently [2]. The ionization mechanism of polyatomic particles and the possibility of using the Saha-Lengmur formula to describe their ionization has been experimentally proved [3]. By now regularities and peculiarities of SI for molecules of various classes of organic/bioorganic compounds have been established allowing the prediction of the ion composition and ion current densities [4].

2.Basic considerations:

The features of thermal desorption of positive multiatomic ions and the possibility of creating simply-designed and effective SI sources of multiatomic ions with the given composition and structure have been considered in the present work.

2.1.Energy "specificity" of ions

This kind of emission is in the thermal equilibrium so that the evaporated particles (both ions and neutrals) exhibit a Boltzman distribution in energy with the temperature equal to the temperature T of the solid involved, by that ions start to move from the emitter surface with equal potential. Therefore, the formation of a beam of these ions is very simple.

2.2. The high selectivity of the process in reference to the ionization potential V of the ionized particles. For instance, if V of two particles differs by 1 eV, the ionization efficiency can vary up to 10^5 times.

2.3. Heterogeneous reactions of original molecules.

The molecules can undergo the chemical transformation on the surface, not only original particles but also the products of their heterogeneous transformations can desorb as ions. If molecules on the surface of a solid transform into i species of new particles, then the incident flux can be formally represented as consisting of i effective fluxes v_i, each of them producing particles of one species only. Now the relation between v_i and the flux v of molecules going to the surface can be written in the form $v_i(T) = \gamma_i(T)v$, where γ_i is the total reaction yield determining the concentration of the given i particles on the surface. γ_i depends not only on the rate constant of the corresponding chemical reaction, but also on the rate constants of all the other processes in which the original molecules and the particles forming from them participate in adsorbed state [4].

The current density $\quad j_i = e\,v_i^+ = e\,v\beta_i\gamma_i,$

where $\beta_i = v_i^+ \big/ v_i$ is the ionization coefficient connected with the degree of SI

$\alpha_i = v_i^+ \big/ v_i^0 = A_i \exp\!\left[e(\varphi - v_i) \big/ kT \right]$ by the relation $\beta_i = \alpha_i/(1+\alpha_i)$, so that expressions for the

current densities (4) reduce to $\qquad j_i(T) = \dfrac{e\,v\gamma_i(T)}{1 + A_i^{-1} \exp\!\left[e(V_i - \varphi) \big/ kT \right]}$

where e is the electron charge, φ is the work function, T is the solid temperature, V_i is the ionization potential, A_i is the ratio of the statistical weights of the states of charged and neutral i-particles.

2.4 .Ion emitters

The ionization efficiency is determined not only by the properties of the ionized molecules, but also by thermoemissive and catalytic properties of the surface, where the ionization occurs. So the choice of the emitter material and the way of its preparation are of primary importance. At present, emitters made from W, Mo, Ni, Re, Pt, Ir and their oxides (or metal-oxygen system) are used. Their thermoemissive properties are known [4]. The best (effective and stable) emitters to operate under vacuum conditions are the emitters from W with the "thick" layer (up to ~μm) of oxides on the surface. Their properties are stable, e.g. up to a doze of $5\cdot10^3$ L molecules of triethilamine. The emitters from oxidized Re have the greater work function. But they are unstable and "poisoned" for a short time. To operate relatively stable, their surface must be continuously oxidized, for example, by continuous leak-in of oxygen up to pressure of ~10^{-3} Pa [5]. The best emitters to operate in the air atmosphere are the emitters from single crystalline Mo doped with elements of the platinum group [6].

2.5.Classes of ionizable compounds [4]

By now, the surface ionization for more than 200 molecules of various organic and bioorganic compounds has been studied. These are mainly the compounds with V-A subgroup heteroatoms: amines, hydrazines and their various derivatives, including compounds of biogenic origin, for instance alcoloids, narcotics and other abused drugs; phosphines, arsines and their derivatives. Aromatic hydrocarbons, benzoil - containing compounds can be ionized. Simple hydrocarbons, alcohols, aldehidy, ketons, nitriles can not be practically ionized.

Nitrogen-containing bases and their derivatives can be more effectively ionized by SI. So, for the adsorption of tertiary amines and their derivatives on the emitter from oxidized metals the experimentally detected density of ion current can be the value of ~0.05 A/Pa·cm^{-2}, i.e. each 2nd-5th adsorbed molecule forms an ion.

2.6. SI mass-spectra (or ion composition) of amines and their derivatives are very simple. They exhibit, as a rule, only few lines: rarely M$^+$ and more often (M-H)$^+$, (M-Ri)$^+$, (M-H-2nH)$^+$, (M-R$_i$-2nH)$^+$, (M+H)$^+$, where M is the original molecule, H is the hydrogen atom eliminated from or added to it, R$_i$ stands for the radical, n is an integer. Practically all ions formed in SI have the even number of electrons and they can be approximated as ions with a quadrivalent, positively charged nitrogen having sp^3 or sp^2 hybrid orbital (Fig. 1).

Fig. 1.

Molecules	Ions		
M	(M+H)$^+$	(M-H)$^+$	(M-R)$^+$
R_1 $\diagdown$ $\;$ $\overset{\displaystyle H}{\underset{\displaystyle H}{\mid}}$ R_2 $\diagup$ N—C—R	$\overset{\displaystyle H}{\underset{\displaystyle R_2}{\mid}}$ $R_1—N^+—R_3$	R_1 $\diagdown$ R_2 $\diagup$ $N^+{=}\overset{}{\underset{\displaystyle H}{C}}—R$	R_1 $\diagdown$ R_2 $\diagup$ $N^+{=}CH_2$

2.7. Ion current dependence on temperature is, as a rule, a typical feature. It comes mainly from the difference in the temperature dependence of the chemical reaction yield resulting in the formation of ionized particles: reactions involving the formation of associates proceed at lower temperatures than is the case with dissociation reactions; and the temperature threshold for the formation of (M-Ri)$^+$ particles is substantially higher than the threshold of hydro-gen

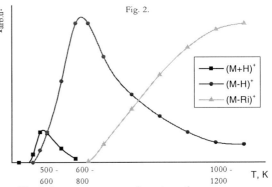

Fig.2: *Ion current as a function of temperature*

atom elimination [4]. The experi-mentally found typical dependence $I(T)$ for alkylamines and their derivatives is given in Fig.2. This characteristic dependence $j(T)$ makes it possible to obtain, by SI, the beams of polyatomic ions with the given, practically isotopic composition with no use of a mass-separator.

2.8. Ion current density or SI of amines on emitters from oxidized W.

Ions (M-H)$^+$ and (M-Ri)$^+$: j~0.04 A/Pa·cm^2 for tertiary amines, ~$10^{-3} \div 5 \cdot 10^{-3}$ A/Pa·cm^2 for secondary, and ~$10^{-4} \div 5 \cdot 10^{-5}$ A/Pa·cm^2 for primary amines.

Ions (M-H-2nH)$^+$ and (M-R-2nH)$^+$. In the ionization of amines with linear substituents, the line intensity of such ions is always substantially lower than that of the (M-H)$^+$ and (M-R)$^+$ ions. In the mass-spectra of N-heterocyclic compounds, the line intensity of the (M-H-2nH)$^+$ ions leading to the ring aromatization can exceed that of (M-H)$^+$.

Ions (M+H)$^+$. For SI under vacuum conditions the current density of these ions is essentially lower than that of (M-H)$^+$ and (M-R)$^+$. However, during the ionization in the air atmosphere j of (M+H)$^+$ ions can be comparable and more than j of (M-H)$^+$ ions.

Thus, by SI it is relatively simple to create fluxes of polyatomic ions, I~mkA and j~mA/cm^2 with the given number of carbon and hydrogen atoms and with the given ion "geometry" (structure) that are defined by the R_1, R_2, R_3 substituents of the molecule. For example, ions can be branch-like if the R_1, R_2, R_3 substituents are alkyl radicals. Ions can be flat if the substituents are aromatic rings.

3.Conditions for a multiatomic ion source

For a multiatomic ion source to operate under vacuum conditions:

1) as an emitter it is necessary to use a tungsten wire is needed which must be recrystallized by heating at T~2000 K for ~2 hours, the temperature increasing up to 2300 K for 2-3 minutes 5-10 times. In such a way, besides the wire recrystallization,the current of alkaline metal ions (Na^+ and K^+) , responsible for the background current – decreases several orders of magnitude and has the value of ~10^{-11} A/cm^2. Then this wire (band) is oxidized in an air atmosphere at P~0.1-1 Torr by heating for 10-30 minutes at T~1000 K.

2) as a substance to be ionized it is necessary to use tertiary amines or their derivatives.

So, for a source of molecular ions with the relatively small number of carbon atoms (from 3 to 10) and with the number of hydrogen atoms ~ 2 times greater than that of carbon atoms, as a substance to be ionized it is necessary to use vapor of simple tertiary alkylamines. These compounds have the considerable pressure of vapor (tens hundreds Torr) at the room temperature. Vapors of these substances are fed to the emitter surface (into the ion source) by the well-known simple systems of vapor feeding.For example, if the simplest trialkylamine – trimethylamine $(CH_3)_3N$ is used then only ions $(M-H)^+$ - $C_3H_8N^+$ with j ~ A/Torr·cm^2 will be desorbed as ions within the temperature range 700 – 1200 K. When treeethylamine $(C_2H_5)_3N$ is used, then within the temperature range 700-800 K practically only ions $(M-H)^+$ - $C_6H_{14}N^+$ with j ~ 5 A/Torr·cm^2 will be desorbed, and in the range of T ~700-1200 K only ions $(M-CH_3)$ – $C_5H_{12}N^+$ with j ~ 4 A/Torr·cm^2.

If the fluxes of $(M-H)^+$ and $(M-R)^+$ ions with a great difference in the number of particles are required, then it is necessary to use alkylamines with substitutions having a great difference in the number of atoms. For example, for $(CH_3)_2N-C_4H_9$ it is possible to produce the fluxes of $(M-H)^+$ - $C_6H_{14}N^+$ ions with j ~ 5 A/Torr·cm^2 at T~800-900 K and the fluxes with the 2 times less number of $C_3H_8N^+$ atoms with j ~ 5 A/Torr·cm^2 at T~1000-1200 K. Emitters from oxidized tungsten make it possible to produce the stable fluxes of ions of these compounds with I~μkA for 10-15 hours of continuous operation. After that they can be "poisoned". To restore them, it is necessary to repeat the above-indicated high-temperature annealing and oxidization.

To produce molecular ions containing several tens of carbon atoms, "heavy" amines are used for which the vapor pressure is very low at the room temperature. Therefore, their vapors are directed to the emitter surface from the Knudsen cell at 300 K < T ≤450 K.

During the ionization of complex amine vapors the time of continuous stable operation of the emitter decreases according to the number of carbon atoms.

Acknowledgement.

The author acknowledge the support of this work by USAID (Grant No. TA-MOU-95 CA15-029) and by the Fund of Uzbek Acadademy of Sciences. (Grant No. 22-99).

References

[1] E.Ya. Zandberg and N.I. Ionov. Surface Ionization. National Science Foundation, Washington, D.C., 1971 [Nauka, Moscow (1969)].

[2] E.Ya. Zandberg, U.Kh. Rasulev, B.N. Shustrov. Dokl. Akad. Nauk. SSSR, 172 (1967) 885.

[3] E.Ya. Zandberg and U.Kh. Rasulev. Sov. Phys. Tech. Phys., 13, (1969) 1450.

[4] U.Kh. Rasulev and E.Ya. Zandberg. Prog. Surf. Sci., 28, №3/4 (1988) 181-412.

[5] E.Ya. Zandberg, E.G. Nazarov and U.Kh. Rasulev. Sov. Phys. Tech. Phys., 35 (1981) 706.

[6] U.Kh. Rasulev, E.G. Nazarov, G.B. Khudaeva. J. Chromatogr. A, 704 (1995) 473.

A. Benninghoven, P. Bertrand, H.-N. Migeon and H.W. Werner (Editors).
Proceedings of the 12th International Conference on Secondary Ion Mass Spectrometry,
Brussels, Belgium, 5-11 September 1999

COMPARISON OF SECONDARY ION FORMATION FROM NITRATE SALTS PRODUCED BY ATOMIC AND CLUSTER PROJECTILES AT keV AND MeV ENERGIES

M. J. Van Stipdonk, V. Santiago and E. A. Schweikert
Center for Chemical Characterization and Analysis, Department of Chemistry,
Texas A&M University, College Station, Texas 77843-3144 USA.
vanstipdonk@mail.chem.tamu.edu

1. Introduction

We have shown that polyatomic primary ions promote an increase in the formation of secondary ions (SI) via rearrangement and reduction reactions relative to ions presumably emitted as intact units from the sample surface [1]. Polyatomic projectile induced reduction of nitrate (NO_3^-) to nitrite (NO_2^-) during ion formation from sodium nitrate ($NaNO_3$) has been studied at the limit of single primary ion impacts [2], and the observations made were reminiscent of those expected due to high overall ion beam doses [3]. We present here a survey of the effect of varying the primary projectile complexity and energy on the yield of secondary ions from $LiNO_3$, $NaNO_3$, KNO_3, and $CsNO_3$ targets. Of particular interest in this study was the influence of the cation on the ion yields and the nitrate reduction observed during polyatomic ion induced sputtering.

2. Experimental Method

Event-by-event bombardment/detection, coincidence counting and a dual Time-of-Flight mass spectrometer [4] were used for these experiments. $(CsI)_nCs^+$ (n = 0-2) primary ions were produced by the impact of ^{252}Cf fission fragments on an aluminized Mylar™ foil coated with a vapor deposited layer of CsI. The coincidence counting protocol allowed all secondary ion spectra at a given projectile energy to be acquired simultaneously; the transmission and detection efficiency, and sample target surface conditions remained constant throughout each experiment. Some ^{252}Cf fission fragments pass through the foil to strike the sample, allowing the collection of plasma desorption and SIMS spectra simultaneously. Secondary ion mass spectra were collected from the $(CsI)_nCs^+$ projectiles at both 10 and 20 keV impact energies.

The number of primary ions incident on the sample was measured using secondary electrons emitted from the target upon projectile impact; only negative spectra were collected. It is assumed that at least one electron was emitted from each projectile impact. Secondary ion yields were calculated by dividing the integrated secondary ion peak areas by the integrated secondary electron peak area associated with a particular primary ion impact, each after appropriate background subtraction.

Sample targets of Li, Na, K and $CsNO_3$ were prepared by drying 10 μL aliqouts of 0.3M aqueous solution onto a stainless steel sample cube in a dark fume hood. All ion yield and yield ratio trends measured were reproduced using multiple sample targets.

288

3. Results and Discussion

Sample targets of each alkali nitrate were bombarded with 10 and 20 keV Cs^+ and $(CsI)_nCs^+$ projectiles (n = 1,2) as well as MeV energy ^{252}Cf fission fragments. In each experimental run, the total incident ion dose never exceeded ~1 x 10^7 ions/cm^2. Any reduction effects observed are therefore attributed to discrete ion impacts and not beam-type dose effects. Figure 1 shows the mass spectra generated from the same $NaNO_3$ target by (a) 10 keV $(CsI)Cs^+$ and (b) ^{252}Cf fission fragments. The spectra are shown to illustrate the qualitative differences in the spectra produced by the two projectiles. The spectra shown in figure 1 are representative of those derived from each alkali nitrate target.

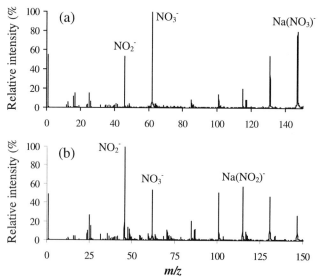

Figure 1. Mass spectra of $NaNO_3$ collected using (a) 10 keV $(CsI)Cs^+$ and (b) ^{252}Cf fission fragment projectiles.

In general, at both 10 and 20 keV impact energy the relative secondary ion yields from each alkali nitrate target sputtered by Cs^+ were an order of magnitude lower than the yields produced by the keV polyatomic ion and fission fragment projectiles. The yields produced by the polyatomic ion and the fission fragments projectiles were comparable in magnitude. The fission fragments produced higher yields of nitrite-containing secondary ions {eg. NO_2^-, $Na(NO_2)_2^-$} from each solid, whereas the polyatomic and mono-atomic projectiles produced higher yields of the nitrate-containing species {eg. NO_3^-, $Na(NO_3)_2^-$}.

A strong cation effect was observed in the ion yield distributions. The relative yield trends are summarized in table 1 for NO_2^-, NO_3^-, $M(NO_2)_2^-$ and $M(NO_3)_2^-$ {where M denotes the alkali cation} from each alkali nitrate sample. For the keV energy projectiles, the yield distribution trends observed were the same at both 10 and 20 keV impact energy. The yields of NO_2^- and NO_3^- with respect to the cation in the nitrate solid follow a trend that reflects the relative heat of formation and free energy for the bulk alkali nitrate solids (in the order Cs>Li>Na>K). The higher abundance of larger polyatomic secondary ions such as $M(NO_2)_2^-$ and $M(NO_3)_2^-$ from Li and $NaNO_3$ can be rationalized based on the high lattice energy and bond strengths for clusters containing the smaller Li and Na cations.

Projectile	Ion	Secondary Ion Yield			
		Highest	$\Rightarrow$	$\Rightarrow$	*Lowest*
$(CsI)Cs^+$	NO_3^-	Cs	Li	Na	K
	NO_2^-	Cs =	Li	Na	K
	$M(NO_3)_2^-$	Li	Na	Cs	K
	$M(NO_2)_2^-$	Li	Na	Cs	K
$(CsI)_2Cs^+$	NO_3^-	Cs	Li	Na	K
	NO_2^-	Li	Cs	Na	K
	$M(NO_3)_2^-$	Li	Na	Cs	K
	$M(NO_2)_2^-$	Li	Na	Cs	K

Table 1. Summary of cation effect on secondary ion yield distribution using $(CsI)Cs^+$ and $(CsI)_2Cs^+$ projectiles at 10 and 20 keV.

The NO_3^-/NO_2^- relative yield ratio from nitrate solids can be used as an indicator of projectile induced chemical damage. We have shown that this ion yield ratio is not sensitive to the projectile impact energy, but increases with increasing projectile complexity [2]. The ratio (and thus the chemical damage) is the result of the high instantaneous atom dose brought on by the impact of a polyatomic primary ion and can be linked to the energy density deposited on impact. Table 2 summarizes the NO_3^-/NO_2^- relative yields produced by impacts of $(CsI)_nCs^+$ projectiles on the four alkali nitrate targets.

Projectile	$LiNO_3$	Sample target $NaNO_3$	KNO_3	$CsNO_3$
10 keV				
Cs^+	2.54	3.23	3.62	3.53
$(CsI)Cs^+$	2.03	2.6	2.83	2.72
$(CsI)_2Cs^+$	1.70	2.09	4.17	1.97
20 keV				
Cs^+	2.62	2.88	2.98	2.84
$(CsI)Cs^+$	2.06	2.56	2.65	2.42
$(CsI)_2Cs^+$	1.69	1.87	2.13	1.99

Table 2. Summary of the NO_3^-/NO_2^- relative yield ratios produced by the keV atomic and polyatomic ion impacts on Li, Na, K and $CsNO_3$ targets.

290

As with the overall secondary ion yields, the cation influences the NO_3^-/NO_2^- yield ratio produced by atomic and polyatomic projectile bombardment. The trend observed for the NO_3^-/NO_2^- relative yield ratio, however, is opposite that observed for the relative ion yields. The ratio is highest for the K salt and lowest for the Li and Cs salts. The difference in trend is more pronounced for the larger polyatomic projectiles. It is interesting to note that the chemical damage trend, the NO_3^-/NO_2^- ratio, measured in our experiments is also opposite the measured yield of NO_2^- formed within alkali nitrate solids following bombardment with ionizing radiation such as high-energy electrons and alpha particles [6]. The latter experiments were conducted by extracting and measuring the amount of NO_2^- within the solid subsequent to irradiation while our experiments involved measuring the NO_2^- emitted from the sample surface. The comparison of the two results indicates that the amount of chemical damage observed in our experiments may depend not only on the amount of reduction occurring, but also on the relative sputter yields from the various targets.

4. Conclusions

We have shown that the cation present in alkali nitrate solids influences both the overall ion yields and the NO_3^-/NO_2^- produced when these solids are bombarded with keV energy atomic and polyatomic projectiles. The yields produced by keV energy polyatomic and MeV fission fragments projectiles are comparable and an order of magnitude higher than keV atomic ion impacts. The amount of chemical damage induced at the single projectile impact level, however, is higher for the more complex keV energy ions and the fission fragment projectiles.

5. Acknowledgement

This work was funded by a grant from the National Science Foundation (CHE-9727474)

References
[1]	M. J. Van Stipdonk, V. Santiago and E. A. Schweikert, J. Mass Spectrom., 34 (1999) 554.
[2]	M. J. Van Stipdonk, D. R. Justes, V. Santiago and E. A. Schweikert, Rapid Comm. Mass Spectrom. 12, (1998) 1639.
[3]	J. Marien and E. De Pauw, Int. J. Mass Spectrom. Ion Physics 43, (1982) 233.
[4]	M. J. Van Stipdonk, R. D. Harris and E. A. Schweikert, Rapid Comm. Mass Spectrom. 10, (1996) 1987.
[5]	M. G. Blain, S. Della-Negra, H. Joret, Y. Le Beyec and E. A. Schweikert, J. Vac. Sci. Technol. A8, (1990) 2265.
[6]	S. R. Logan and W. J. Moore, J. Chem. Phys., 67, (1963) 1042.

A. Benninghoven, P. Bertrand, H.-N. Migeon and H.W. Werner (Editors).
Proceedings of the 12th International Conference on Secondary Ion Mass Spectrometry,
Brussels, Belgium, 5-11 September 1999

DECAY FRACTIONS OF INORGANIC CLUSTER IONS SPUTTERED BY ATOMIC AND POLYATOMIC PRIMARY IONS

M. J. Van Stipdonk, V. Santiago and E. A. Schweikert
Center for Chemical Characterization and Analysis, Department of Chemistry,
Texas A&M University, College Station, Texas 77843-3144 USA.
vanstipdonk@mail.chem.tamu.edu

1. Introduction

Polyatomic primary ions produce 10-100 times higher secondary ion (SI) yields than atomic projectiles at comparable impact energy or velocity. The yield increases are due to non-linear processes in the stopping of the polyatomic projectiles. Recently, we have demonstrated that artifact ion (i.e. ions indicative of chemical damage) yields are sensitive to the choice of polyatomic primary ion [1-3]. For instance, fast rearrangement and/or reduction reactions are more apparent in the mass spectra produced by cluster projectiles. The reactions are sensitive to the energy deposited per unit volume deposited in the surface region of the solid.

Yet to be explored in the area of sputtering by cluster projectiles is the SI internal energy. The internal energy determines the amount of prompt and metastable fragmentation and thus influences the qualitative and quantitative features of a secondary ion mass spectrum. We present here a preliminary investigation of the decay fractions for secondary cluster ions sputtered from lithium nitrate by keV energy $(CsI)_nCs^+$ and MeV energy ^{252}Cf fission fragment projectiles.

2. Experimental Method

These experiments were conducted using event-by-event bombardment/detection, coincidence counting and a custom dual-Time-of-Flight (TOF) SIMS instrument. The original instrument design was modified by the addition of a three-grid retarding field assembly located mid-way through the secondary ion TOF leg. In all other cases, the configuration and operation of the instrument are as described in reference 4.

$(CsI)_nCs^+$ (n = 0-2) primary ions were produced by the impact of ^{252}Cf fission fragments on an aluminized Mylar™ foil coated with a vapor deposited layer of CsI. Some ^{252}Cf fission fragments pass through the foil to strike the sample, allowing the collection of plasma desorption and SIMS spectra simultaneously. The coincidence counting protocol allowed all secondary ion spectra at a given projectile energy to be acquired simultaneously; the transmission and detection efficiency and sample target surface conditions remained constant throughout each experiment. The background pressure during the decay fraction measurements was ~1 x 10^{-4} Pa, a pressure at which sputtered secondary ions may be activated by collisions with rest gas molecules. Because the ion and neutral (from in-flight dissociation) relative yields from multiple primary projectiles were collected simultaneously, dissociation due to in-flight collisions cancel out and relative changes in decay fraction are therefore attributed to internal energy effects linked to the primary ion impact.

The peaks present in a conventional linear TOF spectrum are composed of both intact ions and neutral and ion fragments from metastable dissociation. The middle grid of the retarding field assembly, when biased, rejects ionized species and allows the selective detection of neutrals from in-flight dissociation reactions. The decay fraction, a quantitative measure of the number of secondary ions that dissociate within the field-free region of the TOF instrument, is calculated by dividing the yield of the neutrals from the dissociation of a particular precursor ion (grid biased) by the ions+neutrals yield (grid grounded).

3. Results and Discussion

Figure 1 compares the mass spectra produced by 20 keV $(CsI)Cs^+$ projectile impacts on a $LiNO_3$ target (a) with the voltage on the middle grid set a 0 kV and (b) with the middle grid biased to –5.2 kV. In figure 1b, the x-axis is labeled as apparent mass, due to the fact that the neutral species derived from in flight dissociation carries only a fraction of the mass of the original cluster ion.

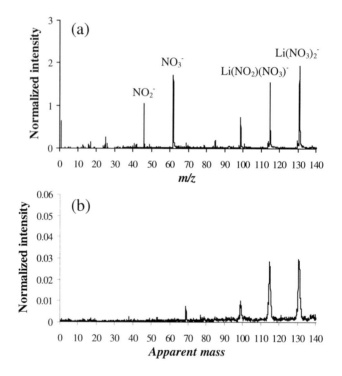

Figure 1.   The (a) ions + neutrals (conventional linear TOF) spectrum and (b) neutral from in-flight dissociation only spectra derived from $LiNO_3$ following the impact of 20 keV $(CsI)Cs^+$ projectiles.

Due to conservation of momentum, the center of mass velocity is retained, giving the neutral a flight time roughly equal to the undissociated precursor cluster ion. The increases in the peak width observed in figure 1b are attributed to kinetic energy release from the in-flight dissociation.

The decay pathways for the secondary cluster ions that are the focus of the decay fraction measurements are provided below. To elucidate the dissociation pathways for the secondary cluster ions sputtered from $LiNO_3$ we tested duplicate samples in a reflectron TOF instrument equipped with a ^{252}Cf source. With the reflectron TOF instrument we could determine the dissocation pathways via the ion-neutral correlation method [5]. It is assumed that the cluster ions sputtered by keV energy primary ions follow the same dissociation pathways as when they are produced by ^{252}Cf fission fragment impacts.

$$\{Li(NO_2)(NO_3)\}^- \quad \Rightarrow \quad Li(NO_2)^\circ + NO_3^-$$

$$\{Li(NO_3)_2\}^- \quad \Rightarrow \quad Li(NO_3)^\circ + NO_3^-$$

Both secondary cluster ions dissociate by shedding the nitrate anion. It is assumed that the neutral species is composed as shown in table 1. The decay fractions measured for the $Li(NO_2)(NO_3)^-$ and $Li(NO_3)_2^-$ secondary ions sputtered from $LiNO_3$ by 20 keV Cs^+, $(CsI)Cs^+$, $(CsI)_2Cs^+$ and ~100 MeV ^{252}Cf fission fragment projectiles are listed in table 2.

	Decay fraction	
	$Li(NO_2)(NO_3)^-$	$Li(NO_3)_2^-$
Primary projectile		
Cs^+	.040 ($\pm$.008)	.036 ($\pm$.007)
$(CsI)Cs^+$	.062 ($\pm$.012)	.051 ($\pm$.010)
$(CsI)_2Cs^+$	.063 ($\pm$.012)	.045 ($\pm$.009)
^{252}Cf Fission fragment	.076 (+.015)	.047 (+.009)

Table 1. Decay fraction for $\{Li(NO_2)(NO_3)\}^-$ and $\{Li(NO_3)_2\}^-$ secondary cluster ions sputtered by 20 keV $(CsI)_nCs^+$ (n=0-2) and ~100 MeV ^{252}Cf fission fragment projectiles. Each decay fraction was measured using three individual sample targets. The standard deviation from the mean is provided in parenthesis following the decay fraction value.

As shown in table 1, the $(CsI)Cs^+$ projectile produced an increase in the decay fraction for both secondary cluster ions when compared to Cs^+. Within the error of the measurements there was no further increase in the decay fraction observed for either the $(CsI)_2Cs^+$ or ^{252}Cf fission fragment projectiles. The decay fractions were consistently higher for the mixed anion cluster species, $Li(NO_2)(NO_3)^-$, indicating that this secondary ion is less stable than the cluster composed of a cation and two nitrate units.

4. Conclusions

Decay fractions for two secondary cluster ions sputtered from lithium nitrate targets by atomic and polyatomic primary ions were measured. In general, these decay fractions, and thus the SI internal energies of the sputtered cluster ions, were higher when polyatomic ions are used as projectiles. In a practical sense, the internal energy of a sputtered SI is an important parameter when reflectron Time-of-Flight (ToF) mass analyzers are employed. Sputtered SI with sufficient internal energy (and dissociation rate constant) will fragment in the field-free region of the instrument and are not reflected for high-resolution mass measurements. Increasing the metastable dissociation of sputtered ions will also be useful for tandem TOF performed using reflectron TOF analyzers and the ion-neutral correlation method. This method relies on the dissociaton of secondary ions within the first field free region of the instrument to determine ion composition and structure.

5. Acknowledgement

This work was funded by a grant from the National Science Foundation (CHE-9727474)

References

[1] M. J. Van Stipdonk, D. R. Justes, V. Santiago, E. A. Schweikert, Rapid Comm. Mass Spectrom., 12 (1998)1639.

[2] M. J. Van Stipdonk, V. Santiago and E. A. Schweikert, J. Mass Spectrom, 34 (1999) 554.

[3] C. W. Diehnelt, M. J. Van Stipdonk and E. A. Schweikert, Phys. Rev. A, 59, (1998) 4470.

[4] M. J. Van Stipdonk, R. D. Harris and E. A. Schweikert, Rapid Comm. Mass Spectrom.10, (1996) 1987.

[5] M. J. Van Stipdonk, D. R. Justes, R. D. English and E. A. Schweikert, J. Mass Spectrom. (1999) in press.

A. Benninghoven, P. Bertrand, H.-N. Migeon and H.W. Werner (Editors).
Proceedings of the 12th International Conference on Secondary Ion Mass Spectrometry,
Brussels, Belgium, 5-11 September 1999

295

FORMATION OF NEGATIVE CARBON CLUSTER IONS
BY MOLECULAR ION IRRADIATION

Hiroyuki Yamamoto*, Fumitaka Esaka[a] and Hidehito Asaoka
Department of Materials Science, [a]Department of Environmental Sciences,
Japan Atomic Energy Research Institute, Tokai, Naka, Ibaraki 319-1195, Japan
*Electronic mail: yamamoto@analchem.tokai.jaeri.go.jp

1. Introduction

Strongly enhanced cluster ion emission has been observed in the present experiments by using SF_5^+ for the primary ion. It is known that when some solid materials are sputtered by ion bombardment, a fraction of the ejected particles agglomerates into several or many atoms. The formation of these clusters in the course of the collision represents one of the most interesting phenomena in the investigation of ion-solid interaction [1-6]. Most of these studies have been performed using irradiation of monatomic ions, or O_2^+ ion to achieve high ionization probability [1-5]. To our knowledge, molecular ions which have several constituent atoms have scarcely been used for these experiments. It has been observed that the sputter yields by molecular ion bombardment are more than ten times greater than those by monatomic ion bombardment at the same velocity [7,8]. It is expected that agglomeration of the sputtered atoms takes place more efficiently with the increase in the sputter yield using molecular ions.

In the present work, molecular ion (SF_5^+) has been irradiated to the diamond thin film. Negative carbon cluster ions (C_n^-) up to $n \leq 12$ have been observed. On the basis of the relationship between relative yields of the cluster C_n^- and the number of constituent atoms, a possible mechanism for the cluster ion emission is considered.

2. Experimental

The incident SF_5^+(m/e=127) ion was produced from SF_6 source gas in a duoplasmatron-type ion source. The mass of the ions was separated by an analyzing magnet. Rare gas ions, Xe^+(m/e=132) and Ar^+(m/e=40), were also irradiated for comparison. The incident energy of the ions was 4 keV, and the flux was 1 $\mu A/cm^2$. The incident angle of the ions was 25° from the surface normal. The diamond thin film was deposited on Si(100) target. The sample surface was kept at room temperature during the bombardment. The base pressure of the system was lower than 2 x 10^{-7} Pa, and the pressure during ion irradiation was kept below 1 x 10^{-6} Pa. Both positive and negative ions emitted from the surface were detected with a quadrupole mass analyzer equipped with a 45° sector field energy filter (Hiden Analytical, Ltd., EQS-500). The mass and kinetic energy of the emitted ions were analyzed simultaneously by this system. The transmittance of the mass spectrometer was calibrated by comparison of observed and standard mass spectra for SF_6 gas.

In order to obtain the relative cluster yields from experimentally observed secondary ion intensity, calculation of the ionization probability of these clusters is required, because the both positive and negative ionization probability of the cluster strongly depends on the cluster size. The relative cluster yields can be obtained from Saha-Eggert equation [9,10], which is widely applied for the secondary ion measurements. In this equation, concentration ratio of sputtered negative ion and neutral atoms is calculated. Several factors other than ionization probability are also required during calculation, such as plasma temperature of irradiated area and temperature-dependent internal partition functions. These values are found from various literatures [11].

3. Results and discussion

Fig. 1 shows the secondary ion spectra observed from the diamond thin film target by bombardment with the respective ions. All spectra were recorded under 4 keV ion bombardment with a flux of 1 μA/cm^2. It is seen that cluster C_n^- ions up to $n \leq 12$ are clearly detected for SF_5^+ irradiation. On the other hand, the intensities of C_n^- clusters by Xe^+ and Ar^+ irradiations are quite low compared with those by SF_5^+ irradiation. For the SF_5^+ irradiation, the F^-(m/e=19) peak was observed in addition to that of C_n^- ions. The F^- ion is observed due to the dissociation and sequential implantation of irradiated SF_5^+ ions. It should be noted that positive cluster ions were scarcely observed, though positive cluster ions (Si_n^+) were mainly observed for Si target [12].

Fig. 2 shows the relationship between the relative cluster yields $Y(n)$ and the number of the constituent atoms (n) on a log-log scale. In the case of carbon target, the yield of monatoms $Y(1)$ is extremely lower than that of other clusters. The relative yields are therefore normalized to dimer $Y(2)=1$. The results show that the relative cluster yields $Y(n)$ roughly exhibit a power-law dependence on the number of atoms in the cluster (n) for each irradiated ion, namely,

$$Y(n) = an^{-\delta} \qquad (1)$$

where a is a constant. Such a relationship has also been observed for sputtered neutral clusters [3,4]. The exponents δ for SF_5^+, Xe^+ and Ar^+ are 1.8, 2.7 and 4.7, respectively. The obtained exponents δ are in the order $\delta(SF_5^+) < \delta(Xe^+) < \delta(Ar^+)$. Two possible effects would influence the order of the exponents. The first one is the mass effect where the sputter yield of carbon increases with the mass of the irradiated ions at 4 keV [13]. The second one is the size effect, in which the polyatomic ions such as SF_5^+ collide with several surface atoms. The number of atoms which participate in the collision increases with the size of the irradiated ion. In both cases, the possibility of cluster formation in-creases with the total sputter yield be-cause the sputtered atoms are emitted close enough in time and space [2].

If the mass effect is dominant, it is expected that the observed δ values of SF_5^+ and Xe^+ are almost the same, since these ions have almost equal mass. However, the δ of Xe^+ is 1.5 times that of SF_5^+. The difference in δ shows that mass effects might not be dominant for cluster emission. On the other hand, the order of the exponents is in fairly good agreement with that of the ion size [14].

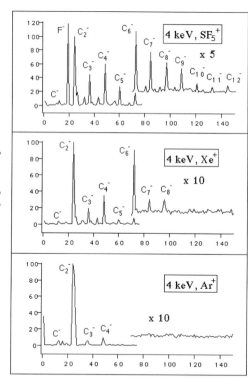

Fig.1 Mass spectra of sputtered C_n^- clusters ions. The species and energy of the irradiated ions are indicated in the respective columns.

When a large polyatomic ion collides with the surface atoms, high-density collision cascades will be formed at the irradiated local area. It is expected that a "non-linear sputtering effect" [15] (extremely high sputtering yields and cluster ion emission) can be observed for the SF_5^+ bombardment though the ion current density is in the order of several $\mu A/cm^2$. In the case of SF_5^+ irradiation, we can consider that carbon atoms emitted by the impacts of the F and S fragments originating from the same SF_5^+ ion are close enough in time and space. These results show that the size of the irradiated ion greatly affects the cluster emission. The size effect might be more remarkable for larger polyatomic ion irradiation.

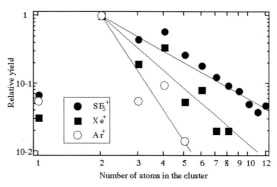

Fig.2 Relationship between relative cluster yields and the number of the constituent atoms in the cluster. The data are normalized to the yield of C_2 dimer.

According to the cluster emission behavior, we can conceive of the emission mechanisms of these clusters. The mechanisms of cluster emission can be roughly divided into the following two models, though the mechanism is not yet fully understood. These are, 1) direct emission of the cluster from the ion-bombarded surface (direct emission model [16]) and, 2) recombination of independently sputtered atoms or ions above the surface (recombination model [17]). The former mechanism can be applied mainly to adsorbates or molecular sol-ids. The latter mechanism is often applied to metals. In the latter, dimers or larger clus-ters are formed from independently sputtered atoms, when they are emitted close enough in time and space and their relative kinetic energies are less than the binding energy of clusters.

The present results show that the power law exponent δ of Xe^+ is 1.5 times that of SF_5^+. Wucher et al. have demonstrated that the total sputter yield increases with the decrease in the power law exponent δ of the cluster yield [4]. On the basis of their results, the total sputter yield of SF_5^+ is estimated to be 2.4 times that of Xe^+. Such a high sputter yield for the molecular ion induces the formation of "nascent" cluster just above the sample surface according to the results of Molecular Dynamics simulation [4]. Just after the nascent cluster formation, sequential decomposition of these cluster ions might take place because the simulation also suggests that these clusters contain a large amount of internal energy. If the "nascent" cluster emission and sequential decomposition actually takes place during molecular ion irradiation, more stable cluster ions show higher intensity, because the stable ions are easily formed and survive the fragmentation process of nascent clusters. We can obtain important information on the cluster formation mechanism by comparison of the intensities and stabilities of these cluster ions.

In fig. 2, a yield variation between clusters containing odd and even numbers of atoms for clusters $C-C_7$ is seen, which is similar to that observed for sputtered metal cluster ions [1]. In the case of the metal cluster ions, the intensity of odd-n clusters is greater than that of even-n clusters. Such behavior of these metal cluster ions can be explained on the basis of an electronic shell model. In positive cluster ion observation, only sputtered particles with positive single-charge have been detected. Therefore, the number of free electrons in n-mer, which are obtained from the valence electrons of constituent atoms is $n-1$ for the metals. Katakuse et al. have shown that even-electron clusters (odd-n clusters) are more stable compared with odd-electron clusters due to spin-spin coupling of valence electrons on the basis of the results for metal cluster ion emission [1].

Contrary to the behavior of metal cluster ion emission, the present results for the negative carbon clusters show that the relative intensity of even-n clusters is greater than that of odd-n

ones. During the collision process, it is expected that the decomposition of the sputtered "nascent" clusters takes place through the electron detachment process [18]. The calculated results of electron affinity for the carbon cluster, which indicate the possibility of electron detachment, show that odd-n cluster display much more lower electron affinity than the even-n species [19]. The results suggest that electron detachment takes place more easily for odd-n clusters. The "odd-n nascent clusters" therefore easily decompose compared with even-n clusters. The experimentally observed "destruction cross section" of the gas phase cluster also shows that odd-n clusters have higher cross sections [18]. The even/odd alternation is therefore observed due to the difference of the stability.

4. Conclusion

On the basis of the present experiments, the following points have been clarified.

1)Strongly enhanced negative carbon cluster ion emission (C_n^-, $n \leq 12$) has been observed by 4 keV SF_5^+ ion ($1 \mu A/cm^2$) irradiation.

2)Relative cluster yields roughly exhibit a power-law dependence on the number of constituent atoms in the cluster. The obtained exponents are in the order of $\delta(SF_5^+) < \delta(Xe^+) < \delta(Ar^+)$. The size of the irradiated ions and the sputtering conditions (e.g., total sputter yields) affect the behavior of the cluster emission.

3)A yield variation between odd-n and even-n clusters is observed from C to C_7. The intensities of even-n clusters (C_2, C_4) are relatively higher than those of neighboring odd-n clusters. This emission behavior of the clusters implies nascent cluster ion emission and the sequential decomposition process.

The authors are grateful to Dr. K. Hojou and Dr. Y. Baba for their helpful discussion and collaboration through the present work.

References

[1] I. Katakuse, T. Ichihara, T. Matsuo, T. Sakurai and H. Matsuda, Int. J. Mass Spectrom. Ion Processes 91 (1989) 99, and references therein.
[2] W. Husinsky and G. Betz, Thin Solid Films 272 (1996) 289.
[3] S.R. Coon, W.F. Calaway, M.J. Pellin and J.M. White, Surf. Sci. 298 (1993) 161.
[4] A. Wucher and M. Wahl, Nucl. Instr. and Meth. B115 (1996) 581.
[5] Indira S. Iyer, R. Mehta, D. Kanjilal and A. Roy, Rad. Effects and Defects in Solids 138 (1996) 145.
[6] W. Szymczak and K. Wittmaack, Nucl. Instr. and Meth. B88 (1994) 149.
[7] M.G. Blain, S. Della-Negra, H. Joret, Y. Le Beyec and E.A. Schweikart, Phys. Rev. Lett. 63 (1989) 1625.
[8] A.D. Appelhans and J.E. Delmore, Anal. Chem. 61 (1989) 1087.
[9] C.A. Andersen and J.R. Hinthorne, Anal. Chem. 45 (1973) 1421.
[10] H.W. Werner, Surf. Interf. Anal. 2 (1980) 56.
[11] e.g. W. Steiger and F.G. R¸denauer, Int. J. Mass Spectrom. Ion Phys., 13 (1974) 411.
[12] H. Yamamoto and Y. Baba, Appl. Phys. Lett. 72 (1998) 2406.
[13] N. Matsunami, Y. Yamamura, Y. Itikawa, N. Itoh, Y. Kazumata, S. Miyagawa, K. Morita, R. Shimizu and H. Tawara, *Energy Dependence of Ion-induced Sputtering of Monatomic Solids*, Inst. of Plasma Phys., Nagoya Univ. (IPPJ-AM-32), 1983, p. 1.
[14] e.g. Ed. David R. Lide, *Handbook of Chemistry and Physics, 77th edition*, CRC, Florida, 1996, p. 9-21.
[15] H.H. Andersen and H.L. Bay, J. Appl. Phys. 45 (1974) 953.
[16] R. De Jonge, K.W. Benoist, J.F.W. Majoor, A.E. de Vries and K.J. Snowdon, Nucl. Instr. and Meth. B28 (1987) 214.
[17] R.A. Haring, H.E. Roosendaal and P.C. Zalm, Nucl. Instr. and Meth. B28 (1987) 205.
[18] H. Shen, C. Brink, P. Hvelplund and M.O. Larsson, Z. Phys. D40 (1997) 371.
[19] Shihe Yang, K.J. Taylor, M.J. Craycraft, J. Conceicao, C.L. Pettiette, O. Cheshnovsky and R.E. Smalley, Chem. Phys. Lett. 144 (1988) 431.

A. Benninghoven, P. Bertrand, H.-N. Migeon and H.W. Werner (Editors).
Proceedings of the 12th International Conference on Secondary Ion Mass Spectrometry,
Brussels, Belgium, 5-11 September 1999
© 2000 Elsevier Science B.V. All rights reserved.

NEGATIVE FULLERENE ION GUN FOR SIMS APPLICATIONS

A. Bekkerman, B. Tsipinyuk and E. Kolodney.

Department of Chemistry, Technion - Israel Institute of Technology ,
Haifa 32000, Israel.. chranato@tx.technion.ac.il

1. Introduction

Due to high secondary ions yield and shallow penetration the use of cluster or polyatomic ions as primary projectiles for static SIMS analysis of organic and inorganic samples have many advantages as compared with atomic ions [1,2]. The use of fullerene ion projectiles as the primary beam for dynamic and static SIMS applications is especially attractive [3,4]. In addition, fullerenes are a good model colliders for many fundamental studies: molecular ions surface scattering, mechanisms of secondary ion emission of macromolecules, charge exchange, sputtering and cluster-surface collisions. Various methods for the generation of positive and negative fullerene ion beams were used: laser ablation and desorption of graphite or fullerene targets, fission fragments impact on a C_{60} coated surfaces, fullerene thermal desorption combined with electron attachment or electron impact ionization, etc.. Attempts were also made to use conventional ion sources (arc-discharge and sputtering type). Most of the above mentioned beam sources have various drawbacks when used for SIMS applications. These may be either the complexity of the source, the need for mass filter due to fragmentation upon ionization, low intensity or poor focusing. In this paper we present an innovative negative fullerenes ion gun which is both simple and reliable, has high beam purity and high brightness. It is based on a new method for the generation of negative fullerene ions recently developed in our laboratory [5]. We present performance data of the fullerene ion gun and report some preliminary results obtained with a new C_{60}^- - SIMS instrument.

2. Experimental

The negative fullerene ion gun was mounted on a molecular beam-surface scattering apparatus as described before [5,6]. The UHV scattering chamber is equipped with two quadrupole mass spectrometers: Balzers QMG-421 and Extrel MEXM - 4000 with 1024 a.m.u and 4000 a.m.u full mass scales respectively. The QMG-421 was mounted on the primary fullerene beam line for measuring its mass composition. The MEXM - 4000 was used for secondary ions registration and was mounted at an angle of 45° relative to the primary beam axis. For measuring the energy spread of the primary beam a VG-100AX hemispherical analyser was mounted on the primary beam line instead of the QMG - 421. Ion current was measured by a Faraday cup placed on a special sample holder fixed on a precision manipulator at the centre of the UHV chamber. A calibrated slit (500 μm width) was mounted in front of the Faraday cup for measuring the beam spot size. A polycrystalline gold surface covered with a thin film of amino acid (DL-Serin) was mounted on the sample holder. The film was prepared by deposition from aqueous solution of DL-Serine (dipping the substrate for a short time in the solution and subsequent drying).

3. The fullerene ion gun – general description and performance data

The negative fullerene ions are generated in a two-stage capillary nozzle with an exit orifice of $100 - 120$ μm [5]. The temperature of the C_{60} vapours at the first stage (the evaporator) is controlled in the range of $650 - 1000$ K and is stabilized to better then 1 centigrade. The temperature of the C_{60} particles exiting the nozzle aperture can be independently varied in the range of T = $1000 - 2000$ K. Since both stages are thermally decoupled the flux is constant irrespective of the temperature tuning of the nozzle stage. The usual working temperature is $1600 - 1750$ K. The nozzle stage is resistively heated by a thin rhenium ribbon that may also be the source for thermal electrons. The ionization process itself is not fully clear yet (electron attachment or negative surface ionization) and is the subject of current research in our laboratory. The fullerene powder (purchased from MER) is placed inside the evaporator in a replaceable ceramic crucible. Acceleration of the negative ions takes place in the region between the nozzle orifice and an extractor electrode. Fullerene ion beams in the energy range of $50 \div 5000$ eV are currently generated. The ion gun optics is composed of two focusing (einzel) lenses, intermediate correction plates, intermediate current collector, gating electrodes for pulsed beam mode operation and quadrupole deflector plates for beam scanning on the sample surface.

Fig.1 shows mass spectra of the negative fullerene ion beam at primary energy E_o =100 eV for two different fullerene powders: (a) - purified C_{60} powder (99.5%) and (b) - refined fullerenes mixture. As can be seen, when pure C_{60} powder is used in the mass spectra the negative ion beam is totally dominated by C_{60}^- ions. For the fullerene mixture the highest peaks are C_{60}^-, C_{70}^- but larger fullerene ions C_n^- (n = 72, 74, 76) of very low intensity were also observed. The high stability of the fullerene molecules prevents unimolecular decomposition in spite of the vibrational excitation inside the nozzle. In all cases only negligible fraction ($< 10^{-5}$) of smaller negatively charged fullerene ions C_n^- (n = 56, 58) were detected.

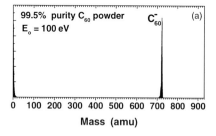
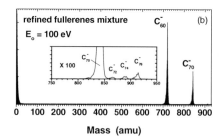

Fig. 1. Mass spectrum of the primary negative fullerene ion beams for different fullerene powders.

Fig. 2 shows the fullerene negative ions current as a function of the acceleration voltage applied between the source orifice and extractor electrode. Measurements are presented for two different values of the total heating power P supplied to the source. A maximal beam current (C_{60}^- ions) of ~10 nA (pure C_{60} powder) was obtained.

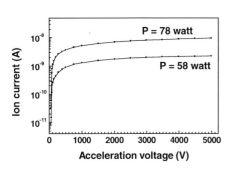

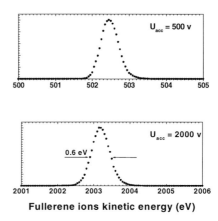

Fig. 2. The C_{60}^- negative ions current as a function of the acceleration voltage $U_{acc.}$

Fig. 3. Energy spectrum of the C_{60}^- ions produced by the ion gun.

One of the most important parameters of an ion source is its energy spread. It affects the ions extraction efficiency, the beam current density and homogeneity and the focusing quality. Fig. 3 shows the energy spectrum of the fullerene negative ion beam measured for two acceleration voltages (500 and 2000 V). As shown in both spectra the full width at half maximum(FWHM) of the kinetic energy distribution is quite narrow and for E_o=2000 eV is limited by the instrumental width (0.5 – 0.6 eV) of the hemispherical energy analyser. Detailed measurements of different energy spectra show that the energy spread of the negative ions is nearly independent of the acceleration potential. For all measurements the kinetic energy of the fullerene ions exceeded the $eU_{acc.}$ values by 1 – 4 eV (depending on the acceleration voltage). This shift probably relates to slight surface charging of the ceramic emitter. The ion beam spot size at the sample was determined from the 10–90% rise (or fall) of the beam intensity when the beam is scanned over the calibrated slit. For beam current <0.1 nA a minimal spot size of 20 μm is currently achievable. This can be useful for microprobe applications.

Another unique feature of our C_{60}^- ion gun is its ability to generate high kinetic energy (50 – 5000 eV) neutral C_{60}^o beams. The highly vibrationally excited C_{60}^- ions produced at the superhot nozzle source gradually decay, during their flight time to the target, into neutral C_{60}^o via vibrationally induced delayed auto-detachment of electrons (thermionic emission) [5]. The neutral fraction is typically 0.1-5% of the total beam flux depending on beam energy and nozzle temperature. For low E_o values (<100 eV) much higher neutrals yield can be achieved. Pure neutral C_{60}^o beam is obtained by deflecting the C_{60}^- ions using the gating electrodes. The use of neutral beams could be advantageous when working with highly insulating targets, avoiding the problematic charging effects associated with ion beams. This operation mode can

302

be considered as the neutral cluster beam analog of the fast atom bombardment (FAB) technique used for desorption mass-spectrometry. It may provide a unique opporto compare SIMS and FABMS for heavy colliding species.

4. C_{60}^- - SIMS Examples

Negative and positive static SIMS spectra of DL-Serine on gold is shown in Fig.4. Pure C_{60}^- primary beam was used at impact energy of 4.5 KeV. The negative secondary ions spectra (NSI) also demonstrate the convenience of using single-element cluster as a projectile since all the impact generated C_n^- fragments (n = 1 – 9) can be easily assigned.

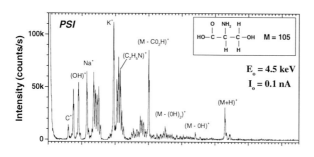

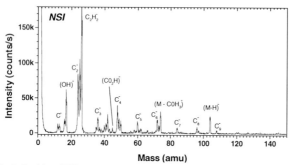

In summary, we believe that using C_{60}^- ion as a SIMS projectile combined with the various features of the C_{60}^- ion gun presented here, will lead to new and interesting organic SIMS applications and will deepen our understanding of the physico-chemical processes underlying the collisional interaction of large particles with surface.

Fig.4. Positive (PSI) and negative (NSI) static SIMS spectra of DL-Serine deposited on a gold surface. Pure C_{60}^- primary beam is used at impact energy of 4.5 KeV and beam current density of 4×10^9 ion $\cdot s^{-1} \cdot cm^{-2}$.

References

[1] R. D. Harris, M.J. Van Stipdonk, and E.A. Schweikert Int. J. of Mass Spect. and ion proc. 174 (1998) 167.
[2] Y.Le Beyec, Int. J. of Mass Spect. and ion proc. 174 (1998) 101.
[3] M.J. Van Stipdonk, R. D. Harris and E.A. Schweikert, Rapid commun. Mass Spectrom. 10 (1996) 1987.
[4] K. Baudin, G. Bolback, A. Brunnelle, S. Della-Negra, P.H. Akansson, Y. Le-Beyec, Nucl. Instruments and Meth. B88 (1994) 160.
[5] A. Bekkerman, B. Tsipinyuk and E. Kolodney Int.J.of Mass Spectrometry,187 (1999) 773.
[6] A. Bekkerman, B. Tsipinyuk, S. Verkhoturov and E. Kolodney J. Chem. Phys. 109 (1998) 8652.

A. Benninghoven, P. Bertrand, H.-N. Migeon and H.W. Werner (Editors).
Proceedings of the 12th International Conference on Secondary Ion Mass Spectrometry,
Brussels, Belgium, 5-11 September 1999

303

SECONDARY ION EMISSION FROM CsI SURFACE BOMBARDED WITH keV MULTIPLY CHARGED NANOCLUSTER IONS OF GOLD

I. Baranov [a], S. Jarmiychuk [a], S. Kirillov [a], A. Novikov [a], V. Obnorskii [a], A. Pchelintsev [a], C. T. Reimann [b], K. Wien [c]

[a] V.G. Khlopin Radium Institute, 2nd Murinskii ave. 28, 194021 St.-Petersburg, Russia, novikov@atom.nw.ru
[b] Department of Material Sciences, Uppsala University, Box 534, S-75121 Uppsala Sweden
[c] Institut fuer Kernphysik, Technische Universitaet Darmstadt, Schlossgartenstr. 9, 64289 Darmstadt, Germany

1. Introduction

Interactions of massive (10^3-10^6 atoms per projectile or more) and slow (0.01-1 eV/amu) projectiles with surface have a number of peculiarities. In this case (1) secondary ion (SI) yields are frequently higher than one, (2) lines of molecular and cluster ions formed by constituents of target material are well pronounced in SI mass-spectra and (3) low or almost no fragmentation is observed [1,2,3,4]. The mechanism of this effective, but "gentle" interaction is far from clear yet. One of the instrument to study the SI emission in this peculiar stopping mode of primary ions is delivered by the fission fragment (FF) induced desorption of metal nanoclusters [4,5]. Recently it was shown that with help of this method it is possible to obtain metal cluster ions with mass of 10^5-10^8 amu and charge of 1-16 e^- [5]. This work continues the investigation of SI emission due to surface bombardment by gold nanocluster ions that was started in [4]. For the first time the dependencies of the total yield of SIs ejected from the CsI target versus the cluster impact parameters are obtained for the metal cluster projectiles in the 3×10^5- 2.5×10^7 amu and 40-450 keV mass and energy ranges. The influence of energy, kinetic and geometrical factors on the process researched is discussed.

2. Experimental technique

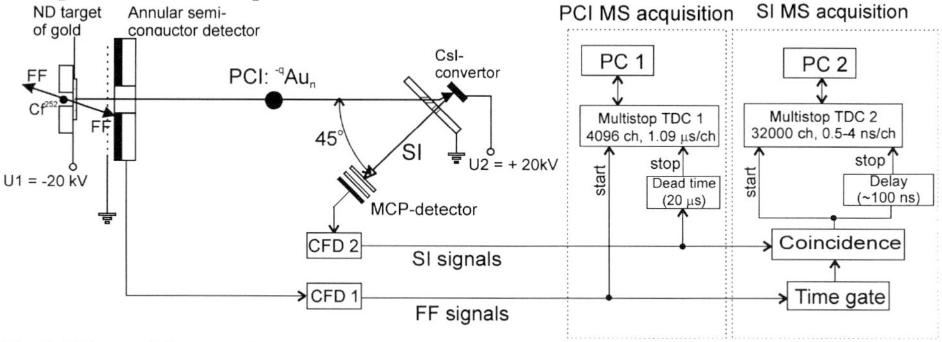

Fig. 1. Scheme of the experiment.

In this work we used the tandem time-of-flight (TOF) mass-spectrometer described in detail in [4] (see Fig.1). Primary ions – negatively charged nanocluster ions of gold (PCI) – were desorbed by FFs from a nanodispersed (ND) target of gold. The ejection of a cluster ion was synchronized with the start pulse produced by a corresponding FF. A PCI with mass m and charge q was accelerated up to $20 \times q$ keV, passed the first flight tube (96 cm), was post-accelerated up to $40 \times q$ keV and impinged on a CsI ion-to-ion converter that was positioned at 45° to the axis of the first flight tube. Positively charged SIs ejected from the converter by the cluster ion impact were accelerated by the converter potential, passed the second flight tube (31 cm) and were detected by the stop detector. On an average, the time of flight for the PCI was 2 to 3 orders of magnitude higher then for the SI. The PCI TOF spectra were recorded with a multistop time-to-digital converter (TDC) (4096 channels, 1.09 μs/ch), signals from FFs being treated as start-signals, those from SIs – as stop ones. The SI TOF spectra were recorded with another multistop TDC (32000 channels, 0.5-4 ns/ch) in the self-coincidence mode, i.e. the signals from SIs were used both as start and stop ones.

Determination of the total SI yield from the self-coincidence spectra [4]. A self-coincidence SI spectrum (see Fig. 3) consists of a strong line at the beginning of the time scale (S_{start} – the number of counts in the self-coincidence line) and a broad distribution of SIs that arrived after the starting one and were ejected from the converter by the same PCI (S_{stop} – the sum of counts in the stop events distribution). Assuming that the SI multiplicity follows a Poisson distribution, the total secondary ion yield Y_{SI} can be determined from the equation

$$S_{stop}/S_{start}+1=Y_{SI}/(1-exp[-Y_{SI}]). \qquad (1)$$

Table A. Mean PCI parameters

Target $\Rightarrow$	#1	#2	#3	#4
$<m>\pm St.D.$, amu	$(5.0\pm4.6)\times10^5$	$(1.1\pm0.6)\times10^6$	$(6.4\pm4.5)\times10^6$	$(1.9\pm1.2)\times10^7$
$<m/q>\pm St.D.$, amu/e⁻	$(3.0\pm1.7)\times10^5$	$(6.0\pm3.9)\times10^5$	$(1.2\pm0.7)\times10^6$	$(2.4\pm1.1)\times10^6$
$<q>$, e⁻	1.8	2.1	5.4	8.5

Masses and charges of PCIs. In order to obtain the dependencies of SI yield versus the cluster impact parameters that are mainly define by m and q of PCIs, the latter were varied in two ways. (1) 4 nanodispersed gold targets were used with different grain size distributions in the range of 3 – 17 nm. This provided 4 statistical ensembles of PCI with significantly different m and m/q distributions and different mean q (see Table A). These characteristics were measured in the previous work [5], for this work the parameters of mass distributions were defined more precisely. (2) The SI spectra were recorded in coincidence with 2 to 3 non-overlapping time (m/q) windows that were set on the TOF spectra of the PCIs ejected from each target. Mean values and deviations of m and q for cluster ions corresponding to the selected m/q sub-ranges were determined via Monte-Carlo simulation. The cluster mass distributions were used as initial data [5]. We used the dependence of mean charge $<q>$ of a gold nanocluster ion versus its size D obtained in [5]

$$<q>=1+a\times D^2 \ (a\approx0.039 \ e^{-}/nm^2, \ D\sim m^{1/3}). \qquad (2)$$

It was assumed that for a certain value of m possible values of q are Poisson-distributed. m and q pairs giving m/q ratio falling into selected sub-range were tracked, their mean values and standard deviations were found. Dependencies $<m>=f(<m/q>)$ and $<q>=f(<m/q>)$ that characterise the particles in the selected ranges are shown on Fig. 2 a, b.

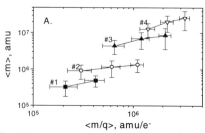 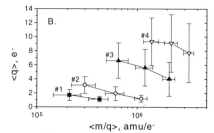

Fig. 2 Mean m, q and m/q of PCIs depending on the ND target (## 1-4) and the time window set on the corresponding PCI TOF spectrum, the standard deviations used as error bars.

Ion-to-ion converter. Mass spectrum and yield of SIs produced by bombardment of insulator layers with polyatomic ions depend heavily on the target preparation method, degree of volume and surface contamination etc. (see e.g. [6]). In this work for obtaining comparable results in the all measurements the same ion-to-ion converter was used, ~500 nm CsI layer being vapordeposited *in vacuo* on a stainless steel substrate. Vacuum in the converter chamber was ~5×10⁻⁷ mbar during the whole measurement cycle.

3. Results

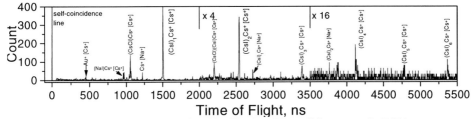

Fig. 3. Self-coincidence TOF spectrum of positive SIs ejected from CsI converter by PCI impacts.

SI mass spectra. A typical TOF spectrum of positively charged SIs ejected from CsI converter by PCI impacts is shown on Fig. 3. The most intense lines correspond to $(CsI)_nCs^+$, n = 0–6 ions and ions of the same composition with one Cs or I atom substituted by Na or Cl respectively, the Cs^+ ion gives maximum yield and is the basic starting ion. A weaker series of the same mass lines can be identified as corresponding to Na^+ starting ion. Presence of Na and Cl is obviously due to the admixture of these elements to the converter material. Ions containing atoms of gold are not observed except for a very weak and hardly identifiable Au^+ peak. Non-zero background is most probably due to the same ions as in peaks when starting ions were those from organic surface contamination [7].

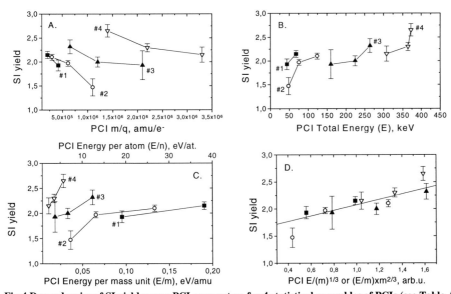

Fig.4 Dependencies of SI yield versus PCI parameters for 4 statistical ensembles of PCIs (see Table A).

Total SI yield. Dependencies of total SI yield versus PCI m/q (Fig. 4a) were measured for 4 statistic ensembles of PCIs (see Table A). Total SI yield in the whole range of varied PCI parameters is 1.4–2.8 ions/impact. Using dependencies $<m>=f(<m/q>)$ and $<q>=f(<m/q>)$ (see Fig. 2 a, b) and value of the total accelerating voltage being 40 kV, dependencies of SI yield versus energy (E) and energy per mass unit (E/m) of PCIs were built (Fig. 4 b, c respectively). It can be seen from Fig. 4 b, c that SI yield increases with growth of E and E/m. However in both cases dependencies for different projectile ensembles are split and transition from E to E/m changes the order they follow. The dependence of SI yield versus $E/m^{1/3} = (E/m) \times m^{2/3}$ parameter seems to be of general character (Fig. 4d).

4. Discussion

Today there are few models and molecular dynamics simulations that describe the interaction of slow (0.01-1 eV/amu) macromolecular and cluster ions containing 10^3-10^6 atoms with surface, e.g. [2,3,8]. Basing on these works the mechanism of secondary ion emission under consideration may be presented as follows. The simultaneous impact of a large number of atoms creates an area of high pressure and temperature (several thousands K) with lifetime in picosecond range. The temperature in the impact area depends on the projectile energy per atom E/n and the lifetime of the high-temperature state is the longer the bigger the cluster size [8]. Fast superheating of target material in the impact area induces non-equilibrium phase transition and transfer of target matter to vacuum in form of atoms and clusters. If the projectile energy per atom is high enough constituents of the projectile can also be sputtered. Charge state of the particles ejected is determined by the distribution of ionic sites on the target surface and maybe on the surface of the projectile before the impact.

The results of this work qualitatively agree with this scenario on the following points. (1) It is observed the high yield of SIs consisting mainly of the constituents of the target material (1.4-2.8 ions/impact). The charge state of ejected particles is obviously formed by a sudden break of heteropolar ionic bounds. (2) Positive gold containing SIs are not practically observed probably due to the affinity of gold to form either neutral or negatively charged secondary particles. (3) Cluster component in the SI mass spectra is well pronounced. (4) Total SI yield in the first approximation is proportional to the $(E/m) \times m^{2/3}$ parameter, the first multiple of which $E/m \sim E/n$ defines the temperature at the region of impact and the second one $m^{2/3} \sim D^2$ defines its size and the lifetime of the high temperature state.

Acknowledgement

The work was supported by the International Science and Technology Center (Project #902).

References

[1] R. Zubarev, I. Bitensky, P. Demirev, B.U.R. Sundqvist, Nucl. Instr. and Meth. B88 (1994) 143.
[2] J. Mahoney, J. Perel, T. Lee, P. Martino, P. Williams, J. Am. Soc. Mass Spectrom. 3 (1992) 311.
[3] W. Knabe, F.R. Krueger, Z. Naturforsch. 37a (1982) 1335.
[4] Van-Tan Nguyen, K. Wien, I. Baranov, A. Novikov, V. Obnorskii, Rapid Commun. Mass-Spectrom. 10 (1996) 1463.
[5] I. Baranov, S. Jarmiychuk, S. Kirillov, A. Novikov, V. Obnorskii, A. Pchelintsev, C.T. Reimann, K. Wien, to be published in Nucl. Instr. and Meth. B (1999).
[6] Peter Stuetzer, Diplomarbeit, TU Darmstadt 1998.
[7] J. Martens, W. Ens, K.G. Standing, A. Verentchikov, Rapid Commun. Mass-Spectrom. 6 (1992) 1463.
[8] G. Betz, W. Husinsky, Nucl. Instr. and Meth. B122 (1997) 311.

SECTION 7 :

POST-IONIZATION, SPUTTERED NEUTRAL MASS SPECTROMETRY

A. Benninghoven, P. Bertrand, H.-N. Migeon and H.W. Werner (Editors).
Proceedings of the 12th International Conference on Secondary Ion Mass Spectrometry,
Brussels, Belgium, 5-11 September 1999

309

ION ENERGY SPECTROSCOPY IN HF-PLASMA SNMS:
GLASS AND CERAMIC MATERIALS

H. Jenett[1], X. Ai[1,2], D. I. Mircea[1,3]

[1] Institut für Spektrochemie und Angewandte Spektroskopie (ISAS), Bunsen-Kirchhoff-Str. 11, Postfach
101352, D-44013 Dortmund, Germany
[2] Beijing University for Science and Technology, China / IFOS, D-67653 Kaiserslautern, Germany
[3] Universitatea „Al.I.Cuza", Facultatea de fizica, Bld. Copou 11, RO-6600 Iasi, Romania

1. Introduction and Overview

Implementing also previous results, this paper briefly describes ion energy spectra (IES) [1] obtained from technologically important, mostly binary B, C, N, O, and Si compounds with HF-plasma SNMS [2,3] and some conclusions with respect to the sputtering behavior of these materials. The background (not the subject) of this paper is that IES may affect SNMS quantification via the energy window used for everyday analyses (see Fig.1 serving as an introductory example and defining some acronyms). This paper will show that in many cases, the IES of postionized secondary neutrals (SN^+) are flatter than expected for Thompson type collision cascades; partly tentative explanations will be given. Among others, B com-pounds are found to be sensitive to O contamination leading to high-energy B^+ contri-

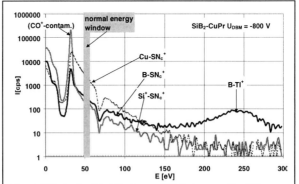

Fig. 1: IES obtained in HF-plasma SNMS from an Cu+SiB$_2$ powder pellet in the direct dc bombardment mode (DBM [2-4]). Near $e_0U_{pl,m} \approx 35$ eV ($U_{pl,m}$: mean plasma - *i.e.* ion generation - potential), background effects (not subtracted) dominate. Between 40 and 100 eV, ionized secondary neutrals from collision cascades (SN_c^+) appear ("dent" near 70 eV: artifact). The broad "B-Tl$^+$" peak near 240 eV comes from BO$_2^-$ negative secondary ions (SI$^-$) having been formed with O contamination, accelerated by the potential difference between the sample surface (on U_{DBM} = - 800V) and the plasma sheath edge, and fractured by electron impact: (800+35) eV-BO$_2^- \rightarrow$ (214+35)eV-B$^+$ + 2(311-35)eV O$^-$ [4]). Lower bombardment voltages |U_{DBM}| shift the low-energy tail of this broad positive tertiary ion (Tl$^+$) peak into the "normal energy window" usually used for quantitative SNMS analyses thereby increasing the as-believed "pure" B-SN$_c^+$ signal.

butions - see Fig.1. In addition to the results in [5,6], it will be shown that also glasses emit high-energy positive secondary ions (SI$^+$) contributing to the positive ion signal which is accepted by the normal energy window (Fig.1) in the square-wave high-frequency sputtering mode (HFM) (see lower part of Fig.5, and [6] with references therein).

2. Experimental

Table 1 contains the list of the investigated compounds. The preparation of the Cu powder pellets (1.9 g Cu + 0.1 g ceramic powder, O content of non-oxides: 0.1-1 wt-%) has been described in [7]. The origins of the massive samples and of the typically several μm thick layers were as follows: massive SiC and massive nitrides, Showa Denko, Tokyo; nitride layers from arc-PVD, University of Dortmund, Germany [8]; TiO$_2$, Goodfellow, UK; Na$_2$O-B$_2$O$_3$-SiO$_2$

glass (molar ratio 1:2:1), Technical University of Clausthal, Germany; sintered (Ti-Al-Si)O$_x$ powder pellets, University of Leipzig, Germany [5,9]. In addition to Tab.1, also an NBS1412 standard sample was investigated.

Tab.1: Overview over metal (M) - non-metal (A) compounds, sample types, properties, and results

com-pound type	M_mA_a	sample[1]			E_b[2] (MA)	IP[3] [eV]	I_{MA}/I_M [%][4]	IES features [5]			addnl.
		m	l	p				M	A	MA	
borides	MgB$_2$			+	n.l.	n.l.	1	c*, Tl$^+$	c*	n.d.	B$_2^+$
	AlB$_2$			+	n.l.	n.l.	0.1	c*, Tl$^+$	c*	n.d.	
	SiB$_2$			+	3.0	n.l.	0.5	c*, Tl$^+$	c*	n.d.	
carbides	SiC	+		+	4.7	n.l.	n.d.	c*(Tl$^+$)	c*(Tl$^+$)	n.d.	
nitrides	BN	+		+	4.0	11.2	<0.1	c*, Tl$^+$	c*	n.d.	
	AlN	+		+	3.1	n.l.	0.1	c*, Sl$^+$	c*	n.d.	
	Si$_3$N$_4$	+		+	4.9	n.l.	1	c*	c*	c*	
	TiN		+	+	4.9	n.l.	1	c*	c*	c	
	CrN	+*		+	3.9	n.l.	5	c*	c*	c	
	ZrN		+	+	5.8	n.l.	2	c*	c*	c*	
oxides	H$_3$BO$_3$			+	8.3	12.8	20	c*	c*	th	
	MgO			+	3.7	7.9	<0.1	c*	c*	n.d.	
	Al$_2$O$_3$	+		+	5.3	9.8	0.7	c*	(c)	c	
	SiO$_2$	+		+	8.3	11.4	3	c*	(c)	c	
	TiO$_2$	+		+	6.9	6.8	10	c*	c*	c	
	Cr$_2$O$_3$		+		4.4	n.l.	1	c*	c*	c	
	Y$_2$O$_3$			+	7.4	6.4	60	c*	c*	c	
	ZrO$_2$		+	+	8.0	6.0	20	c*	c*	c	
mixed oxides (glasses, ceramic)	Na$_2$O-B$_2$O$_3$-glass	+			2.6 8.3	n.l. s.a.	1 20	Na: th, Sl$^+$ B: c, Tl$^+$	(c)	n.d. th	
	(Ti-Al-Si)O$_x$	+			s.a.	s.a.	s.a.	(th), c, Sl$^+$	s.a.	s.a.	
silicides	TiSi$_2$			+	n.l.	n.l.	1	c	c*	c	Si$_2^+$
	CrSi$_2$			+	n.l.	n.l.	2	c	c*	c	
	CoSi$_2$			+	2.8	n.l.	4	c	c*	c	
	ZrSi$_2$			+	n.l.	n.l.	2	c*	c*	c	

[1] m: massive, l: layer; p: Cu powder pellet, * Cr$_3$N layer. - [2] Bond strengths from [10], n.l.: not listed, s.a.: see above. [3] Ionization potentials, see [11-13] and ref. therein. - [4] MA molecule over M atom int., data preferentially from m- or l-sample; n.d.: not detectable (interferences). - [5] c*: energy distributions flatter than for Cu$^+$; n.d.: not detectable (interferences, low int.); (c): c* case not excluded (low int.).

IES were acquired with the HF-plasma SNMS instrument INA-3 as described in [1,3,4,6]. Conductive samples were sputtered in DBM using Ar$^+$ primary ions from the plasma with energies of $(U_{DBM} +U_{pl,m})e_0$ (U_{DBM} = -800...-1000V). Insulators were sputtered in the HFM with a square-wave amplitude of U_{HFM} = -800V and a typical negative and positive (U_{HFM}= 0V) half-wave duration of Δt^-=3.6µs and Δt^+=0.4 µs, respectively (see also [6] and Fig.5). For comparison, background IES with U_{DBM} or U_{HFM} = 0V were acquired and subtracted. The electrode potentials of the 90° electrostatic energy filter between the Ar plasma and the quadrupole (Balzers QMG 511) were scanned with an energy window of 2 eV according to the equations given in [1]. - Looking for further mechanisms which might affect SNMS quantification, we also measured the relative molecule MA signal intensities I_{MA}/I_M obtained with the normal, static, about 8eV wide energy window (Fig.1) in ordinary mass spectra.

3. Results, discussion (Tab.1)

As displayed for the SiB$_2$+Cu-powder pellet in Fig.1, even the low O contents of 0.1-1% may cause the emission of secondary BO$_2^-$ ions from *borides* and other B containing samples. Like those from the H$_3$BO$_3$+Cu pellet discussed in [4], they are strongly forward focussed towards the detection system and partially fractured to B$^+$ by energetic electrons in the plasma. Because of the Franck-Condon principle of molecule fragmentation, TI$^+$-IES are broad; in the case of B$^+$, this may be one reason for its comparatively flat IES. We compare all IES with the one of Cu$^+$ obtained in every case either from the pellet matrix or from the Cu mask on the sample surface. In [11] we showed that plasma

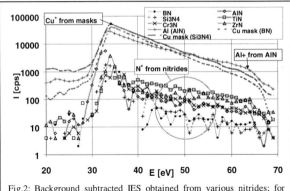

Fig.2: Background subtracted IES obtained from various nitrides; for comparison also Cu$^+$-IES arising from metallic Cu masks on insulating nitride samples, and Al$^+$-IES from massive AlN

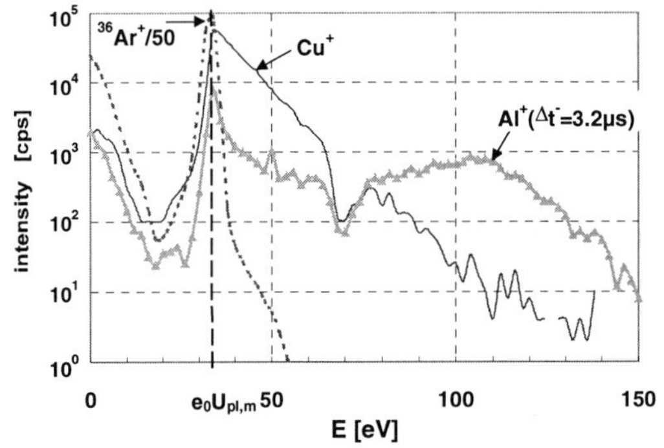

dwell time corrected Cu$^+$- and Al$^+$-IES obtained with U$_{DBM}$ = -1000eV fit well to the TRIDYN data in [14]; for Ar$^+$ primary ion energies of 2 keV on Al, Cu, and Mo, we have shown good fits to the Thompson formula in [1]. This holds also for a Cu+Al-powder pellet [11] showing that the surface morphology developing under sputtering inhomogeneous Cu pellets exerts no significant influence on the measured IES.

The right-hand part of Tab.1 indicates that most IES of metal M$^+$ and non-metal A$^+$ are found to be flatter than that of Cu$^+$. This holds not only for the borides and SiC where we

Fig.3: Background subtracted IES obtained on a sintered, 3 mm thick Al$_2$O$_3$ sample with Cu mask with a 3.2 μs negative half-wave duration Δt$^-$

detected more or less appreciable TI$^+$ contributions, but also for the massive (or thick-layer) *nitride* samples (Fig.2), even the electrically conductive ones. The latter finding implies that high-energy SI$^+$ - accelerated in HFM by high ΔU$_s$ at the start of Δt$^-$ (Fig.5) from massive ceramic *oxides* (Fig.3, see also [5,6]) including glasses (Fig.4) - cannot be the reason for that flatness. That unusual IES flatness is tentatively explained as follows: i) As shown in [15-17] for M = U (also: Zr, Mo) and A = O, low-energy M and A atoms from a collision cascade can be scavenged from the secondary neutral (SN) flux by associative ionization according to M + A → MA$^+$ + e$^-$, i.e., molecular SI$^+$ formation right above the surface. ii) Excited secondary neutrals (SN*) with U$_0$ greater than the U$_0$ of ground-state SN from the pure metal [18], i.e., an additional contribution of high-energy SN, might increase the intensity of the high-energy tail. But in contrast to the conclusions of [18] we never found such SN* to be the dominant part of an SN$^+$ spectrum. Such would have shown up in high-energy components like those given in Figs. 3 and 4 for SI$^+$, but without the peak energy shifting with Δt$^-$ in HFM [5,6]. Another feature appearing in HFM on massive insulating oxides only are "thermal", postion-

312

ized secondary neutral "SN_{th}^+" peaks of M = Al, Ti (from ceramics), K, Na, Li (from glasses). They show roughly the same shape as the Ar^+-IES in Fig. 3 and as BO^+ from the Na_2O-B_2O_3-SiO_2 glass (and from the H_3BO_3+Cu-pellet in [11]). We tentatively regard the SN_{th}^+ particles as former SI^+ having been retracted during Δt^- to the surface, discharged and electron-stimulated desorbed by the electron saturation current flowing at the start of Δt^+ ("SI^0", see Fig.5; for ESD particle energy distributions see also [19]).

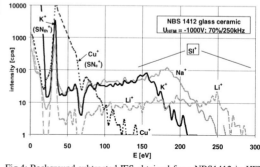

The center of Tab.1 shows that the lowest relative molecule intensities I_{MA}/I_M are especially obtained for cases where E_b < IP. This yields evidence that an appreciable part of sputtered molecules might disappear by fragmentation into neutrals - or add to the M^+ channel by ionic fragmentation. This has to be investigated in more detail in future work.

Fig.4: Background subtracted IES obtained from NBS1412 in HFM with Δt^-=2.8µs. The reproducible mass effect on the alkali SI^+ energies: $E(Li^+)>E(Na^+)>E(K^+)$ is under investigation.

References

[1] H.Jenett, V.-D.Hodoroaba, J. Vac. Sci. Technol. A 15 (1997) 3158
[2] D.Briggs, M.P.Seah (eds.), Practical Surface Analysis (2nd Ed.) Vol. 2: Ion and Neutral Spectroscopy. Wiley, Chichester (1992)
[3] H.Jenett, J.D.Sunderkötter,T.Niebuhr, M.F. Stroosnijder, in: G.Gillen et al. (eds.), SIMS XI, Wiley, Chichester 1998, pp. 619
[4] H.Jenett, V.-D.Hodoroaba, in: G. Gillen et al. (eds.), SIMS XI, Wiley, Chichester, 1998, p. 673
[5] X.Ai, H.Bubert, H.Hutter, M.Gritsch, H.Börner, J. D. Sunderkötter, H.Jenett, Fres.J.Anal.Chem., accepted
[6] H.Jenett, V.-D.Hodoroaba, H.Börner; in: G.Gillen et al. (eds.); SIMS XI, Wiley, Chichester, 1998, pp. 685
[7] H. Jenett, M. Luczak, O.Dessenne: Anal. Chim. Acta 297 (1994) 285
[8] F.W.Bach, H.D. Steffens (eds.), Verbundwerkstoffe, KONTEC, Hamburg, 1999
[9] H.Börner, H.Jenett, V.-D.Hodoroaba in: G.Gillen et al. (eds.), SIMS XI, Wiley, Chichester, 1998
[10] D.R.Lide (ed.), CRC Handbook of Chemistry & Physics 78th edn., CRC Press, Boca Raton, 1997
[11] H.Jenett, X.Ai, V.-D.Hodoroaba, Nucl. Instrum. Meth. B 155 (1999) 13
[12] S.P.Karna, F.Grein, Mol. Phys. 56 (1985) 641
[13] L.Operti, E.C.Tews, T.J.MacMahon, B.J.Freiser, J.Am. Chem. Soc. 111 (1989) 9152
[14] T.Mousel, W.Eckstein, H.Gnaser, Nucl. Instrum. Meth. B 152 (1999) 36
[15] P.Williams, R.L.Hervig, *these proceedings*
[16] A.E.Morgan, H.W.Werner, Surf. Sci. 65 (1977) 687
[17] W.L.Fite, H.H.Lo, P.Irving, J. Chem. Phys. 60 (1974) 1236
[18] W.Husinsky, G.Betz, I.Girgis, J. Vac. Sci. Technol. A 2 (1984) 698
[19] H.Overeijnder, M.Szymónski, A.Haring, A.E.deVries, Rad. Effects 36 (1978) 63

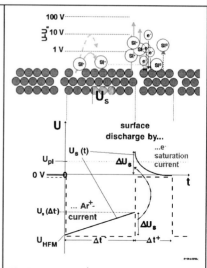

Fig.5: Scheme of SI^+ retraction and desorption in HFM; U_s: sample surface potential; dashed line: applied square-wave voltage

A. Benninghoven, P. Bertrand, H.-N. Migeon and H.W. Werner (Editors).
Proceedings of the 12th International Conference on Secondary Ion Mass Spectrometry,
Brussels, Belgium, 5-11 September 1999

ELECTRONIC PROCESSES DURING THE EMISSION
OF ION-BEAM SPUTTERED METAL ATOMS
STUDIED BY DOUBLE-RESONANT LASER IONIZATION

V. Philipsen, J. Bastiaansen, E. Vandeweert,
P. Lievens, and R.E. Silverans

Laboratorium voor Vaste-Stoffysica en Magnetisme, K.U.Leuven
Celestijnenlaan 200 D, B-3001 Leuven, Belgium
Corresponding author : erno.vandeweert@fys.kuleuven.ac.be

1. Introduction

The high sensitivity and spatial resolution with which secondary ions are collected upon impact of an energetic projectile form the basis of many applications in surface characterization, as can be deduced from the large number of contributions to the series of SIMS Conferences. However, it is also well known that the overwhelming majority of the desorbing species leave the surface as neutral atoms distributed among different electronic states. Quite a number of analytical problems could benefit from the development of efficient and simple detection strategies for these particles. In an ongoing effort to better understand the fundamental mechanisms beyond sputtering of excited particles, resonance ionization mass spectrometry (RIMS) was recently used as a universally applicable and very sensitive technique for the quantitative determination of population partitions of atoms sputtered in ground and metastable electronic states [1-5]. In this contribution we complement our measurements of the ground and metastable state population of keV Ar$^+$ sputtered Ni and Co (3,5) with those of sputtered Sr. All these elements have metastable states with different electronic configurations in a broad excitation energy range. This makes them excellent probes to study electronic processes that occur during the emission of ion-beam sputtered metal atoms. The combined results on the sputtering of Ni, Co, and Sr are interpreted based on resonant charge transfer between the sputtered particles and the metal.

2. Experimental setup and procedures

The RIMS apparatus for the sputtering studies reported here consists of an UHV chamber in which an ion gun directs 3 - 15 keV Ar$^+$ ions onto the target foils at 45° incidence in a long pulse mode (ca. 3µs) for the population partition measurements. The plume of sputtered particles is intersected, parallel to the foil, by two overlapping laser beams from a pulsed optical parametric oscillator and a pulsed dye laser system. These tunable laser systems deliver laser pulses of ~6 ns in the wavelength range from 225 to 1600 nm with pulse energies from 4 mJ in the UV up to 50 mJ in the visible range. The atoms emitted in a polar angle interval of ~10° around the surface normal and photo-ionized by the laser beams are detected in a time-of-flight mass spectrometer.

Special care was taken to reduce the degree of contamination of the sample surfaces, in particular of the Sr sample, as much as possible. Before each measurement prolonged sputter cleaning was performed until the metallic surface was recovered and the number of secondary electrons emitted from oxidized surfaces was minimized.

To quantitatively determine the population partition of atoms sputtered in the ground and metastable electronic states, an experimental procedure based on two-step two-color resonance laser ionization was used. The first step sequentially saturates the excitation of atoms in the envisaged states into a selected intermediate state. A second and independent ionization step is used to ionize the atoms. Where possible, the same intermediate state was used to deduce directly the population partition from the relative photoion signals regardless of the ionization efficiency. If this was not feasible, as in the Sr-experiment because the ground and metastable states have different parity, care was taken to saturate both the excitation and ionization steps while keeping the ionization volume constant. To enhance the sensitivity of the method, double-resonant schemes were used in which the ionizing laser was tuned to resonant transitions into autoionizing states situated just above the ionization limit. More details on the experimental setup and procedures can be found elsewhere (3).

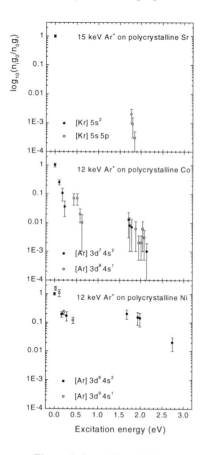

3. Results and discussion

The measured population distributions over the ground and all metastable states of Sr atoms sputtered from pure polycrystalline targets are presented in Fig. 1 (upper panel) and compared with previously measured Co and Ni distributions [3,5]. The populations are given relative to the ground state as function of the excitation energy above this state. Because very long ion pulses were used, the measured populations are an integration over all kinetic energies of the ejected atoms. The atomic states of Sr, Co, and Ni belonging to multiplets with a completely filled outer shell (respectively [Kr] $5s^2$ for Sr and [Ar] $3d^{x-1}$ $4s^2$ for Co (x = 8) and Ni (x = 9)) are presented by solid symbols, whereas open symbols are used for states with partially filled outer shell configurations (respectively [Kr] $5s$ $5p$ for Sr and [Ar] $3d^x$ $4s^1$ for Co and Ni).

From these experiments we conclude that all states with excitation energies as high as 2.7 eV are substantially populated. Another salient feature observable in the Co and Ni population partitions of the low-lying states with excitation energies up to 1 eV, is the systematic shift of the population on the states with a $3d^x$ $4s^1$ configuration (open dots) to higher values with respect to the states with a completely filled $3d^{x-1}$ $4s^2$ configuration (filled dots).

Figure 1. Population distributions of sputtered Sr, Co, and Ni atoms versus excitation energy. The populations (n_i) are divided by their statistical weight (g_i) and given relative to the ground state.

These results cannot be explained by the more popular models, including collisional excitation and non-radiative de-excitation used earlier to interpret population partitions of atoms sputtered in the ground state and metastable states. An up-to-date overview of the current hypotheses of the fundamental processes involved can be found in [6]. Recently, we pointed out that both the significant population on high-lying states and the enhanced population of the states with a $3d^x 4s^1$ configuration provide evidence for the dominant role of resonant electron tunneling during the emission process [3,5]. In the following, we present a combined interpretation of the population partition of sputtered Co, Ni and Sr atoms within a multichannel resonant electron transfer model.

In the resonant electron transfer (RET) model the interaction between a sputtered particle and a metal surface is treated as a charge transfer involving electronic states with different characteristics. The metal is thereby treated as a lattice of ions immersed in a sea of valence electrons. These electrons occupy the valence band states that form an energy continuum. As a result of the collision cascade created by the energetic projectiles, a sputtered particle escapes from the metal as a positive ion that can be neutralized when only one electron makes an energy-conserving transition from its valence band state into a discrete atomic state. The electron transfer probability in this time-dependent and initially strongly coupled system is found to depend on several parameters. These include the coupling strength between the atomic state and the band states in the metal, the extent of spatial overlap between atomic and metallic electron wave functions and the perpendicular velocity of the sputtered particle.

In most studies, like the ones presented here, the atoms have a complicated electronic structure and several more or less equivalent electron transfer channels are competing because in general more atomic states are accessible. A full theoretical treatment of this problem is hampered because the set of coupled rate equations that describe the time dependent occupation probability of each atomic state cannot be solved due to the lack of detailed knowledge about the differences in coupling strength and spatial extension of the wave functions. However, some general qualitative trends can be formulated. With respect to the population partitions, all atomic states lying below the Fermi energy at large distances between the metal and the sputtered particle will have a substantial probability to be populated, and the further below the Fermi level the higher this probability will be. Secondly, those atomic states with electronic wave functions similar to those of the valence electrons in the metal, will be preferentially populated due to the higher coupling strength.

Sr, Co and Ni have bulk work functions of 2.6, 5.0, and 5.2 eV respectively and atomic ionization potentials of 5.7, 7.9, and 7.7 eV. All states with excitation energies up to 3.1 eV for Sr, 2.9 eV for Co, and 2.5 eV for Ni are at large surface-to-atom distances energetically in resonance with occupied valence band states. The overall picture of the population distributions shown in Fig. 1, therefore agrees with the RET model. All states within the energy window defined by the metal valence band are populated.

The configuration-dependent population on Sr, Co, and Ni states far below the Fermi level can also be explained within the RET-picture taking into account the band structure of the different metals. Indeed, the probability that an electron tunnels between the metal and the departing ion is determined by the degree of coupling between the final atomic state and the metallic states. The fact that the valence band electronic structure of Co and Ni is predominantly $4s^1$ in character [1,3,4], explains the enhanced population of the states with a $3d^x 4s^1$ configuration (shown with open symbols in the lower panels of Fig. 1). The observed decrease in the population of the members within each low-lying multiplet with increasing excitation energy indicates that the competition between the different neutralization channels

316

within one multiplet is governed by the energy difference between the atomic state and the Fermi level. The band structure of pure Sr metal deep below the Fermi level is known to be highly *s*-like. The probability that a neutralizing electron ends up in the $5s^2$ ground state is thus highly favored above a transfer into one of the metastable members of the excited multiplet characterized by a $5s\,5p$ configuration. In this experiment, this translates into a relatively low occupation of the latter states.

Within the simplified RET model presented here, the populations on highly excited Co and Ni states are less prone for a straightforward interpretation. Most probably the energy difference between the atomic states and the Fermi level is too small compared to the initial broadening and upward shift of the states while the escaping particle is still close to the metallic surface. At short distances, these levels will thus lie partly above the Fermi level, and the final population will strongly depend on the specific coupling strengths of the different competing neutralization channels.

4. Conclusions

We used RIMS to determine the population partition of Sr atoms sputtered in the ground and metastable states. The results have been interpreted in combination with the partitions previously obtained for Co and Ni. Because of the different electronic configurations of both the atom and the bulk metal and the extended range of excitation energies of the metastable states, these elements proved to be excellent probes for the electronic processes that occur during ion beam sputtering. The observations are strongly indicative that resonant electron transfer is the dominant mechanism behind the emission of metal atoms in excited states.

Acknowledgments

This work is financially supported by th e Fund for Scientific Research - Flanders (F.W.O.), the Flemish Concerted Action (G.O.A.) Research Programme and the Interuniversity Poles of Attraction Programme - Belgian State, Prime Minister's Office - Federal Office for Scientific, Technical and Cultural Affairs. P.L. is a Postdoctoral Research Fellow of the F.W.O.

References

[1] C. He, Z. Postawa, S.W. Rosencrance, R. Chatterjee, B.J. Garrison, and N. Winograd, Phys. Rev. Lett. **75** (1995) 3950.

[2] G. Nicolussi, W. Husinsky, D. Gruber, and G. Betz, Phys. Rev. B **51** (1995) 8779.

[3] E. Vandeweert, V. Philipsen, W. Bouwen, P. Thoen, H. Weidele, R.E. Silverans and P. Lievens, Phys. Rev. Lett. **78** (1997) 138.

[4] W. Berthold and A. Wucher, Phys. Rev. Lett. **76** (1996) 2181.

[5] P. Lievens, V. Philipsen, E. Vandeweert, and R.E. Silverans, Nucl. Instrum. Meth. B**135** (1998) 471.

[6] B.J. Garrison, N. Winograd, R. Chatterjee, Z. Postawa, A. Wucher, E. Vandeweert, P. Lievens, V. Philipsen, and R.E. Silverans, Rapid Commun. Mass Spectrom. **12** (1998) 1246.

A. Benninghoven, P. Bertrand, H.-N. Migeon and H.W. Werner (Editors).
Proceedings of the 12th International Conference on Secondary Ion Mass Spectrometry,
Brussels, Belgium, 5-11 September 1999

317

ADVANCES IN TRACE METAL CONTAMINANT ANALYSIS BY LASER-SNMS

Lorenza Moro[1] , Paolo Lazzeri[2], Kuang Jen Wu[3]

[1]SRI International, 333 Ravenswood Av. Menlo Park, CA 94025, USA
[2]Istituto per la Ricerca Scientifica e Tecnologica, Povo-Trento, Italy
[3]Charles Evans & Associates, 301 Chesapeake Drive, Redwood City, CA 94063, USA

1. Introduction

The detection and control of metallic contaminants on silicon surfaces is essential for development of silicon circuit technologies.[1]   The current methods for detection and quantification of surface and near surface impurities include total reflection x-ray fluorescence (TXRF), time-of-flight secondary ion mass spectrometry (ToF-SIMS) and vapor phase decomposition (VPD) coupled with different types of mass spectroscopy. Each of these techniques comes with its unique analytical limitations for characterizing surface metal contaminants. These techniques all have a nominal detection sensitivity of ~5×10^9 atoms/cm^2. This research project, laser-secondary neutral mass spectrometry (laser-SNMS), focuses specifically on the development of a analytical technique for trace metal contaminants on Si. The analytical concept is illustrated in Figure 1. Surface metal impurities are desorbed/ablated with a pulsed UV laser, the desorbed neutrals are then intercepted and post-ionized by a second laser and mass analysis of these ions is performed with a time-of-flight mass spectrometer.

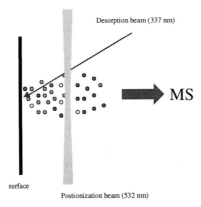

Fig. 1   Schematic diagram of Laser-SNMS setup. A high power density picosecond Nd:YAG laser is used for post-ionization of the laser ablated neutrals.

2. Experimental

Laser-SNMS studies were performed with a Physical Electronics TOF-SIMS instrument at

Charles Evans & Associates. The standard instrument is equipped with In^+ liquid metal ion gun (LMIG) for ToF-SIMS analysis. A N_2 laser (λ=337nm) at output energy of 2-10 μJ/pulse and beam size (10-40 μm) is used for desorption. Photoionization of laser desorbed neutrals is performed using the second harmonic (λ=532 nm, 2.33 eV) of a 35-ps Nd:YAG laser with output energies of 35-40 mJ/pulse. Power density as high as 10^{14} W/cm^2 can be achieved with this laser. At this high power density, saturated ionization of the desorbed neutrals can be readily achieved.[2,3] An important aspect of this instrumental configuration is that laser-SNMS and ToF-SIMS studies can be conducted on the same instrumental platform.

Reference silicon wafers for this study were prepared by spin coating metals onto silicon surfaces. The surface metal concentration of these samples ranges from 5×10^{13} to 1×10^{10} atoms/cm^2. The concentrations of the surface metals were determined independently by TXRF, and TOF-SIMS. In an effort to minimize data variation from surface inhomogeneity, the ToF-SIMS analyses were conducted on spots next to the Laser-SNMS sampling area.

3. Results and Discussion

A positive ion laser-SNMS spectrum obtained from a reference Si wafer sample is shown in Figure 2. The results were accumulated over approximately 100 laser shots and each laser shot was taken from a new spot. As a result of high power density for post-ionization, molecular species are fragmented. When operating at an optimum configuration, there are essentially no molecular ions or cluster ions present in the spectrum. Therefore, there are no organics interferences in the mass spectrum. This important characteristic not only permits easy data interpretation but also suggests that high mass resolution and mass accuracy is not required for surface metal applications since there is no need to separate the atomic ions from organic or cluster ions.

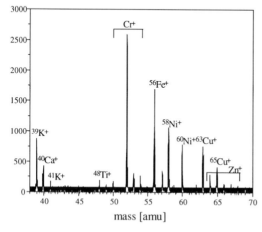

Element	TXRF [atoms/cm^2]	ToF-SIMS (Ga) [atoms/cm^2]
S	$7.3*10^{12}$	/
Cl	$1.2*10^{13}$	/
K	$3.8*10^{12}$	$2.1*10^9$
Ca	$6.3*10^{12}$	$1.3*10^9$
Cr	$4*10^{10}$	$1.3*10^{10}$
Ti	$6.5*10^{10}$	
Mn	$8.0*10^9$	
Fe	$5.1*10^{11}$	$1.2*10^{11}$
Ni	$1.4*10^{11}$	$6.5*10^{10}$
Cu	$5.0*10^{10}$	$6.8*10^{10}$
Zn	$5.0*10^{11}$	$2.5*10^{11}$

Fig. 2   Positive ion laser-SNMS spectrum obtained from a spin-coated reference wafer sample. The table summarizes the surface metal concentrations determined by TXRF and ToF-SIMS. The discrepancy between K and Ca surface concentration is attributed to the different sampling areas of TXRF and ToF-SIMS.

The spectrum shown in Figure 3 was obtained from a reference wafer containing 8×10^{10} atoms/cm² of Ni and 5×10^{11} atoms/cm² of Zn. The spectrum was accumulated over approximately 200 laser shots. The ^{62}Ni isotope has 3.6% abundance and corresponds to a surface concentration of 2.9×10^9 atoms/cm². Therefore, the results indicate that with the current instrument configuration, the detection sensitivities of laser-SNMS for transition metals are in the low-10^9 atoms/cm². The run-to-run reproducibility of the analysis on the same sample is approximately 25%. ToF-SIMS analysis on the same sample has shown comparable variations suggesting that a substantial contribution to this variation may come from real non-uniformities in the element distribution across the surface.

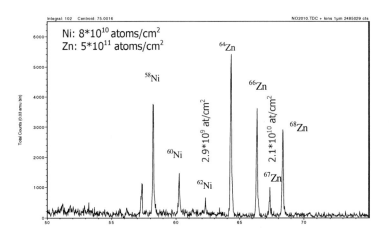

Fig. 3   Positive ion laser-SNMS spectrum obtained from a spin-coated reference wafer sample. The surface metal concentration was determined by TXRF and ToF-SIMS.

The ionization yields of Laser-SNMS is directly related to the ionization potential of the elements. The range of IP's for the elements listed in Figure 2 is between 4.34 eV for K to 9.39 eV for Zn. At 2.33 eV photon energy, these elements require 2 – 5 photons for the formation of M⁺ ions. Under a given photon power density, the ionization yield is higher for elements with lower IP such as K than for higher IP such as Zn. A theoretical calculation of the ionization yields of metals indicates that uniform ionization yields can be achieved at approximately 5×10^{14} W/cm². However, such high power density is accomplished using a tightly focused laser spot. As a consequence, the ionization volume is significantly reduced by the small laser spot. Therefore, the effective ionization yields, i.e. the total number of ions formed, are much smaller under these conditions. The effective ionization yields can be increased by defocusing the post-ionization laser, thereby increasing the ionization volume. When decrease the power density to 5×10^{12} W/cm², the calculation indicates that the difference in ionization yields between 2 and 5 photon ionization process spreads to approximately an order of magnitude. Assuming uniform neutral density within photo-ionization volume, the calculation suggests the relative sensitivity factors (RSF's) of these elements should be within a factor of 10.

320

Our experimental studies of RSF's of laser-SNMS were conducted on several reference wafers. The power densities were in the range of 5×10^{12} to 10^{14} W/cm^2 and the results are summarized in Figure 4. The RSF's of six elements plotted as a function of their photoionization process are illustrated. Notice that the RSF's for the elements investigated by laser-SNMS are within an order of magnitude. This is in good agreement with the theoretical calculation on the ionization yields for different order photoionization processes. Furthermore, a linear correlation between surface concentration and peak intensity was observed. Therefore, with a minor correction, the surface metal concentration can be extrapolated directly from the measured peak intensity. Further improvements in detection sensitivity could be accomplished by optimizing the laser desorption and post-ionization steps.

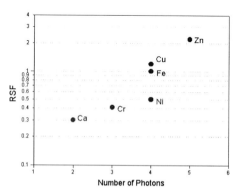

Fig. 4   RSF's derived from laser-SNMS measurements. RSF's are normalized to Fe+ signal intensity. The values of RSF increase as the number of photon required for photoionization increase.

4. Summary

We have shown a laser-SNMS approach for surface metal applications. Using a high power density, short pulse width post-ionization laser configuration, the technique enables (1) high detection sensitivity at low-10^9 atoms/ cm^2 level, (2) no organic interference thereby permits easy data interperation and (3) RSF's span only an order of magnitude between K and Zn. Work is currently in progress to develop a methodology for absolute quantification of trace metal contaminants on Si surfaces.

5. Acknowledgement

This work is supported by a grant from National Science Foundation (DMI-9705609). Collaborative Research Grant from NATO for travelling expenses of P. Lazzeri is acknowledged.

References
[1] "*The National Technology Roadmap for Semiconductors*", Semiconductor Industry Association, San Jose, California, 1997
[2] C.He, J.N. Basler, C. H. Becker, *Nature*, **385**, 797 (1997)
[3] C.H. Becker, J. S. Jovis, *J. Vac. Sci. Technol.* **A12**, 2352 (1994)

A. Benninghoven, P. Bertrand, H.-N. Migeon and H.W. Werner (Editors).
Proceedings of the 12th International Conference on Secondary Ion Mass Spectrometry,
Brussels, Belgium, 5-11 September 1999
© 2000 Elsevier Science B.V. All rights reserved.

RESONANT POSTIONIZATION OF NEUTRAL SPECIES DESORBED BY keV Ar+ BOMBARDMENT OF C6H6/Ag(111)

C. A. Meserole[1], E. Vandeweert[2], R. Chatterjee[1], A. Sostarecz[1], B.J. Garrison[1], N. Winograd[1], and Z. Postawa[3]

Corresponding author: cam30@psu.edu

[1]Department of Chemistry, The Pennsylvanian State University, University Park, PA 16802

[2]Laboratorium voor Vaste-Stoffysica en Magnetisme, Celestijnenlaan 200 D,B-3001 Leuven, Belgium

[3]Institute of Physics, Jagellonian University, ul. Reymonta 4, PL 30-059 Krakow 16 Poland

1. Introduction

It is not well understood how intact molecules can be desorbed from a surface subsequent to a violent collision between a surface and massive particles having orders of magnitude more kinetic energy than the energy needed to hold an organic molecule together. In order to gain insight into such phenomena, a simple system consisting of benzene, C_6H_6, physisorbed onto cold Ag (111) is studied. Time-of-flight (TOF) and energy and angle resolved neutral (EARN) distributions are employed in this work.

This system is an ideal model system for such studies for a variety of reasons. Silver is unreactive toward benzene [1]; therefore, the system is reversible and reproducible for a variety of C_6H_6 coverages. Furthermore, the possibility of chemical reactions between the adsorbate (C_6H_6) and the substrate (Ag) that could alter the binary nature of the system can be largely neglected. Another important attribute of this system is that both the (molecular) adsorbate and (atomic) substrate can be resonantly ionized. C_6H_6 can be resonantly ionized by one-color two-step processes [2, 3]. Ag substrate atoms in the atomic ground state can be resonantly ionized with a two-color two-step process, while highly excited metastable Ag atoms, having 3.75 eV excitation energy, can be resonantly ionized with a one-color one-step process [4].

2. Experimental Setup

Details of the instrument used for these studies are provided elsewhere [5]. Prior to dosing the C_6H_6 is purified by several freeze-pump-thaw cycles in order to remove dissolved gaseous impurities, and the Ag(111) is sputter cleaned, annealed, and then cooled to 120 K. The C_6H_6 exposure is controlled by monitoring the chamber pressure as a function of time.

Desorption events are initiated by a 200 ns Ar+ pulse accelerated to 8 keV and focused to a 3 mm spot. The Ar+ dose is restricted to 10^{11} Ar+/cm^2 to minimize surface damage. The angle of incidence is 45° for (TOF) experiments and 0° for EARN experiments. Desorbed particles are detected by multiphoton postionization and time of flight mass spectrometry. A gated, position-sensitive microchannel plate detector is utilized to detect the postionized species and to discern angular information.

The output from a frequency doubled Nd:YAG pumped tunable dye laser is used for resonant photoionization of the species of interest. The dye laser output is focused to a ribbon about 1 cm in front of the sample. For ionizing C_6H_6 ejected in the zero level of the molecular ground state 259.01 nm radiation is used, while 266.82 nm radiation will ionize vibrationally excited C_6H_6 having one quantum in the v_6'' vibrational mode [2, 3]. The output of two dye lasers, 328.2 nm and 272.4 nm, is used for probing Ag in the atomic ground state [4]. However, only a single photon of 272.2 nm radiation is needed to postionize Ag emitted in a highly excited metastable state, Ag* [4].

3. Results and Discussion

The desorption of the C_6H_6 is coverage dependant [1, 3]. In the low coverage regimes the C_6H_6 desorption process is largely ballistic in nature. However, in the very high coverage regime the mechanism appears to be thermal-like. The yields and the angle and energy distributions of the substrate atoms for a variety of C_6H_6 exposures not only suggest the role that the substrate plays in the C_6H_6 desorption, but also provide information concerning the effects of organic overlayers on the emission of substrate species.

The effect on the emission of Ag atoms by the addition of C_6H_6 to the surface of the Ag crystal is found to be dramatic. The yield, which is determined by integrating the angle-integrated energy distributions, of the substrate atoms as a function of C_6H_6 exposure decreases rapidly when about 7 L, or 1 ML, of C_6H_6 is on the surface. The addition of C_6H_6 to the surface differently affects the emission of the ground state and metastable state atoms. For instance, the addition of 7 L of C_6H_6 will cut the ground state yield in half, while the metastable yield is reduced to 20% of the yield from a clean substrate. At multilayer coverages the yields slowly decrease to 11% and 7% at 100 L for the ground state and metastable state, respectively, when compared to the clean substrate. Since the metastable atoms are larger than the ground state atoms, they will have a higher probability of colliding with the organic overlayer. Through these collisions, they can undergo collisional deexcitation, and

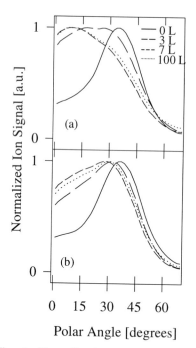

Fig. 1. Normalized energy-integrated polar angle distributions of the silver monomer subsequent to 8 keV Ar⁺ bombardment for a variety of benzene exposures. (a) Distributions of metastable atoms. (b) Distributions of ground state atoms.

therefore it is expected that the metastable yields would be more sensitive to the presence of the overlayer.

The energy-integrated angular distributions of Ag and Ag* exhibit a coverage dependence. As the coverage of C_6H_6 is increased, the prominent peak at 35° off-normal becomes shifted to the normal direction and is substantially broadened (Fig. 1). However, the shift is much more noticeable in the metastable case (Fig. 1a) than for the ground state (Fig. 1b). Because the Ag* atoms can undergo collisional deexcitation, they may be detected as ground state Ag atoms, and not Ag*. If this happens, then the off-normal peak in the Ag distribution will be bolstered by the deexcited Ag* atoms, while the off normal peak in Ag* distribution will diminish. The increased number of particles emitted in the normal direction may be caused by the randomized scattering as a result of the molecular adsorbate on the surface or possibly by an ion milling process whereby the incident primary ions create channels in the organic overlayer that are oriented largely perpendicular to the surface. It is through these channels that the substrate atoms preferentially travel away from the target.

The angle-integrated kinetic energy distributions of the Ag and Ag* are also affected by the presence of the organic overlayers. Upon the addition of C_6H_6 to the surface, the energy distributions tend to become more narrow (Fig. 2). A possible explanation for the observed trend is that the more translationally energetic silver atoms are more likely to impart some of their kinetic energy to the C_6H_6 molecules, leading to the desorption of the C_6H_6, than the slower silver atoms. As a result, the detected Ag atoms will have reduced kinetic energy, and therefore will enhance the low energy portion of the energy distribution and make the energy distributions decay more rapidly.

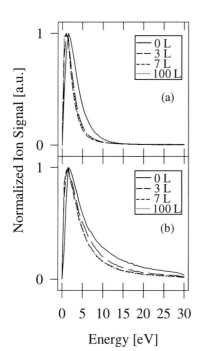

Fig. 2. Normalized angle-integrated kinetic energy distributions of the silver monomer subsequent to 8 keV Ar^+ bombardment for a variety of benzene exposures. (a) Distributions of meta-stable atoms. (b) Distributions of ground state atoms.

Because the yield of the silver atoms is greatly diminished by 100 L of C_6H_6 exposure, it stands to reason that direct collisions between the silver atoms and C_6H_6 molecules, which play a major role in the C_6H_6 desorption at monolayer coverage, near the C_6H_6/vacuum interface are unimportant for multilayer samples. However, it appears that all of the major changes affecting the distributions of the substrate atoms occur in the submonolayer to monolayer regime, and the addtion of multilayers of C_6H_6 to the surface produces only subtle changes in the distributions of the substrate atoms.

4. Conclusion

State selective TOF and EARN distributions of the adsorbate and substrate species allow for a detailed look at the processes leading to the desorption of atoms and of intact molecules subsequent to energetic particle bombardment of surfaces. The processes leading to the desorption of intact C_6H_6 molecules are coverage dependant.

The addition of the organic overlayers on the Ag (111) dramatically affects the angle and energy distributions of the emitted silver atoms. In both cases of the ground state and metastable state atoms, the energy distributions tend to become more narrow after the surface has been exposed to C_6H_6. However, the changes are more pronounced in the Ag* distributions than the Ag distributions. The angular distributions are also affected by the presence of the organic overlayers; however, the Ag* atoms appear to be more affected than the Ag atoms. In both cases, the off-normal ejection peak associated with clean Ag (111) tends to shift toward the normal direction and also tends to broaden. The yields of both the Ag and Ag* atoms initially tend to decay rapidly as a function of C_6H_6 exposure, but initially the yields of the Ag* atoms decay more rapidly than the Ag yields. However, beyond roughly 1 ML, the yields of both types of atoms tend to decay less rapidly. The trends observed in the angle and energy distributions and the yields of the Ag and Ag* are generally similar. However, the trends of Ag* seem to be more exaggerated than is observed for Ag, presumably because the larger Ag* atoms can more readily collide with the overlayer molecules and deexcite.

Acknowledgements

The financial support of the National Science Foundation, the National Institutes of Health, the Office of Naval Research, and the Polish Committee for Scientific Research Fund and Maria Sklodowska-Curie Fund MEN/NSF-96-304 are gratefully acknowledged.

References

[1] R. Chatterjee, D.E. Riederer, Z. Postawa, and N. Winograd, J. Phys. Chem. B **102**, 4176 (1998)
[2] J.H. Calloman, T.M. Dunn, and I.M. Mills, Phil. Trans. Roy. Soc. London **259A**, 499 (1966).
[3] C.A. Meserole, E. Vandeweert, R. Chatterjee, B.R. Chakraborty, B.J. Garrison, N. Winograd, and Z. Postawa, AIP Conf. Proc. **454**, 210 (1998).
[4] W. Berthold and A. Wucher, Phys. Rev. B **56**, 4251 (1997).
[5] P.H. Kobrin, G.A. Schick, J.P. Baxter, N. Winograd, Rev. Sci. Inst. **57**, 1354 (1986).

A. Benninghoven, P. Bertrand, H.-N. Migeon and H.W. Werner (Editors).
Proceedings of the 12th International Conference on Secondary Ion Mass Spectrometry,
Brussels, Belgium, 5-11 September 1999
© 2000 Elsevier Science B.V. All rights reserved.

325

QUANTITATIVE NON-RESONANT POSTIONIZATION EXPERIMENTS WITH FEMTOSECOND LASER PULSES

Teiichiro Kono[a], Vasil Vorsa[b], Shixin Sun[b] and Nicholas Winograd[b]

[a,b]184 Materials Research Institute Building, University Park 16802 USA

[a]2-1 Samejima, Fuji, Shizuoka, 416 Japan

a8911363@ut.asahi-kasei.co.jp

1. Introduction

Nonresonant postionization of sputtered neutral atoms offers the possibility of detecting most elements in the periodic table with similar sensitivity and with reduced matrix effects. However, to obtain quantitative data, the photoionization step must be saturated. Ti:Sapphire-based lasers produce a very high power density of pulses and are considered to be the most likely candidate for that purpose. Even with the power of these systems the laser still needs to be focused to attain saturation. In this case it is difficult to ionize all of the particles in the sputtered plume.

The calculated ionization probabilities for different elements along the radius of a gaussian laser beam are shown in Figure 1. In this scenario, the elements display an intensity disparity due to the variation of the ionization volume. It is apparent that some coefficient such as the relative sensitivity factor needs to be introduced. One way to correct for this difference is to obtain the ratio of the signal intensity to the sample concentration for each element. However the concentration of each species in the postionization volume does not necessarily reflect the concentration in the sample. Another way is to measure the ionization cross section. Once you obtain the ionization cross section (σ), it is possible to calculate the concentration from the signal intensity and the laser beam profile.

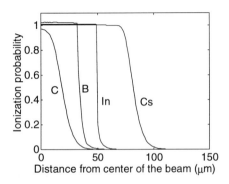

Fig. 1. Ionization probabilities along the radius of a gaussian beam for different elements. See Eq. 1-4.

2. Experimental

Time of Flight SIMS equipped with a Ga^+ ion source in conjunction with the Ti:Sapphire laser system [1] was used for all the postionization experiments. The Ti:Sapphire laser system produces pulse energies of 3.3 mJ, 1.2 mJ, 400 uJ and 45 uJ with pulse widths of 100 fs, 150 fs, 200 fs and 300 fs for 800 nm, 400 nm, 267 nm and 200 nm wavelengths, respectively. The focused laser beam profile was measured by a microscopic objective and a CCD camera. The beam power was attenuated through reflections by optical wedges and a combination of a waveplate and a polarizer.

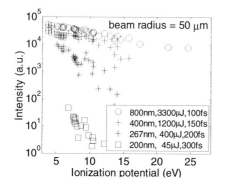

Fig. 2. Calculation results of ion intensities for representative elements plotted against ionization potential. O:800 nm, + :400 nm, *:267 nm, □:200 nm. Gaussian beam was used for calculation. See Eq. 1 and 2.

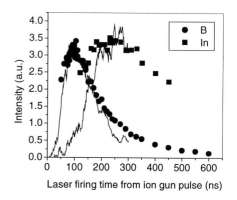

Fig. 3. Intensity vs time difference between laser pulse and ion pulse. ●, ■:Experiment, —:simulation. The primary ion pulse width was fixed at 40 ns.

Since our system produces four different wavelengths, the choice of wavelength for quantitative analysis purposes is of interest. It could be estimated by calculating σ obtained from theoretical calculations [2]. Results from these calculations are shown in Figure 2. The most favorable wavelength for quantitative analysis is 800 nm due to the relatively weak dependence on ionization potential.

Because of the variation in the energy distribution of sputtered neutrals for different elements, the time sequence of laser pulse, ion pulse and extraction voltage as well as the length of the primary ion pulse play important roles in quantitative analysis. The change in the intensities for B and In when changing the laser pulse timing with respect to

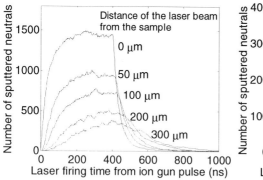

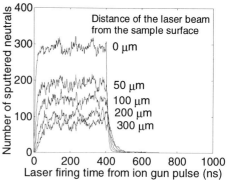

Fig. 4. The calculated number of sputtered neutrals inside the photoionization volume (60 .m in radius) for 400 ns ion pulse width plotted against laser firing time from ion gun pulse. Right:Boron, left:Indium.

the ion pulse timing is shown in Figure 3. These elements show different maxima which would lead to errors in quantitation. To avoid this situation, we increase the pulse width up to 400 ns and fire the laser pulse before the end of the ion gun pulse. As shown in Figure 4 the distance of the laser beam from the surface also affects quantitation. The smaller the distance, the better the quantitation. However, even when firing the laser beam at the maximum point for both elements, there still exist large differences in the number of neutrals in the postionization volume, especially when the laser beam size is small as shown in Figure 4. Nevertheless, since the energy distribution is not strongly dependent on the matrix, once the ratio of the neutrals inside the postionization volume to all the neutrals is measured for a standard sample, the concentration in the postionization volume can be converted to the one in the sample by multiplying these factors.

3. Measurement of ionization cross section

The calculation model to obtain the ionization cross section used here is based on the following formulas[2-5].

$$N_i = N_0 \iiint \max\left(P_{MPI}(x,y,z), P_{TI}(x,y,z), P_{BSI}(x,y,z)\right) dx\, dy\, dz \quad (1)$$

$$P_{MPI}(x,y,z) = 1 - \exp\left(-\sigma_k \int F^k(x,y,z,t)\, dt\right) \quad (2)$$

$$P_{TI}(x,y,z) = \left(\frac{3e}{\pi}\right)^{\frac{3}{2}} \frac{Z^2}{3n^3} \frac{(2l+1)}{2n-1} \int \left(\frac{4eZ^3}{(2n-1)n^3 F(x,y,z,t)}\right)^{2n-\frac{3}{2}} \exp\left(-\frac{2Z^3}{3n^3 F(x,y,z,t)}\right) dt \quad (3)$$

$$P_{BSI}(x,y,z) = \begin{cases} 1 & \max(F(x,y,z,t)) \geq F_{BSI} \\ 0 & \max(F(x,y,z,t)) < F_{BSI} \end{cases} \qquad F_{BSI} = \frac{\varepsilon_0^2 h^2 c}{e^3 m_e a_o} \frac{E^2}{Z} \quad (4)$$

where N_i is the number of ions created by the laser pulse, N_0 is the initial number of neutrals per unit volume, and P_{MPI}, P_{TI}, P_{BSI} are ionization probabilities for multiphoton ionization, tunnel ionization and barrier suppression ionization respectively. F is the field strength of light which is a function of time and position, k is the number of photons necessary for ionization and σ_k is the k photon order ionization cross section. Z is the multiplicity of ion, and l and n are principal and orbital quantum numbers.

To verify the model, power dependence measurements were carried out for several elements. The results for Xe are shown in Figure 5. We report pulse energy instead of power density because of difficulty in defining the power density for a non-gaussian beam. The result yields $\sigma_3 = 10^{-79.5}$ /cm^{6}s^2. Using this approach, the fit value of σ is found to be independent of beam profile.

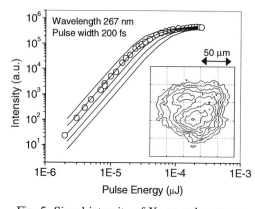

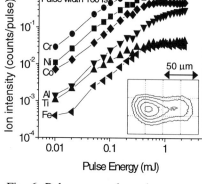

Fig. 5. Signal intensity of Xe vs pulse energy. o:experiment, line:calculation with -log(σ_3)= 79.2, 79.5, 79.8, 80.1, 80.4 from top. The inset shows the measured beam profile used in this measurement and calculation.

Fig. 6. Pulse energy dependence curves for elements in the stainless steel. The inset shows the measured beam profile used in this measurement and calculation.

Using this method we examined a stainless steel reference sample obtained from NIST. The sample was ion-etched in the spectrometer to remove surface impurities. The power dependence curve is shown in Figure 6. Up to 1 mJ all elements show the same slope of 1.3 which means the ionization for all elements is saturated. The leveling off observed in the high pulse energy region is due to the onset of multiply charged ions and the saturation in detection system. The intensity ratio of Ni, Cr, Ti, Al, Co and Fe at 0.1 mJ were 25.0, 58.2, 1.6, 3.1, 11.6, 0.7 respectively whereas the composition ratio provided by NIST is 52.2, 23.6, 3.6, 3.5, 16.1, 0.97. If the concentrations of each elements are calculated from these intensities using the approach outlined for Xe and the ratio of the number of sputtered neutrals inside the postionization region is known, the results should coincide with the sample composition. The results presented here provide an initial framework for acquiring quantitative elemental information. The next step in our experiments is to acquire a library of cross sections and the relative number of neutral particles in the laser beam.

The authors acknowledge the office of Naval Research and the National Science Foundation for financial support.

References

[1] K. F. Willey, C. L. Brummel, N. Winograd, Chem. Phys. Lett. **267** (1997) 359
[2] P. Lambropoulos and X. Tang, J. Opt. Soc. Am. B **4** (1987) 821
[3] F A Ilkov, J E Decker and S L Chin, J. Phys. B At. Mol. Opt. Phys. **25** (1992) 4005
[4] V. P. Krainov and B. Shokri, JETP **80** (1995) 657
[5] M. V. Ammosov, N. B. Delone and V. P. Krainov, Sov. Phys. JETP **64** (1986) 1191

A. Benninghoven, P. Bertrand, H.-N. Migeon and H.W. Werner (Editors).
Proceedings of the 12th International Conference on Secondary Ion Mass Spectrometry,
Brussels, Belgium, 5-11 September 1999

TOF-SIMS AND LASER-SNMS ANALYSIS OF SUB-μm PARTICLES

F. Kollmer[1], R. Kamischke[1], R. Ostendorf[1], A. Schnieders[1], C.Y. Kim[2], J.W. Lee[3],
A. Benninghoven[1]

[1]Physikalisches Institut der Universität Münster, D-48149 Münster, Germany
[2]LG Corporate Institute of Technology, 137-140 Seoul, South Korea
[3]Department of Physics, Hallym University, South Korea

1. Introduction

The identification and characterization of sub-μm particles is a key-issue for many applications. Examples are aerosol particles from polluted air [1], uranium particles collected in the environment of nuclear power plants, nanoparticles and particle distributions on catalyst surfaces. A further example is particulate contamination during semiconductor fabrication as a major cause for device failure. The *National Technology Roadmap for Semiconductors* [2] determines the size of structures and the tolerable defect sizes in future microelectronics. According to the 98 Roadmap update the critical particle analysis size is currently 60 nm. For the analysis of 25 nm particles, needed in the year 2008, up to now no solutions are known.

In this investigation, we compared the capabilities of TOF-SIMS and Laser-SNMS for particle analysis by a standard set of samples *(Table 1)*. Both techniques combine high sensitivity and high lateral resolution as a prerequisite for the analysis of smallest particles. In Laser-SNMS useful yields up to 1 % and above are achieved [3], provided a high fraction of the predominantly neutral sputtered species is postionized.

Further analytical techniques for sub-μm particle characterization are scanning electron microscopy with energy dispersive X-ray analysis (SEM/EDS) and scanning Auger electron spectroscopy (SAM). A comparison of the particle analysis capabilities of SEM/EDS, SAM and TOF-SIMS is given in literature [4, 5]. Whereas SEM/EDS, AES and Laser-SNMS reveal quantitative elemental information, TOF-SIMS is the only method capable of providing detailed molecular and elemental information. Quantification, however, is hampered by the "matrix effect".

Although the primary system is similar for SEM/EDS and SAM, the spatial resolution is limited by different effects. Escape depths of several μm for the X-rays complicates analysis of particles < 100 nm with SEM/EDS. Auger electrons escape from a near surface region of 5 nm or less [6]. For flat surfaces the spatial resolution of SAM is mainly limited by the size of the primary electron beam [7]. In the case of smaller particles scattered primary electrons pass through the side of the particle and degrade the spatial resolution drastically [8]. The spatial resolution of sputtering based surface mass spectrometry (TOF-SIMS, Laser-SNMS) is mainly limited by the size of the primary ion beam (< 80nm).

2. Experimental

By applying a combined TOF-SIMS/Laser-SNMS instrument, a direct comparison of both techniques was possible. The use of a 30 keV fine focused Ga⁺ source [8] and a gridless reflectron based time-of-flight instrument guarantees high lateral (<100 nm) and mass resolution at high transmission. For nonresonant postionization an excimer-laser ($\lambda = 193$ nm and $\lambda = 248$ nm) was applied.

To compare the particle analysis capabilities of TOF-SIMS and Laser-SNMS a standard set of samples was prepared *(Table 1)*. The particle material was supplied in powder form and in a suspension, respectively. The particle material in powder form was first suspended in methanol. Subsequently the suspensions were diluted several times. After each preparation step the suspensions were placed in an ultrasonic bath to prevent clustering of the particles. For particle deposition on GaAs substrates 2.5 μl of the suspension was spincoated. Obtained area particle densities were about 2-3 particles in a field of 10 x 10 μm².

To confirm particle size and size distributions on the prepared wafers, field emission scanning electron (FE-SEM) images were performed with an Hitachi S-5000 "in lens" microscope. To enhance contrast the samples were coated under rotation with 1.5 nm Pt/C.

particle	size (nm)
Al_2O_3	1000
Al_2O_3	13
Au	1-2
$CaCo_3$	230
CeO_2	3-12
Fe_2O_3	15
Fe_2O_3	500
Si_3N_4	100
TiO_2	20-50
ZnO	20-80

Table 1: particle sizes in the raw material

3. Results and discussion

Table 2 presents yields (detected Me^+ ions / PI) obtained for TOF-SIMS as well as for Laser-SNMS for a variety of metal samples. Yields were acquired for both ozonized and presputtered surfaces. Presputtering was carried out with a fluence of $F_{SP} = 4 \cdot 10^{15}$ cm^{-2}. Since the ozonized surface is covered with a contamination and oxide layer, the Laser-SNMS yields distinctly increase after presputtering. In contrast the yields for TOF-SIMS decrease as a result of presputtering.

The high sensitivity for atomic species in Laser-SNMS is achieved by reaching saturation of the non-resonant ionization process within a rather large ionization volume. Observed differences in sensitivity are due to differences in the sputter yields, to the effective ionization volumes and to different angular and velocity distributions of the sputtered neutrals.

As an example we will discuss the results for CeO_2 particles. *Figure 1* shows TOF-SIMS, Laser-SNMS and FE-SEM images of CeO_2 particles on GaAs substrates. The FE-SEM image displays a typical cluster consisting of several 10 nm particles. Individual cluster sizes varied from 35 nm to 100 nm.

	Yield / 10⁻²			
	SNMS		SIMS	
	oz.	presp.	oz.	presp.
Ag	9,9	137	1,5	0,002
Al	0,86	1,06	0,67	1,3
Al	6,88**	7,97**		
Au	13,0	56,2	0,25*	0,004*
Ce	1,38	9,27	0,05	0,08
Cr	0,77	5,20	0,56	0,0004
Cu	18,1	63,7	0,51	0,02
Fe	12,8	34,3	0,37	0,08
Ge	1,15	2,65	0,46	0,01
Pb	5,20	32,9	0,23	0,02
Si	0,54	1,32	0,53	0,009
Ti	0,22	4,24	0,21	0,59
W	0,17	3,1	0,002	0,01
Zn	1,20	35,2	0,03	0,007
U**	2,32	2,17	0,002	0,002

Table 2: Yields on ozonized and presputtered surfaces ($F_{PI} = 4 \cdot 10^{15}$ cm^{-2}) for postionized neutrals and positive secondary ions (* negative secondary ions) Postionization: $\lambda = 248$ nm, $E_{pulse} = 150$ mJ, (** $\lambda = 193$ nm, $E_{pulse} = 25$ mJ)

For particle identification with both techniques TOF-SIMS and Laser-SNMS the primary ion fluence had to exceed the static limit. In Laser-SNMS the Ce^+ signal as well as the Ce^{2+} and the CeO^+ signal was used for particle detection / identification. In TOF-SIMS only the CeO^+ signal was intense enough to perform particle detection. The larger scale images in the first row present typical particle densities.

The second row of figure 1 shows images acquired by total consumption of a single particle

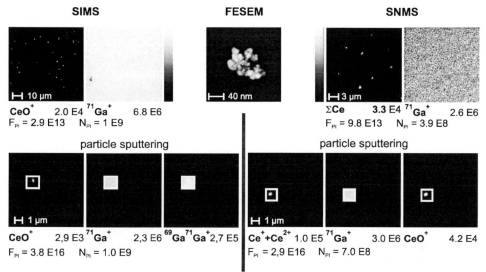

SIMS

H 10 µm

CeO^+ 2.0 E4 $^{71}Ga^+$ 6.8 E6
F_{PI} = 2.9 E13 N_{PI} = 1 E9

particle sputtering

H 1 µm

CeO^+ 2,9 E3 $^{71}Ga^+$ 2,3 E6 $^{69}Ga^{71}Ga^+$ 2,7 E5
F_{PI} = 3.8 E16 N_{PI} = 1.0 E9

FESEM

H 40 nm

SNMS

H 3 µm

ΣCe 3.3 E4 $^{71}Ga^+$ 2.6 E6
F_{PI} = 9.8 E13 N_{PI} = 3.9 E8

particle sputtering

H 1 µm

$Ce^+ + Ce^{2+}$ 1.0 E5 $^{71}Ga^+$ 3.0 E6 CeO^+ 4.2 E4
F_{PI} = 2,9 E16 N_{PI} = 7.0 E8

Figure 1: High resolution TOF-SIMS, Laser-SNMS and FE-SEM images of CeO_2 particles on GaAs. The subscript shows the substance name, the number of detected ions, the primary ion fluence F_{PI} and the total number of primary ions N_{PI}. In TOF-SIMS the signal of Ce^+ interferes with the substrate signal $^{69}Ga^{71}Ga^+$.

cluster. To reach high fluences even with the low primary ion currents of the analysis beam, the analyzed area has to be minimized. In case of TOF-SIMS high repetition rates (10 kHz) enable the use of primary ion currents of 50 pA DC, corresponding to a focus below 100 nm. Due to the limited repetition rate of the excimer laser (50 Hz) and the registration, Laser-SNMS requires a primary ion current of 1 nA DC to reach satisfying fluences in acceptable times. This could be achieved only by increasing the primary ion beam to about 200-300 nm. Since the Ce signal results from a convolution between the primary ion current density and the particle, the particle size could not be concluded from the obtained images. Indication of particle sizes much smaller than the primary ion beam diameter was given by the intense substrate signal from the particle area. In addition the reconstructed spectra *(Figure 2)* prove only minor differences in the substrate signal between the particle area and the environment.

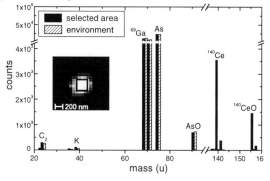

Figure 2: reconstructed **Laser-SNMS** spectra of the selected area and the environment

Reconstructed depth profiles for both TOF-SIMS and Laser-SNMS are presented in *Figure 3* and *Figure 4*, respectively. The decreasing Ce and CeO signals indicate that by a fluence of 10^{16} PI/cm^2 the cluster was removed completely. The constant ratio of Ce and CeO, however, proves that the oxidation state on the surface and in the particle volume is similar. Whereas the substrate signal of ^{71}Ga

for TOF-SIMS is influenced by the matrix effect, in Laser-SNMS it is nearly independent from the chemical environment.

Based upon a useful yield of $1.4 \cdot 10^{-2}$ for Ce^+, the number of removed Ce atoms could be calculated to $3.9 \cdot 10^6$, equivalent to a volume of $1.6 \cdot 10^{-16}$ cm^3 for CeO_2. This volume corresponds to a sphere with a diameter of 70 nm. Assuming a flat 2-dimensional cluster consisting of particles of the nominal size of 10 nm this amount corresponds to a resulting cluster size about 150 nm.

4. Conclusion

We have shown that TOF-SIMS and particularly Laser-SNMS are very sensitive tools for the characterization of small metal/metaloxide particles. Although the oxide character of the investigated particles is advantageous for TOF-SIMS, the sensitivity is even higher with

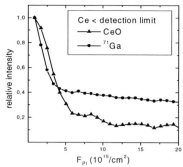 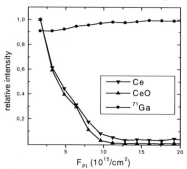

Figure 3: reconstructed **TOF-SIMS** depth profile from the selected area in figure 2. Acquisition time ~ 10 min

Figure 4: reconstructed **Laser-SNMS** depth profile from the selected area in figure 2. Acquisition time ~ 20 min

Laser-SNMS. Achieved yields for both TOF-SIMS and Laser-SNMS are high enough for the characterization of particles well below the present spot size of the primary ion beam. The combination of TOF-SIMS and Laser-SNMS is a promising approach for quantitative elemental as well as molecular particle analysis, in the < 100 nm range.

Acknowledgment
The authors gratefully acknowledge the supply of particles by S. Stipp (Geologisk Institut Kobenhavns Universitet, Kopenhagen, Denmark), H. Orthner (Gerhard-Mercator-Universität, Duisburg, Germany), R. Holm (Bayer AG, Leverkusen, Germany), N. Erdmann, and O. Stetzel (Europ. Inst. for Transuranium Elements, Karlsruhe, Germany). Thanks are alo due to R. Reichelt (Institut für Med. Physik und Biophysik, Münster, Germany) for FE-SEM measurements.

References
[1] F. Faude, J. Goschnick, Fres. J. Anal. Chem. **358,** 67 (1997)
[2] National Technology Roadmap for Semiconductors 1988 update, 181 (1998)
[3] M. Terhorst, R. Möllers, E. Niehuis, A. Benninghoven, Surf. Interf. Anal., **18,** 824 (1992)
[4] K. Childs, D. Narum, L.A. La Vanier, P.M. Lindley, B.W. Schuler, G. Mulholland, A.C. Diebold, J. Vac. Sci. Technol. A **14**, 2392 (1996)
[5] A.C: Diebold, P. Lindley, J. Viteralli, J. Kingsley, B. Y. H. Liu, K. Woo **A16**, 1825 (1998)
[6] K. Childs, D. Narum, L.A. LaVanier, P.M. Lindley, B.W. Schueler, G. Mullholland, and A.C. Diebold, J. Vac. Sci. Technol. A **14**, 2392 (1996)
[7] M.M. El Gomati and M. Prutton, Surf. Sci. **72,** 485 (1978)
[8] A. Umbach, A. Hoyer, and W.H. Bruenger, Surf. Interf. Anal. **14**, 401 (1989)
[9] J.Schwieters, H.-G. Cramer, T. Heller, U. Jürgens, E. Niehuis, J. Zehnpfennig and A. Benninghoven, J. Vac. Sci. Technol. **A9**, 2864 (1991)

A. Benninghoven, P. Bertrand, H.-N. Migeon and H.W. Werner (Editors).
Proceedings of the 12th International Conference on Secondary Ion Mass Spectrometry,
Brussels, Belgium, 5-11 September 1999

333

CHEMICAL CHARACTERIZATION OF MODIFIED NANOTIPS BY TOF–SIMS AND LASER–SNMS

R. Kamischke[1], F. Kollmer[1], H. Fuchs[1], R. Stark[2], W. Heckl[2], and A. Benninghoven[1]

[1]Physikalisches Institut der Universität, Wilhelm-Klemm-Str. 10,
D-48149 Münster, Germany

[2]Institut für Kristallographie und Mineralogie der Universität,
Theresienstr. 41, D-80333 München, Germany

1. Introduction

For many applications detailed information on the chemical surface composition with extremely high spatial resolution is essential. Atomic Force Microscopy offers highest spatial resolution but does not provide chemical information. However, the combination with TOF–SIMS and Laser–SNMS, the most sensitive techniques for chemical surface mapping with good lateral resolution, allows to determine the surface chemistry of nanostructures. For many applications detailed information on the chemical surface composition of the used AFM-nanotip is a key issue. This hold e.g. for their use as chemical sensors, where the tip surface is chemically modified, or for sub-amol nanoextraction of sample material by direct contact with the tip. We show first results of TOF–SIMS and Laser–SNMS analyses of AFM cantilevers.

2. Experimental

All experiments were carried out in a gridless reflectron based time of flight instrument with a fine focused Ga+ liquid metal ion source (focus ≤ 80 nm) [1]. For nonresonant postionization an excimer laser with wavelengths of 248 and 193 nm was applied. This instrument allows a direct comparison of high lateral resolution TOF–SIMS and Laser–SNMS analyses of the same sample. Whereas Laser–SNMS analysis requires a pulsed extraction field for the postionized species, TOF–SIMS measurements can be performed by applying a static or a pulsed extraction field. Typical acquisition times for SIMS and SNMS are about three and six minutes per scan, respectively.

Special efforts had to be put on the sample preparation of the investigated AFM cantilevers. Distortions of the extraction field due to sample geometry, shadowing effects, vibrations of the tip and charging had to be reduced to a minimum level. Therefor the AFM-cantilevers were prepared in a special sample holder, guaranteeing a good contact to the substrate (stainless steel) and maintaining the possibility to focus the laser beam closely above the cantilever tip. Presputtering of the samples had to be minimized due to the small amount of material deposited on the tip and being available for an analysis. Therefor experimental parameters where adjusted on a standard sample before turning to the relevant sample. Presputtering for sample adjustment was below $4 \cdot 10^{12}$ PI/cm^2.

334

3. Samples

The experiments concentrated on two areas of interest. One deals with the immobilization of polylysine on nanotips, done with Si₃N₄ cantilevers (see *figure 1*) with tip heights of ~4 µm. The front part of the cantilever including the tip was Au coated. Polylysine (459 kda) was immobilized on the substrate using an alkanthiole as linker. These nanotips are used for investigating the interaction of the polylysine with a given surface by AFM. TOF–SIMS and Laser–SNMS are used to monitor the success of the surface modification.

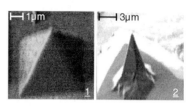

Fig.1: SE images of cantilever nanotips. Picture 1 and 2 show a Si₃N₄ and a Si tip, respectively

Secondly we deposited sample material on AFM Cantilever tips. For these experiments Si tips (see *figure 1*)with a tip height of 10-15 µm were used. The sample was first imaged in the AFM tapping mode to localize the region of interest. Afterwards material was extracted mechanically from the sample by applying loading forces of several µN and scanning over the surface for some µm. The extracted material adheres to the tip and is analyzed using TOF–SIMS / Laser–SNMS. We show results of Ag extraction from a single crystal.

4. Results and discussion

High lateral resolution imaging for a Si₃N₄ Cantilever nanotip is demonstrated in *figure 2*. Since the lateral resolution is limited to 80 nm and the tip radius is about 20 nm, it is not possible to characterize the tip itself. However, imaging the cantilever including the tip pyramid with SIMS provides detailed information on the elemental and molecular surface composition. The brightness contrast for different areas of the tip pyramid illustrate different sputter yields caused by different angles of the primary ion incidence.

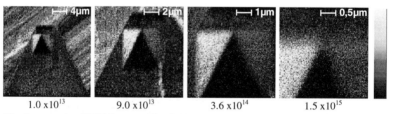

$$1.0 \times 10^{13} \qquad 9.0 \times 10^{13} \qquad 3.6 \times 10^{14} \qquad 1.5 \times 10^{15}$$

Fig. 2: negative SIMS images of a Si₃N₄ AFM cantilever nanotip. All images show Cl⁻. The subscript reveals the applied fluence (PI/cm²).

4.1 Surface modification

Figure 3 presents SNMS (193 nm) results of polylysine immobilized on an Au coated cantilever. Only the front part was Au coated to avoid cantilever bending due to different expansion of Au and Si₃N₄. Laser–SNMS using a wavelength of 193 nm has been proved to be an adequate technique to analyze amino acids [2]. Usually amino acids show a [M-COOH]⁺

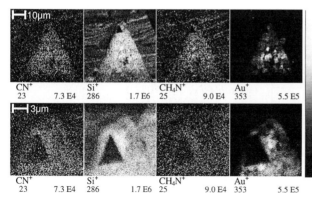

CN⁺ 23 7.3 E4 Si⁺ 286 1.7 E6 CH₄N⁺ 25 9.0 E4 Au⁺ 353 5.5 E5

CN⁺ 23 7.3 E4 Si⁺ 286 1.7 E6 CH₄N⁺ 25 9.0 E4 Au⁺ 353 5.5 E5

Fig.3: SNMS (193 nm) results of polylysine immobilized on a cantilever. In the subscript of each map the maximum number of counts per pixel and the integral number of counts are given.

and several nitrogen containing signals. However, lysine shows only fragments at low masses like CN⁺ or CH₄N⁺ *(figure 3)*. There are some more significant ions which interfere with substrate signals. Obviously polylysine was adsorbed on the tip pyramid, allowing the conclusion that the polylysine transfer to the tip was successful. Mapping areas down to this size, the static limit (~10¹³ PI/cm²) is exceeded within a few scans, so the amount of material accessible for this analysis was extremely small. This demands for a minimum of presputtering.

4.2 Nanoextraction

Ag loaded nanotips were analyzed using three different operation modes: SNMS (248 nm) and positive SIMS with static or pulsed extraction. For SNMS the sample was analyzed as received, whereas for SIMS measurements the sample was fully oxidized by an ozone treatment. All three methods demonstrate the capability to locate the nanotip on the cantilever and allow the detection of the deposited material, as shown in *figure 4*. Due to the extreme sharpness of this kind of tip static fields are distorted which leads to a lack of signal from the sides of the tip using the static extraction SIMS mode, whereas results of SNMS and SIMS with pulsed extraction show signal from the whole tip. Since neutrals are not at all influenced by electric fields, the signal from the side of the tip is significantly higher applying SNMS compared to SIMS with pulsed extraction.

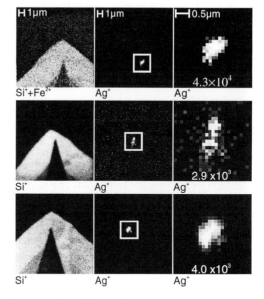

Fig.4: Ag loaded Cantilever (10µN loading force, 10 linescans for 2,5µm). First row: SNMS 248nm; second row: SIMS, static extraction; third row: SIMS, pulsed extraction. In the right column the total numbers of Ag counts normalized to the fluence are given.

mode	surface condition	Yield [10^{-2}] (#counts / #PI)
SNMS (248nm)	native	24.5
	ozone	9.9
	presputtered	137.0
Positive SIMS	ozone	1.5
	presputtered	0.0018
Negative SIMS	ozone	0.0069
	presputtered	0.0048

Table1: Yields for Ag, obtained for SNMS (248 nm) and SIMS with static extraction for an Ag standard.

Extracted Ag material is detected by all three modes on the uppermost tip area. Analyzing the Ag intensities just for the tip region as shown in column 3, the total counts for SNMS and SIMS show a similar ratio as the corresponding yields (see *table 1*).

From a cantilever with a smaller amount of Ag transferred to the tip all material could be sputtered during a SNMS measurement as demonstrated in *figure 5*. Applying a total primary ion fluence of $4 \cdot 10^{14}$ PI/cm², the Ag atoms are completely removed from the tip. Assuming a useful yield of $8 \cdot 10^{-3}$ the total number of Ag atoms deposited on the tip is estimated to be approximately $4 \cdot 10^4$. This amount is equivalent to less than 1amol.

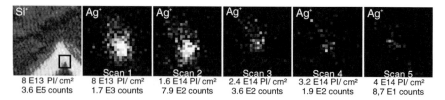

| Si⁺ | Ag⁺ | Ag⁺ | Ag⁺ | Ag⁺ | Ag⁺ |

| 8 E13 PI/ cm² 3.6 E5 counts | 8 E13 PI/ cm² 1.7 E3 counts | 1.6 E14 PI/ cm² 7.9 E2 counts | 2.4 E14 PI/ cm² 3.6 E2 counts | 3.2 E14 PI/ cm² 1.9 E2 counts | 4 E14 PI/ cm² 8,7 E1 counts |
| Scan 1 | Scan 2 | Scan 3 | Scan 4 | Scan 5 | |

Fig.5: Ag loaded cantilever (10µN loading force). The first image shows an area of 15x15 µm², the others are zoomed into the marked tip area of 2.5x2.5 µm². In the subscript of each map the applied fluence and the total number of counts are given.

5. Conclusions

Combining AFM and TOF–SIMS / Laser–SNMS is a way to obtain information from nanostructures. We have shown that TOF–SIMS and Laser–SNMS are powerful tools for the chemical characterization of modified cantilever and nanotips. We proved the capability of manipulating and analyzing sub-amol amounts of sample material and the suitability to determine the success of chemical surface modification of nanotips. The high yields particularly for SNMS allow most sensitive surface analysis and elemental surface mapping with high lateral resolution.

Acknowledgement

The authors acknowledge support by Y. Oberndörfer and A. Janshoff, Physikalisches Institut der Universität, Münster, Germany for donating cantilever samples.

References

[1] R. Möllers, thesis, Universität Münster, Germany (1996)
[2] J. Schwieters, H.-G. Cramer, T. Heller, U. Jürgens, E. Niehuis, J. Zehnpfennig, and A. Benninghoven, J. Vac. Sci. Technol. **A 9**, 2864 (1991).

A. Benninghoven, P. Bertrand, H.-N. Migeon and H.W. Werner (Editors).
Proceedings of the 12th International Conference on Secondary Ion Mass Spectrometry,
Brussels, Belgium, 5-11 September 1999
© 2000 Elsevier Science B.V. All rights reserved.

THREE-DIMENSIONAL MODELING OF A TIME-OF-FLIGHT MASS SPECTROMETER: OPTIMIZATION OF SNMS/SIMS TRANSMISSION USING SIMION[*]

Igor V. Veryovkin, Wallis F. Calaway, and Michael J. Pellin

Material Science and Chemistry Divisions, Argonne National Laboratory,
Argonne IL 60439, U. S. A., e-mail: verigo@anl.gov

1. Introduction.

The software package SIMION 3D© [1] has been used to model the surface analysis by resonance ionization of sputtered atoms (SARISA) SNMS/SIMS instrument, that was developed and built at Argonne National Laboratory [2]. The SARISA instrument (Fig.1), which operates on the time-of-flight principle, has a unique design that uses two hemispherical energy analyzers for energy- and angular-refocusing of sputtered ions and photoionized neutrals. Another feature of the instrument is that the same "front end" ion optics is used for focusing primary ions with normal incidence and for extracting and focusing secondary ions and postionized neutrals. The motivation of this work is to develop a time-of-flight mass spectrometer (TOF MS) with improved useful yield (atoms detected per atoms sputtered) and mass resolution. This is to be accomplished (1) by obtaining accurate quantitative estimates of the instrument transmission and time resolution, (2) by identifying a rational alignment procedure for optimizing these parameters, and (3) by exploring changes in the ion optics design that would lead to these improvements. The techniques and approach used here should be *generally useful to design electrostatic and magnetic mass spectrometers.*

2. The Model.

Virtual ion optics components (called "instances") were assembled together on a SIMION workbench. Ion trajectories through each component were then calculated under control of the corresponding set of user programs written in the Hewlett Packard calculator based RPN language. Since some of the components of SARISA are identical, the same potential arrays and user programs were used twice to save computer memory. There are 21 "instances" controlled by 18 programs written for 18 unique potential arrays. To correctly define boundaries of electric fields, all the important and complex virtual components were "built" as three dimensional (3D) "instances". Typically, this has been done for areas where cylindrical elements (lenses) were interacting with planar elements (deflectors). The major 3D components are as follows: (1) the "front end" focusing region for primary and secondary ions, which consists of two Einzel lenses separated by planar ion beam deflectors; (2) the system of horizontal deflecting plates separated by resistively coated vertical side plates used to bend the primary ion beam onto the secondary ion axis; (3) entrance and exit regions of the

---

[*]Work supported by the U. S. Department of Energy, BES-Materials Sciences, under Contract W-31-109-ENG-38, and by NASA under Grant No.1559.

specially designed hemispherical energy analyzers with resistive disks, which provide an accurate termination of the electric field lines within the analyzers; and (4) the Colutron™ ion source with its velocity filter, which includes shims plates for shaping the electric field within the filter. The resistive coating used in the energy analyzers and in the bending system was simulated by introducing a number of intermediate electrodes into the corresponding potential arrays. This

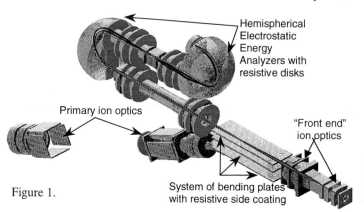

Hemispherical Electrostatic Energy Analyzers with resistive disks

Primary ion optics

"Front end" ion optics

Figure 1.

System of bending plates with resistive side coating

allowed precise modeling of the resistive coating regions with floating electric potentials. The model part corresponding to the Colutron™ ion source can be used as a separate independent and accurate model of this ion source.

To investigate the influence each component has on the final transmission of the SARISA instrument, 3D computer displays of ion trajectories were constructed. These simulations have identified several changes in operating conditions that improved instrument transmission. A set of user programs is used (1) to control voltages applied to all the virtual electrodes, (2) to control appearance ("birth") of ions with predetermined initial coordinates, velocities and angles of motion within any of 21 "instances" and (3) to monitor ions parameters during their flight through the ion optical system. An algorithm has been developed that allows a means of estimating the instruments transmission. This algorithm allows small sets of ions (up to 27) with definable initial parameters to be created internally by SIMION in real time. Due to limitations of the build-in RPN compiler of SIMION, large sets of ions (200 and more) are imported from ASCII files generated externally. In this case, the ion generating part of the user programs is skipped and only subroutines that monitor ion parameters and set voltages on virtual ion optics electrodes are used. These two modes of operation provide substantial flexibility when using the computer model as discussed below.

1. The *alignment mode* is used for quickly identifying the optimal alignments of the instrument for ions with initial kinetic energies equal to the most probable energy. In this mode, the ion generating routine calculates (a) the emission of secondary ions homogeneously distributed within a controllable solid angle from a circular spot with a controllable position and diameter ("SIMS regime") or (b) the appearance of postionized sputtered neutrals homogeneously distributed within a volume of controllable size located at a controllable distance from the controllable emission spot mentioned above ("SNMS regime"). For neutrals, angles of the initial ion motion are calculated from the relationship between locations and sizes of the emission spot and the cylindrical ionization volume. Octagons are used to simulate circles of the emission spot and the ionization cylinder.

2. The *transmission mode* makes use of externally generated files containing initial parameters for the ions. The algorithm for calculating initial parameters is the same as used internally by SIMION. However, in this mode, it is possible to generate large sets of ions

(>30) with varying initial energies, coordinates, angles of motion, times of birth etc. Any appropriate external software can be used for this purpose. A larger number of ions and a wide variety of initial parameters are used in the *transmission mode* to more accurately calculate the transmission. Despite the fact that it is not difficult to generate sets of thousands of ions representing all the possible angles and energies, sets of hundreds of ions seem to be sufficient for good accuracy.

In both operating modes, SIMION monitors the parameters of ions as they fly through SARISA. These parameters are read by the set of user programs to calculate transmission and time resolution. Voltages for SARISA that are optimized in the *alignment mode* are then used in the *transmission mode* to obtain more precise quantitative estimates of transmission and time resolution. Two definitions for the transmission of the instrument are used: (1) the *ordinary transmission* is the ratio of the number of detected ions to the number of emitted ions, and (2) the *weighted transmission* is the ratio of the sum of weighting factors of detected ions to the sum of weighting factors of emitted ions. *By introducing weighting factors, the angular and energy distributions of emitted particles can be taken into account.* After the last ion has been generated, the programs calculate minimal and maximal times of flight for the set of ions. Those times are used to estimate the time resolution of the system as the ratio between the average time of flight and the difference between maximal and minimal times of flight. The average time of flight of ions is defined as a ratio between the sum of products of times of flight of detected ions to their weighting factors and the sum of the weighting factors of detected ions.

3. Results and discussion.

Estimates of the transmission of the SARISA instrument, operated in the SIMS regime with the extraction voltage of secondary ions of 1 kV, were obtained by performing the following computer "experiments". A total of 49 emission spots each with a diameter of 0.3 mm were equally spaced within a square (6 mm×6 mm) on the target. From each spot 241 secondary ions are emitted with energies of 5 eV and 20 eV. Emission angles (φ) for the ions were selected over the range 0° to 180° in steps of 1.5°. This caused the ions to be equally spaced over the emission hemisphere. Results of the computer

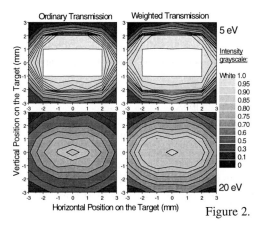

Figure 2.

experiments to estimate transmission are shown in Figs. 2 and 3. Figure 2 shows ordinary and weighted transmission maps for secondary ions. The used non-linear grayscale is selected to emphasize areas with the transmission higher than 0.7. The weighting factor used to calculate the transmission was $\cos^n \varphi$, where $n = 1$. As seen in Fig. 2, the weighted transmission is higher than the ordinary transmission because ions emitted with oblique angles do not substantially contribute to the detected signal. From the maps shown in Fig.2, ion optics elements that limit the transmission of SARISA can be identified. The low transmission areas of the map are formed by shadowing of the flying ions by specific elements that can be identified by analyzing ion trajectories. Examining the high transmission rectangular area for 5 eV in Fig. 2, leads to the conclusion that the high transmission area in the vertical dimension (±1 mm) is limited by the bending plates (14 mm high), and the high transmission area in the horizontal dimension (±2 mm) is controlled by the Einzel lenses (inner diameter 24 mm) in front of the entrance to the first hemispherical energy analyzer. The same conclusions can be derived by examining the 20 eV data. Further, the asymmetry of the transmission in the vertical direction for 5 eV can be traced to the hole in the bending plates used to introduce the primary ion beam. Thus, full-scale 3D modeling of the ion optics allowed tracing features that could not be identified by using two-dimensional approaches.

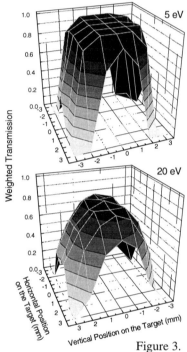

Figure 3 shows the weighted transmission for the two ion energies as 3D plots. A linear grayscale linked to the Z axis is used to indicate the corresponding transmission. The XY plane of Fig. 3 corresponds to the target surface mapped in Fig. 2. Note that the transmission of the instrument is lower than unity (typically, 0.8-0.85) for 20 eV ions even if they are emitted from the center of the target, since fast ions moving at oblique angles do not reach the detector. In general, the simulation proves the high transmission of the SARISA instrument assumed in Ref. [3]. Despite of the low extraction voltage of 1 kV, the weighted transmission is equal to unity for secondary ions with energies less than 10 eV, which covers the range of the most probable energies for the majority of secondary ions.

Figure 3.

4. Conclusions.

A computer program that models secondary ion and postionized neutral trajectories through the SARISA instrument has been developed. The program has been tested by determining the transmission of secondary ions for two different ion energies. Results indicate that the model accurately reflects the transmission of the SARISA instrument. The developed algorithm for creating ions and monitoring their parameters is generic and can be used for examining other SIMS/SNMS instruments and ion sources.

References.

[1] "SIMION 3D Version 6.0," David A. Dahl, 43rd ASMS Conference on Mass Spectrometry and Allied Topics, May 21-26 1995, Atlanta, Georgia, p. 717.

[2] M. J. Pellin, C. E. Young, W. F. Calaway, J. W. Burnett, B. Jorgensen, E. L. Schweitzer and D. M. Gruen, Nucl. Instr. and Meth. B18 (1987) 446.

[3] C. S. Hansen, W. F. Calaway, B. V. King, and M. J. Pellin, Surf. Sci. 398 (1998) 211.

A. Benninghoven, P. Bertrand, H.-N. Migeon and H.W. Werner (Editors).
Proceedings of the 12th International Conference on Secondary Ion Mass Spectrometry,
Brussels, Belgium, 5-11 September 1999
© 2000 Elsevier Science B.V. All rights reserved.

INVESTIGATION OF THE FORMATION OF SPUTTERED OXIDE CLUSTERS WITH THE LASER ASSISTED SPUTTERED NEUTRAL MASS SPECTROMETRY TECHNIQUE (LASNMS)

J. Vlekken[1], D. Polus[1], M. D'Olieslaeger[1], W. Vandervorst[2] and L. De Schepper[1]

[1]Limburgs Universitair Centrum, Institute for Materials Research, Materials Physics Division,
Universitaire Campus, Wetenschapspark 1, B-3590 Diepenbeek, Belgium
[2]IMEC vzw, Kapeldreef 75, B-3001 Leuven, Belgium

1. Introduction

The formation of clusters in sputtering processes is a complicated process depending on the nature of the formed clusters. Under the assumption of a binary collision cascade, sputtered clusters can be formed by either of the following two mechanisms [1] :
a) an atomic combination mechanism where the constituent particles of the cluster are sputtered independently and combine above the surface.
b) a direct emission mechanism where only one of the constituent particles is set in motion to an outward direction by the binary collision cascade. Under fulfilment of certain energy considerations, co-emission of one (or more) particle can occur resulting in the sputtering of a cluster.
It was shown by Oechsner [1] that for strong (ionic) bonds between next neighboured atoms A and B at the sample surface and for great differences between the atomic masses of A and B, co-emission of an AB pair is possible when the heavy species becomes knocked on. This was experimentally demonstrated for MO clusters, with M a heavy metal, sputtered from heavy metal oxides.
According to the model of Oechsner and co-workers [1-3], the partial sputtering yield of metal monoxide molecules (MO) and metal atoms (M) sputtered from these metal oxides can be written as:

$$Y_{MO} = Y_0 . c_M^s . c_O^s . p \tag{1}$$

$$Y_M = Y_0 . c_M^s . (1 - c_O^s . p) \tag{2}$$

where c_M^s and c_O^s denote the surface concentration of M and O respectively and p denotes the probability for co-emission. In equation (1) c_M^s represents the probability of hitting a M atom at the surface from below and $c_O^s . p$ describes the probability that this atom is then ejected as a part of a MO cluster. If it can be assumed that the measured SNMS signals are proportional to the partial sputter yields it can be written that :

$$\frac{I_M}{I_{MO}} = \frac{D_M}{D_{MO}} . \frac{1}{p} . \left(\frac{1}{c_O^s} - p \right) \tag{3}$$

with D_M and D_{MO} the SNMS sensitivity factors of the corresponding elements. Furthermore, if it can be assumed that Y_0 only depends little on the oxygen surface concentrations, equation (1) will be maximum if $c_O^s = 0.5$. Starting from this reference value, a self-callibration can be applied using equation (1). It can be calculated that :

$$c_O^s = 0.5\left\{1 \pm \left(1 - I_{MO}/I_{MO}^{max}\right)^{1/2}\right\} \qquad (4)$$

The validity of eqs. (3) and (4) can be checked by plotting I_M/I_{MO} vs $1/c_O^s$. This is expected to give a linear relation and has already been observed for oxidised Ta and Nb surfaces [3,4]. In this paper we will show that SiO-molecules sputtered from an oxidised Si-surface do also follow these relations and are as a consequence also probably formed by a direct emission process. Finally, the parameter p and the relative sputter yields of the Si and SiO particles will be determined.

2. Experimental

In this paper, the sputtering of SiO clusters from a SiO_2 sample under an Ar^+ bombardment is studied using the Laser Assisted Sputtered Neutral Mass Spectrometry (LASNMS) technique. The experiments are carried out with a femto-second laser system that is used to apply Non-resonant Multiphoton Ionisation (NRMPI). This is a non-selective ionisation process that has the advantage that a detailed knowledge of the electronic energy levels of the elements is not necessary and that all elements can be monitored at the same time. As well the formation mechanism as the partial sputter yield of the oxide clusters will be investigated.

The SIMS system of the post-ionisation equipment was constructed by IMEC, and is based on a conventional Cameca IMS SIMS instrument. For a detailed description of the SIMS-system we refer to the work of De Bisschop et al. [5]. In the present study, a Si-sample with on top a SiO_2 layer of 40 nm was bombarded with Ar^+ ions with an accelerating energy of 5 kV and an incidence angle of about 45° off normal. The beam intensity was adjusted to 12 nA and had a diameter of 50 μm. The beam was scanned over a square area of 300 μm². In order to avoid crater edge effects and to achieve a high depth resolution during profiling an electronic gate was used. The sample was set to a potential of 3.1 kV resulting into a primary ion impact energy of 1.9 keV. The pressure in the sample chamber was better than 10^{-6} Pa.

The non-resonant post-ionisation of the sputtered neutral particles was achieved using a solid-state laser system (Super-Spitfire) fabricated by Spectra-Physics and a harmonic generator of Uniwave Technology. Using the Ti-sapphires of the Super-Spitfire, femto second pulses (130 fs) at a wavelength of 800 nm and a pulse energy of 2.6 mJ are produced at a repetition rate of 1 kHz. Based on this fundamental beam, photons with wavelengths of 400nm (second harmonic), 266 nm (third harmonic) and 200 nm (fourth harmonic) can be created in the harmonic generator. The third and fourth harmonic photons have an energy of respectively 4.66 eV and 6.2 eV. The pulse widths are smaller than 250 fs and 300 fs and the pulse energies are 300 μJ (1.2 GW peak power) and 30 μJ (0.1 GW peak power) respectively.

Finally the beam is focussed at 1 mm in front of the sample using a spherical plano-convex lens. This allows to have a laser beam in front of the sample crater as large as approximately 350 μm in diameter what results in power densities of 10^{12} W/cm^2 and 10^{11} W/cm^2 for the third and fourth harmonic respectively. These power densities for the third harmonic (266 nm) are high enough to ionise almost all elements efficiently with an ionisation potential less than 14 eV by a 2- or 3-photon process. For the results described in this paper we used the third harmonic (266 nm) with an energy of 250 μJ per pulse.

3. Results and discussion

Figure 1 shows a depth profile of the SiO$_2$/Si structure. It can be observed that the ^{30}SiO signal shows a peak at the SiO$_2$/Si interface. Assuming that the ^{30}SiO clusters are formed by a direct emission process, this corresponds to the condition where $c_O^s = 0.5$. Using the ^{30}SiO peak intensity and equation (4), we calculated the oxygen surface concentration. As can be seen from Figure 2, the oxygen surface concentration at the SiO$_2$ sample corresponds well to the oxygen bulk concentration. As a consequence no preferential sputtering seems to occur under the given bombarding conditions. Furthermore, it can also be observed that a weak oxygen surface concentration is also present when bombarding the Si-substrate. This is due to

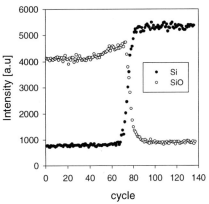
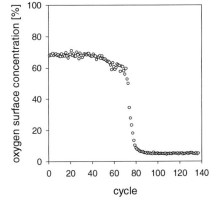

the rest gas in the spectrometer (6.4 10^{-7} Pa).

Fig. 1: SNMS depth profile SiO$_2$/Si sample   Fig. 2: Calculated oxygen surface conc.

Next, these calculated oxygen concentrations were used to plot I_{Si}/I_{SiO} vs $1/c_O^s$. As can be observed from figure 3, a very good linear relation is obtained. This indicates that a direct emission process as described for the heavy metal oxides probably forms also the SiO clusters. Finally, it can easily be observed from equation (3) that the intersection of the linear curve with the X-axis corresponds to the value p and that the absolute value of the intersection of the linear curve with the Y-axis corresponds to D_{Si}/D_{SiO}. From the linear fit of Figure 3 it could be calculated that p = 0.89. This is close to the value reported for TaO-clusters

344

sputtered from an oxidised Ta-metal (p ~ 0.86) [3]. For the ratio D_{Si}/D_{SiO} a value of 0.277 was obtained. Using this value we determined the ratio of partial sputter yields Y_{SiO}/Y_{Si}. This result is shown in Figure 4. As can be seen, Y_{SiO}/Y_{Si} is equal to 1.47 in the SiO_2 sample. This signifies that the measured mono-atomic Si-signal is not representative anymore for the sputtered Si-flux. As a consequence, the quantitation of Si-oxides can not be done using only the mono-atomic SNMS signals. This was also observed for Ta-oxides [4] and is probably, as suggested before, a general phenomenon for oxides.

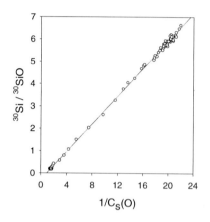

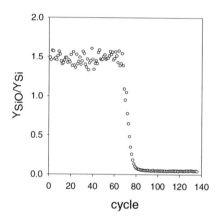

Fig. 3: Ratio of Si and SiO versus 1/calculated oxygen surface concentration

Fig. 4: Ratio sputter yield of SiO on Si

4. Conclusions

In this paper it was shown that a direct emission process as was already described previous for heavy metal oxides probably forms also the SiO clusters sputtered from a SiO_2 sample. Furthermore it could be calculated that the chance for the co-emission of an O-atom with a Si-atom is equal to $0.89.c_O^s$. Finally we could experimentally define that the partial sputter yield of SiO on Si is equal to 1.47.

Acknowledgements
This research was performed in the framework of the FWO-program No G.0099.97.

References

[1] H. Oechsner, SIMS III proceedings, Springer-Verlag, New York, 1982, p. 106
[2] H. Oechsner, H. Schoof and E. Stumpe, Surface Science, 76 (1978) 343
[3] A. Wucher, H. Oechsner, Nucl. Instr. Meth. In Phys. Res., B18 (1987) 458
[4] A. Wucher, K. Franzreb, H.-J. Mathieu and D. Landolt, Surface and Interface Analysis, 23 (1995) 844
[5] P. De Bisschop, D. Huyskens, M. Meuris, W. Vandervorst, B. Rasser and F. Costa de Beauregard, SIMS VII, John Wiley & Sons, Chichester, 1990, p. 907

SECTION 8 :
DATA PROCESSING

A. Benninghoven, P. Bertrand, H.-N. Migeon and H.W. Werner (Editors).
Proceedings of the 12th International Conference on Secondary Ion Mass Spectrometry,
Brussels, Belgium, 5-11 September 1999

347

ANALYSIS OF ORGANIC CONTAMINANTS ON SILICON WAFERS
BY MEANS OF MULTIVARIATE CALIBRATION

Sandro Ferrari [&1], F. Zanderigo [#], G. Queirolo[#], M. Borgini[§] and C. Pellò[§],
Laboratorio MDM - INFM, via Olivetti 2, I-20041 Agrate Brianza (Mi) - Italy.
E-mail: mdmlab@progetto3000.it
[#]STMicroelectronics, Agrate Brianza, I-20041, Italy
[§]MEMC, Novara, I-28100, Italy

1.Introduction

Trace organic contaminants adsorbing on the surfaces of silicon wafer have a detrimental effect on the performance of semiconductor devices [1,2,3,4,5]. One of the most critical sources of organic contamination are the plastic boxes where the wafer are stored, which tend to release oligomers, plasticizers, antioxidants and surfactants [6]. A number of techniques have been applied to analyze organic contaminants like XPS, thermal desorption spectrometry (TDS) thermo-desorption gas-chromatography mass-spectrometry (TD-GC/MS) and ToF-SIMS. Thanks to high sensitivity and specificity ToF-SIMS can be advantageously applied to the analysis of organic contaminants, although some limitation must be taken in account. First of all, providing quantitative information is extremely difficult due to the need of calibration curves for any of the species analyzed and to matrix effects. In addition data interpretation is extremely complicated in the common situation where many and unknown contaminants are present at the same time. In this paper we address the problem of data interpretation by means of Principal Component Analysis (PCA). PCA has been applied to static SIMS data interpretation in a number of paper [7,8,9]. Nevertheless application of statistical method must be done with care and always verifying the results by more traditional estimations.

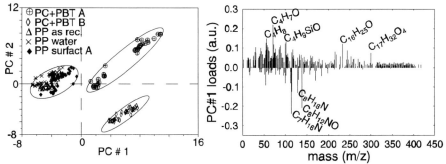

Figure 1: Scores of the first against the second PC relative to the analysis made on PP boxes cleaned with different protocols and two different boxes made of PC+PBT and loadings relative to PC #1 where the most relevant masses are assigned to the most probable formulas.

---

[1] Corresponding author.

2.Experimental details

P-type (Boron doped) 200mm, CZ-Si <100> wafers were stored for one hundred and fifty days in six different boxes. Four of them were made of Poly-Propylene (PP) and were cleaned in DI water using different protocols. In particular the first one adding a surfactant (PP surf A) with protocol A, the second with the same surfactant but with a different protocol (PP surf B), the third with protocol B but without surfactant (PP water) and the last was used as received by the supplier (PP as rec). Two boxes were made of Poly-Carbonate and Poly-Butylene-Terephtalate (PC+PBT A and B) and they were manufactured by two different suppliers. Positive mass spectra were acquired by means of a CAMECA ION-TOF (IV) operated with a 25 kV Ga gun in high mass resolution mode. Analyses were performed in static conditions. Seventeen spectra were collected for each wafer spanning different areas of the surface. Principal Component Analysis (PCA) was performed on a matrix composed of 496 peaks and a total of 204 spectra. Pre-treatment of data was done by adding a value of hundred to every element of the matrix, normalizing peak intensities to $^{30}Si^+$ signal, taking the logarithm and mean centering.

3.Results and discussion

PCA was initially performed on the whole set of data to evaluate differences between PP boxes and PC+PBT boxes. Since one of the PP boxes (PP surf B) was showing strong differences from every other PP box, it was left out during this part of the analysis to allow a better estimation of differences between PP and PC+PBT boxes. PP boxes and PC+PBT boxes can easily be separated by the first PC while the second is able to separate PC+PBT A from B as shown in figure 1. From the loadings of PC #1 it is possible to observe that oxygen containing peaks have loadings with positive values and are associated to PC+PBT, while nitrogen containing peaks are associated to PP boxes. Nitrogen containing peaks are most likely originated by surfactants used to clean the boxes, while those with oxygen (and without nitrogen) are coming from additive, plasticizers and possibly by unpolymerized oligomers. The highest and the lowest valued peaks in the loadings are plotted for every box type in figure 2. Mass 114 assigned to $C_7H_{16}N$ is relative to an amine that was present on the PP as received by the supplier and not removed by any of the treatments. Mass 71 assigned to C_4H_7O is characteristic of PC+PBT boxes. Although it is mostly present on PC+PBT A also B has a significant amount of this species present as compared to PP boxes. It is probably a fragment generated by unpolymerized monomers of PC/PBT.

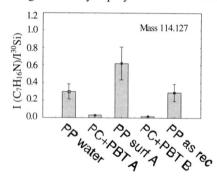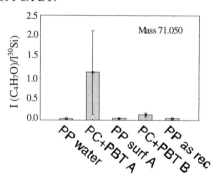

Figure 2: Peak intensities of masses with max. and min. loading value as observed in fig. 1.

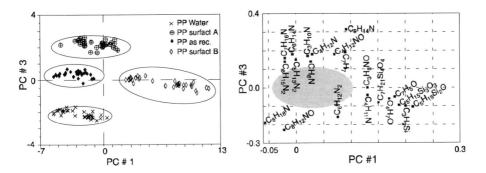

Figure 3: Scores of the first against the third PC relative to the analysis made on PP boxes cleaned with four different protocols and loadings relative to PC #1 and PC #3 plotted one against the other. The shadowed area is where most of the loadings fall. There is a parallelism between loadings and scores so that, the peaks falling in the same area of a set of samples are usually intense in this set of samples.

A second PCA was performed to study the effect of box cleaning on wafer cleanliness. The first and the third principal components are effective in separating all four PP boxes as can be seen in figure 3. The distribution of the loadings in the plane PC#1-PC#3 can help to relate particular peaks with the boxes from which the samples are coming. PP surface B is associated with a set of peaks $C_xH_ySi_zO_p$ that can be associated with the presence of siloxanes. The third PC is projecting *PP surfact A* in the positive semi-plane and *PP water* in the negative. Peaks that are significant in PC#3 are mostly containing nitrogen and can be related to amine. In this case the distribution of the peaks in the loadings plane can not be directly related to the relative intensities among the samples as can be seen in figure 4. In this case two peaks very close in the plane of figure 3 show a different trend among the samples. Samples may have complex relations with the loadings as in this example and in order to draw correct conclusion significant peaks must always be studied in a univariate way.

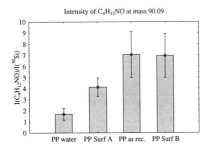

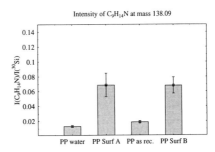

Figure 4: Peak intensities of masses showing opposite loadings values in PC #3, but similar behavior, showing how PCA analysis can be misleading.

4.Conclusions

PCA showed to be very effective in discriminating among different boxes as demonstrated by the separation of the samples in the scores PC-plane and gives some indication on the nature of the contaminants responsible of the differences. Nevertheless this kind of analysis is not sufficient to give a satisfactory description of the studied system and a single peak analysis was necessary to fully understand the contamination occurring in the boxes. A more sophisticated multivariate analysis more focussed on samples discrimination and classification will be performed to improve the information obtainable by the multivariate approach.

This work showed that the choice of the box and his cleaning protocol has a remarkable effect on the nature and amount of contamination on the silicon wafer and stimulates further studies on this topic in the future.

Acknowledgement. This work has been supported by European Community as part of project ESPRIT 28091 FABTOF.

References

[1]. K. Saga and T. Hattori, *J. Electrochem. Soc.*, **143**(10), (1996), 3279.

[2]. T. Hattori Ultraclean Surface Processing of Silicon Wafers, Springer-Verlag, Berlin,1998.

[3]. L.A. Fergason, *Microcontamination*, pp33-40, April, 1986.

[4]. E.J. Mori, J.D.Dowdy, and L. Shive, *Microcontamination*, pp35-38, Nov. 1996.

[5]. P. Sun, M. Adams, L. Shive, and S. Pirooz, SPIE, **3215**, pp118-127, Oct. 1997.

[6]. K. J. Budde, W. J. Holzapfel and M. M. Beyer *J. Electrochem. Soc.*, **142**(3), (1995), 888.

[7]. X. Vanden Eynde and P. Bertrand, *Surf. Interf. Sci.*, **25**, (1997) 878.

[8]. Å. Öhrlund, L. Hjertson and S. Jacobsson, *Surf. Interf. Sci.*, **25**, (1997) 105.

[9]. A. Chilkoty and B. D. Ratner, *Anal. Chem.*, **65**, (1993), 1736.

A. Benninghoven, P. Bertrand, H.-N. Migeon and H.W. Werner (Editors).
Proceedings of the 12th International Conference on Secondary Ion Mass Spectrometry,
Brussels, Belgium, 5-11 September 1999
© 2000 Elsevier Science B.V. All rights reserved.

IMAGE ANALYSIS METHODS FOR THE QUANTIFICATION OF ION IMAGES

A. Spool, K. Kuboi

IBM Corporation, 5600 Cottle Road, San Jose, CA 95193
spool@us.ibm.com

1. Introduction

While the quantification of SIMS spectra has become a common undertaking, only qualitative information is generally obtained from the mass selected images the SIMS technique now routinely produces. For example, the segregation of Cobalt onto magnetic recording disk surfaces after treatment with elevated temperature and humidity is now typically quantified using TOF-SIMS [1]. The Nickel which may also segregate to the surface of the those disks with Aluminum / Magnesium electroless plated Nickel substrates, especially in the presence of corrosive agents, is generally inhomogeneous across the surface in ways that vary from disk to disk. This inhomogeneity has been noted qualitatively before [2], but no attempt has been made to systematically assess the ion images. As an example of how quantitative information can be obtained from SIMS images using image analysis methods that are by now standard [3], we here present a quantitative assessment of such Nickel images.

2. Experimental

Magnetic recording disks of various types and vintages were exposed to elevated temperatures and humidity. TOF-SIMS data were obtained from the disks using a PHI-Evans Trift I system equipped with an In^+ Liquid Metal Ion Source. The ion source was set to a beam voltage of 15 kV, which in conjunction with a 3 kV extraction potential at the sample meant that the primary ions struck the samples with 12 kV impact energy. The ion source was tuned for the good lateral resolution (sub-micron resolution) which in this instrument meant that beam bunching was not employed and that the mass resolution of the spectrum was relatively poor (m/Δm for Ni was approximately 10^3). Nonetheless, the mass resolution was sufficient to resolve the Ni peak from any others. For these experiments, data acquisition was performed for 5 minutes on each sample, using approximately 10 ns pulses of a 600 pA DC Ion Beam. Ion images were obtained on the instrument using PHI's WinCadence software and transferred via the Windows NT clipboard to Adobe Photoshop Version 5.0 for further analysis. The Image Processing Toolkit Version 2.5 was used to enhance the capabilities of the Adobe Photoshop program so we could perform many of the algorithms described below.

3. Results and Discussion

Figure 1 shows two ion images from two different disks, showing qualitatively different distributions of Ni. The human eye readily distinguishes that the first image has more spots, while the second has fewer, but larger spots. The images are quite grainy, however, since the Ni being detected is present in a low concentration (a good reason to use SIMS for this

352

measurement) and because we have many of these measurements to do and so don't want to spend too long on any one of them.

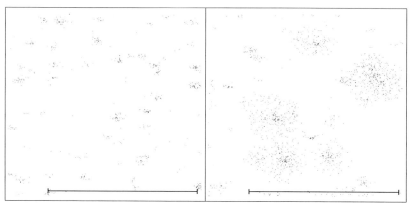

Figure 1: Mass selected Ni Ion Images from Two different disks (bar is 100 microns long)

The trick is to process these images as the human eye would, grouping those pixels together that are clearly part of the same feature, but to do it using set algorithms that will produce consistent results on image after image. One method for doing this shown below was obtained via an empirical trial and error method.

a. Remove the scale bar by subtracting a "blank" image (one with no ion counts) from the image of interest.
b. Autoscale the image (to set the pixel with the greatest number of counts in the image to black, the background to white) [4].
c. Apply the rank operation [5] "Darkest" to expand the dark pixels (reduce the background areas between the black pixels). The operation ranks the pixels by setting the central pixel to the darkest value in the 5 pixel wide circular neighborhood.
d. Apply 3 successive close operations [6]. The close operation consists of a dilation operation (adding a black pixel next to every existing black pixel) followed by an erosion operation (setting a pixel to white that is next to a background / white pixel). The effect of the close operation is to fill in the gaps in the center of your otherwise still grainy features.
e. Apply 1 added erosion operation.
f. Apply 2 successive open operations [6]. The open operation is the opposite of the close operation, as one might expect. It is the combination of an erosion operation followed by a dilation operation. An open operation has the effect of removing lone black pixels from the middle of otherwise white areas.
g. Apply the watershed operation [7] if desired. This operation, based on a Euclidean Distance Map, separates overlapping features (one is assuming the features one wants to count would have been somewhat circular if they hadn't run into each other). This operation can create errors including dependency on over all image intensity and can produce overly fragmented features.

h. Measure the resulting image [8]. One can count features, measure their sizes (area), measure the total percentage of the viewed area subtended by the features, and so on.

The images that result from this algorithm when it is applied to the images in Figure 1, are shown in Figures 2 and 3.

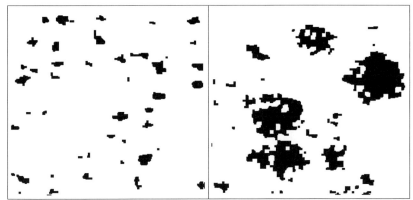

Figure 2: Images from figure 1 processed through the above algorithm, without watershed.

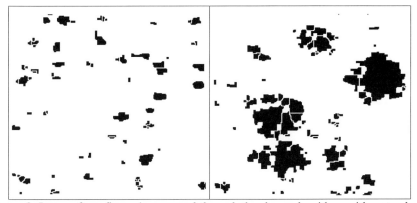

Figure 3: Images from figure 1 processed through the above algorithm, with watershed.

The choice of whether to use the watershed operation or not, or indeed how to process the image at all is largely a matter of judgement. The important point is that once one chooses an algorithm, one can apply it in exactly the same way to a series of images and thus come up with measurements of the images that are directly comparable.

An example of some measurements that can be made is shown in Table I. Note that the primary effect of the watershed operation is to change the number of features, but that this is at least a consistent effect. The Ni density described in the table is the number of Ni counts (in raw SIMS signal) divided by the area (in square microns) subtended by the features containing the Ni. The area is derived from the size of the raster and an analysis of the above images which gives the percent area of the features. More counts from a sample with smaller features will give a larger Ni density. Higher Ni density for a given Ni signal level means that the Ni detected is more segregated and more likely to have depth, and therefore be undercounted by surface analysis techniques such as SIMS and ESCA.

Table 1. Measurements of Processed Images (Figures 2 and 3)

Sample	Watershed	^{58}Ni Counts	# Features	% Area	cts/feature	Ni density
1	No	818	44	5	19	0.97
2	No	1704	32	17	53	0.59
1	Yes	818	74	5	11	0.97
2	Yes	1704	81	17	21	0.59

Additional measurements that can be made in this application include the determination of the average ratio of the long axis of the features with the short axis (determining how round the features are) and the measurement of the relative orientation of the features' long axes (whether the Ni spots elongate along, for example, polish marks).

4. Conclusions

The images that SIMS instruments produce can be quantified just as readily as the SIMS spectra can. The mature field of Image Processing can now be brought to bear on the SIMS field, as we have demonstrated in this paper.

References

[1]   L. J. Huang, Y. Hung, and S. Chang, *Secondary Ion Mass Spectrometry, Proceedings of the 11th International Conference*, G. Gillen, R. Lareau, J. Bennett and F. Stevie ed., Wiley, Chichester, 1998, 563-566.

[2]   T. J. Schuerlein, C. A. Evans, P. M. Lindley, *ibid*, 615-618.

[3]   J. C. Russ, *The Image Processing Handbook*, CRC Press Inc., Boca Raton, 1995.

[4]   J. C. Russ, *ibid*, 271-272.

[5]   J. C. Russ, *ibid*, 249-250.

[6]   J. C. Russ, *ibid*, 433-451.

[7]   J. C. Russ, *ibid*, 1995, 469-474.

[8]   J. C. Russ, *ibid*, 481-515.

A. Benninghoven, P. Bertrand, H.-N. Migeon and H.W. Werner (Editors).
Proceedings of the 12ᵗʰ International Conference on Secondary Ion Mass Spectrometry,
Brussels, Belgium, 5-11 September 1999

355

DEVELOPMENT OF A WINDOWS NT-BASED DYNAMIC SIMS SOFTWARE PROGRAM FOR INSTRUMENT CONTROL AND DATA REDUCTION ACROSS DIFFERENT INSTRUMENT PLATFORMS

P.J.McNitt[1], J.J.Hagen[2], D.J.Martel[2] and R.A.Register[1]

1. Physical Electronics, 575 Chesapeake Dr., Redwood City, CA 94063, U.S.A.
Pmcnitt@phi.com
2. Charles Evans & Associates, 301 Chesapeake Dr., Redwood City, CA 94063, U.S.A

1.Introduction

The workplace environment in which the analyst operates has changed dramatically with the advent of operating systems that permit parallel use and interaction of multiple applications. In this paper we report on new software, running under Windows NT, that provides instrument control and data reduction for magnetic sector, time of flight, and quadrupole SIMS instruments. The benefits of working within the Windows environment are well known, and for the SIMS analyst include easy integration of SIMS data and images into standard business applications. The new software addresses the limitations imposed by previous operating systems while incorporating and building upon various features that made the previous software a widely used tool.

All data and all acquisition and instrument parameters are individually time stamped so that any and all changes of state during an experiment can be accounted for during data reduction. Individual time stamping, combined with powerful 'calculation trees' (the integration of raw data with mathematical functions, and analytical parameters) allows the user to create arbitrarily complex curves and avoid some processing artifacts. A solid object-oriented design, incorporating ActiveX, and structured file storage (allowing forward and backward file compatibility) have aided in the implementation of complex features, such as curve arithmetic and layering.

Other features of the software, such as auto analysis and batch processing of data will also be discussed.

2.Advantages of Windows NT

The prevalence of Windows in the commercial environment makes it an obvious choice of platform for the development of next-generation data acquisition and reduction software. The data display and data navigation tools are very similar in 'look and feel' to the Windows Explorer, an interface instantly familiar to most users.

Data is either loaded or acquired in to a 'browser'. Fig 1 shows a typical Profile Browser. The display is divided into four main areas. The 'Tree View' in the upper left corner of the screen offers a hierarchical view of all aspects of the data. The 'List View', immediately below the tree view, shows details of the data selected in the tree view. For example, if

'Acquisitions' are selected in the tree view, the list view displays, in a sortable list, all the acquisitions loaded into the browser and their properties. Navigating down into the tree view reveals data in more and more detail, much like viewing the directory structure of a disk drive with the Explorer. This flexibility of data display will easily handle addition of new and more complex data reduction functionality in the future. Multiple selection in the list view allows rapid application of the same operation to many data objects simultaneously, specifying a single RSF for species across multiple acquisitions, for example.

The graph (on the right side of the browser) offers many new formatting and display options, such as complete control of label font, size, position, and color, data point symbols, *etc.* Graphs can be saved to file or the clipboard in both BMP and Windows Metafile format allowing use in other software such as word processors, immediate e-mailing or posting on a web site. Data can also be saved to a file or the clipboard, giving immediate access to spreadsheets like Excel and more powerful scientific analysis packages.

Immediately below the list view is an area reserved for tools that require interaction with the graph. Dose calculations, for example, require the user to select end points and a base line; these parameters can be entered graphically or via text edit controls (fig. 1). Once the parameters have been specified, other curves can be selected from the list view, and the dose is shown. Interaction between the various parts of the browser minimizes the number of steps needed to accomplish any given task.

3.Cross Platform Capability

The modular architecture of the software allows data reduction capability to be rapidly shared across instrument platforms. 'Browsers' are developed for each type of acquisition (profiling, spectra, imaging, *etc.*) as ActiveX controls, allowing them to be used in different software packages without modification. As an example the profile browser (discussed above) developed for dynamic SIMS (Phi Quads and CAMECA) is being adopted by the Phi TOF-SIMS software and the imaging browser from the TOF platform will be used in dynamic SIMS.

4.Data Structures

Individual time stamping of data allows for improved accuracy of established data reduction techniques particularly for shallow implants or isotope ratio measurements. It will also make many new features possible, such as the addition or removal of species during an acquisition on a quadrupole or TOF instrument (all data cycles were previously assumed to be of the same duration).

The user will be able to model time varying phenomena in ways not possible with the previous generation of SIMS software. In layered samples for instance, the analyst previously declared separate RSFs and sputter rates for each layer. However, no account could be made for the continuous transition of the RSFs and sputter rates at layer boundaries, resulting in significant artifacts. The new software permits the calculation of smoothly varying RSFs and sputter rates in any interface region. The challenge for analysts will be to derive functions that successfully model the transitions.

All critical acquisition parameters and instrument settings are also time-stamped. Any instrument parameter such as the raster size could be changed at any point during a profile. The exact time and magnitude of the change is recorded within the raw data. These changes can then be factored back into the quantification routines.

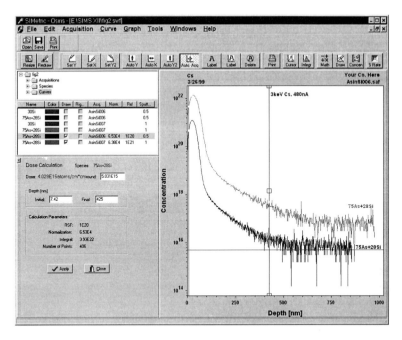

Fig 1. Profile Browser

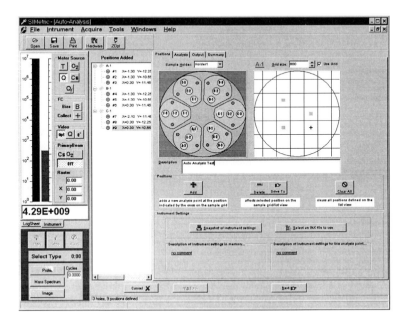

Fig. 2. Automated Analysis setup dialog box.

Another fundamental feature of the program's architecture is the 'calculation tree'. This is used to tie raw data sets together with mathematical processing to produce arbitrarily complex curves, including curve arithmetic between different acquisitions. This is important where conflicting requirements for high data density and good detection limits make it necessary to acquire different species in separate acquisitions, and then use one to normalize the others. This situation is familiar to users of CAMECA dynamic SIMS instruments.

The software has been designed to allow advanced users to write their own functions that can be 'plugged in' and added to the set of possible arithmetic functions.

5.Miscellaneous Features

As the demands of the production environment increase, some form of automated analysis becomes highly desirable. WinCadence (TOF) and Simetric (Quadrupole) instrument control software from Physical Electronics both have automated analysis capability (fig 2). In order to process the large amounts of data being generated from an automated instrument in a timely fashion, batch processing is necessary. Such a tool has been developed in the new data reduction software, modeled after the 'Load Similar' function in the old DOS version of the software (but without many of the limitations). The batch processing is much more powerful, and allows the user to simultaneously process many raw data files. Batch processing is not limited to simply producing similar graphs, but will handle other processing such as a dose calculation for each data set.

Instrument control voltages and profile setup parameters are automatically stored as part of each data file, allowing an instrument state associated with a specific set of data to be recalled later. A 'filtering' mechanism permits the importing of specific voltages from any data or instrument setting file, such as the mass spectrometer or primary column voltages, without affecting other settings. Acquisition data that has been partly or fully quantified may be stored as a separate 'workfile'.

The data reduction part of the software is compatible with data files generated within the older DOS-based programs, and with profiling data from TOF-SIMS instruments.

6.Conclusion

The SIMS instrument control and data acquisition software will operate on a number of instrument platforms. These include the new generation of quadrupole SIMS and time of flight instruments from Physical Electronics, in addition to CAMECA IMS-3F/5F dynamic SIMS instruments using their original control electronics, and CAMECA IMS-3F/5F controlled with the newly available electronics upgrade from Masstek Services Ltd. Support of new instrumentation will be relatively straightforward (such as ongoing development of Quadrupole and TOF-SIMS instruments by Physical electronics, and possibly CAMECA IMS-6F).

Data reduction tools and techniques build on more than 10 years of development of the previous generation of software, and the experience and input of many SIMS analysts. The power and stability of Windows allow the programmer to provide a familiar set of tools for the user to integrate their data in to the modern business model.

A. Benninghoven, P. Bertrand, H.-N. Migeon and H.W. Werner (Editors).
Proceedings of the 12ᵗʰ International Conference on Secondary Ion Mass Spectrometry,
Brussels, Belgium, 5-11 September 1999

359

THE COMBINED WIENER FILTERING / MAXIMUM ENTROPY DECONVOLUTION IN DATA PROCESSING OF SIMS MEASUREMENTS: MASS RESOLUTION ENHANCEMENT *

Igor V. Veryovkin[a], Ina Constantinides, Annemie Adriaens[b] and Freddy Adams

Department of Chemistry, University of Antwerp (U.I.A.), Universiteitsplein 1,
B-2610 Antwerp (Wilrijk), Belgium e-mail: inaco@uia.ua.ac.be

1. Introduction

During the past ten years, mathematical deconvolution procedures have been successfully applied to results of SIMS depth profiling [1] and permitted noticeable improvements of the depth resolution. Such data processing procedures may also be applied to mass spectra and energy distributions of secondary ions measured by secondary ion mass spectrometers. An improvement of mass spectral resolution of such instruments by fine tuning procedures is limited since it affects their dynamic range: to enhance the mass resolution, slits in magnetic sector instruments or primary ion pulses in time-of-fight instruments should be narrowed, which makes the detected signal lower. Therefore optimal alignments of the mass spectrometers are always a compromise between gaining the resolution and losing the signal (and vice versa). The use of deconvolution procedures might enhance the mass spectral resolution without deteriorating the dynamic range because it can reconstruct the «true» (i.e. *high resolution*) spectra from the *high intensity* spectra «corrupted» by a low resolution measuring procedure. It was an intention of this work to develop a simple deconvolution procedure capable of performing these operations with experimental data measured by a magnetic sector instrument.

2. The Method

In general, the measuring process is imperfect so that what comes out from the mass spectrometer is a corrupted signal $c(t)$. Here, using the variable t (times) corresponds to the fact that the mass spectrum is a finite set of data points measured with some (equal) sampling interval. This signal may be less than perfect in either or both of two respects. First, the apparatus may not have a perfect «delta-function» response, so that the true signal, $u(t)$, is convolved with some known response function $r(t)$ to give a smeared signal, $s(t)$,

$$s(t) = r(t) * u(t) = \int_{-\infty}^{\infty} r(t-\tau)u(\tau)d\tau \qquad \text{or} \qquad S(f) = R(f)U(f) \qquad (1),$$

where S, R, U are the Fourier transforms of s, r, u, respectively.

---

* The contribution to the «IMMACO» Project (European Commission, DG XII, SMT4-CT96-2055), and partially supported by INTAS (Project 96-470).

[a] I. Veryovkin is the corresponding author and indebted to the Belgian Federal Office for Scientific, Technical and Cultural Affairs (DWTC/OSTC). Present address: Materials Science and Chemistry Divisions, Argonne National Laboratory, 9700 S. Cass Avenue, Argonne. IL 60439, U.S.A.; e-mail: verigo@anl.gov.

[b] A. Adriaens is indepted to the Flemish Fund for Scientific Research (FWO).

Second, the measured signal, $c(t)$, may contain an additional component of noise $n(t)$:

$$c(t) = s(t) + n(t) \qquad (2).$$

The restoration of the true signal, $u(t)$, from the experimental signal, $c(t)$, is not a trivial task. This inverse problem is ill-posed, and some form of regularization is needed to recover $u(t)$ [2]. For this purpose, forward methods (like Maximum Entropy Method - MEM, Ref.3) and inverse methods (based on the Fourier transform properties of the convolution integral shown in Eq.1) can be used. Inverse methods are simpler and faster than forward methods but may produce extreme noise amplification and physically unrealistic negative regions in the deconvolved signal. The inverse method, which takes into account and eliminates the noise component from the measured signal, was developed by N. Wiener [4]. A power spectrum of the measured signal in *a frequency domain*, which corresponds to the sampling interval, should be analyzed in order to build the *Optimum* (Wiener) filter $\Phi(f)$, which, when applied to the measured signal $C(f)$ and then deconvolved by response function $R(f)$, produces a signal $\tilde{U}(f)$, which is as close as possible to the uncorrupted signal $U(f)$:

$$\tilde{U}(f) = \frac{C(f)\Phi(f)}{R(f)} \qquad (3).$$

By performing the inverse Fourier transform of $\tilde{U}(f)$, the deconvolved signal, $\tilde{u}(t)$, which is a maximum likelihood estimate of the true signal, $u(t)$, can be then obtained. Wiener Filtering is based on the fact that, in the majority of cases, a clear distinction between frequency components of the smeared signal, $s(t)$, and noise, $n(t)$, is possible, which allows approximating the power spectrum by a sum of two model functions describing each of the spectrum components. Usually, least square fitting techniques are used for this identification purpose. Unfortunately, an arbitrary selection of the fitting functions can dramatically affect results of such an inverse deconvolution procedure.

In the present work, instead of looking for the best fitting functions for modeling the noise and smeared signal components of the power spectrum, we proposed to build them by using the *linear prediction* technique. As shown in Fig.1, such an approach permits replacing arbitrarily chosen functions by those reconstructed using statistically evident information, as follows: (1) For the sampling frequency range where the noise is hidden under the smeared signal component, the noise can be predicted by using the visible noise (high frequency «tail» of the power spectrum) as a *basis data set* for the linear prediction. It is especially useful for cases with poor signal-to-noise ratios because visible noise components of the corresponding power spectra cover the major part of the frequency range. In such cases, a prediction for few data points can be done using many data points, which makes the accuracy of the prediction procedure sufficient and provides reliable results. (2) For the same range, the smeared signal component is visible, and the difference between the power spectrum of the measured signal and the predicted noise spectrum can be calculated and used as a basis for a linear prediction. In this case, the range where the smeared signal is predicted should not be wider than the range where the signal is visible. This helps to avoid prediction errors that are quite probable when many data points are predicted using few data points. (3) Looping calculations subsequently repeating predictions 1 and 2 can be performed to minimize the difference between the sum of these predictions and the power spectrum of the measured signal. Noise and smeared signal components reconstructed in this way provide accurate results for building the Optimum

(Wiener) filter, which can suppress the noise component by several orders of magnitude and can be used both for the noise filtering and for the deconvolution procedures.

Figure 1 gives the essence of the proposed algorithm by showing the shape of the filter (a) and the power spectrum (b). Both correspond to experimental data discussed below. For calculating linear prediction coefficients necessary for the reconstruction of the signal and noise components, *Burg's algorithm* [5], which is based on the Maximum Entropy Method, has been selected. *Another issue* is producing the power spectra of the measured signal. For this purpose, two approaches generally can be used: (1) the Fast Fourier Transform (FFT) technique, which is the conventional method in use, and (2) the linear

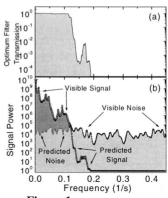

Figure 1.

prediction technique, which is known to provide better estimates for some special cases. We used and compared both approaches and found that the latter stabilizes the algorithm described above. For calculating the power spectra, the same Burg's linear prediction algorithm [5] as in the filtering procedure was used. This algorithm is known in this context as Maximum Entropy Spectrum Analysis (MESA). Thus, we performed Wiener filtering by using MEM technique both for producing power spectra of measured signal and for the reconstruction of the information from these spectra.

3. Results and discussion

To examine the proposed data processing procedure, the CAMECA IMS-4F double focusing secondary ion mass spectrometer has been used in a series of measurements. Mass spectra of positive secondary ions sputtered by 5.5 keV ions of alkali metals (Cs^+, $^{85}Rb^+$, $^{87}Rb^+$, and Na^+) from standard reference materials (leaded bronze, C50.04-2, and gunmetal, C70.32-1, prepared by the BNF Metal Technology Center, UK) have been obtained. To compare experimental data corresponding to different mass resolutions, the measurements were performed for several different alignments (widths) of slits of the instrument. Low resolution spectra were then processed in order to restore «high resolution» spectra and compared with experimental high resolution mass spectra. To compare the deconvolved and experimental spectra, a special procedure providing the same (high) mass resolution in both spectra was used for definition of the response function $r(t)$ from Eq.1. In essence, for the data measured with low resolution, we used response functions sufficient to improve the mass resolution so that it matched data measured with high resolution.

It is infeasible to determine in an accurate experimental or analytical manner the actual response function of the SIMS instrument. Such a *mass resolution function* (MRF) can be mass dependent due to the non-linearity of the mass scale. This requires developing a special procedure capable of taking the non-linearity into account. Nevertheless, this limitation can be passed over when performing deconvolution of data for a reasonably narrow mass range. Then the variation of the resolution function versus mass can be neglected, in the first approximation, so that the same function can be used within the entire selected range. We determined such a resolution function from a comparison between experimental measurements

362

performed with high and low resolution for the selected range. In this approach, the low resolution experimental data can be considered a convolution of the high resolution experimental data with such a mass resolution function. To identify this function, it is necessary to choose one peak with high intensity, which has a good signal-to-noise ratio, and is believed not to have any interference with other masses. For experiments with Cs^+ ion bombardment carried out within mass range 380 to 400 a.m.u., the peak at 399 a.m.u., corresponding to Cs_3^+, was selected. For the high resolution mass spectrum, this peak was fit by the Gaussian function. This was then used as a *temporary* response function in deconvolution of the corresponding Cs_3^+ peak of the low resolution mass

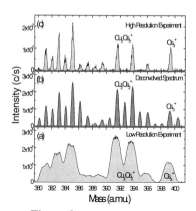

Figure 2.

spectrum. The Wiener filtering algorithm described above can be used in such a deconvolution procedure, and its result can be fit by the Asymmetric Double Sigmoidal function, which, when convolved with the experimental high resolution mass spectrum, transforms it into the spectrum measured with low resolution. This peak function can be used to enhance the mass resolution of the latter spectrum. In this case, the response function is applied to deconvolution of the data corresponding to the entire mass range of interest. It is important to notice that the shape of the mass peaks is inconsequential for the procedure so that, in principle, the peak functions we selected can be replaced by any other appropriate peak functions. Sufficiently narrow sampling interval of the experimental data can produce a spectrum with any desired mass resolution. Figure 2 shows the mass spectra for leaded bronze under low (a) and high (c) resolution, and the corresponding deconvolved spectrum (b). The deconvolution results (Fig.2b) obtained from the low resolution spectrum (Fig.2a) are compared with the high resolution spectrum (Fig.2c); the capability of the developed procedure to enhance mass spectral resolution is clearly seen. This capability was useful in our experiments with different alkali metal primary ions (to be published elsewhere) because measurements with Rb^+ and Na^+ were carried out at lower ion currents and wider slits than those for Cs^+. At this point, we can conclude that the method outlined above is robust and can be used in other spectrometric and spectroscopic experiments where resolution enhancements are required, taking care that the variation of the resolution function can be neglected within processed spectrum range.

Acknowledgements

Authors are thankful to Dr. W. F. Calaway for his useful comments and help.

References

[1]   D. P. Chu and M. G. Dowsett, Phys. Rev. B56 (1997) 15167
[2]   L. L. Scharf, *Statistical Signal Processing: Detection, Estimation and Time Series Analysis*, Addison-Wesley, Reading (MA) – Menlo Park (CA) – New York, 1990
[3]   E. T. Jaynes, Phys. Rev. B 106 (1957) 620
[4]   N. Wiener, *Extrapolation, Interpolation and Smoothing of Stationary Time Series with Engineering Applications*, Technology Press and Wiley, New York, 1949
[5]   [5] J. P. Burg, *Maximum Entropy Spectral Analysis*, Ph.D. Thesis, Stanford University, Stanford (CA), 1975

SECTION 9 :
QUANTIFICATION

A. Benninghoven, P. Bertrand, H.-N. Migeon and H.W. Werner (Editors).
Proceedings of the 12th International Conference on Secondary Ion Mass Spectrometry,
Brussels, Belgium, 5-11 September 1999
© 2000 Elsevier Science B.V. All rights reserved.

AN INVESTIGATION OF MATRIX EFFECTS IN THE ANALYSIS OF FLUORINE IN HUMITE-GROUP MINERALS

Luisa Ottolini[*] & Fernando Cámara[§]

CNR-Centro di Studio per la Cristallochimica e la Cristallografia, Via Ferrata 1
I-27100 Pavia, Italy.

1. Introduction

Some previous works by EMPA (Electron Micro-Probe Analysis) have revealed the difficulties in determining F in several matrices. In a comparison among minerals, F content derived by EMPA agreed with wet chemical analysis with the exception of topaz [1]. Although topaz (17.6 wt.% F) contains more F than the norbergite (13.5 wt.% F), the $FK\alpha$ peak heights resulted nearly identical, with a net content for F in topaz 20% too low. However, a study of the $FK\alpha$ peak shape showed that the areas of the two peaks are different, 20% larger for the topaz than for norbergite. Peak shifts and changes in peak shape were also detected for a variety of minerals. For topaz (which represents the most dramatic case), it seemed that a measurement of the area would be more convenient than that of the peak intensity [1]. But, probably, this would not be a general, practical procedure given the low count rates of less than 1 cps for most minerals [1]. Other limiting factors which have hampered an accurate fluorine analysis by EMPA are the presence of interferences, the influence of sample chemical composition on the X-ray intensity and the lack of suitable standards. A matter of concern has been the strong dependence of count rate from crystal orientation. Under *routine* EMPA conditions, $FK\alpha$ X-ray intensities of Durango fluorapatite sections with the surface perpendicular to the c axis increase up to 100% during the first 60 s of exposure to the beam [2]. After longer periods, the intensity falls to values below the initial intensity. This effect evidences the strongly anisotropic character of the X-ray intensity emission. Sections parallel to the c axis show a similar behavior but on a scale approximately 20 times longer. No change in $FK\alpha$ intensity was evidenced in topaz, whereas in fluorite one observes a decline in intensity with increasing duration of beam exposure. Experiments on F-bearing amphiboles and micas with non-controlled crystallographic orientation did not reveal any significant increase in intensity, nor anisotropy for $FK\alpha$ X rays [2].

It seems therefore that many problems affect the measurement of F by EMPA, a few of them not entirely understood. To overcome peak shift and peak shape changes it would be required to integrate the peak area, which is very time-consuming. One alternative method is to use Area Peak Factors (APFs) [3]. The APF factor is calculated starting from one standard and one unknown sample (S and U, respectively) where $APF = (I_U^I \cdot I_S^P)/(I_U^P \cdot I_S^I)$. I_U^I is the integrated intensity of the unknown; I_S^P is the peak-intensity of the standard; I_U^P is the peak-intensity of the unknown; and I_S^I is the integrated intensity of the standard. In EMP analytical work, however, such a procedure is not yet much diffused. A few examples of application of

---

[*] Corresponding author. E-mail address: ottolini@crystal.unipv.it
[§] Present address: Univ. Sciences & Technologie de Lille, Bat C6, F-59655 Villeneuve d'Ascq-Cedex, France

APFs concern the quantification of boron in some binary borides [4], of nitrogen [5] and oxygen [6].

Not much SIMS data for fluorine has been available until now. Problems in F quantification are mainly due to the lack of well-characterized reference samples for any matrix of interest, and the presence of matrix effects [7, 8]. These latter are a complex function of chemical composition, crystal structure and/or crystallographic orientation of the sample. Due to the complexity of sputtering/ionization process, they cannot be easily predicted for a given mineral chemistry. They generally change when changing matrix composition and are believed to increase with the concentration of the element itself. As for orientation matrix effects, no systematic fluorine investigation has been carried out so far by SIMS, so that when one speaks about matrix effects, one mainly refers to chemical matrix effects.

Fluorine has been analyzed by SIMS using either positive or negative secondary ions. Positive F ions are very intense at low secondary ion energies and this was ascribed to the efficiency with which secondary electrons can desorb F ions from the sample [9]. Significant matrix effects for F are reported in literature between F-bearing minerals and glasses [10]. Monitoring high-energy positive secondary ions revealed useful in reducing the influence of non-linear effects and a working curve for fluorine in a set of silicates (kornerupine, phlogopite, amphibole and topaz) was obtained [11]. The discrepancy between ion and electron microprobe values (these latter assumed as the reference for SIMS) has been $\sim \pm 20\%$ for F concentrations > 0.1 wt.%. The relative-to-Si ion yield for fluorine, $IY(F/Si)$, under these experimental conditions, is about two orders of magnitude lower than that of other light elements, for instance, lithium [$IY(Li/Si) \sim 1.5$] due to the relatively high ionization potential for fluorine, i.e., 17.42 eV against 5.39 eV for Li. A calibration line was obtained monitoring low-energy positive secondary ions in humite-group minerals [12]. Negative secondary ions for F are much more intense than positive ones: 1 count/s $F^- \sim > 1$ ppm for 1 nA O^- and secondary ions with 50 ± 20 eV. Matrix effects were also detected among F-rich amphibole, apatite, and rhyolite glasses [13].

2. Experiments

With the aim of gaining an insight into the matrix effects affecting the microanalysis of fluorine, we have selected humite-group minerals [nMg$_2$SiO$_4$•Mg(F,OH)$_2$, where n=1 stands for norbergite, n=2 for chondrodite, n=3 for humite, and n=4 for clinohumite] and we analyzed them by EMPA and SIMS. In the absence of substitutions other than (F,OH), they represent a magnesium-silicate matrix with an approximate constant Si/Mg ratio and a variable quantity of OH or F. Moreover, in order to isolate the matrix effects related to Si and/or Mg contents, we selected a fluoborite [Mg$_3$(OH,F)$_3$(BO$_3$)] sample, which presents a composition similar to that of humite-group minerals, but without Si.

The chosen series of samples are (in order of increasing F content): clinohumite, chondrodite, norbergite and fluoborite. The crystals were mounted in epoxy resin and polished. In order to investigate the possible role of crystal orientation on $FK\alpha$ X-ray emission and fluorine ionization, we determined the different crystal orientation with a diffractometer before embedding the grains in epoxy. In humite-group minerals F is concentrated in bands perpendicular to b axis: therefore the angle between the incident beam and those planes was calculated for each crystal. Two crystals of norbergite, one of clinohumite and one of chondrodite were embedded with b axis parallel to the electron beam, whereas one crystal of clinohumite and one of chondrodite were embedded in a general position with none of their cell-axes parallel to the e-beam (electron beam). Another crystal of norbergite was mounted with its *a* axis at 35° to the e-beam ("disoriented" crystal). The two fluoborite samples were embedded with their *c* axis perpendicular and parallel to the e-beam, respectively. SIMS investigations were carried out by means of a Cameca IMS 4f ion microprobe. The experimental set up involves the use of high-energy positive secondary ions: $^{19}F^+$, $^{24}M^+$ and $^{30}Si^+$ isotopes in the range 75-125 eV, $^{16}O^-$ primary ions, 2 nA current intensity and a ~ 5-μm ∅. The reference F concentrations were obtained by EMPA. We used a RAP crystal [Rubidium Acid Phthalate] as the analyzer crystal, 7 and 15 keV electron beam energy for F (15 keV for all major constituents), 20 nA current intensity and a 30-μm ∅ electron beam. $\phi(\rho z)$ corrections were employed.

3. Results

In the present paper, we show the results and the extent of matrix effects we can encounter when working with *routine* EMP procedures in the analysis of fluorine in silicates and Mg-bearing samples. A detailed description of the procedure for our calculations of APFs, the related corrections as well as the SIMS results relative to Si are reported in [14]. New accurate F calibration curves for SIMS have been worked out taking Mg (Fig. 1 a,b) as the reference element for the matrix.

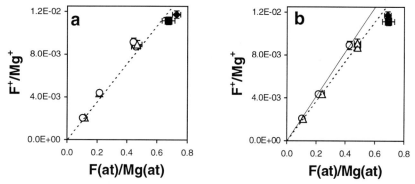

Fig. 1. Working curves obtained by plotting ion intensity ratio (F^+/Mg^+) vs. at.% concentration ratio F(at)/Mg(at). Fluoborite samples are reported for comparison. F concentrations from EMPA obtained at 15 keV (a), and 7 keV (b). Symbols, as it follows: empty circles = humite-group "disoriented" crystals; triangles = "oriented" ones; filled symbols = fluoborite samples, square = *c* axis parallel to e-beam, diamond = *c* axis perpendicular to e-beam. Errors (±2σ) smaller than symbol or shown by error bars. Reprinted from [14] with the permission of the Mineralogical Society of America.

In Fig. 1a the agreement between experimental data and fitted line was generally within or comparable to the experimental error. In only few cases, the discrepancy was higher. "Disoriented" norbergite does not lie on the line; the two fluoborite crystals showed a comparable IY(F/Mg) (= 0.016), lower by ~ 9% rel. than that of the regression line. Within humite-group minerals, the major discrepancy between EMPA and SIMS (Δ% = ~ 16% rel.) is shown by norbergite with a "general" orientation. The maximum difference among all IYs is ~ 25% rel.

In Fig. 1b, we see that the "disoriented" samples, i.e., samples mounted in a general orientation to the electron beam show an ion yield higher than that of the "oriented" ones

368

(= 0.018): Δ% = ~ 14% rel. This holds for humite-group minerals, suggesting that we should use these two lines. Indeed, the correlation is very good ($R^2 = 1$) for both lines that define two different trends as a function of orientation. The fluoborite crystals show a comparable (Δ% = ~ 6% rel.), lower IY. The maximum difference among all these ion yields is still ~ 25% rel.

4. Discussion

The matrix effects related to crystallographic orientation seem to be more evident for F concentrations derived at 7 keV e-beam energy (we remember that Mg content in all these samples has been obtained at 15 keV). At low energy, effects due to absorption of $FK\alpha$ intensity in the matrix are probably higher. SIMS analysis enhances these differences with the net result of two perfectly linear calibration curves for "disoriented" as well as "oriented" samples.

In case of fluoborite samples -that have the highest F content in the set (~ 20 wt.% F)-, matrix effects are more significant for the crystal with its c axis parallel to the electron beam, which shows the lowest SIMS F concentration.

When working under these experimental conditions the present results must be taken into account since the IY derived from a "disoriented" norbergite and used as a F-reference sample to quantify an unknown fluoborite could result in up to ~ 25% inaccuracy, depending on matrix effects that may be ascribed to both chemistry and crystallographic orientation.

Acknowledgements. The Authors are indebted to S. Bigi (University of Modena) for making EMP analyses, R. Gastoni (CNR-CSCC, Pavia) for crystal mounting, and M. Palenzona for ion-microprobe maintenance.

5. References

1. T.N. Solberg, Microbeam Analysis, San Francisco Press, San Francisco, 1982, p 148.
2. F.C. Jr. Stormer, M.L. Pierson and R.C. Tacker, Amer. Mineral. 78 (1993) 641.
3. G.F. Bastin, and H.J.M. Heijligers, Electron Probe Quantitation, Plenum Press, New York, N.Y., 1991, p 145.
4. G.F. Bastin, and H.J.M. Heijligers, Internal Rep. Eindhoven Univ. of Technology, Eindhoven, The Nederlands, 1986.
5. G.F. Bastin, and H.J.M. Heijligers, Internal Rep. Eindhoven Univ. of Technology, Eindhoven, The Nederlands, 1988.
6. G.F. Bastin, and H.J.M. Heijligers, Microbeam Analysis, San Francisco Press, Inc., San Francisco, California, 1989, p 207.
7. R.L. Hervig, W.T. Kortemeier and D.M. Burt, Amer. Mineral. 72 (1987) 392.
8. A.P. Jones and J.V. Smith, Neues J. Min. Monatshefte 5 (1984) 228.
9. P. Williams, Practical Surface Analysis (2nd edition), John Wiley & Sons, New York, 1992, p 177.
10. V.I. Kovalenko, R.L. Hervig and M.F. Sheridan, Amer. Mineral. 73 (1988) 1038.
11. L. Ottolini, P. Bottazzi, A. Zanetti, SIMS IX Proceedings, John Wiley & Sons, Chichester, 1994, p 191.
12. J.R. Hinthorne and C.A. Andersen, Amer. Mineral. 60 (1975) 143.
13. P.D. Ihinger, R.L. Hervig and P.F. McMillan, Reviews in Mineralogy, v. 30, Volatiles in Magmas, 1994, p 67.
14. L. Ottolini, F. Camara and S. Bigi, Amer. Mineral. 85 (2000), in press.

A. Benninghoven, P. Bertrand, H.-N. Migeon and H.W. Werner (Editors).
Proceedings of the 12th International Conference on Secondary Ion Mass Spectrometry,
Brussels, Belgium, 5-11 September 1999

369

CHARACTERIZATION OF PATTERNED WAFERS BY TOF-SIMS

T. Schuerlein[1], I. Mowat[1], R. Brigham[1], J. Metz[1], H. Li[2] and D Hymes[2]
[1]Charles Evans & Associates, Redwood City, CA [2]OnTrak Systems, Milpitas, CA

1. Introduction

The development of Cu metallization for semiconductor interconnects has lead to a large number of challenges [1]. One of these has been to understand and control the level of Cu left on the dielectric surface after processing. Copper, unlike its predecessor aluminum, cannot easily be dry etched. This has led to the development of a new technology for the production of metal interconnects, the damascene process. The detection of metallic contaminants between closely spaced Cu lines on a dielectric film (typically SiO_2) presents a challenge that cannot be readily addressed by the familiar techniques of Total Reflection X-ray Fluorescence (TXRF), Vapor Phase Decomposition (VPD), or dynamic SIMS. Time-of-Flight Secondary Ion Mass Spectrometry (TOF-SIMS) has several unique characteristics that allow it to be employed in such investigations.

In its simplest form, the damascene process involves the production of a patterned dielectric film and the subsequent deposition of Cu into the dielectric "mold". Excess Cu is polished off via a chemical mechanical polish (CMP), and then the wafer is treated with a post-CMP clean. As might be expected from an abrasive polish step, the damascene process is inherently dirty. The optimization of the CMP and post-CMP clean is of great importance to keep residual levels of Cu and other metal low on the dielectric surface. It is the dielectric surface that will be of interest in these investigations.

2. Experimental

Wafers with copper interconnects were polished back to the underlying field oxide (TEOS) film using a CMP process under investigation by LAM Research (Milpitas, CA). The wafers were then cleaned with an OnTrak Synergy™ system using various proprietary copper cleaning protocols.

TOF-SIMS data was acquired on a TRIFT II instrument. All data were acquired with a $^{69}Ga^+$ primary ion beam. Data was acquired using both high image resolution and high mass resolution settings with beam currents ranging from 200 pA to 2 nA. High mass resolution data was acquired with a 12 keV impact energy, with a corresponding mass resolution of typically >6500 and beam diameter of ca. 1-2 µm. High image resolution data was acquired with an impact energy of 22 keV, and a spot size of ca. 0.2 µm. The mass resolution in this mode was sufficient to separate species with mass deficits from those with mass excesses, SiCl and Cu were not separated, nor was ^{30}Si and ^{29}SiH.

TXRF data was acquired on a TECHNOS 610. The excitation source was a 40 Watt Mo anode.

3. Results and Discussion

With the exception of some work of metals on polymers [2], quantification by TOF SIMS has typically been restricted to the native oxide of silicon wafers [3,4] using high mass resolution analysis conditions. The current experiment requires the quantitative analysis of metals on a SiO_2 surface using high image resolution (low mass resolution). These two changes in the typical experimental protocol will be addressed.

To determine if quantification of metals on TEOS could be reliably performed using relative sensitivity factors (RSF's) generated from the native oxide on silicon wafers, a Cu coated wafer was prepared that had a large (10 cm) region in the center polished down to bare TEOS. Both TOF-SIMS and TXRF were performed on this sample. The results are shown in Table 1. The TOF-SIMS quantification, using an archival RSF, is within a factor of ~ 2 of the TXRF values for copper on this sample. A detection limit of about 5×10^9 atoms/cm^2 was extrapolated from this high mass resolution data, the detection limit in imaging mode was ~5 times higher. The trend in the copper concentration across three locations in this region of the sample showed very similar behavior for the two techniques. These data indicate that TOF-SIMS can be a useful tool for the quantitative measurement of metallic contaminants on TEOS.

The ability of TOF-SIMS to provide accurate quantification is compromised when the contamination levels are significant. The simple mathematical expression used for quantification:

$$Concentration_{Cont} = RSF * Counts_{Cont}/Counts_{Sub}$$

where "Cont" and "Sub" refer to the contaminant and substrate, respectively. This equation assumes that the substrate ion intensity is not affected by contaminant concentration. This assumption does not hold when contamination levels are high. Additionally, at significant contaminant concentrations, the ion yield of the contaminant and substrate may be affected due to a change in the matrix effects.

Analyses were performed on a sample using high mass resolution and high image resolution gun conditions to determine if quantification of metals on a SiO_2 surface was reliable under the protocols required for the analysis between closely spaced Cu lines. Concentrations obtained under the two different conditions were typically within 10% of each other, which is within the reproducibility of the measurement, indicating that high image resolution TOF data can be used to get semi-quantitative results.

	TOF	TXRF	TOF/TXRF
Right	5.6E13	3.8E13	1.5
Center	4.4E13	2.5E13	1.8
Left	4.4E13	2.2E13	2.0

Table 1: Cu atomic concentrations (in atoms/cm^2) at three locations of a large polished TEOS area on a Cu CMP wafer.

Data was acquired on two samples that had undergone different post-CMP cleaning processes, A and B. On these films, the Cu lines were separated by 10 μm of TEOS. This data is shown in Figure 1. In these images the brighter intensity reflects a stronger Cu signal.

Line-scans of the images are taken across the highlighted line. These data show a lower inter-line Cu concentration indicating that cleaning procedure B is more effective than procedure A. The calculated Cu concentrations for these two samples are *ca.* 6 x 10^{15} atoms/cm^2 and 4 x 10^{13} atoms/cm^2, respectively. The Cu concentrations on sample A were high enough that the absolute quantification is in doubt; however, the observed increase in Cu levels on sample A compared to sample B is significant.

Data acquired from Cu lines that were 1 μm wide separated by 1 μm TEOS, the data are shown in Figure 2. These results show that the image resolution on these insulating substrates is not sufficient to provide clear demarcation of the lines. It is also possible that the TOF data between these densely packed lines is representative of the surface and the surface is very smeared. Regardless of the absolute levels of Cu between the conductors, it is evident that the residual metal levels for clean A are higher than those for clean B.

In a separate experiment TOF-SIMS was used to investigate the distribution of contaminants between widely spaced features. The distribution of contaminants in larger areas may provide a clue to the origin of the contamination and allow for its removal. Cu features that were separated by 3 mm were studied with data acquired at 200 μm intervals. Figure 3 shows the distribution of several contaminants, including mobile ions, in this region. Cu levels are highest near the Cu features, indicating that smearing, not redistribution of Cu from the slurry is the major contributor to the metallic contamination. Unlike the remainder of the contaminants, Li is seen to have a non-uniform distribution through the analysis region, increasing from right to left.

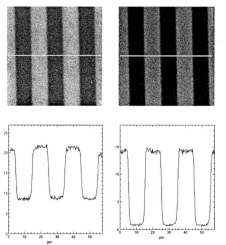

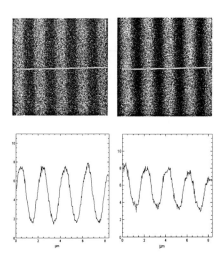

Figure1: Cu ion images and accompanying line scans of 10 μm Cu and TEOS lines with two cleaning procedures, A (left) and B (right).

Figure 2:Same as Figure 1 for 1 μm Cu and TEOS lines.

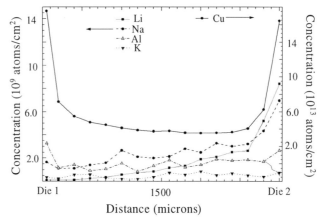

Figure 3: Distribution of elements between die.

4. Conclusions

Measurements were made to assess the ability TOF-SIMS to perform quantitative analysis by comparison with TXRF results. It was determined that quantification of low level metallic contaminants is possible by TOF-SIMS in high mass and high image resolution modes. Semi-quantitative analyses can be performed on 10 μm areas, with useful information available from line widths as small as 1 μm.

References

[1] J. Heidenreich, et. al., Proc. of the IEEE IITC, pg. 151-153 (1998).
[2] A. Golata, SIMS XI Orlando, FL, unpublished.
[3] B. Schueler, Microcontam. Con. Proc. 783 (1994).
[4] A. Schnieders, R. Mollers, A. Benninghoven, J. Vac. Sci. Technolo. B **14**, 2712 (1996).

A. Benninghoven, P. Bertrand, H.-N. Migeon and H.W. Werner (Editors).
Proceedings of the 12th International Conference on Secondary Ion Mass Spectrometry,
Brussels, Belgium, 5-11 September 1999

DEPTH PROFILING BARIUM ON AG(111)

O.M.N.D.Teodoro and A.M.C.Moutinho

GIDS/CeFITec- Physics Department

Faculty of Sciences and Technology, New University of Lisbon

Campus da Caparica, 2825-114 Caparica, Portugal

Corresponding author: O.M.N.D.Teodoro, Dep. Física da FCT/UNL

Campus da Caparica, 2825-114 Caparica, Portugal, e-mail: orlando@ideafix.df.fct.unl.pt

1. Introduction

Deposition of barium on clean metals is often performed to change the electronic properties of metal surfaces. This adsorption produces a well known decrease on the surface work function and the consequent change on the ionization probability of the particles emitted out of the surface. Applications are devices for production of negative ions, high emission and long life cathodes and thermionic energy conversion[1].

In this work, we aim to study the stability of thin barium films evaporated over the (111) face of a silver crystal. The goal was to get insight in the growing mechanisms and check if there was place for diffusion.

2 Experimental

The work has been done in a multitechnique surface analysis system [2]. Three main techniques are available: SIMS, XPS and AES. The analyzer for SIMS is a quadrupole based instrument and two ion guns are fitted: one cesium gun and one electron bombardment ion gun (normally operated with argon at 4 keV). Further details are provided in reference [2].

The silver crystal was sputtered and annealed before barium deposition, to ensure a clean surface. XPS and AES were used to check the cleanliness of the surface. Then, the barium was evaporated from a SAES getter heated by an electrical current during a fixed time period. These type of sources provide a stable and reproducible flux of metal atoms as long as the heating current has a constant intensity. All depositions have been done at room temperature.

The work function was measured by the onset method [3] that have been recently introduced in the apparatus. This method takes advantage of the AES instruments and also allows imaging of the surface. Basically, the shift in the onset energy of the secondary electrons emitted from the surface due to the primary beam (electron or ion beam), is monitored. This shift is compensated throughout an electronic unit, and the voltage needed for compensation provides the relative work function measurement.

The film was evaporated in time steps. In between, the surface was analyzed by AES and the work function was measured. After deposition SIMS depth profiles were acquired.

Since the barium films were very thin (in the order of the nm) depth profiles were taken rastering the 4 keV Ar$^+$ primary beam over a large area (300 nA in $\approx$50 mm^2), to achieve a very low erosion rate of the order of 0.1 Å/s. Only the ions emitted from the central rastered area were detected.

374

3. Results and Discussion

For submonolayer coverages, the work function showed the usual behavior— first a steeply decrease down to a minimum of 2.35 eV and then a slow increase. The Auger silver signal decreases and the barium signal rises from zero, as expected. Figure 1 shows this variation (note the presence of two vertical scales).

However, for longer deposition times we found that the work function will never increase to 2.7 eV (the work function of bulk barium) and the Auger silver signal will never reach zero intensity, no matter the amount deposited. Even taking in account that the escape depth of Auger electrons can be 1 nm or larger, the silver signal should continuously decrease with the deposition of barium.

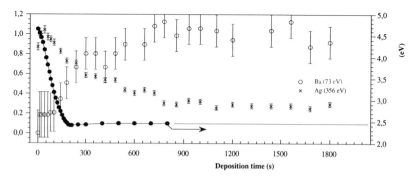

Fig. 1— Relative Auger intensities during the deposition of barium on Ag(111). The work function variation is also plotted (right axis). It is evident that the Ag signal never vanish and the work function never reach 2.7 eV the bulk barium value, no matter the deposition time. Each 300s of deposition time is approximately the equivalent of one complete monolayer.

Other depositions have been done for very long time (several hours) and the *Auger* silver signal remained constant and approximately equal to 40% of the clean silver intensity. A similar result has been previously observed (not for so long deposition times) and it was attributed to uncompleted coverage of silver by barium since the surfaces have incommensurate structures [4]. This explanation was based in the fact that the barium atoms are bigger than silver atoms and Ba crystal is bcc while the Ag crystal is fcc. Thus, barium would grow with holes over the surface. However, for very long deposition times (the equivalent of more than 50 monolayers), the amount of barium should be more than enough to completely cover the surface. This was never detected in our experiments.

Furthermore to the assumption of incommensurated surfaces, we have to consider the hypothesis of diffusion between the surface and the bulk. Thus, SIMS and work function depth profiles have been done to check the in-depth distribution of barium on the silver crystal.

The acquired depth profiles are shown in Fig. 2 a) and b). These profiles have been taken immediately after deposition and hours later in order to verify the existence of diffusion.

The depth profile a) was performed immediately after deposition. In the absence of diffusion, a typical delta layer profile could be expected. However, the profile shows the expected Ba^+

peak at the surface but simultaneously a constant Ag^+ intensity throughout the surface to the bulk (no measurable decrease of Ag^+ at the surface was found). This fits with the Auger data where the silver signal is detected in the surface even after the deposition of barium.

In the profile obtained 3 days later from a similar film, surprisingly both Ba^+ and Ag^+ displayed one clear peak at the surface. Then the Ag^+ intensity decreases to a constant value (half peak height) and the Ba^+ intensity decreases almost to zero. The long tail of Ba^+ can be partially attributed to memory factors in the instrument.

The observance of an Ag^+ peak at the surface is remarkable and requires discussion. Why is the silver mixed with the deposited barium on the surface? How can the Ag^+ intensity be higher at the surface than in the 99,999% pure silver bulk?

Since ionization probability depends strongly in the surface work function one could think that during the removal of barium the work function would drastically change the ionization probability. Indeed, this is expected to be true, but the effect will work in the opposite direction. During the sputtering of the barium layer(s) the work function becomes higher than increasing the positive ionization probability. This would produce fewer positive ions at start (low work function) and more when the bulk is reached.

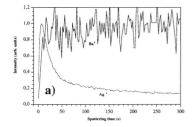 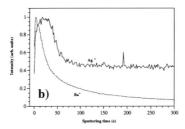

Fig. 2— Depth profiles of barium on Ag(111). The erosion rate was of the order of 0.1 Å/s.

    a) Profile acquired immediately after the deposition of barium during 1100s. The surface does not look completely covered with barium. (The slow decay in the barium distribution can be partially attributed to memory factors on the apparatus).

    b) Profile acquired 3 days after the deposition of barium (1800 s). Both Ba^+ and Ag^+ display much higher intensities at the surface (see text for explanation).

The reason should be related with different erosion rates in the surface and in the bulk. Thus, we propose the following explanation, based in the change of the surface energy.

The surface energy is 1.84 eV for barium and 2.97 eV for silver (polycrystalline). Since the sputter yield depends inversely on the surface energy, barium is sputtered faster than silver.

From our measurements, it was clear that after barium deposition, spontaneous diffusion of silver took place. This is probably due to the fact that barium atoms do not fit in the surface. A chemical reaction should occur and an intermettalic compound is formed. The detection of ion $BaAg^+$ corroborate this presumption.

The phase diagram [5] shows that Ag_5Ba, Ag_2Ba, $AgBa$ and Ag_2Ba_3 are stable compounds. Moreover, the Ag_2Ba_3 compound has the lowest melting point (340°C compared with 722°C for pure barium) and the higher lattice parameters. This suggests very weak bonds between the atoms of this molecule and with the surface.

Thus, it should be formed a new compound with a very low surface energy being possible to be sputtered at very high rate. When the bulk is reached, the surface energy gets higher and then the removal rate becomes lower and constant.

The co-adsorption of O_2 in between two depositions of barium was also performed to attempt to stop the diffusion. Indeed, the co-adsorption of oxygen before a second deposition of barium, was found to block the diffusion of silver to the surface. The depth profile (not shown), display a clean barium surface without silver, a barium oxide layer and then a barium-silver compound (discernible from the $BaAg^+$ peak). The work function with the second deposition of barium after the adsorption of O_2 could finally reach the bulk barium value (≈ 2.7 eV). These results are being presented elsewhere[6].

4. Conclusions

The deposition of barium on silver showed a very peculiar behavior. No continuous growth of barium was found. Our results indicate the occurrence of diffusion of silver atoms to topmost layers and the formation of an intermetallic compound with a rather low surface energy.

This finding, relates to the depth calibration of high resolution depth profiles. In some cases, it should taken in account the possible presence of compounds with very low surface energy.

References

[1] R.W. Gurney, Phys.Rev., 47 (1935) 479.

R.W. Verhoef, M. Asscher, Surf. Sci., 391 (1997) 11.

G.G. Magera, P.R. Davis, J.Vac. Sci. Technol., A11 (1993) 2336.

[2] O.M.N.D.Teodoro, J.A.M.C.Silva and A.M.C.Moutinho, Vacuum, **46** (1995) 1205.

[3] G. Bachmann, H. Oechsner, J. Scholtes, Fresenius Z.Anal.Chem., 329 (1987) 195.

G. Bachmann, W. Berthold, H. Oechsner, Thin Sol.Films, 174 (1989) 149.

[4] U.van Slooten, W.R.Koopers, A.Bot, H.W. van Pinxteren, A.M.C.Moutinho, J.W.M.Frenken, A.W.Kleyn, J .Phys.: Condens. Matter, **5** (1993) 5411.

[5] G. Bruzzone, M. Ferreti, F. Merlo, J.Less-Common Met., 128 (1987) 259.

[6] O.M.N.D. Teodoro, J.Los and A.M.C. Moutinho, TE838S ECOSS 18, 1999.

A. Benninghoven, P. Bertrand, H.-N. Migeon and H.W. Werner (Editors).
Proceedings of the 12th International Conference on Secondary Ion Mass Spectrometry,
Brussels, Belgium, 5-11 September 1999

377

QUANTIFICATION OF OXYGEN AT THE INTERFACE BETWEEN POLY SILICON FILM AND SILICON SUBSTRATE

T. Miyamoto, E. Hayashi, N. Morita, N. Nagai, T. Hasegawa, M. Hatada, A. Karen
and A. Ishitani

Toray Research Center, Inc.
3-7 Sonoyama 3-chome, Otsu, Shiga 520-8567, Japan
E-mail:Takashi_Miyamoto@trc.toray.co.jp

1. Introduction

The recent process control for Si-LSI production often demands measurement of the very thin oxide film thickness below 1 nm at the interface between poly-Si film and Si-substrate. For this range of thin films, RBS, AES, TEM, FTIR or nuclear reaction analysis(NRA) are not precise enough. XPS is a good technique for a top surface film[1], but not suitable to a buried film. On the other hand, we can precisely measure total amount of oxygen around the interface by SIMS due to its excellent sensitivity, and then the result can be converted to the thickness under an adequate assumption of the film density. But the accuracy of SIMS result may deteriorate because of the possible change of RSF in the film[2-5]. In this work we studied the dependence of the SIMS results on a variety of measurement conditions.

2. Experimental

We examined four samples of silicon oxide films A to D at the interface between poly-Si films of 400nm thick and Si(100) substrates. FTIR measurement using IFS-120HR (BRUKER) gave the oxide thickness of about 0.6-0.2 nm for them, decreasing according to the order of the sample IDs. SIMS depth profiling was performed using a Cameca IMS-4f under the conditions #1 to #8 listed in the Table1, where the incident angles are from the surface normal. The crater depths were measured by a Sloan DEKTAK 3030ST profilometer. Quantification was done with an oxygen implanted Si standard sample, assuming the natural abundance of the isotopes in the oxide films. The possibility of the slight change in the sputter

Table 1. SIMS depth profiling conditions

Condition#	Primary ion	Secondary ions	Impact energy	Incident angle
#1	Cs+	$^{16}O^-$ / Si$^-$	14.5 keV	25°
#2	Cs+	Cs_2O^+ / Cs_2Si^+	5.5 keV	42°
#3	Cs+	CsSiO$^+$ / CsSi$^+$	5.5 keV	42°
#4	Cs+	CsO$^+$ / CsSi$^+$	5.5 keV	42°
#5	Ar+	$^{16}O^-$ / Si$^-$	19.5 keV	26°
#6	Ar+	$^{16}O^+$ / Si$^+$	10.5 keV	37°
#7	($^{16}O_2$)$^+$	$^{18}O^-$ / Si$^-$	17.0 keV	25°
#8	($^{16}O_2$)$^+$	$^{18}O^+$ / Si$^+$	8.0 keV	39°

rate at the oxide was neglected. The crater bottoms after SIMS measurements were analyzed by XPS to see the surface chemical composition for the conditions #7 and #8. XPS measurement was done by a VG ESCALAB 220iXL, after samples were transferred under nitrogen ambience.

In order to compare the RSFs of oxygen in a Si substrate and a SiO_2 film under the conditions #1-#8, another set of SIMS depth profilings were done for ^{16}O or ^{18}O implanted Si-substrates and a thermal oxide film of 100nm thick on a Si-substrate. The implantation energies were 80keV for ^{16}O and 100 keV for ^{18}O. The doses were 2E15 and 5E14 atoms/cm^2 for ^{16}O and ^{18}O, respectively. The oxygen density in the thermal oxide was determined as 4.7E22 oxygen atoms/cm^3 by RBS. The matrix reference intensities were measured in the substrates. The RSFs in the oxide were calculated assuming the natural abundance of the isotopes. The procedure of calculating the RSFs is illustrated in Fig.1.

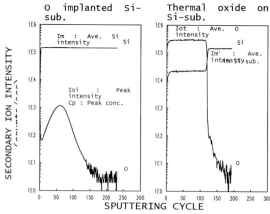

$$O - RSF(Si) = \frac{Cp}{Ioi} Im$$

$$O - RSF(SiO_2) = \frac{4.7E22}{Iot} Im'$$

Fig.1 Illustration of the procedure of calculating the RSFs. Cp is the peak concentration of the implanted Oxygen.

3. Results and discussion

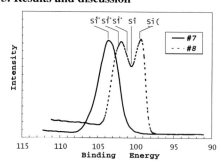

Fig.2 XPS spectra of the crater bottoms after the SIMS measurements under the conditions #7 and #8.

Figure 2 shows the XPS spectra of the crater bottoms in the Si substrate after the SIMS measurements under the conditions #7 and #8. The sputtered surface was fully oxidized under the condition #7 with lower incident angle of $(^{16}O_2)^+$, which is consistent with Reuter's data[6]. We can expect this surface oxide suppresses the RSF change through the buried oxide film.

Figure 3 shows the film thickness of four samples obtained with the eight conditions in Table 1. The oxide films were assumed to be SiO_2 with the density of 7.05E22 atoms/cm to convert the total amount of oxygen around the interface obtained by SIMS to the film thickness. Because the suppression of the RSF change is thought to be most effective for the thinnest oxide film, we normalized the results to give the same thickness for the sample D as 0.343 nm determined under the condition #7. Each point in Fig.3 denotes the average of two or three analyses.

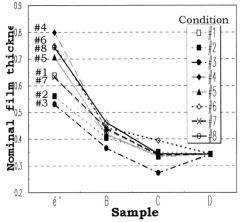

Fig.3 Nominal thickness of oxide films measured
under the conditions in Table 1. The results
were normalized to give the same thickness
for the sample D.

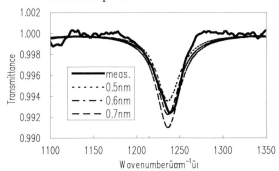

Fig.4 FTIR data of the sample A and the results of
the simulation assuming three different thickness
value of the oxide film.

For the thickest film A, we obtained FTIR spectrum shown in Fig.4 The spectrum showed almost the same peak shape as for ordinary SiO_2, while the other samples gave the distorted peak shape which means the structural change in the oxide film. The simulation of the FTIR spectra for the various thickness of SiO_2 films gave the film thickness of 0.60nm for the sample A. The procedure of the simulation is according to Fresnel equations [7].

The SIMS procedure gave the film thickness of 0.63nm for the sample A under the condition #7 as seen in Fig.3. This value agrees with the above FTIR result very well, considering the possible error in SIMS standard. This agreement means that the condition #7 gives the accurate thickness for this kind of thin oxide films.

In Fig.3, the condition #1 (Cs+ primary, $^{16}O^-$ and Si^- secondary ions) gives very good agreement for all the samples with the condition #7 which is thought to be almost free from the matrix effect. Therefore the most common SIMS analysis condition #1 for oxygen in Si happens to give very accurate quantification for thin oxide film buried in Si, at least up to 0.6 nm.

The variation of the nominal thickness of each sample tends to increase with the film thickness in Fig.3. This means that the matrix effect was not negligible in the thicker films and the actual RSFs in those films were different from the RSFs in Si substrate. The ratios of oxygen RSF in Si substrate to oxygen RSF in thermal oxide film under the conditions #1 to #8 are listed in Table 2. As the doses of ^{16}O and ^{18}O implanted to Si-substrates are expected to have the errors of about 10%, the values in Table 2 include similar errors. Under the conditions #1 and #7, oxygen RFSs are nearly the same in Si and the thermal oxide. However, oxygen RSFs are smaller in the thermal oxide than in Si substrate for #4,5,6,8, which leads to an

Table 2. Oxygen RSF ratio in Si vs. thermal oxide

Measurement condition	#1	#2	#3	#4	#5	#6	#7	#8
RSF ratio	1.0	0.47	0.05	18	18	7.4	0.75	3.8

380

overestimate of the amount of oxygen in an oxide film when the RSF in Si substrate is used for the quantification as in Fig.3. This is consistent with the tendency of the nominal film thickness of sample A seen in Fig.3. On the other hand, the conditions #2 and #3 gave the deviation of the RSF ratios and the film thickness in the opposite direction to the conditions #4, 5, 6, 8. This tendency is recognized more clearly in Fig.5 over the whole conditions and samples. Figure 5 shows the plots of the nominal oxide film thickness vs. the oxygen RSF ratio in Table 2. If the buried oxide is thin enough to be free from the matrix effect for all the measurement conditions, the plots for each sample should be flat. But even in the thinnest film, we can see the same tendency as in the thickest film A.

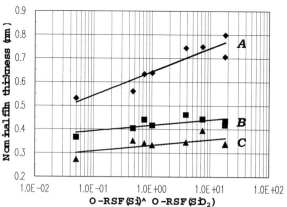

Fig.5 Plots of the nominal oxide film thickness vs.
oxygen RSF ratio in Table 2. A-C are sample

4. Conclusions

When we use SIMS to quantify the oxygen at the interface between poly-Si film and Si substrate, we should be careful about the matrix effect even for very thin oxide films. We found two specific measurement conditions which are thought to be free from the matrix effect for the oxide film at least up to 0.6 nm thick.

The authors would like to thank Mr. T. Hoshi of ULVAC-PHI, Inc. (Japan) for valuable discussions.

References

[1] J. R. Shallenberger, D. A. Cole, S. W. Novak, R. L. Moore, M. J. Edgell, S. P. Smith, C. J. Hitzman, J. F. Kirchhoff, E. Principe, S. Biswas, R. J. Bleiler, W. Nieveen and K. Jones, Abstracts of XIIth International Conference on Ion Implantation Tecnology, June 22-26, 1998, Kyoto, P1-135
[2] J. A. Kilner, R. J. Chater and S. D. Littlewood, SIMS VI, Wiley, 1988, p.299.
[3] S. B. Patel, G. P. Beyer and J. A. Kilner, SIMS IX, Wiley, 1994, p.154.
[4] I. Kawashima and Y. Homma, SIMS IX, Wiley, 1994, p.215.
[5] Y. Kataoka and Y. Toda, SIMS IX, Wiley, 1994, p.402.
[6] W. Reuter, Nucl. Instrum. Methods Phys. Res. B15(1986)173
[7] B.Harbecke, Appl.Phys.B39(1986), 165

A. Benninghoven, P. Bertrand, H.-N. Migeon and H.W. Werner (Editors).
Proceedings of the 12th International Conference on Secondary Ion Mass Spectrometry,
Brussels, Belgium, 5-11 September 1999

QUANTITATIVE TOFSIMS DEPTH PROFILING OF ULTRA THIN SILICON OXYNITRIDE FILMS

T. Conard, H. De Witte, M. Schaekers, W. Vandervorst[+]
IMEC, 75 Kapeldreef, 3001 Leuven, Belgium
+ also at INSYS, KU Leuven, Belgium
e-mail: tconard@workmail.com

1. Introduction

The downscaling of microelectronic devices leads to the use of thinner and thinner gate dielectrics, down to 2-3 nm. These dielectrics face thus a large reliability challenge and silicon oxynitride has emerged as one of the viable alternatives to SiO_2. The exact incorporation of nitrogen in these films (concentration and distribution) in function of the experimental preparation conditions (gas, temperature, ...) is still not yet perfectly understood. In addition, the very low thickness of the films puts high demands on analysis profiling techniques such as SIMS. We investigate here a number of different processes in order to study both the profiling capabilities of TOFSIMS and the elemental distribution of oxygen and nitrogen in the films.

2. Sample description

Two series of samples were considered in this study. The first one is composed of a 2.5 nm nitrided oxide film chemically etched by HF in order to reduce the oxide thickness. First the oxide was formed by conventional O_2 annealing followed by the nitridation by NO annealing for 15 min at 850 C.

The second series of samples consisted of ~2.5 nm nitrided SiO_2 prepared with a similar process but with different nitridation conditions between 750 and 850 C and with pure or diluted NO.

Additionally, a sample was made using a "reverse process" i.e. first the NO annealing followed by an H_2O annealing. The exact characteristics of all films analyzed are given in Table 1

3. Results and discussion

In order to address the two main questions (concentration and depth distribution of the nitrogen), two independent approaches were used. First, for very thin films, XPS (X-ray Photoelectron Spectroscopy) is a well-suited technique to determine the elemental concentration composition of the films but requires some hypothesis on the structure of the film. Second, low energy SIMS depth profiling can easily give a depth distribution but is limited by two problems: the precise location of the oxide-substrate interface and difficulties in the quantification, the so-called matrix effect. The quantification in TOFSIMS has to be made using peaks integrals or peaks intensities corrected by a relative sensitivity factor. We will first present quantification-related issues before addressing the impact of the process conditions on the nitrogen content and its distribution. The summary of the quantification results is presented in Table 1.

Table 1: Sample characteristics, atomic concentration of nitrogen at the interface determined by XPS and TOFSIMS and oxide thickness determined by XPS and Spectroscopic Ellipsometry

Wafer fabrication	Post processing	At. Conc. (at/cm^2)		Oxide thickness (Å)	
		XPS	TOFSIMS	XPS	SE
O$_2$ + NO annealing					
NO57: 850 C 15 min	HF 2%	2.0E14	2.2E+14	4.7	5.7
NO67: 850 C 15 min	HF 2%	2.6E14	2.8E+14	5.1	6.7
NO80: 850 C 15 min	HF 0.1%	7.1E14	5.9E+14	8.6	8
NO106: 850 C 15 min	HF 0.1%	1.3E15	1.1E+15	12.2	10.6
NO144: 850 C 15 min	HF 0.1%	1.5E15	1.5E+15	15.8	14.4
NO189: 850 C 15 min	HF 0.1%	1.4E15	1.5E+15	21.4	18.9
NO254: 850 C 15 min	HF 0.1%	1.4E15	1.7E+15	30.4	25.4
15' NO 850C	None	1.4E15	1.3E+15	31.8	25.0
15' NO 800C	None	1.1E15	1.1E+15	29.9	21.9
15' NO 750C	None	6.0E14	7.2E+14	32.1	22.8
5' NO 750C	None	2.6E14	2.8E+14	31.1	23.1
5' NO diluted 750C	none	ND	1.3E+14	30.3	27.3
15' NO 850°C + 10' H$_2$O 750°C	none	1.5E15	1.3E+15	31.0	25.0

3.1 XPS

XPS measurements of ultrathin films can provide an absolute measurement of the film thickness assuming that the electron mean free path is known, which is the case for SiO$_2$ on Si. The oxide thicknesses measured by XPS and ellipsometry are presented in Table 1.

The N content can be determined in two ways after correction of the intensities with the sensitivity factors. On one hand the ratio N/SiO$_2$ is calculated as the intensity ratio of the N$1s$ and the Si$2p$ peak from SiO$_2$. This gives the average nitrogen composition of the oxide film assuming a homogeneous distribution of nitrogen in the oxide layer. On the other hand, assuming that the nitrogen is present as a delta layer at the SiO$_2$/Si interface

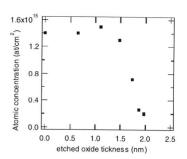

Figure 1: N surface atom density as a function of the etched oxide thickness

and assuming an identical electron mean free path for the N$1s$ and Si$2p$ peaks in the oxide layer, the N/Si ratio gives the atomic N concentration at the interface in at/cm^2. This last method was used as we expected the nitrogen to be concentrated on the SiO$_2$/Si interface.

Figure 1 presents the N/Si (atoms/cm^2) as a function of the etched oxide thickness for the first series of samples. The surface concentration determined with this methods clearly shows a plateau for during the etching of the first 1.5 nm. This clearly indicate that the nitrogen is not present in the first 1.5 nm of the oxide. The decrease for higher etched thickness can therefore be explained by the effective removal of N in the etching process confirming that the nitrogen is well located close to the interface.

An angle dependent XPS measurement on the 2.54 nm oxide sample also shows that at a take-off angle of 10 deg, no nitrogen is observed anymore, confirming the absence of nitrogen in the uppermost surface oxide layer. It is however difficult to go much further in the XPS data interpretation.

3.2 TOF-SIMS quantification

Using the dual beam experimental set-up (IONTOF IV) different matrix clusters can be investigated at the interface position [1]. Following the method described in [1], we used Ar$^+$ sputtering and positive ion detection for the analysis. To address the quantification problem, a comparison of TOFSIMS intensities of the Si$_2$N cluster and of XPS concentrations was carried out (see Table 1). This comparison shows a very good correlation between the two signals and a linear fit produces a sensitivity factor of 4.68E9 atoms/cm^2 for the Si$_2$N TOFSIMS intensity with a relative standard deviation of 13%.

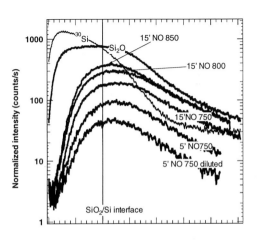

Figure 2 shows an overlay of the Si$_2$N ion clusters for samples with different process conditions. One typical Si$_2$O and the ^{30}Si ion profiles are also shown. The

Figure 2: TOFSIMS depth profile of nitrided SiO$_2$ with different process condition. The SiO$_2$/Si interface is aligned

positioning of the interface is indicated as a vertical line and aligned between the different samples. It can clearly be observed that the maximum of the intensity of the Si$_2$N cluster corresponds to the interface position and thus that the nitrogen is located at the interface. It is also confirmed that nitrogen is not present at the surface of the oxide. The small differences in oxide thickness observed by XPS or ellipsometry are also observed by TOF-SIMS (data not shown).

Figure 3 presents the quantification obtained both by XPS and by TOFSIMS using the above given sensitivity factor. This clearly shows the importance of the annealing temperature, of the annealing time and of the NO concentration. It also shows that, as expected, the quantification with TOFSIMS is still possible for the lowest N concentration while XPS does not detect nitrogen anymore.

The influence of the process conditions on the nitrogen incorporation is also evidenced by comparing two profiles obtained with a 15 min NO anneal at 850 as a first or as a second process step (Figure 4). We found from the TOFSIMS quantification that when the NO anneal is performed first, the overall N content is 1.31E15 at/cm^2 while when it is performed second, the nitrogen content is 1.64E15, a significant difference. However, XPS shows (within the measurement errors) an equal content for the two samples. The explanation comes from the depth distribution of the nitrogen in the oxide. It is indeed observed in the TOFSIMS profile that the nitrogen signal is much more present at the surface than for sample NO254. A simulation of the XPS intensities with the TOFSIMS profiles shows that, indeed, the two different nitrogen distributions produce an equivalent XPS signal. This simulation corrects the TOFSIMS profile, taking into account the XPS electron mean free path in the analyzed sample. The difference in depth of the nitrogen maximum explains thus the difference in the quantification.

3.3 Comparison with other techniques

A similar experiment was realized on the same samples with low energy dynamic SIMS using Cs^+ sputtering and detection of Cs clusters [3]. The quantification obtained is in very good agreement with the quantification obtained here. The two depth profiling methods are thus equivalent. Sample NO254 was also investigated with H-ERD depth profiling, confirming the presence of nitrogen predominantly at the SiO_2/Si interface[2].

4. Conclusions

This study shows that combining XPS and TOFSIMS depth profiling with Ar^+ sputtering and positive ion detection allows a quantitative analysis of the nitrogen distribution in a thin SiO_2 nitrided film with an accuracy of about 10%. It also shows the influence of process on the nitrogen incorporation in thin SiO_2 films.

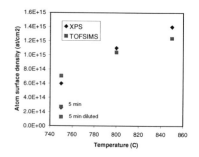

Figure 3: Comparison of TOFSIMS and XPS quantification of the NO process condition

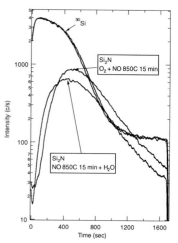

Figure 4: TOFSIMS depth profiles of two process condition with NO annealing at 850C for 15 min

References

[1] H. De Witte, T. Conard, W. Vandervorst and R. Gijbels, SIMS XII, Brussels, 1999
[2] B. Brijs, J. Deleu, T. Conard, H. De Witte and W. Vandervorst, K. Kimura, G. Dollinger, M. Dobeli, IBA-14, Dresden, Germany, July 26-30, 1999
[3] W. Vandervorst, T. Conard and H. De Witte, G.A. Cooke, SIMSXII, Brussels, 1999

A. Benninghoven, P. Bertrand, H.-N. Migeon and H.W. Werner (Editors).
Proceedings of the 12th International Conference on Secondary Ion Mass Spectrometry,
Brussels, Belgium, 5-11 September 1999
© 2000 Elsevier Science B.V. All rights reserved.

RELATIVE SENSITIVITY FACTOR REPRODUCIBILITY
WITH MAGNETIC SECTOR TYPE SIMS

S.Y. Hong, T.E. Hong, J.P. Lee, M.N. Yoon, K. Min and S.Y. Lee
Hyundai Electronics Industries Co., R&D Division
Ichon, Kyunggi 467-701 , Korea.

1. Introduction

Comparing with Quadrupole Type SIMS (Q-SIMS), Magnetic Sector Type SIMS (M-SIMS) gives relative high mass resolution and high transmission due to the bias voltage applied to the sample. However, this sample bias produces analytical artifacts such as the deviation of Relative Sensitivity Factor (RSF). In the case of Q-SIMS, the Relative Standard Deviation (RSD) of RSF is less than 1% with different windows of a sample holder [1], but M-SIMS does not give so small deviation. This deviation is mainly caused by the distortion of extraction field with sample holder and the incorrect setting of energy slit with spectrometer[2].

In this article, we show that the windows, which means the sample position in the sample holder, actually cause the analytical artifacts and there are changes in RSD of RSF due to the sample holder type and the window position in the sample holder with M-SIMS by the statistical approach[3].

2. Experimental

Sample was prepared by usual ion implantation onto Si (100) p-type wafer. The boron ion implantation was performed by Varian E-500HP with 80 keV energy and total dose of 5.0E13 ions/cm^2. The conditions of tilt and twist angles are 7 degree and 22 degree, respectively. Three sample holders were tested in this experiment : 3 holes, multiple type (4 holes) and 9 holes. All measurements were performed with a Cameca IMS-6f ion microscope operating at 12.5keV of primary energy and 5 keV of secondary energy. $^{11}B^+$ and $^{28}Si^{++}$ positive ions were collected from a circular area of 60 μm in diameter centered within a 250x250μm^2 raster size by Electron Multiplier to avoid the instrumental factors itselves[4]. To eliminate the electrostatic field distortions between the sample and immersion lens caused by the edge of the sample holder window, we monitor the depth profile data within an area of 1000 μm in diameter centered in the window by using the auto centering system which is provided with the IMS-6f automation system. The instrument was tuned for flat-topped peaks, and the energy slit was centered and fully opened throughout all measurements to prevent the spectrometer factors as discussed in Ref.[2]. From these measurements, we gathered the 61 values of RSF data from 3, 4, and 9 hole sample holder (3 holes : 9, 4holes : 16 and 9 holes : 36 data, see Fig. 1). In this study, we used the RS/1 Explore program and the calculation of One-way ANOVA, Two-way ANOVA and Box-plot as the statistical approach to confirm the main factor, which gives the variation of RSF for usual SIMS measurements.

3. Result and Discussion

The RSD of the mean RSF values is 5.84% for the 3 holes, 66.7% for the 4 holes, and 14.3% for the 9 holes. Then we used the One-way ANOVA calculation to find the major effect of the deviation of RSF. Table 1 summarizes the results of calculation and shows that the deviation to be attributed to the different types of sample holder is 21.66% and another error factor is 78.34%. This means that the deviation of RSF will be affected by the another error factor more than sample holder type itself although it should be noted that sample holder type is significant enough because the p value is 0.001.

To identify the other error factor, which is more effective to the deviation of RSF, we applied the One-way ANOVA calculation again with the effect of the window position for each type of sample holder as shown in the figure 1. These results reported in table 2 show that the window position term is more effective to explain the deviation of RSF. window position term is more effective to explain the deviation of RSF.

ANOVA Unweighted Comparison of Means		
Source	Degree of Freedom	% Variable of Explanation
Holder	2	21.66
Error	57	78.34
Total	59	100.00
$F(2.57) = 7.88, P = 0.001[3]$ IQR of RSF = 0.37[3], Residual = 0.271 Root Mean Squared Error = 0.17065		

Table 1. One-way ANOVA of the type of sample holder

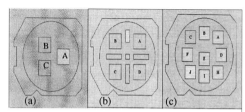

Fig. 1. Schematic diagram of back-side sample holder and analysis point ; (a) is 3-hole, (b) is 4-hole, and (c) is 9-hole sample holder.

Therefore, the RSD of RSF mainly depends on the window position comparing with the sample holder type.

ANOVA Unweighted Comparision of Means								
3 Hole Sample Holder			4 Hole Sample Holder			9 Hole Sample Holder		
Source	Degree of Freedom	% Variable of Explanation	Source	Degree of Freedom	% Variable of Explanation	Source	Degree of Freedom	% Variable of Explanation
Window	2	94.69	Window	3	97.07	Window	8	96.82
Error	6	5.31	Error	11	2.93	Error	27	3.18
Total	8	100.00	Total	14	100.00	Total	35	100.00
$F(2.6) = 53.54, P = 0.0001$ IQR of RSF = 0.15 Residual = 0.04 RMS Error = 0.02357			$F(3.11) = 121.28, P = 0$ IQR of RSF = 0.19 Residual = 0.048 RMS Error = 0.030526			$F(8.27) = 102.91, P = 0$ IQR of RSF = 0.0345 Residual = 0.06 RMS Error = 0.038309		
Trend Test : Not defined for unranked predictor								

Table 2. One-way ANOVA ; position of the windows

Furthermore Two-way ANOVA was applied to both the sample holder type and the window position. The results also show that the sample holder type explains 23.1% of deviation, whereas the window position explains 55.3% of deviation of RSF. This means that the window position is the most significant factor to the deviation of RSF as shown in Table 3.

Analysis of Varience Using an Interactive Model Unweighted Comparision of Means				
Source	Degree of Freedom	% Variable of Explanation	F-Ratio[3]	Significance[3]
Holder	2	23.1	57.002	0.0000
Window	2	55.3	136.629	0.0000
Residual	55	21.3	13.872	0.0000
Interaction	4	11.2		
Error	51	10.3		
Total	59	100.0		
IQR of RSF = 0.37, Residual = 0.106, Error = 0.067 RMS Error = 0.052255, F-Ratio for Holder & Window based on Error line				

Table 3. Two-way ANOVA of sample holder & window

Finally, we also confirmed that there is a trend which shows the deviation of RSF can be divided in 3 groups. This tendency is clearly observed on the Box-plot of all RSF data shown in figure 2. Following the figure 2, each marked circle, rectangle, and triangle of the RSF data point for each sample holder type, 3 hole, 4 hole and 9 hole, can be grouped separately and this group is consistent with the Table 4 summarizes the RSD of RSF after grouping in the case of 9 hole sample holder, and we found that the RSD can be reduced to 1.2% when the window position is grouped as shown in figure 3. The reason why the RSD of RSF is reduced when each window position will be grouped comes from the method of mounting the sample holder. In the case of CAMECA IMS series, three screws are used the parallelism between the immersion lens and the sample surface. Consequently, it is necessary to adjust carefully these screws to minimize the deviation of RSF. Furthermore, it is also necessary to qualify the deviation of RSF for every sample holder to determine the window groups, which shows the smallest RSD. In this experiment, we found that the 1st group had the smallest RSD as shown in figure 3, but this group maybe changed by how to adjust the mounting screws from time to time.

	1st window group	2nd window group	3rd window group
# of data	18	19	23
Mean	1.53E19	1.34E19	1.14E19
ʃ	4.83E17	1.22E18	1.14E19
RSD	1.20%	9.09%	9.83%

Table 4. RSD after window grouping as three group

388

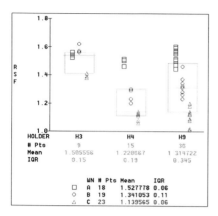

Fig. 2. Box-plot of RSF for each sample holder type, 3 holes(H3), 4 holes(H4) and 9 holes(H9)

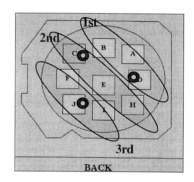

Fig. 3. Grouping of the sample holder and the double marked circle shows the position of screw

4. Conclusion

We have studied the deviation of RSF in 3, 4, and 9 hole sample holder type to analyze the main factor which gives the deviation. Following this study, we firstly confirmed that the deviation mainly came from the difference of window position although the sample holder type was also meaningful. The deviation of RSF with different window position can be divided by 3 groups due to the use of sample mounting screws. Therefore, the RSD of RSF can be reduced to 1.20% when the window position is selected carefully to analyze the depth profiling.

References

[1] S.B. Patel and J.L. Maul, "Proceeding of Ultra Shallow Junction "99, 212 (1999).
[2] P.H. Chi and D.S. Simons, "Proceeding of Secondary Ion Mass Spectrometry VII", 127 (1989).
[3] In this paper, we used statistical terminology to explain the effect of each factor. F-ratio, Significance, IQRs has its own meaning in statistics and the detail can be found elsewhere, e.g.: G. E. P. Box, W. G. Hunter, and J. S. Hunter, "Statistics for Experimenters", John Wiley & Sons, Inc. New York (1978), D. C. Montgomery, "Design and Analysis of Experiments" (4th edition) John Wiley & Sons, Inc. New York (1997)
[4] R.G. Wilson, F.A. Steve and C.W. Magee, "Secondary Ion Mass Spectrometry : A Practical Handbook for Depth Profiling and Bulk Impurity Analysis", John Wiley & Sons, Inc. New York, p3.1-1 (1989).

A. Benninghoven, P. Bertrand, H.-N. Migeon and H.W. Werner (Editors).
Proceedings of the 12th International Conference on Secondary Ion Mass Spectrometry,
Brussels, Belgium, 5-11 September 1999

ON THE INFLUENCE OF CESIUM IMPLANTATION ON THE EMISSION OF POSITIVE SECONDARY IONS: DUAL BEAM EXPERIMENTS WITH CAMECA ION-TOF SIMS

Igor V. Veryovkin[*], Erik Cuynen[**], and Pierre Van Espen[***]

Department of Chemistry, University of Antwerp (U.I.A.), Universiteitsplein 1,
B-2610 Antwerp (Wilrijk), Belgium e-mail: cuynen@uia.ua.ac.be

1. Introduction

It is well known that the presence of alkali atoms on the metal surface lowers its work function (WF) [1]. Recently, initial stages of Cs incorporation on surfaces irradiated by keV Cs$^+$ ions have been studied by SIMS and the relationship between the WF changes and the positive ion emission of Cs and Cs-carrying diatomic cations was shown [2]. Experimental dependencies of the WF values and the intensity of secondary ions on the Cs concentration were obtained in Ref.2 for *dynamic* SIMS conditions when the Cs implantation and the SIMS analysis (i.e. sputtering) were performed *simultaneously*, and the Cs concentration had to be estimated by computer simulations. The use of a dual beam technique under *static* SIMS conditions permits separation of these two processes so that the ion emission from Cs doped layers can be studied by using other (than Cs$^+$) ion beams that do not change the WF of the surface. In this case, it is important that the dose of the Cs implant is controllable and the static analysis of the same sample area can be performed *before* and *after* the implantation. This makes possible starting experiments at a clean surface with a known WF, which helps to estimate ionisation probabilities that can be used for performing quantitative SIMS analyses.

2. Experimental: the motivation and the method

It was an intention of this work to apply the electron tunneling model of the ionization of sputtered atoms [1] to SIMS quantification without use of standard reference materials (SRM) in a conventional way with calculation of relative sensitivity factors (RSF). The proposed quantification procedure uses the theoretical description from Ref.1. This predicts an exponential dependence for the ionization probability of positive sputtered ions,

$$P^+(\Phi + \Delta\Phi) \cong \exp\left[-\left(I - (\Phi + \Delta\Phi)\right)/\varepsilon_p\right], \qquad (1)$$

where I is the ionization potential of the corresponding atom; Φ is the WF of a *clean* surface; $\Delta\Phi$ is the WF shift corresponding to the *actual* surface (the difference between Φ and the WF of the actual surface), which can be affected by the Cs implantation; and ε_p is a parameter that

---

[*] I. Veryovkin is the corresponding author and indebted to the Belgian Federal Office for Scientific, Technical and Cultural Affairs (DWTC/OSTC). Present address: Materials Science and Chemistry Divisions, Argonne National Laboratory, 9700 S. Cass Avenue, Argonne, IL 60439, U.S.A.; e-mail: verigo@anl.gov

[**] E. Cuynen is indebted to the Flemish Institute for the Promotion of Scientific-Technological Research in the Industry (IWT).

[***] P. Van Espen is indebted to the Flemish Fund for Scientific Research (FWO).

depends on the emission velocity of the departing ion. Values of I and Φ are known/tabulated, and the value $\Delta\Phi$ is controllable/measurable in dual beam experiments. Thus, the parameter ε_p can be determined by measuring the secondary ion current, $J^+(\Phi+\Delta\Phi)$, for different WF values and normalizing them to the ion current corresponding to the clean surface, $J^+(\Phi)$, as follows:

$$\frac{J^+(\Phi+\Delta\Phi)}{J^+(\Phi)} = \frac{j_0 \cdot T \cdot Y \cdot P^+(\Phi+\Delta\Phi)}{j_0 \cdot T \cdot Y \cdot P^+(\Phi)} = \frac{\exp\left[-(I-(\Phi+\Delta\Phi))/\varepsilon_p\right]}{\exp\left[-(I-\Phi)/\varepsilon_p\right]} = \exp\left[-\frac{\Delta\Phi}{\varepsilon_p}\right], \quad (2)$$

where j_0 is the primary ion current, T is transmission of the SIMS instrument, Y is sputtering yield of the corresponding element, and P^+ is defined by the Eq.1. If alignments of the instrument and the current of the analyzing ion beam are the same for all the measurements, then the values of j_0, T, and Y can be excluded from the normalization ratio. For different elements of the sample, the parameter ε_p can be determined from the Eq.2 by an exponential fit. Then ratios between sputtering yields of any two elements (e.g., elements #1 and #2) can easily be determined by the second exponential fitting procedure:

$$\frac{J_1^+(\Phi+\Delta\Phi)}{J_2^+(\Phi+\Delta\Phi)} = \frac{j_0 \cdot T \cdot Y_1 \cdot P_1^+(\Phi+\Delta\Phi)}{j_0 \cdot T \cdot Y_2 \cdot P_2^+(\Phi+\Delta\Phi)} = \frac{Y_1}{Y_2} \cdot \frac{\exp\left[-(I_1-(\Phi+\Delta\Phi))/\varepsilon_{p1}\right]}{\exp\left[-(I_2-(\Phi+\Delta\Phi))/\varepsilon_{p2}\right]} =$$
$$= \frac{Y_1}{Y_2} \cdot \exp\left[\frac{I_2-(\Phi+\Delta\Phi)}{\varepsilon_{p2}} - \frac{I_1-(\Phi+\Delta\Phi)}{\varepsilon_{p1}}\right] \quad (3),$$

where Φ, I_1 and I_2 are known, $\Delta\Phi$ is controllable and the parameters ε_{p1} and ε_{p2} can be determined from Eq.2. Keeping element #2 the same and varying element #1 in Eq.3, a series of Y_1/Y_2 ratios corresponding to the percentage of elements in the analyzed sample can be obtained, which fulfills the quantification task.

To examine the proposed procedure, a series of experiments using the CAMECA ION-TOF IV SIMS instrument has been carried out. The instrument used 10 keV Ar^+ ions to analyse clean surfaces and surfaces dosed by 3 keV Cs^+ ion beam. In this case, changes of the WF due to the Cs implantation and their influence in the positive ionization probability were determined by measuring the mass spectra of positive ions. These dependencies were measured for different positive atomic ions from a standard reference material, SRM 1155 (stainless steel, 65.5% Fe, 18.4% Cr, 12.1% Ni) under high vacuum conditions ($\cong 10^{-8}$ Torr). The SRM was selected for examination purposes only. To test the quantification procedure, it was planned to use it as a sample with unknown composition. The work function ($\Phi = 4.75$ eV) for clean stainless steel surfaces was found in Ref.3. Three areas were selected on the sample surface for independent Cs implantations lasting 4 s, 5 s and 6 s. To vary concentrations of the Cs implant, the Cs^+ ion beam (5 nA ion current) was raster scanned over the surface with different square areas (1000 μm, 750 μm, 500 μm, 300 μm, and 200 μm). The Ar^+ ion microbeam (0.60 pA ion current) used for SIMS analysis was *always* scanned over a smaller area (100 μm) than the Cs^+ dosed area. The WF changes ($\Delta\Phi$) were assumed to be homogeneous. *Under the same alignments* of the ion optics of the instrument, six mass spectra were measured for each dosed spot on the sample surface. The first spectra was always recorded *before* implanting Cs, and five others were measured *after* that.

3. Results and discussion

Time-of-flight (TOF) spectra corresponding to Fe^+, Cr^+ and Ni^+ secondary ions were analysed. All the tendencies observed for the three ions were similar. Fig. 1 shows TOF Fe^+ peaks from two spots on the sample where the Cs implantation lasted 4 s and 6 s. Data corresponding to the 5 s implantation laid between these two groups of peaks. A comparison between the groups reveals differences in their positions and in shapes of peaks corresponding to similar conditions of the Cs implantation. In our opinion, this has to be considered as an *experimental artifact* originating from the

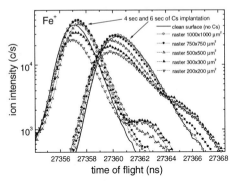

Figure 1. Fe^+, peak shape and position

alignment of the ion optics for optimal transmission of secondary ions from the 4°s spot only (the other two spots were examined by moving the sample holder). In comparison to the Fe^+ peak from the clean surface of the 4 s spot, which is nearly perfectly symmetric, an asymmetry of the corresponding peak from the 6 s spot indicates slightly non-optimal alignment for the latter case. The observed $\cong 3$ ns shift in time corresponds approximately to 2 eV in energies, which is 0.1% of the accelerating voltage (2 kV) applied between the sample and the extracting electrode, which are several mm from each other. Non-parallel motion of the sample holder might add/subtract several μm to/from this distance, deteriorating the alignment and shifting the group of peaks several eV.

Nevertheless, when analyzing a single spot (with the same extraction distance since the sample is not moved), the influence of the Cs implantation on the intensities and positions of the ion peaks can be clearly observed. To demonstrate trends, we consider results from 5 s and 6 s spots too. The logarithmic scale of Fig.1 also shows changes in peak shapes; i.e. the growth of an additional peak («shoulder»), which is shifted towards longer TOF with increasing Cs concentration and has approximately two orders of magnitude lower intensity than the maximum. For reflectron TOF instruments, this shift can indicate an emission of Fe^+ ions with different energy distributions from the same sputtered area. It may be that implanted Cs atoms are changing the surface binding energy for Fe atoms. Thus, the «shoulders» may suggest presence of microscopic areas with different surface binding energy. The concentration of these spots increases with increasing Cs concentration so that the «shoulder» peaks are transformed into continuum widening the main peak. It should be noticed that when plotting the peaks of mass spectra normalized to their maximum on a linear scale, the visible differences («shoulders») are diminished, and it makes the peaks appear nearly identical but slightly shifted. This is why WF shifts ($\Delta\Phi$) have been determined in the following way. The Asymmetric Double Sigmoidal peak function was used to fit TOF peaks (plotted in the *linear* scale) corresponding to clean surfaces. Fitting parameters defining the peak shape were then fixed, and this function was used to fit peaks observed under the Cs implantation. To improve accuracy of the WF shift determination, «shoulders» have been excluded from the fitting range and only parameters defining the peak size and position were varied during this procedure.

392

This approach precisely determines the position of the main peak since a large number of data points is used in the fitting procedure. The dependencies of the WF shifts and signal intensities on the Cs dose are shown in Fig.2 for Fe^+ ions. The influence of Cs implantation is clearly seen for both cases. These results are in a good agreement with experimental results of Ref.2 and a number of other experiments; namely, lowering the WF *reduces* the probability for forming *positive* ions and increasing the WF *increases* this probability. The surprising observation of the latter case for larger raster sizes of the 4 s spot can be explained by low Cs doses (less than 10^{14} at/cm^2). This corresponds to initial stages of Cs incorporation when the equilibrium in surface conditions is not yet reached. Using a logarithmi scale, Fig.3 shows the dependencies of the «normalised ion intensity vs WF shift»

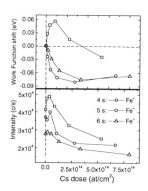

Figure 2. WF-shifts and intensity vs. Cs-dose

(Eq.2). Normalising the data to those obtained for clean surfaces allows comparison between different spots. The curvature of the data is in good agreement with Ref.2. Results for the 4 s

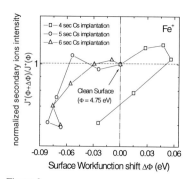

Figure 3.

spot are different from those for 5 s and 6 s due to the apparent sensitivity of instrument alignment on the distance between the sample and the extracting electrode, as mentioned above. Optimising extraction conditions for each spot would produce more reproducible and comparable results since the proposed normalisation procedure means overlapping undoped peak shapes. Therefore a special attention should be paid in future experiments to the alignment of the instrument for each spot with different implantation time. A lack of experimental data points did not allow us to use the dependencies shown Fig.3 in the quantification procedure. Identifying a region where $\Delta\Phi$ has the expected exponential behaviour by

using only three data points is *too arbitrary*. The number of useable data points can be increased by using a wider range of raster sizes and implantation times. At this point, we can conclude that using the dual beam technique in static SIMS mode allows estimating the influence of Cs implantation on the ionization probabilities of positive ions, which is the first step for quantitative SIMS analysis using the method outlined above. Future experiments will provide additional data points thus permitting a test of the proposed method.

Acknowledgements
Authors are thankful to Dr. W. F. Calaway for his useful comments and help.

References.
[1]   M. L. Yu, in *Sputtering by Particle Bombardment III*, ed. By R. Behrish and K. Wittmaack, Springer, Berlin, 1991, p.91.
[2]   H. Gnaser, Phys. Rev. B54 (1996) 17141.
[3]   S. G. Walton, J. C. Tucek, and R. L. Champion, J. Appl. Phys. 85 (1999) 1832.

A. Benninghoven, P. Bertrand, H.-N. Migeon and H.W. Werner (Editors).
Proceedings of the 12th International Conference on Secondary Ion Mass Spectrometry,
Brussels, Belgium, 5-11 September 1999

393

IMPROVING RSF REPRODUCIBILITY OF B IN Si
FOR ACCURATE SIMS QUANTIFICATION[*]

Qin Chao[1], Gui Dong[1], Zhu Yizheng[1], Wang Youzheng[1], Cha Liangzhen[1]
Ma Nongnong[2], Liu Rong[2]

[1]Department of Electronic Engineering, Tsinghua University, Beijing, China, 100084
chalz@mail.tsinghua.edu.cn
[2]The 46th Institute, Ministry of Electronic Industry, Tianjin, China, 300192

1. Introduction

The quantification of B in Si has been selected as the first international standard to be established in SIMS area by ISO/TC 201/SC 6. In the first ISO round-robin test[1], results have been obtained from 16 labs in the world. The unknown boron atomic concentration in the sample WRR1-U was determined by 12 labs using CAMECA IMS instruments with O_2^+ primary beam under positive mode. The average value of the boron atomic concentration reported is 4.32×10^{18} atoms/cm^3 and the relative standard deviation (RSD) is 7.1%. However, the reproducibility of the relative sensitivity factor (RSF) among the labs was different significantly[2]. Thus, RSF reproducibility, the basis of accurate SIMS quantification, needs to be investigated in some detail.

Data accumulated in this round-robin test show that the RSD of RSFs obtained from three testing points near the central region of the sample window changes from 0.3% to 4.7% for the reference material WRR1-C, and from 0.7% to 13% for WRR1-A even when the same type of CAMECA instruments were used under the same operation mode. The atomic concentrations of B in Si are $(8.52 \pm 0.32) \times 10^{15}$ and $(1.09 \pm 0.01) \times 10^{19}$ atoms/cm^3 for WRR1-A and C, respectively. The detected ion of $^{11}B^+$ was selected by all the labs. However, the reference secondary ions selected were different, including atomic ions of $^{28}Si^+$ and $^{30}Si^+$, cluster ions of $^{58}Si_2^+$ ($^{28}Si^{30}Si^+$ or $^{29}Si_2^{29}Si^+$) and $^{59}Si_2^+$ ($^{29}Si^{30}Si^+$), as well as doubly charged ion of $^{28}Si^{++}$[2].

The dependence of RSF reproducibility upon testing position and the selection of reference ion have been systematically investigated. The discussion of the experimental result and the suggestion to improve the reproducibility of RSF measurement are also presented in this paper.

---

[*] This work is supported by the Doctoral Dissertation Foundation of Graduate School, Tsinghua University

2. Experimental

All measurements were performed on a CAMECA IMS-4f ion microscope using 8.0 keV O_2^+ primary ions. The boron-doped bulk silicon sample (WRR1-C) was tested in this study. A multi-window sample holder was used to mount the sample. The detected secondary ion of $^{11}B^+$ and different kinds of reference ions such as $^{28}Si^+$, $^{30}Si^+$, $^{58}Si_2^+$, $^{59}Si_2^+$ and $^{28}Si^{++}$ were selected to study the dependence of RSF reproducibility on the combination of the detected and reference ions.

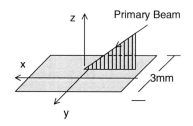

In order to investigate the dependence of RSF reproducibility on testing position, line scans were carried out with a computer-controlled step-motor in two mutually perpendicular directions across the sample under a 3×3 mm² window, as shown in Fig. 1. In fact, not the primary beam but the sample holder was moved with a step length of 60 μm. Secondary ions were collected only from the central region of the 60×60 μm² rastered area.

Fig. 1 Schematics of scan directions

3. Results

3.1 Normalized ion intensities versus testing position

The results of line scans along X and Y direction are shown in Fig. 2 and Fig. 3, respectively. The intensities of different kinds of secondary ions have been normalized to their maxima. It can be observed that 1) The intensities vary according to the change of the testing position. Abrupt falling of ion intensity appears near the edge of the window; 2) The discrepancy of the variations is significant. Some signals vary intensively, while others rather smoothly; 3) Different variation tendencies between the two directions are apparent. The curve slopes in Fig. 3 are more gentle and their contours more centrally symmetrical, in comparison with those in Fig. 2.

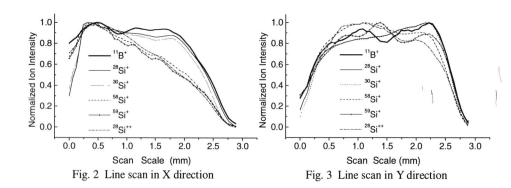

Fig. 2 Line scan in X direction   Fig. 3 Line scan in Y direction

3.2. Relative ion intensities versus testing position

For the RSF method, the relative ion intensities of the reference ions to the detected ion $^{11}B^+$ are important. Processed results from X direction line scans are plotted in Fig. 4, where the intensity ratios have been normalized to their maxima. It is obvious that the intensity ratios of $^{28}Si^+/^{11}B^+$ and $^{30}Si^+/^{11}B^+$ are roughly independent of the testing position, while other ratios vary more or less significantly across the window. The RSDs of the intensity ratios obtained from the testing position in the central 2 mm of the sample are summarized in Table 1. One can see that in comparison with the cluster ions or the doubly charged ions of silicon, the atomic ions of $^{28}Si^+$ and $^{30}Si^+$ as reference ion will make the value of RSF more stable in a quite broad region of the window.

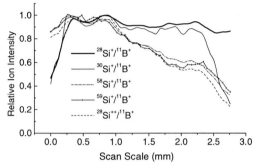

Fig. 4 Relative ion intensity in X direction

Table 1. RSD of intensity ratios in the central 2 mm of the sample in X direction

Intensity Ratio	$^{28}Si^+/^{11}B^+$	$^{30}Si^+/^{11}B^+$	$^{56}Si_2^+/^{11}B^+$	$^{58}Si_2^+/^{11}B^+$	$^{59}Si_2^+/^{11}B^+$
RSD	3.0%	5.7%	33.4%	18.7%	20.8%

Practically, the testing points should normally be chosen close to the central point of the window, rather than being decentralized across the window. Hence, good reproducibility of no more than 1% can be obtained in this experiment when using $^{28}Si^+$ as reference ion.

4. Discussion

All these results can be partly explained by the reported distortion of the CAMECA extraction field. Due to the existence of the metal window on the sample, the expected planar, parallel and equally spaced potential contours are distorted near the edges of the window[3]. It can be easily understood that ions with different energies will be affected differently. Those of low energies are more susceptible to the distortion because of their low initial velocities.

Thus, information concerning the energy distribution of the secondary ions can contribute to the comprehension of the measured reproducibility. By decreasing the energy window width and introducing an offset into the target voltage in a stepwise manner, the energy distribution can be acquired on CAMECA instruments. The detailed method has been discussed by A. Adriaens and F. Adams before[4]. The energy window width here was set to 2 eV and the step size of the offset was 0.5 V. For each offset value, the sample was sputtered until stable secondary signals were maintained The experimental results of the secondary ion energy distribution are shown in Fig. 5. For comparison, each curve has been normalized to its maximal intensity. As it is well known, the energy distribution curves of silicon secondary ions are very much different for atomic and cluster ions. Among them, atomic ions of $^{28}Si^+$ and $^{30}Si^+$ have the most similar distributions with that of the detected ion of $^{11}B^+$.

Combining Fig. 5 with Fig. 2, one can find that ions with similar energy distributions, e.g. $^{58}Si_2^+$ and $^{59}Si_2^+$ or $^{28}Si^+$ and $^{30}Si^+$, always have similar intensity changes in line scans. Thus, it can be reasonably concluded that ions with similar energy distribution will be influenced by the field distortion in similar way. Hence, one can expect to obtain good reproducibility of RSF from a given combination of detected ions and reference ions, presupposing they have similar energy distributions.

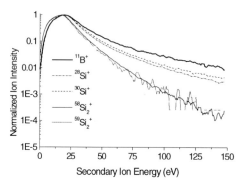

Fig. 5 Energy distribution of secondary ions

Furthermore, when scanning along X direction, the obliquely introduced primary beam is affected differently by the distorted field on the two sides of the window center, resulting in asymmetrical curves in Fig. 2. While along Y direction, the curves tends to be more gentle and symmetrical, as shown in Fig. 3.

5. Conclusion

The dependence of RSF reproducibility upon testing position and the selection of the reference ion have been investigated. It can be concluded that during practical measurement, better reproducibility will be obtained when the three testing points are selected along Y direction, rather than X direction. The atomic ion $^{28}Si^+$ or $^{30}Si^+$ as reference ion is a better selection to get good reproducibility than cluster ions or doubly charged ions of silicon, because the former ones have similar energy distribution with that of $^{11}B^+$ and will be influenced by the field distortion in similar way. Thus, under well controlled conditions, good RSF reproducibility of less than 1% is not difficult to obtain from the three testing points on the sample WRR1-C when using $^{11}B^+$ as the detected ion and $^{28}Si^+$ or $^{30}Si^+$ as the reference ion.

References

[1] Y. Homma *et al.*, Proceedings of SIMS X, Wiley, Chichester, 1997, p 681
[2] ISO Document Number: ISO/TC 201/SC 6 N28, 1996
[3] W.M. Lau, D.R. Cochrane and J.D. Brown, Nucl. Instr. and Meth. B16 (1986) 391
[4] A. Adriaens and F. Adams, Proceedings of SIMS IX, Wiley, Chichester, 1994, p 76

A. Benninghoven, P. Bertrand, H.-N. Migeon and H.W. Werner (Editors).
Proceedings of the 12th International Conference on Secondary Ion Mass Spectrometry,
Brussels, Belgium, 5-11 September 1999

CALCULATION OF THE ENERGY DEPENDENCE OF THE ION COLLECTION EFFICIENCY OF THE CAMECA IMS-3F SIMS INSTRUMENT

D. Karpuzov[2*], K. Franzreb[1], and N. S. McIntyre[1]

[1] Surface Science Western, Univ. of Western Ontario, London, Ontario N6A 5B7, Canada
[2] Institute of Electronics, Bulgarian Academy of Sciences, Sofia 1784, Bulgaria
* Corresponding author, E-mail: karpuzov@surf.ssw.uwo.ca

1. Introduction

The transmission of a secondary ion, species X with energy E, through a SIMS instrument is described by an energy-dependent function, $T_X(E)$. Since the ion optics in modern mass spectrometers is complex, and since ion ejection during sputtering cannot be predicted easily, the ion transmission function is often not well-known and difficult to determine experimentally. Estimates of the dependence of T_X on the initial ion emission energy, E, are of interest for optimizing operation conditions for specific SIMS analysis requirements and for the correction of secondary ion energy distribution raw data.

2. Ion collection for the extraction geometry of the Cameca IMS-3f

Attempts to correct ion energy distribution data for instrumental transmission can be made, based on the operation of the Cameca IMS-3f magnetic sector SIMS instrument in the 'sample bias scan' mode [1-5]. In this case, the energy dependence of the ion transmission, $T_X(E)$, may be assumed to be determined by the collection efficiency for secondary ion extraction [2,5] for ion emission from a point source on the ion-optical axis:

$$(1) \quad T_X(E) \approx \int_0^{2\pi} (\int_0^{\theta_{max}(E)} N_X(\theta, \varphi, E) \cdot \sin(\theta)\, d\theta)\, d\varphi \, / \int_0^{2\pi} (\int_0^{\pi/2} N_X(\theta, \varphi, E) \cdot \sin(\theta)\, d\theta)\, d\varphi.$$

The calculations presented here refer to this simplified case. Experimental results, however, may deviate somewhat because (i) lens aberrations are neglected in the model and (ii) when the lateral size of the analyzed sample area is not small anymore. In the above definition, with $0 < T_X(E) \leq 1$, the term $N_X(\theta, \varphi, E)$ is the a priori unknown element- and sample-specific angular emission distribution of a sputter-ejected ion, X, at any given emission energy, E. θ is the polar angle (measured with respect to the surface normal) and φ is the azimuth. $\theta_{max}(E)$ is the maximum initial emission angle of an ion with kinetic emission energy E, that may still be collected due to ion acceleration along the surface normal. $\theta_{max}(E)$ depends on the specific extraction geometry of the Cameca IMS-3f SIMS instrument. Based on ion optical calculations made by Slodzian [6,7], approximate formulae for $\theta_{max}(E)$ had been provided by Reed and Baker [1], and later by van der Heide [3] and Wittmaack [5]. The ion collection efficiency,

$T_X(E)$, was estimated by Schauer and Williams [2] (for p=1, cosine), by van der Heide [3] (for p=0, isotropic), and by Zalm and by Wittmaack [5] (for general power p) for angular ion distributions, that were assumed to be independent of φ, E and to be given by a polar cosine power law:

(2) $N_X (\theta, \varphi, E) - (\cos(\theta))^p$,

(3) $T_X(E) = 1 - (1 - (\sin(\theta_{max}(E)))^2)^{(1+p)/2}$,

(4) $\sin(\theta_{max}(E)) \approx a/(8 \cdot g \cdot D) \cdot (4500 \text{ eV} / E)^{1/2}$,

where the instrument specific parameters [1] a=400 :m (diameter of the biggest aperture of the contrast diaphragm), g=0.28 (angular cross-over magnification) and D $\approx$ 4.5 mm (distance from sample to the extraction plate). The power p may be mass- or element-specific (i.e. p_X). In this definition $T_X(E)$ is 1 for E≤7 eV, and becomes small but not zero in the field-free case (i.e. sample bias zero; E=4500 eV). At large emission energies, of about E > 20 eV, a simple inverse energy dependence of $T_X(E) \sim E^{-1}$ (with a mass-independent slope of -1) follows from (3) for any cosine power-law approximation [5],

(5) $T_X(E) \sim (1+p_x)/E$.

3. Results of MARLOWE computer simulation of $N_X(2,v,E)$ and $T_X(E)$

The goal of the present study is to calculate, rather than assume [2,3,5], angular emission distributions of $N_X(2,v,E)$ with the MARLOWE sputter code for various projectile→sample combinations, and then determine $T_X(E)$ with eq.(1) and compare it with the prediction of eqs.(3-5). Owing to non-normal ion surface bombardment (under ≈30° with respect to the surface normal) asymmetric angular distributions may be expected, that depend on the projectile to target mass ratio [8]. The study of these effects for galena, PbS, under oxygen or cesium bombardment was therefore of particular interest [9, 10]. A detailed description of the computer simulations will be presented elsewhere [10]. A dynamic version of MARLOWE has been applied that takes near-surface composition changes during sputtering of PbS into account [9,10]. For comparison, results for Ar sputtering of elemental Al are also included. We note that codes for computer simulation of the sputtering, such as MARLOWE, cannot predict subsequent charge transfer during sputter ejection. The calculated results of $N_X(\theta, \varphi, E)$ are therefore representative for the sputtered neutral species X [11] and will differ somewhat from the respective unknown ion angular distribution. Secondary ion distributions of $N_X(\theta, \varphi, E)$ may be modified by energy- and angular-dependent electron transfer approximated by $\sim c_x \cong \exp(-v_0/(v(E) \cong \cos(\theta)))$ [5,11]. The order of magnitude of the pre-exponential factor c_x is not known with sufficient accuracy. It is not predicted well by theoretical models and may be element- and sample-specific.

Figure 1 shows calculated differential sputter yield, $N_X(\theta, E)$ (after integration over the azimuth v) for both the light (^{32}S) and heavy (^{208}Pb) component X sputtered from galena with 8 keV oxygen (^{16}O) under 35°. Strong variations of the angular distributions with emission energy E are clearly visible. Hence, a factorization ansatz to assume $N_X(\theta,E)$. $N_{1X}(\theta)$. $N_{2X}(E)$ would be difficult to justify in this case. Analogous results found for sputtering of S and Pb from PbS under ^{133}Cs bombardment will be given in ref.[10].

Figure 2 shows calculated ion collection efficiencies $T_X(E)$ for ^{32}S and ^{208}Pb sputtered from PbS with 8 keV ^{16}O. The values for S are found to be about a factor of 1.5 to 2 larger than those of Pb. (This ratio is similar for projectiles of ^{133}Cs [10]). Deviations from the

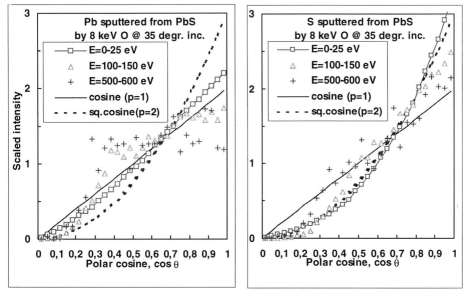

Fig.1: Simulated emission polar-angle distributions, $N_X(2,E)$, of ^{208}Pb and ^{32}S sputtered from PbS with 8 keV ^{16}O at 35°. Emission energies, E, are shown in the legend.

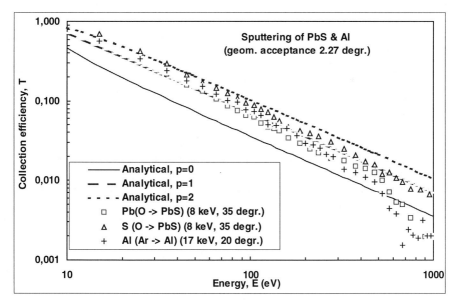

Fig.2: Collection efficiencies, $T_X(E)$, for PbS and Al calculated for the Cameca IMS-3f set-up.

prediction of each of the cosine power-law approximations (shown for p=0,1,2) are observed. The results follow directly from the angular distributions given in Fig.1. The data calculated for Al under 17 keV Ar bombardment confirm these trends. At high emission energies (E>500 eV for Pb and Al here) cosine power-law approximations (eqs. 3-5) seem to overestimate the ion collection. (Note that statistical inaccuracy in this range may be up to 50 % for S and 100 % for Pb and Al). An approximation of $T_X(E) \sim E^{-k}$, with a slope k of 1.1-1.2 is suggested by the present calculations to fit most of the E-range considered.

4. Summary and Conclusion

Calculations of the collection efficiency for secondary ion extraction (so called energy-dependent transmission function $T_X(E)$) for the geometry of the Cameca IMS-3f SIMS instrument, based on simulated angular and energy dependence of the sputter yield show that the assumption of a unique instrumental transmission function of $T(E)$ is not quite accurate. Strictly speaking, $T_X(E)$ is specific for each element and sample, owing to its dependence on the angular distribution of the sputtered ion species at each emission energy, $N_X(\theta, \varphi, E)$. The present results show energy- as well as mass-dependent deviations from eq.(3) that has been suggested for $T_X(E)$ under the assumption that angular ion emission distributions might be described by a single polar cosine power law (with any mass-specific power of p_x). The calculations confirm a crude approximation by $T_X(E) \sim E^{-k}$ with a slope k of roughly 1.1-1.2 for the range of E from 50 to at least 500 eV. For a system with large mass difference, such as sputtering of ^{32}S and ^{208}Pb from PbS, the ion collection efficiency is found to be larger for the lighter sample constituent. Hence, an element-specific error, as high as up to a factor of 2, may be introduced, if such a mass dependence of $T_X(E)$ is neglected.

Acknowledgment
The financial assistance of the Center for Chemical Physics, UWO providing for the visit of one of the authors (D.K.) is gratefully acknowledged.

References

[1]   D. A. Reed and J. E. Baker, Nucl. Instrum. Methods 218, 324 (1983).
[2]   S. N. Schauer and P. Williams, Phys. Rev. B46, 15452 (1992).
[3]   P. A. W. van der Heide, Surf. Sci. Lett. 302, L312 (1994).
[4]   K. Franzreb et al., Surf. Interface Anal. 26, 597 (1998).
[5]   P. C. Zalm, private communication (1998);
      K. Wittmaack, Surf. Sci. 429, 84 (1999).
[6]   G. Slodzian, in: N.B.S. Special Publication, no. 427 (1975), p.33.
[7]   G. Slodzian, Surf. Sci. 48, 161 (1975); G. Slodzian, in: Applied Charged Particle Optics. Ed. A. Septier (Academic, New York, 1980), p.1.
[8]   G. Betz and G. K. Wehner, in: Sputtering by Particle Bombardment II, Ed. R. Behrisch (Springer, Berlin, 1983), p.45.
[9]   D. Karpuzov, K. Franzreb, A. R. Pratt, and N. S. McIntyre, SIMS XII (this proceedings).
[10] D. Karpuzov, K. Franzreb, A. R. Pratt, and N. S. McIntyre, to be published.
[11] B. van Someren et al., Surf. Sci. 423, 276 (1999).

A. Benninghoven, P. Bertrand, H.-N. Migeon and H.W. Werner (Editors).
Proceedings of the 12th International Conference on Secondary Ion Mass Spectrometry,
Brussels, Belgium, 5-11 September 1999

QUANTIFICATION OF ELEMENTS AT THE Si/SiO$_2$ INTERFACE

T. Janssens, W. Vandervorst[1]

IMEC, Kapeldreef 75, B-3001 Leuven, Belgium
[1] also: KULeuven, INSYS, Kard. Mercierlaan 92, B-3100 Leuven, Belgium
email: Janssent@imec.be

1. Introduction

The matrix effect at the Si/SiO$_2$ interface can be minimised by using measuring conditions that fully oxidise the Si surface. But this prevents an accurate interface localisation, because the change in matrix ion intensities is used to locate the position of the interface. The aim of this study is to measure simultaneously the correct position and concentration of dopants and contaminants in a Si/SiO$_2$ multilayer.

An oblique angle of incidence combined with intermediate oxygen flooding is used to establish intermediate oxidation levels thereby reducing the matrix effect but still maintaining accurate interface localisation. The remaining ionization degree changes at the Si/SiO$_2$ interface are corrected based on a point by point correction algorithm thereby taking into account the detailed dependencies on the oxygen concentration. In this context three items needed to be studied: (i) a proper Matrix Ion Species Ratio (MISR) to be used as an internal indicator for the degree of oxidation of the Si surface, (ii) the influence of the oxygen surface concentration on the ionization degree of different elements and (iii) the changes of different matrix ions at the oxide interface relative to the correct interface position.

2. Experimental

The SIMS measurements are performed in a Cameca 4f with a 3 keV O$_2^+$ primary ion beam. The angle of incidence is 52°. The imaged field is 60μm and the used contrast aperture 60μm. The oxidation degree of the Si is altered by changing the oxygen pressure above the sample surface. The pressure is varied between 2e-9 Torr and 5e-6 Torr. The use of a grazing angle of incidence (52°) combined with intermediate flooding conditions enhances the formation ripples on the crater bottom. The surface roughness makes it impossible to determine useful yields at 3 keV O$_2^+$ and 52° for oxidation conditions, characterised by an MISR 57/60 between 9 and 0.5. In order to prevent fast ripple formation in this region an angle of incidence of 35° is used (10.5keV O$_2^+$).

3. Results and discussion

3.1 Matrix ion species ratio as oxygen indicator

The matrix effect at the Si/SiO$_2$ interface, induced by the variation in oxygen concentration at the sputter surface, can only be corrected for if the oxygen concentration at the Si surface is known in every measurement point. Previous studies showed that a ratio of two Si$_x$O$_y^{+q}$ clusters can be used as an in situ indicator of the oxidation degree [1,2]. This ratio is called the Matrix Ion Species Ratio or MISR.

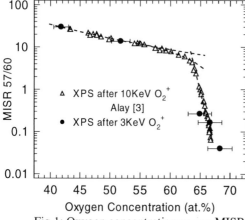

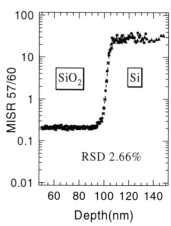

Fig.1: Oxygen concentration versus MISR

Fig.2: reproducibility MISR: overlay of 3 identical SiO₂/Si structures

The ratio Si_2^+/SiO_2^+ is chosen as MISR because this is the cluster ratio with the largest dynamic range at the Si/oxide interface. The SiO_2^+ cluster is enhanced by a factor 100, while the intensity of Si_2^+ is only slightly enhanced, passes through a maximum and then decreases to the stationary level in SiO_2, where $I(SiO_2)/I(Si)$ is 0.57(Fig. 4 and 5). When the oxygen content of the Si surface is changed from 40 and 66 at.% by oxygen flooding, the cluster ratio Si_2^+/SiO_2^+ is enhanced by more then two orders of magnitude. The isotopes m/e=57 and m/e=60 are selected to monitor Si_2^+ and SiO_2^+, because they do not saturate the electron multiplier at the highest oxidation degrees, and because the MISR 57/60 has a good reproducibility. The relative standard deviation (RSD) of the oxygen indicator MISR57/60 amounts to 2.66% if three profiles of the same structure are compared (Fig.2).

To determine the relation between the MISR 57/60 and the real oxygen concentration at the Si surface (Fig.1), XPS results [3] of Si surfaces, measured after 10 keV O_2^+ bombardment at different angles of incidence, are used. Additional to this data we determined the oxygen concentrations at the Si surface after 3 keV O_2^+ bombardment for different oxidation conditions, the angle of incidence fixed at 52°, with XPS (Fig.1). When the oxygen concentration is smaller then 58 at.% or larger then 63.6 at.% the matrix ion species ratio Si_2/SiO_2 can be described as a power of the oxygen concentration, in the region between these 2 values the dependency is linear.

3.2 Ionization degree versus oxidation conditions

With the use of MISR 57/60 it becomes possible to follow the instant degree of oxidation of the Si surface during depth profiling. A point by point concentration calibration of an element at the oxide interface is now possible if the exact dependence of that element on the changing oxidation degree of Si is known. Therefore the response of the useful yields of different dopants and contaminants on changing oxidation conditions is studied here. Useful yields are determined by measuring ion implanted reference material in Si. The degree of oxidation is changed by adjusting the oxygen pressure above the Si surface and monitored by the selected MISR.

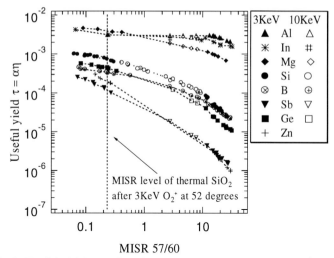

MISR 57/60

Fig.3: Useful yields as a function of matrix ion species ratio Si_2^+/SiO_2^+

A detailed picture of the enhancement of the ionization degree of various elements by oxygen is shown in Fig.3. In order to be able to compare results that are measured at different times, the useful yield of Si is used as a reference signal to correct for transmission efficiency fluctuations. The curves in Fig.3 allow the calibration of the concentration scale at the Si/SiO_2 interface. The matrix effect in the dopant profile disappears; the ionization degree of matrix ion signals still changes at the interface. This creates the possibility to locate the interface, while the correct concentration profile is measured simultaneously. In Fig.3 special attention is drawn to the oxidation condition where MISR 57/60 amounts to the value 0.23. This value equals to the value of the Si_2^+/SiO_2^+ ratio that is measured when a thermal oxide is profiled with a 3 keV O_2^+ primary ion beam at an angle of incidence of 52 degrees under vacuum conditions (Fig.2). Additional increase of ionization degrees of elements sputtered from SiO_2 is possible by using flooding conditions (e.g. 24.5% for Si and 41% for Ga).

3.3 Interface localisation
At grazing angles of incidence the Si surface is only partially oxidised by the O_2^+ bombardment. At 3 keV O_2^+ under 52 degrees and ultra high vacuum conditions the oxygen concentration at the surface amounts to 40 atomic percent (Fig.2.). Under these conditions the matrix effect can be used to determine the correct position of the oxide interface. Oxide layers with different thickness, ranging from 3 to 30 nm, are grown on Si. The thickness of the oxides is determined with ellipsometry before the samples are buried under 100nm poly Si. These buried oxide layers are used to relate the change of the matrix ion intensities to the exact position of the Si/SiO_2 interface. To prevent charging in the insulating layers (oxide and undoped Si toplayer) the samples are bombarded with an electron beam during profiling. The changes of Si^+, SiO^+, SiO_2^+, O^+, Si^{++} and Si_2^+ intensities at the interfaces of a 23.8nm thick buried oxide layer are shown in Fig.5. The dynamic range of the different species, defined as the ratio of the intensity in SiO_2 to the intensity in Si, is displayed in Fig.4 and is independent of the oxide thickness as long as the oxide is thicker then 9.6 nm.

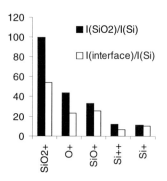

Fig.4: dynamic range and interface level for the different ion species

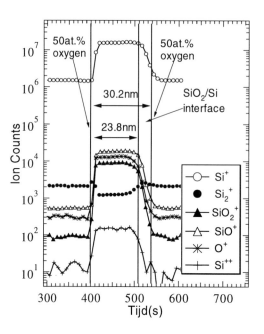

Fig.5: 100nm polySi/23.8nmSiO₂/Si

If the 50% level of the dynamic range would be used to set the interface position, then the position would be dependent on the used ion species [4]. The leading edges of the ion signals at the oxide layer are steep. The Si/SiO$_2$ interface is defined as the location with 50 at.% oxygen content. This point is found by using the relation between MISR 57/60 and the oxygen concentration in Fig1. From the known oxide thickness and the measured erosion rates in Si and SiO$_2$ the original SiO$_2$/Si interface position can then be calculated. The 50 at.% oxygen position at the trailing edge is shifted to a larger depth then the real interface position due to ion beam mixing. For the used experimental conditions this shifts amounts to 6.4nm. The position of the SiO$_2$/Si interface in an unknown structure can now be found as the position where the matrix ions changed by a certain amount. This amount is displayed as I(Interface)/I(Si)in Fig.5 for each species studied.

4. Conclusion
A procedure to determine simultaneously the correct position and concentration of elements in a Si/SiO$_2$ system at the interface is developed. An oblique angle of incidence is used to be able to locate the interfaces by the matrix effect. The ratio of Si$_2^+$(m/e=57) on SiO$_2^+$(m/e=60) is used as in situ oxygen indicator, because of it's high dynamic range and good reproducibility. The useful yields of different elements are determined as a function of this MISR 57/60 by measuring reference material under different flooding conditions. This allows a point by point concentration calibration, based on useful yields.

References:
[1] F.Michiels, L.Butaye, F.Adams, Surf.Int.Anal., vol14, (1989), 170
[2] G.Stingeder, J.Anal.Chem.,327, (1987), 225
[3] J.L.Alay, W.Vandervorst, Phys.Rev.B, vol50, 20 (1994)15015
[4] F.Degreve, Ph.GED, Surf.Int.Anal., vol5, 2 (1983), 83

A. Benninghoven, P. Bertrand, H.-N. Migeon and H.W. Werner (Editors).
Proceedings of the 12th International Conference on Secondary Ion Mass Spectrometry,
Brussels, Belgium, 5-11 September 1999
© 2000 Elsevier Science B.V. All rights reserved.

GENERALISATION OF THE "CORRELATION PLOT" METHOD FOR STANDARD-FREE QUANTIFICATION OF SIMS AND SNMS MEASUREMENTS FOR SAMPLES CONTAINING THREE OR MORE ELEMENTS

M. Gastel[1], S. Flege[2], U. Breuer[3], H.M. Ortner[1]

[1]Fachgebiet Chemische Analytik, [2]Fachgebiet Dünne Schichten, Fachbereich
Materialwissenschaft, TU Darmstadt, Petersenstraße 23, 64287 Darmstadt;
[3]Zentralabteilung für Chemische Analysen, Forschungszentrum Jülich GmbH,
52425 Jülich, Germany. - email: gastel@hrzpub.tu-darmstadt.de

1. Introduction

One of the main problems in secondary ion mass spectrometry is still quantification. The only reliable method - besides using postionization techniques, where a calculation of the relative sensitivity factors is possible with sufficient reliability in most cases [1-3] – is still the use of reference samples with known concentrations. Because very often there are no reference standards available, several attempts have been made to establish a standard-free quantification scheme, beginning from thermodynamic equilibrium models in the early 70s [4] to the infinite velocity method [5]. All of these methods had only limited success, and there is still a lack of good quantification methods.

Based on earlier work [6], in 1994 Gnaser [7] proposed a method to perform a standard-free quantification of MCs^+-SIMS depth profiles of binary systems using a "correlation plot" with the ion intensities of both elements as the ordinates. Provided there are no matrix effects, all measurement points lie on a straight line, and the slope of the line gives the ratio of the relative sensitivity factors. In this paper, we examine whether this method can be generalized for samples containing more than two elements.

2. Theoretical Considerations

Let us first consider a situation where

- the total sputter yield Y is constant
- the relative sensitivity factors are not depending on the concentrations (i.e. no matrix effects)

Let I^i be the measured ion intensity, c^i the concentration and S^i the sensitivity factor of element i. I_p is the primary ion current and Y the total sputter yield. n is the number of elements in the sample. Then the measured ion intensity can be expressed as

$$I^i = I_p Y c^i S^i \qquad (1)$$

All concentrations must sum up to 1:

$$\sum_i c^i = 1 \tag{2}$$

This leads to the following vector equation:

$$\vec{I} \bullet \vec{S} = I_p Y \tag{3}$$

where $\vec{I} = \left(I^1, I^2, \cdots, I^n\right)$, $\vec{S} = \left(1/S^1, 1/S^2, \cdots, 1/S^n\right)$ and "$\bullet$" is the scalar product. (3) is the "Hesse" form of an equation that describes an (n-1)-dimensional affine hyperplane in the n-dimensional space. The geometrical interpretation of (3) is, that all vectors $\vec{I}$ consisting of the measured ion intensities for all elements at one measurement point form a hyperplane (n=3: a plane; n=2: a straight line like shown by Gnaser in [7]), and the vector $\vec{S}$ that is perpendicular to this hyperplane contains the sensitivity factors. This offers an easy way for the determination of the sensitivity factors by calculating the hyperplane that is the best fit to all measurement points $\vec{I}$. This is relatively easy using a least square fit: The distance between one measurement point $\vec{I}$ and the «best fit hyperplane» H is

$$dist(\vec{I}, H) = \left|\vec{I} \bullet \vec{S} - I_p Y\right| \tag{4}$$

So we have to minimize the function

$$D(\vec{S}) = \sum_i dist(\vec{I}_i, H)^2 = \sum_i \left(\vec{I}_i \bullet \vec{S} - I_p Y\right)^2 \tag{5}$$

The summation index i runs from 1 to the number of measurement points. In the minimum the gradient of this function must be zero:

$$0 = \nabla D(\vec{S}) = 2\sum_i \left(\vec{I}_i \bullet \vec{S} - I_p Y\right)\vec{I}_i \tag{6}$$

This is a linear equation system; the number of equations is the number of elements in the sample. The factor $I_p Y$ can be put into the sensitivity factors because only relative values need to be known. Doing so, the equation system (6) is for a sample with 3 elements:

$$\begin{pmatrix} \sum_i I_i^1 I_i^1 & \sum_i I_i^1 I_i^2 & \sum_i I_i^1 I_i^3 \\ \sum_i I_i^2 I_i^1 & \sum_i I_i^2 I_i^2 & \sum_i I_i^2 I_i^3 \\ \sum_i I_i^3 I_i^1 & \sum_i I_i^3 I_i^2 & \sum_i I_i^3 I_i^3 \end{pmatrix} \begin{pmatrix} 1/S^1 \\ 1/S^2 \\ 1/S^3 \end{pmatrix} = \begin{pmatrix} \sum_i I_i^1 \\ \sum_i I_i^2 \\ \sum_i I_i^3 \end{pmatrix} \tag{7}$$

With (6) or (7) the (relative) sensitivity factors can be calculated from the measured ion intensities.

3. Experimental

We investigated the applicability of this method for MCs$^+$-SIMS and e-beam SNMS. For MCs$^+$-SIMS we used a Cameca ims 5f machine with a Cs ion gun. The energy of the Cs$^+$ primary ions was 5.5 keV. The SNMS measurements have been carried out on a FISONS SIMSLAB with e-beam postionization option with Ar$^+$ primary ions.

For our investigation we used multilayer samples of ternary metallic alloys. Different samples of the systems Ni$_x$Cu$_y$Zr$_z$, Al$_x$Cu$_y$Zr$_z$ and Al$_x$Ni$_y$Zr$_z$ have been prepared using molecular beam epitaxy. All samples contain 8 or 9 layers (30 nm each) of different composition. We chose metallic systems to keep the artefacts from charging or matrix effects as low as possible.

4. Results

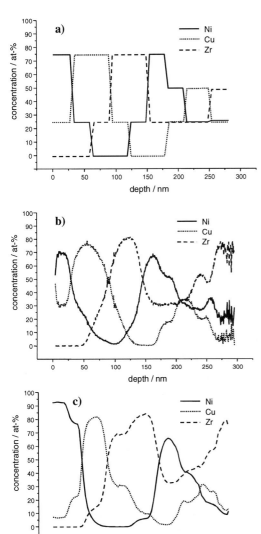

a) System Ni-Cu-Zr

The sample is a multilayer system, consisting of nine layers with concentrations to be seen in Table 1. Fig. 1a shows the depth profile as it is expected from the deposition parameters. Fig. 1b shows the SNMS depth profile which was quantified using the new quantification algorithm. Fig. 1c shows the same for MCs^+-SIMS. Note that before using eq. (7), all measured intensities have been normalized to the measured intensity of Cs^+ ions in order to correct for changes in sputter rate and surface potential. Without this correction, no meaningful results could be received.

It can be stated that the quantification is reasonably good in both cases, although for some layers in the case of the MCs^+-SIMS profile (e.g. layer no. 2) the quantification gives wrong results. This shows that the assumption that there are no matrix effects is not valid in case of the MCs^+-SIMS profile. Table 1 gives an overview over the relative sensitivity factors for each layer, calculated from the measured ion intensities and the known concentrations, compared to the values one gets for the whole profiles following eq. (7). In the case of SNMS the values from eq (7) are in good agreement with the mean values of the RSFs. In the case of MCs^+-SIMS the agreement is not so good. The table shows that in this case the matrix effects are not neclectable (indicated by different RSFs for the different layers).

Fig.1: Depth profile of NiCuZr-Multilayer sample, a) calculated from the deposition rates, b) SNMS, c) MCs+-SIMS, b) and c) quantified using eq. (7)

b) Systems Al-Cu-Zr and Al-Cu-Ni

Similar experiments have been performed for multilayer samples of the systems Al-Cu-Zr and Al-Cu-Ni. For Al-Cu-Zr the MCs^+ results are of similar quality like in the Ni-Cu-Zr system. The concentrations calculated using eq. (7) do not differ by more than a factor of 2 from the real ones, and for most layers the results are much better. However, there are problems with SNMS in this system: While the RSFs for Ni and Al seem to be quite reasonable, the Cu concentration is underestimated by a factor of about 10. In the Al-Cu-Ni system, the method fails totally for MCs$^+$-SIMS and also for SNMS.

Table 1: Concentrations (in at-%), measured and calculated RSFs for the NiCuZr sample

	concentrations			relative sensitivity factors MCs$^+$-SIMS			relative sensitivity factors SNMS		
Layer #	Zr	Ni	Cu	Zr	Ni	Cu	Zr	Ni	Cu
1	0	75	25		4.5	0.24		2.3	1.7
2	0	25	75		5.2	0.13		2.4	1.4
3	25	0	75	0.36		0.96	2.5		1.5
4	75	0	25	0.43		0.72	2.2		1.3
5	75	25	0	0.58	0.54		2.0	2.4	
6	25	75	0	0.80	2.7		3.0	2.4	
7	25	50	25	1.0	2.7	0.58	3.2	3.0	1.2
8	25	25	50	1.2	2.5	0.46	3.8	3.9	1.2
9	49	26	25	1.8	2.3	0.83	2.5	2.9	1.2
mean value				0.89	2.92	0.56	2.74	2.76	1.36
equation (7)				0.89	4.68	1.17	2.74	2.36	1.60

5. Discussion

In principle, the approach of the correlation plot can be used not only for binary sample like shown by Gnaser, but also for samples with more than two elements. However, the method only works if there are no big matrix effects, and therefore an application to classical SIMS (without MCs$^+$ detection) seems to be hopeless. We had some success in quantifying MCs$^+$-SIMS and SNMS depth profiles of ternary metallic alloys, but there have also been similar samples where the method failed. We did not test the method for samples containing more than three elements, but most probably then the problems increase. More work has to be done to prove in which systems the method is valuable.

References

[1] A. Wucher, J. Vac. Sci. Technol. A6 (1988) 2287
[2] A. Wucher, F. Novak, W. Reuter, J. Vac. Sci. Technol. A6 (1988) 2265
[3] M. Gastel, U. Breuer, H. Holzbrecher, J.S. Becker, H.J. Dietze, M. Kubon, H. Wagner, Fresenius J. Anal. Chem. 353 (1995) 478
[4] J.M. Schroer, NBS Spec. Publ. 427 (1975) 121
[5] P.A.W. van der Heide, M. Zhang, G.R. Mount, N.S. McIntyre, Surf. Interf. Analysis 21 (1994) 747
[6] P.M. Hall, J.M. Morabito, D.K. Conley, Surf. Sci. 62 (1977) 1
[7] H. Gnaser, J. Vac. Sci. Technol. A12 (1994) 452

A. Benninghoven, P. Bertrand, H.-N. Migeon and H.W. Werner (Editors).
Proceedings of the 12th International Conference on Secondary Ion Mass Spectrometry,
Brussels, Belgium, 5-11 September 1999

409

QUANTITATIVE CHARACTERIZATION OF SURFACE IMPURITIES BY TOF-SIMS: ANALYSIS OF 12 ELEMENTS ON 19 MATRICES

M. Juhel
FRANCE TELECOM, BD, CNET
28, chemin du vieux chêne MEYLAN F-38243 FRANCE
marc.juhel@cnet.francetelecom.fr

1. Introduction

Time of flight secondary ion mass spectrometry (TOF-SIMS) has been proven to be one the most sensitive methods for analyzing trace metal surface contaminants. This technique combines high sensitivity, detection of light elements and a good spatial resolution. Unfortunately TOF-SIMS, like dynamic SIMS, is unable to give quantitative results without calibration standards.

Most of recent works for quantification of metallic contamination has been done on silicon oxide, for other surfaces very few data are available [1], [2].

In this study we compare the useful yield of 12 elements (Be, Mg, Al, Si, Cr, Mn, Co, Fe, Ni, Cu, Mo and Ag) on 19 matrices from semiconductors, insulators, alloys, metals and polymers. The goal of this study is to give quickly the magnitude order of metal contamination found on a semiconductor device.

2. Experimental

For the preparation of standards we used a sputter deposition technique with a commercial system (PECS 682 from GATAN). The main advantage of this system is the rotation of the sample holder, which allows a uniform deposition on 10 different samples in parallel. Semiconductor and metal matrix were exposed to sputter deposited contamination in two series of 10 samples. For each series we put one sample of silicon, for the contamination quantification. On silicon we used RSF to determine the sputter deposited contamination (these RSF come from analysis of spin-coating standard with a VPD-AAS quantification). In fact, and this is the main limitation of these experiments, we assume that the surface contamination is the same on all samples. In practice volatile organo-metallic compounds could be formed and induce dispersion in the results. In order to avoid some time evolution of the contamination the samples were analyzed immediately after the deposition.

TOF SIMS analysis were performed using a Physical Electronics TRIFT-II instrument with a 15kV gallium beam and a dose of 10^{13} ion/cm^2, the mass resolution was 6000 on 28Si+.

3. Results and discussion

Table 1 shows the different matrices and metal contaminants used in this study. For some matrices the level of metal impurities of the surface before the contamination was to high to enable the analysis, for example Al traces were found on iron. These cases are shown in dark grey and 'C'.

The results of our study are summarized in table 1, we give the calibration factor for all matrices by reference to silicon. This calibration factor is defined by the relation 1:

$$(1) \quad \text{cal. factor (element A)}_{\text{matrixM}} = \left(\frac{\text{I element A}}{\text{I matrix M}}\right)\text{matrix M} \Big/ \left(\frac{\text{I element A}}{\text{I 28 Si}}\right)\text{silicon}$$

The RSF of an impurity A on a matrix M can be estimated by the relation 2:

$$(2) \quad \text{RSF(impurity A)}_{\text{matrix M}} = \text{RSF(impurity A)}_{\text{Silicon}} \times \text{cal. factor}_{\text{Silicon to matrix M}}$$

matrix	matrix reference	metal trace contaminants										
		Al	Mo	Cu	Co	Fe	Ag	Mg	Cr	Mn	Be	Ni
Si	28Si	1.0	1.0	1.0	1.0	1.0	1.0	1.0	1.0	1.0	1.0	1.0
Si3N4	28Si	1.0	1.1	0.8	0.7	1.2	1.0	1.0	0.8	1.0	1.1	1.0
SiO2	28SI	1.0	0.8	0.6	0.8	0.7	0.6	0.9	0.7	0.8	0.9	0.8
Ta	181Ta	5.1	8.4	5.0	4.9	4.5	4.3	5.0	4.7	5.2	3.7	5.1
TaN	181Ta	4.4	6.0	C	4.5	3.9	4.5	4.4	3.9	4.5	5.1	4.6
Al	27Al	M	2.8	C	0.3	0.3	0.3	0.3	0.2	0.3	0.4	0.3
Ge	74Ge	1.1	2.0	0.8	1.3	1.4	1.0	1.1	1.3	1.5	1.4	1.6
TiN	48Ti	0.4	0.7	0.1	0.5	0.3	0.3	0.3	0.3	0.3	0.4	0.4
W	184W	8.6	14.6	3.3	6.1	17.0	4.6	5.0	9.3	10.0	9.2	8.0
Photoresist	12C	2.2	4.3	3.0	3.1	3.8	2.8	3.4	4.3	3.0	8.8	3.0
GaAs	71Ga	0.3	0.4	C	0.3	0.4	0.3	0.2	0.4	1.6	0.4	0.4
Cu	63Cu	0.3	0.3	M	0.3	0.3	0.4	0.2	0.3	0.3	0.3	0.3
Wafer Box	12C	38.7	22.7	15.2	14.0	19.0	15.0	24.0	22.7	21.9	16.3	12.9
Mo	98Mo	2.2	M	4.1	0.5	0.9	4.0	1.8	2.2	1.0	1.8	0.7
Pb	208Pb	0.5	0.6	0.5	0.4	0.4	0.4	0.3	0.5	0.4	0.4	0.4
Fe	56Fe	C	C	C	0.5	M	0.5	0.5	0.6	9.6	0.6	1.4
Ni	58Ni	0.7	0.5	C	0.3	1.2	0.3	0.4	0.5	C	0.5	M
Sn	120Sn	2.6	1.6	C	1.0	2.2	0.3	1.7	1.4	1.4	1.0	1.9
Zn	64Zn	0.7	0.5	0.6	0.4	0.6	0.3	0.6	0.6	0.7	0.6	0.5

Table 1: Calibration factor of an impurity A in a matrix M by reference to silicon RSF. The matrix mass used for reference is on the second column. (M = matrix interference and C = contamination lower than detection limit).

Surface contamination on semiconductor device

In a second experiment we utilized a sample with two different matrices SiO2 and Cu. On this surface we make a deposition of chromium, aluminum, magnesium, cobalt and nickel contamination in the range 10^{13} at/cm^2. This high level of impurities enables to make imaging of the contaminants. Figure 1 shows the sample dimensions and topography. For these analysis the lateral resolution was 3µm and the mass resolution 4000 on 28Si.
On figure 2 we can see uniform distributions of Cr+, Al+, Mg+, Co+ and Ni+ ions counts, the surface ions yields of these impurities seems to be the same on SiO2 and Cu.

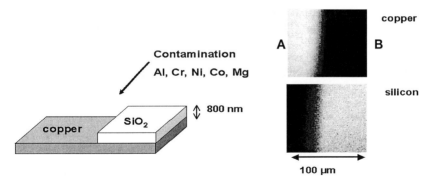

Figure 1: Contamination of a Cu/SiO2 patterned sample.

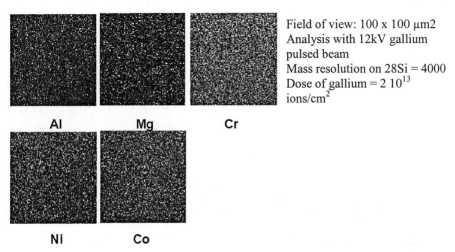

Field of view: 100 x 100 $\mu m2$
Analysis with 12kV gallium
pulsed beam
Mass resolution on 28Si = 4000
Dose of gallium = $2\ 10^{13}$
ions/cm^2

Fig.2: Mapping of Al, Cr, Ni, Mg, and Co contamination on Cu/SiO2 pattern (positive SIMS)

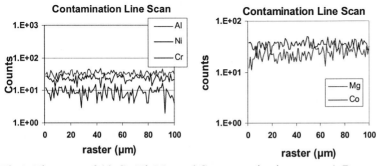

Fig.3: Line scan of Al, Cr, Ni, Mg, and Co contamination across A-B

In order to determine with more precision the ion yield variations we plotted on figure 3 the intensity line scan of the impurities: we can see an uniform distribution. The surface ion yields of these elements are the same on SiO2 and Cu. The type of contamination could explain this: unlike ion implantation sputter deposition is a low energetic process. The impurities are not inside the SiO2 or Cu matrices but are adsorbed on their surface

On figure 4 we try to compare the ion yield variations between all the matrices used in this study. We plot for each matrix the ratio I (impurity A)/ I (impurity Cr). The choice of Cr for the normalization is arbitrary and this able us to see the variation of impurity ion yields between the different matrices. In this plot we remove the points in dark grey on table1 (data lower than the detection limit). In fact the precision of the experiment is not enough to conclude if the relative ion yields variation shown on figure 4 are real or not. But as we mentioned before the goal of the study is to get the magnitude order of contamination on a large number of matrices. In this precision range the relative variation of sensitivity factors from one matrix to another is found to be quite stable.

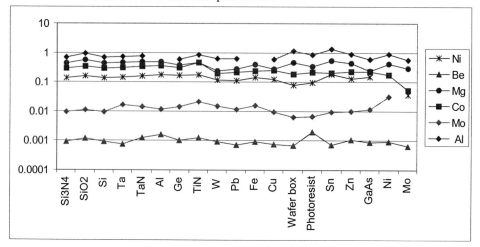

Fig4: Plot of the ratio I (impurity A)/ I (impurity Cr) for different matrices.

4. Conclusion

We found this sub-monolayer deposition technique helpful when standard calibration method such as VPD-AAS are not available, for example on organic material. It is a fast way to get magnitude order of contaminants on any material.
The results show that the ionization yield of impurities has not a strong matrix dependence for this type of low energy contamination.

References

[1] A. Schnieders, R. Mollers and A. Bennighoven, J. Vac. Sci. Technol. B 14 (1996) 2712.
[2] M.A. Douglas and P.J. Chen, Surf. Interface Anal. 26 (1998) 984.

A. Benninghoven, P. Bertrand, H.-N. Migeon and H.W. Werner (Editors).
Proceedings of the 12th International Conference on Secondary Ion Mass Spectrometry,
Brussels, Belgium, 5-11 September 1999
413

DETECTION OF NITROGEN IN SILICON IN THE LOW PPB-RANGE

Hubert Gnaser

Institut für Oberflächen- und Schichtanalytik and Fachbereich Physik,
Universität Kaiserslautern, D-67663 Kaiserslautern, Germany

1. Introduction

Secondary-ion mass spectrometry (SIMS) is a well-established technique for surface and thin film analysis. Generally, the detection sensitivity in SIMS is very high: concentrations in the ppb- or even sub-ppb-range can be achieved for many elements [1]. For example, we have demonstrated recently [2] that Te-atoms can be detected in GaAs at an atomic density level of some 10^{12} atoms/cm^3 corresponding to an atom fraction of ~ 10^{-10} or less. Unfortunately, detection limits are generally worse for (light) elements which are present in the gas phase of the analytical instrument (e.g., H, C, N, or O); the potentially limiting factor for the detection of those elements at very low concentrations arises due to adsorption of residual-gas species on the surface of the eroded specimen [3,4,5,6], resulting in an *apparent* concentration level superimposed onto the *actual* concentration of this element in the sample.

This work intends to illustrate that, at least in specific cases, the detection limits can be extended into the ppb-range also for those elements. The example presented refers to the detection of nitrogen in silicon. By a variation of the erosion rate during the analysis and by correlating the ion signals of N and of another adsorbate species *not* present in the specimens (e.g., H or O), the lowest detectable (bulk) concentration of N can be inferred to be about 5×10^{13} N-atoms/cm^3. Apparently, this detection sensitivity is favored by the efficient formation and ionization of NSi$^-$ ions: roughly 5% of the sputtered N atoms are *detected* as NSi$^-$ molecular ions. (Because N does not form a stable negative ion and the yield of positive N$^+$ ions is very low, the preferred detection scheme is via negative NSi$^-$ molecular ions.)

2. Experimental

The measurements were performed on a standard SIMS instrument (Cameca IMS-4f [7]) using 14.5 keV Cs$^+$ primary ions (incidence angle ~ 26° off normal) and detecting negative secondary ions. Typically, an ion beam of 70 nA beam current (30 μm spot size) was used and raster-scanned across the sample surface; to achieve the variation of the erosion rate discussed below, the nominal size of the scanned area was varied in several distinct steps (up to 11) from (150 μm)^2 to (30 μm)^2. The sputtered ions were detected from a circular area of 30 μm in diameter, centered within the bombarded area. The double-focusing mass spectrometer of the instrument was operated at low mass resolution ($M/\Delta M$ ~ 300) and the slit in its energy-dispersive plane was open (ΔE ~ 100 eV) for most of the measurements. The so-called "150-μm-transfer lens" was employed (which does not provide the ultimate transmission of the instrument but is the usual operation condition) and the second largest angular-acceptance diaphragm in the mass spectrometer entrance plane ("150-μm contrast aperture") was utilized. Under these conditions the total instrument transmission is estimated to fall in the range of 10–15% [2]. The base pressure in the analysis chamber of the instrument amounted to $< 1 \times 10^{-9}$ mbar; with the ion beam operating, the pressure increased to about $(1-1.5) \times 10^{-9}$ mbar. This rise is largely due to beam-induced desorption of adsorbates from surfaces hit by the ions. Upon prolonged operation of the beam the pressure decreases gradually and the background level of gas-phase species is reduced by about a factor of two over a running time of several hours.

Several different Si specimens were used in this work; they were doped with nitrogen at concentration levels of up to about 2×10^{15} N-atoms/cm^3. As silicon is known [8] to amorphize at a fluence of about 10^{14} ions/cm^2 under irradiation conditions comparable to the present ones, the steady-state sputtering conditions of this work refer to an amorphous state of the near-surface region of the samples.

3. Results and discussion

For elements contained in gas-phase species present in the instrument, the adsorption of the latter on the surface may result in an apparent concentration of this element if the reemission due to sputtering occurs in the form used to analyze the element in the mass spectrometer. This apparent concentration level due to residual-gas adsorption, c^{rg}, adds to the concentration, c^0, of this element actually contained in the specimen, giving a total detected concentration c_X^{tot} for element X

$$c_X^{tot} = c_X^{rg} + c_X^0. \qquad (1)$$

Obviously, c^{rg} depends on the number of gas-phase species, i.e. on the pressure in the vicinity of the irradiated surface. This kind of background is exemplified in Fig. 1 which displays the depth distribution of ^{14}N implanted in silicon (energy: 80 keV; fluence: 1×10^{15} cm^{-3}). To record this concentration profile the specimen was eroded at a rate of 1.9 nm/s and NSi$^-$ ions were monitored. The depth scale was calibrated from the total crater depth determined by stylus profilometry and the concentration was established using the nominal fluence value; the latter also yields the relative sensitivity factor for the quantification of other N-containing samples. From these data the ratio of *detected* NSi$^-$ ions per *sputtered* N-atom was derived to be 0.05. This astonishingly high number implies that roughly 30–50% of the N-atoms are emitted as NSi$^-$ ions. Very probably this is due to the strong bonding of the NSi molecule (dissociation energy 5.2 eV) and the high electron affinity of NSi$^-$ (3.3 eV). The concentration profile in Fig. 1 clearly demonstrates that, beyond a depth of ~ 0.6 μm, the N-concentration stays constant at a

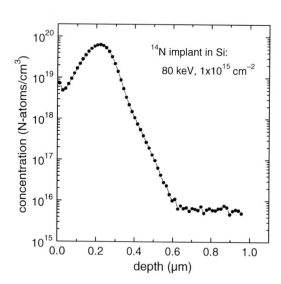

Fig. 1. ^{14}N implantation profile in Si. The sample was sputtered with 14.5 keV Cs$^+$ ions and NSi$^-$ molecular ions were monitored. The erosion rate was 1.9 nm/s.

level of about 6×10^{15} N-atoms/cm^3. This limited detection level is due to the adsorption of N-containing species on the Si surface.

Apart from the pressure which cannot be varied easily, the apparent concentration level depends on the erosion rate of the specimen [4,5,6]. This is due to the fact that, for a given (constant) adsorption rate of gas-phase species, the ratio of the gas-phase to sample atoms in the sputtered flux decreases with increasing erosion rate. In the experiment, the erosion rate was varied by changing the nominal ion-beam scan width, while keeping the acceptance area of secondary ions constant. Decreasing the scan width thus results in a proportional increase of the intensities of species contained in

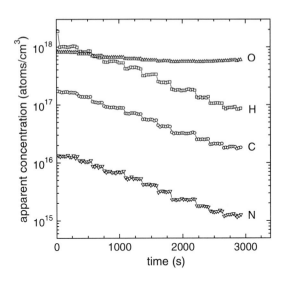

Fig. 2. The apparent concentration due to gas-phase adsorption of H, C and N decreases with increasing erosion rate. The oxygen concentration in this specimen is about 5×10^{17} cm^{-3}.

the specimen (e.g., Si$^-$ in the present situation), whereas the signals of gas-phase induced ions (e.g., H$^-$) stay constant. (The strict inverse proportionality between nominal scan width and intensity breaks down when the former approaches the ion-beam size; then, the erosion rate does not increase by the same amount as the decreased scan area would indicate and is, therefore, not precisely known.) Fig. 2 depicts these effects, showing the reduction of the concentration due to gas-phase adsorption with increasing erosion rate for the elements hydrogen, carbon and nitrogen. (Oxygen is contained in this sample at a concentration of about 5×10^{17} cm^{-3}.) Further evaluation of the data (see below) does show, however, that both C and N are also contained in this specific sample, albeit at concentrations lower than the lowest concentration levels attainable for them by the erosion-rate variation (1×10^{15} atoms/cm^3 for N and 2×10^{16} atoms/cm^3 for C).

The apparent concentrations of two gas-phase species (say X and Y) are linearly related

$$c_X^{rg} = k\, c_Y^{rg}, \qquad (2)$$

where k depends on their relative densities in the gas phase and the adsorption probabilities. For the sensitive detection of an analyte in the sample (N in the present case) we may correlate its *total detected* concentration with the *apparent* concentration of an element that is not contained in the specimen (e.g. H$^-$) using Eqs. (1) and (2):

$$c_N^{tot} = c_N^0 + k\, c_H^{rg}. \qquad (3)$$

Varying c_H^{rg} by means of the erosion rate, a linear relation between c_N^{tot} and c_H^{rg} can be expected; the intercept should then yield c_N^0, the N concentration in the sample. Fig. 3 demonstrates this approach for the data given in Fig. 2. It depicts the detected N concentration

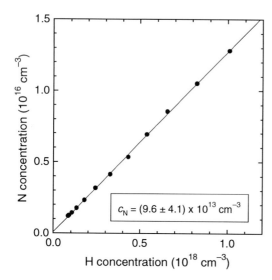

Fig. 3. Correlation between the total N concentration and the apparent concentration of H. The intercept of the straight line yields the actual N concentration c_N^0 in this sample.

which is composed both of the gas-phase component and of the actual amount in the sample as a function of the apparent H concentration. The intercept of the straight-line fit to the data with the N-concentration axis gives the actual concentration of N in this sample, $c_N^0 = (9.6\pm4.1)\times10^{13}$ cm^{-3}. An analogous evaluation for the C-concentration yields $c_C^0 = (3.9\pm0.6)\times10^{15}$ cm^{-3}. In both cases, these real concentrations are by a factor of about ten lower than the lowest concentrations that can be reached by the increase of the erosion rate. Nevertheless, the data obtained thereby have a critical influence on the precision of the determination of the actual sample concentration (cf. Fig. 3).

4. Conclusion

The very low concentration levels of N that are accessible in this way are of paramount importance for investigations which examine the nitrogen incorporation in silicon crystals [9]. Preliminary results from a more detailed study showed that an N atomic density $c_N^0 \sim 5\times10^{13}$ N-atoms/cm^3 [corresponding to an atomic concentration of 1 ppb ($\equiv 10^{-9}$)] constitutes the present detection limit for N in Si achievable by this approach.

References

[1] R.G. Wilson, F.A. Stevie, C.W. Magee, *Secondary Ion Mass Spectrometry*, Wiley, New York (1989).
[2] H. Gnaser, Surf. Interf. Anal. **25**, 737 (1997).
[3] C.W. Magee, E.M. Botnick, J. Vac. Sci. Technol. **19**, 47 (1981).
[4] K. Wittmaack, Nucl. Instrum. Methods **218**, 327 (1983).
[5] Y. Homma, Y. Ishii, J. Vac. Sci. Technol. A **3**, 356 (1985).
[6] J. Kobayashi, M. Nakajima, K. Ishida, J. Vac. Sci. Technol. A **6**, 86 (1988).
[7] H.N. Migeon, C. Le Pipec, J.J. Le Goux, in *Secondary Ion Mass Spectrometry SIMS V*, eds., A. Benninghoven, R.J. Colton, D.S. Simons, H.W. Werner, Springer, Berlin (1986), p. 155.
[8] H. Gnaser, *Low-Energy Ion Irradiation of Solid Surfaces*, Springer, Berlin (1999).
[9] R.S. Hockett, C.A. Evans, P.K. Chu, in *Secondary Ion Mass Spectrometry SIMS VI*, eds., A. Benninghoven, A.M. Huber, H.W. Werner, Wiley, Chichester (1988), p. 441.

A. Benninghoven, P. Bertrand, H.-N. Migeon and H.W. Werner (Editors).
Proceedings of the 12th International Conference on Secondary Ion Mass Spectrometry,
Brussels, Belgium, 5-11 September 1999

417

HIGH ENERGY METHODS FOR QUANTITATIVE STATIC SIMS

John C. Huneke and Robert W. Odom

Charles Evans & Associates, Redwood City, CA 94063

1. Introduction

Secondary ion mass spectrometry has developed into a widely applied technique for microanalytical, thin film analysis to trace element levels. However, SIMS is significantly limited for applications requiring accurate concentration measurements, since SIMS sensitivities are widely variable, depending on elemental composition of the sputtered sample and the relative concentrations of sputtering ion and analyte. The so-called "Infinite Velocity Method" (IVM) for quantitative SIMS analysis has demonstrated near unit sensitivity which essentially eliminates the requirement for extensive standards analysis for those elements studied[1]. Higashi and Homma recently developed and applied an alternate formalism (the so-called High Energy Method or HEM) from which they conclude that HEM provides a method for determining trace concentrations within a factor of 2 for the elements these researchers investigated[2]. The successful application of either of these formalisms to static SIMS data would be an important development since the environment for sputter ionization, determined by the nature of the adsorbed contaminants on the surface, is generally unpredictable under static conditions.

This study provides results of HEM TOF-SIMS measurements on a variety of known standard metal alloys, III-V semiconductors, and thin films on Si. The goals of this work include:

(1) Assess the viability of HEM for TOF-SIMS analysis

(2) Evaluate relative sensitivity factors (RSFs) for TOF-SIMS as a function of element, concentration and matrix composition and

(3) Demonstrate quantitative HEM TOF-SIMS analysis of surface films.

2. The High Energy Method

Higashi and Homma introduced the HEM mode of analysis as a simpler, instrument independent, IVM formalism. Using the relationships from van der Heide, et al.[1], the relative concentrations [C] are expressed by Higashi and Homma as

$$[C_A/C_R] = \{[I_A(E_2)/I_R(E_2)]^{\sqrt{E_2}/(\sqrt{E_2}-\sqrt{E_1})}\}/\{[I_A(E_1)/I_R(E_1)]^{\sqrt{E_1}/(\sqrt{E_2}-\sqrt{E_1})}\} \qquad (1)$$

for the analyte element A relative to the reference element R, measured at two separate energies E_1 and E_2. If one includes the B term for the dependence of ion formation on secondary ion velocity ($I^+=B\exp(-v_0/v)$) as well as the relative multiplier detection efficiency (Q_i), Eq(1) becomes

$$\log[B_A/B_R \bullet Q_A/Q_R \bullet C_A/C_R] = [\sqrt{E} \bullet \log\{I_A(E)/I_R(E)\} - \sqrt{E_0} \bullet \log\{I_A(E_0)/I_R(E_0)\}]/(\sqrt{E}-\sqrt{E_0}) \qquad (2)$$

where E_0 is the initial energy of measurement (greater than about 30 eV). It is normal to correct ion counting results for quantum yield if at all possible. If not, it is usual to take $Q_A/Q_R \cong 1$.

The term $B_A/B_R \bullet Q_A/Q_R \bullet C_A/C_R$ is then evaluated from the slope of the line through experimental data plotted on a graph of $\sqrt{E} \log[I_A(E)/I_R(E)]$ vs. $\sqrt{E}$. Assuming $Q_A/Q_R=1$, the ratio of the modified relative concentrations to known concentrations for standard metals gives B_A/B_R, which is effectively the relative ion yield of the high energy method.

3. Experimental Procedures

3.1 Time of Flight Secondary Ion Mass Spectrometry

Static SIMS results were obtained using the PHI TRIFT I TOF instrument, an imaging time-of-flight mass spectrometer in which secondary ions are accelerated to 3 kV and transported into the mass spectrometer by the combined immersion lens, transfer lens ion optics [3]. A sequence of three spherical 90° electrostatic analyzers provides energy and stigmatic focusing. The sputtered ion beam is maximally dispersed in energy at a crossover in the middle of the second ESA. A fixed slit placed near this crossover defines a 10 eV energy acceptance. The sample surface is sputtered using a focused, pulsed In^+ ion beam under static SIMS conditions. The sample stage incorporates liquid nitrogen cryocooling.

Analytical Procedure

Each sample was cleaved to an appropriate size and mounted with no chemical or mechanical cleaning. Cut and polished standard metal alloy samples and bulk wafer samples which required sputter equilibration and cooling were mounted in a specifically designed carrier. Bulk sample surfaces were sputter equilibrated over a larger area (~120 μm^2), and the surface was briefly resputtered after each analysis to compensate for any compositional drift. Secondary ion energies were sampled at 5 eV, 30 eV, 60 eV, 90 eV, 120 eV, and 150 eV. Energy definition was accomplished by maximizing the ion transmission through the energy slit at the basic acceleration potential V, and subsequently altering the ion optical potentials of all lens and ESA elements at constant ion accelerating voltage V by the fractional amount $(V+\Delta E)/V$.

3.2 Representative Results for HEM TOF-SIMS

Comparison of HEM TOF-SIMS to IVM Dynamic SIMS Data for Standard Metal Alloys

A useful mode of comparing measured and true compositions is the relative ion yield defined as

$$RIY = \{I(A)/I(B)\}_{Meas} / \{[A]/[B]\}_{Standard} \qquad (3)$$

The relative ion yield is also independent of composition and thus the specific standard sample, since the different measurement process parameters and relative compositions are taken into account. A RIY of 1 indicates unit sensitivity and measured ratios would give an accurate measurement of composition with no further adjustment.

NIST SRM 1133

NIST SRM 1133 is a solid form of the particulate SRM 648, which was used by van der Heide, et al. [1] to demonstrate the IVM technique with dynamic SIMS. The static SIMS analysis using the high energy method was performed on a polished sample of SRM 1133. The sample was cooled by liquid nitrogen to approximately –130 K.

Figure 1 is a plot of the ion current ratios for Al, Cr, and Fe relative to Ti at various energies in accordance with Eqn. (2). The parameters of the best fit line are provided on the plot, and the relative concentrations were calculated from the slopes of the lines. A slope of –1 indicates a relative concentration of 0.1. All correlations are linear over the higher energy range (30 eV to 150 eV). Since all curves should pass through the origin (0,0), a positive intercept of the fit line with the ordinate is a measure of the increased ion production of X relative to Ti at low secondary ion energies.

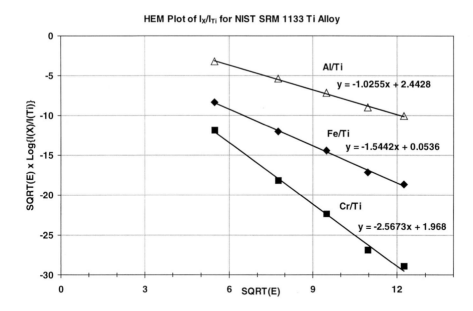

Figure 1. HEM ToF-SIMS Plots of Al, Fe and Cr Intensities Relative to Ti

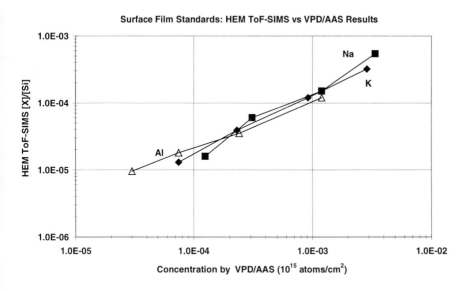

Figure 2. HEM TOF-SIMS Concentrations for Na, Al and K Trace Levels on Si Wafers

The modified relative concentrations calculated from the slopes of the fitted data are summarized in Table 1. These concentrations are normalized to standard compositions to provide relative ion yields. Relative ion yields from HEM TOF-SIMS analysis are compared to the RIY values calculated from the data of Lodding, et al.[4] as well as values from a library of dynamic SIMS (DSIMS) relative ion yields presented by Wilson, et al.[5]. The relative ion yields were normalized to a RIY(Cr) ≡ 6, since Fe is a minor component and thus subject to more variability and interference. The data of Lodding, et al. [4]) is tabulated as both corrected and uncorrected for electron multiplier yield variations, since the ToF-SIMS data were not so corrected. The RIY from HEM TOF-SIMS and IVM dynamic SIMS are remarkably similar for the major components Al, Sn, Ti, Zr, and Cr.

Comparison of HEM TOF-SIMS to VPD/AAS for Na, Al, and K Contamination on Si Wafers.

The results of the HEM TOF-SIMS analysis of Si wafers coated with Na, Al and K at trace levels are plotted in Figure 2 against the data acquired by vapor phase deposition atomic absorbtion spectroscopy (VPD/AAS) on these samples. The correlations are reasonable for all three elements over the range studied (2 ppm to 0.1% coverage of the Si surface.) For K and Al, the correlations are not linear but show a systematic decrease of sensitivity with decreasing concentration. Such behavior can be understood in terms of both the distributions of the impurities over the Si substrate and the analytical depths of the techniques

The ratio of alkali to Si measured by HEM ToF-SIMS is also an order of magnitude lower than values determined by VPD/AAS, again highlighting the fact that the alkalis have a distribution different from the Si. The alkali rich film is a thin layer resident on a thick surface oxide of Si.

References

[1] Van der Heide, P. A. W., Zhang, M., Mount, G. R., and McIntyre, G. *Sur. Inter. Anal.*, 1994, v. 21, pp. 747.

[2] Higashi, Y. and Homma, Y.; *J. Anal. Sci.*, 1998, v. 14, pp. 281

[3] Schueler, B., Sander, P., and Reed, D. A., *Vacuum*, 1990, v. 41, pp. 1990

[4] Lodding, A., van der Heide, P., Brown, J., and Sodervall, U., *Mikrochim. Acta*, 1997, v. 125, pp. 317

[5] Wilson, R. G., Stevie, F. A., and MaGee, C. W., *Secondary Ion Mass Spectrometry*, Wiley, New York, 1989

Acknowledgements
Partial Support for this work was provided by NSF SBIR Grant DMI 9760853

Table 1. Relative ion yields of selected elements from NIST SRM 1133 measured by HEM TOF-SIMS with In^+ sputtering and IVM dynamic SIMS with O_2^+ sputtering.

Element	Ionization Potential (eV)	Dynamic SIMS Ion yield	ToF-SIMS	Dynamic SIMS/O_2^+ Lodding, et al. (1997)	
				Corr.	Uncorr.
Al	5.99	30	7.4	5.7	7.5
Ti	6.82	12	11.5	9.1	12
Cr	6.77	≡6	≡6	≡6	≡6
Fe	7.87	1.5	18	4.6	3.7
Zr	6.84	16	13.6	15.4	13.5
Sn	7.34	1.4	0.66	1.6	0.83

A. Benninghoven, P. Bertrand, H.-N. Migeon and H.W. Werner (Editors).
Proceedings of the 12th International Conference on Secondary Ion Mass Spectrometry,
Brussels, Belgium, 5-11 September 1999

421

AN INVESTIGATION ON THE EFFECTS OF SURFACE TOPOGRAPHY ON DEPTH RESOLUTION IN SECONDARY ION MASS SPECTROMETRY

L. Kiong, A.T.S. Wee*, R. Liu, S.L. Lim
Department of Physics, National University of Singapore,
Lower Kent Ridge Road, Singapore 119260
*email: phyweets@nus.edu.sg

1. Introduction

In recent years, there has been an increase in interest in the effects of surface topography on depth resolution in SIMS. There have been several studies investigating sputtering-induced surface roughness [1-3], as well as a few studies concerning the modeling of SIMS depth profiles [4-5]. However, more could be done to quantify the effects of surface roughening in the SIMS depth resolution functions (DRF) in order to provide more physical validity to these mathematical models. Using the atomic force microscope, the post-sputtering crater bottoms may be investigated by analysing the surface topography. Investigations on the dependence of surface characteristics such as roughness as a function of the depth resolution have the potential to yield a deconvolution scheme that will enable us to explain the depth resolution of SIMS profiles. In this study, a chromium-chromium oxide multilayer standard was used. The profiles were fitted using a modified mixing, roughness and information depth (MRI) model proposed by S. Hofmann [6] and the roughening parameter used to achieve the fit was compared with the corresponding AFM roughness data. We show that there is good correlation confirming the usefulness of the model.

2. Experimental

The chromium-chromium oxide NIST SRM 2136 multilayer sample consists of eight Cr layers (approx. 30 nm thick) that have been sputter deposited onto a polished Si(100) substrate [7]. The outer surface of each of these Cr layers was oxidized forming seven very thin (2-3 monolayers) Cr oxide layers. For this paper, we fitted the SIMS profiles obtained from a Cameca IMS 6f instrument using a 3 keV Cs^+ primary ion beam at a calculated incident angle of 40°. The raster size was about 100 x 100 μm^2. Similar Cr^+ and O^+ profiles were obtained up to the fifth Cr oxide layer which showed well separated peaks for which the fitting could be performed. Separate craters were also prepared by terminating the sputtering at the centre of the first five peaks to investigate crater bottom roughening by AFM. AFM measurements were performed on a Digital Instruments D3000 AFM using a silicon tip in tapping mode.

3. Results

Fig. 1 shows AFM images obtained after 3 keV Cs^+ sputtering was stopped at the first to fifth Cr oxide layers as indicated. The centroids of the Cr^+ or O^+ profiles would correspond to the positions of the oxide layers. The images show an obvious increase in surface roughness with increasing sputter depth. Height histograms of these images show that the height distribution is approximately Gaussian. The root-mean-square (R_{rms}) roughness values for the six craters were determined to be: (a) 2.73 nm, (b) 3.15 nm (c)

4.47 nm, (d) 5.72 nm, (e) 6.67 nm, (f) 7.37 nm. A plot of R_{rms} as a function of sputter depth yields a straight line (with a zero offset due to initial surface roughness) with a linear correlation of 0.983. This indicates that roughness increases with depth under these sputtering conditions.

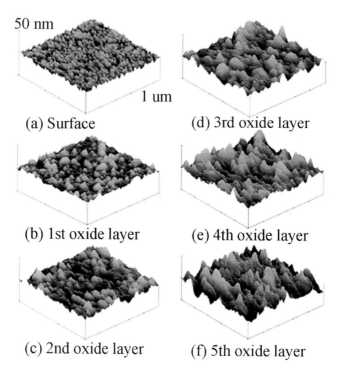

50 nm

1 um

(a) Surface   (d) 3rd oxide layer

(b) 1st oxide layer   (e) 4th oxide layer

(c) 2nd oxide layer   (f) 5th oxide layer

Figure 1. 1.0 x 1.0 μm^2 AFM images of (a) the surface and (b)-(f) after 3 keV Cs^+ sputtering to the first to fifth Cr oxide layers respectively.

3.1 Profile fitting

Although the Cr^+ yield was higher, only the O^+ profiles were used in the theoretical peak fitting. This circumvents the need to account for the increase in Cr^+ yield at the oxide layers due to the matrix effect since the Cr^+ ionization yield is strongly enhanced in Cr oxide. On the other hand, the O^+ signal should be reflective of the oxygen concentration in the oxide layers. We have chosen to use the mixing, roughness and information depth (MRI) model proposed by Hofmann [4,6] as a basis for our profile fitting since this semi-empirical model attempts to quantify the fundamental physical mechanisms of atomic mixing, surface roughness, and information depth. We have for the purposes of this work simplified the MRI model by neglecting the factor of information depth since in SIMS (as opposed to AES), the sputtered species originate predominantly from the first monolayer [7]. In the curve fitting process the convoluted profiles are compared with the actual experimental depth profiles to determine if the fit is good. Such a forward method is done rather than to deconvolute the actual experimental profiles because inverse methods tend to be more inconsistent with experimental data [6]. The elements of the DRF in our modified MRI model, taking into account only mixing and roughness, is summarized by the following basic equations [6,8]:

$$X_A^l = [1 - \exp(-\frac{z - z_1 + w}{w})]$$

(1)

for the region $z_1 - w < z < z_2 - w$ where 'l' denotes the leading edge and w the mixing length,

$$X_A^t = [1 - \exp(-\frac{z_1 - z_2}{w})][\exp(-\frac{z - z_2 + w}{w})]$$

(2)

for the region $z > z_2 - w$ where 't' denotes the trailing edge. The final equation (3) is then the convolution of the mixing function described by equations (1) and (2) with a Gaussian function representing surface roughening, where σ denotes the roughening parameter:

$$X_A^b = \frac{1}{\sqrt{2\pi}\sigma} \int_{z-3\sigma}^{z+3\sigma} X_A^{l,t}(z') \exp[\frac{(z-z')^2}{2\sigma^2}]dz'$$

(3)

Thus, the overall computed profile X_A^b is the convolution of a profile depicting the effects of atomic mixing, $X_A^{l,t}$ with a Gaussian function. We assumed that each Cr oxide layer is 1 nm thick (corresponding to 2-3 monolayers) and that its theoretical distribution is a rectangular function. Fig. 2 shows the raw data and fitted profiles for the first 4 Cr oxide layers. The w and σ values for the fitted profiles are listed in Table 1. Table 1 also shows the corresponding FWHM of the experimental AFM height distribution measured from the approximately Gaussian height distribution of each AFM image.

(a) Expt. FWHM (AFM)	w	σ	(b) Fitted FWHM (FWHM=2.35σ)	(a)/(b) (Expt/Fitted FWHM)
6	1.6	1.2	2.8	2.1
10	2.2	2.1	5.0	2.0
11	2.9	2.8	6.6	1.7
13	3.4	3.0	7.1	1.8

Table 1. Experimental and theoretical fitting parameters of the profiles in Fig. 2.

424

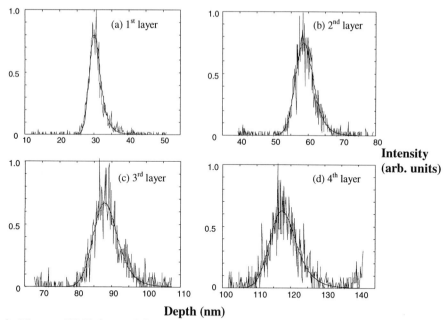

Figure 2. The raw SIMS data and fitted profiles of the first four Cr oxide layers.

4. Conclusions

The model provides a reasonably good fit to the experimental profile (Fig. 2), but it can be seen from the last column in Table 1 that the experimental FWHM is about a factor of two larger than the theoretically fitted FWHM. This systematic error is not unexpected since besides roughening, other factors that have not been accounted for include surface flatness, non-rectangular Cr oxide profile, segregation of oxide, diffusional mixing and recoil implantation [5]. Furthermore, the erosion rate is also a function of roughening, making an association of the peak width and the broadening effect more complex. Nevertheless, we have shown that the experimental roughness data have comparable values and similar trends with the roughness parameter used in the fitting routine, and that the development of surface topography is indeed a major factor in the degradation of the depth resolution. Further work is in progress to test this model with delta profiles in other matrices.

References

[1]   T. Wohner, G. Ecke, H. Roβler and S. Hofmann, Surf. Interface Anal. 26 (1998) 1.
[2]   S. Rusponi, G. Constantini, C. Boragno and U. Valbusa, Phys. Rev. Lett. 81 (1998) 4184.
[3]   J.S. Pan, S.T. Tay, C.H.A. Huan and A.T.S. Wee, Surf. Interface Anal. 26 (1998) 930.
[4]   S. Hofmann and Johannes Schubert, J. Vac. Sci. Technol. A 16 (1998) 1096.
[5]   M.G. Dowsett, R.D. Barlow and P.N. Allen, J. Vac. Sci. Technol. B 12 (1994) 186.
[6]   S. Hofmann, Surf. Interface Anal. 21 (1994) 673.
[7]   S. Hofmann, Appl. Surf. Sci. 70/71 (1993) 9.
[8]   L. Kiong, Physics Honours dissertation, National University of Singapore (1999).

A. Benninghoven, P. Bertrand, H.-N. Migeon and H.W. Werner (Editors).
Proceedings of the 12th International Conference on Secondary Ion Mass Spectrometry,
Brussels, Belgium, 5-11 September 1999

TOF-SIMS ANALYSIS OF SURFACE METAL STANDARDS PRODUCED BY ION IMPLANTATION THROUGH A REMOVABLE LAYER

D.F.Reich[a], B.W.Schueler[a], F.A.Stevie[b], J.M.McKinley[b], and C.N.Granger[b]

[a]Physical Electronics, 575 Chesapeake Dr., Redwood City, CA 94063, U.S.A.,
bschueler@phi.com
[b]Lucent Technologies, 9333 S.John Parkway, Orlando, FL 32819, U.S.A.

1. Introduction

Shrinking device geometry and the associated use of ultra-low energy (ULE) ion implants with junction depths of <20nm present a new analytical challenge for SIMS, since the major portions of these implants are located in the immediate vicinity of the sample surface. It has thus become necessary to determine the surface concentration of the implant, as well as metal contaminants. Surface quantification not only requires appropriate analytical techniques and protocols but also reliable calibration standards.

This paper describes the TOF-SIMS analysis of surface metal standards, which were produced by ion implantation through a removable oxide layer. Ion implantation can deposit precisely controlled amounts of virtually any element into a solid material. The implantation into a substrate will, however, result in the implant peak concentration at some distance below the surface (the projected range) and the concentration at the surface to be poorly defined. Ion implantation through a SiO_2-layer and subsequent removal of the oxide layer should result in a well defined surface concentration of the implant. The nominal surface metal concentration of the implant standards is compared to the results of the surface concentration derived by the TOF-SIMS analysis, using independently derived relative sensitivity factors (RSFs). Furthermore, the effects of organic surface contamination and sample pre-treatment will be reported.

2. Experimental

Surface metal concentration standards were produced at Lucent Technologies by ion implantation through a removable oxide layer [1]. In this study, the ion implantation was performed through a 100nm thick SiO_2-layer. The ion implantation energy was chosen such that the peak concentration peak concentration of the implant is located at the Si/SiO_2 interface. The SiO_2-layer was then etch-removed to expose the implant peak using a 3 minute HF-etch followed by a DI-water rinse. The removable SiO_2-layer thickness of 100nm was chosen because it can be easily and reproducibly grown under semiconductor processing conditions. B, Al, Ca, Mg, Fe, Cu, P, and As were implanted through the removable oxide.

TOF-SIMS positive secondary ion analysis of the implant standards was performed on a PHI TRIFT II mass spectrometer using a bunched liquid metal ion gun operating at 15keV beam energy. Standard analytical conditions as used in the analysis of trace metals on silicon wafers were applied, i.e. using an analytical area of 40μm x 40μm and an analysis time of 10 minutes, the analysis was *integrated* over a depth of approx. 1nm. The metal concentration was first measured by analyzing the «as received» surface, i.e. the inevitably present organic surface contamination layer was included in the analysis. The analysis was repeated again after a period of 4 months. The samples were also analyzed following a 2 second sputter cleaning with a 20nA, 15keV Ga primary ion beam over an area of 300μm x 300μm. This procedure removes the organic contamination by sputtering away from the top monolayer.

3. Results and discussion

Figure 1 shows the comparison of the nominal concentration of the implant standards with the extrapolated concentrations as measured by TOF-SIMS. A bunched 15keV In primary ion beam was used to analyze the «as received» surface. The surface concentration for the different metals was evaluated from the TOF-SIMS measurements using RSFs, which had been determined in independent studies by cross-calibration with TXRF and VPD/AAS. The concentration was then derived from the estimated analysis depth of 1nm. As can be seen from Fig.1, the correlation between the standard concentrations for the various elements with those

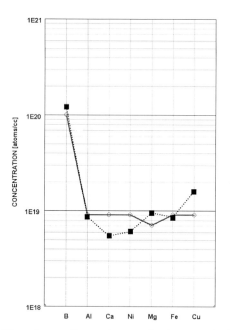
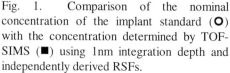
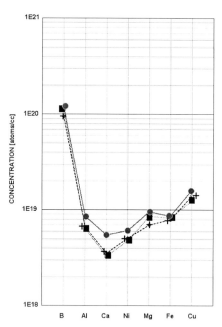

Fig. 1. Comparison of the nominal concentration of the implant standard (O) with the concentration determined by TOF-SIMS (■) using 1nm integration depth and independently derived RSFs.

Fig. 2. Three TOF-SIMS surface measurements taken on three instruments over a period of 5 month. ●: 1st measurement, In+ ion beam , ■ : 2nd measurement 4 month later, Ga+ ion beam, ✣: 3rd measurement 5 month later, Ga+ ions

determined by TOF-SIMS is rather good. Especially B, Al, and Fe show excellent agreement. These RSFs were derived from VPD/AAS measurements on well characterized samples. The observed mean error between standard and the measured values is 30%. This deviation is entirely within the expected range since a number of RSFs have been determined by cross calibration with TXRF.

There has been some uncertainty as to whether such measurements are affected by prolonged storage of the samples, for instance due to the accumulation of organic contaminants. Figure 2 shows the summary of three measurements, which were taken on three instruments over the period of 5 months. The first measurement was taken with a bunched In^+ primary ion beam whereas the subsequent measurements were obtained using a Ga^+ primary ion beam with the same number of primary ions per pulse. The overall change of the measured concentrations, using standard RSFs, is rather weak. It is seen that B, Ni, Fe, and Cu are barely affected by the time between measurements and the different primary ion species. The spread in the B, Ca, and Mg concentration is somewhat larger in the overall set of measurements but is negligible when comparing only the data taken with a Ga^+ primary ion beam over a period of one month. The somewhat larger deviation between measurements taken with Ga^+ and In^+ may be due to a slightly larger total integration depth when using In^+. Overall, the measurements do not indicate any significant change of the sample surface with time.

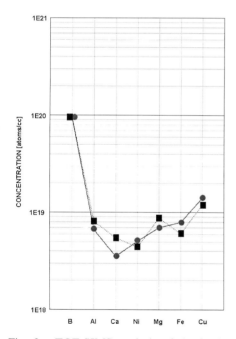 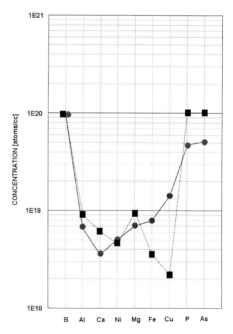

Fig. 3. TOF-SIMS analysis of the implant standards taken at the surface (●) and after pre-sputtering with $2x10^{14}cm^{-2}$ 15keV Ga (■) to remove the organic surface layer.

Fig. 4. TOF-SIMS surface concentrations measured at the surface (●) and at 2nm (■) depth by sputtering with 500eV O_2^+ with O_2-leak. RSFs for P and As were determined from the implant standard at 2nm depth.

The thickness of the organic surface layer influences the analysis depth for a given set of analysis conditions. The effect of sputter removal of the organic surface layer using 15keV Ga^+ (dose: $2x10^{14}ions/cm^2$) on the surface concentrations measured on the implant standards is illustrated in Figure 3. In general, the effect of sputter removal of the organic layer on measured surface concentrations is rather weak. A slight systematic increase in the Al, Ca, and Mg as well as a small decrease in the Fe and Cu concentration is noted. With the exception of Fe, the surface concentrations exhibit a somewhat closer match to the nominal surface concentrations of the implant standards. Similar to sample aging, the effect of sputter removal of the organic layer is weak and is likely negligible if the integration depth of the analysis is slightly increased.

The concentration profile of the implant standards is assumed to be constant over a depth of several nm. The removal of some nm from the sample surface should not significantly influence the metal concentration. Figure 4 shows the comparison of the surface metal concentrations determined by TOF-SIMS at the top surface and after the top 2nm were removed by sputtering with a 500eV O_2^+ primary ion beam and using an O_2-leak. The data points for P and As are included to show the qualitative behavior of the RSFs. The RSFs for P and As were calculated using the nominal dose of the implant standard from the analysis taken at 2nm depth. It is seen that for B, Al, Ca, Ni, and Mg, the measured surface concentrations after removal of the top 2nm is virtually identical to the results obtained after sputter removal of the organic surface layer. Fe and Cu, however, exhibit a significant drop in measured concentration by factors >2. This discrepancy may either be due to a preferential segregation of Fe and Cu at the surface or an unexpected increase in the RSFs. The opposite behavior is observed with P and As, where an apparent surface depletion is indicated. It should be mentioned that the same qualitative behavior was observed for these four elements when the sputter removal was carried out using a 15keV Ga^+ primary ion beam with O_2-leak.

4. Summary

The TOF-SIMS analysis of ion implant standards produced by implantation through a removable oxide layer demonstrates close agreement of the nominal and extrapolated surface concentrations at the top 1nm of the surface. The measured dose at the surface as well as after organic removal was found to yield repeatable surface concentrations over an extended time period. With some exceptions, only very minor changes in the measured concentrations were found for the various analytical conditions. The apparent enrichment of Fe and Cu and apparent depletion of P and As at the outermost 1nm of the surface are not fully understood and require further study. Additional work is in progress to apply these standards to TXRF measurements.

References
[1] F.A.Stevie, et.al., Proc. USJ Conf., NC, 1999

A. Benninghoven, P. Bertrand, H.-N. Migeon and H.W. Werner (Editors).
Proceedings of the 12th International Conference on Secondary Ion Mass Spectrometry,
Brussels, Belgium, 5-11 September 1999

SURFACE ANALYSIS BY TOF-SIMS AND LASER POST-IONISATION SNMS OF ION INDUCED MODIFIED Si OXIDE AND Mo OXIDE SURFACES

J. Cardenas, N. P. Lockyer and J. C. Vickerman

Surface Analysis Research Centre, UMIST, Manchester M60 1QD, UK

1. Introduction

The surfaces of inorganic solids have been investigated by SIMS using both qualitative and quantitative methods. Investigations of oxides has shown that the molecular ion yield of $MeO_x^{+/-}$, where Me denotes the metal atom and x=1,2,3.., is a sensitive indicator for elucidating chemical information[1-2]. In particular, the relative ion yield of $MeO_x^{+/-}$ as function of x has shown to be described by a Gaussian function whose centroid for negative ions (G_-) and positive ions (G_+) is correlated with the valence of the metal ion in the oxide and with the surface binding energy, respectively[3]. More recent investigations suggest that the average of G_- and G_+ vary linearly with the composition[4].[4] However, the present investigation provides evidence that G_+ is strongly correlated with the surface composition.

2. Experimental

Time-of-flight SSIMS and Laser postionisation SNMS were used to conduct measurements on thin (2-5nm) Si oxide and Mo oxide layers on a Si wafer and a Mo/Si structure, respectively. The Mo layer was electron beam evaporated to a thickness of ~60nm. The sample surfaces were typically eroded using a Ga^+ ion beam, consisting of a current between 2 and 10 nA and rastered over an area of ~500x500μm^2, with an incidence energy of 12.5 keV and an incidence angle of ~32° followed by the analysis performed using the same ion beam. The dose during the erosion and during the subsequent data acquisition exceeded $1x10^{14}$/cm^2 and was less than $2x10^{12}$/cm^2, respectively. The post-ionisation was performed using a laser light focused to a spot of ~10μm in diameter, with a density of ~$1x10^{14}$W/cm^2, and a wavelength of 532 nm. The mass resolution during the SSIMS and the SNMS measurements was typically ~1000 at mass 56 and ~300 at mass 28, respectively.

3. Results and discussion

Figure 1 shows the normalised intensity of the peaks at mass 56, 72, and 88 corresponding to Si_2, Si_2O, and Si_2O_2, respectively, from SIMS mass spectra obtained for the Si oxide sample. The spectra were acquired after having exposed the surface to a Ga^+ dose of $\sim1.2\times10^{14}/cm^2$ and $\sim2.4\times10^{14}/cm^2$. The solid lines describe Gaussian functions, fitted by a least square algorithm to the peaks, whose center positions are denoted by G_+^A and G_+^B for the ion dose of $\sim1.2\times10^{14}/cm^2$ and $\sim2.4\times10^{14}/cm^2$, respectively. Figure 2 shows the dependence of G_+ as a function of the exposed Ga^+ dose, which depicts a significant variation at $\sim1\times10^{14}Ga^+/cm^2$. This dependence suggests that the original surface was oxygen deficient and due to the ion bombardment experienced a transition at an ion dose of $\sim1\times10^{14}Ga^+/cm^2$ to a more oxygen rich surface. The integrated peak area for mass 28 in the mass spectra obtained by laser post ionisation of secondary neutrals has an inverse relation as a function of dose in agreement with the SIMS results (Fig. 2). Noteworthy is that the transition occurs for a relatively low dose which would imply that preferential sputtering cannot be the main driving force for the compositional change of the surface. In addition, SiO_2 does not undergo preferential sputtering during ion bombardment[5]. It is therefore tempting to suggest that oxygen diffuses, due to ion beam atomic mixing, preferentially as has been observed in dynamic SIMS[5].

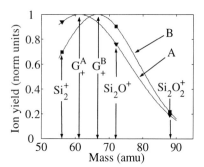 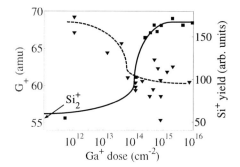

Fig. 1. Yield of $Si_2O_y^+$ molecular ions (y=0,1,2) obtained from a SSIMS spectra after having exposed the Si oxide sample to a dose of $1.2\times10^{14}/cm^2$ (A) and $2.4\times10^{14}/cm^2$ (B).

Fig. 2. The dependence of G_+ (see fig. 1) and the postionisation yield of Si secondary neutrals versus the Ga^+ dose.

When Mo oxide is ion bombarded, Mo sputters preferentially and it has been shown that MoO_3 is reduced to MoO_2[6]. Figure 3 shows the dependence of G_+ as a function of the Ga^+ dose for Mo oxide, which reveals an opposite behaviour than for the Si oxide sample and a gradual transition. This is in agreement with a gradual change of the composition due to preferential sputtering. The compositional change of the surface was confirmed by laser post ionisation of secondary neutrals, where the ion yield in Fig. 3 consists of the sum of the integrated peak areas of Mo^+ and Mo^{2+} which reveal an inverse relation to the SIMS results. The ion yield in Fig. 3 is the sum of Mo^+ and Mo^{2+} normalised to the sum of Mo^+ and Mo^{2+} and Ga^+ in the Mo layer of the MoO_x/Mo/Si multilayer structure. In addition to Mo^+ and Mo^{2+} there were peaks in the SNMS spectra which are most probably associated with MoO^+ and Ga^+. The intensity of MoO^+ and Ga^+ were not more than 15% and 25%, respectively, of the sum of the peaks associated with Mo. The implanted Ga was observed for ion doses exceeding $\sim 4 \times 10^{14}$ and $\sim 1 \times 10^{14}$ in the SiO_x/Si sample and in the MoO_x/Mo/Si sample, respectively.

These results suggests that variations in G_+ are strongly associated with changes in surface stoichiometry and not necessarily to changes in surface binding energy as suggested by Plog et al.[3]. Furthermore, our results are in agreement with SSIMS investigations on reduced TiO_2 where the ratio TiO^+/Ti^+ was shown to vary linearly with the Auger O/Ti peak ratio suggesting a linear dependence with composition [6].

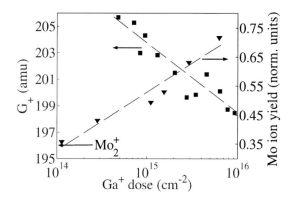

Fig. 3. The dependence of G_+ (see fig. 1) and the post ionisation yield of Mo secondary neutrals versus the Ga^+ dose.

4. Conclusion

The SSIMS mass spectra and laser postionisation SNMS of thin Si oxide and Mo oxide layers were acquired after having exposed the samples to a Ga^+ dose between $\sim 1 \times 10^{14} Ga^+/cm^2$ and $\sim 1 \times 10^{16} Ga^+/cm^2$. The SSIMS results were analysed within a procedure similar to the partial charge model. The results from the two experimental methods are in agreement and suggest that SSIMS for positive ions is sufficient to investigate the surface composition.

Acknowledgements

Samples were kindly provided by Dr. A. Mouroux.

References

[1] N. M. Reed and J. C. Vickerman, Proc. SIMS VII, (John Wiley and Sons Ltd., Monterey, USA, 1989), p. 793.
[2] C. Plog, L. Wiedmann, and A. Benninghoven, Surf. Sci., 67 (1977) 565.
[3] C. Plog and W. Gerhard, Proc. SIMS II, (Springer, Stanford, USA, 1979), p. 37.
[4] D. Lipinsky, L. Wiedmann, and A. Benninghoven, Proc. SIMS X, (John Wiley and Sons Ltd., Münster, Germany, 1995), p. 235.
[5] Th. Albers, M. Neumann, D. Lipinsky, L. Wiedmann, and A. Benninghoven, Surf. Interf. Analysis, 22 (1994) 9.
[6] J. Marien and E. De Pauw, Proc. SIMS III, (Springer , Budapest, Hungary, 1981), p. 377.

A. Benninghoven, P. Bertrand, H.-N. Migeon and H.W. Werner (Editors).
Proceedings of the 12th International Conference on Secondary Ion Mass Spectrometry,
Brussels, Belgium, 5-11 September 1999

433

IN SITU ION IMPLANTATION FOR QUANTITATIVE SIMS ANALYSIS OF ELECTRONIC MATERIALS

Richard T. Lareau[1] and Frank Chmara[2]

[1]Army Research Laboratory, Adelphi, MD 20783-1197 USA
RLareau@ARL.MIL
[2]Peabody Scientific, P.O. Box 2009, Peabody MA 01960 USA

1. Introduction

This work focuses on a recent application of the in situ ion implantation technique to quantify dopants and impurities in electronic materials by SIMS. A negative ion sputter source was attached to the primary ion column of a Cameca IMS-6f magnetic sector SIMS instrument to provide a wide variety of sputtering species. These new species can be used as alternative SIMS primary ions, including negative cluster and polyatomic ions, or used to generate internal calibration standards with in situ ion implantation [1-3]. Presently, there are numerous external (ex situ) ion implanted calibration standards for SIMS, however, those available are only for the more common semiconductor materials, such as, Si, SiO2, GaAs, etc. Several reasons exist for utilizing the in situ ion implantation method, including, wide range of elements or isotopes available, rapid choice of implant specie, ability to perform microarea implants into test pads or active device areas, selective depth implants by pre-sputtering down to the depth of interest, improved quantitative accuracy, and on-demand and inexpensive implantation method. For research laboratories investigating the growth and processing of advanced electronic materials, including: wide-band gap (WBG) materials (SiC, GaN, AlN, etc.); III-V materials (Al_xGa_yAs, GaAs, DyAs, InP, etc.); II-VI materials (CdTe, HgCdTe, etc.), and dielectric materials, etc., the urgent need for on-demand and selected-area ion implantion/quantification is essential.

2. Experimental

For the first time, a commercially available negative ion sputter source (Peabody Scientific, PSX-120, Peabody, MA, USA), typically used with many ion accelerators, was attached directly onto the primary ion column of a Cameca IMS-6f SIMS instrument (in place of the standard duoplasmatron ion source). The negative ion sputter source, based on the Middleton design [4], uses surface ionization of cesium from a cylindrical ionizer filament, accelerated by a high-energy extraction field to the cathode target. This results in the sputtering and extraction of copious amounts of negative ions from the target into the entrance of the primary ion column. The primary column is equipped with an optional extended, mass-range, primary-beam mass filter, permitting selection and filtering of the desired specie. To date, C, O, N, B, Si, Al, Fe, Ni, and Ag ions have been generated and implanted into test samples. Unlike commercial external ion implanters, this method permits use of much smaller "maskless" implant areas (typically on the order of 500 μm x 500 μm or smaller), and hence, lower ion implant currents. The total ion energy used for the implants was 20-30 keV, resulting in a range of 200-1000Å in most of the materials studied.

The accuracy of the in situ ion implantation technique depends on several factors. First, one must be able to measure the implanted ion dose (current and area) accurately. For current measurements, a biased electrometer is connected to the sample's high voltage connection, and measurements of the ion current are monitored using a Faraday cup designed in the center of the sample holder. In addition, the ion current must be stable over the standard implant time; this is typically 10-20 minutes, depending on the implant ion current used. The negative ion sputter source provides a stability of approximately a few percent over a 20-minute period. The area of the ion implant must also be precisely known. To accomplish this, calibration of the negative ion rastered image to a known grid calibration standard can be used, or alternatively, a longer implant time providing a deeper sputter crater can then be calibrated via a standard surface profilometer.

After the in situ ion implant into the analytical sample was completed, post-implant analysis of this region was performed with the cesium microbeam ion source. For this study, typical conditions of 14.5 keV Cs^+ primary ion impact energy, 250 µm x 250 µm raster area, and a 30% acceptance area were used. Since the ion implants are near surface at these energies, the non-equilibrium region was avoided by performing a pre-sputter with the Cs^+ ion beam before the in situ ion implant process was performed. An implant with a large raster area of 500 µm x 500 µm over a few minutes was sufficient to remove the top surface contamination and to establish steady state sputtering rates in the matrix which can be monitored observing the depth profile and stopping after the equilibrium levels have been established. Thus, the procedures of pre-sputter, implantation, and post-analysis make up the full process of in situ ion implantation.

An example of the utility of this technique is illustrated with the quantitative analysis of N- and Al-doped epitaxial SiC layers (a test WBG structure). As there are no known commercial SIMS reference standards for N and Al in SiC, in situ ion implants of both species directly into the analytical sample provided for a fast and accurate measurement of the doping levels for each layer, and provided quick confirmation of the grower's nominal doping levels. After the profile through the implant distribution, the residual background levels correspond directly to the doping levels in the analytical sample. Figure 1 is a qualitative SIMS depth profile of the device layers; the main areas of interest are highlighted in the figure as points A and B (an Al-doped plateau and an N-drift region, respectively). For both in situ ion implants, Cs^+ pre-sputtering was used both to reach the equilibrium sputter rate for Cs^+ in SiC and to selectively (in both the lateral and depth directions) sputter down to the analytical areas of interest. Both N and Al ion implant conditions were set at −15 keV primary ion, +10 keV secondary accelerating potential (resulting in 25 keV impact energy), and a few nA of implant energy into a 500 µm x 500 µm implant area.

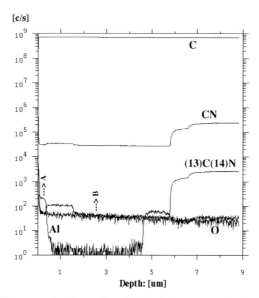

Fig. 1: SIMS sputter depth profile of epitaxially grown thin-film WBG test structure. Point A is the Al-doped plateau and point B is the N-drift region.

3. Results and Discussion

Figure 2 is a SIMS depth profile for a 25 keV, 8e15 N/cm^2, approximately 25 degree implant angle, in situ ion implant into the SiC epi layer. This implant resulted in a peak concentration of approximately 4e20 N/cm^3 at a range of 330 Å. The calculated background or N drift concentration determined from this measurement was 1.5e17 N/cm^3, which was close to the nominal growth concentration of 2e17 N/cm^3.

Similarly, Figure 3 is a SIMS depth profile for a 25 keV, 1.0e16 Al/cm^2, approximately 25 degree implant angle, in situ ion implant into the same SiC epi structure (Al-doped layer). This implant resulted in a peak concentration of 2.6e21 Al/cm^3 at a range of 226 Å. It is clear from both Figure 2 and 3 that the analytical sputter equilibrium was achieved readily, due to the Cs$^+$ pre-sputter step, and that a major percentage of the ion implant was retained in the SiC layer (over 95% in both cases). Results for both implants were compared to ion implant simulations (Profile Code and SRIM [5-6]), and agreed well. The measured dopant concentration for the Al plateau region was 2.5e18 Al/cm^3, which is low compared to the nominal growth target of 1e19 Al/cm^3. This does not necessarily indicate inaccuracies in this implant or technique, as the nominal growth levels for this material were known to be in error from electrical characterization of the material. Hence, a need exists to verify the accuracy of this technique with the use of a SIMS certified standard.

436

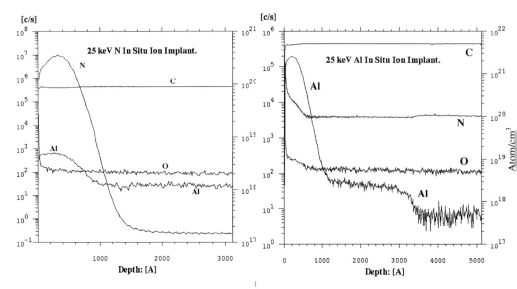

Fig. 2: N In Situ Ion Implant into N-drift region.

Fig 3: Al In Situ Ion Implant into the Al-doped plateau region.

4. Conclusion

These results clearly illustrate the utility of the negative ion source for the generation of a wide variety of ion implant species. Both N and Al in situ ion implants into the SiC WBG epi test layers indicate the potential of quantitative analysis by this technique. The overall accuracies of the in situ ion implantation technique cannot be determined from the above application, and future work is under way to implant B into Si and directly determine the quantitative accuracy using a B in Si NIST standard reference material (SRM) [7]. Previous work has indicated that the accuracy is better than 10% [1]. In addition, plans are currently under way to use species from this new ion sputter source to fabricate near-surface, selective-area device implant regions as part of the processing of new test device structures.

References
[1] R.T. Lareau and P. Williams, *Mat. Res. Soc. Symp. Proc.* **48**, 273, (1985).
[2] H.E. Smith and G.H. Morrison, *Anal. Chem.*, 57, 2663, (1985)
[3] G.Gillen, P. Chi, and D.S. Simons, *SIMS VII Proc.*, 697, (1989).
[4] R. Middletown, *Nucl. Instr. Methds.*, **214**, 139-150, (1983).
[5] Profile Code, Vers. 3.2, Implant Sciences Corp., Wakefield, MA USA.
[6] SRIM 1999, IBM-Research, Yorktown, NY USA.
[7] NIST SRM #2137, Boron Implant in Silicon, NIST, Gaithersburg, MD USA.

SECTION 10 :
SURFACE ANALYSIS

A. Benninghoven, P. Bertrand, H.-N. Migeon and H.W. Werner (Editors).
Proceedings of the 12th International Conference on Secondary Ion Mass Spectrometry,
Brussels, Belgium, 5-11 September 1999

439

CHARACTERISATION BY TOF-SIMS AND AUGER SPECTROSCOPY OF FINGERMARKS REVEALED BY VACUUM METAL DEPOSITION

D. Léonard[a]*, G. Stauffer[b], N. Xanthopoulos[a], C. Champod[b] and H.J. Mathieu[a]

[a]Laboratoire de Métallurgie Chimique (LMCH), Département des Matériaux, Ecole Polytechnique Fédérale de Lausanne (EPFL), CH-1015 Lausanne - EPFL, Switzerland

*corresponding author: Dr Didier Léonard (email: didier.leonard@epfl.ch)

[b]Institut de Police Scientifique et de Criminologie (School of Forensic Science), Université de Lausanne BCH, CH-1015 Lausanne-Dorigny, Switzerland

1. Introduction

Among the various methods used to detect fingermarks, Vacuum Metal Deposition (VMD) is a method of choice for two main reasons:

- its excellent sensibility for detecting fingermarks deposited on non-porous surfaces such as glass and polymer substrates [1];

- the possibility of putting VMD in a complementary sequence with other chemical or physical detection techniques [2].

The process consists of the consecutive vacuum metal depositions of a very thin Au layer (~2 nm) and of a Zn layer of adequate thickness (~5 nm) to achieve a good contrast. The method was empirically developed and more insight on surface characterisation is needed to identify the exact roles of Au and Zn layers. More precisely, it is not clear if gold condenses on fingermark residues or not, while it is clear that Au promotes Zn condensation and acts as a presensitizing layer [3]. Thus, the basic questions are the following: is Au deposited only on the substrate, facilitating Zn adhesion on these parts, or is Au deposited everywhere but diffuses through the fingermark residues leading to Zn evaporation only on areas where Au is still significantly present? Understanding of the process may help to increase the sensibility of the VMD method or to develop procedures allowing a measure of the age of a fingermark residue.

Imaging Time-of-Flight Secondary Ion Mass Spectrometry (ToF-SIMS) and Auger spectroscopy are used to answer more specifically the three following questions: how are Au atoms distributed on the surface after Au evaporation? A similar question exists for Zn after direct Zn deposition (no Au pre-deposition), and finally is there any interaction between Au atoms and fingermark residues (such as diffusion as proposed by Margot and Lennard [2])?

2. Experimental Conditions

Vacuum metal depositions for revealing latent fingermarks were performed using an Edward model 3AM VMD apparatus. The substrate to be examined was arranged perpendicularly above the twin filaments at a distance of 30 cm before the system was evacuated to a pressure of 10^{-5} torr. Then, 2–3 mg of gold was rapidly heated to 1600°C in one of the filaments and allowed to evaporate completely. The temperature of the second filament was then raised slowly until the zinc began to melt. Evaporation continued until a contrast was achieved between the fingerprint ridges and the substrate. The fingermarks obtained are negatives since the valleys, where there is no residue, are developed by the zinc.

All the samples discussed in this study where prepared on Si wafer substrates to allow both ToF-SIMS and Auger spectroscopy analyses. The following samples were prepared: (1) fingermarks deposited on the Si wafer substrates; (2) same as (1) followed by an evaporation of Zn in excess (compared to the empirical process); (3) same as (1) followed by an evaporation of Au in excess (6mg); (4) same as (1) followed by the whole VMD process (Au then Zn) and finally (5) same as (4) but with an evaporation of Zn in excess.

The ToF-SIMS system used in this study was a commercial ToF-SIMS mass spectrometer (described in detail elsewhere [4-5]) from PHI-EVANS (PHI-EVANS Trift 1). The DC 15 keV $^{69}Ga^+$ ion beam current was pulsed at 5 kHz repetition rate (pulse width of about 7 ns (unbunched)). ToF-SIMS image acquisition was performed in high mass resolution conditions (bunched ion beam) using a charge compensation in the negative ion acquisition. The analysed area was estimated to be a square of 420 x 420 μm^2. The total ion dose for a 30 min spectrum was below $1 \cdot 10^{12}$ ions/cm^2, which is within the so-called 'static' SIMS conditions [6].

Auger spectroscopy measurements were performed using a Perkin Elmer PHI 660 Auger system. The spectra were acquired using the following experimental conditions: primary beam energy 3 keV, primary beam current 5 nA and beam diameter 0.25 µm. Sputtering was performed with 2 keV Ar^+ ions and the sputter rate was 2 nm/min when measured on Ta_2O_5.

3. Results and Discussion

When operated in the usual empirical conditions, vacuum metal deposition leads to a clear optical contrast. ToF-SIMS imaging reveals that as expected from the optical evaluation, Zn is present in the regions where no fingermark residue is present but also that Au is observed in the regions corresponding to the fingermark residues along with characteristic peaks of these residues such as Na^+, K^+ and Ca^+. This is even still the case when after Au evaporation, an evaporation of Zn in excess is performed. Figure 1 illustrates this case with images from the following ions: Na^+, $^{64}Zn^+$ and Au^- (the latter in a region close to that displayed in the two other images). This thus indicates that even after Zn evaporation, Au is still observed in the fingermark residues region along with residues characteristic peaks; Au is not only deposited between the fingermarks but also on the fingermark residue.

ToF-SIMS imaging of samples on which only Zn in excess was evaporated (no Au pre-evaporation) illustrates that Zn preferentially condenses on areas not covered by fingermark residue (see Na^+ and $^{64}Zn^+$ images in Figure 2). From these results, one could argue that the Au pre-evaporation is not needed to get an optical contrast. This is true for the Si wafer substrate used in this study, but it has been empirically shown that it is not the case for all substrates. Moreover, in this case, it took longer and it was more difficult to obtain this contrast compared to the usual process which includes a pre-evaporation of Au. This is an empirical confirmation of the role of Au as a presensitizing agent for Zn condensation [3].

On the sample for which only a Au evaporation in excess was performed (no Zn evaporation followed), it appears that Au is observed almost everywhere (see Au^- image in Figure 3) even though a difference in signal can still be observed between covered and uncovered regions (as better displayed with Au^+ and Na^+ images in Figure 3).

All the above results consistently indicate that (a) Au is deposited everywhere; (b) Zn deposited alone fills (with difficulty) primarily the substrate regions and (c) when applied in excess on the Au pre-evaporated sample, Zn does not completely cover the fingermarks even though Au is detected at the fingermark top surface and an enhancement in Zn condensation on Au coated substrates is empirically observed. One hypothesis is that Au diffuses into the fingermark residue and does not enhance zinc condensation on it due to its limited quantity at the top surface. The difference in Figure 3 in intensity for Au characteristic peaks between uncovered and covered substrate regions could corroborate such hypothesis. However, matrix effects should not be excluded to explain such a difference in secondary ion detection.

Auger spectroscopy is used as an external confirmation of our hypothesis. Figure 4 (a) is a SEM image of a selected region of the sample for which only Au evaporation in excess was performed. Three areas are numbered and correspond to the following: 2 is in the region where fingermark is present, while 1 and 3 correspond to regions where no fingermark residue is present. Figure 4 (b) displays the sputter profiles for two elements (Au and Si) in these three selected areas. It clearly appears that for area 2, Si is observed from a higher depth than in the two other areas. At the same time, Au is observed in this area 2 in the whole depth of material covering the Si substrate confirming the diffusion hypothesis.

Surface analysis results have shown that evaporated Au condenses on fingermarks but also partly diffuses into them. Its absence or relatively lower quantity at the surface hinders condensation of Zn on the marks. This better understanding could lead to a better application of the method: for example, a better revelation of aged fingermarks after rejuvenating them to allow this diffusion phenomenon. Even surface analysis techniques could be useful if it appears that differences can be observed as a function of ageing, allowing dating of fingermarks, a recurrent question in forensic science without any validated answer.

References

[1]   Home Office Scientific Development Branch, HMSO, London, 1986
[2]   P. Margot and C.J. Lennard, IPSC, Lausanne, 1994
[3]   D.S. Hambley, PhD dissertation, London: Royal Holloway College, Department of Physics, 1972
[4]   B.W. Schueler, Microsc. Microanalysis Microstructure 3 (1992) 119.
[5]   K. Franzreb, H.J. Mathieu and D. Landolt, Surf. Interface Anal. 23 (1995) 641.
[6]   D. Briggs in Practical Surface Analysis, Second Edition, Volume 2. Ion and Neutral Spectroscopy, D. Briggs and M. P. Seah (Eds), John Wiley, Chichester, 1992, 367

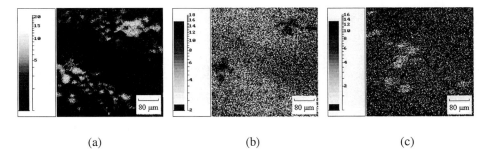

(a)   (b)   (c)

Fig. 1. Na+ (a), ^{64}Zn+ (b) and Au- (c) images of a selected area of a Si wafer on which fingermarks were deposited and then the usual Au evaporation was performed, followed by an evaporation of Zn in excess. It should be noted that for the negative ion image, there is a slight shift in comparison with the two positive ion images.

442

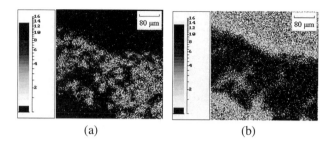

(a)   (b)

Fig. 2. Na⁺ (a) and ^{64}Zn⁺ (b) images of a selected area of a Si wafer on which fingermarks were deposited and then Zn was evaporated in excess.

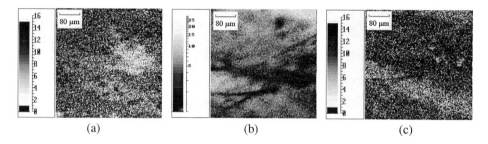

(a)   (b)   (c)

Fig. 3. Na⁺ (a), Au⁻ (b) and Au⁺ (c) images of a selected area of a Si wafer on which fingermarks were deposited and then Au was evaporated in excess.

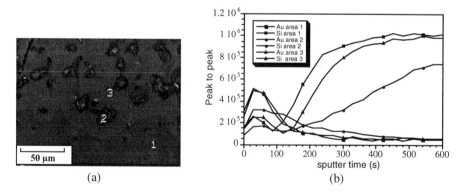

(a)   (b)

Fig. 4. (a) SEM image of a selected region of the sample for which only a Au evaporation in excess was performed (1, 2, 3: see text); (b) Auger spectroscopy sputter profiles of Au and Si for the three areas defined in Fig. 4 (a).

A. Benninghoven, P. Bertrand, H.-N. Migeon and H.W. Werner (Editors).
Proceedings of the 12th International Conference on Secondary Ion Mass Spectrometry,
Brussels, Belgium, 5-11 September 1999
443

TOF-SIMS STUDY ON ADSORPTION OF PHOSPHATE TYPE LUBRICANT ADDITIVES ONTO FRICTION SURFACES OF FERROUS MATERIALS

*A. Murase and T. Ohmori

Toyota Central R&D Labs., Inc.,
Nagakute, Aichi, 480-1192, Japan
*E-mail: e0483@mosk.tytlabs.co.jp

1. Introduction

Lubricant additives which are added into oils are known to perform by forming an organic and/or inorganic thin film on the friction surface, and the information of structure of the film is extremely important for the analysis of the lubrication mechanism. Usually, for this purpose, top-surface analysis such as X-ray photoelectron spectroscopy (XPS) or auger electron spectroscopy (AES) have been widely used [1]-[3]. However, these analytical techniques have not been sufficient for the analysis of organic chemical structure of the thin film formed on a friction surface, because the main function of these techniques is element analysis. Therefore, the authors have attempted to analyze organic chemical structures of thin films formed on friction surfaces by Time-of-Flight Secondary Ion Mass Spectrometry (TOF-SIMS), which is not only suitable for the analysis of thin films as well as XPS or AES, but also is expected to provide the information about organic chemical structure. This paper describes the analysis of the adsorption of phosphate type lubricant additives onto the friction surfaces of ferrous materials by TOF-SIMS.

2. Experimental

As model compounds of phosphate type lubricant additives, tri-n-butylphosphate, di-n-butylphosphate, tri-n-butylphosphite, di-n-butylphosphite, triphenylphosphate, diphenylphosphate, triphenylphosphite, and diphenylphosphite were used. They were dissolved with paraffinic oil into 0.5 % in P concentration for the lubrication tests. All of the additives were commercially available reagents.

The lubrication tests were performed with a ring-on-block type friction test instrument at 230N, 1.8m/sec, and 80°C for 1 hour. By this test, friction coefficient and the width of wear scar were evaluated. The friction surfaces of the tested blocks were washed with n-hexane before TOF-SIMS measurements.

TOF-SIMS measurements were performed with a Physical Electronics TFS-2100 (TRIFT2) instrument. High mass resolution spectra of M/dM>5000 at m/z 27 ($C2H3^+$) or m/z 25 ($C2H^-$) were acquired using bunched $^{69}Ga^+$ ion pulse with an impact energy of 15keV, an ion current of 600pA for 1 pulse, and a pulse frequency of 10kHz. Total ion doses in these measurement were approximately $<1 \times 10^{12}$ ions/cm^2.

444

3. Results and discussions
3.1 Lubrication test
The values of the friction coefficient and the width of wear scar, which were obtained by the lubrication tests for 1 hour, are shown in Table 1.

The friction coefficient: All of the systems can be classified into two types. Di-n-butylphosphate, di-n-butylphosphite, diphenylphosphate, and triphenylphosphite have small values of the friction coefficient. On the other hand, tri-n-butylphosphate, tri-n-butylphosphite, triphenylphosphate, and diphenylphosphite have large values almost same as that of a non-additive system (paraffinic base oil only).

The width of wear scar: In all of the lubricant systems, the values were smaller than that in the non-additive system.

Table 1. Results of the lubrication tests

	Tri-n-butyl-phosphate	Di-n-butyl-phosphate	Tri-n-butyl-phosphite	Di-n-butyl-phosphite	Triphenyl-phosphate	Diphenyl-phosphate	Triphenyl-phosphite	Diphenyl-phosphite	Base oil
Friction coefficient	0.08	0.01	0.07	<0.01	0.07	<0.01	<0.01	0.08	0.09
Width of wear scar (mm)	0.45	0.60	0.52	0.41	0.61	0.31	0.38	1.20	3.74

3.2 TOF-SIMS analysis
As an example of TOF-SIMS spectra, the positive and the negative ones of the friction surface tested with triphenylphosphate are shown in Fig.1. In all lubricant systems, the main ion of positive spectra were Fe^+ which is origined mainly from the base material. This result means that the thickness of organic layer formed over the friction surface is less than the sampling depth of a TOF-SIMS analysis i.e. 1 nm on the average. On the other hand, in negative spectra, fragment ions of phosphate i.e. PO_2^- or PO_3^- were clearly detected. This result means that the organic layer contains the phosphates adsorbed onto ferrous base material.

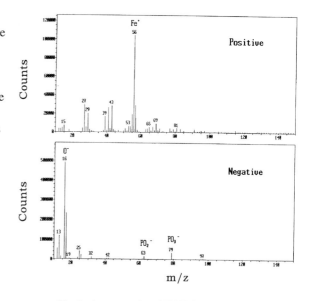

Fig.1 An example of TOF-SIMS spectra. Friction surface tested with triphenylphosphate.

As reaction products between the alcohol or phenol units of the lubricants and Fe, CH$_3$OFe$^+$ (m/z 86.91) and C$_6$H$_5$OFe$^+$ (m/z 148.97) were detected for butylester systems and phenylester systems, respectively, as shown in Fig.2. The amount of these reaction products was found to be anti-correlated with the width of wear scar, as shown in Fig.3. This result suggests that the amount of these products are an indication of the lubricity of phosphates lubricants.

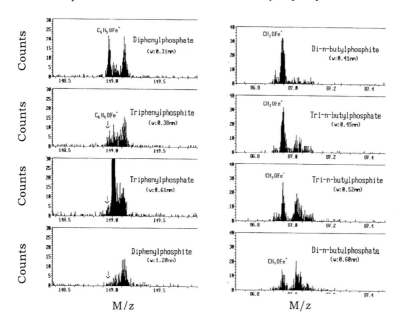

Fig. 2 Positive TOF-SIMS spectra of friction surfaces.

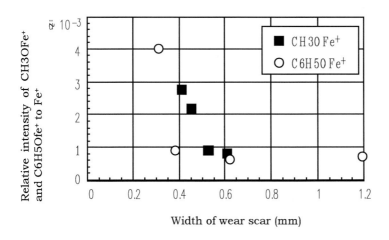

Fig. 3 Relation between the width of wear scar and the intensity of CH$_3$OFe$^+$ or C$_6$H$_5$OFe$^+$.

As reaction products between the phosphoric units of the lubricants and Fe, $FeP_3O_9^-$ (m/z 293), $Fe_2P_3O_{10}^-$ (m/z 365), and $Fe_3P_3O_{11}^-$ (m/z 437) etc, which indicate an existence of Fe-polyphosphate, were detected for all phosphates systems, as shown in Fig.4. The amount of these reaction products were found to be correlated with the friction coefficient. Although an existence of Fe-polyphosphate has been suggested by Cann et al [4] and Martin et al [5], the result of TOF-SIMS clearly demonstrates an evidence of the existence.

Reaction products between paraffinic base oil and Fe, such as CH_3Fe^+, $C_2H_5Fe^+$ etc, were detected for all kind of lubricant systems including non-additive oil. The amount of these products were found to be correlated with the width of wear scar.

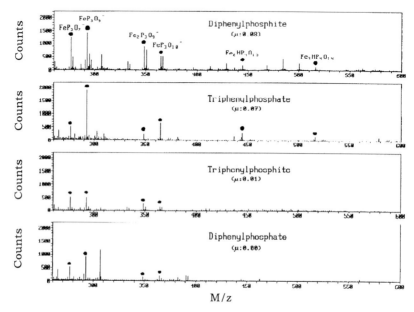

Fig.4 Negative TOF-SIMS spectra of friction surfaces.

4. Conclusion

By TOF-SIMS analysis of friction surfaces, Fe-alcoholate, Fe-phenolate and Fe-polyphosphate were detected as reaction products between phosphate type lubricant additives and Fe. The amount of these products were found to be correlated with the friction properties such as a friction coefficient and a wear scar.

References

[1] J.H. Sanders, J.N. Cutler and G. John, Appl. Surf. Sci. 135 (1998) 169
[2] M.E. Napier and P.C. Stair, J. Vac. Sci. Technol. A. 9 (1991) 649
[3] L.L. Cao, Y.M. Sun and L.Q. Zheng, Wear, 140 (1990) 345
[4] P.M.E. Cann, G.J. Johnston and H.A. Spikes, I. Mech. E. C208/87 (1987) 543
[5] J.M. Martin, M.Belin and J.L. Mansot, ASLE, 29 (1985) 523

A. Benninghoven, P. Bertrand, H.-N. Migeon and H.W. Werner (Editors).
Proceedings of the 12th International Conference on Secondary Ion Mass Spectrometry,
Brussels, Belgium, 5-11 September 1999

FUNCTIONALITIES OF A Fe-BASED CATALYST EVIDENCED BY ToF-SIMS IN RELATION WITH THE ELECTROREDUCTION OF OXYGEN IN POLYMER ELECTROLYTE FUEL CELLS

M. Lefevre[1], J-P Dodelet[1†], P. Bertrand[2]

1. INRS-Énergie et Matériaux, 1650 Blvd Lionel Boulet, C.P. 1020, Varennes, Quebec, Canada J3X 1S2.
2. PCPM, Université Catholique de Louvain, 1348 Louvain-La-Neuve, Belgium

1. Introduction

Polymer electrolyte fuel cells (PEFCs) are highly efficient and low polluting electrochemical power systems based on the oxidation of hydrogen by oxygen. They are of interest for mobile and stationary applications[1-3]. PEFCs' commercial prototypes use Pt-based catalysts to oxidize hydrogen and reduce oxygen. However, Pt is an expensive metal of low abundance and it would be advantagious to replace Pt with non-noble metal electrocatalysts. In that respect, it has been demonstrated that catalysts for the electrochemical reduction of oxygen are obtained from N_4-Metal macrocycles such as Fe or Co porphyrins when these macrocycles are adsorbed on carbon black and are pyrolyzed at 500-700 °C in an inert atmosphere [4-6]. The catalytic site obtained in that temperature range has a N_4-Metal structure bound to the carbon support [5]. It is efficient but unstable in fuel cells. The stability of these catalysts is drastically improved when the same precursors are pyrolyzed at higher temperatures $\geq$ 800 °C [7]. In that case, the N_4-Metal site is destroyed. The structure of the new catalytic site is still unknown. Catalytic activity and probably the same catalytic site are also obtained by pyrolyzing at elevated temperature various metal precursors adsorbed on carbon black in the presence of an adsorbed or of a gaseous nitrogen precursor [8].

Recently we discovered that it is possible to generate simultaneously the carbon support and the catalytic site by pyrolyzing at 900 °C in NH_3, Fe^{II} acetate adsorbed on perylene tetracarboxylic dianhydride (PTCDA; Fig. 1). In this work, Fe^{II} acetate will be adsorbed onto PTCDA and pyrolyzed in NH_3 at various temperatures ranging between 400 and 1000 °C in order to vary the catalytic activity. The same samples have been analyzed by ToF SIMS in order to find an eventual trend between some of the detected ions and the catalytic activity and therefore to obtain structural information on the high temperature catalytic site for

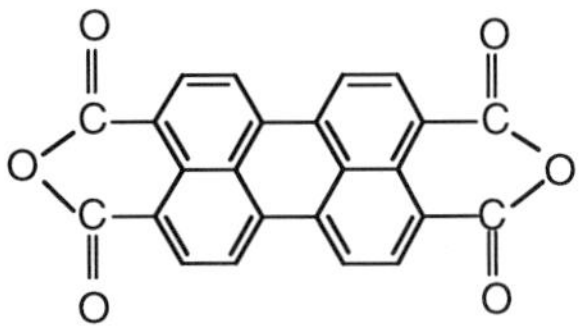

Fig. 1 Molecular structure of 3,4,9,10 perylene tetra-carboxylic dianhydride.

---

† Corresponding Author : dodelet@inrs-ener.uquebec.ca

oxygen reduction. The Fe loading was set at 2000 ppm which is the optimum loading [9]. The use of Fe^{II} acetate instead of iron porphyrin is interesting because, contrary to the porphyrin, there is a drastic change in the catalytic activity with the pyrolysis temperature so it is expected that SIMS analysis will also be sensitive to that change. The use of PTCDA as a precursor for the carbon support is important in this context because : (i) it contains fewer metallic impurities, (ii) has a simpler positive SIMS spectrum than carbon black and (iii) does not contain nitrogen.

2. Experimental

2.1 Purification of PTCDA

Commercial PTCDA contains at least 1000 ppm Fe. To clean it, PTCDA is set in suspension during one night in a 1:2 mixture of concentrated HCl and de-ionized water (d-H$_2$O). This suspension is filtered and rinsed with d-H$_2$O. PTCDA is dried during one night at 75 °C. This procedure is repeated twice.

2.2 Pyrolysis of PTCDA

PTCDA in a quartz boat is introduced into a quartz tube (5 cm diam). Ar is circulated in the tube for 30 min. Then the tube is placed in a split-oven and a gas mixture NH$_3$: H$_2$ is added to Ar in the following proportions : 1:2:1, respectively. H$_2$ is necessary to keep a reducing atmosphere during pyrolysis. The oven temperature is now set at 400 °C for 1h. Then the oven temperature is raised to until 900 °C where it remains for another hour. Finally, the quartz tube is removed from the oven and cooled under Ar. Pyrolyzed PTCDA is finely ground.

2.3 Preparation of the catalyst

The amount of Fe^{II} acetate required to obtain 2000 ppm Fe in the catalyst is mixed for 1h with a suspension of pyrolyzed PTCDA in 100 ml of d-H$_2$O. The mixture is placed in an oven at 75 °C for one night in order to evaporate H$_2$O. The resulting material is placed in a quartz boat and introduced into the quartz tube previously described. The pyrolysis temperature is set at either 400, 500, 600, 700, 800, 900, or 1000 °C. The ambient gas for pyrolysis is a 1:1 mixture of Ar and H$_2$. This represents a second pyrolysis step.

2.4.Electrochemical measurements

The catalyst's activity is measured using a rotating electrode. The sample preparation is as follows : 16 mg of the catalyst is ultrasonically mixed during 15 min with 400 µl of a Nafion solution and 400 µl of H$_2$O. 10 µl of the suspension are spread on the disk of the electrode (0.5 cm diam) which is then dried at 75 °C in air. The electrochemical cell contains an O$_2$ saturated solution of H$_2$SO$_4$ at pH =1. A first voltammetric cycle is recorded in stationary conditions (0 rpm) between 0 and 0.7 V vs SCE, then the electrode is rotated at 1500 rpm to confirm mass transport limited O$_2$ reduction.

2.5 Surface analysis

The surface of the catalyst is analyzed by ToF SIMS (Charles-Evans and Associates) using Ga$^+$ 15 keV primary ions with a resolution of 10000 for Si on a Si wafer. For the samples a resolution of about 4000 at the Si mass is obtained. For the analysis, the catalysts are pressed into an In sheet and 4 regions are analyzed for positive and negative ions. A 6 keV post acceleration is used with a 0-10000 mass analysis. The primary ion fluence is below 10^{12} ions/ cm^2, remaining therefore in the static SIMS range.

3. Results and Discussion

3.1 Electrochemical tests

The evolution of catalytic activity for O_2 reduction with the pyrolysis temperature is displayed in Fig. 2. The catalytic activity rises quickly above 500 °C to reach a maximum at about 800 °C. PTCDA alone, pyrolyzed in the same conditions (o) has little catalytic activity, as does Fe^{II} acetate adsorbed onto pyrolyzed PTCDA but without a second pyrolysis step (●) at room temperature in Fig. 2). The appearance of catalytic activity requires the simultaneous presence of a carbon support, a source of N, a source of Fe and heat-treatment at high temperature (at least 600 °C as shown in Fig. 2).

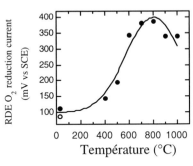

Fig. 2 Evolution of the catalytic activity vs pyrolysis temperature for Fe^{II} acetate adsorbed (●) onto PTCDA and for PTCDA pyrolysed alone (O).

3.2 SIMS analysis

In this communication, all catalysts contain the same precursors, the only variable being the pyrolysis temperature of the second pyrolysis step. Several characteristic C and N-containing ion peaks of PTCDA pyrolyzed at 900 °C are reported in the first line of Table 1. These peaks are normalized against C$^+$ which is the main ion present in all catalysts. The absence of peaks $C_7H_7^+$ and $C_5H_5^+$ which are the signature of aromaticity of carbon blacks is striking in that sample. For the samples containing the Fe^{II} acetate precursor, the same C and N-containing ions are found but Fe$^+$, FeH$^+$, FeO$^-$ and FeOH$^-$ are also present.

Table 1. Example of characteristic ions in the SIMS spectra.

I/I$_C$	$C_2H_3^+$	$C_3H_5^+$	$C_4H_7^+$	$C_5H_{12}N^+$	Fe$^+$	C_2^-	C_5^-	CN$^-$
Mass	27.0457	41.0725	55.0993	86.1565	55.8470	24.0220	60.0550	26.0177
Blank	0.32	0.18	0.06	0.05	0	4.05	0.01	3.99
Unpyrolysed	0.36	0.18	0.05	0.04	0.56	2.85	0.01	3.22
400 °C	0.64	0.38	0.12	0.07	0.45	4.28	0.01	6.74
500 °C	0.71	0.42	0.13	0.08	0.29	4.39	0.01	6.81
600 °C	0.50	0.29	0.09	0.05	0.26	4.19	0.02	5.72
700 °C	0.32	0.18	0.06	0.05	0.14	4.57	0.01	4.84
800 °C	0.48	0.28	0.08	0.05	0.04	4.15	0.01	4.85
900 °C	0.47	0.25	0.07	0.04	0.03	4.28	0.01	2.52
1000 °C	0.35	0.17	0.05	0.04	0.03	5.36	0.01	1.57

Table 1 presents the relative intensities of a series of typical ions measured for catalysts obtained by pyrolyzing the starting material (unpyrolysed) at various temperatures. The

450

intensity's evolution of all ions does not correspond to the evolution of the catalytic activity given in Fig. 2.

As it was previously demonstrated that C, N, and Fe were all important for the occurrence of catalytic activity, we focused our attention on ions that contained all these elements even if their contribution to the spectra was very small. Therefore, we looked after $FeN_xC_y^+$ type of ions and their change in intensity with temperature. The intensity of a particular ion, FeN_1C_2 for instance, was normalized by dividing by the total integrated intensity of all $FeN_xC_y^+$ ions. $FeNC^+$, FeN_2C^+ and $FeN_2C_4^+$ ions have been found with normalized intensities equivalent to about 10^{-1}, the other $FeN_xC_y^+$ ions having a normalised intensity of 10^{-3} each. The normalized signals of $FeNC^+$ and FeN_2C^+ ions decreases with the temperature rise while that of $FeN_2C_4^+$ is reported in Fig. 3. This curve is similar to that of the evolution of the catalytic activity (Fig. 2). Therefore, this ion is possibly related to a precursor which is the catalytic site or a fraction of that site.

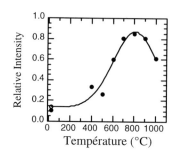

Fig. 3 Relative intensity of $FeN_2C_4^+$ as a function of the pyrolysis temperature of the catalyst (●), O represents pyrolysed PTCDA at 900 °C.

4. Conclusions

- It is necessary to have C, N, and Fe as well as a high temperature heat-treatment to obtain catalytic activity for O_2 reduction.
- The $FeN_2C_4^+$ secondary ion is possibly related to the catalytic site (or part of it).

References

[1] K.B. Parter. J. Power Sources 61 (1996) 105.
[2] A.J. Appleby. Philos. Trans. R. Soc. London Ser. A: 354 (1996) 1681.
[3] S. Gottesfeld, T.A. Zawodzinski. Adv. Electrochem. Sci. Eng. 5 (1997) 195.
[4] K. Wiesener. Electrochim. Acta (1986) 1073.
[5] J.A.R van Veen, H.A. Colijn, J.F. van Baar. Electrochim. Acta 33 (1988) 801.
[6] E. Claude, T. Addou, J.M. Latour, P. Aldebert. J. Appl. Electrochem. 28 (1998) 57.
[7] G. Faubert, G. Lalande, R. Côté, D. Guay, J.P. Dodelet, L.T. Weng, P. Bertrand, G. Dénès, Electrochim. Acta 41 (1996) 1689.
[8] R. Côté, G. Lalande, D. Guay, J.P. Dodelet, G. Dénès, J. Electrochem. Soc. 145 (1998) 2411.
[9] G. Faubert, R. Côté, J.P. Dodelet, M. Lefèvre and P. Bertrand. Electrochimica acta 44 (1999) 2589.

SECTION 11 :
DEPTH PROFILING

A. Benninghoven, P. Bertrand, H.-N. Migeon and H.W. Werner (Editors).
Proceedings of the 12th International Conference on Secondary Ion Mass Spectrometry,
Brussels, Belgium, 5-11 September 1999
© 2000 Elsevier Science B.V. All rights reserved.

DEPTH PROFILING OF BORON ULTRA-SHALLOW
IMPLANTS USING SUB-KEV OXYGEN ION BEAMS

Y. Kataoka and Y. Tada

Fujitsu Laboratories Ltd.,

10-1 Morinosato-Wakamiya, Atsugi 243-0197, Japan

1. Introduction

Reductions in the scale of semiconductor devices require accurate and reproducible SIMS measurements with sub-nm depth resolutions in the near surface region. Quantitative analysis of shallow doping distribution is currently one of the major challenges for SIMS. Depth resolution can be significantly improved by using lower primary ion energy at normal incident angle. A combination of oblique incident angles and oxygen flooding has also been used to improve depth resolution. However, recent studies have shown that artifacts, such as enlarged transient width and surface roughening, require case for accurate depth profiling under this condition.[1),2),3)]

Shallow junctions are formed mainly by low energy ion implantation. However, low ion implantation results in a high percentage of the implantation present in the near surface region and changes the matrix composition and the crystallographic orientation. These effects cause changes in secondary ion yields and errors in quantification of shallow depth profiles. The purpose of this study is to find reasons for changes in secondary ion yield in order to improve the accuracy of boron shallow depth profiles.

2. Experiment

To investigate the changes in secondary ion yields, we implanted $^{11}B^+$ into Si with doses of 5×10^{13} and 1×10^{15} cm^{-2} at 1 keV. For the shallow depth profiling, we used an ATOMIKA 4500 ion microprobe. With this instrument, we can acquire depth profiles with primary ion energies in the sub-keV range.

We rastered O_2^+ primary ions over an area of 250×250 cm^2 at 0.25 to 0.75 keV. The primary ion current was 50 nA, and the vacuum inside the sample chamber was 5.0×10^{10} Torr. To obtain high depth resolution, we measured the depth profiles at an incident angle of $0°$.

We also measured energy spectra by changing the target potential with depth profile measurements.

3. Results and discussion

Figure 1 shows the depth profiles of $^{11}B^+$ and $^{30}Si^+$ for the boron implanted into silicon crystals with a dose of 1×10^{15} cm^{-2} at 1 keV. These profiles are obtained using the primary energy of 0.5 keV at an incident angle of $0°$.

454

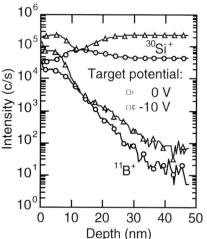

Fig. 1 Depth profiles of B and Si for boron implanted silicon with a dose of 1 x 10^{15} cm^{-2} at 1 keV

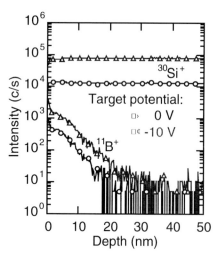

Fig. 2 Depth profiles of B and Si for boron implanted silicon with a dose of 5 x 10^{13} cm^{-2} at 1 keV.

In figure 1, the ^{30}Si$^+$ profile and ^{11}B$^+$ profile exhibit the same kind of variation at the depth between 6 nm and 30 nm, but the variation is different from that for the target potential of 0 V and −10 V. Figure 2 shows the depth profiles of the boron implanted silicon crystals with a dose of 5 x 10^{13} cm^{-2} at 1 keV. In figure 2, we observe no variation in secondary ion yields.

These results suggest that the high-dose ion implantation causes the variations in secondary ion yields. To observe the dependence on the target potentials, we measured depth profiles a range of for different target potentials. Figure 3 shows ^{30}Si$^+$ depth profiles obtained using the primary energy of 0.5 keV. The Si yields are suppressed with decreasing target potential. To examine this effect in more detail, we measured the energy spectra for different depth profiles and plotted the peak positions and FWHM of the energy spectra versus the sputtered depth. In figure 4, the peak position and FWHM are significantly changed at the depth between 6 nm and 30 nm. This result suggests that secondary ion yields are caused by charge build-up.

To compensate the charge build-up, we measured depth profiles for the boron implanted silicon with light emitted by a halogen lamp under the bombardment of O$_2^+$ at energies of 0.25, 0.5 and 0.75 keV. Figure 5 shows the silicon depth profiles for the target potential of −20 V obtained with light and figure 6 shows the silicon depth profiles obtained without light. Comparing figure 5 with figure 6, we can see that the charge build-up is reduced with decreasing the O$_2^+$ energies and with light irradiation.

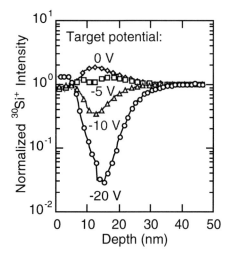

Fig. 3 Depth profiles of $^{30}Si^+$ for different target potentials

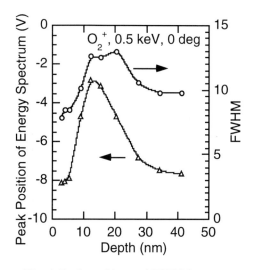

Fig. 4 Peak position and FWHM versus sputtered depth

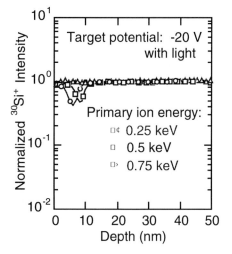

Fig. 5 Depth profiles of $^{30}Si^+$ measured with light for boron implanted Si with a dose of 1×10^{15} cm^{-2} at 1 keV

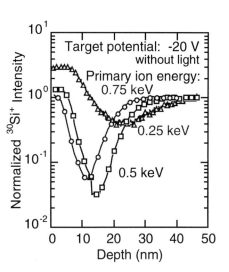

Fig. 6 Depth profiles of $^{30}Si^+$ measured without light for boron implanted Si with a dose of 1×10^{15} cm^{-2} at 1 keV

456

Figure 7 and figure 8 show the depth profiles of B and Si obtained under the bombardment of O_2^+ at energies of 0.25 and 0.5 keV with light, respectively. In figure 7, we can't see the variations in the secondary ion yields at a 0.25 keV-bombardment. On the other hand, in figure 8, we still observe the changes in secondary ion yields at a depth of 10 nm. From these results, we can see that using a lower energy bombardment with light is effective in order to improve the accuracy of boron shallow profiles.

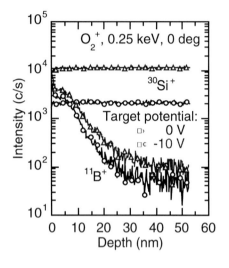 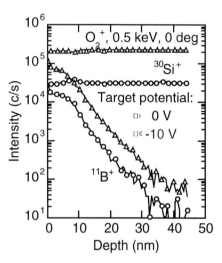

Fig. 7 Depth profiles of $^{11}B^+$ and $^{30}Si^+$ obtained 0.25 keV O_2^+ bombardment with light

Fig. 8 Depth profiles of $^{11}B^+$ and $^{30}Si^+$ obtained 0.5 keV O_2^+ bombardment with light

4. Conclusion

We investigated reasons for the variations of secondary ion yields in analysis of ultra-shallow boron implanted silicon crystals. From the analyses of energy spectra, we found that boron and silicon yields are influenced by charge build-up. We also found that using a lower energy bombardment with light is effective in order to improve the accuracy of boron shallow depth profiles.

References
[1] K. Wittmaack and S. F. Corcoran, J. Vac. Sci. Technol. **B16**, 272 (1998).
[2] G. R. Mount, S. P. Smith, C. J. Hitzman, V. K. F. Chia and C. W. Magee, in Proceedings of the 1998 Int. Conf. on Characterization and Metrology for ULSI Technology, NIST, Gaithersburg MD, March 23-27, 1998.
[3] J. Bennet and A. Diebold, Paper presented at this conference.

A. Benninghoven, P. Bertrand, H.-N. Migeon and H.W. Werner (Editors).
Proceedings of the 12th International Conference on Secondary Ion Mass Spectrometry,
Brussels, Belgium, 5-11 September 1999
© 2000 Elsevier Science B.V. All rights reserved.

SUPPRESSION OF SODIUM DIFFUSION IN SIMS DEPTH PROFILING OF POLYMER MATERIAL

R.Mimori, A.Shimizu, E.Hayashi, M.Hatada, A.Karen and A.Ishitani

Toray Research Center Inc.
3-7, Sonoyama 3-chome, Otsu, Shiga 520-8567, Japan
E-mail : Reiko_Mimori@trc.toray.co.jp

1. Introduction

In general, it is difficult to perform an accurate SIMS depth profiling analysis of Na in some insulators[1], since the Na atoms can easily migrate through the sample during the measurement due to the electric field and/or the local heating caused by the primary beam bombardment. As regards SiOx, several studies have been done aiming to suppress the migration. The techniques reported were as follows: the self-charge compensation method[2], chemical etching with HF solution[3], sample cooling[4], N_2^+[5] or O^-, O_2^-, NO_2^-[6] primary beam bombardment.

In the polymer industry, we often need to know the true depth distribution of Na in polymer materials to control the surface property. In this study, we investigated the depth profile of Na in a polyethylene terephthalate(PET) substrate covered with a thin copolyester film containing sodium 5-sulfoisophthalate. We will discuss the effects of primary beam species, bombardment conditions(such as impact energy, incident angle, beam spot size and current density), electron flooding, the roughness and the chemical composition of the sputtered surfaces, which might be related with the deterioration of the Na profile.

2. Experimental

The sample was prepared as follows: the aqueous solution of a copolyester composed of terephthalic acid(34.8mol%), isophthalic acid(11.7mol%), sodium 5-sulfoisophthalate (3.5mol%) and ethylene glycol(50.0mol%) was spin-coated onto a PET substrate. Depth profiling was done with an Atomika A-DIDA3000 quadrupole SIMS instrument. Both O_2^+ and Cs^+ primary beams were used at the beam currents ranging from 15 to 50nA. Rasters ranging from 200 to 600μm squares were used for 3-12keV O_2^+ bombardment at 2° from the surface normal and 12keV Cs^+ at 45°, and rasters ranging from 200μm x 280μm to 400μm x 570μm rectangles were used for 12keV O_2^+ at 45°. Positive secondary ions were collected from the center 30% of the raster. In order to avoid charging problems, we used either of the following methods : 1)500eV electron flooding during the measurement, or 2)conductive coating with platinum (~6nm) before the measurement. The crater depths were measured by a Sloan Dektak 3030ST profilometer. The roughness of the sputtered surfaces was observed by AFM, Digital Instruments Nano Scope IIIa, and the chemical compositions of the sputtered surfaces were analyzed by XPS, VG Scientific ESCALAB 220iXL.

458

3. Result and Discussion

Figure 1 shows profiles of $^{23}Na^+$, $^{12}C^+$ and $^{28}Si^+$ in the sample (without Pt coated), obtained by 12keV O_2^+ and Cs^+ primary beams at 45° with electron flooding. Si^+ peaks found at about 0.1μm originated from silicone as the lubricant applied to the surface of the commercial PET substrate, therefore Si^+ peaks indicate copolyester/PET interfaces. Although both primary beams had the same impact energy and incident angle, Na^+ profiles were completely different. In the case of the Cs^+ primary beam, the migration of Na was drastically suppressed. The changes of secondary ion intensities at 0.3-0.4μm in Fig.1(b) is likely due to a ripple on the surface as observed by AFM.

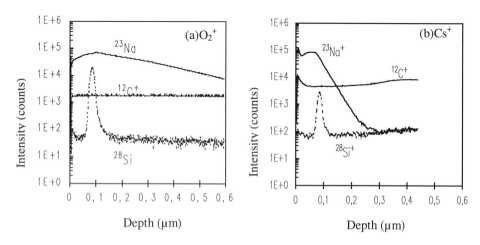

Fig.1 Depth profiles of Na^+, C^+ and Si^+ in the sample. Primary beams used: (a)12keV O_2^+ at 45°, (b)12keV Cs^+ at 45°.

We investigated how the migration behavior depended on the impact energy and the incident angle of O_2^+. Figure 2 shows the decay length of Na^+ (distance over which the Na^+ intensity drops by a factor of 1/e) under several measurement conditions. The impact energy had a minor effect on the migration for O_2^+ at 2°. Though we changed the incident angle from 2° to 45° at 12keV O_2^+, the decay length was almost same as that obtained at the condition of 2° incidence using 3keV O_2^+. All the measurement conditions for O_2^+ caused much deeper migration of Na than the condition with a Cs^+ primary beam at 12keV.

We checked the Na profiles with some other measurement conditions. Firstly, to exclude the influence of electron flooding, we carried out the depth profiling of the Pt coated sample without electron flooding under all the conditions corresponding to Fig.2. This change made no essential difference. Secondly we examined the effect of primary beam spot size. For 12keV O_2^+, a Na^+ profile obtained with the focused beam(the diameter: 20μm) was completely the same as that obtained with the deliberately defocused beam(70-80μm).

The diameter of 12keV Cs^+ beam spot was 30-40μm. The spot size was determined from the sidewall of the craters as measured by a profilometer between the 84% and 16% points[1]. Finally, we examined the effect of primary ion current density. For 12keV O_2^+ at 45°, 200μm x 280μm raster made no difference from 400μm x 570μm raster in Na profiles. Therefore, electron flooding, primary beam spot size and current density have no substantial effect.

In order to estimate the Na detection limit under Cs^+ bombardment we performed SIMS measurements of Na implanted in PET with a dose of 5.5E14cm^{-2} at 80keV. The limit of the count rate of Na^+ gave the detection limit of about 1E15 cm^{-3}.

Figure 3 shows the AFM images of the sputtered surfaces at the depth of about 0.2μm by O_2^+ or Cs^+ bombardment. Though both surfaces were different in topography, there was no great difference in the roughness on them. This is consistent with the fact that the trailing edges of both Si^+ peaks at the interfaces in Fig.1 show the similar steepness.

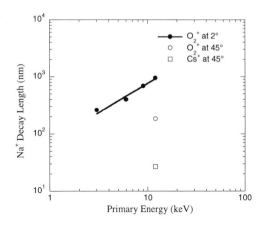

Fig.2 Plots of decay length of Na^+ in PET substrate vs. primary beam energy under the different conditions with electron flooding.

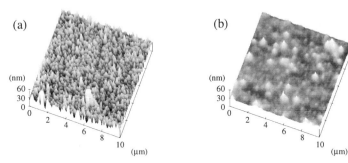

Fig.3 AFM images of the sample surfaces sputtered with (a)12keV O_2^+ at 45°, (b)12keV Cs^+ at 45°.

Figure 4 shows the XPS spectra of the sputtered surfaces at about 0.1μm (where Si^+ intensity dropped by about one decade from the peak top at the interface) by O_2^+ and Cs^+ bombardments. The samples were transferred from the SIMS to the XPS instrument under nitrogen ambience. The surface sputtered by O_2^+ was entirely composed of amorphous carbon. On the other hand, the polar groups such as COO, C=O, C-O were observed on the

460

surface sputtered by Cs⁺. If these functional groups were formed during profile measurements with Cs⁺, it seems to be possible that Na atoms were bound to them with a kind of electrostatic interaction which might be related to the suppression of Na migration.

4. Conclusion

We investigated the depth profiles of Na in a PET substrate covered with a copolyester film containing sodium 5-sulfoisophthalate. SIMS depth profiling was performed using O_2^+ or Cs^+ primary beams in positive ion detection mode. As a result, we found that the migration of Na was drastically suppressed by the use of a Cs^+ primary beam. This migration during O_2^+ bombardment doesn't seem to be dependent on electron flooding, primary beam spot size and current density. The impact energy and incident angle affected it to some extent. The chemical composition of the sputtered surfaces might be related with this phenomenon. Further study to explain the mechanism of the migration will be needed. The sensitivity of Na^+ with a Cs^+ primary beam was high enough to perform the analysis in PET.

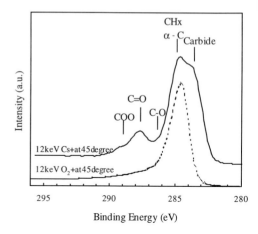

Fig.4 XPS C1s spectra of the sample surfaces sputtered with 12keV O_2^+ at 45°, and 12keV Cs^+ at 45°

References

[1] R.G.Wilson, F.A.Stevie and C.W.Magee, *Secondary Ion Mass Spectrometry*, John Wiley & Sons, New York, 1989

[2] R.Nagayama, S.Makinouchi, A.Takano, M.Tezuka, K.Takahashi and M.Kudo, *Proceedings of SIMS VII*, John Wiley & Sons, Chichester, 1990, p655

[3] R.Watanabe and M.Kudo, *Proceedings of SIMS X*, John Wiley & Sons, Chichester, 1997, p495

[4] Y.Hayashi and K.Matsumoto, *Proceedings of SIMS IX*, John Wiley & Sons, Chichester, 1994, p864

[5] R.Saito, Y.Ichinohe, and M.Kudo, *Proceedings of SIMS XI*, John Wiley & Sons, Chichester , 1998, p379

[6] S.G.Simakin, *Proceedings of SIMS XI*, John Wiley & Sons, Chichester , 1998, p213

A. Benninghoven, P. Bertrand, H.-N. Migeon and H.W. Werner (Editors).
Proceedings of the 12th International Conference on Secondary Ion Mass Spectrometry,
Brussels, Belgium, 5-11 September 1999

461

DUAL BEAM DEPTH PROFILING WITH GALLIUM AND ARGON PRIMARY IONS: A TOF-SIMS STUDY

A.Licciardello, L.Renna, A.Torrisi, S.Pignataro

Dipartimento di Scienze Chimiche - Viale Andrea Doria, 6 - 95125 Catania, Italy

e-mail: alicciardello@dipchi.unict.it

1. Introduction

The use of gallium primary ions in secondary ion mass spectrometry is widely spreading in connection with the increasing need for high lateral resolution imaging and micro area depth profiling for the characterization of solid surfaces and interfaces. However artifacts may be produced by such non-inert primary beams, but only a few papers have been published on this topic [1,2]. By contrast, the effect of use of oxygen beams has been extensively investigated since several years [3,4], including beam induced relocation of impurities in the matrix [5,6]. In previous work [1] we reported that a double peak in the gallium yield is observed at the interface when a SiO_2/Si system is profiled by means of a gallium beam. In the present paper we revisit this topic and report new data, obtained by using the dual ion beam depth profiling technique [7] in a TOF-SIMS apparatus. We used an Ar^+ beam for erosion and a Ga^+ beam for analyzing the crater bottom. Such approach has the advantage of allowing the independent control of the erosion and analysis conditions and, in the case under discussion, allows to largely uncouple the introduction of the gallium impurity from the effects connected with the energy deposition and formation of the altered layer. The experimental results will be discussed in terms of Ga segregation at the interface. Also, SNMS data will be presented shortly, supporting the interpretation of the SIMS results.

2. Experimental

Samples of suitable size have been obtained from silicon wafers covered by a thermally grown oxide. This oxide was 85 nm thick with ± 1% thickness homogeneity.

Dual ion beam SIMS profiles have been obtained by using a TOFSIMS-IV instrument (CAMECA), equipped with a pulsed liquid metal source (working with isotopically enriched ^{69}Ga) and a EI gas source. As sputter beam we used Ar^+ (1÷5 keV, 40 nA, (300 x 300) μm^2 raster). The analysis beam is Ga^+ (15÷25 keV, 1÷2 pA), rastered (30 μm x 30 μm) at the center of the sputter crater. In order to achieve a stable surface potential, pulsed electron flooding was used. The most part of measurements were made in the so-called blinking mode, i.e. by alternating a "long" sputtering and analysis cycles (1-2 s each). This mode allows a good charge compensation and signal stability.

EI-SNMS profiles were obtained in a quadrupole-based SIMS apparatus (VG SIMSLAB), by using a continuos Ga^+ beam, in the energy range 4÷10 keV.

3. Results and discussion.

Figure 1 shows a typical dual ion beam depth profile of a SiO_2/Si sample. The Si^+ and SiO^+ signals show the expected – and well known - trend, with a fall of the yield at the interface, caused, for silicon, by the change of the ionization probability, due to the decrease of oxygen

462

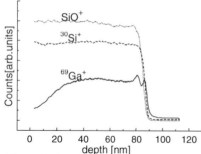

Fig. 1. Typical depth profile of the SiO₂/Si system, obtained in dual ion beam mode (erosion beam 3keV Ar⁺; analysis beam 25 keV Ga⁺).

concentration. As to the Ga⁺ yield, it shows an initial increase, due to the implantation of gallium from the analysis beam, a sputter equilibrium region and, near the interface, a characteristic structure with two peaks, the second peak being located approximately at the same depth of the inflection point of the silicon signal. After the interface the Ga yield decreases, for the same reason as the Si yield. The behaviour of gallium signal at the interface is qualitatively similar to that observed previously [1], which was obtained in very different experimental conditions, namely by using a high current density Ga primary beam for both erosion and analysis, in a quadrupole based instrument. It should be stressed that the two profiling experiments involve very different steady state level for implanted gallium. Indeed at sputter equilibrium, by using a continuous single beam of gallium, one can estimate that the gallium concentration in SiO_2 is of the order of $10 \div 30$ at%, the exact value depending on energy and angle-of-incidence of the beam. This figure has to be compared with a value of the order of 10^{13} Ga atoms cm^{-3} estimated for dual beam depth profiling under the conditions used in the present experiment [8]. Hence, in the dual beam experiment, the concentration of the implanted gallium, being at dopant level, does not change appreciably the matrix composition. In order to explain the behaviour of the gallium signal at the interface (i.e. the two-peak structure), different hypotheses can be put forward. A first possibility is that changes of sputtering rate or of ionization yield, or both, in the interfacial transient region are responsible for the observed profile [2]. By contrast, one could hypothesize that the observed profile (although convoluted by the ion yield changes in the interfacial region) reflects, at least qualitatively, a real variation of gallium concentration at the interface. In a recent work [8] we show that the first peak can be interpreted in terms of changes in sputtering rate in the transient region and that the peak at higher depth from the surface cannot be accounted for by a sputter rate variation. In a previous paper [1] we hypothesized that such peak is due to gallium segregation at the SiO_2/Si interface. The relocation of gallium at SiO_2/Si interface has been discussed in related experiments [5,6] dealing with impurity transport in silicon under O_2^+ bombardment. The approach consists in studying the O_2^+ SIMS depth profile of a thin film of the impurity under study deposited onto a silicon substrate [5]. Indeed, at near normal incidence O_2 bombardment is known to promote the formation SiO_2 layer. From this kind of experiments Wittmaack [5] concluded that Ga gives rise to moderate segregation at SiO_2/Si interface, whilst Honma [6] proposed that "gallium is distributed uniformly in the surface SiO_2 layer rather than being segregated at the SiO_2/Si interface". Then, it is clear that the observed phenomenology deserves further investigation. We explore the behaviour of gallium at the interface by independently changing the energy of the sputter and analysis beams respectively. In Fig. 2 four Ga profiles obtained in dual ion beam mode are reported. Depth calibration has been obtained by using the inflection point of the SiO⁺ signal as marker for the interface, and the intensity scale has been normalized, for each profile, to the respective ³⁰Si steady state value in SiO_2. The spacing of the double-peaked structure is influenced by Ar sputter beam energy (see profiles *a*, *b*, *d*, obtained at fixed Ga⁺ energy and at different Ar⁺ energies), but doesn't depend on the energy of the gallium probe (compare profiles *b* and *c*, both obtained at the

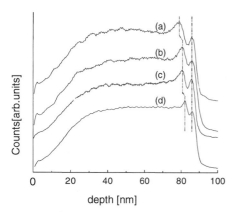

Fig.2. Gallium TOF-SIMS profiles, obtained in different beam conditions: a) Ga 25keV, Ar 5keV; b) Ga 25keV, Ar 3keV; c) Ga 15keV, Ar 3keV; d) Ga 25keV, Ar 1 keV. The profiles have been shifted each other along the vertical axis in order to improve the readability of the figure.

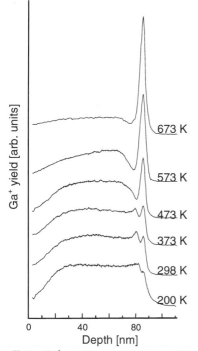

Fig.3. Ga+ profiles obtained at different temperatures, as indicated in the figure. (Erosion beam, 3keV Ar+; analysis beam, 25 keV Ga+)

same Ar+ energy (3 keV) and with 25 keV and 15 keV Ga+ beam respectively). This clearly confirms that the effect is connected with the thickness of the altered layer [1], that can be assumed to be produced by the high current density sputter beam only.

A further insight in the interpretation of the phenomenology under discussion is given by temperature dependent experiments in the range 200-673 K. Figure 3 reports the gallium profiles, calibrated and normalized in the same way as in figure 2. It turns out from the figure that the peak at higher depth is still present at low temperature and its intensity increases by increasing temperature. Two different behaviour regimes can be observed. At lower temperatures (approximately up to ~400 K), the shape of the profile remains substantially unchanged. In particular the width of the double peaked structure is constant and the intensity of the interface peak increases moderately. Above 400 K the intensity of the interface peak increases strongly and the peak at shallower depth disappears, completely overcome by the large "valley" on the oxide side of the interface peak. Moreover, at high temperature, the intensity of gallium in the central region of the oxide (where a plateau due to the sputter equilibrium is present at lower temperatures) decreases as temperature increases. It is worth to note that, at variance of the Ga signal, the $^{30}Si^+$ and SiO^+ signals remain practically unchanged by the temperature variation, and are very similar to those shown in figure 1. The observed phenomenology appears to be consistent with gallium segregation at the interface, and consequent formation of a depletion region in the oxide side. This is consistent with the findings of [5] and at variance of the conclusions of ref.[6]. The driving force for segregation could be the much lower solubility of gallium in SiO_2 than in silicon [9]. The occurrence of segregation, however, needs a transport mechanism for gallium. At low temperatures the mobility of implanted Ga is confined in the altered layer region, and is

464

probably due to ballistic mechanisms (such as recoil mixing) and/or to diffusion *via* the defects produced by the collision cascade. Both the mechanisms are indeed compatible with the energy dependence of the width of the double-peaked structure. The strong increase of the intensity of the interfacial Ga peak at high temperatures, instead, appears to be due mainly to thermal diffusion through the oxide bulk, that occurs even when the altered layer region is still away from the interface. It is indeed well known that Ga diffusion in SiO_2 is much faster than in Si [6,9].

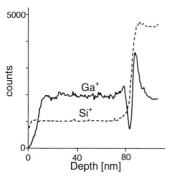

Fig.4. SNMS depth profile of the SiO_2/Si system obtained by using a continuous 6keV Ga beam. The Ga signal is the sum of ^{69}Ga and ^{71}Ga

A support to the above observations is given by SNMS experiments, that will be fully discussed elsewhere [10]. Here we only note that the SNMS profiles (see Fig.4) show a strong similarity with the SIMS profile although, according to the lack of significant matrix effect in SNMS, no fall of the Ga signals is observed after the interface. Incidentally, this allows to rule out the possibility that the interface peak is due to change in Ga ionization yield. Moreover, the area of the "valley" before the interface peak is of the same magnitude as that of the interface peak. This strongly supports the idea that gallium transport occurred, from SiO_2 oxide to the interface and also suggests that the eventual relocation of the Ga implanted in silicon behind the interface gives, if any, a minor contribution to the peak.

4. Summary

The double-peak structure of Ga signal, observed at SiO_2/Si interface when profiling with Ga ions has been studied by using a dual ion beam sputtering approach. The experimental results indicate that, whilst the first peak can be accounted for by sputter rate variation in the transient region, the Ga peak at the SiO_2/Si interface is due to gallium segregation at the interface.

Acknowledgement

Work supported by U.E. through the Italian Network of Mass Spectrometry. MURST and CNR (Rome) are acknowledged for partial support.

References

[1] A.Licciardello, A.Torrisi, S.Pignataro, Surf. Interface Analysis, 14 (1989) 491
[2] H.E.Bishop, S.J.Greenwood, Surf. Interface Analysis, 17 (1991) 325
[3] K.Wittmaak, in *Secondary Ion Mass Spectrometry SIMS XI*, G.Gillen, R.Lareau, J.Bennett, F.Stevie (Eds), Wiley, New York, 1998, p.11
[4] J.S.Williams, *ibid.*, p.3
[5] K.Wittmaack, Nucl.Instr.Methods B19/29 (1987) 484
[6] Y.Honma, T.Maruo, Surf. Interface Analysis, 14 (1989) 725
[7] K.Iltgen, C.Bendel, E.Niehuis, A.Benninghoven, in *Secondary Ion Mass Spectrometry SIMS X*, A.Benninghoven, B.Hagenhoff, H.W.Werner (Eds), Wiley, N.Y., 1997, p.375
[8] A.Licciardello, L.Renna, S.Pignataro, Surf. Interface Analysis, in press
[9] H.F.Wolf, in *Semiconductors*, pp. 356-361, Wiley, New York (1971)
[10] A. Licciardello, V. Ignatova, in preparation

A. Benninghoven, P. Bertrand, H.-N. Migeon and H.W. Werner (Editors).
Proceedings of the 12th International Conference on Secondary Ion Mass Spectrometry,
Brussels, Belgium, 5-11 September 1999

SIMS ANALYSIS OF H, N, B IN THIN GATE OXIDE OF MOS LSI

S. Miwa[a], Y. Kudo[a], S. Kawado[a] and F. Nishiyamab[b]

[a]Frontier Science Labolatories, Sony Corp.,Yokohama, Japan
[b]Hiroshima University, Higashi Hiroshima Japan

1. Introduction

The gate oxide in a metal-oxide-semiconductor (MOS) structure is one of the most essential factors in the development of ultra-large-scale integrated circuits (ULSI). It is well-known that Hydrogen (H) can terminate dangling bonds of crystals and sometimes passivate carriers in semiconductor materials. H also affects the charges traps in the silicon dioxide (SiO_2) layer and the formation of SiO_2/Si interface [2]. On the other hand, silicon oxynitride (SiO_xN_y) has been adopted for the gate insulator of p-channel MOSFETs in ULSIs smaller than the quarter-micron design rule because SiO_xN_y can suppress the penetration of Boron (B) from the gate electrode, polycrystalline silicon (poly-Si), to the Si substrate[2]. The gate oxide of ULSIs is now thinner than 4nm and it has become important to characterize such a thin oxide. Secondary ion mass spectrometry (SIMS) is the most powerful tool for detecting impurities. It is very difficult, however, for SIMS to analyze such thin films because it is necessary to reduce the energy of primary ions. In this work, we have investigated the hydrogen concentration in thin SiO_2 (<10nm) films. We have also determined the nitrogen (N) or B distribution in p-MOS structures with thin oxynitride films (~2.5nm).

2. Experiments

Thermally oxidized thin SiO_2 films on a Si(001) substrate were prepared. The gasses used for the oxidation and sample description are summarized in Table I. The measurements were carried out using a Cameca ims-4f ion micro-analyzer with a KMASS1000 option, whose vacuum system was modified by us. The base pressure of the analysis chamber was maintained at under 1×10^{-10} Torr. Samples of a p-MOS structure with a SiO_2 or a SiO_xN_y layer were also prepared. A 2.5nm-thick SiO_xN_y film was grown by rapid thermal oxynitridation (RTON) using NO gas. The N distribution in the SiO_xN_y film and B distribution in the poly-Si/oxide/Si structure were measured using both a PHI ADEPT1010 and a Cameca ims-4f ion micro-analyzer.

3. Results and discussion

Table I   description of thermaly oxide samples

sample	oxide thickness (nm)	growth temperature (° C)	oxidation gasses
1	10.7	850	O_2+H_2
2	9.5	850	O_2+D_2
3	7.0	850	O_2+D_2-->O_2+H_2
4	5.0	850	O_2+H_2
5	5.0	850	O_2+D_2

Table I shows the secondary ion intensity of $^1H^-$ and $^{267}HCs_2+$ ions obtained with various energy of Cs^+ primary ions. As the SiO_2 layer is very thin, the tail of the H signal at the

466

surface reaches the SiO_2/Si interface by the knock-on effect in the case of 5.0keV and 14.5keV Cs^+ primary ions, as shown in Fig.1. The signal of the surface is derived from surface contaminants which are impossible to remove. Therefore a reduction of primary ion energy is necessary and in this experiment the energy of primary ions is 1keV for the detection of $^{267}HCs_2+$. The quality of the vacuum during the measurement is also important because the measurement of atmospheric gas elements like H is limited by the residual gasses in the chamber [6]. The pressure during the measurement is lower than 1×10^{-10} Torr, so the background signal of the residual gasses is low. Using 1keV primary ions we compared the H and deuteron (D) distribution in the SiO_2 films shown in Table I. $^{267}HCs_2+$ and $^{268}DCs_2+$ profiles for the samples 2 are shown in Fig.2. H is clearly observed at the SiO_2/Si interface in both samples 1 and 2, as shown in Fig.1 and Fig.2. Even though the SiO_2 film of sample 2 was grown using D_2 and O_2 gasses, H exists at the interface. H was detected at the SiO_2/Si interface in all samples and the signal intensity is almost the same. This result suggests that some H on Si substrate remained after the oxidation. That H is combined with surface dangling bonds after a diluted HF solution was used to etch, prior to the oxidation process remained. The concentration of D detected in sample 2 is about 1×10^{-13} cm^{-2} determined by nuclear reaction analysis [3] and is higher than that in sample 3 and 5. This means that the hydrogen coming from the gasses used for oxidation is easily moved and diffused.

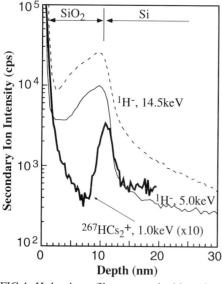 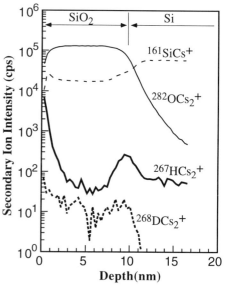

FIG.1 H depth profile measured with various energy of primary ions; 14.5keV and 5.0keV for $^1H^-$ detection and 1.0keV for $^{267}Hcs_2+$

FIG.2 H and D depth profiiles in a 9.5nm-thick SiO_2 grown by D_2 and O_2 gasses

We have measured the N distribution in the SiO_2/Si structure using both the MCs^+ technique. In general, for the detection of N in Si or SiO_2, $^{42}SiN^-$ is used as a secondary ion because of its high sensitivity. In this case , however, N profile near the SiO_2/Si interface is important , so that we have tried MCs^+ technique in order to avoid the matrix effect. Figure 3(a) and 3(b) show the secondary ion intensity obtained using the MCs$^+$ technique at different incidence angles and at the energy of 750eV and 500eV, respectively. As shown in Fig.3(a) and 3(b), the Si secondary ion intensity of Si layer near the SiO$_2$/Si interface strongly depends on the incidence angle of primary Cs$^+$ ions and that a stable Si intensity can be obtained only with certain incidence angles. The angles are 55° for ^{161}SiCs$^+$ detection with 750eV, 70° for ^{161}SiCs$^+$ detection with 500eV. In the view point of the reproducibility, the incidence angle of 70° is so high angle that, in fact, the profile obtained with 70° is less reproducible than that with 55°. On the other hand, the O profile obtained by ^{149}OCs$^+$ at the energy of 750eV is, however, not accurate because its intensity decreases rapidly near the SiO$_2$/Si interface. The slope of the ^{149}OCs$^+$ profile in the Si layer is also steeper than that of ^{147}NCs$^+$. We compared the ^{149}OCs$^+$ profile with that of ^{282}OCs$_2$$^+$ using a Cameca ims-4f and they are shown in Fg.3(c). The O profile of ^{282}OCs$_2$$^+$, as shown in Fig.3(c), is a reasonable representation. In practice, we need the combination both reproducible and high depth-resolution (low-energy) measurements.

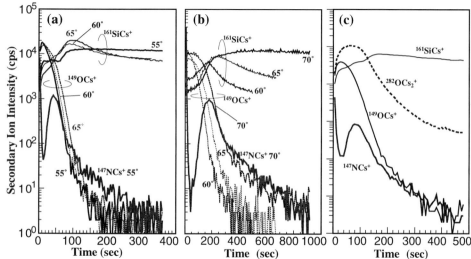

FIG.3 The secondary ion intensity as a time of function time for MCs$^+$ ions with 55°-70° incidence angl (a) at the energy of 750eV , (b) at the energy of 500eV and (c) ^{149}OCs$^+$ and ^{282}OCs$_2$$^+$ by using a Cameca ims-4f at the energy of 850eV

Figure 4(a) shows the B diffusion from the poly-Si layer to the Si substrate through SiO$_2$ or SiO$_x$N$_y$. O2+ primary ions are used to detect ^{11}B$^+$ secondary ions with a normal incidence angle and with the energy of 500eV. Figure 4(a) clearly shows the effectiveness of films for the suppression of the B diffusion. The B concentration at the oxide region is higher than that in the poly-Si layer. The same phenomenon is observed in O$_2$$^+$ primary ions with a 45° incidence angle and with an O$_2$ gas leak and the B concentration at the oxide region is higher than that obtained with normal incidence O$_2$$^+$ primary ions. Figure 4(b) shows the ^{144}BCs$^+$ profile obtained by 850eV Cs$^+$ primary ions near the interface of poly-Si/SiO$_x$N$_y$/Si. In Fig.4(b) no enhancement by the oxide layer is observed. These results imply that the oxide layer enhances ^{11}B$^+$ ion signals even with normal incidence O$_2$$^+$ or with an O$_2$ gas leak. The sensitivity of ^{144}BCs$^+$ is, however, less than that of ^{11}B$^+$ secondary ions by O$_2$$^+$ primary ions.

468

4. Conclusion

We have studied the SIMS analysis of MOS structure used in advanced ULSIs. In such an analysis it is important not only to use the low-energy primary ions but to determine the optimum measurement conditions such as the appropriate secondary ion species and the incidence angle of primary ions.

Acknowledgment

The authors would like to thank Dr.T.Hoshi, Dr.Z.P.Lee and Dr.H.Tomizuka of ULVAC-PHI, Inc. for measurements using a PHI ADAPT1010.

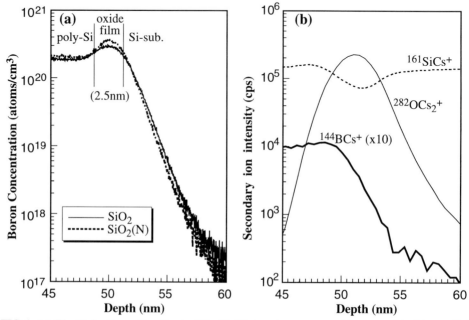

FIG.4 (a) The B depth profile of poly-Si/oxide/Si structure measured by normal incidence O_2^+ primary ions. (b) the distribution of 144BCs$^+$ at the poly-Si/SiO$_2$/Si by using a Cameca ims-4f at the energy of 850eV

References

[1] A.Yokozawa and Y.Miyamoto, Phys. Rev. B55, p.13783 (1997)
[2] T.Aoyama, S.Ohkubo, H. Tashiro, Y.Tada, K.Suzuki and K.Horiuchi, Jpn.J.Appl.Phys.37, p.1244 (1998)
[3] Handbook of Modern Ion Beam Materials Analysis, Material Research Society

A. Benninghoven, P. Bertrand, H.-N. Migeon and H.W. Werner (Editors).
Proceedings of the 12th International Conference on Secondary Ion Mass Spectrometry,
Brussels, Belgium, 5-11 September 1999

REDISTRIBUTION OF BORON DURING SIMS DEPTH PROFILING USING OXYGEN BEAM BOMBARDMENT

Larry Wang, C. Tian and Stephen P. Smith

Charles Evans and Associates, 301 Chesapeake Drive, Redwood City, CA 94063

1. Introduction

Boron is the major p-type dopant currently used in production Si semiconductor processing. A typical doping process includes ion implantation and subsequent annealing to electrically activate the implanted species [1]. Due to its excellent detection sensitivity and depth resolution, SIMS depth profiling is commonly used to determine the concentration and distribution of boron in Si.

Boron depth profiling provides important information that can be used in process control, failure analysis, and process modeling. Accurate and reproducible SIMS measurements are especially important in modeling and process control of advanced CMOS processes.

Because boron is an electro-positive species, it is typically analyzed using oxygen beam sputtering. Boron positive ions (B^+) are detected. With an 8 keV O_2^+ primary beam at 42^0 incident angle, SIMS profiling of B^+ has two well-know problems: (1) the first 200 Å region of the profile can not be accurately quantified due to transient effects; and (2) sputtering induced roughness will become significant at about 2 to 5 microns sputter depth, causing degradation of SIMS depth resolution and uncertainty in the concentration quantification [2, 3].

In this paper, we discuss a newly discovered SIMS artifact that causes distortion in certain portions of SIMS depth profiles for B in Si. The distortion appears to be due to lateral redistribution (or segregation) of boron caused by previous profiling in the adjacent sample region (<3mm separation between analysis craters). We will show examples of this artifact, and present the results of different analysis approaches.

2. Experimental

All SIMS measurements were performed on a CAMECA ims 4f instrument equipped with both oxygen and cesium primary beam sources. SIMS analyses were performed with 8 keV and 3 keV O_2^+ beams, and a 14.5 keV Cs^+ beam. Beam currents were between 50 nA to 500 nA for the O_2^+ beams, and 100 nA for the Cs^+ beam. Typical raster sizes were 150 to 200 microns and the collection area was 80 microns in diameter.

---

*Corresponding Author. **lwang@cea.com**

All samples were implanted with one or more [11]B implants at energies greater than 50 keV. The dose of each implant is between 5e12 at/cm^2 to 5e13 at/cm^2. All samples, except the sample in Fig. 1(a), were annealed. Samples used in Fig. 1 are device samples with 200-500 micron pads. Samples used in Fig. 2 are unpatterned blanket wafers.

3. Results

3.1 Example of boron redistribution

An apparent redistribution of boron has been observed in several annealed, ion-implanted samples. After the first SIMS profile, all subsequent profiles taken in the neighborhood of a previously sputtered crater on these samples show a characteristic distortion ("dip" and "bump") in a portion of the depth profile. These "dip" and "bump"

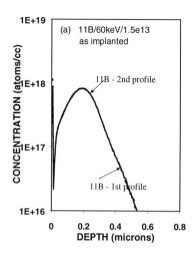 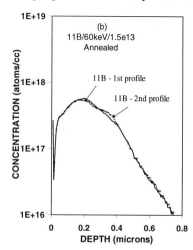

Fig. 1 SIMS profiles of [11]B implanted samples. (a) as-implanted, (b) annealed

distortions occur at depths between 0.1 to 0.5 microns, and they are reproducible in all subsequent profiles. Some examples of these features are shown in Fig. 1 and Fig. 2. These profiles were obtained using an 8 keV O_2^+ primary ion beam.

The sample used in Fig. 1(a) was as-implanted. Two SIMS profiles were taken in a 200x350 micron pad and the two profiles are indistinguishable. The sample used in Fig. 1(b) received the same boron ion implant as that in Fig.1, but was also annealed. In this case, the second profile, again taken from the same pad as the first profile, showed a "dip" and a "bump" at about 0.3 microns depth.

3.2 Effect of analysis location on the redistribution of boron

In Fig. 2 are shown [11]B profiles measured at several different locations of a single sample. The blanket wafer was implanted twice, with 1e13 at/cm^2 [11]B at 80 keV and

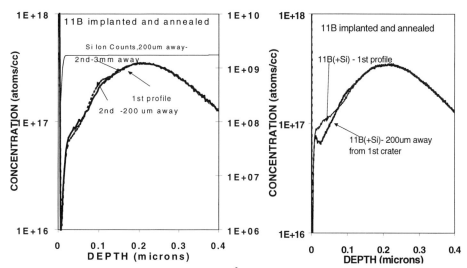

Fig.2 11B implanted (80keV 1e13 at/cm^3 and 360keV 5e12 at/cm^3) and annealed wafer sample. 8keV O_2^+ sputtering.

Fig.3 11B implanted (80keV 1e13 at/cm^3 and 360keV 5e12 at/cm^3) and annealed wafer sample. 14.5keV Cs^+ sputtering.

5e12 at/cm^2 [11]B at 360 keV. The wafer was annealed at 800°C in a nitrogen environment for 20 minutes. The first SIMS profile of [11]B was obtained from a freshly cleaved piece (1st profile). The next profile taken immediately adjacent to the first profile (200 microns away from the first profile) shows the formation of a "bump" at about 0.11 micron. A Si profile taken in the same region shows that the "bump" appears at a depth well beyond the surface transient region. Another set of profiles was measured at 1.5 mm (not shown) and 3 mm (2nd –3mm away) distance from the first crater on the sample, respectively. The profile taken at 1.5 mm from the first crater still shows a slight difference from the first profile. The profile taken at 3 mm from the first crater appears to be unaffected by the artifact.

3.3 Effect of O_2^+ beam density and energy, and measurement as BSi$^-$ using a Cs beam

The same sample used to obtain the profiles shown in Fig. 2 was also measured with an 8 keV O_2^+ beam with a reduced primary beam current of only 10% of that used for Fig. 2, and also was profiled with a 3 keV O_2^+ beam. The boron redistribution effect was seen in both of these cases.

The sample was also analyzed using a Cs^+ beam by measuring the BSi$^-$ molecular ion, as shown in Fig. 3. A similar redistribution artifact also appears to exist in this data.

4. Conclusions

The boron profile distortion artifact illustrated here under O_2^+ sputtering has been observed repeatedly in many different samples. The following statements summarize our observations to date:

1. Oxygen beam sputtering of *some boron implanted and annealed* samples may cause distortion of subsequent B^+ profiles acquired from adjacent locations on the same sample. The extra "dip" and "bump" that appears in the subsequent profiles appears to be due to redistribution of the implanted boron under the influence of the SIMS primary oxygen ion beam.

2. The boron redistribution effect is most severe immediately adjacent to the initial sputtering location on the sample, and dies out laterally within a distance of about 3 mm from the previously sputtered crater.

3. This lateral redistribution of boron can occur under both 3 keV and 8 keV O_2^+ primary ion beam sputtering. It can also occur over a wide range of primary ion beam current densities. Further study is needed for Cs^+ primary ions.

The above observations show that great care must be taken to acquire accurate repeat SIMS analysis profiles of B in ion implanted silicon wafers. The driving forces behind the observed redistribution are not clear at present and additional experiments are required to fully characterize this artifact.

References

[1] *Ion Implantation and Ion Beam Processing of Materials*, G.K. Hubler, et al., eds., MRS Symposia Proceedings 27, (North-Holland, New York) 1984.

[2] *Secondary Ion Mass Spectrometry. A Practical Handbook for Depth Profiling and Bulk Impurity Analysis*, R.G. Wilson, F.A. Stevie and C.W. Magee, John Wiley & Sons, New York, 1989.

[3] *Secondary Ion Mass Spectrometry. Basic Concepts, Instrumental Aspects, Applications and Trends*, A Benninghoven, F.G. Rüdenauer and H.W. Werner. John Wiley & Sons, New York (1987).

A. Benninghoven, P. Bertrand, H.-N. Migeon and H.W. Werner (Editors).
Proceedings of the 12th International Conference on Secondary Ion Mass Spectrometry,
Brussels, Belgium, 5-11 September 1999
© 2000 Elsevier Science B.V. All rights reserved.

SHAVE-OFF DEPTH PROFILING OF MULTI-LAYER SAMPLES USING A GALLIUM FOCUSED ION BEAM SIMS

B. Tomiyasu[a], S. Sakasegawa[a], T. Toba[a], M. Owari[b] and Y. Nihei[a]

a: Institute of Industrial Science, The University of Tokyo,
7-22-1 Roppongi, Minato-ku, Tokyo 106-8558, Japan.
e-mail : bunbu@cc.iis.u-tokyo.ac.jp
b: Environmental Science Center, The University of Tokyo,
7-3-1 Hongo, Bunkyo-ku, Tokyo 113-0033, Japan.

1. Introduction

SIMS is one of the most effective techniques for depth profiling of elements in solid materials. In conventional SIMS depth profiling, it is required that the analyzed surface is always parallel to the initial one. In the case of sputtering of micro particles and samples with rough surfaces, however, it is impossible to keep a parallel surface because of the topographic effect on the sputter-etching rate. Thus, it is difficult to obtain an accurate depth profile of these surface layer regions by conventional methods. Recently, there are several research reports on profiling by micro-machining and imaging the cross-section of samples [1,2].

We have developed a shave-off analysis for a single micro particle using a Ga^+ focused ion beam (Ga-FIB) SIMS [3]. Since the topographic effect can be canceled, the shave-off depth profiling is one of the most powerful techniques to obtain accurate elemental depth distributions with high depth resolution from small particles and the samples with rough surfaces [4,5]. In order to clarify the factors determining the depth resolution and to estimate the ultimate depth resolution of shave-off depth profiling, model calculations to simulate shave-off processes on a double layer sample were performed. An experiment was also performed on a TiN thin layer sample to compare depth resolution.

2. Shave-off depth profiling of a multi-layer sample

2.1 Procedure of shave-off depth profiling

Figure 1 shows the procedure for shave-off depth profiling of a multi-layer sample. In order to apply the shave-off depth profiling to the bulk samples, the micro-machining processes of a sample (a,b) were required. The surrounding part of the analyzing surface layer region was sputtered by raster scan of high current Ga-FIB. This rough micro-machining process made a cube with rough walls on a substrate. The surfaces of cube were micro-machined for flat ones by shave-off scan [3] of low current and fine Ga-FIB. After these micro-machining processes, the sample was tilted at 90 degrees precisely, and analyzed by

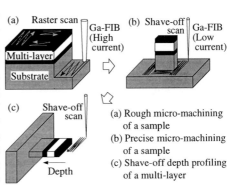

Figure 1 Procedure for shave-off depth profiling of a multi-layer sample.

shave-off depth profiling (c). By these processes, we could get the changes of secondary ion intensities as a function of the scanning position of a primary ion beam. Because the accuracy of a scanning position of ion beam had no relation with the analyzed depth in shave-off depth profiling, the depth resolution of obtained profiles was not dependent on the analyzed depth.

2.2 Computer simulation of shave-off depth profiling

Figure 2 shows the calculation model of the shave-off depth profiling of a multi-layer sample, and the parameters in this computer simulation. Under the shave-off depth profiling, the sample was cross-sectioned as in the figure. The parameters of the primary ion beam were a beam diameter d, a beam current I_p and a shave-off scan speed v_Z. The beam profile was defined as a Gaussian distribution. The another key parameters were as follows: the width (height) of analyzed layer L_X (L_Y), the angles between an X (Y) direction of primary beam and an X (Y) direction of interface of thin layers θ (ϕ) and the unit time of ion detection t.

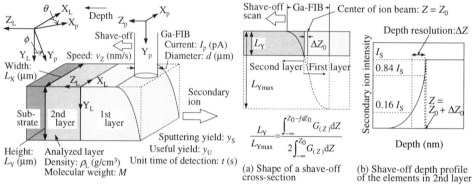

Figure 2 Calculation model of the shave-off depth profiling of a multi-layer sample.

(a) Shape of a shave-off cross-section

(b) Shave-off depth profile of the elements in 2nd layer

Figure 3 Shape of cross-section and expected shave-off depth profile from second layer.

The shape of cross-section of the analyzed layer and a shave-off depth profile were simulated using the calculation model and parameters. The solid curved line in figure 3(a) shows the expected shape of the cross-section when the first layer is sputtered out by Ga-FIB. If the height of analyzed layer was large enough, the Ga-FIB sputtered the sample with length L_{Ymax}. Because the beam profile was defined as a Gaussian distribution, the shape of cross-section was expressed as the integral of Gaussian distribution. The length L_{Ymax} was calculated by the parameters in Fig. 2. The distance between a center of Ga-FIB and the interface of sample ΔZ_0 was calculated by the equation in Fig. 3(a). The expected intensity was increased in proportion to the integral of Gaussian distribution until the center of Ga-FIB reached to the depth $Z_0 + \Delta Z_0$. After that the intensity was kept constant value of I_S. We defined the depth resolution ΔZ as the length between depths where the intensities were 0.16 I_S and 0.84 I_S.

In this calculation model, the depth resolution was calculated by the parameters in Fig. 2. We estimated the relationships between a depth resolution and calculation parameters. Figure 4 shows the relationship between a depth resolution and a diameter of Ga-FIB. Because the diameter of Ga-FIB generally depends on the beam current, we assumed typical combinations of beam diameter and current of the apparatus used in this study. Recently the combination of 10 nm of beam diameter and 1 pA of beam current has been realized in Ga-FIB technology, so the depth resolution under this beam condition was also calculated (broken line). It is clear that the shave-off depth resolution was higher using a finer Ga-FIB.

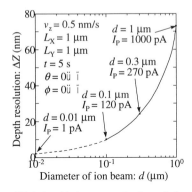

Figure 4 Relationship between a depth resolution and a diameter of Ga-FIB.

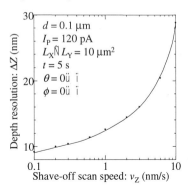

Figure 5 Relationship between a depth resolution and a shave-off scan speed.

The relationship between a depth resolution and a shave-off scan speed is shown in Fig. 5. The high depth resolution was realized under slow shave-off scan. The sputter volume of the sample in unit time of secondary ion detection was dependent on the shave-off scan speed. The slowest scan speed of our apparatus was 0.39 nm/s.

Figure 6 shows the relationship between a depth resolution and the angle between an X (Y) direction of primary beam and an X (Y) direction of interface of thin layers θ (ϕ) (see in figure 2). In this calculation, the width of cross-section was 5 μm, and height was 2 μm. The best depth resolution was estimated to be 3 nm when the angles of θ and ϕ were 0 degrees and −0.4 degrees, respectively, under the optimum condition. This simulation result suggested that the cross-section of the sample was not parallel to the incidence angle. The depth resolutions were deteriorated rapidly by displacement from the optimum. It was clear that the angles of θ and ϕ are the most important parameters in this depth profiling.

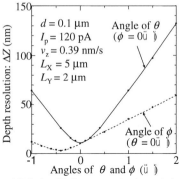

Figure 6 Relationship between a depth resolution and angles θ and ϕ.

From the simulation results of the relationship between depth resolution and these experimental parameters, we expected the best depth resolution for shave-off depth profiling. The best depth resolution was estimated as 1.4 nm under the condition of 10 nm beam diameter, 1 pA beam current, 0.1 nm/s shave-off scan speed, 1 μm^2 size of cross-section area and 1s unit time of detection. The simulation showed that the accurate depth profile with a high depth resolution was obtained by the precise shave-off depth profiling.

3. Experiment: shave-off depth profiling

We analyzed the multi-layer sample by shave-off depth profiling under the conditions given by on the results of computer simulation. The multi layer sample consisted of 3 thin layers: TiN thin layer (100 nm), Al thin layer (500 nm), TiN thin layer (100 nm), surface, and Si substrate. The experimental condition was as follows: 0.1 μm beam diameter, 120 pA beam current, 0.39 nm/s shave-off scan speed, 1.4 μm width of cross-section area, 5 μm height of cross-section area and 5s unit time of detection. During the measurements, secondary ions of m/z = 24-48 range were detected simultaneously by a parallel detection system. Using the beam scan rotation system, the angle θ was precisely aligned to 0 degrees.

Figure 7 shows the shave-off depth profile of a TiN thin layer, which is the third layer from the sample surface. When the analyzed depth was shallower than 600 nm, the intensity of $^{48}Ti^+$ increased gradually. The intensity was constant between the depths of 600-635 nm, and decreased rapidly for depths deeper than 635 nm. Based on the definition of the depth resolution in this study, the experimental shave-off depth resolutions were estimated to be 30 nm from changes in the front edge and 20 nm from changes in the backside edge. The simulation with the beam parameter values used in this experiment yielded the depth resolution of 10.4 nm. The

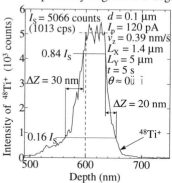

Figure 7 Shave-off depth profile of the TiN thin layer (3rd layer from the surface).

depth resolution obtained from experimental results was at least twice that expected by the simulation. The disagreement of these resolutions can be attributed to the misalignment of ϕ by +0.19 degrees in the experiment. Thus, the precisely tilting system of a sample is needed to obtain shave-off depth profiling with the best depth resolution.

4. Conclusion

The simulation revealed that the key factors to realize the best depth resolution are alignment of the primary beam and the sample, small diameter of Ga-FIB, and shave-off scan speed. The simulation showed the best depth resolution of 3 nm with precise alignment of the primary beam and the sample under the current experimental conditions. From the experimental results on depth profiling of a TiN thin layer, a depth resolution of 20-30 nm was obtained. When the ultra fine focused ion beam with a diameter of 10 nm is used as the primary beam, the practical depth resolution of 1.4 nm is expected for the analysis of the sample with 1 μm² cross section. Thus, we conclude that the shave-off depth profiling is one of the most effective techniques for accurate depth profiling.

5. References

[1] B. Tomiyasu, H. Komatsubara, I. Fukuju, M. Satoh, M. Owari and Y. Nihei, in *Secondary Ion Mass Spectrometry SIMS XI*, eds. by G. Gillen, R. Lareau, J.Bennett and F. Stevie, John Wiley & Sons, Chichester (1998) 1069.

[2] R. Gibbons, M. G. Dowsett, G. A. Cooke, C. Hill and P. J. Pearson, in *Secondary Ion Mass Spectrometry SIMS XI*, eds. by G. Gillen, R. Lareau, J.Bennett and F. Stevie, John Wiley & Sons, Chichester (1998) 313.

[3] H. Satoh, M. Owari and Y. Nihei, J. Vac. Sci. Technol., **B6** (1988) 915.

[4] B. Tomiyasu, H. Komatsubara, M. Satoh, S. Sakasegawa, M. Owari and Y. Nihei, in *Secondary Ion Mass Spectrometry SIMS XI*, eds. by G. Gillen, R. Lareau, J.Bennett and F. Stevie, John Wiley & Sons, Chichester (1998) 383.

[5] B. Tomiyasu, I. Fukuju, H. Komatsubara, M. Owari and Y. Nihei, Nuclear Instrument and Methods in Physics B, **136-138** (1998) 1028.

A. Benninghoven, P. Bertrand, H.-N. Migeon and H.W. Werner (Editors).
Proceedings of the 12th International Conference on Secondary Ion Mass Spectrometry,
Brussels, Belgium, 5-11 September 1999
© 2000 Elsevier Science B.V. All rights reserved.

SIMS CHARACTERIZATION OF ULTRA-THIN INTEGRATED OXYNITRIDE (ION) FOR THE GATE DIELECTRIC

L. Wu , J.J. Lee, H-H Tseng, D. Sieloff, D. O'meara and P. Tobin
Advanced Products Research and Development Laboratory
Motorola Inc.
3501 Ed Bluestein Boulevard
Austin, Texas 78721
Tel: (512)-933-6479, FAX: (512)-933-2705 ra5468@email.sps.mot.com

1. Introduction

There are two major challenges as gate dielectric thickness decreases in order to satisfy the device geometry reduction: high leakage current and dopant penetration. Integrated nitride becomes an attractive candidate for a thin gate dielectric due to its high dielectric constant, which reduces leakage current, and its resistance to dopant diffusion, which minimizes boron penetration [1-2]. Since these thin film (35Å) dielectrics are often fabricated with multiple steps and in-situ silicon capped to prevent oxide growth, SIMS characterization becomes very challenging due to the complicated matrix and depth resolution requirements. In this study, we have determined the nitrogen distribution using CsN+ secondary ion and also monitored the subtle chemical and matrix changes as a function of film process using matrix sensitive secondary ion SiN-. Comparison of CsN+ profile and SiN- profile are discussed.

2. Experimental

The thin integrated oxynitride characterized in this study was fabricated in several steps. First a thin oxide is grown, followed by an oxynitride deposition in a commercial RTCVD silicon nitride reactor. A post anneal step is used to modify film thickness, composition and electrical properties. Samples with three different post anneal steps were studied: no post anneal, N2 post anneal and N2O+N2 post anneal. A 100Å silicon cap was used to prevent further oxide growth on all samples.

Ion Film	~35Å	~100Å Si Cap Layer
		Additional SiO$_2$ depending on Post Anneal step
		Deposited **Oxynitride**
		Grown SiO2
		Si Substrate

Scheme: Cross section of Integrated oxynitride (ION)

SIMS analysis was performed by using three different SIMS tools: Cameca-6f magnetic sector SIMS, Cameca TOF IV TOF SIMS and Atomika 4500 quadrupole SIMS. For analyses on the Cameca SIMS, a 10nA Cs+ beam with Ep=6 keV, Es=4 keV at 60 degree [3] was applied as monitoring both CsN+ and CsO+ was necessary to improve the data quantification [4-6]. A 3nA 600eV Cs+ beam at 45 degrees was used during the TOF SIMS analysis while monitoring SiN- and SiO-. A 50nA low energy Cs+ beam at 1 keV and 60 degrees was used on the Atomika 4500.

SIMS quantification is based an oxynitride standard previously characterized with quadrupole SIMS. All the profiles shown are on the same common intensity scale.

3. Results and Discussions

Cameca SIMS results: A very small change in the position of the nitrogen peak as a function of post anneal steps was observed, as displayed in Figure 1. With no post anneal and N2 post anneal, the nitrogen peak was near the Si cap / ION film interface. N2 post anneal provided further nitrogen incorporation, and thus exhibited the highest nitrogen peak among the three samples. For N2O+N2 post annealed sample, nitrogen peak was completely contained within the thin oxide due to additional thin oxide formation with N2O+N2 anneal prior to Si capping. This additional thin oxide also prevented further nitrogen incorporation, even with the N2 presence during the anneal. Therefore the nitrogen content remained unchanged in comparison with the unannealed sample.

TOF SIMS results : In Figure 2, the TOFSIMS SiN- peak of the no post annealed sample and N2 post annealed sample appears distorted towards the Si cap/ ION interface in comparison to the Cameca SIMS profile, apparently due to ion yield enhancement at the Si cap / oxynitride interface. A very slight shoulder peak on the right side of the SiN- profile appears to reflect the very small matrix difference between the thin oxynitride and initial thin oxide formed during the ION process. However, for the N2O+N2 annealed sample, because the nitrogen peak was completely inside the oxide prior to Si cap, matrix effects are reduced and the artificial shoulder peak was minimized. This result suggested that a sandwich layer composed of oxide/ oxynitride / oxide stack was formed inside the ION film after N2O+N2 anneal.

Atomika SIMS results : Consistent profiles between Atomika and Cameca SIMS, as demonstrated in Figure 1 and Figure 3, suggest that depth resolution is likely not limited by beam energy but roughness of the sample surface by silicon capping. The roughness of the capping Si layer was further revealed by AFM imaging.

4. Conclusions

Ultra-thin integrated oxynitride films can be characterized by utilizing several SIMS techniques. By monitoring cesium cluster ions, nitrogen and oxygen distribution profile can be achieved by using either a Cameca-6f magnetic sector SIMS or an Atomika 4500 quadruple SIMS. By monitoring matrix sensitive secondary ion SiN- and SiO- in TOFSIMS analysis, subtle chemical and matrix change can be revealed. Based upon the SIMS results, improved understanding about post anneal steps was gained. N2 post anneal only increased the content of the nitrogen in the film but did not change the nitrogen peak position. Additional thin oxide

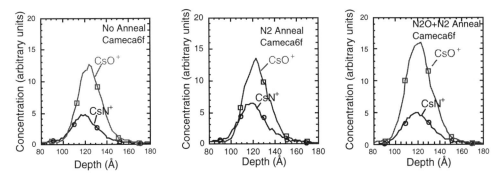

Figure 1 Cameca SIMS results analyzed at Ep=6KeV, Es=4KeV, 60°.

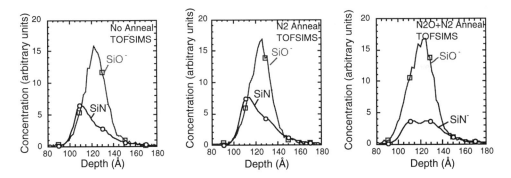

Figure 2 TOF SIMS results analyzed at Ep=600eV, 45°.

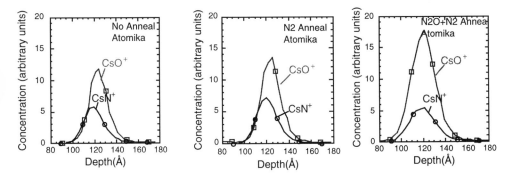

Figure 3 Atomika SIMS results analyzed at Ep=1KeV, 60°.

formed by N2O+N2 post anneal prevented further nitrogen incorporation into the oxide and placed the nitrogen peak completely inside the oxide.

Acknowledgment

The authors thank Fabio Pintchovski, and Joe Mogab for their support of this work. Authors also thank Jerry Hawkins for the helpful technical discussions.

References

[1]. H.H.Tseing, D. O'Meara, P. Tobin, V. Wang, X. Gao, R. Hegde, I. Yang, P. Gilbert, R. Cotton and L. Hebert, *IEDM*, Vol. 29, No. 5.1, (1998) pp793.

[2]. R.I. Hegde, B. Maiti, and P. J. Tobin, *Journal of the Electrochemical Society*, Vol. 144, No. 3, (1997) pp1081.

[3]. L. Wu, T. Neil, D. Sieloff and R.I. Hegde, *Secon dary ion mass spectrometry SIMS XI*, eds. By G. Gillen et, John Wiley & son U.S.A, p245

[4]. M.R. Frost and C. W. Magee, *Applied Surface Science*, 104/105 (1996) 379-384.

[5]. C. W. Magee, W.L. Harrington and E. M. Botnick, *Int. J. Mass Spectrosc. Ion proc.* 103 (1990) 45.

[6]. Y. Gao, *J. Appl. Phys.* 64(1988) pp3760.

[7]. *Secondary Ion Mass Spectrometry:A Practical Handbook for Depth Profiling and Bulk Impurity Analysis.* ed by R. G. Wilson, F. A. Stevie and C. W. Magee. John Wiley & Sons.U. S. A. (1989).

A. Benninghoven, P. Bertrand, H.-N. Migeon and H.W. Werner (Editors).
Proceedings of the 12th International Conference on Secondary Ion Mass Spectrometry,
Brussels, Belgium, 5-11 September 1999

481

OXYGEN BOMBARDMENT INDUCED ZINC SEGREGATION
DURING DEPTH PROFILING OF ZnO/Si LAYERED STRUCTURES

U. Zastrow, B. Rech, A. Mück and W. Beyer

Institute of Thin Film and Ion Technology
Research Centre Juelich GmbH, D-52425 Jülich, Germany
e-mail: u.zastrow@fz-juelich.de

1. Introduction

Aluminum doped zinc oxide (ZnO:Al) is transparent as well as conductive and applied as electrical contact in opto-electronic devices like silicon based solar cells and optical sensors. The use of O_2^+ primary ions at normal incidence for SIMS depth profiling of ZnO/Si layered structure provides high ion yields for dopants in Si and avoids sputtering induced roughening.

In the present paper we focus on the influence of the O_2^+ bombardment on the Zn relocation leading to artificial Zn profile broadening in Si. We calculate the inherent Zn mass transport from the decay in the Zn depth profiles. Furthermore we discuss the Zn transport in terms of (i) the oxygen injection into the surface layer as well as of (ii) the cascade mixing process. For this purpose the latter effects both are derived from Monte-Carlo calculation (TRIM [1]).

2. Experimental

The ZnO:Al films are deposited by rf-magnetron sputtering from ZnO (2% Al_2O_3) targets. SIMS analysis is carried out with an Atomika 4000 instrument using O_2^+ primary ions at near-normal incidence and primary energies of 1.5 to 12 keV. Depth scaling is achieved by stylus surface profiling (Dektak). The Zn concentration in Si is quantified via ^{64}Zn implantation. Monte-Carlo simulation of the oxygen bombardment is performed applying the TRIM-95 routine [1] and using standard displacement and binding energies of 15 and 2 eV, respectively.

3. Results and Discussion

Applying perpendicular O_2^+ bombardment for SIMS depth profiling of ZnO/Si layered structures, Zn is found to show an anomalous decay behavior after sputtering through the ZnO/Si interface. The apparent depth distribution of Zn in Si fits complementary error function (erfc) and can therefore be confused with diffusion of Zn during device fabrication. However, complete removal of the ZnO layer by etching in HCl solution prior to SIMS analysis gives evidence that no diffusion of Zn into Si has taken place. In Fig.1a the Zn depth profiles of ZnO/Si layered structure are plotted for various primary O_2^+ energies E. Constant amount of Zn (areal density $\phi_0 \sim 5 \times 10^{15}$ cm^{-2}) is found to be involved in the decay process leading for all primary energies to error function type depth distributions $C = C_0 \mathrm{erfc}\{(z-z_0)/\xi\}$ with z_0 the depth at the ZnO/Si interface and with $C_0 \propto E^{-1}$ and $\xi \propto E$, approximately. Using 12 keV primary ions this decay behavior is found to be indepent of the Si doping (as checked for n$^+$-type {4 mΩcm}, p$^+$-type {2 mΩcm} and n$^-$-type {5 kΩcm} material) as well as of the erosion velocity v (as checked for 0.1 nm/s ≤ v ≤ 2 nm/s), indicating that neither electric field-induced [e.g. 2,3] nor diffusion-limited [4] migration of Zn significantly influences its profile broadening during near-normal O_2^+ sputter depth profiling. Therefore the system Zn in Si is

482

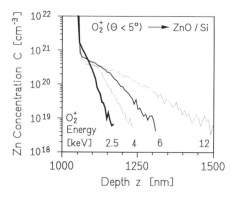

Fig.1a Depth profiles of the apparent Zn concentration behind the ZnO/Si interface ($z_0 \sim 1050$nm) for various primary energies.

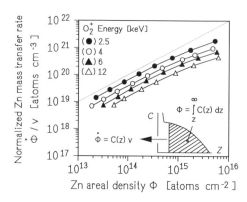

Fig.1b Zn mass transfer rate (normalized to erosion velocity v) versus Zn areal density in Si as derived from the data shown in Fig.1a.

well suited to study the mass transport through the O_2^+ bombardment induced altered layer. A SiO_2 layer is formed [e.g. 5] which is moving into depth due to sputter removal. In Fig.1b the Zn mass transfer rate (normalized to erosion velocity v) through this surface layer is plotted for various primary ion energies versus Zn areal density. The data are derived from the depth profiles presented in Fig.1a. Observed at the migrating surface the normalized Zn mass transfer rate (equivalent to $d\phi/dz$) can be expressed by the product of two independent functions: $d\phi/dz = C_0(E) f(\phi)$. With decreasing ϕ the transient Zn concentration in Si ap-proaches exponential decay $C(t) \propto \exp(-z(t)/\lambda(E))$ resulting in $d\phi/dz = \lambda(E)^{-1}\phi$. The latter is in-dicated in Fig.1b by the straight line ($\lambda = 10$ nm) as guide for the eye. Note that the graph $d\phi/dz$ versus ϕ provides more unambiguous information about the physical process than the discussion of concentration C versus depth z: because in the mass transfer differential equations both, $C_0(E)$ as well as $\lambda(E)^{-1}$, simply act as scaling factors. Turnig the attention to the altered surface layer, its internal

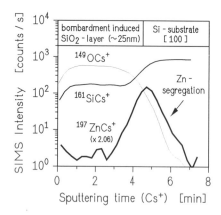

Fig.2a Internal profile of the 12 keV O_2^+ sputtering induced altered layer as recorded *in-situ* about 50 nm after passing through the ZnO/Si interface.

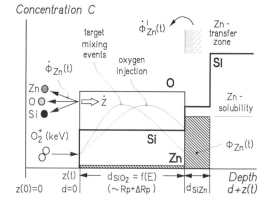

Fig.2b Schematic diagram of the O_2^+ sputtering induced SiO_2 layer, the Zn segregation at the SiO_2/Si interface and the depth distributions of injected oxygen primary ions and mixing events.

profile is shown in Fig.2a. It is observed ~ 50 nm after O_2^+ sputtering through the ZnO/Si interface. The profile data, which are recorded *in-situ* using the MCs^+ technique [6], demonstrate that Zn strongly segregates at the sputtering induced SiO$_2$/Si interface. In Fig.2b the schematic diagram of this altered layer is drawn. The thickness of the SiO$_2$ layer, which migrates into depth due to sputter erosion, depends on primary energy E and is known to correspond roughly to the sum of projected range and straggeling of the primary ions (Rp+Δ Rp) [5,7]. According to Fig.2a the majority of Zn retained in Si originates from Zn segregation at the SiO$_2$/Si subsurface while the Zn concentration within the oxide layer is quite low. Therefore the Zn transfer from the buried SiZn layer into the SiO$_2$ should be rate limiting for the Zn mass transfer through the sputtered surface. The thickness of the SiZn layer d_{SiZn} has to increase for higher Zn areal density ϕ. Assuming the Zn transfer to originate from a thin zone close to the oxide (which is likely due to the depth limited primary beam - sample interaction) the SiZn layer expansion can explain the increasing deviation from the $d\phi/dz \propto \phi$ relation with increasing ϕ (observed in Fig.1b). The O_2^+ bombardment of the sample leads to (i) oxygen injection into the altered layer as well as to (ii) target atom relocations due to cascade mixing. In order to investigate the influence of both processes, (i) and (ii), Monte-Carlo simulation of the oxygen implantation into the altered layer structure is performed using the TRIM-95 routine [1]. The following procedure is applied for each primary ion energy used. First Rp and ΔRp are determined by TRIM evaluation of the oxygen ion trajectories in pure SiO$_2$. Second the SiO$_2$/SiZn/Si layer system is created according to Fig.2b. Here $Si_{0.5}Zn_{0.5}$ compound is assumed for the middle layer. Taking the total Zn areal density ($\phi_0 \sim 5\times10^{15}$ cm^{-2}, as discussed in Fig.1a) into account the SiZn layer thickness is estimated to ~20 Å indepently of the primary energy. Third the TRIM routine is used to calculate the oxygen implantation into the complete layer system, the routine resulting in depth distributions of injected oxygen and target vacancy densities per impining primary ion. At last the calculated distributions are normalized per sputter removed Si atom, the Si sputter yield for each primary energy taken from the literature [8]. The last step enables the direct comparison of both effects, (i) and (ii), with the Zn mass transfer data discussed in Fig.1b. The results of this procedure are plotted in figures 3a and 3b versus normalized depth.

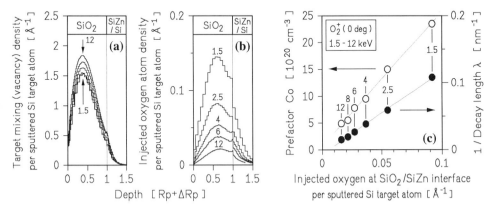

Fig.3 Monte-Carlo simulation (TRIM-95) of the O_2^+ sputtering induced **(a)** target mixing and **(b)** oxygen injection, both versus normalized depth. The numbers in the plots indicate the O_2^+ primary ion energy. **(c)** Prefactor C_0 and inverse decay length λ^{-1} versus average injected oxygen density, the latter calculated from 10Å depth interval centered at the SiO$_2$ / SiZn interface.

The target mixing (vacancy) density weakly depends on the primary ion energy, as illustrated in Fig.3a. In contrast the injected oxygen density is observed to increase strongly with decreasing O_2^+ ion energy, as demonstrated in Fig.3b. These results suggest that the pro-nounced increase in the Zn mass transfer rate with decreasing bombardment energy is induced by the increase in the oxygen supply rather than by changes in the cascade mixing effect. In order to check this suggestion quantitatively we evaluate the injected oxygen density at the $SiO_2/SiZn$ subsurface, where the rate limitation for the Zn mass transfer should occur. The TRIM routine can produce artificial peaks and dips at layer edges [1], these artifacts caused by missing coincidence of the compound layer boundary with the edge of the atomic layer. Therefore 10 Å depth intervals (i.e., roughly four atomic layers), centered at the $SiO_2/SiZn$ interfaces, are used to calculate the average density of implanted oxygen. Its comparison with the mass transfer scaling factors is plotted in Fig.3c. Both, $C_0(E)$ and $\lambda^{-1}(E)$, are found to be approximately proportional to the density of oxygen injected at the interface region. This pro-portionality supports the association of the Zn mass transfer with the presence of free oxygen. We propose the following explanation: Metallic Zn is mobile in Si to move into depth pushed by the buried edge of the migrating oxide. Once formed into ZnO, zinc is immobilized and gets incorporated into the SiO_2 matrix. Due to the large difference in heat of formation, Si-O: ~ 799 kJ mol^{-1} compared to Zn-O: $\leq$ 276 kJ mol^{-1} [9], ZnO will not be formed in the presence of elemental Si [10]. However, as soon as SiO_2 stoichiometry is reached due to progressive O_2^+ sputtering, the excess of injected oxygen should enable ZnO formation at the buried edge of the silicon oxide. This formation process would consequently lead to the experimental results observed in this study. Finally we remark that the proposed mechanism could fit to any O_2^+ sputtering induced impurity segregation decaying in silicon with $\lambda \propto E$, approximately.

4. Conclusion

The use of perpendicular O_2^+ bombardment for depth profiling of ZnO/Si layered structure is found to result in error function type decay behavior of Zn in Si. Inherent Zn segregation at the O_2^+ sputtering induced SiO_2/Si interface is detected *in-situ* by MCs$^+$ profiling. By varying the primary ion energy and deriving the associated oxygen injection into the altered layer from Monte-Carlo calculation (TRIM), the Zn mass transfer through the sputtered surface is shown to be approximately proportional to the amount of free oxygen at the $SiO_2/Si(Zn)$ subsurface.

Acknowledgement   The authors would like to thank H. Siekmann for ZnO film deposition.

References
[1] J.F.Ziegler, J.P.Biersack, U.Littmark, *The Stopping and Range of Ions in Solids*, Pergamon Press, New York (1985); J.F. Ziegler, *TRIM v. 95.4*, IBM-Research, Yorktown NY (1995)
[2] K. Wittmaack, Y.Homma, Appl. Phys. Lett. <u>58</u> (1991) 2138
[3] U.Zastrow, W.Beyer, J.Herion, Fres. J. Anal. Chem. <u>346</u>, (1993) 92
[4] C.Tian, G.P.Beyer, W.Vandervorst, K.Maex, J.A.Kilner in: A. Benninghoven et.al. (eds) *Secondary Ion Mass Spectrometry - SIMS X, Wiley, Chichester* (1997) p. 383
[5] W.Vandervorst, J.Alay, B.Brijs, W.DeCoster, K.Elst in: A. Benninghoven et.al. (eds) *Secondary Ion Mass Spectrometry - SIMS IX*, Wiley, Chichester (1994) p. 599
[6] U.Zastrow, J.Fölsch, A.Mück, K.Schmidt, L.Vescan in: *SIMS X*, see ref. 4, (1997) p. 541
[7] J.A.Kilner, G.P.Beyer, R.J.Chater, Nucl. Instr. and Meth. B <u>84</u>, (1994) 176
[8] K.Wittmaack, Phil. Trans. R. Soc. Lond. A <u>354</u>, (1996) 2731
[9] *CRC Handbook of Chemistry and Physics*, CRC Press, Palm Beach FL (1978) p. F-224
[10] W.DeCoster, B.Brijs, W.Vanderforst in: *SIMS X*, see ref. 4, (1997) p. 529

A. Benninghoven, P. Bertrand, H.-N. Migeon and H.W. Werner (Editors).
Proceedings of the 12th International Conference on Secondary Ion Mass Spectrometry,
Brussels, Belgium, 5-11 September 1999
© 2000 Elsevier Science B.V. All rights reserved.

AN AFM AND TEM STUDY OF RIPPLE TOPOGRAPHY GROWTH DURING SIMS ULTRA SHALLOW DEPTH PROFILING OF Si

P.A.W. van der Heide[1], M.S. Lim[2], S.S. Perry[2], J. Kulik[3].
[1]Materials Research Science and Engineering Centre (MRSEC),
[2]Chemistry department,
[3]Texas Centre for Superconductivity,
University of Houston, Houston, Texas 77204-5500, U.S.A.

1. Introduction

The formation of surface topography has long been realised to have detrimental effects on depth resolution during Secondary Ion Mass Spectrometry (SIMS) depth profiling[1,2]. This surface roughening occurs as a result of the sputtering process and comes in many forms, i.e., ripples, cones, pits, pyramids, etc. These effects have been assumed to occur following prolonged sputtering, i.e., to depths approaching 1 μm or more. Recent studies carried out in this laboratory however have revealed that ripple topography can occur close to the onset of sputtering, or more precisely, just following the native oxide region on Si wafers[3].

This study examines the ripple topography growth observed during the ultra shallow depth profile analysis of two Si wafers bearing low energy implants (<10keV) of As and Sb via Atomic force microscopy (AFM) and transmission electron microscopy (TEM). X-ray Photo electron spectroscopy (XPS) was also used to examine the surface composition of the sputtered and unsputtered surfaces.

2. Experimental

The samples consisted of two doped Si wafers; one was implanted with As^+ at an energy of 1 keV to a dose of 1×10^{14} atoms/cm^2 and the other with Sb^+ at an energy of 5 keV to a dose of 1×10^{14} atoms/cm^2. These substrates possessed native oxides of 0.93 (As) and 0.97 nm (Sb) in thickness. These dimensions were defined via XPS, on a PHI 5750 instrument using a procedure described elsewhere[4].

SIMS analysis was carried out on a Phi 6600 SIMS instrument. A 1-5 nA, 750 eV, Cs^+ primary ion beam was directed at 60° with respect to the sample normal. A primary ion raster pattern of 500x500 um was used and the secondary ions of O^-, Si^-, As^- Sb^-, $AsSi^-$ and $AsSb^-$ emanating from the central 10% region of the sputtered area were recorded. All secondary ion signals were kept below 1 MHz. A variable O_2 leak ($1\text{-}10 \times 10^{-8}$ torr) was also employed during analysis (this unconventional set of analytical parameters was used since an O_2 leak was previously found to result in a loss of depth resolution[2,3]). Depth scales were derived through the use of previously defined sputter rates (SiO_2/Si=0.9). The term "apparent depths" is used since a linear sputter time to depth relation was assumed.

Surface topography measurements were collected over 250 x 250 nm regions within the respective SIMS craters using contact mode AFM on a homebuilt instrument using RHK AFM 100 and STM 1000 control electronics and software. Low resolution and high resolution cross sectional images of the sputtered surface and underlying region were collected on JOEL 2000FX and 2010-F TEM instruments.

3. Results and discussion

In Fig. 1(a) are shown examples of some Sb depth profiles collected with and without the use of an O_2 leak and with and without the prior evaporation of Cs onto the sample surface. (Cs evaporation was carried out via an SAES source situated in an attached reaction chamber to examine, as with the O_2 leak, the transient effects active[3]). Of special note here are the broadened profiles seen when using the O_2 leak. With the exception of the transient region, the $SbSi^-$ profiles were seen to both match (see inset if Fig. 1(a)) and exhibit the same trends (broadening) as the Sb^- profiles under O_2 leak conditions. The lack of the surface spike in the more intense $SbSi^-$ profiles noted when analysing this sample without an O_2 leak (see inset of Fig 1(a)), results from the fact that this signal appears to be free of the matrix effects influencing the Sb^- signal[3]. A similar broadening effect was noted during the analysis of the As implanted Si wafer. The results from the $AsSi^-$ secondary ions are shown in Fig. 1(b). This broadening, also seen in the As^- profiles, increased at elevated O_2 leak pressures.

Surface topography measurements were collected from craters sputtered to a depth of 30 nm (taken at the end of the Sb^- profiles) and 3 nm (taken by stopping the profile at the position where the $AsSi^-$ exhibited a peak intensity) with and without the use an O_2 leak. The results are shown in Figs. 2(a) and 2(b). Line scan analysis of the AFM images reveals that the periodicity and amplitude of the ripples is about 15 nm and

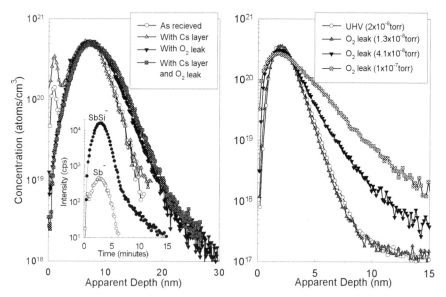

Fig. 1(a) Concentration vs depth profiles obtained from Sb^- under the specified Sb^- and $SbSi^-$ profiles in inset.   **Fig. 1(b)** Concentration vs depth profiles obtained from the $AsSi^-$ signals under the conditions. O_2 leak pressures listed.

0.5 nm respectively. Little difference was seen between the structure of the ripples between the two samples. The fact that ripple topography was observed at a sputtered depth of only 3 nm indicates that these ripples are initiated within, or just following, the native oxide region on Si and are due, in some manner, to the presence of O₂.

Fig. 3(a) through 3(c) show TEM cross sectional images of the Sb implanted Si wafer prior to, and following SIMS analysis in which the O₂ leak was used. From these, the unsputtered surface is seen to have an ~1 nm native oxide (consistent with the 0.97 nm derived via XPS) on top of a 12 nm amorphous region (this would have been caused during the implantation process) followed by the crystalline Si substrate. The sputtered surface, shown in Figs. 3(b) and (c) (sputtered to a depth of 30 nm), exhibited a rumpled amorphous SiO_2 layer (composition defined via XPS analysis) of ~2 nm in thickness. This would have formed during the sputtering process via the adsorption of O₂ present in the vacuum chamber during sputtering. The fact that the range (normal to the surface) for the Cs^+ primary beam used is 2.1 nm (derived using TRIM) suggests that the damage induced by the Cs^+ ion beam facilitates in the formation of the relatively thick oxide (this is twice as thick as the respective native oxides). The high resolution image shown in Fig. 3(c) reveals that the rippling extends to the SiO_2/Si (single crystal) interface.

Though these results suggest that the loss in depth resolution noted in Figs. 1(a) and 1(b) stems from ripple topography formation, segregation of these dopants to the SiO_2/Si interface has also been shown to occur[5]. Such an SiO_2 layer is continuously formed during the depth profile analysis of these samples when an O₂ leak is used. This SiO_2 formation is also believed to be the driving force behind the initiation of the ripple topography, suggesting that all these are indeed interrelated.

Sb in Si without O₂ leak (30nm crater depth),   As in Si without O₂ leak (3nm crater depth).

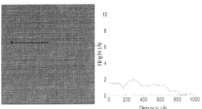
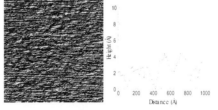

Sb in Si with O₂ leak (30nm crater depth),   As in Si with O₂ leak (3nm crater depth).

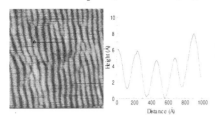
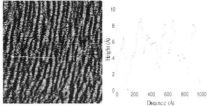

Fig. 2(a) AFM images of SIMS crater base from Sb implanted Si wafer. Line scans are shown on the right.   **Fig. 2(a)** AFM images of SIMS crater base from As implanted Si wafer. Line scans are shown on the right.

488

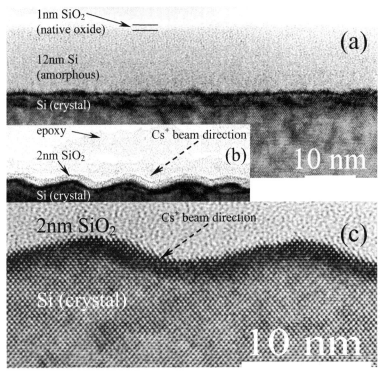

1nm SiO₂
(native oxide)

12nm Si
(amorphous)

Si (crystal)

epoxy

2nm SiO₂

Si (crystal)

Cs⁺ beam direction

(a)

(b)

10 nm

2nm SiO₂

Cs⁺ beam direction

(c)

Si (crystal)

10 nm

Fig. 3(a) High resolution TEM image of the unsputtered Sb implanted Si wafer.
Fig. 3(b) Low resolution TEM image of a sputtered region of the Sb implanted Si wafer.
Fig. 3(c) High resolution TEM image of a sputtered region of the Sb implanted Si wafer.

4. Conclusions

AFM and TEM studies reveal ripple topography within the SIMS craters generated via Cs⁺ primary ion bombardment. This occurred within the first few nm on n-type Si (with 0.93 and 0.97 nm native oxides), when exposed to O_2 during sputtering. TEM and XPS analysis show a rumpled 2 nm SiO_2 layer on top of a crystalline Si lattice, i.e., the rippling extends to the SiO_2/Si interface. No rippling or SiO_2 layer was observed in an O free environment, indicating that the oxidation of Si plays a critical role.

Acknowledgements

This work was funded in part by the MRSEC program of the National Science Foundation under award number 9632667.

References

[1] P.C. Zalm, *Rep. Prog. Phys.*, 58, (1995), 1321.
[2] A. Ishitani, A. Karen, Y. Nakagawa, M. Uchida, M. Hatada, K. Okumo, R. Soeda, *SIMS VIII proceedings*, John Wiley & Sons, New York, (1992), 315.
[3] P.A.W. van der Heide, M.S. Lim, S.S. Perry, J.W. Rabalias. Submitted to *J. Chem. Phys.*, (1999).
[4] D.F. Mitchell, K.B. Clark, J.A. Bardwell, W.N. Lennard, G.R. Massoumi, I.V. Mitchell, *S.I.A.*, 21, (1994), 44
[5] W. Vandervorst, R.R. Shepard, M.L. Swanon, H.H., Plattner, O.H. Westcoft, J.V.Mitchell, *Nucl. Instru. Meth.* B 15, (1986), 201.

A. Benninghoven, P. Bertrand, H.-N. Migeon and H.W. Werner (Editors).
Proceedings of the 12th International Conference on Secondary Ion Mass Spectrometry,
Brussels, Belgium, 5-11 September 1999

NATIVE OXIDE EFFECT ON ULTRA-SHALLOW ARSENIC PROFILE IN SILICON

M.Tomita, C.Hongo and A.Murakoshi*

Corporate Research and Development Center, Toshiba Corp., Yokohama 235-8522, Japan
*Microelectronics Engineering Laboratory, Toshiba Corp., Yokohama 235-8522, Japan
E-mail:mitsuhiro.tomita@toshiba.co.jp

1.Introduction

Ultra-shallow dopant implantation will be conducted in developing ULSIs in the future, and precise determination of the dopant profile is necessary for estimating dose and junction depth. In the case of ultra-shallow arsenic implantation, in which the profile peak is located in the native oxide film on the silicon substrate or near the interface, it has been said that the profile is influenced by the native oxide, and, consequently, quantification of arsenic becomes more difficult [1]. In RTA samples annealed after shallow arsenic ion implantation, the total arsenic dose measured by SIMS (Cs primary ions used and $AsSi^-$ and Si_2^- (reference ion) ions detected) was found to be larger than that of as-implanted samples, as shown later. This unexpected increase of the dose is thought to be caused by the native oxide or interface effect. It is said that the oxygen flooding method yields the accurate dose of arsenic [1], but does not provide accurate junction depth because of its low ion yield.

In this study, the profiles of arsenic which had been implanted into silicon substrates were measured using cesium primary ions in order to clarify the native oxide and interface effects on the arsenic ion and silicon reference ion yields.

2. Experimental

Throughout this study, silicon (100) wafers having arsenic ions implanted by an Applied Materials ion implanter were used. Some of the wafers were annealed after arsenic ion implantation by RTA under a nitrogen ambient without applying any SiO_2 capping layer. Arsenic ion implantation and anneal conditions are shown in table 1. Furthermore, arsenic ion implanted SiO_2 (7.5 nm)/silicon (100) wafers were used.

Table 1 Sample details

Wafer	Arsenic ion implantation condition		RTA condition	
	Energy (keV)	Dose (ions/cm^2)	Temperature (°C)	Time (sec)
Si(100)	1.0	2.0E14	1000	30
Si(100)	0.5	6.3E13		
SiO$_2$/Si(100)	7.0	6.3E14		

All SIMS measurements were performed with an ATOMIKA 4000 instrument. Using a Cs ion beam having an energy of 1 keV and an incident angle of 60 degrees, [103]AsSi⁻ ions were detected for arsenic profile measurements and $^{57}Si_2^-$ and $^{30}Si^-$ ions were detected as reference ions. Depth scale calibrations were performed using crater depth which was measured with a profilometer DEKTAK 3030. The sputtering rate difference between native oxide and silicon was ignored.

3. Results and discussion

For determining arsenic profiles in silicon by SIMS, AsSi⁻ ions are usually detected because of its high ion yield, and Si_2^- ions are used as the reference ion of the AsSi⁻ measurements. It is said that Si_2^- ions have a similar energy distribution as AsSi⁻ ions and that the combination of these ions yields good reproducibility for quantification of arsenic concentration. This combination is employed because slight extraction field variations due to small differences in sample alignments affect the yields of secondary ions having different energy distributions [2].

In order to investigate if the AsSi⁻–Si_2^- combination gives the best results in ultra-shallow arsenic profile determination, we measured arsenic-implanted samples after RTA, as shown in Fig. 1.

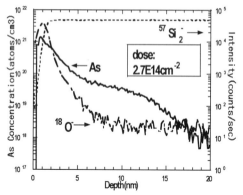

Figure1. Arsenic concentration profile of 1000°C, 30 sec RTA sample. Arsenic ion implantation conducted at 1keV, 2.0E14cm⁻².

The arsenic profile was calculated by point-to-point normalization (AsSi⁻/Si_2^-) and arsenic concentration was calibrated using the RSF (relative sensibility factor) obtained from the measurement of 7keV arsenic ion implanted samples. It is seen that the arsenic peak of the profile is located in the native oxide. Surprisingly, the total dose of measured arsenic in the RTA sample, 2.7E14cm⁻² is larger than the implant dose, 2.0E14cm⁻² (the measured total dose of an as-implanted sample is 1.9E14cm⁻²), although the amount of arsenic in silicon is said to decrease by out-diffusion to the annealing ambient [3]. This unexpected phenomena was observed repeatedly.

In order to further investigate this unusual phenomenon, we studied arsenic ion implanted samples (0.5 keV, 6.3E13 cm⁻²) in which the arsenic peak is located at the interface between the native oxide and the silicon substrate. The result is shown in Fig. 2. Si⁻ ions were also detected as the reference ion besides Si_2^- ions. The arsenic concentration of each sample was quantified by the three methods: (1) AsSi⁻/Si_2^- point-to-point normalization, (2) AsSi⁻/Si⁻ point-to-point normalization and (3) normalization with the average intensity of Si_2^- ion at the silicon substrate. Table 2 shows the total dose of arsenic determined by these three methods.

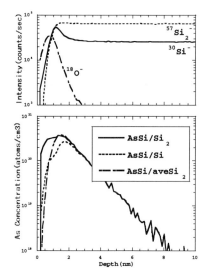

Table 2 measured total dose of arsenic with three quantification methods.

Method	Total dose (atoms/cm^2) (ratio to the implant dose)
Method (1) (AsSi$^-$/Si$_2^-$)	8.8E13 (+40%)
Method (2) (AsSi$^-$/Si$^-$)	5.7E13 (-9%)
Method (3) (AsSi/ave.Si$_2^-$)	7.2E13 (+13%)

Figure 2. Arsenic concentration profiles of arsenic ion implanted sample (0.5 keV, 6.3E13 cm^{-2}) with three quantification methods.

The total dose of the 0.5 keV arsenic ion implanted sample is found to be 40% larger than implant dose, when method (1) is used. Although it is expected that implant dose is identical with existing arsenic dose in the sample, because the implant dose is too low to cause self-sputtering. This increase is the same phenomenon as observed in RTA samples. On the other hand, smaller differences of −9% for method (2) and +13% for method (3) were found, though this difference might be too large to evaluate arsenic dose in ULSI manufacturing. The result of method (3) shows a small enhancement of the AsSi$^-$ ion yield in the native oxide and/or at the interface between the native oxide and the silicon substrate. Hence it is clear that the overestimation with method (1) is caused by the reduced ion yield of the Si$_2^-$ reference ion in the native oxide and/or at the interface. It is thought that in silicon oxide oxygen cuts the Si–Si bond, thus reducing the yield of the Si$_2^-$ ions produced by the direct emission process. In method (2), the Si$^-$ reference ion yield is enhanced to a greater extent than the AsSi$^-$ ion yield at the interface, thus causing slight underestimation of arsenic dose.

To study that method (2) and (3) provide better arsenic profiles and doses, arsenic ion implanted SiO$_2$(7.5nm)/Si samples were measured. The measurements reveal which causes the overestimation for method (1), the oxide effect or the interface effect. Concentration-calibrated profiles are shown in Fig. 3. A result of Monte Carlo simulation of the implanted arsenic profile is also indicated for comparison with the quantified profiles. When calibrated by method (1), the profile in the inside of the SiO$_2$ film and silicon substrate shows good agreement with the simulated profile, although only one RSF for the silicon substrate was used. The ion yield ratios in the inside of the SiO$_2$ and the silicon for AsSi$^-$ ion and Si$_2^-$ reference ion should be almost same.

492

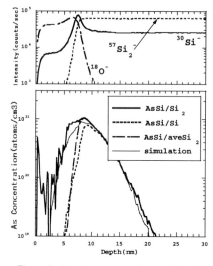

Figure 3. Arsenic concentration profiles of arsenic ion implanted (7keV, 6.3E14cm^{-2}) SiO^2(7.5nm)/Si sample with three quantification methods.

It means that there is no oxide effect for arsenic quantification by method (1). However in the near-interface region, the arsenic concentration estimated by method (1) is larger. This interface effect is caused by the different ion yield changes at the interface and in the silicon for AsSi$^-$ and Si2$^-$ ions. The arsenic concentration by method (2) is too small at any depth except inside of the silicon substrate. On the other hand, the profile by method (3) is a little larger at the deeper side of the interface and smaller at the shallower side of the interface. Method (3) might be better method for determining the total dose, but it does not provide accurate dose because the AsSi$^-$ ion yield shows a complicated change near the interface region. Furthermore, it is thought that accurate dose evaluation of shallow arsenic profiles should be done by other SIMS analysis (oxygen flooding [1]), TXRF [3] or chemical analysis.

4.Conclusions

We have studied the native oxide effect on the arsenic profile and dose. When AsSi$^-$/Si$_2^-$ point-to-point normalization, a common method for arsenic quantification, is applied, arsenic dose is overestimated because of the reduction of Si$_2^-$ ions and the enhancement of the AsSi$^-$ ion yield at the interface between the native oxide and the silicon substrate. This overestimation is caused by the interface effect, not by the oxide effect. Hence, the total dose of RTA samples which has a arsenic peak near the interface is overestimated. A calibration method without point-to-point normalization might provide better results but this is not sufficiently accurate for ULSI manufacturing use. If we need more accurate values of junction depth and its dose, we must determine a profile by Cs-SIMS and dose by other analytical methods.

References

[1] G. R. Mount, C. J. Hitzman, S. P. Smith and P. VanLierde, Secondary Ion Mass Spectrometry SIMS XI, edited by G. Gillen, R. Lareau, J. Bennett and F. Stevie, John Wiley & Sons, 1998, p317
[2] Practical Surface Analysis, second edition, volume 2, Ion and Neutral Spectroscopy, edited by D. Briggs and M. P. Seah, John Wiley & Sons, 1992, p196
[3] D. F. Downey, C. M. Osburn and S. D. Marcus, Solid State Technol., Dec.(1997) 71
[4] H. Schwenke, J. Knoth, L. Fabry, S. Pahlke, R. Scholz and L. Frey, J. Electrochem. Soc., 144, 11(1997) 3979

A. Benninghoven, P. Bertrand, H.-N. Migeon and H.W. Werner (Editors).
Proceedings of the 12th International Conference on Secondary Ion Mass Spectrometry,
Brussels, Belgium, 5-11 September 1999

493

THE MODELLING AND SIMULATION OF OXYGEN UPTAKE DURING SPUTTER DEPTH PROFILING UNDER OXYGEN FLOOD CONDITIONS

R.Badheka [1] , D. G. Armour[2], S. Whelan[3], J. A .van den Berg[3], A. Chew[4] and D. E. Sykes[4]

1 Shimadzu Research Laboratory (Europe) Ltd, Wharfside, Trafford Wharf Road, Manchester, M17 1GP.Ranjan@srlab.co.uk

2 Applied Implant Technology, Foundry Lane, Horsham, West Sussex, RH13 5PY.

3 Department of Physics, University of Salford, Salford, M5 4WT.

4 Loughborough Surface Analysis, PO Box 5016, Unit FC, Gas Research and Technology Centre, Ashby Road, Loughborough, Leicestershire, LE11 3WS.

1. Introduction

The development of so-called eV ion implantation processes for the production of the 30nm deep junctions required for 100nm transistors has created the need for accurate, quantitative depth profiling of extremely shallow implants. In the depth range involved, both the concentration and depth calibration of SIMS profiles is complicated by the changes in composition and hence sputtering yield and ionization efficiency which unavoidably accompany the initial interaction of the probe beam with the sample. Even under bombardment conditions designed to minimize this transient period, a significant fraction of the impurity distribution is eroded during the period in which the chemical state of the near surface region is changing.

The use of oxygen flooding in conjunction with an oxygen probe beam leads to a more rapid stabilization of both the sputtering rate and ionization efficiency. However, even under bombardment conditions that are optimized for high resolution, initial non-linearities in the depth scale make a significant contribution to the overall error in the profile measurement.

In an attempt to assess the magnitude of these errors and to provide a means of correcting the depth scale in SIMS depth profiles, a model of oxygen uptake, based on a surface composition dependent sticking coefficient, has been incorporated into the IMPETUS code [1]. Comparison with experimental measurements has provided a valuable insight into the processes occurring in the transient period and has enabled the parameters describing the overall sticking-sputtering-incorporation process to be evaluated. On the basis of the model, simulations of the transient oxygen and silicon ion yields have been carried out in order to re-calibrate experimental, constant erosion rate based depth scales.

2. The Model.

Silicon samples introduced into a SIMS instrument for analysis have at least a natural oxide layer on the surface and are exposed to a stream of oxygen. This in general, is introduced in such a way that there is no simple relationship between the arrival rate of oxygen molecules at the surface and the oxygen partial pressure in the analysis chamber. Simultaneous bombardment with energetic oxygen ions further complicates the adsorption process. Under these circumstances only global parameters can be used in the model. The arrival rate of oxygen molecules at the surface is defined by a parameter, β which can only be evaluated for specific conditions by comparison of the simulations with experimental data. The sticking coefficient is described by a function which assumes that the oxygen is accommodated to an effective depth of 1 -2 monolayers to take into account microscopic roughness, and that on formation of SiO_2 in this near-surface region, no further oxygen can be accommodated. The overall function which describes the oxygen up-take in a given (ion dose) step is a half Gaussian. Its value falls to below the 1% level after 3 monolayers. This is then combined with a factor, $(1 - \lambda)$, in which λ equal to unity corresponds to the formation of SiO_2. The adsorbed oxygen then becomes part of the solid and undergoes all the atomic mixing processes included in the IMPETUS simulation in the subsequent dose step. Under these circumstances, the flood oxygen that sticks is given by:

$$Fl(x) = \beta(e^{-x^2/2s})(1 - \lambda)$$

where s represents the spread of the Gaussian and the other parameters have already been defined.

This oxygen is added to the incident term in the representation of the incident ions:

$$F(\text{new incident })(x) = Fr(x) + Fl(x)$$

This term, in turn, becomes part of the injecton current expression in the mixing simulation, i.e. Since the solid will expand by an amount given by $\int Fl(x)$, the erosion rate

$$q_i(x) = \int F(new \sim incident)(x) + \frac{\partial}{\partial x}(D_i\theta_i)$$

requires appropriate adjustment.

In addition to the above features, it was found that the flood conditions and the associated increase in oxygen content in the surface layer led to a need to increase the arsenic surface binding energy to avoid excessively rapid depletion. Incorporation of this flood model into the IMPETUS code, which is a numerical implementation of a mathematical model of atomic mixing [2], has provided a means of investigating the initial transient and ultimate equilibrium sputtering behaviour of a solid undergoing sputter depth profiling in the presence of oxygen flooding. Comparison of the simulated and experimental silicon and oxygen profiles have been carried out using the ionization enhancement factor derived from isotopic doping measurements [3].

3. Results

One of the major difficulties in comparing experimental SIMS data with the results of simulations for a wide range of bombardment conditions is that the overall sensitivity of the SIMS instrument is very specifically related to the detailed machine settings. For the Cameca IMS-4f instrument used for the present work, changes in primary beam energy led to unavoidable variations in beam current and profile, which, for operation under oxygen flood conditions caused changes in the balance between ion and atom arrival rates. These changes, which are exacerbated by varying the raster amplitude, affect the transient oxygen up-take and can profoundly influence both the sputtering rate and ion yield. The additional effects of adjustments to the field and contrast aperture settings that affect the transmission function of the instrument make it necessary to make comparisons using parameters which are specific to particular data sets.

The results shown in Figure 1 for the oxygen yield transients were obtained by varying the oxygen flood, monitored experimentally via the pressure in the target chamber, while keeping all other settings constant. Under these circumstances, it is possible to define a consistent set of parameter values in the flood model. The yield transients are plotted on a normalised dose axis which was obtained from a comparison of the experimental and simulated doses required to reach a specified large depth (30 or 50nm). This enables the

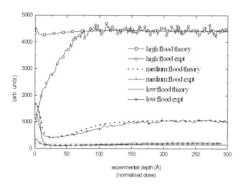

Figure1. Oxygen yield transient under different flood conditions

results to be compared without the complexity of non-linearities in the depth scale. The good agreement between the measured and simulated profiles in terms of the normalised dose required to reach equilibrium indicates that the main features of the oxygen build-up and its effects on the sputtering yield and hence the depth scale can be described by the model.

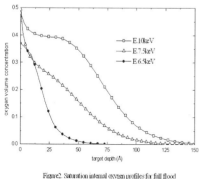

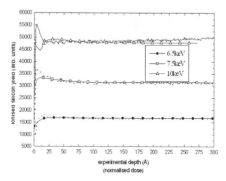

Figure2. Saturation internal oxygen profiles for full flood conditions for different energies

Figure3. Silicon yield comparisons for various Cameca energies

However, there are very clear yield differences for the high flood conditions.

On the basis of this agreement it is possible to use the code to model the build up of oxygen at different bombardment energies for the same flood condition. For a value of β corresponding to the 'over-saturation' condition used in the experiments, the equilibrium oxygen profiles shown in Figure 2 were obtained. The significant differences between these profiles, (and in the way in which they evolve) emphasises the complexity of the flood process. The main purpose of this work was to develop a means of assessing the depth scale errors in the first 1 –2nm of SIMS depth profiles of shallow implants. The silicon ion transients for Cameca source voltages of 10, 7.5 and 6.5kV under full flood conditions are shown in Fig 3.

It can be seen that the yields do not stabilise until eroded depths of 3.5, 2.5 and 1nm respectively. This means that the erosion rate is changing throughout these depths and the calculated erosion rates versus eroded depth in Figure 4 indicate the depth errors involved. The equilibrium erosion rates at full flood were calculated to be reduced by factors of 3.17 at 10kV, 1.4 at 7.5kV and 1.92 at 6.5kV. These reductions are similar in magnitude to those seen in other work.

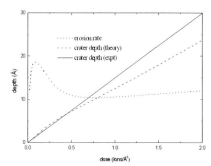

Figure 4. erosion versus crater depth for 10keV bombardment

4.Summary

The depth profiling of very shallow layers using oxygen ions in conjunction with oxygen flooding of the surface has been simulated in order to assess the errors in the depth scale associated with the assumption of a linear depth scale. At this stage, effects such as surface roughening and the detailed role of angle incidence and energy of the primary beam have not been included in the model despite their known importance.

[4 – 6] Purely on the basis of oxygen build-up and the associated changes in sputter yield and atomic mixing, it has been shown that the errors in depth calibration can be significant. However, the factors included in the present model do not fully describe the processes under full flood conditions.The contribution of the surface roughening with the experimental conditions may be one reason for the differences in calculated and measured ion yields.

References

[1] M Wadsworth, D G Armour, R Badheka and R Collins. Int. J. of Numerical Modelling: Electronic Networks, Devices and Fields, 3, 157-169 (1990)
[2] R Collins, J J Jimenez-Rodrigues, M Wadsworth, and R Badheka. J. Appl. Phys., 64, 1120 (1988).
[3] J A Kilner, S D Littlewood, R Badheka, M Wadsworth, D G Armour and J A van den Berg. Materials Science and Engineering, B12, 83-89, (1992).
[4] M G Dowsett, R D Barlow and P N Allen. J. Vac. Sci. Technol. B12, 186 (1994).
[5] K Wittmaack and S F Corcoran. J. Vac. Sci. Technol. B16, 272 (1998).
[6] K Wittmaack. J. Vac. Sci. Technol. B16(5), 2776 (1998).

A. Benninghoven, P. Bertrand, H.-N. Migeon and H.W. Werner (Editors).
Proceedings of the 12th International Conference on Secondary Ion Mass Spectrometry,
Brussels, Belgium, 5-11 September 1999
© 2000 Elsevier Science B.V. All rights reserved.

DECONVOLUTION OF SIMS DEPTH PROFILES: TOWARD THE LIMITS OF THE RESOLUTION BY SELF-DECONVOLUTION TEST

G. Mancina[1], R. Prost[2], G. Prudon[1], B. Gautier[3], J.C. Dupuy[1]

[1] INSA Lyon, LPM, UMR 5511, 69621 VILLEURBANNE Cedex, FRANCE.
[2] INSA Lyon, CREATIS, UMR 5515, 69621 VILLEURBANNE Cedex, FRANCE.
[3] LMIT, Pole Univ. des Portes du Jura, 25211 MONTBELIARD Cedex, FRANCE.

1. Introduction

The techniques of microelectronics devices elaboration are now able to produce thin layers which thickness does not exceed one monolayer. The analysis of such structures requires an optimal depth resolution. Secondary Ion Mass Spectrometry fills partially the requirements, but the resolution has still to be improved. In the steady state of the analysis (outside the surface transitory), the deconvolution of SIMS depth profiles by means of an iterative algorithm with hard constraints and Miller regularization allows a complete or partial restoration of the measured profiles, keeping in mind that the noise in the data is the main obstacle which prevents from a perfect restoration. It has been shown that this deconvolution method is reliable and that it allows to noticeably improve the depth resolution [1, 2, 3]. In this paper we study the potential and the limits of the technique, applying it to simulated profiles featuring a perfect delta layer of Boron in Silicon, analyzed using O_2^+ primary ion beam, in the secondary ion positive mode of the CAMECA IMS3F/4F instrument. The self-deconvolution, i.e. the deconvolution of a perfect delta-doping layer convolved by a Depth Resolution Function (DRF), with some additional noise, allows to define the limits of the deconvolution procedure. We will see that the resolution gain depends on the SIMS analysis conditions. The self-deconvolution is the least favorable case: it deals with the finest profile that one can measure. The high frequencies are the most difficult to restore; this test gives the ultimate resolution that one can obtain with a deconvolution technique in practical situations.

2. Deconvolution conditions
2.1 Simulations

We use an iterative algorithm with hard constraints and Miller regularization [1]:

$$x^{(n+1)} = C\, x^{(n)} + \mu^{(n)} V^{(n)} \qquad x^{(0)} = H^T y$$

where $A = (H^T H + \alpha\, D^T D)$, $V^{(n)} = [H^T y - AC\, x^{(n)}]$, $\mu^{(n)} = \|V^{(n)}\|^2 / V^{(n)T} A V^{(n)}$, y is the measured profile, $x^{(n)}$ is the deconvolved profile at the nth iteration, H is a Toeplitz matrix built from the DRF, α is the regularization parameter and D is the regularization operator. The matrix D insures that the final profile is quite smooth, and prevents that a small error in the data y results in a large error in the deconvolved profile. The scalar α adjusts the compromise between fidelity to the data and fidelity to the prior knowledge of smoothness of the deconvolved profile. It is estimated by generalized cross-validation. The hard constraints operator C is used to incorporate *the natural positivity of the concentrations* and *the finite extent* of the profile.

It is well known that the higher the energy of impact of the primary ions, the broader the DRF, and then the more severe the convolution. It means that the measured profile is very different from the original profile. Consequently the restoration is more difficult. In the same way, the noise in the data decreases the performances of the deconvolution.

We simulate a Boron delta-doping in Silicon by convolving a numerical Dirac (a null vector except in one point) with an analytical DRF of variable width, directly related to the penetration depth of the primary ions R_p. A noise is added to this profile and results to the "simulated measured profile". The deconvolution procedure uses the same DRF as in the initial convolution. Following the work of M.G. Dowsett and al. [4], we used a semi-empirical analytical expression for describing the DRF measured in SIMS depth profile of a Boron delta layer in Silicon under O_2^+ bombardment:

$h(z) = Dexp(z) * G(z)$, where $Dexp(z)$ is an asymmetrical double exponential and $G(z)$ a Gaussian centered in $z = 0$:

$$D\exp(z) = Ae^{\frac{z-z_0}{\lambda_u}} \; (z < z_0), \; D\exp(z) = Ae^{-\frac{z-z_0}{\lambda_d}} \; (z > z_0), \; G(z) = \frac{B}{\sqrt{2\pi}\,\sigma} e^{\frac{-z^2}{2\sigma^2}}$$

The DRF parameters λ_u, λ_d and σ are functions of R_p, which depends on the primary energy Ep and on the incident angle θ: $\lambda_u \approx 10.9$ Å, $\lambda_d = 15.5 + 0.302\, R_p$, $\sigma = 12.9 + 0.131\, R_p$.

We have simulated delta-doping profiles for different penetration depths R_p: 10, 40, 70, 100 et 140 Å, which respectively correspond to 1.5, 3, 5.5, 8 and 13 keV/O_2^+ primary energy, and a 35dB signal-to-noise ratio (random noise, realistic noise level), then a 20dB signal-to-noise ratio (very noisy profile). $R_p = 10$ Å is very difficult to obtain with the CAMECA IMS3F in standard conditions. We have to polarize the sample holder with 2250 V to get this value within acceptable incidence conditions ($\theta < 65°$), and then we obtain $R_p = 10$ Å for $Ep = 1.5$ keV at $\theta = 65°$. The iterative algorithm is stopped when the deconvolved profile is nearly invariant: the area $dA^{(n)}$ between the curves $x^{(n)}$ and $x^{(n-1)}$ is quite similar to the area $dA^{(n-1)}$. The algorithm is stopped when this area is sufficiently small compared to the area A of the measured profile. In our simulations, we chose $dA^{(n)}/A = 2.10^{-5}$ as stop criterion.

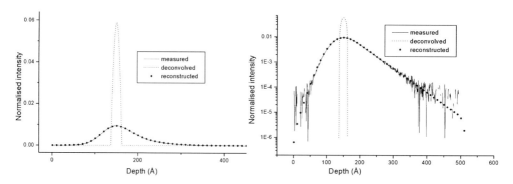

Figure 1: Deconvolution of a delta-doping with $R_p = 100$ Å, S/N = 35 dB. Linear and logarithmic scales.

It is known that when the DRF is broader than the profile to be measured, the deconvolution is only partial [5]. Here the conditions are extreme since the profile has a quasi-null width; thus we know the real profile will never be completely restored. In our simulations, the maximum of a deconvolved profile is 4 to 6 times higher compared the measured profile, but it nevertheless remains 10% lower than the height of the real profile. *The gain of depth resolution* is defined as the ratio of the widths at half maximum (FWHM) of the measured and deconvolved profiles. It varies between 4 and 5 depending on the noise level and the primary energy. For example, an

apparent FWHM at 8 keV/O_2^+ of 92 Å is noticeably lowered to 19 Å after deconvolution. Previous values of the resolution gain gave a limit of 2.3 [5]. In this study, the gain is 4-5, and this improvement is due to three factors :
i) the important number of iterations, ii) the additional support constraint, iii) the one point definition of the Dirac.
Figure 1 shows the deconvolved profile for a 100 Å penetration depth with a 35dB signal-to-noise ratio. The restoration of the initial symmetry is quasi-perfect and the exponential slopes due to atomic mixing are totally removed. The reconstruction of the profile is perfect over the entire length (re-convolution of the deconvolved profile by the DRF), which proves that the procedure is reliable and stable. Here the observed gain of depth resolution is 4.8, and the maximum of the peak is 6.2 times higher than that measured.
The following table shows the gain of depth resolution depending on the depth penetration and the noise level:

R_p(Å)	10	10	40	40	70	70	100	100	140	140
S/N(dB)	35	20	35	20	35	20	35	20	35	20
n iterations	8996	2508	12359	4184	11692	5094	11041	5347	10217	7426
FWHM(y)	48	48	64	64	78	78	92	92	112	112
FWHM($x^{(n)}$)	11	15	13	17	15	19	19	23	23	25
FWHM gain	4.4	3.2	4.9	3.8	5.2	4.1	4.8	4.0	4.9	4.5
max(y)*10^{-2}	1.81	1.87	1.39	1.44	1.13	1.20	0.94	1.00	0.78	0.80
max($x^{(n)}$)*10^{-2}	10.0	6.75	8.50	6.05	6.94	5.40	5.89	4.73	4.75	4.26
Max. gain	5.5	3.6	6.1	4.2	6.1	4.5	6.2	4.7	6.2	5.2

Notice that the number of necessary iterations is lower when the noise level is higher (S/N ratio = 20dB). Indeed the noise in data reduces the effectiveness of the deconvolution algorithm. Convergence is thus reached more quickly, but the deconvolution is less effective. The difference between the gains obtained with S/N = 35dB and S/N = 20dB decreases when the energy increases. This phenomenon is due to the broadening of the DRF.

2.2 Applications to real depth profiles
We also analyzed a sample containing several delta-doping of B : Si using different impact energies. The DRF was fitted on the most superficial delta-doping. At 8 keV, the gain of depth resolution is 7.0 (Figures 2a and 2b), and is 4.5 at 1 keV.

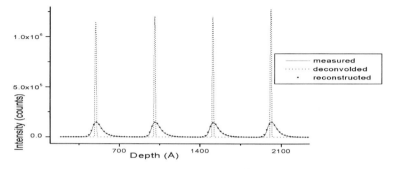

Figure 2a: Deconvolution of a B: Si multi delta-doping. R_p = 100 Å (8keV/O_2^+). Linear scale.

500

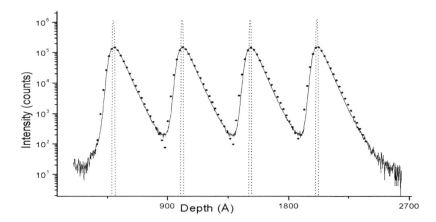

Figure 2b: Deconvolution of a B: Si multi delta-doping. $R_p = 100$ Å $(8keV/O_2^+)$. Log. Scale

It can be noticed that, compared to the simulations, the reconstruction is not perfect: this is due to the uncertainty in the fitting of the true DRF parameters [3]. This shows an additional application of self-deconvolution in evaluating the quality of the delta-doping (real or pseudo-delta), highlighted by an "over-deconvolution " of the measured profile [3].

3. Conclusion

We studied the performances of the deconvolution in the case of the B : Si delta-doped layers analyzed under O_2^+. Simulations show that a gain resolution of 4.5 to 5 can be obtained for primary energies of the ion beam up to 13 keV. The exponential slopes of the profiles introduced by the collisional mixing are removed by the deconvolution procedure. The noise in the data decreases the performances of deconvolution. The width of the DRF is also a factor of degradation: even if the depth resolution gain is almost identical for all primary energies, the deconvolved profile is closer to the real profile at low energies. These simulations show the ultimate resolution that has been reached using SIMS measure assisted by our deconvolution procedure (approximately 10 Å at 1.5 keV/O_2^+). But this is possible only at the detriment of the analysis sensitivity, if no oxygen flooding is present.

References

[1] B. Gautier, J.C. Dupuy, R. Prost, G. Prudon, Surf. Interf. Analysis, 24 (1996) 733-745.
[2] B. Gautier, G. Prudon, C. Dubois, J.C. Dupuy, Proceedings SIMS XI (1997) 347-350.
[3] B. Gautier, G. Prudon, J.C. Dupuy, Surf. Interf. Analysis, 26 (1998) 974-983.
[4] M.G. Dowsett, G. Rowlands, P.N. Allen, R.D. Barlow, Surf. Interf. Analysis, 21 (1994) 310-315.
[5] B. Gautier, *Etude de la résolution en profondeur lors de l'analyse par SIMS*, Thèse de Doctorat, INSA de Lyon,1997, p 148-152.

A. Benninghoven, P. Bertrand, H.-N. Migeon and H.W. Werner (Editors).
Proceedings of the 12th International Conference on Secondary Ion Mass Spectrometry,
Brussels, Belgium, 5-11 September 1999
© 2000 Elsevier Science B.V. All rights reserved.

DECONVOLUTION OF THE SIMS DEPTH PROFILING OF As IMPLANTED INTO Si AT ULTRA-LOW ENERGY

S. Whelan[1], D.G. Armour[2], R. Badheka[3], J.A. van den Berg[1], A. Chew[4] and D.E. Sykes[4]
[1] Department of Physics, Joule Lab. University of Salford, Salford M5 4WT, UK.
s.whelan@physics.salford.ac.uk
[2] Applied Implant Technology, Foundry Lane, Horsham, West Sussex, RH13 5PY, UK.
[3] Shimadzu Research Lab. (Europe) ltd. Wharfside, Trafford Wharf Road, Manchester
M17 1GP, UK.
[4] Loughborough Surface Analysis, PO Box 5016, Unit FC, Gas Research and Technology
Centre, Ashby Road, Loughborough, Leicestershire, LE11 3WS, UK.

1. Introduction

The predicted dimensions of CMOS electronic devices in the year 2001, as set out in the semiconductor roadmap, will lead to the requirement of shallow junctions at 1000Å, with carrier concentrations of 5×10^{19} atoms/cm^3 at the source-drain regions [1]. Ultra-low energy ion implantation is the favoured technique for the fabrication of such devices. Accurate characterisation of the implanted dopant (shape, range and concentration) will improve our understanding of the low energy implantation process.

The ion beam bombardment process during SIMS analysis produces a change in the surface composition resulting in non-linear sputter yields [2] and a change in the ionisation efficiencies of the sputtered ions. Whilst acceptable for SIMS analysis of deep implanted layers (>100Å), the assumption of a constant erosion rate leads to a distortion in the measured profile which gives unacceptable errors when measuring shallow profiles.

The IMPETUS code [3] with the incorporation of an oxygen uptake model [4] has been used to simulate the non-constant sputter yields expected in sputter depth profiling. The effects of ionisation are calculated using the technique described in [5]. The experimental implanted profiles of low energy arsenic were investigated with high resolution medium energy ion scattering (MEIS) and SIMS. The MEIS measurements give a direct indication of the non-mixed, as-implanted dopant profile. The comparison of the experimental profiles with the calculated profiles using IMPETUS has highlighted the errors associated with the assumption of the constant erosion rate.

2. Experimental

SIMS analysis was performed on a Cameca IMS-4f using O_2^+ primary ion bombardment and positive secondary ion detection. Sputter depth profiling was carried out with source potentials at 10 kV, 7.5 kV and 6.5 kV with a constant target voltage of 4.5kV, giving ion energies of 2.75 kV, 1.5 kV and 1 kV respectively. The sensitivity of the SIMS technique is related to the conditions used in the SIMS experiment. The use of ion beams of different energies resulted in a change of the primary ion beam current and ion beam size. Therefore to maintain workable transmission factors the raster size was adjusted accordingly. Oxygen flooding was used to enhance the arsenic ionisation yields and to minimise the non-linearities associated with the surface transient region. The optimum pressure was found at 7×10^{-6} mbar. The conversion from sputtering time to depth assumed that the erosion rate was constant throughout analysis.

The ion implantation was carried out on the ultra low energy ion implanter at the University of Salford. Implantation was performed at 2.5 kV for all of the samples analysed. The arsenic doses implanted were 1.5E15 atoms/cm^2 (low) and 6E15 atoms/cm^2 (high).

MEIS, a high depth resolution variant of RBS-channelling, was used in the double alignment mode to measure the non-substitutional arsenic distributions. The implants analysed have been shown to retain the complete arsenic distribution in non-substitutional positions. A depth resolution of 11 Å was obtained using a 200 kV He$^+$ probe beam directed along the <111> in direction and the <233> out direction (60° scattering). The energy of the backscattered ions was converted into a depth scale assuming the surface energy approximation.

Rutherford backscattering spectrometry (RBS), has been employed to calculate the amount of arsenic retained within the sample after implantation to validate the implant model of IMPETUS. The random mode of operation was used, so that effectively every atom in the material was exposed to the ion scattering beam (unlike in the double alignment mode), to measure the arsenic retained for a range of doses from 1.5E15 to 1.5E16 atoms/cm^2 .

3. Results and discussion

Figures1a and 1b show the high and low dose arsenic profiles measured with MEIS and SIMS at energies of 2.75 kV, 1.5 kV and 1kV per ion. The arsenic yields in the SIMS spectra have been converted into atomic concentrations. As expected, the use of different analysis conditions when depth profiling led to changes in the observed measurements. The height of the silicon ion yield and its shape during the surface transient region was dependent upon any slight changes in any of the parameters of the experiment. The shape of the silicon ion yield at the surface and the relative heights between different analysing energies were used to establish the input parameters required for simulation.

The assumption of a constant erosion rate when converting the sputtered distribution into a depth profile leads to unacceptable errors in the depth scale. Therefore when considering the SIMS experimental profile we define the measured depth as the apparent depth. The apparent depth resolution (slope of the trailing edge) was constant for the analysis of both high and low dose implants for each energy used. Hence the arsenic concentration at high dose, contained within a small region close to the surface, was not high enough to contribute to a change in mixing. Apparent depth resolutions of 125 Å/decade, 80 Å/decade and 53 Å/decade were obtained for ion energies of 2.75 kV, 1.5 kV and 1kV respectively.

The arsenic atomic concentrations at the peak position is increased for the lower energy SIMS analysis, due to the lower levels of atomic mixing. As the mixing broadens the peak there is a corresponding decrease in the peak height. It is observed that for the high dose analysis (performed at a faster rate compared to the low dose analysis) the arsenic peak is shifted towards the surface. The shift is more apparent for the higher energy analysis. This shift in the peak is due to the accommodation of incident ions into the matrix [6]. The surface transient region was measured as the apparent width of the unstable Si^{30} ion yields observed in the near surface of the sample. The surface transient effects become dominant when sputtering profiles with mean projected ranges below 100 Å. Saturation of the surface with oxygen was used to stabilise ion yields. The smallest apparent surface transient obtained was 30Å, achieved with 1.5 kV analysis of a low dose implant with a primary ion current of 0.05μA. Whereas 2.75 kV analysis of a high dose implant with a primary ion beam current of 0.2μA resulted in an apparent transient region extending to 130Å. N.B. Even for the experimental conditions giving a reduced apparent transient region, a large fraction (>50 %) of the arsenic is contained within the inequilibrium phase. The presence of arsenic in the sputtered sample was shown to enhance the silicon ion yields (not shown). This enhancement was subsequently incorporated into the ionisation calculation of IMPETUS.

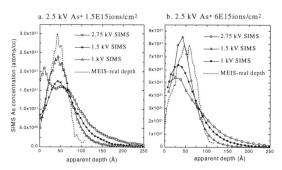

Figure 1. The arsenic profiles measured with MEIS and SIMS

Figure 2 shows the comparison between the experimental data for the dose retention of the implanted arsenic and the dose retained for the simulated implants. The collection curves show a very close agreement between experimental results and theoretical predictions. As dose levels increase, the range of arsenic is reduced and the amount of arsenic retained reaches a saturated level (~1.5E16 atoms/cm^2). At high dose, even though the calculated retained doses show a good agreement between the experimental and simulation results, the profile shapes do not agree. This disagreement is believed to be due to the effects of precipitation and segregation (N.B. not incorporated into the implant model). Therefore for high dose simulations the MEIS profile was used as the implant profile.

Figure 3, shows the comparison between the experimental SIMS profiles and those calculated theoretically for high energy (2.75 kV/ion) analysis of a high dose implant and low energy (1kV/ion) analysis of a low dose implant. The experimental measurements of the crater depth are based upon the linear scaling of the total crater depth after erosion. We define a pseudo-depth in which the total theoretical crater depth is converted into a linearly scaled depth over the dose interval simulated. The differences between the real depth (including mixing) and the

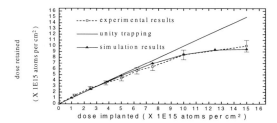

Figure 2. Dose retention curves for experimental and simulation

504

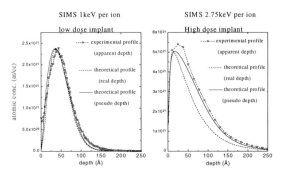

figure3. The simulated depth profiles and the experimental depth profiles

for SIMS analysis at energies of 2.75keV and 1 keV

pseudo and experimental apparent depths (including mixing and the errors connected with the assumption of a constant erosion rate) can be observed. The heights of the arsenic peak for the simulations are scaled with the peak heights of the experimental SIMS profiles. Evaluation of the peak positions and the slopes of the trailing edges is required in order to assess the validity of the atomic mixing incorporated into the IMPETUS model. Within the accuracy of the experiment the theoretical predicted peak positions and the slopes of the trailing edges of the pseudo-depth profiles match closely to the experimental depth profiles. The difference between pseudo and experimental depth with real depth for high energy analysis of a high dose implant is greater than that of the lower energy analysis. This is due to the bigger changes in the erosion rate experienced within the surface transient regions of the analysis. The peak shift can be seen to be ≈ 10Å.

4. Summary

In summary, it has been shown that the assumption of a constant erosion rate during experimental SIMS analysis with energies above 1kV per oxygen ion, introduces unacceptable errors in the depth scale of low energy ion implanted dopant profiles. The calculation of a pseudo-depth from the simulated results have been compared to experimental SIMS profiles and have been shown to agree within the errors of the experiment.

References

[1] The National Technology Roadmap for Semiconductors (SIA San Jose C.A 1994).

[2] C.W. Magee, G.R. Mount, S.P. Smith, B. Herner and H-J. Gossmann, J.Vac.Sci. Technology. B 16(6) (1998)3099.

[3] M. Wadsworth, D.G. Armour, R. Badheka and R. Collins. Int. J. of Numerical Modelling Electronic Networks, Devices and Fields, 3 (1990) 157

[4] R. Badheka, D.G. Armour, S. Whelan, J.A. van den Berg, A. Chew and D.E. Sykes, in proceedings of SIMS12, Brussels 1999.

[5] J.A. Kilner, S.D. Littlewood, R. Badheka, M. Wadsworth, D.G. Armour and J.A. van den Berg, Materials Science and Engineering, B12 (1992) 83.

[6] R. Badheka, M. Wadsworth, D.G. Armour, J.A. van den Berg and J.B. Clegg, Surface and Interface analysis 15 (1990) 550.

A. Benninghoven, P. Bertrand, H.-N. Migeon and H.W. Werner (Editors).
Proceedings of the 12th International Conference on Secondary Ion Mass Spectrometry,
Brussels, Belgium, 5-11 September 1999

ROUGHENING OF Si(100) AND Si(111) BY 1 keV OBLIQUE O$_2^+$ BEAMS

Zhengxin Liu and Paul F.A. Alkemade

Delft Institute of MicroElectronics and Submicrontechnology (DIMES), Department of
Applied Physics, Delft University of Technology, P.O. Box 5046, 2600 GA, Delft, The
Netherlands
liu@cerberus.dimes.tudelft.nl, alkemade@dimes.tudelft.nl

1. Introduction

Surface roughening is one of the factors that limit the applicability of SIMS. Until recently surface roughening under O$_2^+$ bombardment was always seen to occur after sputter removal of several micrometers of material [1], usually well beyond the range of interest. The increased need for analysis of ultra-shallow layers has led to the use of low-energy primary ion beams. However, it was observed recently that surface roughening with oblique, low energy O$_2^+$ beams can start very early [2], sometimes already at a depth of a few tens of nanometers. Moreover, the magnitude of the roughness is a very strong function of the angle of incidence [3,4]. For Si, there are a few angular ranges where roughening is negligible, offering good conditions for shallow depth profile SIMS analysis [3,4].

The phenomenon of early surface roughening is not understood, although it is speculated that local, inhomogeneous oxidation is an important factor [2,5,6]. But before better understanding can be obtained, more experimental data are needed. In this work we measured the onset of roughening of Si(100) and Si(111) as functions of the polar and azimuthal incidence angle and the primary beam current density.

2. Experimental

Pieces of 1x1 cm^2 from 4-inch B doped (10^{18}/cm^2) Si(100) and Si(111) wafers were used in this study. No surface cleaning was applied. We glued the samples into a square depression in a flat, 3 cm diameter stainless steel plate; the depth of the depression corresponds to the thickness of the sample. We used these sample holders because they hardly disturb the instrument extraction field and, thus, the incidence angle. The azimuthal orientation of the holder was adjustable, though not in vacuum. Hence, all measurements were performed in exactly the same geometry but with different azimuthal orientations. The selected azimuths were measured with respect to the cleavage (<011>) direction with a precision of ±3°.

In the first set of experiments, we bombarded the samples with a 100 nA O$_2^+$ beam in an IX70S magnetic sector instrument. Crater sizes were typically 500x800 µm^2; incidence angles, θ, between 51° and 65°, the azimuthal angles selected correspond to low-index crystal and random directions (see Fig. 3). We did not apply oxygen flooding. The pressure during analysis was ~10^{-8} Pa. For the determination of θ, we used the procedure of Ref. [7]. Final crater depths were measured with a Tencor 200 Alpha Step. The secondary ion intensities of ^{11}B$^+$, ^{16}O$^+$, ^{30}Si$^+$, ^{44}SiO$^+$, ^{57}Si$_2^+$, and ^{60}SiO$_2^+$ were recorded. We terminated most measurements when constant intensities were reached again after the roughening transition. From measurements that were stopped at the onset of roughening, we concluded that the sputter rate after the transition was ~30% lower than before.

In another set of measurements, we varied the beam current between 10 and 400 nA.

3. Results

Figure 1(left) shows the secondary ion intensities for the Si(100) sample at an azimuthal angle, φ, of $0°$ with respect to the [011] surface direction. After ~1500 s, the O, Si, SiO and SiO$_2$ intensities started to rise, B remained constant, and Si$_2$ dropped slightly. The Si(111) sample shows the same behaviour, but the intensities changed only after ~2100 s.

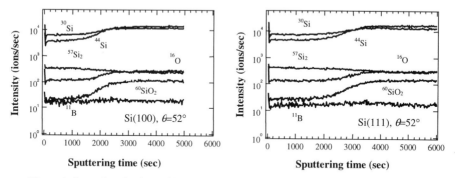

Figure 1. Secondary ion intensities for Si(100) and Si(111) bombarded by 1 keV O$_2^+$ at θ=52° .

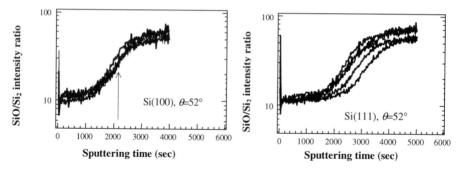

Figure 2. Ratio of SiO/Si$_2$ signals from Si(100) and Si(111) at θ=52° and various φ.

Figure 2 shows the SiO/Si$_2$ ratio for various azimuths. We define the roughening transition time, or fluence, as the time (fluence) when the SiO/Si$_2$ ratio on a log plot is halfway between the initial and the final level, see the arrow. Figure 3 shows the relation between the transition fluence and the azimuthal angle. The low-index crystal directions that are aligned within ~5° to the incidence direction are indicated; 'rnd' means random, viz. no low-index direction nearby. Although the Si(111) data do show quite some variations, there does not seem to be a clear relation between the azimuthal crystal direction and the roughening transition. In any case, the roughening of Si(111) occurs later than in Si(100). Figure 4 shows the relations between the apparent roughening depth, z_r, and the incidence angle ($z_r = z_f / t_f \times t_r$; where t_r = roughening transition time, z_f = final depth and t_f = total time). One sees that the polar incidence and the primary beam current have a large effect on the apparent roughening depth. Note that we did not take the change in sputter rate into account.

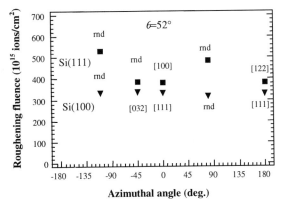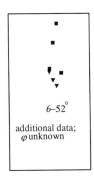

Figure 3. Relation between roughening fluence and azimuthal angle, φ, for Si(100) and Si(111).

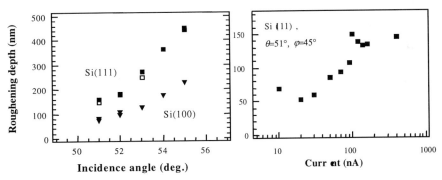

Figure 4. Roughening transition depths versus incidence angle (for 100 nA) and primary beam current (left: for Si(111): □ φ=0°, ■ φ=45°; for Si(100): ▼ φ=0°).

4. Discussion

It is generally assumed that the surface layer during a dynamic SIMS analysis is being amorphized completely after the initial transient phase [8]. For instance, Lewis *et al.* [9] have studied roughening of various faces of Si by 6-8 keV inert ion bombardment and did not find any surface orientation dependence. Furthermore, as far as we know, no differences in sputter rates or ion intensities for various faces of the same material have been reported in the literature. In contrast, the present experiments do show consistent differences in the onset of roughening between Si(100) and Si(111).

The occurrence of roughening during inert ion beam bombardment is the result of a subtle balance between processes that enhance local disorder (*viz.*, deviations from the mean surface height) and those that reduce disorder [10]. Thermal and beam induced surface diffusion smooth the surface. The same holds for viscous flow of the amorphous top layer [11]. When reactive ion beams, *e.g.* O_2^+, are being used, local phase changes may also occur, causing local variations in sputter rate and, thus, surface roughness [2,5,6].

If the surface layer is completely amorphized, then one does not expect any crystal orientation dependence. If, on the other hand, the surface was not damaged at all during dynamic SIMS (a *contradictio in terminis*), then effects similar to channeling of high energy ions in RBS analysis are to be expected. We note that for our low energy O_2^+ beam the typical angular width for channeling effects would be ~10° [12]. Neither of these limiting cases apply for our experiments: Figures 1-3 show that roughening of Si(111) occurs ~30% later than of Si(100). The roughening depths differ even more (Fig. 4): by a factor of ~1.7. The average sputter yield – number of Si atoms removed per ion – was for Si(111) ~30% higher. Although higher sputter yields are commonly related to lower surface oxygen concentrations, the ratio of the various secondary ion intensities is the same for Si(100) and Si(111), see Fig.1.

Remarkable is the current dependence of the roughening depth: shallower at lower currents. We have two possible explanations. Either, the defects induced by impinging ions at low currents have more time to anneal out, so that the surface layer does not amorphize sufficiently and smoothing by viscous flow is weak. This situation is comparable to the high-temperature (250 °C) roughening of Ge by Xe [11]. Or, there is enhanced phase segregation at low currents: the longer times between the removal of successive layers allow the phase segregation via thermal surface diffusion to proceed further.

Our observations on the dependence of surface roughening on crystal orientation and beam current are inconsistent with some of the principles of SIMS. Of course, roughening is *not* a normal SIMS phenomenon and, as long as roughening is avoided, most low-energy SIMS analyses are still trustworthy. In any case, our measurements provide clues for the understanding of early surface roughening of Si by oblique, low-energy reactive ion beams. But more independent evidence is needed. There are factors that have not been considered in this work, such as the state of the original surface and the effect of the finite pressure.

5. Summary and conclusion

Early surface roughening by oblique, low-energy (<1 keV) beams is a major concern for ultra-high depth resolution SIMS analysis. This work shows that one of the paradigms in dynamic SIMS analysis of semiconductor materials – an amorphous altered layer is being formed under ion beam bombardment with no memory of the original crystal structure – is not strictly valid, at least at low energies and oblique incidence. We do see differences in surface roughening and in sputter rates between Si(100) and Si(111). Furthermore, there is also a clear current dependence of surface roughening: lower beam currents imply shallower roughening, probably because of reduced smoothing by viscous flow or enhanced phase segregation. To conclude: especially for low energy SIMS, one has to choose the analytical conditions very carefully.

References

[1] F.A. Stevie, P.M. Kohara, D.S. Simons and P. Chi, J. Vac. Sci. Technol. A 9 (1988) 2246
[2] Z.X. Jiang and P.F.A. Alkemade, *Secondary Ion Mass Spectrometry,* SIMS XI, ed. by G. Gillen, R. Lareau, J. Bennett and F. Stevie, Wiley, Chichester, 1998, p. 431
[3] Z.X. Jiang and P.F.A. Alkemade, Appl. Phys. Lett. 73 (1998) 315
[4] C.W. Magee, G.R. Mount, S.P. Smith, B. Herner and H.-J. Gossman, J. Vac. Sci. Technol. B 16 (1998) 3099
[5] K. Wittmaack, J. Vac. Sci. Technol. A 8 (1990) 2246
[6] K. Elst, W. Vandervorst, J. Alay, J. Snauwert and L. Hellemans, J. Vac. Sci. Technol. B 11 (1993) 1968
[7] Z.X. Jiang and P.F.A. Alkemade, Surf. Interface Anal. 25 (1997) 817
[8] K. Wittmaack, in: *Practical Surface Analysis, Vol. 2,* ed. by D. Briggs and M.P. Seah, Wiley, Chichester, 1992, p. 112.
[9] G.W. Lewis, M.J. Nobes, G. Carter and J.L. Whitton, Nucl. Instrum. Meth. 170 (1980) 363
[10] R.M. Bradley and J.M.E. Harper, J. Vac. Sci. Technol. A 6 (1988) 2390
[11] E. Chason, T.M. Mayer, B.K. Kellerman, D.T. McIlroy and A.J. Howard, Phys. Rev. Lett. 72 (1994) 3040
[12] D. Onderdelinden, Appl. Phys. Lett. 8 (1968) 189.

A. Benninghoven, P. Bertrand, H.-N. Migeon and H.W. Werner (Editors).
Proceedings of the 12th International Conference on Secondary Ion Mass Spectrometry,
Brussels, Belgium, 5-11 September 1999
© 2000 Elsevier Science B.V. All rights reserved.

FURNACE AND RTP NITRIDATION OF ULTRATHIN OXIDE FILMS BY NO AND N2O: SIMS AND TOF-SIMS CHARACTERISATION

M. Bersani, M. Sbetti, L. Vanzetti, and M. Anderle

ITC-irst, Centro per la Ricerca Scientifica e Tecnologica
Via Sommarive 18, 38050 Povo (TN), Italy
e-mail: bersani@itc.it

1. Introduction

Silicon oxide nitridation process is widely used to achieve high quality ultrathin (7 nm or less) gate oxide [1, 2]. The need of this kind of dielectric films is due to the progressive scaling down of MOS devices into the submicron regime. Different precursors (N_2O [1, 3, 4] and NO [5, 6]) are used in the nitridation, in order to modify the physical, chemical and electrical behaviour of the film; moreover, also the thermal treatments, either in traditional furnace [1, 6] or by rapid thermal process (RTP) [3], can control the properties mentioned before.In all these cases one of the main issues is to evaluate a meaningful nitrogen quantitative depth distribution.

In this work we have characterised oxynitride layers using complementary techniques: SIMS and ToF-SIMS. The quantitative SIMS profiles show the accumulation of nitrogen close to the SiO_2/Si interface: in the different samples nitrogen amount and profile shape have been correlated to the process parameters. ToF-SIMS depth profiles show the in-depth behaviour of matrix molecular ions: this feature is useful to define several layers in the oxynitride film.

2. Experimental

In this work we have analysed four oxynitride samples prepared by thermal oxidation of Si wafers, followed by nitridation treatments. The samples have been nitridated by NO or N_2O precursors in conventional furnace or by rapid thermal process (RTP). The oxynitride layer thickness is 5.4 nm for RTP samples, and 7.0 nm for furnace ones.

SIMS measurements have been carried out by a CAMECA 4f equipment. A Cs^+ primary beam with an impact energy of 2.25 keV and an incidence angle of 60° has been used. The choice of this energy matches the need for good depth resolution together with reliable and effectively fast measurements [7]. MCs^+ secondary ion species have been monitored in order to reduce matrix effects [8]. Nitrogen RSF in silicon dioxide and silicon has been measured using two suitable implants. To obtain a more accurate quantification of nitrogen in the SiO_2/Si interface region, the RSF was applied as a function of the oxygen signal variation, as reported elsewhere [7]. Under the used analytical conditions the depth resolution was limited to about 2.6 nm. The ToF-SIMS depth profiles have been performed by a CAMECA ION ToF IV. As analysis beam a 25 keV Ga^+ gun has been used, rastered over a 50x50 μm^2 area with a 1.1 nA of current, combined with a 900 eV Cs^+ beam for sputtering, over a 150x150 μm^2 area.

3. Results and discussion

Figure 1 shows the nitrogen quantitative depth profiles of the four samples. The zero position in the x-axis is fixed at the SiO_2/Si interface. In this way a direct comparison between the profiles is possible. The nitrogen profiles of the two NO samples present very similar behaviour, pointing out that the different thermal treatments have the same effectiveness. The nitrogen amount in N_2O samples is lower and depends on the thermal treatment. In both the NO cases, the nitrogen maximum is closer to the interface with respect of the N_2O sample.

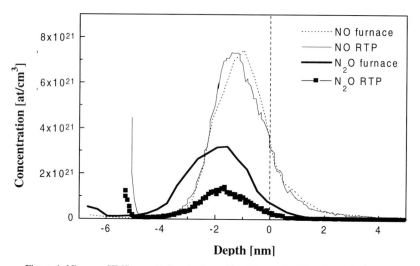

Figure 1. Nitrogen SIMS quantitative depth profiles. The vertical line shows the interface position.

Figure 2 shows the ToF-SIMS depth profiles of matrix Si_xO_y species (Fig. 2a and 2b) and of molecules containing nitrogen (Fig 2c), in the NO RTP sample. The evaluation of the sputtering rate can not be done by conventional stylus profilometer, because the sputtered crater is too shallow. The Si_xO_y profiles have been used to obtain a more accurate idea of the position of the SiO_2/Si interface. We have fixed the interface position at 50% of Si_3 signal. The depth of the 50% of all the Si_xO_y signals is plotted in Figure 2d. It appears to be correlated with the silicon and oxygen amount in the different molecules. Figure 2d shows in addition the peak position and FWHM of four $Si_xN_yO_z$ molecules. The presence of oxygen in the molecules seems to shift the peak positions towards the oxide surface. On the contrary, the SiN peak is much closer to the SiO_2/Si interface, with a worse decay length in the Si substrate.

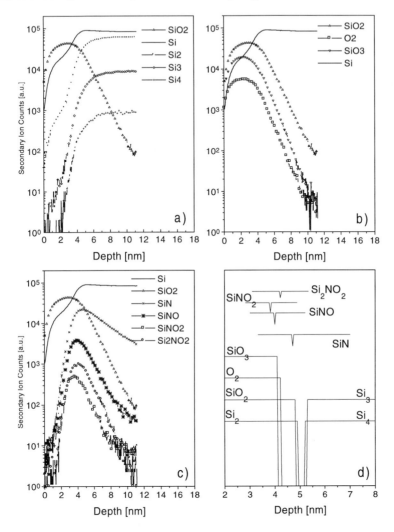

Figure 2. ToF-SIMS depth profiles of NO RTP sample.

Figure 3 shows the ToF-SIMS depth profiles of the SiN, SiNO, and Si_2NO_2 molecules for all the studied samples.

512

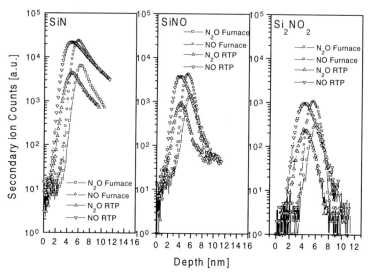

Figure 3 ToF-SIMS depth profiles of the SiN, SiNO, and Si_2NO_2 molecules for all the samples.

The three species are representative of the nitridation amount. In fact, the ratios of the peak maxima follow the quantitative SIMS results reported in Figure 1.

Both SIMS and ToF-SIMS depth profiles confirm the presence of a well defined nitrided region between oxide layer and silicon substrate.

References

[1] E. C. Carr and R.A. Buhrman App. Phys. Lett. 63 54 (1993)

[2] T. Hori, H. Iwasaki and K. Tsuji, IEEE Trans. Electron. Devices ED36, 340 (1989).

[3] D. Bouvet, P.A. Clivaz, M. Dutoit, C. Coluzza, J. Almeida, G. Margaritondo and F. Pio, J. Appl. Phys. 79, 7114 (1996).

[4] P.J. Tobin, Y.Okada, S.A. Ajuria, V. Lakhotia, W.A. Feil and R. Hedge J. App. Phys. 75 1811 (1994)

[5] M. Bhat, L. K. Han, D. Wristers, J. Yian, D. L. Qwong and J. Fulford, Appl. Phys. Lett. 66, 1225 (1995).

[6] R.I. Hedge, P.J. Tobin, K.G. Reid, B. Maiti and S.A. Ajuria, Appl. Phys. Lett. 66, 2882 (1995).

[7] M. Bersani, M. Fedrizzi, M. Sbetti, M. Anderle, in Characterisation and Metrology for ULSI Technology, AIP Conference proceeding 449, ed. by D.G. Seiler, A.C. Diebold, W.M. Bullis, T.J. Shaffner, R. McDonald and E.J. Walters, 892-896, Woodbury, New York (1998).

[8] Y. Gao J. Appl. Phys. 64, 3760 (1988)

A. Benninghoven, P. Bertrand, H.-N. Migeon and H.W. Werner (Editors).
Proceedings of the 12th International Conference on Secondary Ion Mass Spectrometry,
Brussels, Belgium, 5-11 September 1999

513

ULTRA-SHALLOW DEPTH PROFILING OF IMPLANTS AND MULTILAYER SAMPLES USING A MODIFIED CAMECA IMS 4F

J.-C. Canry and A. Brown

CSMA Ltd, Armstrong House, Oxford House, Manchester M1 7ED, UK
jccanry@csma.ltd.uk, alanbrown@csma.ltd.uk

1. Introduction

The latest challenge for SIMS analysts is to accurately measure the profile shapes for low energy ion implantation within the first few tens of nanometers of the substrate surface. The analytical options currently available involve using either normal incidence (0 degree) or oblique angle bombardment. Quadrupole-based SIMS instruments, operating at low extraction fields, have the flexibility to vary the angle of incidence of the primary beam from normal to glancing incidence without significantly compromising secondary ion transmission. Magnetic sector instruments, however, have generally fixed sample orientations and scope for varying primary beam angle of incidence is determined by a combination of primary and secondary ion accelerating voltages. In this paper we report on the optimisation of a modified Cameca ims 4f instrument for ultra-shallow depth profiling. Data from delta-doped layer structures and a series of silicon samples implanted with boron, in the range 2.5keV - 250eV, analysed under a set of standard optimised conditions are presented. Some of these samples were also analysed on a Quadrupole SIMS instrument with normal incidence bombardment. The profile shapes, sputter rates and detection limits obtained on both types of instruments are discussed and also compared with published data from similar samples.

2. Experimental

Magnetic sector SIMS depth profiles were acquired using a Cameca ims 4f instrument at CSMA Ltd., Manchester, UK. The instrument has been modified to provide continuously variable primary beam voltages from 1.5 to 17.5 kV. The secondary ion extraction is also variable from 1.125 kV to 4.5kV in three steps with the additional option of continuous variation between 0.4 kV and 2.5 kV. For the analyses, an O_2^+ primary beam with a net energy varying between 500eV and 1.5 keV was used in conjunction with oxygen flooding (5e-6 Torr). Typically, a beam current of ca. 50 nA was used and the rastered area varied from 250 x 250 [m² and upwards.

Quadrupole SIMS (QSIMS) depth profiles were acquired using a 1keV or 250eV O_2^+ at normal incidence. The rastered area was typically ca. 250 x 250 μm² at 1keV primary beam energy and the beam current was ca. 80 nA.

The crater depths were measured by Dektak Profilometry using replicate measurements across the X and Y directions. Comparison of Dektak measurements from two separate laboratories for several craters showed agreement within ± 1% on a depth of 300nm.

Part of the samples consisted of boron implanted silicon wafers, where the implant energies varied from 250eV to 2.5keV. Both "as implanted" and "annealed" types of samples were analysed. The other sample investigated was a delta-doped boron in silicon multilayer structure comprising 16 discrete layers as later described. All samples were analysed as received with no special surface treatment, pre-conditioning or cleaning.

3. Results

Figure 1 shows an overlay of the boron profiles for three annealed implanted Si samples (0.5, 1.0 and 2.5keV implant energies) analysed at normal incidence with a Quadrupole SIMS instrument and at oblique incidence with the Cameca 4f instrument. Similar profile shapes are obtained with both types of instruments and a good agreement on the depth and concentration calibrations can be generally observed. The slightly higher dose measured by QSIMS for profiles (1) and (2) may be due to the different reference samples used for the calibration of QSIMS and Cameca data. QSIMS data show detection limits in the range 2-5e16cm^{-3} whereas this parameter is consistently lower by a factor of 2-5 in the Cameca data. This is probably the combined result of optical gating superimposed on the conventional electronic gate in the Cameca instrument. For these samples, raw data comparisons (not reported) show that the time to complete the profiles are generally comparable under the set of analysis conditions used although the Cameca achieves this using lower beam currents and typically larger raster sizes. This observation is not surprising since normal incidence inherently leads to significantly reduced sputter rates.

Figure 2 shows an overlay of five depth profiles for a 500eV B implant in a Si wafer sample (as implanted) obtained on the Cameca instrument at five different impact energies ranging from 500eV to 1.5keV. It should be noted that as the primary beam impact energy is reduced, the impact angle increases to the point where at 500eV the retarding effect of the fixed secondary extraction voltage used on the sample (2.25kV) is so great that a grazing beam (close to 90° to the sample normal) is obtained. For impact angles below 52°, the Si matrix signal remained constant. However, above 54° (1.18keV impact energy), the matrix signal became increasingly distorted with increasing impact angles. Other authors reported such distortions of the matrix signal with impact angle [1] which may correspond to non-linear sputtering or roughening effects. The constancy of the matrix signal does not necessarily imply the absence of non-linear effects since ion yield and sputter rate variations may cancel each other out. As shown on Fig. 2, the apparent width of the profiles reduces with impact energy. However, no significant improvement in the resolution of profile features (surface peak and maximum of B implantation range) in the 0 - 5nm depth range is observed. This again is probably a result of non-linear effects and/or roughening taking place in this regime and possibly beyond [2, 3] under the low energy beam conditions used for the analyses. Interestingly, the junction depths measured at 1e19at.cm^{-3} of boron for 500eV impact energy are comparable to literature data for similar (but not identical) B implants analysed at, for example, 250eV normal incidence or 400eV 45° incidence on QSIMS instruments [4].

Comparative depth profiles of a 250eV B implanted Si sample (annealed) is presented in Fig. 3. This time, there is a significant difference in the apparent width between the QSIMS and Cameca profiles. In the latter case, the profile appears closer to the surface. This may be again indication of non-linear sputter rate and roughening effects. The accuracy of the depth scale calibration may also be partly responsible for such a shift. It should be noted that for the higher

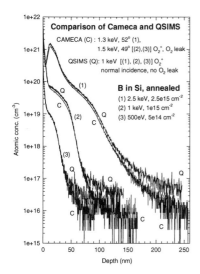

Fig 1. Comparison of Cameca and QSIMS profiles obtained on a series of B implanted Si samples.

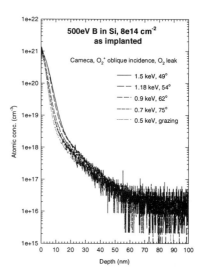

Fig 2. Cameca profiles of a 500eV B implant in Si analysed with different primary beam energies.

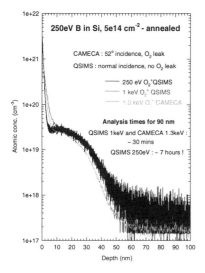

Fig 3. Comparison of Cameca and QSIMS profiles obtained on a 250eV B implant in Si.

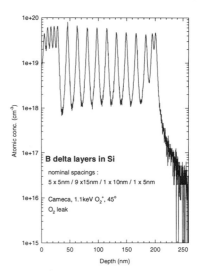

Fig 4. Cameca profile of a B delta-doped multilayer structure in Si.

beam impact energies, the dynamic range is limited by the high background of boron in the sample. In contrast, the detection limit of the ultra-low energy QSIMS profile (250eV) appears to be limited by the counting statistics. Comparison of the sputter rates shows that for both QSIMS and Cameca at 1 - 1.3keV impact energies, a depth of 90nm containing the whole profile was reached after ½ hour whereas 7 hours were necessary to complete the same profile under ultra-low energy depth profiling conditions with the QSIMS instrument.

Fig 4 shows the Cameca profile obtained on a B delta-doped multilayer structure in silicon. The data show that a good depth resolution can be maintained over a depth range of 200nm. The last two layers, which have a nominal separation of 5nm, are well resolved. With the future knowledge of the exact positions of deltas in a given sample, it should be possible to evaluate, by measurement of any shifts of the deltas towards the surface, the extent of non-linear sputter rate. This is at present beyond the scope of this paper.

4. Conclusions
Analysis of a series of B implanted Si samples with 1keV normal incidence QSIMS and 1.3keV, 52° - 1.5keV, 49° oblique incidence magnetic sector SIMS showed that the profile shapes were similarly defined with both types of instruments.

There is evidence from this work (and literature) for non-linear effects and possibly roughening for oblique incidence bombardment with O_2 leak which is dependent of the primary energy and incidence angle. These effects are clearly visible in the magnetic sector profiles for impact angles above 54° and may therefore restrict the choice of analytical conditions for low energy profiling on this type of instrument.

A significant benefit in analytical throughput using oblique incidence is evident. The inherently reduced sputter rates at normal incidence can lead to prohibitively extended analysis times, especially under ultra-low energy profiling conditions (~250 eV).

The magnetic sector data show consistently lower detection limits by up to a factor of 5, compared to QSIMS data. The determination of junction depths in the range 1e16 - 1e17 cm^{-3} may therefore be better achieved on an appropriately configured magnetic sector SIMS instrument.

Acknowledgements
Samples of boron implanted into silicon wafers were provided by the University of Salford, UK, Courtesy of Dr. J. A. van den Berg.
The delta-doped boron in silicon multilayer sample was kindly provided by the University of Warwick, Advanced SIMS Projects Group, Courtesy of Professor Mark Dowsett.

References
[1] M. Schuhmacher, B. Rasser and D. Renard, in SIMS XI, G. Gillen, R.Lareau, J. Bennett, F. Stevie, Eds, John Wiley & Sons, Chichester, 1997, p. 695.
[2] K. Wittmark and S.F. Corcoran, J. Vac. Sci. Technol. B16(1) (1998) 272.
[3] K. Wittmark, J. Vac. Sci. Technol. B16(5) (1998) 2776.
[4] ULE SIMS brochure, Evans Europa.

A. Benninghoven, P. Bertrand, H.-N. Migeon and H.W. Werner (Editors).
Proceedings of the 12th International Conference on Secondary Ion Mass Spectrometry,
Brussels, Belgium, 5-11 September 1999
© 2000 Elsevier Science B.V. All rights reserved.

COMPARATIVE ANALYSIS OF BORON DELTA-DOPING LAYERS IN SILICON USING Xe+ AND O_2^+ PRIMARY IONS

J.C. Dupuy[a], P. Holliger[b], G. Prudon[a], N. Baboux[a], G. Mancina[a], C. Dubois[a]

[a]Laboratoire de Physique de la Matière, UMR CNRS 5511, INSA LYON, 69621 Villeurbanne Cedex, France

[b]CEA LETI, 17 rue des Martyrs, 38054 Grenoble Cedex 9, France

1. Introduction

Silicon microelectronics uses increasingly shallower doping profiles, and *SIMS* analysis is required to supply the concentration profiles with a continuous improvement in depth resolution. This improvement can be reached by signal treatment via a deconvolution procedure [1,2], but an initial experimental profile has to be very good: the present tendency is to lower the energy of the primary ion beams. This decrease in energy can be achieved by using a conventional ion source, for example O_2^+ source optimized to work at very low energy (a source with a floating potential, or with acceleration-deceleration) or also by using cluster ions like SF_5^+ [3], which allows to divide up the total energy among the six cluster atoms. Another way, however, is not to be disregarded: the use of heavier ions, like xenon, which has the advantage of inducing a narrower damage zone than oxygen, and at the same time of decreasing the effects of collisional mixing. We propose a comparative experimental study, as well as a *SRIM98* code simulation study.

2. SIMS experiments

An epitaxial silicon sample consisting of several delta-doping layers of boron located at different depths was analyzed by a *CAMECA IMS 5F* ion microscope equipped with an

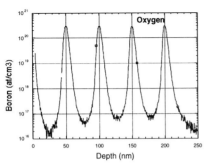
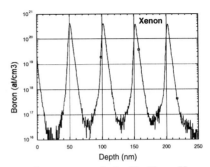

Figure 1.   a : oxygen analysis, 2keV per O_2 b : xenon analysis, 2keV per Xe

oxygen ion source and a xenon ion source [4]. The analysis with xenon was carried out with oxygen flooding and different experimental conditions were used. Figure *1* shows an example obtained with *5 kV* source tension, and a sample voltage of *3 kV*, this leads to an energy of *2 keV* per *Xe* or per *O$_2$* and to an incident angle of the order of *52°*. A set of similar measurements was performed with the different experimental conditions. Figure *2* represents a compilation of the results. There are two important parameters concerning the depth resolution : the exponential decay length λ_d and the standard deviation of the DRF σ_{tot} .The results for λ_d and σ_{tot} are given versus the primary ion range R_p.

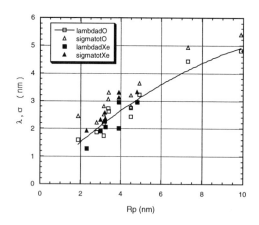

Figure 2 : compilation of results with oxygen and with xenon. For the same R$_p$ of the primary ions, the results with xenon are at least as good as those obtained with oxygen.
λ_d is the decay length and σ_{tot} the total standard deviation of the response to the delta layer.

3. SRIM simulations

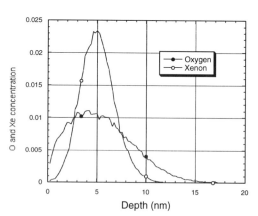

Figure 3 : The oxygen and the xenon implantation with the same energy (4 keV per O$_2$ or per Xe) at 47°. The concentrations are in atoms per Angstrom and per ion (the dose for the oxygen is 90% of the xenon dose, because the backscattering cannot be neglected for the oxygen). We note that the R$_p$ are close (5 nm for Xe, 5.5 nm for O), but the ΔR$_p$ is smaller for Xe than for O.

The SRIM [5] simulations were made for different experimental conditions used in a CAMECA, and it was assumed that the energy of O$_2$ was divided equally among the two atoms. Figure 4 gives the values obtained for the quantities of interest (projected range R$_p$ and its standard deviation, range of damage R_d and its standard deviation) under the experimental conditions used during SIMS analysis.

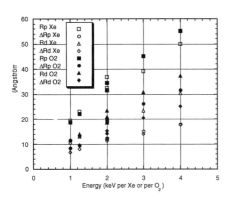

Figure 4: Projected range (Rp), range of damage (Rd), and their standard deviations (labeled ΔRp and ΔRd). The conditions of energy and incident angle are the ones used in SIMS. We note double values for 2 keV, which have been obtained for two pairs of source-sample voltage values (5 kV/3kV and 4 kV/2 kV).

4. Discussion and conclusion

Collisional mixing is the principal mechanism for the broadening of SIMS profiles in the case ofboron in silicon, and the implantation depth of the primary ions, characterized by R_p, is generally considered as the principal factor. In fact, the important parameter is the thickness of the primary ion energy deposition zone, in which the diffusion takes place, but one has to add a factor, which takes into account the competition between the mixing rate and the sputtering rate. The choice for the parameter R_p to characterise the collisional mixing is, nevertheless, proved a posteriori from Figure 5 :

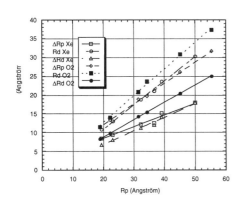

Figure 5 : ΔR_p, R_d and ΔR_d variations for oxygen and for xenon versus R_p. The quasi-linear nature of all the variations allows to take R_p as a single characterisation parameter.

520

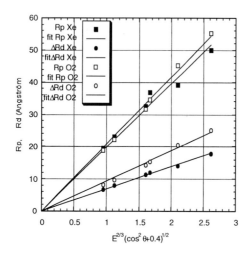

Figure 6 : variation law of R_p and ΔR_d.

At high energies these parameters are quite linear [6] vs $E^n\cos\theta$. At low energies it is necessary to introduce a term of $\sin^2\theta$ [7]. A good linear fit is obtained when using the function :

$$k\, E^{2/3} \sqrt{\cos^2\theta + 0.4}$$

where E is the energy in keV per Xe or per O_2, and R_p or ΔR_d are expressed in Angström. We obtain for k :

for the xenon :
19.73 for R_p and 6.89 for ΔR_d,

and for the oxygen :
20.77 for R_p and 9.33 for ΔR_d.

Two opposing factors govern the broadening of the profiles analysed with oxygen and with xenon under the same experimental conditions : on one hand the zone of energy deposition is narrower for xenon as compared to oxygen at the same energy, but on the other hand for the same voltage the energy per xenon atom is twice that per oxygen atom. In spite of this, for the same voltage, the exponential decays are as compared to O2+ and the total broadening of the profile is slightly smaller with xenon. The fact of a double energy of xenon is, hence, completely counterbalanced by the smaller thickness of the damage zone. In conclusion, the expected gain is marginal, but xenon remains competitive to oxygen and its use must be studied also for the analysis in the surface transient, where it must not give rise to transitory incorporation.

References

[1] B. Gautier, R. Prost, G. Prudon, and J.C Dupuy, Surf and Interface Anal. **24**,733,(1996)

[2] P. N. Allen, M. G. Dowsett, R. Collins, Surf. Interface Anal. **20**, 696, (1993)

[3] F. Kötter, E. Niehuis, A. Benninghoven, Proc. of SIMS XI, G. Gillen et al. ed.,J. Wiley, 459 (1998)

[4] B. Blanchard, P. Holliger, Proc. of SIMS XI, G. Gillen et al. ed.,J. Wiley, 265 (1998)

[5] J. F. Ziegler, J. P. Biersack, U. Littmark, The Stopping and Range of Ions in Solids. Vol. 1. Pergamon Press, New York (1985)

[6] J. C. Dupuy, G. Prudon, C. Dubois, P. Waren, D. Dutartre, Nucl. Instr. Methods **B 85**, 379 (1994)

[7] Z. X. Jiang, P. F. A. Alkemade, Surf. Interface Anal. **27**, 125 (1999)

A. Benninghoven, P. Bertrand, H.-N. Migeon and H.W. Werner (Editors).
Proceedings of the 12th International Conference on Secondary Ion Mass Spectrometry,
Brussels, Belgium, 5-11 September 1999

521

SOLID STATE REACTIONS WITH F IN SIO$_2$.
SIMS STUDY AND COMPUTER SIMULATIONS

A.A.Efremov, G.Ph.Romanova, V.G.Litovchenko

Institute of Semiconductor Physics, NAS of Ukraine,
45 Pr. Nauki, 252028 Kiev, Ukraine
E-mail: Lvg@Div9.Semicond.Kiev.UA

1. Introduction

The doping SiO$_2$ films with fluorine is considered now as one of the possibilities to increase the quality of MOS IC including ultra large scale integrated (ULSI) application[1,2]. The most important effects of fluorination are the improvement of the resistance of MOS structures to radiation (hot electron induced degradation), the suppression of the interface trap generation, and the decrease of mechanical stresses in SiO$_2$-Si structures [1,2]. The models proposed for the description of F induced chemical bonds reconstruction [3,4] need to be supported by more detailed microscopic information about depth distribution of not only fluorine itself, but also of other impurities and defects. Similar conclusion is valid for description of irradiation induced structural transformations in SiO$_2$:F. In the present paper we consider the above mentioned aspects of the SiO$_2$ fluorination both experimentally by SIMS and theoretically by computer simulations (CS) of fluorine interaction with SiO$_2$ matrix. The CS will allow us to predict the irradiation induced redistribution of supposed *precursors* for different secondary ions (SI) and discuss both oxide structure transformations and SIMS depth profiles upon more sound theoretical background.

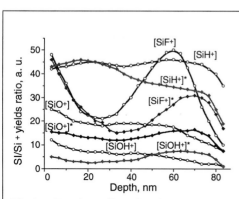

Fig.1: Depth profiles of SI for SiO$_2$ doped with HF at the initial stage of oxidaton:
[SiF$^+$]→SiF$^+$/Si$^+$($\times 10^4$);
[SiH$^+$]→ SiH$^+$/Si$^+$($\times 10^3$);
[SiOH$^+$]→ SiOH$^+$/Si$^+$($\times 10^2$);
[SiO$^+$] →SiO$^+$/Si$^+$ ($\times 10^3$);
[ ] for as-grown oxide; [ ]* after γ-irradiation

2. Experimental

We have used two different types of fluorine treatment: F$^+$ implantation (35 keV, D=10^{12}-10^{16} ion/cm^2) in thermal dry oxide (d$_{ox}$ = 200 nm) and introducing of HF into oxidizing ambient at initial stage of silicon oxidaton (d$_{ox}$ = 80 nm). The influence of γ–irradiation on both types of fluorinated SiO$_2$-Si structures

522

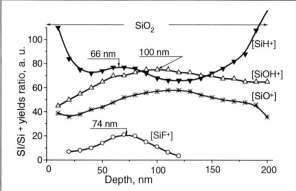

Fig. 2 Depth profiles of SI for as-implanted SiO$_2$ (F$^+$, 10^{14} ion/cm^2)

[SiF$^+$]→ SiF$^+$/Si$^+$($\times$10^5);   [SiH$^+$]→ SiH$^+$/Si$^+$($\times$2$\circ$10^3),

[SiOH$^+$]→ SiOH$^+$/Si$^+$($\times$5$\circ$10^3), [SiO$^+$]→ SiO$^+$/Si$^+$($\times$2$\circ$10^3).

Arrows indicate precise positions of maxima.

was studied on the samples irradiated from γ-source (^{60}Co) at the dose 5 Mrad .

In order to determine the fluorine distribution over the depth of the SiO$_2$ film the monitoring of [^{47}SiF]$^+$ cluster was performed. One could not expect that the yield of this SI corresponds to fluorine concentration in SiO$_2$. It should reflect the concentration of respective precursors, namely ≡Si–F DB, i.e. the fluorine bounded in the SiO$_2$ network. Taking into account the isotopic ratios, the shares of such SI as [^{30}Si^{16}OH]$^+$, [^{29}Si^{16}OD]$^+$, and [^{29}Si^{18}O]$^+$ were subtracted from 47th mass peak. The correct monitoring of single atomic ^{19}F$^+$ SI is more difficult due to the superposition of such peaks as ^{19}[H$_3$O]$^+$ or (more probably) ^{19}[HDO]$^+$ [5].

3. Results and discussion

The SIMS data were interpreted in the framework of the conception of *precursors* [6]. According to it each type of the secondary ion (SI) is formed from one (or several) *precursors*, i.e. such fragments of sputtered matrix which are similar to respective SI in composition *and local atomic arrangement*. In particular, it was established experimentally that ≡Si–O DB is the most probable precursor for SiO$^+$ SI. [7] Fluorine incorporated during oxidation has a U-shaped distribution. (Fig. 1). It is mostly localized near SiO$_2$-Si interface. After γ-irradiation this maximum decreases. SiO$_2$:F films differ from a standard film by relatively higher content of

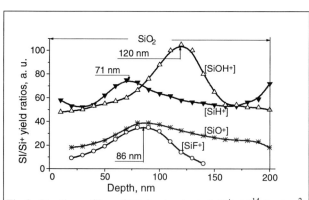

Fig.3: Depth profiles of SI for implanted (F$^+$, 10^{14} ion/cm^2) and γ-irradiated SiO$_2$.

[SiF$^+$]→ SiF$^+$/Si$^+$($\times$10^5);   [SiH$^+$]→ SiH$^+$/Si$^+$($\times$$\circ$10^3),

[SiOH$^+$]→ SiOH$^+$/Si$^+$($\circ$10^3), [SiO$^+$]→ SiO$^+$/Si$^+$($\circ$10^3).

Arrows indicate precise positions of maxima.

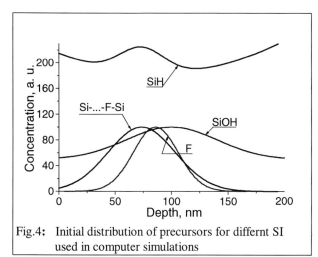

Fig.4: Initial distribution of precursors for differnt SI used in computer simulations

hydrogen (SiH^+, $SiOH^+$). SiH^+ depth profile is uniform but $SiOH^+$ has a maximum near the outer surface of the film. After γ-irradiation the region near the interface is found to be depleted with SiH complexes and enriched with SiOH ones.

SIMS depth profiles for F^+ implanted and γ–irradiated SiO_2 films are both Gauss-like (Fig. 2). In the former case the profile corresponds to the theoretical distribution ranges. Taking into account simul-taneous formation of $\equiv Si$-F and $\equiv Si$–O DB it is expected to observe a correlated increase of SiO^+ and SiF^+ yields. However, in postimplanted samples these two profiles do not coincide completely. $\equiv Si$–O DB are formed also due to pure ion beam induced processes (e.g. due to recoil). On the other hand some part of fluorine may remain in the SiO_2 network as interstitials and not form the precursors for SiF^+. After γ-irradiation, when additional $\equiv Si$– and $\equiv SiO$ DB are introduced, complete incorporation of fluorine in SiO_2 matrix takes place. For this reason SiF^+ yield increases (under the same fluorine concentration!) and correlation between SiO^+/Si^+ and SiF^+/Si^+ depth distributions becomes yet more pronounced. The increase of implantation dose results in respective increase of SiO^+/Si^+ ratio. (Fig, 3) In all cases γ-irradiation intensifies this effect. It should be noted that the most complete irradiation induced fluorine re-incorporation after implantation is observed at the optimum implanted dose about $10^{14} cm^{-2}$.

4. Computer simulations

Computer simulations of the structure reconstruction proces-ses have been performed. The interaction between fluorine, hydrogen, native (intrinsic) and irradiation induced defects was described in the framework quasichemical approach descri-bed in [8]. Good accordance with the experiment has been achieved in the framework of such models: (i) During oxidation fluorine incorporates

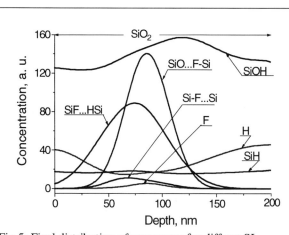

Fig.5: Final distribution of precursors for differnt SI after γ-irradiation obtained in computer simulations.

and forms stable $\equiv$Si-F$^{-\delta}$...$^{+\delta}$H-Si$\equiv$ defects. For this reason correlation between Si-F^{+} and SiH^{+} SI is observed. γ- irradiation leads to the bonds reconstruction, accompanied by the release of mobile hydrogen and practically immobile interstitial fluorine: $\equiv$Si-F$^{-\delta}$...$^{+\delta}$H-Si$\equiv$ + γ →$\equiv$Si-...-Si$\equiv$ + H↑ + F. These two impurities interact with γ induced DB in two opposite parts of the SiO$_2$ film: $\equiv$Si-O-Si$\equiv$+γ→$\equiv$Si-O..-Si; $\equiv$Si-O...-Si$\equiv$+F→$\equiv$Si-O...F-Si$\equiv$; $\equiv$Si-O+H→$\equiv$Si-OH+-Si$\equiv$ As a result new $\equiv$Si-OH and $\equiv$Si-O...F-Si$\equiv$ defects are formed and some share of fluorine are proved to be released. For this reason SiF+/Si+ ratio decreases after irradiation as one can see from Fig. 1. (ii) During F^{+} implantation about one half of impurity atoms stop in interstitial positions (Fig.4). The rest proves to be trapped by primary beam induced vacancies $\equiv$Si-...-Si$\equiv$ and therefore, metastable defects such as $\equiv$Si-F...-Si$\equiv$ are created (see Fig.2, curve 1 and Fig. 4,5). As in previous case γ- irradiation results in the release of high mobile hydrogen atoms (from SiH complexes), which fill the DB above mentioned: $\equiv$Si-F...-Si$\equiv$ + H → $\equiv$Si-F...H-Si$\equiv$ (see Fig.2,3 curves 1). Another process where H participates is $\equiv$Si-O...-Si$\equiv$ + H → $\equiv$Si-OH ...-Si$\equiv$ (see Fig. 2,3 curve 3 and Fig. 4,5). The second slower process is the interstitial fluorine reincorporation due to γ-induced DB formation: F + $\equiv$ Si-O...-Si$\equiv$ → $\equiv$Si-O...F-Si$\equiv$. (see Fig.2, curve 4). It should be emphasized a good accordance between experimental SI profiles and calculated distributions of their supposed *precursors*.

Hence computer simulation (Fig. 4,5) allows us to reveal creation of several types of F-containing complexes in fluorinated SiO$_2$ films: (a) interstitial F; (b) $\equiv$Si-F...-Si$\equiv$; (c) $\equiv$Si-F...O-Si$\equiv$; (d) $\equiv$Si-F...H-Si$\equiv$. Hypothesis about high mobility of fluorine itself is not confirmed. On the contrary, the high mobility of hydrogen is very important here. In particular γ-irradiation leads to transfer of hydrogen from SiH complexes to SiOH ones. According to simulations the most complete fluorine re-incorporation occurs at the optimum F+ dose (about 10^{14} cm^{-2}) where maximum steady-state concentration of $\equiv$Si...Si$\equiv$ defects induced by implantation itself in SiO$_2$ matrix is achieved. Subsequent increase of the dose increases only interstitial fluorine rather than bound one.

5. Conclusion

SIMS depth profiling of two type of fluorinated SiO$_2$ film before and after γ-irradiation have been performed. Comparison of SIMS data with the results of computer simulation of γ-irradiation induced processes in SiO$_2$:F shows that fluorine may be present in SiO$_2$ in «interstitial» form and may be included in such structural defects as $\equiv$Si-F...-Si$\equiv$, $\equiv$Si-F...O-Si$\equiv$, $\equiv$Si-F...H-Si$\equiv$.

References

[1]   Y. Nishioka, Y. Ohiji, N. Natuaki et al., Electron Dev. Lett. 10 (1989) 141.
[2]   N. Yasushiro, I. Toshiyuki and O. Kiyonori, IEEE Trans. Nucl. Sci., NS 37 (1990) 2026.
[3]   W.-T. Tseng, Y.-T. Hsieh and C.-F. Lin, Solid State Technology, 61 (1997) 185
[4]   T. Homma, R. Yamaguchi and Y. Murao, J. Electrochem. Soc, 140 (1993) 687.
[5]   B. Yu, N. Konuma and E. Arai, J. Appl. Phys., 70(1991) 2408.
[6]   A. Benninghoven, SIMS- III, Proceeding, (1982) 438.
[7]   V.G. Litovchenko, A.A. Efremov, and G.Ph. Romanova, SIMS XI, Proceeding, (1997).
[8]   V. Litovchenko, A. Efremov, B. Romanyuk. et al., J.Electrochem. Soc., 145 (1998) 2964.

A. Benninghoven, P. Bertrand, H.-N. Migeon and H.W. Werner (Editors).
Proceedings of the 12th International Conference on Secondary Ion Mass Spectrometry,
Brussels, Belgium, 5-11 September 1999

SIO₂ NUCLEATION ENHANCED BY CARBON.
SIMS DEPTH PROFILING OF SIMOX

A. A. Efremov, G. Ph. Romanova, V. G. Litovchenko and P. I. Didenko

Institute of Semiconductor Physics, NAS of Ukraine, 45 Pr. Nauki, 252028 Kiev, Ukraine
E-mail: Lvg@Div9.Semicond.Kiev.UA

1. Introduction

Buried SiO_X in silicon prepared by the relatively low dose ($\sim 10^{17}$ cm^{-2}) oxygen implantation is a suitable model system consisting of silicon and oxygen nonuniformly distributed over the depth in different local atomic configurations. Additional implantation with C^+ allows to control the process of precipitation of SiO_2 in Si [1] and change the characteristics of the buried layer [2]. When such a system is sputtered with O_2^+ ions in SIMS analysis the unique large variety of phases containing silicon and oxygen is realized *in situ* on the surface and in a subsurface layer

The subsurface layer being modified by primary ions should consists of (i) SiO_2 precipitates in silicon; (ii) silicon inclusions in SiO_2; (iii) metastable suboxides; (iv) weakly bonded oxygen introduced directly by primary beam and released from bound state due to ion beam mixing. All these components would influence on SI emission in different manners (being *precursors* [3,4]) and more insight in the origin of different SI may be done from SIMS depth profiles measured for such type of matrix.

The main goals of the present work are: 1) to reveal the role of the afore-mentioned phases in the formation of matrix SI such as Si^+, Si_2^+, Si_3^+, SiO^+, O^+, 2) to estimate how much the primary beam *in situ* modifies initial chemical and phase compositions of the sputtered surface, and 3) to clear out some peculiarities of SiO_2 nucleation and oxygen redistribution enhanced by carbon. In discussion we shall use the results of computer simulation (CS) of the dynamics of structural and compositional changes in SIMOX caused by carbon implantation [2].

2. Experiment

CZ-Si (100) 10 Ω•cm wafers were implanted with O^+ ($D_o = 1 \cdot 10^{17}$ cm^{-2} and E=150 keV, $R_p = 363$ nm). After this, C^+ implantation was carried out with different doses and energies. Subsequently, the samples were annealed at $T_A = 1150°$ C in Ar ambient. Depth profiling of the samples was done with O_2^+ primary beam at decline incidence using CAMECA–4f. C^+ was implanted to the «left» (120 keV, $R_p = 320$ nm) or to the «right» side (160 keV, $R_p = 407$ nm) of the buried suboxide. On this basis below we denote the samples as <L> («left implanted») and <R> («right implanted») respectively.

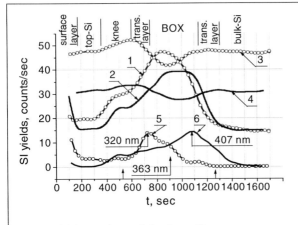

Fig. 1. Initial experimental depth profiles
1, 2 - Si$^+$ (x10^{-6})
3, 4 - Si$_2^+$ (x10^{-3}),
5 - C$^+$(x 0.2),   6 - C$^+$ (x0.1)
1, 3, 5 correspond to <L> and
2, 4, 6 – correspond to <R> samples respectively.

3. Basic results

In Fig 1 Si$^+$, Si$_2^+$ and C$^+$ secondary ions (SI) SIMS depth profiles for <L> and <R> SOI structures are compared. The following features should be noted:

1) In spite of oxygen ions were used for SIMS analysis Si$^+$, SiO$^+$, as well as O$^+$, reproduce well the depth distribution of the bound oxygen in SIMOX structure. (SiO$^+$ and O$^+$ depth profiles are similar to Si$^+$ one and not shown in Fig.1) In this case also absolute values of the yields depend relatively weak on the carbon peak position, but the shape of profiles is sensitive to carbon distribution.

2) For <L> samples the maximum of Si$^+$ yield is about *20% higher* than for <R> ones.

Both AES data and computer simulations of BOX growth [2] confirm the most effective accumulation of oxygen within narrow Si layer for this case.

3) At the same initial spatial distribution of implanted oxygen the formed buried dielectric is found to be shifted to the place of implanted carbon peak position. The shift is observed for all profiles of secondary ions and is about of 20 nm. Therefore, the pronounced gettering effect of oxygen by carbon in silicon occurs.

4) Depth profiles of C$^+$ SI correspond in general features to implanted ions range distributions. However, when carbon atoms were implanted to the silicon enriched left region of the SIMOX structure the C$^+$ secondary ions yield which is sensitive to the presence of C-O complexes in the matrix was *two times lower*.

5) Depth profile of Si$_2^+$ SI has a minimum in the middle of the buried oxide where relatively few silicon inclusions in SiO$_2$ matrix occur and a pronounced maximum in the narrow sublayer («knee») of upper silicon (Fig.1). According to independent data «knee» sublayer consists of a lot of small SiO$_2$ precipitates separated each from other only by thin streaks of silicon phase [2]. Such mixture of the both phases are proved to be the most favourable for Si$_2^+$ SI formation under O$_2^+$ sputtering. Absolute value of Si$_2^+$ yield depends also on micro- and macrostructure of SIMOX as a whole and is *two times higher* for <L> samples. The depth profiles of Si$_3^+$ SI resemble «overturned» profiles of oxygen sensitive ions and have similar peculiarities (These initial experimental data are not shown in Fig.1, but general behaviour of Si$_3^+$ yield depth profiles are similar to their normalized profiles in Fig. 2 and 3). As well as for Si$_2^+$ <L> samples demonstrate *two-times higher* absolute values of Si$_3^+$ yield.

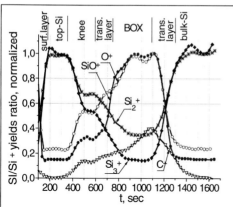

Fig. 2. The SI yields normalized on Si$^+$ depth profile for <R> samples.

4. Discussion of macro- and micro-structure of SIMOX

Yet initial depth profiles of SI allow us to reveal several sublayers in SIMOX. However, profiles normalized to one basic one (e.g. on Si$^+$ SI) prove to be more usefull to reveal the structure peculiarities within SIMOX in detail. The are at least seven sublayers in SIMOX where different SI yield behaviour is observed (Fig. 1-3):

1. Bulk and Top-silicon. Here the normalized yield values of SiO$^+$, and O$^+$ are minimum, i.e. both contain similar concentration of bound oxygen. However, for <L> samples Si$_2$/Si and Si$_3$/Si ratios are noticeably higher for bulk silicon (Fig. 3). If we take into account stimulating role of carbon in SiO$_2$ precipitation, the last may be treated as a consequence of more perfect large blocked structure of bulk silicon and more dispersed SiO$_2$ phase in it due to the *lower concentration of carbon* in this region in comparison with <R> samples.

2. Knee is located just to the right from the top silicon. Knee's position does not depend on parameters of carbon implantation. Therefore, its appearances is caused by oxygen implantation itself, namely by primary defects which enhance the growth of SiO$_2$ phase. The knee is characterized by the increased yield of Si$_2^+$ and Si$_3^+$ SI as well as SiO$^+$. According to independent data [2] the knee corresponds to satellite sublayer saturated with small (~100-200 μ) SiO$_2$ and Si inclusions. We suppose that Si$_2$-O and Si$_3$-O fragments in matrix located in the vicinity of multiple SiO$_2$/Si boundaries (as well as the same fragments formed *in situ* due to ion-beam mixing) are probable precursors for respective SI. As to SiO$^+$ SI their precursors are Si-O dangling bonds [3] which should present abundantly in such heterogeneous region. The shape of the knee depends on carbon peak position. For <R> samples the knee has a tendency to form a maximum separated from the main distribution of bound oxygen, because the latter is shifted more to the right. This is confirmed also by CS [2]. It is clear especially from SiO$^+$ normalized profile. On the contrary, SI O$^+$ yield (as well as Si$^+$) is less sensitive to this peculiarity.

3. Left edge of buried layer is the next sublayer after the knee. Its the most interesting peculiarity is a quite different behaviour of SiO$^+$ and O$^+$ normalized

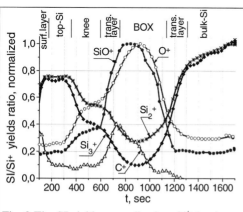

Fig. 3 The SI yields normalized on Si$^+$ depth profiles for <L> samples.

yields. The nature of the difference may be deduced easier if we firstly analyse the profiles for the <L> SIMOX. Here SiO^+/Si^+ ratio has the maximum just at the carbon peak position, where according to [1] enhanced SiO_2 precipitation and growth should take place. Therefore, *big* SiO_2 inclusions, which are *at small distances* each from other are more favourable for SiO^+ SI generation under O_2^+ sputtering. On the contrary, smaller and more distant inclusions, which are formed at lower carbon concentration should be dissolved due to ion-beam mixing under sputtering. As a result large amount of weakly bonded interstitial oxygen O_i is released *in situ* and gives an additional pronounced share in detected O^+ yield. In [5] we have shown that use of O^+/Si^+ ratio depth profile allows us to emphasize just this component in O^+ yield as one can see also in Fig 4. If we come back to <R> SIMOX we can conclude by analogy (higher O^+/Si^+ and lower SiO^+/Si^+ ratios) that small SiO_2 inclusions are within thin silicon region between separated satellite sublayer and main layer of buried dielectric.

4. Middle part of buried oxide is quite different for <L> and <R> structures. As one can see from Fig. 2 normalized yields of SiO^+ and O^+ allow to reveal *two maxima* in the middle part of the <R> samples, besides the right maximum position coincides with one for carbon. The left maximum is near the maximum of implanted oxygen distribution, where its high concentration proved to be enough for intensive precipitation independently on carbon. The appearance of both maxima are well predicted by CS [2]. According to Fig. 3 <L> samples contain larger SiO_2 inclusions on the left side of the middle part (where carbon was implanted) and smaller precipitates are on the right side. Si_2^+ and Si_3^+ yields drop within middle part of main SiO_X layer and their precursors are probably ultra-small silicon inclusions in SiO_2 phase [6]. For <L> samples both Si_2^+/Si^+ and Si_3^+/Si^+ ratios continuosly rise in the beginning of bulk Si region. The last may be explained by more «diffused» right boundary of BOX in this case, containing a more dispersed SiO_2 phase.

5. Conclusion

The enhancement of C^+ SI yield by oxygen in local atomic environment in silicon matrix is observed. The peculiarities of Si^+, SiO^+, O^+ depth profiles are caused by their sensitivity to bound oxygen. Depth profiles of Si_2^+, Si_3^+ yields are found to be sensitive to dispersed silicon phase in SiO_2. The use of normalized yields gives the possibility to detect weakly bonded oxygen released *in situ* during SIMS analysis. Local enhancement of SiO_2 nucleation caused by introduction of carbon is supported by SIMS data. It results, nevertheless, in the global transformations of buried oxide micro- and macrostructure stimulating complex redistribution of implanted oxygen.

References

[1] A. Borghesi, B. Pivac, A. Sasela and A. Stella, J. Appl.Phys. **77** (1995) 4169.
[2] V.G. Litovchenko, A.A. Efremov, B.N. Romanyuk, V.P. Melnik and C. Claeys, J. Electrochem. Soc. 145 (1998) 2964.
[3] A. Benninghoven, SIMS -III, Proceeding (1981) 438
[4] G.Ph. Romanova, A.A. Efremov and P.I. Didenko, SIMS-VI, Proceeding (1987) 335.
[5] V.G. Litovchenko, A.A. Efremov, G.Ph. Romanova et al, in: Optoelectronics and Semiconductor Technique, 30 (1995) 3, Naukova Dumka Press, Kiev, Ukraine.
[6] P.I.Didenko, A.A. Efremov, V.S.Khomchenko, et al Phys. Status. Solidi (a) 100 (1987) 501.

A. Benninghoven, P. Bertrand, H.-N. Migeon and H.W. Werner (Editors).
Proceedings of the 12th International Conference on Secondary Ion Mass Spectrometry,
Brussels, Belgium, 5-11 September 1999

529

DUAL ION BEAM ANALYSIS OF SiO₂/Si INTERFACE

S. Hayashi and K. Yanagihara

Advanced Technology Research Labs., Nippon Steel Corporation
20-1 Shintomi, Futtsu, 293-8511, Chiba, JAPAN, e-mail: shun@re.nsc.co.jp

1. Introduction

This is important to quantify harmful metallic elements in the SiO_2 gate oxide of the metal oxide semiconductor (MOS) transistor structure. SIMS depth profiles provide a useful method to detect and locate small amounts of impurities. However, SIMS has inherent difficulties with quantification because of matrix effects, *i.e.*, different secondary ion yields for different concentrations of oxygen. The sputtering rate can also be different for different layers. In the case of MOS structures, the oxide layer gives rise to a large matrix effect compared with silicon. Laser post-ionization SNMS has been applied to the quantitative determination of metallic element in a SiO_2/Si structure [1]. However, this technique cannot compensate for the sputtering rate change. On the other hand, lower energy ion beams have been used to minimize atomic mixing for evaluating shallow junctions. At the same time, a lower energy oxygen beam can form the thin oxide layer at the sputtered surface. From this point of view, this feature is expected to lead to reduce matrix effect for SiO_2/Si interface. However, depth profiles using lower energy oxygen ion beam are time consuming. In our study we used a sub-keV O_2^+ ion beam for oxygen enrichment on the Si surface and a Cs^+ ion beam for sputtering the Si surface.

2. Experimental

All SIMS depth profiling measurements were used the PHI-6650 instrument. A 250 eV O_2^+ ion beam with various ion beam current and a 1 keV Cs^+ with a current of 1 nA was used to get depth profile. Both beams impinged on the sample surface at 60 degrees from the normal. Both beams were aligned to raster-scan the same 200 μm square for the depth profile. An analyzed area of 4% in the center of the eroding area was chosen and an electron flooding gun was used for charge compensation.

Sample 1: B^+ implanted Si to determine dependence of useful yield on primary O_2^+ energy.

Sample 2: 10 nm thick SiO_2 film on (100)Si to determine depth profiles of SiO_2/Si interface under various dual ion beam SIMS conditions.

Sample 3: Cu implanted 100nm thick SiO_2/Si sample

To show application of technique. Sample was prepared by implanting SiO_2(100 nm)/Si(100) wafer with Cu ions to a dose of 1E16 ions/cm^2 at 82 kV by a MEVVA (Metal Vapor Vacuum Arc) ion implanter, which had the Cu^+:Cu^{2+}:Cu^{3+} percentage ratios of the charge distributions as 44:42:14, at Nippon Steel[2].

3. Results and discussion

Fig.1 shows the dependence of useful yields, on oxygen primary ion beam energy for B^+ implanted Si sample. Under O_2^+ bombardment with impact energy below 500 eV, the useful yields of the atomic ions, B^+ and Si^+, drastically increase. Oxygen enrichment at the sputtered surface leads to an increase of ionization probability. Subsequently, we used a Cs^+ ion beam to obtain higher sputter yield.

The primary ion energy was 1 keV and current was 1 nA at 200 x 200 µm^2. The changes of secondary ion yields due to rise of oxygen enrichment at the sputtered surface were investigated using a 10 nm thick SiO_2 on Si substrate(Sample 2). Fig. 2 shows the depth profiles of $^{30}Si^+$ taken under various dual ion beam conditions.

Using only Cs^+ ion beam, $^{30}Si^+$ has a difference between SiO_2 and Si of one order of magnitude. Using oxygen flooding, $^{30}Si^+$ signals were made flat through SiO_2/Si interface. However, using an oxygen ion beam, higher $^{30}Si^+$ can be obtained by means of enrichment of oxygen at the sputtered surface various dual ion beam SIMS conditions.

With a 250 eV oxygen ion beam at currents of 0, 16, and 50 nA, $^{30}Si^+$ signals increase. In the case of the 50 nA Cs^+ ion beam, the $^{30}Si^+$ depth profile is close to that taken by oxygen ion beam with oxygen flooding. It shows that saturation of oxygen enrichment during SIMS analysis can be achieved.

Finally, we applied this technique to obtain the depth profile of Cu impurity around the SiO_2/Si interface. Fig. 3 shows profiles of Cu simulated by Monte Carlo calculations and obtained using dual ion beam SIMS. The theoretical profile shows that implanted Cu distributes from the SiO_2 layer through the interface to the Si substrate. However, Cu^+ in the Si substrate seems to be very low in the dual ion beam SIMS measurement.

Table 1 shows the Cu distribution ratios calculated from the detected ion intensity ratios between in SiO_2 and in Si substrate. Chemical analysis data was taken by using wet-etching technique and ICP-MS. This value is almost equal to the theoretical data expected from the Monte Carlo simulation. However, the value by dual ion beam technique is far from the expected one by one order of magnitude. As compared with our laser post-ionization results, there is too much difference. In this condition, Si^+ signals apparently saturate. The disagreement would be caused by the difference of Cu and Si. Cu is nobler and has lower oxygen affinity than Si. In this condition , the sputtered surface would not be completely

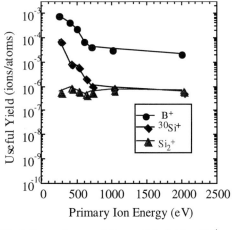
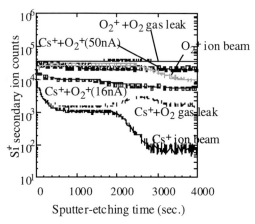

Fig.1 Dependence of the useful yields of B^+, $^{30}Si^+$ and Si_2^+ on O_2^+ ion beam energy.

Fig.2 Depth profiles of the $^{30}Si^+$ taken under various dual ion beam SIMS conditions.

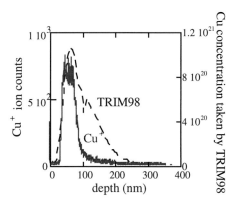

Fig. 3 Theoretical and experimental (dual ion beam) SIMS profiles of Cu^+

532

oxidized during dual ion beam analysis.

Table 1. Cu distribution ratios between in SiO_2 and in Si substrate taken by various SIMS
related techniques.

	Cu distribution ratio (in SiO_2/Si)
Chemical analysis	1:1.9
Conventional SIMS	1:0.0092
Laser post-ionization	1:2.3
This study(dual ion beam)	1:0.19

4. Conclusions

Dual ion beam SIMS can achieve higher secondary ion yield than that with oxygen flooding in the case of using Cs^+ ion beam. Atomic ion signals of Si^+, however, saturate using lower energy O_2^+ ion beam, while Si_2^+ does not. In this condition oxide layer production during SIMS analysis does not take place.

Furthermore, dual ion beam technique has difficulties for quantification:

1)oxygen amounts at the surface should be well controlled in order to saturate the secondary ion yields.

2)Surface roughening should be restrained to obtain an accurate depth profile.

3)Ion beam induced segregation should be taken into account.

However, shallow junction profile of the dopants taken by SIMS with low energy ion beam has similar difficulties for a quantitative interpretation.

References

[1] S. Hayashi, SIMS IX,1994,p339.
[2] J. Sasaki and I. G. Brown, J. Appl. Phys., 66(1989)5198.

A. Benninghoven, P. Bertrand, H.-N. Migeon and H.W. Werner (Editors).
Proceedings of the 12th International Conference on Secondary Ion Mass Spectrometry,
Brussels, Belgium, 5-11 September 1999
© 2000 Elsevier Science B.V. All rights reserved.

ULTRA LOW ENERGY CS BOMBARDMENT
ON A MAGNETIC SECTOR SIMS INSTRUMENT

E. De Chambost, B. Boyer, B. Rasser, M. Schuhmacher

CAMECA, 103 bd Saint Denis, BP6, 92403 Courbevoie Cedex, France

1. Introduction

The development of the ultra shallow junction technology for the semiconductor devices requires SIMS tools capable of measuring in-depth distribution of dopants within the first tens of nanometers underneath the sample surface. This means that the sample surface must be sputtered with a sub-keV impact energy for the primary ions. Previous works have shown that such low energy range can be reached for O_2^+ bombardment and positive secondary ion analysis on conventional magnetic SIMS [1]. On the CAMECA IMS 6f, because the secondary extraction field acts as a decelerating electrode for the primary particles sub-keV impact energy have been demonstrated [2] [3]. For Cs^+ bombardment and negative secondary ion analysis, impact energy below 1.5keV can not be reached because, in this case, the target acts as an accelerating electrode for the primary ions.

It has already been demonstrated that, in terms of beam density, a floating primary column design offers improved performance at very low primary impact energy [4]. CAMECA has developed a new ion optical arrangement for magnetic sector SIMS instruments compatible with a very low impact energy (< 250 eV) for negative secondary ion analysis under Cs bombardment. This new ion optical design is based on a floating type primary column and a new secondary ion extraction system.

2. The primary column design

The new floating primary column designed by CAMECA is fitted at 60° with respect to the secondary axis. It can be equipped with a Cs source and/or a duoplasmatron source. Accordingly to the floating column principle, all the electrostatic lenses and deflectors are biased with respect to an electrostatic chamber while this chamber is biased with respect to the grounded vacuum chamber in the range of [-20 kV, +20 kV]. The primary ions reach the sample surface with an impact energy adjustable from 250 eV to 10 keV while they are keeping their acceleration energy (ranging from 1 keV to 10 keV) in the column. The last focusing lens, not included in the floating column is biased directly with respect to the ground. It is worthwhile to mention that this floating primary column is equipped with a variable shaped beam system, a continuous beam current monitoring and a Wien mass filter.

The variable beam concept is illustrated in the figure 1. Instead of focusing onto the sample a cross-over image, a cross-over image at scale 25 is used for illuminating a square aperture, so-called stencil, which is imaged onto the sample surface at scale 1/25. This shaped beam principle allows to restrict the cross-over to its central part where the brightness is maximum, and therefore to suppress any cross-over tail. This shaped beam scheme would require a single

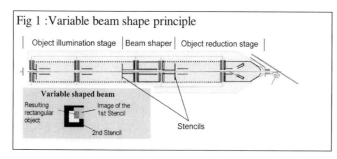

Fig 1 : Variable beam shape principle

stencil. The variable shaped beam scheme consists of a pair of identical stencils. The first one is imaged onto a second one by means of an electrostatic lens. A deflector located in the middle of this lens allows to shift the first stencil square image with the second square stencil, thus achieving the variable rectangle object which is reduced and focused onto the sample. Practically, with a 60° axis, a W × H rectangle with W=2H must be formed to image a square probe in the sample surface plane. Note that this variable shaped beam concept allows to modify the spot size by means of a single deflector, all the lenses being kept at the same bias. Figure 1 shows that the column is entirely symmetric with respect to the shaping deflector center. The two square stencils are mechanically fixed. The Wien mass filter is incorporated in the illumination stage of the column.

The continuous primary beam intensity monitoring consists of sampling the current in a Faraday cup (equipped with a repeller) every frame of the primary beam raster. The primary beam is deflected into the Faraday cup by means of a fast beam blanking for a time corresponding to n lines (typically 20) of the 1024 lines rastered per frame.

3. The secondary ion extraction system

Like for CAMECA IMS 6f instruments, the sample can be biased from -10 kV to +10 kV with respect to the ground. A strong secondary extraction field becomes a major issue at low impact energy. This problem is overcome on TOF SIMS instruments by uncoupling the sputtering process and the analysis processes [5]. However this technique reduces the useful yield since most of the sputtered matter is not collected by the mass spectrometer. Another approach is a shaping of the secondary extraction field in order to minimize its effect on the primary beam trajectory [6].

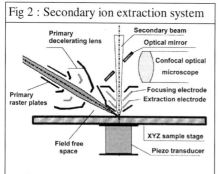

Fig 2 : Secondary ion extraction system

The secondary extraction system represented in Figure 2 consists of providing a field free space from the last primary lens to the secondary extraction field and to uncouple the extraction and focusing functions of the immersion lens. The first immersion lens shielding electrode, brought at the sample potential, has an aperture radius of 2.5mm reducing to this size the extraction area. The uncoupling of both extraction and focusing functions is achieved by including in the immersion lens two independently biased electrodes. It is therefore possible to produce an extraction field as low as required to accommodate low impact energy operation mode, while keeping a high secondary acceleration voltage. Lowering the extraction field has a counterpart which is a chromatic aberration produced by the extraction space. The properties of this immersion lens cannot be presented in detail in this paper. However it must be mentioned that, compared to the IMS 6f immersion lens, the increase of the extraction field chromatic aberration aforementioned is compensated by a reduction of the spherical aberration (factor 2 to 4), the off-axis aberrations (field curvature, coma, distortion) and the conventional lens chromatic aberration as well. It results that there is no loss of transmission compared to the CAMECA IMS 6f.

The figures of merit of this new extraction configuration are : a) impact energy as low as 250 eV can be reached with a secondary extraction field of 3 kV for combining at the same time high depth resolution, high sensitivity and high mass resolution, b) the incidence angle is almost insensitive to secondary polarity and impact energy changes (for instance, at 500 eV the incidence angle is 64° and 58° for positive and negative mode respectively).

An optical microscope (Figure 2) allows to view the sample surface at normal incidence. By combining both this microscope and a Z-axis stage motion (based on piezo transducers), an autofocus routine tunes the Z position of the stage with a precision of ± 2μm and therefore contributes to provide an excellent measurement repeatability.

4. Experimental results

The first CAMECA IMS Wf instrument is equipped with this new ion optical arrangement [7]. Experiments at high and low impact energy have been successfully run. At high impact energy, the analytical performance are the same as the CAMECA IMS 6f. This paper will therefore presents results for low impact energy only.

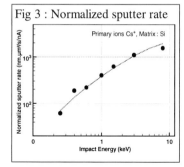

Fig 3 : Normalized sputter rate

Analytical performance in the impact energy range [250eV, 10keV] has been investigated. First results show that a Cs^+ probe carries 40 and 30 nA at 1 keV and 500 eV impact energy, respectively. At 250 eV, a beam intensity of 15 nA and a raster size of 400×400 μm² yields to a sputter rate of 0.3 nm/mn in silicon. The variation of the normalized sputter rate (i.e. sputter yield) in Si as a function of the impact energy is plotted in Figure 3. A drop of the sputter yield by more than one decade when the impact energy decreases from 10 keV to 250 eV can be observed.

Three different samples have been analyzed to demonstrate the analytical performance at low impact energy Cs for negative secondary ion analysis on CAMECA magnetic sector SIMS instruments : *Gate oxide* (3 nm thick), *P implant* (1 keV, 10^{15} at/cm² dose), *As implant* (1 keV, 5 10^{14} at/cm²).

The *Gate oxide* profile measured at 250 eV impact energy is plotted in Figure 4. It shows a well resolved oxide layer with a flat plateau for Si signal. The insert shows the variations of the Si profile shape as a function of the impact energy (250, 400 and 600 eV). The *P implant* profile measured at 600 eV impact energy is plotted in Figure 5. The mass resolution was 3500, the raster size 250×250 μm² and the analyzed area 40×40 μm². The primary beam intensity measured during the profile is also plotted. Owing to the secondary acceleration voltage set at 5 kV more than 100 c/s are measured for a P concentration of 10^{18} at/cm³.

536

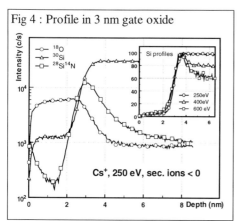

Fig 4 : Profile in 3 nm gate oxide

Cs+, 250 eV, sec. ions < 0

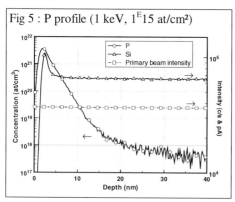

Fig 5 : P profile (1 keV, 1^E15 at/cm²)

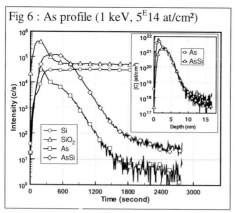

Fig 6 : As profile (1 keV, 5^E14 at/cm²)

Note that the profile dynamic range is limited to less than 5 decades because of a cross contamination of the extraction plate due InP sample analyses run on the same instrument. The *As implant profile* measured at 250 eV impact energy is plotted in Figure 6. The mass resolution was 3500, the raster 400 × 400 µm² and the analyzed area 60 × 60 µm². The As⁻ profile shows a peak at the interface SiO₂/Si not observed for the AsSi⁻ profile. It could be an evidence of a stronger dependence of the As⁻ ion yield on the oxygen content than for AsSi⁻. More investigation are required to conclude. The insert shows the overlay of the two As profiles (the concentration of the As⁻ profile has been normalized to fit with the trailing edge of the AsSi⁻ profile).

5. Summary

The combination of both a floating primary column and a new secondary ion extraction system on CAMECA magnetic sector SIMS provides capabilities for analysis under Cs bombardment with an impact energy as low as 250 eV in both polarities. The low impact energy can be reached with a secondary extraction voltage of 3 kV to maintain high sensitivity and high mass resolution performance featuring sector SIMS instruments.

References

[1] Z.X. Jiang and P.F.A. Alkemade, JVST B16, 1998, p 373.

[2] M. Schuhmacher, B. Rasser, D. Renard, SIMS XI proceedings, 1997, p 695.

[2] M. Schuhmacher, B. Rasser, F. Desse, USJ 99, proceedings JVST, 1999 (in press).

[3] M.G. Dowsett, N.S. Smith, R. Bridgeland, D. Richards, A.C. Lovejoy, P. Pedrick, SIMS X proceedings, A. Benninghoven et al. eds, J. Wiley, Chichester, 1995, p.367.

[4] K. Iltgen, C. Bendel, E. Niehuis, A. Benninghoven, SIMS X proceedings, 1995, p 375.

[5] M.G. Dowsett, S.P. Thompson, C.A. Corlett, SIMS VIII proceedings, 1991, p.187.

[6] T. Bitner, E. de Chambost, P. Monsallut, B. Rasser, M. Schuhmacher, These proceedings.

A. Benninghoven, P. Bertrand, H.-N. Migeon and H.W. Werner (Editors).
Proceedings of the 12th International Conference on Secondary Ion Mass Spectrometry,
Brussels, Belgium, 5-11 September 1999

ANOMALOUS SURFACE TRANSIENT OF BORON IN Si

P.F.A. Alkemade[a] and Z.X. Jiang[b]

[a]DIMES, Delft University of Technology, P.O. Box 5046, 2600 GA Delft, The Netherlands
[b]Institute of Micro Electronics, Singapore Science Park II, Singapore 117685
alkemade@dimes.tudelft.nl, zhixiong@ime.org.sg

1. Introduction

Ultra shallow B implantation in Si will become one of the most important fabrication steps for the coming generations of CMOS transistors. This development requires the availability of a materials analytical technique with high accuracy, both in terms of composition and depth [1]. At present the capabilities of SIMS for this purpose are being discussed widely. It has, *e.g,* been recognised that B delta-doped Si samples are indispensable for this explorative work. However, recent discussions about the quality of certain SIMS analyses or special test samples led to the speculation that boron does not behave in SIMS as nicely as usually is expected [2]. Some observed discrepancies in measured delta peak intensities point to an anomalously long surface transient for B in Si. It is obvious that consistent experimental data are required to resolve this pressing issue.

This work is a contribution to the debate. We measured secondary B^+ intensities from homogeneously and delta-doped Si samples, bombarded by 1 and 2 keV O_2^+ at oblique incidence without oxygen flooding. We explain tentatively the observed intensity variations in terms of surface topography, phase separation and B segregation.

2. Experimental

Two sets of samples were used. The first was taken from a homogeneously B doped (10^{18}/cm^3) 4"-Si(100) wafer, named Si(B). We did not apply any surface cleaning. The second set consisted of Si(100) samples with an MBE-grown Si overlayer with two B deltas and one Ge delta, named Si(BGeBδ). The B deltas with each a nominal content of 1×10^{14}/cm^2, were located at a depth of 14 and 41 nm respectively. The Ge delta - which had no function in this work - was at 28 nm. More details about this samples will be published elsewhere [3].

We used the oxygen beam of a VG IX70S magnetic sector instrument. The impact energy was 1 or 2 keV; the incidence angle, θ, was varied between 45° and 80° [4]. Sputter rates were determined by measuring final crater depths or - for the Si(BGeBδ) sample - from the known spacing between the B deltas. There was no oxygen flooding.

3. Results

Figure 1 shows measurements at E_p=1 and 2 keV. Note the linear scale and the scaled intensities of Ge and Si. The transition depth for $^{30}Si^+$ - where 95% of the final intensity is reached - is 6 nm at 1 keV (calculated assuming a constant erosion rate) and 9 nm at 2 keV. The ratio of the areas below the two B peaks as a function of θ is shown in Fig. 2. One sees that the ratio is almost independent of θ. The average ratio is 0.91±0.02 for E_p=1 keV and 0.99±0.03 for E_p=2 keV.

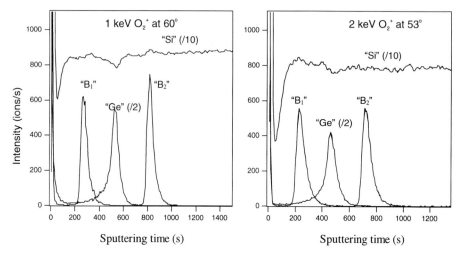

Figure 1. SIMS profiles of B and Ge deltas in Si.

Figure 3 shows the relative signals of various secondary ions versus depth from the Si(B) sample. The secondary intensities of $^{16}O^+$, $^{57}Si_2^+$, $^{60}SiO_2^+$, and $^{72}Si_2O^+$ reach equilibrium within ~5 nm from the surface. Some signals show irreproducible 'long' term variations of <7%, especially in the outermost ~50 nm, see also Fig. 1. The intensity of $^{11}B^+$ on the other hand always continued to rise well beyond the surface transient region of the matrix related ions. This effect was observed repeatedly in many samples from the same or similar wafers.

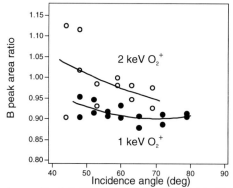

Figure 2. Ratio of B delta peak areas *vs.* θ (B_1/B_2). Full curves guide the eye.

Figure 4 is an overview of four series of measurements on Si(B). The curve through the data points is a fit of a function that approaches exponentially the equilibrium level. The typical rise length is 72 ± 10 nm. The ratio of the fitted intensities at 14 and 41 nm - *viz.*, the depths of the B deltas in the Si(BGeBδ) sample - is 0.94, in agreement with the measured delta area.

ratio at E_p=1 keV and θ=60°: 0.92 ± 0.02. The E_p=2 keV measurements of Fig. 3 show, in contrast, a much smaller difference in behaviour between B and the other secondary ions: $^{16}O^+$ and $^{57}Si_2^+$ reach equilibrium (95% level) after 8 ± 1 nm, while $^{11}B^+$ after 15 ± 2 nm.

We note that we did also a measurement on a heavily contaminated (*viz.*, by skin contact) Si(B) sample. It showed an intense Na^+ signal from various spots of the bombarded surface and a weak C^+ signal. Nevertheless, the same prolonged B transient was observed. And in another measurement we recorded both $^{10}B^+$ and $^{11}B^+$. Apart from the usual isotopic abundance difference and statistical noise, both profiles were the same.

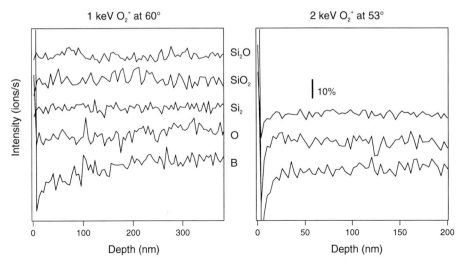

Figure 3. Secondary ion intensities of various ions. The vertical scale is linear and has offsets of 15% between neighbouring traces; see also the 10%-bar

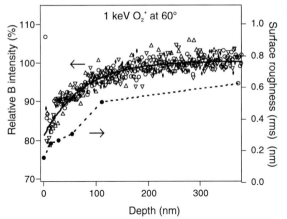

Figure 4. Four series of measurements of the B signal (1 keV 60°); the curve is a fit (see text). Filled circles are the surface roughness, as measured by AFM [7] (right hand scale).

4. Discussion

The 1 keV SIMS measurements show that the intensity of B^+ from the outermost ~100 nm of Si is systematically 5-15% lower than from deeper layers. In contrast, $Si_nO_m^+$ ions ($0 \leq n, m \leq 2$) reach 95% of their final level within ~5 nm. For 2 keV beams, B^+ reaches its final level much earlier, though still later than $Si_nO_m^+$ ions. Thus, B has an anomalously long surface transient at low energies (≤ 1 keV), oblique incidence and no flooding.

If one detects too few secondary ions, one may conclude that (1) there are less atoms of that specific element present; (2) that the atoms have been relocated before emission; (3) that the sputter rate is not constant; (4) that the ionisation probability is lower; or (5) that the emission angles are different. Explanation 3 does not seem to hold in this case: all other secondary ions do not show any reproducible variation. If significant B relocation occurs, e.g., by beam-induced indiffusion, then B^+ reaches equilibrium later than the other secondary ions. However, the measurements of the delta doped samples do not show any shift (within ~1 nm [3]), but do show the same loss of intensity. Thus, explanation 2 does not apply.

The comparison between the 1 and 2 keV measurements indicates that the B concentration is constant in the homogeneously doped sample and that both B deltas in the Si(BGeBδ) sample have indeed the same content. Thus, explanation 1 is not valid either. We note that we do not have an independent measurement of the B content in both deltas.

The remaining explanations are changes in ionisation or in emission angle. It is generally believed that there is dynamic equilibrium when constant intensities of all matrix signals have been reached. Then, the overall composition of the altered layer does not change anymore, as long as no layer of different composition is reached. Only the development of a surface topography might affect the secondary ion intensities [6]. At oblique incidence and low beam energies, minor surface ripples develop rather quickly. Using AFM we have observed [7] ripples already at a depth of 13 nm, though the height variations were less than 0.3 nm (root-mean-square, rms), barely more than for the original surface. Although the ionisation probabilities and the emission angle distribution depend on the (local) surface inclination, a 5-15% increase in ion yields upon such a small increase in surface roughness, is not likely. Hence, an additional mechanism should be involved. It is conceivable that the formation of minor ripples is accompanied by a small phase segregation. Indeed, the occurrence of *major* surface roughening by reactive ion beams is often explained in terms of the formation of local oxide islands [8]. We hypothesise that with the emergence of minor ripples, some areas get enriched with oxygen. These areas attract B atoms from neighbouring regions, probably by surface diffusion. Indeed, the rms roughness in Fig. 4 shows a similar approach to a constant level. When a B atom is sputtered from such an oxygen rich area, the probability for ionisation is enhanced. This small phase separation plus the B segregation lead to a continuous increase in B^+ yields. Only after a finite beam dose, the surface topography, phase separation, and B segregation reach a stationary level, and the B^+ ion yields become stable.

We note here that similar loss of B^+ intensities have been observed under nominally full oxidising conditions [9]. The proposed model may still be applicable if one assumes that also under these conditions local variations in topography and oxygen content are present.

5. Summary and conclusion

Low-energy (1 keV) SIMS measurements with O_2^+ ions at oblique incidence show that the intensity of B secondary ions from the outermost ~100 nm of B-doped Si is lower than from deeper layers. In contrast, $Si_nO_m^+$ secondary ions ($0 \leq n, m \leq 2$) reach equilibrium levels within 5-10 nm from the surface. It is suggested that minor surface rippling causes the anomalous B transient. We stress that 10% lower B^+ yields from the outermost layers of Si are not insignificant. Because semiconductor industries will increase their demands for high precision and ultra-shallow doping profiling in Si, confirmation of the anomalous B transient in other samples or with other instruments and, if possible, a full explanation are urgently needed now.

References

[1] See, *e.g.*: P.K. Chu, S.P. Smith and R.J. Beiler, J. Vac. Sci. Technol. B 14 (1996) 3321
[2] 5th Intern. Workshop on Ultra Shallow Depth Profiling, Research Triangle, NC, 29 March–2 April, 1999
[3] Z.X. Jiang and P.F.A. Alkemade, J. Vac. Sci. Technol. B (submitted)
[4] Z.X. Jiang P.F.A. Alkemade, E. Algra and S. Radelaar, Surf. Interface Anal. 25 (1997) 285
[5] Z.X. Jiang and P.F.A. Alkemade, Surf. Interface Anal. 27 (1999) 125
[6] F.A. Stevie, P.M. Kohara, D.S. Simons and P. Chi, J. Vac. Sci. Techn. A 6 (1988) 76
[7] Z.X. Jiang and P.F.A. Alkemade, J. Vac. Sci. Technol. B 16 (1998) 1971
[8] K. Wittmaack, J. Vac. Sci. Techn. A 8 (1990) 2246
[9] These proceedings.

A. Benninghoven, P. Bertrand, H.-N. Migeon and H.W. Werner (Editors).
Proceedings of the 12th International Conference on Secondary Ion Mass Spectrometry,
Brussels, Belgium, 5-11 September 1999

ROUND ROBIN STUDY OF ULTRA SHALLOW B DEPTH PROFILING EXPERIMENTAL CONDITIONS

Joe Bennett and Alain Diebold

SEMATECH
Austin, Texas 78741
Joe.Bennett@Sematech.org

1. Introduction

In recent years several methodologies have been proposed for profiling ultra shallow dopants, in particular low energy B implants. These methods include low energy ion bombardment at normal and grazing incidence angles, with or without oxygen backfill, using quadrupole, magnetic sector, and TOF-SIMS instruments. One potential difficulty in determining the merit of the different approaches arises from the use of different test samples to investigate the methodologies. In an effort to simplify direct comparisons of the different methodologies SEMATECH is sponsoring an investigation of ultra shallow B depth profiling experimental conditions.

For this study a set of three samples are being sent to multiple laboratories for analysis under various experimental conditions. The participants are being asked to report several important parameters obtained from the samples. Together these data will be used to evaluate the usefulness of the different methodologies.

2. Experimental

Over 30 sets of samples have been distributed. Each sample set consists of: 1) a 1.2×10^{19} atoms/cm^3 ^{11}B bulk doped sample (calibrated against the NIST ^{10}B SRM) to be used as a reference material, 2) a 500 eV, $\sim 1 \times 10^{15}$ atoms/cm^2 ^{11}B implanted sample, taken from an unannealed, pre-amorphized Si wafer, and 3) a 15 layer B delta structure sample (Figure 1.) taken from a 4" wafer grown by Prof. E. H. C. Parker at the University of Warwick (growth temperature 430C, deltas nominally 5×10^{13} atoms/cm^2, layer spacings of ± 1 nm).

Each participant was requested to profile the samples under specific conditions to ensure complete coverage of the various approaches. In the event the participants were not able to achieve the requested profiling conditions, they were free to choose their own.

The bulk-doped standard sample was to be analyzed three times to determine an average RSF. Using the same conditions, the implant sample was to be profiled three times and the average dose reported. The junction depth, X_j at 5×10^{17} atoms/cm^3, was also to be reported. From the delta structure sample the depth of the first and fifth layers were to be reported. The participants were free to choose the method by which the depth scale was calibrated. Most chose to measure the crater of one (or more) profiles using stylus profilometry and assume a constant sputter rate for subsequent profiles. Some participants measured every crater.

542

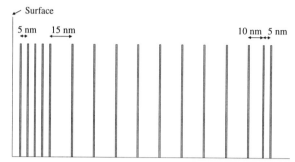

Surface

5 nm   15 nm   10 nm 5 nm

Figure 1. Representation of the B delta-doped structure .

3. Results and Discussion

At the time this manuscript was prepared results had been received from 12 participants. A summary of the results is listed in Table 1. Data from 250 eV O_2^+ bombardment at $0°$ and $40°$, with or without oxygen backfill, and from molecular ion species bombardment have not yet been reported.

Table 1. Summary of experimental conditions and results.

Species	Impact Energy	Angle	Backfill	Dose (atoms/cm^2)	X_j (nm)	1st layer (nm)	5th layer (nm)	Instr. Code*
O_2^+	500 eV	0°	No	6.05e14	12.4	3.4	22.2	17 A
O_2^+	500 eV	0°	No	6.93e14	13.4	3.4	22.2	19 B
O_2^+	500 eV	40°	Yes	6.40e14	13.1	4.1	23.7	08 C
O_2^+	500 eV	44°	Yes	6.59e14	13.7	4.1	23.2	18 D
O_2^+	500 eV	45°	Yes	5.88e14	13.4	4.1	22.5	15 E
O_2^+	500 eV	45°	Yes	7.40e14	13.4	4.1	22.5	06 B
O_2^+	1000 eV	54°	Yes	6.06e14	14.2	3.6	21.3	10 F
O_2^+	1000 eV	60°	Yes	---------	------	3.9	20.9	22 C
O_2^+	1500 eV	50°	Yes	6.30e14	16.7	3.2	22.0	05 G
O_2^+	1500 eV	50°	Yes	6.10e14	15.7	3.4	21.9	11 D
O_2^+	1500 eV	50°	Yes	5.53e14	16.3	3.1	23.4	16 D
O_2^+	1500 eV	50°	Yes	6.33e14	22.2	3.6	22.5	07 D
O_2^+	1500 eV	50°	No	9.37e14	23.7	4.4	22.5	07 D

* Sample set number and instrument: A = Atomika 4100; B = ADEPT 1010; C = PHI 6650; D = Cameca 6f; E = Cameca ION-TOF IV; F = Cameca 4f; G = PHI 6600

3.1 Bulk doped standard

The ^{11}B distribution in the bulk doped standard did not appear to be uniform over the first 20 nm. This phenomenon was observed for all energies and angles (Figure 2) and could lead to an error in determining the RSF if the B-to-Si ratio had not yet reached a constant value. The range of the reported RSF values was 2×10^{21} to 9×10^{22}.

3.2 500 eV ^{11}B implant

The spread in the ^{11}B implant doses reported in Table 1 is about 15% (1σ). If the results from sample set #7 obtained without O_2 backfill are excluded the spread is reduced to about 8%. Some of this spread could be due to errors originating from the RSF determination as

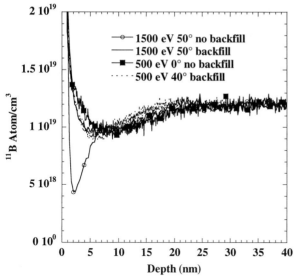

Figure 2. Depth profile of 11B bulk doped Si sample sputtered under different primary ion conditions.

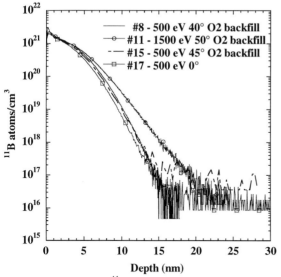

Figure 3. 500 eV ^{11}B implant profiled under different primary beam conditions

described previously. The average dose for samples profiled with 500eV O_2^+ was 6.56 x 10^{14} ± 0.55 atoms/cm^2.

The average for 1500 eV O_2^+ bombardment (excluding sample set #7) was 6.06 x 10^{14} ± 0.36 atoms/cm^2. The average junction depth, X_j for all profiling conditions was 15.6 ± 3.6 nm. X_j was 13.1 ± 0.47 and 17.7 ± 2.8 for 500 eV and 1500 eV bombardment, respectively.

Representative profiles of the 500 eV ^{11}B implant obtained under various sputtering conditions are shown in Figure 3. As expected, the profiles obtained under 500 eV O_2^+ bombardment are significantly more shallow than the data obtained by 1500 eV sputtering.

Clearly the increased primary ion energy and incidence angle of the 1500 eV bombardment conditions leads to poorer depth resolution. It is not clear from the results received to date if there is a significant and reproducible difference between data obtained under 500 eV O_2^+ bombardment at 0° and 40° or 45° (the study called for six different participants to profile with 500 eV O_2^+ bombardment at 0° and 40°; results have been received from four). The sensitivities and dynamic ranges of the different approaches are similar. A more detailed investigation of these parameters as well as analysis time will be conducted as more results are reported.

544

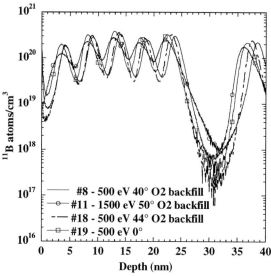

Figure 4. Depth profiles of B delta structure obtained under different sputtering conditions.

3.3 B delta structure

Representative profiles of the delta structure obtained under various sputtering conditions are shown in Figure 4. The average depths of the first delta layer as determined under 500 eV and 1500 eV O_2^+ bombardment conditions were 3.8 ± 0.3 nm and 3.3 ± 0.2 nm, respectively. This difference is statistically significant (p = 0.03). Within the 500 eV results it appears as if the depths recorded under 0° bombardment are shallower than those recorded at 40° - 45°. This is somewhat contradictory to previous studies that suggested that oblique angle incidence sputtering introduces surface roughening and differential sputtering artifacts [1,2]. However, the data in those studies did not include the primary beam energy and angle range used in this investigation. More results will have to be reported before a definitive conclusion is reached. It is interesting to note that there is no significant difference in the average depths of the fifth layer, 22.7 ± 0.6 nm for 500 eV bombardment and 22.4 ± 0.7 nm for 1500 eV bombardment. The precision of the measurements is also better than the results for the first layer. It is important to consider the method used to calibrate the depth scale for this sample (as well as the implant sample) because measuring craters ≤ 50nm could introduce some error.

4. Acknowledgements and Participants

Special thanks to Sean Corcoran of Intel Corporation for allowing us to build off his initial round robin study and for his advice and helpful comments. The participants and their affiliations:

Paul Ronsheim, IBM Microelectronics
Michel Schuhmacher, Cameca Instruments, Inc.
Rainer Loesing, North Carolina State University
Jennifer McKinley, Lucent Technologies
Tom Mates, University of California, Santa Barbara
Gary Mount, Charles Evans & Associates

Philip Merrill, Evans Texas
Charles Magee, Evans East
Sean Corcoran, Intel Corporation
Alan Brown, CSMA Ltd.
Ewald Niehuis, Tascon GmbH

References

[1] K. Wittmack and S. Corcoran, *J. Vac. Sci. Technol. B*, **16**, (1998) 272.
[2] Z. X. Jiang and P. F. A. Alkemeade, *App. Phys. Lett.*, **73**, (1998) 315.

A. Benninghoven, P. Bertrand, H.-N. Migeon and H.W. Werner (Editors).
Proceedings of the 12th International Conference on Secondary Ion Mass Spectrometry,
Brussels, Belgium, 5-11 September 1999
545

ON THE ANGULAR DEPENDENCE OF PROFILE BROADENING IN SILICON UNDER OXYGEN AND NITROGEN BOMBARDMENT

M.Petravic, P.N.K.Deenapanray, C.M.Demanet[#], and D.W.Moon[*]

Department of Electronic Materials Engineering, Research School of Physical Sciences and
Engineering, The Australian National University, Canberra ACT 0200, Australia
[#] Department of Physics, University of Transkei, Umtata, Postbag 5100, South Africa
[*]Surface Analysis Group, KRISS, Yusung P.O. Box 102, Taejon 305-606, S.Korea

1. Introduction

The choice of impact angle for primary ion beam in SIMS analysis affects the sputtering yield of matrix and the depth resolution of impurity profiles. In general, both these quantities increase with the angle of incidence. Several theoretical models predict a $(\cos\theta)^{-f}$ dependence for polycrystalline and isotropic materials [1,2], with the exponential factor f between ~1 and ~5/3 [1]. The theoretical predictions usually break down in following cases: i) at the glancing incidence, when most of atom recoils are generated close to the surface and the reflection coefficient of the primary beam becomes large; ii) at the near-normal incidence for reactive ion bombardment which induces formation of chemical compounds at the surface. In this paper we explore in some detail the later point. We present the angular dependence of depth resolution in Si under O_2^+ and N_2^+ bombardment in the transient region between the pure matrix (or the substoichiometric compound) and the stoichiometric compound (SiO_2 or Si_3N_4) formed under ion bombardment. The angular dependence of compound formation has been reported previously [3,4]. The critical angle for oxide formation changes from 25° for 4 keV/ion bombardment to 34° for 14.5 keV/ion bombardment. The nitride formation follows the similar pattern, but overstoichiometric, rather than stoichiometic layers are formed at these angles.

2. Experimental

In this study we used Cz Si wafers of (100) orientation (1-10 Ωcm) ion-implanted with Ni, Na, F and Ga and the Si samples with buried marker layers grown either by MBE (B, Ge and Sb delta-layers) or the ion-beam sputter deposition technique (GaAs layers). All SIMS measurements were performed in a quadrupole type SIMS instrument (Riber MIQ 256) in which the primary beam energy and angle of incidence can be changed independently. Typically, a 4-14 keV/ion O_2^+ or N_2^+ beam, focused to a spot <60 μm in diameter and rastered over an area of 400x400/cosθ μm², was employed and secondary ions were collected from the central 10% of the eroded area. The roughness at the bottom of some craters created on a Si wafer was examined by the atomic force microscopy (AFM).

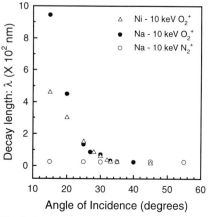

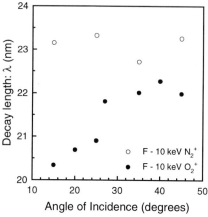

Fig.1 Decay length of Ni and Na implanted into Si as a function of the impact angle.

Fig.2 The angular dependence of λ for F in Si under O_2^+ and N_2^+ bombardment.

3. Results and Discussion

We describe the depth resolution of SIMS profiles by the decay length λ which defines the exponential decay of the trailing edge of a profile. The angular dependence of λ in Si under oxygen and nitrogen bombardment at near-normal incidence may reflect several distinctive processes.

The large decay lengths, as a consequence of large degradation of SIMS profiles, have been found for some mobile atoms in Si [5,6]. In Fig.1 we illustrate this effect for profiles of Ni and Na implanted into Si. Below 30° (measured from the surface normal) λ exhibits a large increase of over an order of magnitude. Such strong effect can be understood in terms of beam-induced segregation of impurity atoms towards the interface between the SiO_2 layer, formed during oxygen bombardment, and the Si substrate. It has been shown that the segregation of Na is dominated by the electric field effects (build-up of an electric field across the insulating SiO_2 layer drives the Na^+ ions to the oxide side of the SiO_2/Si interface) [7,8], while the migration of Ni to the Si side of the interface is dominated by the oxidation thermodynamics (the high heat of Ni-oxide formation and the high solubility of Ni in amorphous Si represents the dominant driving force in this case) [6]. Following the thermodynamic arguments, one would expect a decrease in λ for an impurity having lower heat of oxide formation than SiO_2, under bombardment conditions favouring the oxide formation at the surface. Indeed, it been shown that impurities such as Al, Mg, Ti, Hf and Zr migrate toward the surface and into the stoichiometric oxide which is formed at the surface. Consequently, the SIMS profiles appear sharper, giving smaller λ-values [8,9]. On the other hand, the field induced segregation should have the same effect on highly electronegative elements, such as F and Cl, which have a tendency to become negatively charged. In Fig.2 we show the angular dependence of λ for F implanted into Si (solid circles). Under the influence of an electric field, the F^- ions start to migrate toward the surface immediately upon formation

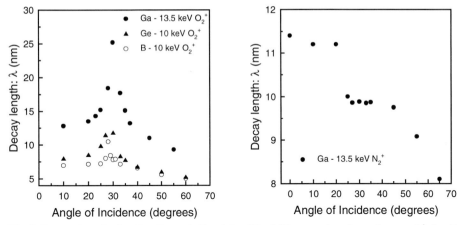

Fig.3 Decay length for B, Ge and Ga delta layers in Si as a function of angle of incidence.

Fig.4 The angular dependence of λ for Ga in Si under 13.5 keV N$_2^+$ bombardment.

of a surface SiO$_2$ layer (below 30°), thus providing sharper SIMS profiles. The effect is more pronounced for stronger fields, i.e. thicker oxide films at lower impact angles.

The bombardment of Si with N$_2^+$ ions may cause similar effects to O$_2^+$ bombardment, as nitrogen and oxygen have similar masses and ranges in Si, show similar sputtering effects and both have the ability to form chemical compounds with Si. However, no anomalous broadening of implanted impurities have been observed under irradiation conditions when a nitride layer forms at the surface, as illustrated by open circles in Fig.1 for Na profiles and Fig.2 for F profiles. These results suggest little segregation and relocation of impurities in Si under nitrogen bombardment and reflect extremely low mobility of impurities in Si nitride.

Another unusual effect in angular dependence of λ has been observed previously only for Ga in Si [10]. The decay length of Ga passes through a distinctive maximum at ~27° for 10 keV O$_2^+$ bombardment. This unusual effect has not been explained so far. In order to examine the origin of this phenomenon, we have undertaken a series of careful measurements for a range of impurities in Si. In addition to Ga (either implanted into Si or from thin buried GaAs layers), we have profiled B, Ge and Sb deltas in Si (these elements do not show anomalous segregation effects in Si which may overrun the maximum in λ). The maximum in λ has been observed for all impurities under investigation (not only buried delta-layers, but implanted ions as well) and at about the same critical angle for a given impact energy. As shown in Fig.3 λ exhibits an maximum ~27° for Ge and B under 10 keV O$_2^+$ bombardment. In addition, we have observed the increase of critical angle with the bombardment energy (see Fig.3 where maximum of λ for Ge under 13.5 keV O$_2^+$ bombardment shifts to ~30°). On the other hand, nitrogen bombardment do not show any maximum in λ, as shown in Fig.4 for Ga profiles. Rather, a few steps are observed at impact angles corresponding to the transition from overstoichiometric to stoichiometric Si nitride (~25°) and then to the substoichiometric compound (~40°) [4]. We note in Fig.3 that λ exhibits a rather sharp maximum around an angle close to the critical angle for oxide formation [3]. It seems that the depth resolution

548

deteriorates only for a small angular interval around this critical angle. For these angles, the surface may not be fully and uniformly oxidised, as only islands of stoichiometric and sub-stoichiometric oxides may be formed. If so, the surface roughening will be higher for this transition state of the surface than for the pure Si (or SiO_2) surfaces. We use the AFM to find a possible correlation between the surface roughness around the critical angle and the position of the maximum in λ. This work is still in progress, but our preliminary results, illustrated in Fig.5 for 14.5 keV O^+ bombardment, clearly indicate that the surface roughness significantly increases around 35° which indeed is the critical angle for oxide formation for this impact energy [3].

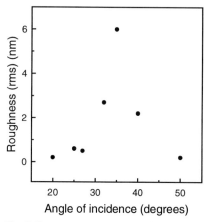

Fig.5 Root mean square of the Si surface roughness as measured by AFM after 14.5 keV O^+ bombardment at different angles.

4. Conclusion

In conclusion, we have shown that λ exhibits different types of angular dependence within the angular interval favouring formation of chemical compounds at the surface. Mobile impurities having higher heat of oxide formation than Si (such as Cu, Ni or Au) or being susceptible to field effects (positively charged ions, such as Na^+) segregate out of oxide showing dramatic increase in λ. Impurities with lower heat of oxide formation (such as Ti, Zr or Hf) or negatively charged impurities susceptible to the field effect (F^- or Cl^-), are driven into the oxide and closer to the surface, thus improving the depth resolution. The increased surface roughening around the critical angle for SiO_2 formation causes deterioration of depth resolution within a small angular window around the critical angle. This effect is pronounced only for the impurities with low mobilities that do not segregate out of oxide.

References

[1]   P.Sigmund, Phys.Rev. **B184**, 383 (1969).
[2]   P.C.Zalm and C.J.Vriezema, Nucl.Instrum.Methods **B67**, 495 (1992).
[3]   P.N.K.Deenapanray and M.Petravic, Surf.Interface Anal. **27**, 92 (1999).
[4]   M.Petravic, J.S.Williams, M.Conway and P.N.K.Deenapanray, Appl.Phys.Lett. **73**, 1278 (1998).
[5]   K.Wittmaack, Appl.Phys.Lett. **48**, 1400 (1986).
[6]   M.Petravic, B.G.Svensson, J.S.Williams and J.M.Glasko, Nucl.Instrum.Methods **B118**, 151 (1996).
[7]   C.W.Magee and W.L.Harington, Appl.Phys.Lett. **33**, 193 (1978).
[8]   M.Petravic, Appl.Surf.Sci. **135**, 200 (1998).
[9]   P.N.K.Deenapanray and M.Petravic, J.Appl.Phys. 85, 3993 (1999).
[10]   Y.Homma and T. Maruo, Surf.Interface Anal. **14**, 725 (1989).

A. Benninghoven, P. Bertrand, H.-N. Migeon and H.W. Werner (Editors).
Proceedings of the 12th International Conference on Secondary Ion Mass Spectrometry,
Brussels, Belgium, 5-11 September 1999

549

ULTRA SHALLOW DEPTH PROFILING AT SILICON SURFACE BY MEANS OF TIME OF FLIGHT SIMS AND QUADRUPOLE SIMS

T.Hoshi, and M.Kudo*

ULVAC-PHI,Inc. 370Enzo, Chigasaki, 253-0084 Japan

*Department of Applied Physics, Sekei University, Tokyo, 180 Japan

1. Introduction

Recently, the need for near-surface analysis in the Si semiconductor industry is increasing, such as analysis of ultra shallow dopants, analysis of <10nm thick gate dielectric films, analysis of surface contamination and so on. Traditional SIMS primary beam conditions, 10-15kV beam energy, can not provide the stable secondary ion signals within the top 10nm of the sample surface. Because the sensitivity-enhancing effects caused by the implantation of the primary beam do not become apparent until the surface has been sputtered to at least twice the depth of the implanted primary ions.

In this study, we investigated the analytical performances of shallow depth profile by using quadrupole based SIMS (Q-SIMS) combined with low energy primary beam and TOF-SIMS with dual beam approach. The samples prepared for this study were shallowly implanted arsenic into silicon wafer and oxide/nitride film formed on silicon wafer(SiON/Si). The results were discussed with respect to the accuracy of quantification (concentration / depth conversion), such as pre-equilibration depth and depth resolution.

2. Experimental

Using shallowly implanted arsenic sample, we investigated the shapes of AsSi$^-$ secondary ion as a function of a primary Cs beam energy. The sputtering condition of Cs beam was 500eV-2keV(60°t) for Q-SIMS and 1keV- 2keV(42°t) for TOF-SIMS, where an incident angle was measured from surface normal. Typical analysis condition of TOF-SIMS was 18keV, 20nA(DC current), 7um raster Ga beam. 10 seconds data acquisition by pulsed Ga beam with 25kHz reputation rate and 5 - 20sec Cs beam sputtering was carried out alternately. TOF-SIMS measurement under 2kV-oxygen beam sputtering was also carried out for the comparison at the native oxide region. Positive ion yields were enhanced by flooding the sample with oxygen (5x10^{-5}Pa) during the TOF-SIMS depth profile. The energy of an implanted arsenic was 5keV(Rp=.7.5nm) to minimize the inference caused by a pre-equilibration region or a native oxide layer on silicon wafer. In case of 500eV implanted energy, a projected range of an implanted arsenic will be located just at the interface between native oxide and silicon substrate. And it will be hard to understand how the energy or angle of the primary beam affecting the shape of the secondary ions.

Using 3nm SiON/Si sample, we investigated the shapes of CsSi$^+$, CsO$^+$ and CsN$^+$ secondary ions as a function of a primary Cs beam energy and incident angle. The sputtering condition of Cs beam was 350 - 750eV(45°-80°), 1-2keV(60°) for Q-SIMS.

During Q-SIMS and TOF-SIMS measurements, conditions of vacuum were 5×10^{-8}Pa and 1×10^{-7}Pa, respectively. The Q-SIMS apparatus used in this study was a Physical Electronics Model ADEPT 1010 and the TOF-SIMS apparatus was a Physical Electronics TRIFT II.

3.Results and discussion

3.1 Quantification (concentration / depth conversion)

For the quantification of near surface region, there are many difficulties; the inaccurate measurement of a shallowly sputtered crater and the changes of both sputtering and secondary ionization yields[1]-[4] before the surface has been sputtered to 2 or 3 times the range of the implanted primary ions. In addition, the sputtered crater of TOF-SIMS measurement has a two step profile which created by Cs or O_2 sputtering and gallium analysis beam, so it is almost impossible to measure the two step crater accurately. In this study, the sputtering rates for the various primary beam conditions used in the profiles shown in Figures were estimated under assumption that the peak of implanted arsenic locates 7.5nm from sample surface or thickness of SiON film is 3nm. No corrections for the changes of the initial sputtering rate have been applied. Furthermore, no corrections for the changes of sputtering rate between SiO_2 and silicon substrate were done. The arsenic concentration was calculated by using a relative sensitivity factor (RSF) which obtained from the dose of implants. Because of these assumptions used in quantification, it is likely that none of the depth profiles represent the "true" implant distribution. However, for the first order approximation, it is useful to discuss the shape of Q-SIMS and TOF-SIMS depth profiles under the assumptions used in quantification, especially from the practical point of view.

3.2 Arsenic profile

Figure 1 shows the typical depth profile obtained by using Q-SIMS and dual beam TOF-SIMS. Arsenic depth profiles are concentration axis and silicon depth profiles are counts axis. The shapes of arsenic profile below 5nm depth were very similar, but with progressive reduction in the decay length (1/e) of arsenic at 1×10^{20}atoms/cm^3 concentration was observed, namely 2nm (Cs 500eV Q-SIMS), 4nm (Cs 2keV Q-SIMS), 4nm (Cs 2keV sputter TOF-SIMS) and 5nm (O_2 2keV sputter TOF-SIMS). As the energy of Cs sputtering deceased, it was observed that the emission of AsSi$^-$ molecular secondary ion was suppressed and the emission of Si$^-$ ion was increased. The suppression of molecular ions and the increasing of atomic ion can be explained by the changing of surface coverage of Cs, because the sputtering yield of silicon was also decreased from 4.8(2keV) to 1.4(500eV), see Figure 3. Although suppression of molecular ion, the detection limit of arsenic was observed below 1×10^{16}atoms/cm^3 by 500eV Cs sputtering condition (Q-SIMS) and around 1×10^{17}atoms/cm^3 for TOF-SIMS. It is clear that evaluation of P-N junction depth, such as 1×10^{17}atoms/cm^3 concentration level, can be better to choose the 500eV Cs sputtering condition from the point of the correct depth measurement and the proper intensity of secondary ion at 1×10^{17}atoms/cm^3 concentration level. At near surface region (0-5nm), the shape of arsenic profile had a strong dependence on the specie of primary beam. Namely O_2 sputtering with oxygen flooding can analyze As$^+$ secondary ion through SiO_2 layer to silicon substrate under similar ionization yields, but AsSi$^-$ or Si$^-$ secondary ion were reduced in the SiO_2 layer in case of Cs sputtering. This is the reason why all Cs sputtering results have the less concentration at near surface region (0-5nm). For precise dose calculation, we should choose the O_2 sputtering and As$^+$ measurement in both Q-SIMS and TOF-SIMS. We can conclude that a sub-keV Cs

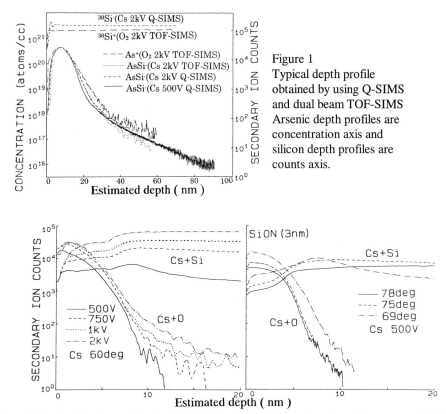

Figure 1
Typical depth profile obtained by using Q-SIMS and dual beam TOF-SIMS Arsenic depth profiles are concentration axis and silicon depth profiles are counts axis.

Figure 2 Typical depth profile obtained by using Q-SIMS as a function of energy and incident angle of Cs beam.

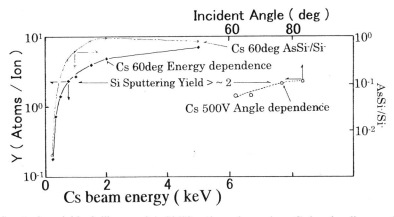

Figure 3 Sputtering yield of silicon and AsSi⁻/Si⁻ ratio under various Cs bombarding conditions

sputtering and AsSi- measurement is better for evaluation of P-N junction depth and an O_2 sputtering and As^+ measurement is for precise dose calculation.

3.3 SiON profile

Figure 2(a),(b) shows the typical depth profile obtained by using Q-SIMS as a function of energy and incident angle of Cs beam. Figure 3 summarize the sputtering yield of silicon under various bombarding conditions of Cs beam. In Figure 2(a), the interface between SiON and Si substrate became unclear as the energy of Cs beam increased. In addition, $CsSi^+$ signal did not become stable until 25nm in Si substrate in case of 500eV Cs bombardment. This fact means that lower Cs energy do not offer best analytical results in SiON/Si depth profile. For 500eV Cs bombardment, the interface became sharper and transient region in Si substrate became smaller in 75 – 80degree incident angle, see in Figure 2(b). Similar trend was observed in 350 – 750eV Cs bombardment; 75-80degree give the sharpest interface and smallest transient region in Si substrate. It is found that each Cs bombarding energies has the best incident angle for the analysis of thin SiON film. Best combinations of energy and incident angle seem that more than 2 Si atoms should be sputtered by 1 Cs primary ion, see in Figure 3.

4. Conclusion

Using shallowly implanted arsenic and thin SiON/Si samples, the analytical results by Q-SIMS and dual beam TOF-SIMS were discussed. For 5keV arsenic implanted samples, it can be concluded that a sub-keV Cs sputtering and AsSi- measurement is better for evaluation of P-N junction depth and an O_2 sputtering and As^+ measurement is for precise dose calculation. For SiON/Si sample, It is found that each Cs bombarding energy has the best incident angle to give the sharpest interface and smallest transient region in Si substrate, such as 75-80deg.

References

[1]M.G.Dowsett; Atomic Layer Characterization ALC97 (1997) 18

[2]C.W.Magee, G.R.Mount, S.P.Smith, B. Herner and H.-J.Gossmann; XII international conference on Ion Implantation Technology, (1998) 1

[3]M.G.Dowsett; SIMS XI , ed by A.Benninghoven et al. John Wiley & Sons(1997) 259

[4]T.Hoshi, R.Oiwa and M.Kudo, J.Surface Science Society of Japan V19 (1998) 527

A. Benninghoven, P. Bertrand, H.-N. Migeon and H.W. Werner (Editors).
Proceedings of the 12th International Conference on Secondary Ion Mass Spectrometry,
Brussels, Belgium, 5-11 September 1999

COMPOSITION PROFILING OF NANOMETRIC OXIDE FILMS
ON Al-4.7 wt% Mg AND IRON (IF-Ti) ALLOYS

G. Plassart[1], G. Rautureau[2], E. Beauprez[2], M. Aucouturier[1]

[1] Université Paris-Sud, Lab. Métallurgie (URA CNRS 1107), Bât. 410, F-91405 Orsay Cedex
[2] DGA, Centre Technique d'Arcueil, 16b Av. Prieur de la Côte d'Or, F-94114 Arcueil Cedex
e-mail : Marc.Aucouturier@metal.u-psud.fr

1. Introduction

Characterisation of ultra-thin surface films, as native oxides on metals, needs the simultaneous use of various methods. Surface analysis methods as X ray-induced Photoelectron Spectroscopy (XPS) bring information on the composition and chemical nature, but may lead to incomplete characterisation, e.g. on amounts of hydrogen and trace elements ; they may also bring biased results due to preferential ion sputtering during profiling (oxide reduction). On the other side, SIMS or GDOS (Glow Discharge Optical Spectrometry) depth-profiling is perturbed by the transitory step of primary beam implantation.

The present paper concerns analyses of oxide films of less than 10 nm thickness formed at low temperature (< 300° C) on two cold-rolled metallic alloys. The analytical SIMS conditions are discussed with respect to the expected results, specially in terms of primary beam implantation. The composition profiles obtained by SIMS are compared to the results of XPS, GDOS and transmission electron microscopy (TEM) [1,2]. A depth distribution scheme of the respective oxides and hydroxides is proposed and discussed.

2. Materials, choice of analytical conditions

The two investigated alloys are : a Al-4.7 wt% Mg alloy (A5182 from Pechiney)of industrial purity (Mn = 0.37, Fe = 0.24, Si = 0.11 wt%) ; an interstitial-free steel with titanium addition (450 ppm) (IF-Ti from Usinor), with very low carbon content (21 ppm), whose main alloying element is Mn (1200 ppm) and main impurity is Al (370 ppm). The Al-Mg alloy is as-cold rolled, the IF-Ti alloy was submitted to a short annealing (a few min. at 770° C in H_2 + N_2) after cold rolling. The sheet surface oxide films are characterised by XPS, GDOS, and TEM [1,2]. Their thickness is respectively ≈ 5 to 20 nm for A5182 and ≈ 5 to 8 nm for IF-Ti.

According to the very small film thickness to be analysed, it was necessary to select carefully the SIMS analysing parameters. It is well known [3] that SIMS profiling from the surface may be drastically perturbed by transitory phenomena as : exaltation effects by surface polluting species ; transitory primary ion implantation ; atomic mixing ; preferential sputtering ; segregation ; etc. In the present case, the polluting layer is part of the study, and the main disturbing effects are transitory primary ion implantation and eventually atomic mixing.

In a previous communication, a simple model was described to calculate the primary beam implantation transitory stage [4]. Following that model and the fact that the investigated layers are mainly constituted of oxidised species, it was chosen to use Ar^+ primary ions (high matrix effects) and to detect positive secondary ions (more grazing beam). As precise beam focusing is important to allow an evenly recessing surface, it was not chosen to decrease the impact energy lower than 5.5 KeV (10 kV acceleration, − 4.5 kV specimen polarisation). In such conditions, the beam impact angle in the Cameca IMS 3F used equipment is 42° with respect to the surface normal. The primary current was 1 to 10 nA (commonly 2 nA) rastered over 250x250 or 500x500 µm². The analysed area was 60 µm diameter. The implantation range R_p from TRIM calculation [5] is 4.2 nm in Al_2O_3 and 4.1 nm in Fe_2O_3, with respective straggling σ_p of 2 nm and 2.2 nm. Application of the model [4] leads to a transitory implantation stage extension over the 10 first nm sputtering from the surface. In fact, as evidenced in the mentioned work [4] and through the following results, the implantation steady state is reached much more rapidly.

In one case, it was necessary to detect negative secondary ions in order to detect low concentration of electronegative species (C, O, OH in IF-Ti film). The impact angle becomes 24,5° for an impact energy of 14.5 KeV ; R_p = 6.7 nm, σ_p = 2.3 nm ; the implantation transitory stage extends theoretically over 10 nm from the surface. Other parameters are identical.

Another difficulty is identification of the chemical origin of the recorded secondary ions. Those layers are of complex chemical nature and exaltation effects are common. As discussed in the following sections, the link between a recorded ion and the originating chemical specie in the film is deduced by comparison with the results of XPS and GDOS analyses.

3. Results and interpretation on Al-Mg alloy

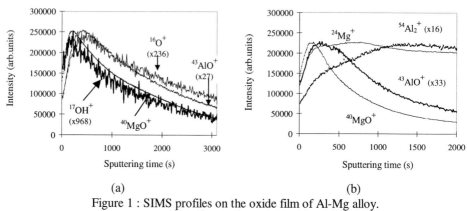

(a)   (b)

Figure 1 : SIMS profiles on the oxide film of Al-Mg alloy.
a : $^{16}O^+$, $^{17}OH^+$, $^{40}MgO^+$, $^{43}AlO^+$;
b : $^{24}Mg^+$, $^{40}MgO^+$, $^{43}AlO^+$, $^{54}Al_2^+$

The MgO^+ profile is different from the Mg^+ profile. It may be seen in figure 1a that the MgO^+ signal follows exactly the OH^+ signal, and can be thus attributed to the hydroxide $Mg(OH)_2$. The occurrence of the MgO^+ and OH^+ maximum before the AlO^+ and Mg^+ maximum indicates that the Mg hydroxide is situated at the extreme surface of the film. This was confirmed by XPS analysis under ion sputtering and GDOS. Semi-quantitative XPS leads to an Al^{3+}/Mg^{2+} ratio of 2 in the film.

The AlO$^+$ signal represents the oxide (Al$_2$O$_3$) and hydroxide (AlOOH + Al(OH)$_3$) compounds, but the position of the OH$^+$ maximum indicates that the hydroxilated species are preferentially situated near the extreme surface. This is also confirmed by XPS and GDOS.

In figure 1b, the Mg$^+$ signal can be unambiguously attributed to MgO. The position of its maximum after AlO$^+$ maximum indicates that MgO is preferentially situated at the oxide/metal interface. But Mg oxide is also present in the whole layer and even in the substrate (i.e. after the stabilisation of the Al$_2$$^+$ signal). Both interpretations (presence of MgO at the oxide/metal interface, presence of oxidised Mg-rich particles in the substrate under the surface film) are confirmed by XPS under ion sputtering, GDOS, and analytical TEM.

Another interesting feature appears in figure 1b : the Al$_2$$^+$ signal exhibits a shoulder inside the oxide layer. It is known that Al$_2$$^+$ emission is favoured by metallic aluminium (Al$^\circ$). This presence of metallic Al clusters in the oxide film has been confirmed by angle-resolved XPS measurements. The formation of those clusters is attributed to a reduction of Al$_2$O$_3$ by diffusing Mg from the substrate [1,6]. A complementary analysis was done on a specimen polished and oxidised in controlled dry oxygen atmosphere, for which the amount of MgO formed is higher than here : the Al$_2$$^+$ shoulder is in that case more pronounced and the presence of Al$^\circ$ is unambiguously confirmed by XPS, thus establishing the proposed interpretation.

4. Results and interpretation on the IF-Ti alloy

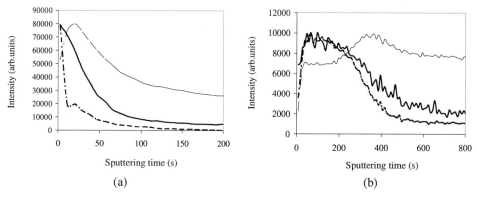

(a)

(b)

Figure 2 : SIMS profiles on the oxide film of IF-Ti alloy.
(a) : negative ions ^{12}C$^-$, ^{16}O$^-$, ^{17}OH$^-$
(b) : positive ions ^{71}MnO$^+$, ^{72}FeO$^+$, ^{112}Fe$_2$$^+$

From figure 2a, it is seen that, although the analysis conditions are not favourable for thin film analysis (negative secondary ions), variations in the carbon profile can be evidenced. This results from a limited internal contamination of the film by the cold rolling lubricant. Comparison of the O$^-$ and OH$^-$ profiles shows that hydroxides are present at the extreme surface but also inside the film. Both results (carbon internal contamination and presence of hydroxides) are confirmed by GDOS and XPS analysis.

By semi-quantitative XPS, the Fe^{3+}/Fe^{2+} ratio is estimated to 3.6.

Figure 2b gives information about the presence of oxidised Mn. Oxidised Mn is even present in the first layers of the substrate, as the MnO$^+$ does not fall to negligible values after

556

the interface, revealed by the FeO$^+$ signal down-drop. The Fe$_2$$^+$ signal exhibits a maximum after the interface. Those observations are attributed to the presence of oxidised Mn-containing compounds and Fe-rich precipitates underneath the interface. This interpretation is confirmed by SEM observation of precipitates, by GDOS analysis, and by complementary experiments on polished and in-situ reoxidised specimens for which the MnO$^+$ signal falls logically to zero after the interface. By semi-quantitative XPS, the Mn$_{ox}$/Fe$_{ox}$ ratio is of the order of 0.2, which is a high enrichment with respect to the substrate composition.

5. Summary and conclusions

Physicochemical characterisation of ultra-thin oxide films on metals can be accomplished by SIMS under the condition that the analytical parameters are carefully selected for that purpose. The interpretation of the profiles, particularly the attribution of the secondary ions detected to given chemical species present in the film can only be done through comparison with other analytical methods as XPS, GDOS and analytical TEM.

The film on as-rolled Al-4.7 wt% Mg is an equimolar Al$_2$O$_3$ + MgO mixture, containing metallic aluminium clusters, surmounted by Al and Mg hydroxides. MgO is concentrated at the oxide/metal interface, but also present in the whole film and underneath the interface.

On the cold rolled and shortly annealed IF-Ti, the oxide film is constituted of an equimolar mixture of Fe$_2$O$_3$ + Fe$_3$O$_4$ containing hydroxilated species on the whole thickness.

For both Al-4.7 wt% Mg and IF-Ti alloys, the principal alloying element (Mg or Mn respectively) is highly enriched in the native film.

Acknowledgement

This work is under the research program "Mise en forme des matériaux, contact métal-outil-lubrifiant" supported by CNRS, IRSID (groupe USINOR) and Pechiney Recherche, involving : Université Paris-Sud Orsay (LMS), Collège de France (PMC), ECL (LTDS), INSA Lyon (LMC), INPT Toulouse (IMF), ENSMP (CEMEF), CNRS (LCA).

References

[1]. S. Scotto-Sherif, E. Darque-Ceretti, G. Plassart, M. Aucouturier, to be published in J. Mat. Sci. (1999)
[2]. G. Plassart, C. Sévérac, A.M. Huntz, M. Aucouturier, Journ. Aut., SF2M, Paris, 1997, Rev. Métall., Sci. Gén. Mat., hors série 1997, 202.
[3]. E. Darque-Ceretti, H-N. Migeon, M. Aucouturier, L'analyse ionique par émission secondaire, in : Techniques de l'Ingénieur, P2618-P2619, (1998-1999).
[4]. A. Boutry-Forveille, G. Blaise, E.A. Garcia, M. Aucouturier, Internat. Conf. "SIMS IX", Yokohama, Nov. 1993.
[5]. J.P. Ziegler, J.P. Biersak, U. Littmark, The stopping and range of ions in solids, Pergamon Press, London, 1985.
[6]. A. Kimura, M. Shibata, K. Kondoh, Y. Takeda, M. Katayama, T. Kanie, H. Takada, Appl. Phys. Lett. 70 (1997) 3615.

A. Benninghoven, P. Bertrand, H.-N. Migeon and H.W. Werner (Editors).
Proceedings of the 12th International Conference on Secondary Ion Mass Spectrometry,
Brussels, Belgium, 5-11 September 1999

CHARACTERIZATION OF ULTRA-THIN OXIDE
AND OXYNITRIDE FILMS

D. F. Reich[1], B. W. Schueler[1] and J. Bennett[2]

[1]Physical Electronics, 575 Chesapeake Dr., Redwood City, CA 94063, U.S.A.,
freich@phi.com
[2] Sematech, 2706 Montopolis Dr., Austin , TX 78741, U.S.A.

1. Introduction

Because of their superior boron diffusion barrier characteristics, thin (<10nm) oxynitride gate dielectrics and their fabrication methods are being studied extensively. The distribution of nitrogen and hence the properties of the film vary with the fabrication process, and it is desirable to be characterize these films with confidence. The characterization of thin oxide and oxynitride films by SIMS is currently performed in our laboratories using quadrupole-based instruments, employing 750-1000eV Cs$^+$ beams at 60° incidence. The CsM$^+$ protocol is used. As the gate oxide thickness is reduced to 2nm it is desirable to achieve better depth resolution in the profiles. Hoshi et al. have noted recently [1] that reducing the Cs$^+$ beam energy further below 750eV at 60° incidence results in complex, non-flat CsO$^+$ and CsSi$^+$ signals in both the oxide and the substrate. The effects are more pronounced as the energy is reduced. Although these specific effects can be avoided using low Cs$^+$ energies and negative secondary ion signals, matrix effects cause SiN$^-$ signals to be enhanced at the interface and well into the substrate, in a manner that is not suggested from CsN$^+$ data on the same sample.

In order to chart the dependence of the CsM$^+$ matrix ion signals upon beam energy and angle, a well-characterized 8nm oxynitride film was profiled with Cs$^+$ beam energies of 500, 600, 750 and 1000eV, and at angles of incidence from 35-80°. Based on these results, a 2.5nm thick nitrided oxide was profiled with 300-500eV Cs$^+$ at glancing angles of incidence (≥ 75°), and appeared to demonstrate high depth resolution and relatively constant matrix signals suitable for the analysis of such thin films. Thicker oxides may be profiled at energies of 750eV or more with less glancing angles of 55-60°.

2. Experimental

The thickness of the oxynitride film studied in this paper was measured by XPS and nuclear reaction analysis, resulting in thickness measurements of 7.7 and 8.3nm respectively. The film thickness was thus taken to be 8nm. This film has an 'equivalent' dose determined by NRA to be 1 x 10^{15} atoms/cm^2, i.e. a peak nitrogen content of ~3 atomic %, located toward the oxide/silicon interface. A Physical Electronics ADEPT 1010 quadrupole SIMS instrument was used to make the SIMS measurements. The instrument has floating extraction primary ion columns. This enables the Cs^+ beam energy to be reduced down to 250eV, while still providing 'useful' beam currents of ~30nA. The instrument is designed for optimized ion extraction at all angles, including non-normal extraction angles, as the sample stage is tilted to achieve different incident primary beam angles. This is achieved with a split (quadrant) secondary extractor

3. Results

A depth profile from the 8nm film using 1keV Cs^+ and 60° incidence is shown in figure 1. The CsO^+ signal equilibrates within 1nm and is approximately constant throughout the 8nm oxide, falling appropriately at the silicon substrate interface. The $CsSi^+$ signal is flat within the oxide, shows a small perturbation at the oxide/silicon interface, rises in the substrate and is constant thereafter. Because the matrix signals are relatively flat, the shape of the CsN^+ signal is assumed to show the true nitrogen concentration profile within the oxide, and 'point-by-point' normalization to a matrix signal need not be considered. The data acquired using 500eV Cs^+ at 60° is shown in figure 2. The $CsSi^+$ signal is no longer as constant within the oxide. It rises at the interface, but then proceeds to fall off (non-linearly) into the substrate. Figures 3a and 3b show the $CsSi^+$ and CsO^+ matrix ion signals as a function of incident beam angle at 1keV. In these and following figures the signals from identical species have been offset from each other for clarity. If constancy of matrix signals within the oxide and substrate are a key criterion, then at 1keV beam energy 55-60° are the most appropriate beam angles of this particular set. The same is true of data obtained at 750eV (not shown). Note that at a glancing angle of 75°, the shape of the $CsSi^+$ changes dramatically into the substrate compared to the case at 70°. Such glancing angles have been used by Morinville and Blackmer [2], who were limited to a minimum beam energy of 1keV, to achieve high depth resolution on thin films. Such glancing angles are in use by Magee and co-workers using the MCs^+ protocol to characterize thin oxides [3].

Figures 4a and 4b show the $CsSi^+$ and CsO^+ matrix ion signals as a function of incident beam angle at 500eV. As the incidence angle is reduced below 55°, the main results are: (a) the $CsSi^+$ signal is progressively reduced in intensity in the substrate compared to the oxide, (b) the enhancement of CsO^+ and $CsSi^+$ at the outermost surface of the oxide is increased, and (c) the sputter rate decreases, resulting in increased analysis times. At incidence angles > 55° and ≤ 70°, the $CsSi^+$ signals are not constant in either the oxide or the substrate, nor are the CsO^+ signals constant within the oxide. The data acquired at 500eV and at glancing angles are quite different however: the $CsSi^+$ and CsO^+ signals obtained at 75° incidence are extremely constant throughout the oxide. At 80° incidence, the $CsSi^+$ signals, although not as flat in the oxide as at 75°, are constant within the near substrate. Figure 5 shows a single data set from the 8nm oxide, acquired using a 500eV Cs^+ beam and at 75° incidence.

Based on the 500eV Cs^+ results from the 8nm film, data was then acquired from a 2.6nm thick nitrided oxide using glancing angles of 75° or 80°, and at beam energies of 300eV, 400eV and 500eV. The data acquired at 300eV and at 80° incidence with is shown in figure 6.

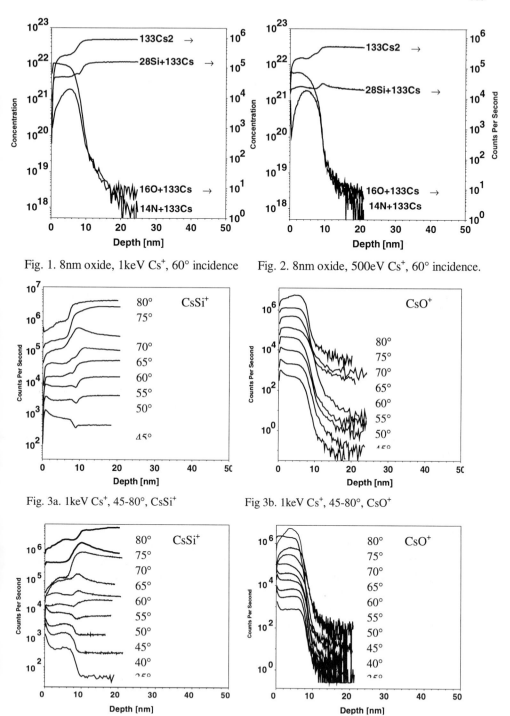

Fig. 1. 8nm oxide, 1keV Cs$^+$, 60° incidence

Fig. 2. 8nm oxide, 500eV Cs$^+$, 60° incidence.

Fig. 3a. 1keV Cs$^+$, 45-80°, CsSi$^+$

Fig 3b. 1keV Cs$^+$, 45-80°, CsO$^+$

Fig. 4a. 500eV Cs$^+$, 35-80°, CsSi$^+$

Fig 4b. 500eV Cs$^+$, 35-80°, CsO$^+$

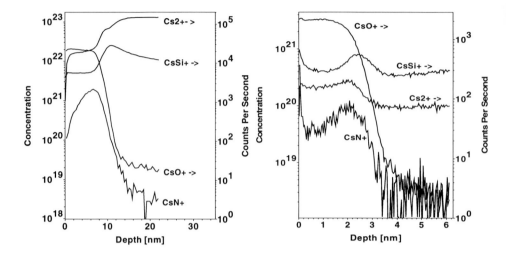

Fig. 5. 8nm oxide, 500eV, 75° incidence   Fig. 6. 2.5nm oxide, 300eV, 80° incidence

4. Discussion and conclusions

The variations of the $CsSi^+$, CsO^+ signals in the present results are complex. At Cs^+ primary beam energies $\leq 750eV$ and at $\leq 55°$ incidence the secondary ion yields tend to show an initial transient over a depth of 0.7-1nm, depending upon the exact conditions. This is due to the initial cesiation of the surface and associated changes in the sputter rate as a dynamic equilibrium is established. This transient results in an enhancement of the $CsSi^+$ and CsO^+ signals, an effect which increases in magnitude with reducing incidence angle for a given beam energy. The opposite effect is observed at incident angles of $\geq 60°$ and $<75°$ at beam energies of $\leq 500eV$. At the oxide/substrate interface another transient occurs in the secondary ion yields as a new material is encountered. With a 1000eV primary Cs^+ beam, the yield of $CsSi^+$ and Cs_2^+ ions equilibrates rapidly in the substrate for all primary incidence angles $> 60°$ (except 75°), resulting in constant signals that are more intense than in the oxide. Such conditions are ideal therefore for the analysis of 'thicker' oxides of 8nm or more. For beam energies $\leq 500eV$, only glancing angles of 70° or more appear to show this same effect. For analysis of ultra-thin oxide layers, where depth resolution is critical, the most promising results appear to be achieved with a low primary energy, such as 300-500eV, and an incidence angle of 75° or 80°. At these high incidence angles, the Cs^+ probe is, of course, highly asymmetrical at the sample surface, and care must be taken to ensure good crater edge rejection, typically using high aspect ratio craters.

References
[1] T. Hoshi, Proceedings of Seikei University Seminar on SIMS, April 1999.
[2] W.R. Morinville and C. Blackmer, Proc. SIMS XI, Wiley & Sons, (1997), pp 297.
[3] C.W. Magee, Evans Analytical Group, Princeton, N.J., private communication.

A. Benninghoven, P. Bertrand, H.-N. Migeon and H.W. Werner (Editors).
Proceedings of the 12th International Conference on Secondary Ion Mass Spectrometry,
Brussels, Belgium, 5-11 September 1999

561

SUB-keV MASS SPECTROMETRY ANALYSES ON
THIN OXYNITRIDE FILMS.

M. Sbetti, M. Bersani, L. Vanzetti, R. Canteri, and M. Anderle

ITC-irst, Centro per la Ricerca Scientifica e Tecnologica
Via Sommarive 18, 38050 Povo (TN), Italy
e-mail: sbetti@itc.it

1. Introduction

Ultrathin (7 nm or less) oxynitrided films have become important materials in ULSI technology today. The characterisation of the nitrogen distribution in these films is an analytical challenge, optimized depth resolution, good sensitivity and reliable quantification being the fundamental issues.

The nitrogen depth distribution in oxynitrides is usually obtained by SIMS analyses in two different analytical conditions, i.e. by monitoring SiN^- [1] or MCs^+ [2, 3] secondary ions. In both cases, the depth resolution is one of the main issues. A shallow projected range of the Cs^+ primary beam is needed to optimise the depth resolution.

For MCs^+ profiles, an impact energy close to 2 keV with a sample bias of 4.5 keV is commonly adopted to profile in a CAMECA instrument [2, 3, 4]. In this configuration, even lower energies would give too grazing impact angles, not ensuring stable and reproducible analytical conditions.

In this work an analytical approach based on low impact energy SIMS profiles is presented. The depth resolution has been evaluated and optimised using different analytical conditions, i.e. varying primary impact energy and angle. The SIMS nitrogen quantitative depth distributions have been confirmed by an HF etch back XPS method [5, 6].

2. Experimental

An oxynitride film (5.3 nm thick) on silicon has been obtained by an NO precursor with a rapid thermal process (RTP). A standard thermal oxide layer on silicon has been analysed to determine the experimental SIMS depth resolution. SIMS analyses have been carried out by a CAMECA 4f using Cs^+ primary beam and monitoring secondary MCs^+ ions. Different impact energies and angles have been used to evaluate both depth resolution and sensitivity. In particular, a 2.25 kV sample bias has been introduced to perform SIMS sub-keV profiles.

The quantitative SIMS nitrogen profiles have been confirmed by XPS analyses performed by a SCIENTA ESCA 200, using HF etch back method [5, 6].

3. Results and discussion

To evaluate the depth resolution in the SIMS measurements a thermally grown oxide layer has been analysed using different primary energies and sample biases. Its SiO_2/Si interface is considered an ideal step.

Table 1: Experimental conditions and measured depth resolution.

Impact Energy [keV]	Sample Bias [keV]	Impact Angle [deg]	Primary Beam Penetration [nm]	Depth Resolution [nm]
3	4.5	52	2.4	3.8
2.75	4.5	54	2.1	3.6
2.5	4.5	57	1.9	3.4
2.25	4.5	60	1.6	2.6
2	4.5	64	1.3	2.5
1.3	2.25	56	1.2	2.2
0.9	2.25	69	0.6	2.0
0.8	2.25	77	0.4	1.3

In table 1 the different experimental conditions are reported together with the calculated [7] Cs^+ projected range and the measured experimental depth resolution, defined as the width between 84% and 16% of the oxygen signal. Under the experimental conditions used the sputtering rates in oxide and silicon matrix do not show a meaningful difference.

In figure 1 we show five representative examples of oxygen depth profiles carried out on the thermal oxide sample. From these analyses the depth resolution values reported in table 1 have been determined.

In order to obtain quantitative profiles we have taken into account the progressive change in RSF through the SiO_2/Si interface, by using a methodology reported elsewhere [2, 5]. The RFS in oxide and silicon matrix has been obtained by suitable implanted standards.

Figure 2 shows the different nitrogen quantitative profiles for the 5.3 nm thick oxynitride sample, carried out at different impact energies. For lower primary beam impact energies the nitrogen peak maximum is shifted towards the SiO_2/Si interface [2]. Furthermore, reducing the impact energy, the FWHM of the nitrogen peak decreases.

Figure 2 shows a clear improvement in depth resolution in the case of sub-keV impact energies, together with a worse detection limit ($\sim 10^{19}$ atoms/cm^3). The analysis time is close to 3 hours, due to the very low primary beam density available in these conditions.

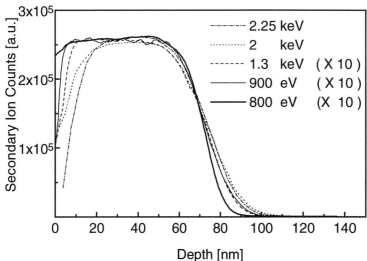

Figure 1. Oxygen SIMS depth profiles of a thermal oxide layer at different energies and angles.

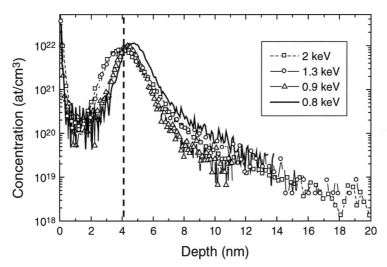

Figure 2. Nitrogen quantitative depth profiles of the oxynitride sample at different energies and angles. The dashed line shows the interface position.

564

The SIMS nitrogen quantitative depth distributions have been compared with HF etch back XPS method. There is a remarkable agreement between the two analytical methods. We have presented elsewhere a detailed comparison between XPS and SIMS results on a complete set of oxynitrided samples [6].

The results show the possibility to obtain a suitable analytical methodology to perform nitrogen quantitative profiles in oxynitride films with a thickness close to 5 nm. The main analytical problems, i.e. the depth resolution and the nitrogen quantification at the interface region, have been examined. For routine analyses a 2 keV primary beam impact energy and a 64° impact angle are sufficient. To improve the depth resolution in a Cameca 4f instrument we had to halve the sample bias. In this way it is possible to reduce the impact energy down to 800 eV at an incidence angle of 77 degrees, and to obtain nitrogen profiles without introducing further analytical artefacts. This enabled us to use, in the sub-keV analyses, the quantification methodology adopted for the profiles obtained at an impact energy of 2 keV.

However, sub-keV analyses have two particular drawbacks in comparison with the routine ones, which are a longer analysis time, due to the very low primary beam density available, and a worse sensitivity.

ToF-SIMS measurements could give complementary information on oxinitride samples [8]. In this case analytical difficulties are accurate nitrogen signal quantification, and the evaluation of the role of SiO_2/Si interface. Further work on these aspects is in progress.

References

[1] E. Brelle, S. Rigo, J.A. Kliner, J.J. Ganem, Appl. Surf. Sci. 81 (1994), 127.
[2] M. Bersani, M. Fedrizzi, M. Sbetti, M. Anderle, Characterisation and Metrology for ULSI Technology AIP Conference proceeding 449 Woodbury NY (1998), 892
[3] P.R. Dakey, S.N. Schauer, R.G. Cosway, and M.D. Griswold in Secondary Ion Mass Spectrometry SIMS XI, eds. By G. Gillen, R. Lareau, J. Bennett, F. Stevie, John Wiley and Sons, Chichester (1998), 253.
[4] L. Wu, T. Neil, D. Sieloff, J.J. Lee and R.I. Hedge in Secondary Ion Mass Spectrometry SIMS XI, eds. By G. Gillen, R. Lareau, J. Bennett, F. Stevie, John Wiley and Sons, Chichester (1998), 245.
[5] M. Bersani, L. Vanzetti, M. Sbetti, M. Anderle, Appl. Surf. Sci. 144-145 (1999), 301.
[6] L. Vanzetti, M. Bersani, M. Sbetti and M. Anderle, to be published on ECASIA'99 Proceedings, Surf. Interface Anal.
[7] W. Vandervost and F. R. Shepherd, J. Vac. Sci. Technol. A5, 313 (1987)
[8] M. Bersani, M. Sbetti, L.Vanzetti, M.Anderle, to be published on SIMS XII Proceedings.

A. Benninghoven, P. Bertrand, H.-N. Migeon and H.W. Werner (Editors).
Proceedings of the 12th International Conference on Secondary Ion Mass Spectrometry,
Brussels, Belgium, 5-11 September 1999

565

QUANTITATIVE DETERMINATION OF OXIDE LAYER THICKNESS AND NITROGEN PROFILES FOR Si GATE OXIDES

O. Brox[1], K. Iltgen[2], E. Niehuis[3], and A. Benninghoven[1]
[1] Physikalisches Institut, University of Münster, Germany
[2] AMD Saxony Manufacturing GmbH, Dresden, Germany
[3] ION-TOF GmbH, Münster, Germany

1. Introduction

Accurate characterization of ultra-thin nitrided gate oxides is crucial for future semiconductor device scaling. Leading edge device technologies are currently using gate oxides of 3 to 4 nm and the National Technology Roadmap for Semiconductor predicts the gate oxide thickness to shrink to 2 to 3 nm until the year 2001. High precision determination of the oxide thickness is necessary to meet these requirements. The quantitative determination of thin oxide layer thicknesses as well as the quantification of nitrogen using TOF-SIMS is difficult. The variation of the sputter yield in a changing matrix is distorting the depth scale whereas changes in secondary ion yields emission lead to problems in determining a concentration scale.

We have investigated the capabilities of TOF-SIMS to control oxide thicknesses down to 2-3 nm and to quantify the nitrogen distribution.

2. Experimental

For our investigations we used a TOF-SIMS III reflectron type instrument build at the University of Münster. This spectrometer is equipped with four ion guns, two for analysis and two for sputtering. The analysis can be performed with a 11 keV electron impact (EI) -gun (Ar^+, Xe^+, O_2^+, SF_5^+ ...) or with a fine focussing 25 keV Ga-LMIG. For both the angle of incidence amounts 45°. For sputtering, an additional EI-gun and a Cs-gun are available. This dual beam technique [1] allows the variation of sputter ion energies between 300 eV and 10 keV. These ion guns are mounted at 52.5° to the surface normal. The impact angle of the sputter ion beams can be varied in a small range by a sample tilt. When depth profiling in the positive secondary ion mode yields can be enhanced by flooding the sample with oxygen ($^{16}O_2$ and $^{18}O_2$).

The investigated gate oxides were thermally grown in an O_2 ambient and subsequently nitrided by N_2O. For all samples the oxide thickness was calibrated by Single Wave Ellipsometry and additionally determined by Transmission Electron Microscopy (TEM).

3. Results and Discussion

3.1 SiO₂ layer. SiO_2 layer thickness can be determined by measuring exactly the position of the Si/SiO_2 interface during SIMS depth profiling with Cs^+ primary ions. This interface is indicated by drastic changes in the yield of characteristic secondary ion species as Si^-, SiO^- and SiO_2^- for example. These changes originate from changes in both sputter yields as well as ionization probabilities, as a result of the changing oxygen and cesium concentrations, when passing the Si/SiO_2 interface. We used the Si^- maximum to determine the interface position.

The expression of this maximum is strongly energy dependent and can be explained by a Cs accumulation at the SiO_2/Si interface [2].

We investigated the influence of different sputter ion energies on the width at which the sputter equilibrium is reached. The determination of this transient width was done using a 18 nm gate oxide. The depth at which the Si^- signal has reached 95% of its equilibrium value is defined as the transient width w_{tr}. Increasing the sputter ion energy leads to a monotonous increase of this transient width, starting at less than 1 nm for very low energies (400 eV) and reaching more than 6 nm for high energies (5 keV).

The position of the Si^- maximum was found to indicate very exactly the oxide layer thickness as determined by TEM. Figure 1 compares the TEM calibrated SiO_2 layer thickness with the sputter time required to reach the Si^- maximum. We found a linear relationship between these two values. The accuracy and precision of this linear behavior are not affected by the sputter ion energy down to a layer thickness of about 3 nm.

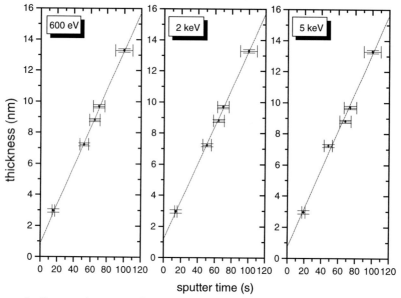

Figure 1: Sputter time as a function of gate oxide thickness for 0.6, 2 and 5 keV Cs^+ sputtering (linear fit)

Thickness calibration of thin oxides by this method seems to be not affected by the width of the transient region. Sputter yields change while reaching the sputter equilibrium are mainly caused by the incorporation of Cs into the surface. Another region of interest is the intersection at about 1 nm which shows no energy dependence (Fig 1). This can be explained by two competing effects. Low sputter ion energies lead to a small transient width but to high Cs surface concentrations which cause a big variation in the erosion rate while reaching the sputter equilibrium, whereas high sputter ion energies causes a large transient region but low Cs surface concentrations with a corresponding small variation in the erosion rate.

3.2 Nitrogen profile. To determine the exact nitrogen concentration scale there are several secondary ions available. In positive SIMS mode nitrogen containing signals are Si_2N^+

emitted under bombardment with noble gas and SF_5^+, or MCs^+ cluster ions (CsN^+, Cs_2N^+) under Cs bombardment. These Cs cluster ions are less influenced by matrix effects. In the negative SIMS SiN^- is emitted with a high secondary ion yield. Due to this fact negative secondary ions were selected for nitrogen quantification.

Quantification of elements in a changing matrix requires the consideration of the corresponding variations in secondary ion yields. The main change while sputtering through thin oxide layers is the removal of the silicon oxide. At any stage of the profiling process the surface oxidation state can be described by the so called lattice valency G^- of the Si-atoms. The model of lattice valency developed by Plog et al.[3] is also valid for Cs sputtered negative SiO_n^- ions [4]. This negative lattice valency is determined from the intensity ratios of secondary ions $Si_mO_n^-$ (m=1), shown in Figure 2. The negative secondary ion intensity as a function of the fragment valency K of a silicon atom in a desorbed secondary ion SiO_n^- can be well fitted by a gaussian curve:

of which the maximum position is called the lattice valency G^-:

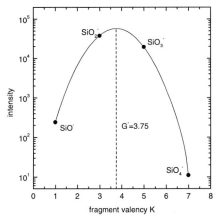

Figure 2: Lattice valency G^- determined by the lattice valency model [2]. The fragment valency is defined by $m*K-2n=q$; q: charge of the fragment ion

To correct changes in ion yield we determined the relation between lattice valency and ionization probability in detail. We used a N-implant standard sample to determine the RSF(SiN$^-$, ^{30}Si$^-$) as a function of the lattice (Fig 3). The variation of the surface oxidation state was done by oxygen flooding.

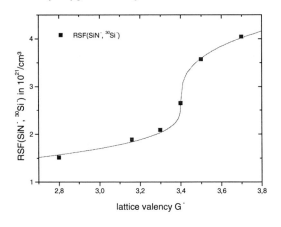

Figure 3: RSF(SiN, ^{30}Si$^-$) as a function of lattice valency G^-

Due to the fact that this relation between G^- and RSF(SiN$^-$, ^{30}Si$^-$) is also influenced by the Cs surface concentration we used fixed sputter conditions of 1 keV Cs$^+$ with an angle of incidence of 52,5°. For a correction of the measured SiN$^-$ signal the lattice valency is required as a function of the sputtered depth. From this relation the relative sensitivity factor can be determined as a function of depth. In addition to this the changing silicon particle density has to be considered. Figure 4 shows the measured SiN$^-$ signal together with the corrected N bulk concentration.

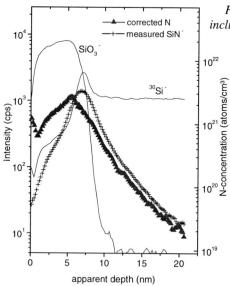

Figure 4: Profile of 7 nm gate oxide including the corrected N concentration

4. Conclusion

It has been shown that SIMS is a practicable tool for thickness determination of thin silicon oxides. The accuracy down to 3 nm is better than 5%. Further improvements can be done using alternating low energy Cs/noble gas sputtering to decrease the transient width without reaching high Cs surface concentrations as they build up during sputtering with Cs$^+$ only [2].

For calibration of the N concentration scale we took the changing surface oxidation state into account. The resulting N concentration has a significant different shape compared to the measured SiN$^-$ signal which shows the strong influence of the matrix effect. The peak concentration was found to be 3.6 at.%, which is in good agreement with a SIMS determination using Cs Cluster ions.

Future developments can be done by the consideration of changing Cs surface concentration caused by segregation effects. Detailed investigations of negative secondary ion emission behaviors from Cs covered surfaces will be presented in the near future.

References

[1]   K. Iltgen, C. Bendel, E. Niehuis and A. Benninghoven, J. Vac Sci. Technol. A, Vol. 15, pp. 460-464 (1997)
[2]   K. Iltgen, E. Niehuis, these proceedings
[3]   C. Plog, L. Wiedmann, A. Benninghoven, Surface Science **67**, 565 (1977)
[4]   K. Iltgen, Dissertation, University of Münster (1997)

A. Benninghoven, P. Bertrand, H.-N. Migeon and H.W. Werner (Editors).
Proceedings of the 12th International Conference on Secondary Ion Mass Spectrometry,
Brussels, Belgium, 5-11 September 1999

569

THE 'NORMAL COMPONENT' OF THE PRIMARY ION ENERGY: AN INADEQUATE PARAMETER FOR ASSESSING THE DEPTH RESOLUTION IN SIMS

K. Wittmaack

GSF–National Research Centre, Institute of Radiation Protection,
85758 Neuherberg, Germany
email: wittmaack@gsf.de

1. Introduction

At present, the most important application of secondary ion mass spectrometry (SIMS) is sputter depth profiling, i.e. the measurement of the concentration of one or more impurities (dopants) as a function of the distance from the surface of the host matrix. One of the key parameters characterising the quality of a sputter profile is the depth resolution. It is well known that an initially sharp doping distribution is broadened by bombardment-induced relocation of target atoms (atomic mixing), a process that is inevitably associated with sputter erosion [1]. Additional broadening may be caused by chemically driven redistribution processes [2,3].

It is important to note that the broadening observed in SIMS depth profiling, in the absence of significant surface roughening, is generally not describable by a symmetric function. Instead the 'resolution function', to be determined by profiling through a narrow 'delta' layer, usually features a peak with a sharply rising front edge and a gradually decreasing exponential tail, the latter being characterised by a decay length λ [4,5]. Owing to the strong asymmetry of the resolution function, the ability to resolve two closely spaced doping features by SIMS depth profiling is determined by the magnitude of λ. Hence it is common practise to discuss aspects of depth resolution in terms of the decay length.

Previous work in this field, reviewed repeatedly [4,6,7,8], has shown that the bombardment-induced profile broadening is not a universal parameter or function, but can differ strongly for different dopant elements in the same matrix as well as for one dopant in different matrices. The other severe problem is that the broadening and related artefacts may be strongly affected by the chemical changes introduced by bombardment with and incorporation of 'reactive' primary ions like oxygen or cesium. The only safe statement one can make is that, in general, the broadening becomes smaller as the energy of the probing beam is reduced. Initiated by the work of Dowsett and coworkers [9], this observation has recently led to an unprecedented step-like improvement in the capabilities of commercial SIMS instrumentation [10] and bombardment with sub-keV ion beams has now become the state of the art.

Whilst the beneficial effect of lowering the beam energy E is well established, measurements of the decay length as a function of the angle of bombardment revealed a rather complex behaviour [6,7]. This paper addresses the question whether the profile broadening observed at oblique primary ion impact can be rationalised by defining some kind of 'normal' or 'effective' energy component. Discussion will be limited to samples which do not show surface roughening or ripple formation under the chosen bombardment conditions.

2. Relevant aspects of primary ion trajectories in magnetic sector field instruments

The idea of defining a 'normal' or 'effective' impact energy is closely related to the frequent use of magnetic sector field instruments for depth profiling by SIMS. The high transmission of such instruments is achieved by applying rather high extraction voltages between the sample and the entrance electrode of the spectrometer, typically 2-5 kV [11]. Furthermore, the extraction field must be very well aligned with respect to the spectrometer axis. Hence the (flat) sample has to be mounted in a highly reproducible manner, with minimum distortions due to the surrounding holder. In other words, it is not possible to mechanically vary the orientation of the sample with respect to the incident ion beam. The primary ion column is oriented at some angle θ_0 to the surface normal of the sample. The true angle θ of ion impact on the sample differs from θ_0 because the beam has to pass through the extraction field.

Knowing θ_0, the terminal voltage V_0 of the ion source, and the target bias V_t (the main body of the spectrometer being at ground potential), it is rather simple to calculate θ for an assumed uniform extraction field. The problem, however, is that the point of impact of the beam on the sample will not be at the crossing point of the axes of the primary ion column and the secondary ion mass spectrometer, but will be displaced due to ion deflection on passage through the extraction field (note that we consider only the beam trajectories in the plane of incidence defined by the axis of the primary ion column and the normal of the sample surface). Correct alignment of the beam with respect to the spectrometer axis can be achieved if θ_0 is changed to $\theta_1 = \theta_0 \pm \alpha$ by deflecting and laterally offsetting the beam prior to entering the extraction field (to some extent, deflection and offset are interchangeable). For Cameca IMS instruments of the 3f-6f series, the problems associated with this procedure have been discussed and explored by Meuris et al. [12] and by Vriezema and Zalm [13]. The offset angles α measured under the conditions of a particular experiment [12] are shown in Fig. 1a as solid circles ($\theta_0 = 30°$, $V_t = 4.5$ kV, $V_0 = 6$ to 15 kV; same polarity of V_0 and V_t). To ease data evaluation, the results were plotted as a function of the reduced final energy (impact energy) ε $= V_f / V_0$, with $V_f = V_0 - V_t$, and were fitted by a second order polynomial (solid curve). The fit suggests that for $\varepsilon = 1$, i.e. in the case of infinite source potential or zero target bias (no deflection in the extraction region), an offset of about 1.4° would have been necessary to direct the primary ions to the nominal point of impact.

In the following discussion we shall assume that the angular offset required for any other initial alignment status of an IMS-3/6f instrument can be derived by simply shifting the solid curve in Fig. 1a in either direction. This simplified procedure is illustrated by the dashed curve in Fig. 1a which is meant to represent a 'perfectly' aligned beam, i.e. $\alpha(\varepsilon = 1) = 0$. Knowing $\alpha(\varepsilon)$ we can calculate $\theta(\varepsilon)$ for the assumed uniform extraction field (no lens effect on passage of the beam through the entrance aperture of the extraction field). The calculation is based on the conservation of energy and momentum. The most simple relation is achieved in terms of the constant momentum parallel to the sample surface [14]

$$\sin\theta = \varepsilon^{-0.5}\sin\theta_1. \tag{1}$$

For the final momentum normal to the surface we have

$$\cos\theta = \varepsilon^{-0.5}(\cos^2\theta_1 - V_t/V_0)^{0.5}. \tag{2}$$

Even though Eq. (1) is more simple than Eq. (2), the latter form has been used quite frequently [12,15,16].

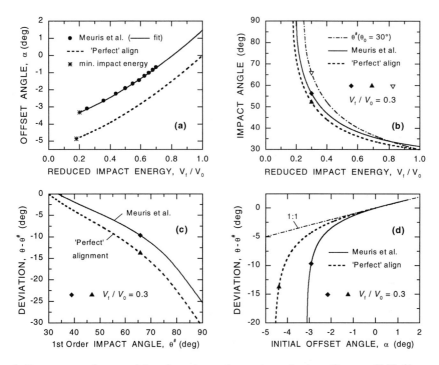

Fig. 1. Parameters characterising the primary ion trajectories in a Cameca IMS-4f magnetic sector field instruments. Original data in panel (a) from Ref. 12. For details see text.

Impact angles calculated by use of Eq. (1) are compiled in Figs. 1b-d. Note that the impact angles for a 'perfectly' aligned beam are even smaller than those reported by Meuris et al. [12]. Although the results of Ref. 12 have been known for more than 10 years by now, incorrect angles $\theta^{\#}(\theta_0 = 30°)$ are commonly quoted in the literature, including recent work. The large error becomes fully evident from Fig. 1c. In the range $0.35 \geq \varepsilon \geq 0.25$ ($57° \leq \theta \leq 90°$), equivalent to low impact energies, the miscalculation of θ may amount to between 7° and 31°.

For $\alpha(\varepsilon = 1) = 0$, a convenient formula for estimating θ is [13],

$$\cos\theta = \cos\theta_0 [1 - c_\theta (\varepsilon^{-1} - 1) \tan^2\theta_0]^{0.5}. \tag{2a}$$

According to Vriezema and Zalm [13] the correction factor c_θ should range between 0.8 and 1. However, fitting Eq. (2a) to the results of Fig. 1b we find $c_\theta \approx 0.75$ for the experimental data of Meuris et al. [12] and $c_\theta \approx 0.65$ for the 'perfect' beam align.

Finally, Fig. 1d illustrates the fact that, in the region of low ε, i.e. strong retardation, beam alignment is very crucial because small changes of α have a large effect on θ (as well as on the point of beam impact on the sample). This explains the poor day to-day reproducibility of beam alignment [13]. The strong dependence of θ on the operator dependent initial beam deflection and offset implies that data obtained on the same type of instrument, at the same source potential and target potential, may differ significantly in impact angle, i.e. the results are not transferable and the erosion rate is not reproducible (even for the same beam current).

3. Origin of the notation 'normal' impact energy

Taking the square of Eq. (2), rearranging and multiplying by the primary ion charge q we get what might be called the 'normal' component of the (final) impact energy E_{fn}, i.e.,

$$E_{fn} = q(V_0 \cos^2\theta_1 - V_t) = q(V_0 - V_t) \cos^2\theta = qV_f\cos^2\theta = E_f\cos^2\theta, \qquad (3)$$

with $E_f = qV_f$. At this point some confusion has entered into the terminology used in the literature. In Ref. 16, for example, E_{fn} has been referred to as the 'effective' beam energy, i.e. the "final kinetic energy component normal to the surface". In the same paper, however, another 'effective' energy E_{eff}, considered to being a good parameter for assessing the depth resolution in the respective SIMS sputter profiling experiments, has been quoted as

$$E_{eff} = E_f\cos\theta. \qquad (4)$$

Neither an explanation for this change in notation nor a justification for this approach has been given. The important point is that E_{eff} according to Eq. (4) has subsequently been used in a variety of papers [17,18,19,20] to argue that the depth resolution obtained with a beam of energy E_f, incident at angle θ, should be equivalent to or as good as a measurements at normal incidence with the lower energy $E_f\cos\theta$. If this reasoning were correct, measurements at impact angles around 60°, for example, could be performed at energies twice as large than at normal incidence to achieve depth profiles of the same quality. Advantages of this procedure would include better beam focusing, higher beam currents and higher sputtering yields.

4. Decay length and internal mixing profile

As pointed out above, the depth resolution achieved in SIMS profiling is commonly discussed in terms of the decay length λ. In the region where the impurity signal decreases as $\exp(\lambda^{-1}z)$, the depth distribution, $N(z)p(z')$, of impurities still present in the sample after erosion to depth z, may be described by an 'internal' mixing profile $p(z')$ of constant shape and an exponentially decreasing total impurity content $N(z)$ [21]. The depth z' is counted from the instantaneous surface and the integral over $p(z')$ is normalised to unity. With this definition the rate of impurity removal, λ^{-1}, may be written [22]

$$\lambda^{-1} = rp^0, \qquad (5)$$

where $p^0 = <p(0 \leq z' \leq \delta)>$ is the near-surface value of $p(z')$, averaged over the escape depth δ of the impurity element. The factor r represents the ratio of the escape probabilities of impurity and matrix atoms [22]. The problem is that neither p^0 not r are currently known in any detail. One might suspect that the width of the internal profile is somehow related to the range of the primary ions, so that p^0 would decrease as the profile broadens with increasing range, but this idea does not hold in quantitative form, as discussed in Sect. 5.

Considering the fact that the (mean) escape depth under SIMS depth profiling conditions is only about 0.2 nm [23,24,25] it is clear that the desired information about the internal profile can only be achieved by a high-resolution technique that allows the impurity concentration to be measured as a function of depth, with essentially monolayer resolution. The resolution obtained in previous work by Rutherford backscattering spectrometry (RBS) was about 2 nm so that only rather extreme cases of bombardment-induced mixing (and segregation) could be explored in reasonable detail [26,27]. It remains to be investigated whether further progress can be achieved by medium-energy ion scattering (MEIS) [28].

5. Dependence of the decay length on bombardment parameters

The effect of bombardment parameters on the decay length may be discussed most conveniently with reference to the results of an experiment that was ideal in the sense that chemically driven transport of impurity and matrix atoms did not take place because the two species were isotopes of the same element. Figure 2 shows a compilation of decay lengths for 30-Si in 28-Si using normally incident primary ions of oxygen, cesium and inert gases [29]. The experiments were performed in a quadrupole-based SIMS instrument in which the impact angle could be varied independent of the primary ion beam energy [30]. The Si-Si system has the additional advantage that the parameter r in Eq. (5) reflects only the isotope effect, i.e. r is close to unity. Two aspects of the data in Fig. 2 are remarkable. (i) The decay lengths for bombardment with cesium and inert gas ions fall on the same curve. (ii) The data for oxygen bombardment, on the other hand, are lower by a factor of 2-2.2.

Also shown in Fig. 2 are ranges of oxygen and inert gas projectiles determined by TRIM computer simulations [31]. At energies below about 1.5 keV the ranges of Xe exceed those of Ne. This somewhat unexpected effect has been verified in a recent study based on additional range calculations and the evaluation of high-precision experimental range data [32].

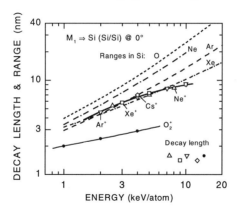

Fig. 2. Energy dependence of the decay length of 30-Si in 28-Si sputter profiled by a variety of normally incident ions [29]. The ranges of oxygen and inert gases in silicon, determined by TRIM simulations [31], are shown for comparison (Ne data interpolated).

For primary ions other than oxygen the decay lengths and ranges in Fig. 2 are roughly the same at low energies, but the energy and mass dependence differ significantly or even strongly (difference by more than a factor of two for 10 keV Ne). Hence we have to conclude that, in general, decay lengths cannot be rationalised in terms of primary ion ranges. As shown below, this statement can be extended to include results obtained as a function of the impact angle.

The lack of a mass dependence may tentatively be explained with reference to Fig. 3a. Even though the p^0-values of the normalised internal profiles are the same for Ne and Xe bombardment, the profiles at larger depth may differ significantly. This is of no relevance for the decay length because λ is only determined by the near-surface value p^0, see Eq. (5), and not by the shape of the internal profile at larger depths.

Figure 3b illustrates the advantageous 'buffer' effect due to bombardment-induced oxidation of silicon, achievable by oxygen impact at normal and near-normal incidence [33]. Mixing during sputtering takes place in the synthesised oxide and the internal profile may have a shape and a p^0-value similar to inert gas ion bombardment (dash-dotted curve). The implanted oxygen can absorb energy that would otherwise be consumed for relocating silicon and impurity atoms. Oxygen, however, is present in the sample only temporarily and memory of all relocation events that have taken place in the oxygen subsystem is lost when the implanted atoms are reemitted in course of sputtering. Furthermore, oxygen is not counted when determining the erosion rate from the depth of the sputtered crater. Hence the decay length actually measured is significantly reduced, by a factor roughly equal to the ratio $\Omega_{Si}/\Omega_{SiO2}$ of the atomic and molecular volumes of Si and SiO_2 [7], see solid line in Fig. 3b.

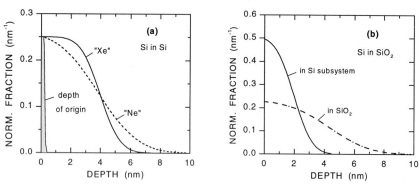

Fig. 3. Schematic illustration of internal mixing profiles produced in silicon under impact of normally incident ions. (a) Inert gas ion bombardment. The depth of origin of sputtered atoms and ions is shown for comparison. (b) Oxide formation by oxygen bombardment. The internal profile narrows significantly if only the silicon subsystem is taken into account.

The arguments provide an explanation for the observation that the decay length of Si (and B) in Si remained essentially constant as the impact angle of 5-10 keV O_2^+ beams was varied between 0° and about 70° [7]. This absence of a sizeable angular dependence of the decay length cannot be rationalised in terms of 'normal' or 'effective' impact energies as defined by Eqs. (3) or (4).

Another example illustrating the non-applicability of the 'normal' energy concept is presented in Fig. 4a which shows decay lengths for Al in GaAs measured on a Cameca IMS-4f under impact of five different primary ion species [34]. Within experimental accuracy all data fall on the same straight line, implying that the decay length does not depend on the mass of the incident ion. This result is very similar to the results for Si/Si bombarded with inert gas and cesium ions, see Fig. 2. Surprisingly, however, the results of Fig. 4a also show that the decay length is independent of the energy per projectile atom. The difference between the experiments of Refs. 29 and 34 is that the latter were performed at oblique angles of incidence, which increased rapidly as the impact energy was reduced (dashed curve in Fig. 4a). At the indicated angles the GaAs sample can be oxidised only slightly [35] so that the favourable oxygen buffer effect (Fig. 3b) does not work. Hence we are dealing with results which may be considered to represent the case of a 'clean' sample (as for inert gas bombardment of Si).

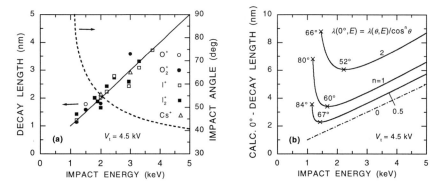

Fig. 4. (a) Energy/angle dependence of the decay length of Al in GaAs measured by SIMS under impact of a variety of primary ion species [34]. The dotted line shows the impact angles according to Fig. 1. (b) Energy dependence of the decay length at normal incidence calculated from the results of (a) under the assumption of a $cos^n\theta$- dependence of the decay length. Some impact angles are marked by crosses.

Now we make the assumption that the E, θ-dependence of λ can be factorized in the form

$$\lambda(E,\theta) = \lambda_0(E)\cos^n\theta, \tag{6}$$

where $\lambda_0(E) = \lambda(E, \theta=0)$. This is what Eq. (4) would predict for the special case n = 1. Figure 4b shows results obtained by rearranging Eq. (6) to determine $\lambda_0(E)$ from $\lambda(E,\theta)$, for different values of n. In the region of interest, i.e. at angles above about 60° (or energies below 2 keV) we find that, in contrast to essentially all published depth profiling data [7], the calculated values of $\lambda_0(E)$ increase very rapidly with decreasing energy, even if evaluation is extended only up to moderately oblique angles (like 80° for n = 1). This result confirms the conclusion that, irrespective of the details of definition, a 'normal' energy component is a completely inadequate parameter for assessing the depth resolution in SIMS.

6. Summary and conclusion

It has been shown that the concept of a 'normal' or 'effective' energy component is closely related to the complex primary ion transport in magnetic sector field instruments. The commonly used method of calculating impact angles for Cameca IMS instruments is severely in error. The true angles of incidence are difficult to determine because primary ion transport to the nominal point of impact on the target can be achieved by different combinations of initial beam deflection and offset. Hence, for the same source and target potential, the actual impact angle can vary significantly between instruments of the same type so that depth resolution data obtained in different laboratories or on different days may not be directly comparable.

In general, decay lengths neither scale with the range of the primary ions nor are they proportional to the artificially defined 'normal' or 'effective' energy component $E_f\cos\theta$. It is of course possible that, in certain cases, one will obtain results in accordance with a $cos^n\theta$ - dependence, for a certain range of angles. But such results should be considered an exception rather than the rule. The mixing and sputtering processes taking place during SIMS depth profiling are so complex that simple relations for assessing the depth resolution do not apply.

I like to thank Helmut Werner for his patient support and Peer Zalm for useful comments.

References

[1] H. H. Andersen, Appl. Phys. 18 (1979) 131
[2] P. Williams and J.E. Baker, Nucl. Instrum. Methods 182/183 (1981) 15
[3] P.R. Boudewijn, H.W.P. Akerboom, M.N.C. Kempeners, Spectrochim. Acta B 39 (1984) 1567
[4] K. Wittmaack, Vacuum 34 (1984) 119
[5] J.B. Clegg and I.G. Gale, Surf. Interface Anal. 17 (1991) 190
[6] K. Wittmaack, in *Practical Surface Analysis* (2nd Edition), Vol. 2: *Ion and Neutral Spectroscopy*, ed. by D. Briggs and M.P. Seah, Wiley, Chichester, 1992, p. 105
[7] K. Wittmaack, Surf. Interface Anal. 21 (1994) 323
[8] P.C. Zalm, Rep. Prog. Phys. 58 (1995) 1321
[9] N.S. Smith, M.G. Dowsett, B. McGregor and P. Phillips, in *Secondary Ion Mass Spectrometry SIMS X*, ed. by A. Benninghoven, B. Hagenhoff and H.W. Werner, Wiley, Chichester, 1997, p. 363
[10] L. Larson, ed., Proc. Fifth Int. Workshop on *Measurement, Characterization and Modeling of Ultra-Shallow Doping Profiles in Seminconductors*, J. Vac. Sci. Technol. B 18 (2000) No. 1
[11] M. Schumacher, B. Rasser, E. De Chambost, F. Hillion, Th. Mootz and H.-N. Migeon, Fres. J. Anal. Chem. 365 (1999) 12
[12] M. Meuris, P. De Bisschop, J.F. Leclair and W. Vandervorst, Surf. Interface Anal. 14 (1989) 739
[13] C.J. Vriezema and P.C. Zalm, Surf. Interface Anal. 17 (1991) 875
[14] W. Szymczak and K. Wittmaack, in *Secondary Ion Mass Spectrometry SIMS VI.*, ed. by A. Benninghoven, A.M Huber and H.W. Werner, Wiley, Chichester, 1988, p. 243
[15] S.R. Bryan, D.P. Griffis and R.W. Linton, J. Vac. Sci. Technol. A 5 (1987) 9
[16] J.L. Hunter, Jr., S.F. Corcoran, D.P. Griffis and C.M. Osburn, J. Vac. Sci. Technol. A 8 (1990) 2323
[17] S.F. Corcoran and S.B. Felch, J. Vac. Sci. Technol. B 10 (1992) 342
[18] P.A. Ronsheim and M. Tejwani, J. Vac. Sci. Technol. B 12 (1994) 254
[19] S.B. Felch, D.L. Chapek, S.M. Malik, P. Maillot, E. Ishida and C.W. Magee, J. Vac. Sci. Technol. B 14 (1996) 336
[20] P.A. Ronsheim and K.L. Lee, J. Vac. Sci. Technol. B 16 (1998) 382
[21] K. Wittmaack, J. Appl. Phys. 53 (1982) 4817
[22] K. Wittmaack, in *Sputtering by Particle Bombardment III*, ed. by R. Behrisch and K. Wittmaack, Springer, Berlin, 1991, p. 161
[23] K.Wittmaack, Phys. Rev. B 56 (1997) R5701
[24] L.G. Glazov, V.I. Shulga and P. Sigmund, Surf. Interface Anal. 26 (1998) 512
[25] V. I. Shulga and W. Eckstein, Nucl. Instrum. Methods B 145 (1998) 492
[26] N. Menzel and K. Wittmaack, Nucl. Instrum. Methods B 45 (1990) 219
[27] W. De Coster, B. Brijs, P. Osiceanu, J. Alay, M. Caymax and W. Vandervorst, Nucl. Instrum. Methods B 85 (1994) 911
[28] J.C. Lee, C.S. Jeong, H.J. Kang, H.K. Kim and D.W. Moon, Appl. Surf. Sci. 100-101 (1996) 97
[29] K. Wittmaack and D.B. Poker, Nucl. Instrum. Methods B47 (1990) 224
[30] K. Wittmaack, Surf. Sci. 345 (1996) 110
[31] J.F. Ziegler, J.P. Biersack and U. Littmark, *The Stopping and Range of Ions in Solids*, Pergamon, New York, 1985
[32] K. Wittmaack and J.P. Biersack, to be published
[33] K. Wittmaack, Surf. Sci. 419 (1999) 249
[34] M. Meuris, W. Vandervorst, P. De Bisschop and D. Avau, Appl. Phys. Lett. 54 (1989) 1531
[35] Y. Homma and K. Wittmaack, J. Appl. Phys. 65 (1989) 5061

A. Benninghoven, P. Bertrand, H.-N. Migeon and H.W. Werner (Editors).
Proceedings of the 12th International Conference on Secondary Ion Mass Spectrometry,
Brussels, Belgium, 5-11 September 1999
© 2000 Elsevier Science B.V. All rights reserved.

HIGH RESOLUTION SIMS ANALYSIS USING A BEVEL-IMAGE TECHNIQUE ON SHALLOW BORON DOPED SILICON

S.Fearn,D.S.McPhail and R.J.Chater

1. Introduction

The depth profiling of shallow implants is especially perturbed by the initial stages of SIMS depth profiling. In this region, before the SIMS signal has reached a steady state, both sputter yield and ionisation rate vary[1]. For accurate depth calibration it is essential that this transient region be minimised so that the dopant profile lies beyond it[2]. With the aim of overcoming these initial transient effects, a 'bevel-image' technique has been developed.

By bevelling a material buried features are exposed as wide surface layers that may be readily analysed via SIMS linescanning or ion imaging. It has been previously displayed that by SIMS linescanning bevelled multi-layer structures that a depth-independent depth resolution could be obtained[3]. However, sensitivity was low due to the small sample analytical volume removed. Through carrying out SIMS ion imaging it is hoped that an improved sensitivity can be achieved.

2. Experimental Procedure

The shallow boron implanted silicon samples that have been studied in this paper were implanted with boron of atomic mass 11 at 10keV and a dose of 4×10^{14}atom/cm^2.

The samples were cut into 1cm^2 pieces and thoroughly cleaned in acetone, methanol and de-ionised water for three minutes each with the aid of an ultra-sonic bath. Once cleaned the samples were mounted onto the bevelling apparatus which has been described elsewhere[3] and then lowered into an etching solution at a constant dip rate of 15mm/min. The samples were etched for approximately 30 seconds producing bevels 7.5mm long.

The etchant used for the bevelling of the boron implanted silicon was composed of 40%HF, 69%HNO$_3$, and glacial CH$_3$COOH. The temperature of the etchant was maintained at 25°C ± 0.5°C using a thermal bath. To ensure that an abrupt interface between the original surface and bevel was achieved a layer of oil was placed on the top of the etchant[3]. The oil also prevents any HF fumes attacking the unetched surface. After bevelling the sample was rapidly removed and thoroughly cleaned using the same procedure described above. The morphology of the bevelled samples was accurately measured using a 3-D optical interferometer (Zygo NewView 200).

A series of profile measurements were made across the width of the bevel so that a good mean slope angle, $\bar{\theta}_{SA}$, could be calculated and any lateral variations in slope angle measured. The accurate measurement of the slope angle down the bevel and the lateral evenness of the bevel are essential for the subsequent conversion of the SIMS ion image data obtained from the bevel into a depth profile. It was observed that the bevels produced were very shallow with slope angles of approximately 100μrads, corresponding to a slope magnification of 10,000. The bevels were also very even and varied by approximately 2%

across their width. Prior to ion imaging, the bevelled sample was pre-etched in HF to remove any native oxide present on the surface. The SIMS ion imaging of the bevelled samples was performed on an Atomika 6500 SIMS instrument using an O_2 beam at 10keV and 4.0nA. The beam size was typically 10μm and the ion image scan size was 1000×1000μm².

The imaging was performed along the original surface and down along the bevel and repeated a total of ten times in the same region, removing approximately 4nm of material, see figure 1. Due to the high magnification of the bevel the B^{11} profile extends some way along the bevel, it was therefore necessary to perform a second set of ion images further along the bevel.

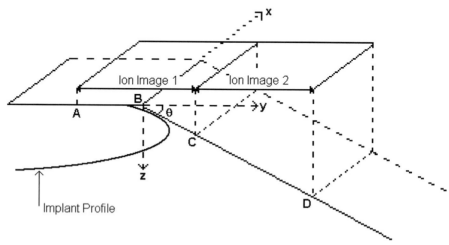

Figure 1 Schematic of the ion imaging process. Secondary ion data is generated from the original surface (AB) and then from points along the bevel (BD). The length AB and bevel slope angle θ are determined using the Zygo interferometer.

3. SIMS Data Conversion

The final ion image data is the averaged counts for the ten images and is composed of a matrix 128×128 pixels which correspond to discrete boron counts. By integrating the counts over the width, x of the matrix, a single column of boron counts can be obtained. This may then be plotted against the imaging distance, down along the sample, producing an 'image-linescan'. An example is shown in figure 2(a).

The boron signal at the bevel interface must then be located as this corresponds to the start of the boron depth profile i.e. 0nm depth, position B on fig.1. This is achieved by measuring the length of the ion image trench that is on the original surface using the Zygo optical profiler at a magnification of ×10. This length can then be subtracted from the original 'image-linescan' (fig 2(a)) and a new 'image-linescan' can be plotted as in fig 2(b) showing the profile from the bevel interface.

Once the start of the boron signal at the bevel interface has been located the distance along the bevel, y from the interface must be converted to the corresponding depth into the material, z to obtain a depth profile. The depth z is related to the distance y by the equation:

$$z = \bar{\theta}_{SA}\, y$$

$$(1)$$

Figure 2 The 'image-linescan' profiles obtained from (a) ion imaging the bevelled sample and (b) from the bevel interface.

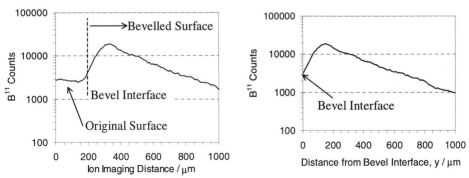

At a magnification of ×10, the lateral error associated with locating the bevel interface is ±1.3μm. However, as the slope angle in the region of the bevel interface was measured to be 100μrads the lateral error corresponds to an error in depth of only ±0.13nm (see eqn 1).

4. Results and Discussion

To demonstrate that the profile obtained via the 'bevel-image' technique had produced a useful depth profile of the 10keV B implant it was compared to a conventional SIMS depth profile. Figure 3 shows the concentration depth profile obtained from the SIMS 'bevel-image' technique compared to a conventional SIMS depth profile at 1keV and normal beam incidence.

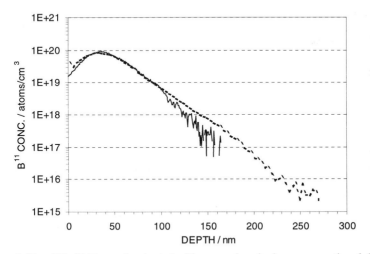

Figure 3 The 10keV Boron implanted silicon analysed via a conventional SIMS depth profile at 1keV (-----), and the 'bevel-image' technique (——).

From Figure 3 it can be seen that the depth profile obtained via the bevel-image technique compares very well with the 1keV depth profile in the boron implant peak region. The leading edge of the 'bevel-image' depth profile is also sharper than the 1keV depth profile. Most importantly the profile obtained using the 'bevel-image' procedure does not suffer from the pre-equilibrium 'spike' that is always present at the start of any conventional SIMS depth profile. This problem is eradicated using the 'bevel-image' technique.

The peaks of the boron implants also compare well with the predicted boron peak position derived from SRIM[4], which was 37nm. The peak depth measured from the 1keV depth profile was 35nm, whereas, the 'bevel-image' depth profiles showed a boron peak depth of 36nm for the bevelled sample.

At a depth of approximately 100nm the profile obtained via the 'bevel-image' technique becomes steeper than the 1keV depth profile. Whereas the 1keV depth profile displays the cumulative effects of SIMS induced broadening and possibly microtopography; the ion imaging was performed on undamaged material and possesses, therefore, an apparent improved depth resolution since the effects of SIMS induced broadening have been reduced.

5. Conclusion

It has been shown that by SIMS ion imaging chemically bevelled shallow boron implanted silicon it is possible to obtain an accurate depth profile of the implant that does not suffer from any of the pre-equilibrium effects that are often associated with conventional SIMS depth profiling. An error is associated with locating the start of the implant boron signal using the 'bevel-image' technique, but this can be accurately assessed, and is also very small at only ±0.13nm. Another advantage of the technique is that the use of low energies for the SIMS analysis is not required, and, moreover the procedure can be carried out using existing SIMS facilities.

The bevelling process is also a quick operation with an etching time of approximately 30 seconds thus many samples may be prepared for SIMS analyses. The total time that was required for the SIMS ion imaging was approximately 30minutes.

It is proposed that this 'bevel-image' technique is very well suited to the accurate analyses of shallow boron implants and can also be applied to shallower implanted materials. Indeed, the procedure has been successfully applied to a 1keV boron implant.

References

[1] J.Maul and S.Patel, **SIMS XI** p707 G.Gillen, R. Lareau., J.Bennet, and F.Stevie, eds., John Wiley and Sons (1998).

[2] D.P.Chu, M.G.Dowsett, T.J. Ormsby, G.A.and Cooke, J. Vac. Sci. Technol. B 16 p302 (1998).

[3] C.M.Hsu, V.K.M.Sharma, M.J.Ashwin, and D.S.M.McPhail, Surf. Int. Anal. 10 p665 (1995).

[4] J.F. Ziegler, and J.P.Biersack, The Stopping and Range of Ions and Solids, Pergamon Press, New York, (1985).

A. Benninghoven, P. Bertrand, H.-N. Migeon and H.W. Werner (Editors).
Proceedings of the 12th International Conference on Secondary Ion Mass Spectrometry,
Brussels, Belgium, 5-11 September 1999

EFFECTS OF USING A ROTATING STAGE ON A CAMECA IMS 6F ON ULTRA SHALLOW JUNCTION PROFILING AND MULTILAYER STRUCTURES

°R. Loesing, +M.Schumacher, °M. S. Phillips, °G. Guryanov, and °D. P. Griffis

°Analytical Instrumentation Facility, North Carolina State University, Box 7531, Raleigh,
NC 27695
+CAMECA- France, 103, bd Saint-Denis, 92403 Courbevoie-France

1. Introduction

Recent investigations have shown that roughness formation during depth profiling of Si using oxygen and SF_5^+ primary ion bombardment, both with and without oxygen flood, has a significant effect on depth resolution [1-3]. It is clearly desirable to use oblique angles for depth profiling since oblique angle sputtering results in higher sputter rates and reduced primary ion beam mixing. Previous experiments employing a rotating stage have shown that sample rotation reduces surface roughness and, as a result, the interface width due to the «360 degree» bombardment for a given surface feature [4-6] provided by sample rotation.

This study investigates the use of a rotating stage on a Cameca IMS 6F with oxygen and cesium beams under various conditions for multilayer structures, boron delta structures and shallow implants. Results are compared on the basis of surface roughness, topography and depth resolution.

2. Experimental

All samples and standards were analyzed using a Cameca IMS-6f, both with and without sample rotation. Analyzed samples consisted of (1) a Ni/Cr depth profiling standard [7] with 12 alternating layers of Ni (53nm) and Cr (64nm) on Si, (2) a Cu layer deposited on Ta deposited on Si, (3) a boron delta structure [round robin sample] with B delta spacing of between 5 and 15nm, and (4) a 10keV, 4e14 atoms/cm^2 Phosphorus implant into Poly-Silicon (4). Samples No.1 and 2 were analyzed with a 10 kV O_2^+-beam and a sample potential of +4.5keV, sample no.3 was analyzed with a collimated 3kV O_2^+-beam and a sample potential voltage of +2kV, sample no.4 was analyzed with a 3kV Cs^+-beam and a sample potential of –1kV. Secondary ions were acquired using the 400µm contrast aperture (CD 1), the 750µm field aperture and the 150µm image field setting resulting in a 60µm diameter optically gated area. Post acceleration of secondary ions was used for extraction potentials at or below 2keV. A mass resolution of 4000 (M/ΔM) was used for the phosphorus analysis. AFM height and phase images were acquired on a Dimension 3000 from Digital Instruments. Crater depths were measured with a P-20 Long Scan Stylus Profilometer from Tencor.

3. Results and Discussion

Figure 1 shows a depth profile of the multilayer Cr/Ni (12 alternating layers with layer thickness of 53nm Ni and 64nm Cr) analyzed with and without sample rotation. Due to the extreme roughness of the crater bottom obtained when the Cr/Ni multilayer sample was depth profiled without rotation (See AFM discussion below), the following normalization procedure was used to facilitate comparison of the two results. The crater obtained with rotation was measured via a stylus profilometer to obtain the depth scale for this sample. The first minimum of the depth profile obtained without rotation was aligned with the first minimum of the rotated depth profile and all subsequent data points were then plotted based on this normalization. Comparison of the depth profiles plotted in the above manner shows a dramatic improvement in depth resolution. The FWHM of the Ni signal stays at a constant value of 62nm if sample rotation is used, while it almost doubles from 65 to 112nm without rotation. AFM micrographs of the craters generated during these depth profiles are shown in Figure 5. Comparison of crater bottom AFM measured roughness resulting from the depth profiling of the sample with (Figure 5A) and without (Figure 5B) sample rotation clearly indicates that the decay of the depth resolution of the non rotated sample is due to the formation of roughness, presumably due differential sputtering resulting from the polycrystalline nature of the metal layers. Measurement of the RMS roughness indicated a factor of 30 decrease in crater bottom roughness from 60nm (no rotation) to 2nm (with rotation). The AFM phase images (Figures 5C and 5D), while not providing any quantifiable information, highlight this difference in roughness. Figure 5c dramatically illustrates the preferential sputtering of the non rotated sample, almost certainly due to the grain structure in the polycrystalline films. These grains appear to have been reduced to circular hillocks of much lower dimension when sample rotation is used. The circular nature of the hillocks are likely the result of having been sputtered from all directions (i.e. 360 degrees) showing the effectiveness of the use of sample rotation to reduce sputter induced roughness.

The improvement in depth resolution obtained when sample rotation is used during the depth profile of a Cu/Ta/Si (currently of great interest to the semiconductor industry) sample is presented in Figure 2. Examination using XRD and TEM as well as studies involving FIB micromachining of this type of sample [8] clearly showed the polycrystalline nature of the Cu layer on this sample. The depth profile of the Cu/Ta/Si sample acquired without sample rotation exhibits severe distortion of the Cu and Ta at the interface making it very difficult to determine its position. With sample rotation, interface definition is dramatically improved.

Profiles obtained from a boron delta layer structure [9] analyzed with a 500eV (normal component) O_2^+ beam without using oxygen flood are presented in figure 3. Depth scale for this sample was calibrated by setting the distance between the 6th and 7th delta to 14.7nm. Although the AFM micrographs of the sputter craters generated with and without rotation (Figure 6a and 6b) shows an decrease in roughness when rotation is used (0.32nm RMS without rotation; 0.24nm RMS with rotation), the depth resolution did not improve. The reduced roughness obtained when using sample rotation results in a more constant sputter rate and a reduction of the total profile shift of 0.7nm compared to the profile obtained without sample rotation.

Apparently under the depth profiling conditions used, factors other then surface roughness dictate depth resolution. Similarly, a 10keV P implant into Poly-Silicon depth profiled using a 3keV (normal impact energy) Cs beam showed no improvement in depth resolution when sample rotation was used. AFM measurement of crater bottoms with and without rotation gave similar values (0.7nm RMS without and 0.9nm RMS with rotation) again indicating that factors other than roughness dictate depth resolution.

4. Summary
The use of sample rotation provides significant improvement in depth resolution when depth profiling polycrystalline metal film samples. Although some improvement in crater bottom roughness was seen for the B delta structure sample, neither the B nor P in Si depth profiles showed any significant improvement in depth resolution.

References:
[1]   G.A. Cooke et al., USJ-99, Research Triangle Park, NC, USA, Proceedings, 41 (1999)
[2]   P.A. Ronsheim and R.J. Murphy, USJ-99, Research Triangle Park, NC, USA, Proceedings, 126 (1999)
[3]   G. Gillen et al., USJ-99, Research Triangle Park, NC, USA, Proceedings, 129 (1999)

[4] M. Schumacher, Presentation at USJ99, Research Triangle Park, NC, USA, (1999)
[5] F. A. Stevie and J. L. Moore, Surf. Interf. Anal., 18, 147 (1992)
[6] E. H. Cirlin et al., J. Vac. Sci. Technol. A5, 9 (1991)
[7] NiCr-2 Depth Profiling Standard, Geller MicroAnalytical Laboratory
[8] J. Phillips et al, 46th AVS International Symposium, Seattle, WA, USA, Proceedings, (1999)
[9] Sample provided by Joe Bennett, SEMATECH

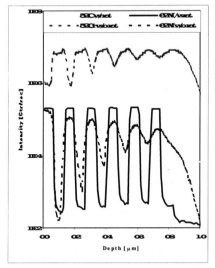

Figure 1: Cr/Ni Multi layer sample analyzed with and without using sample rotation. The profiles are normalized in depth to the first Cr minimum

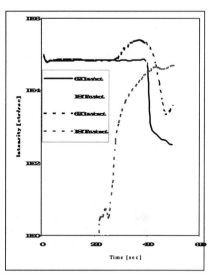

Figure 2: Copper-layer deposited on Tantalum analyzed with and without sample rotation

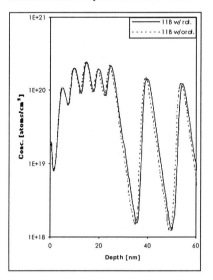

Figure 3: Boron delta-layer structure analyzed with and without sample rotation

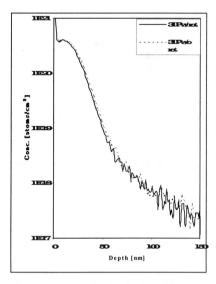

Figure 4: 10keV P-implant implanted into Poly-Silicon analyzed with and without sample rotation

584

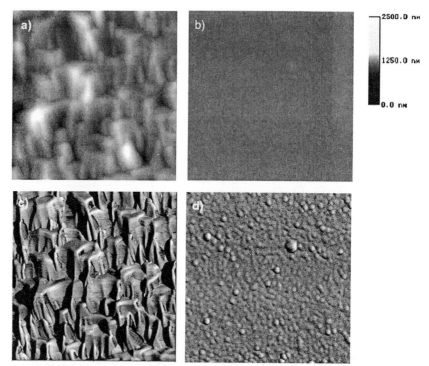

Figure5: 5x5um AFM images of the Ni/Cr-Multilayer sputter crater buttom
a) Height image, no sample rotation   b) Height image, with sample rotation
c) Phase image, no sample rotation   d) Phase Image, with sample rotation

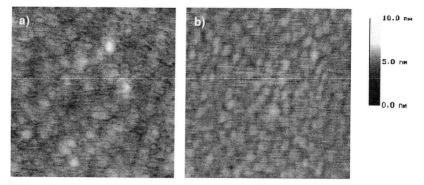

Figure 6: 1x1um AFM images of the Boron delta doped sputter crater bottom
a) Height image, no sample rotation   b) Height image, with sample rotation

A. Benninghoven, P. Bertrand, H.-N. Migeon and H.W. Werner (Editors).
Proceedings of the 12th International Conference on Secondary Ion Mass Spectrometry,
Brussels, Belgium, 5-11 September 1999
© 2000 Elsevier Science B.V. All rights reserved.

NEAR SURFACE CONCENTRATION DEPTH PROFILING OF LOW-ENERGY BORON IMPLANTED SILICON MEASURED USING CHEMICAL BEVELLING AND SIMS LINESCAN ANALYSIS

D.S. McPhail[1], R.J. Chater[1], K.P Johansen[1], S. Fearn[1], G. Cooke[2] and M. Dowsett[2]

[1] Department of Materials, Imperial College of Science Technology and Medicine,
Prince Consort Road, London SW7 2BP UK - d.mcphail@ic.ac.uk
[2] Department of Physics, University of Warwick, Coventry CV4 7AL UK

1. Introduction

Sub-keV dopant implantation is a recent development in VLSI technology that has enhanced device packing densities and switching speeds. The accurate experimental measurement and quantification of these ultra-shallow dopant profiles is essential both for process development and troubleshooting, the more so since theoretical modeling at these low energies may be inaccurate. Thus, there is a need to improve the existing analytical techniques and to develop new strategies in order to achieve sub-nm depth resolution of shallow dopants. This sub-nm depth resolution should be retained to a depth of several hundred nanometers.

The secondary ion mass spectrometry (SIMS) depth profiling community has responded to this challenge by developing a new generation of primary ion guns that can deliver high beam currents at energies as low as 200eV [1]. The low beam energies associated with these 'floating low energy ion guns' (FLIG) reduce the primary ion range and the associated beam induced mixing to a fraction of a nanometre. One might, therefore, expect SIMS depth profiles to have become accurate to a fraction of a nm. There are, however, several problems associated with low energy SIMS depth profiling that may distort the analytical data. As the dopant profile contracts some of the artifacts associated with SIMS depth profiling such as surface transients (due, for example, to native oxides, contaminants and charging effects) and segregation may become more significant. Also it has recently become clear that micro-topography can evolve very rapidly during low energy SIMS depth profiling if the beam is not at normal incidence [2]. The rapid drop in silicon sputter yield at beam energies below 1keV is also a serious limitation of low energy SIMS depth profiling substantially increasing analysis time (and cost) and increasing the possibility of instrumental drift. Given these problems, some of which may prove intractable, it is important that the SIMS community develops alternative analytical strategies. One alternative to low energy SIMS depth profiling presented here involves the synthesis of ultra-shallow bevels into the semiconducting material using a wet chemical etch. The bevels are produced by lowering the sample into the etchant at a constant speed / dip rate. The bevel magnification is simply the dip rate divided by the etch rate. These bevels can then be linescanned or imaged in the SIMS machine and the data quantified to produce a plot of concentration against depth.

2. The Bevel-and-Image Approach

The advantages of this approach are that:

- The bevelling process is simple and rapid (a few minutes).

- Bevel magnifications in the range 100-10,000 can be synthesized by varying the dip rate or the etch rate. If the magnification is 10,000 a 1nm feature is projected on the bevel plane as a 10μm stripe.
- The wet etching process introduces very little damage into the surface of the material.
- The SIMS analysis (linescan or image) takes only a few minutes.
- The bevel shape and the associated SIMS linescan along the bevel are a permanent record of the depth of origin of the secondary ions.
- It is not essential that the bevel is linear since the shape may be inferred from optical interferometry depth maps (instruments such as the ZYGO Newview has sub-nm resolution). A depth coordinate may then be assigned to each point on the linescan.
- The depth resolution is independent of the position along the bevel from which the data is generated (assuming the bevel magnification is constant). The depth resolution of an atomically abrupt feature is given by [1]; $\Delta Z(fwhm) = (W/M) + (di + t)$ where W is the beam width, M the bevel magnification, t the layer thickness and di is a term which includes the information depth , any microtopography and beam induced mixing.
- SIMS analysis takes a few minutes.

Hsu and McPhail [3] have shown that such an approach when applied to III-V systems (AlGaAs and InGaAs based multi-quantum-wells) can produce a trailing edge depth resolution of less than 0.3nm. Recently we have been developing this approach for silicon based semiconducting materials. Fearn [4] has developed a suitable etching system and has produced a series of bevels in silicon and silicon based materials that meet the requirements of the bevel and linescan approach. Fearn has described the etching process and its application to 10keV B in Si implants in these proceedings [4]. She has demonstrated that that implant, which has a peak 36nm below the sample surface, can be accurately assessed using a bevel-and-image approach. Indeed the resolution in that bevel-and-image analysis was better than in the corresponding 1keV SIMS depth profile. Furthermore, and most importantly, the surface spike observed in the boron SIMS depth profile was absent from the bevel-and-image data. Finally she has shown that when there are no lateral variations in the bevel it is possible to add 128 linescans together (i.e. to use image rather than linescan data) leading to an improvement in sensitivity of over two orders of magnitude.

In this paper we report on the use of the bevel and linescan approach to measure an ultra-shallow boron implant (1keV) with a peak just a few nanometres beneath the surface. We have compared the data with that from a low energy SIMS depth profile conducted on the Atomika 4500 at Warwick University.

3. Experimental

A lightly doped p type silicon wafer was implanted at 1 keV with B^{11} at a dose of 5×10^{15}atom/cm^2. The samples were cut into 1cm^2 pieces and thoroughly cleaned in acetone, methanol and de-ionised water for three minutes each with the aid of an ultra-sonic bath. Once cleaned the samples were mounted onto the bevelling apparatus which has been described elsewhere [3] and then lowered into an etching solution at a constant dip rate of 15mm/min. The samples were etched for approximately 30 seconds producing bevels 7.5mm long. The etchant used for the bevelling of the boron implanted silicon was composed of 40%HF, 69%HNO$_3$, and glacial CH$_3$COOH (ratio 5:70:17). The temperature of the etchant was maintained at 25°C ± 0.5°C using a thermal bath. To ensure that an abrupt interface between the original surface and bevel was achieved a layer of oil was placed on the top of the etchant [3]. The oil also prevented any HF fumes attacking the unetched surface. After bevelling the sample was rapidly removed and thoroughly cleaned using the same procedure described above[4]. Bevels were assessed for surface roughness using a Quesant Atomic Force Microscope and the bevel shape was assessed using a ZYGO Newview Scanning Interferometer. After producing the bevel the native oxide was removed using a HF dip prior to linescan analysis. The dopant implant concentration profile was measured using the Atomika 4500 instrument at Warwick University. A 500eV beam focused to ~5μm was scanned down the bevel. The linescan was 1000μm long. After SIMS analysis, the bevel shape was measured with nanometre accuracy using a microscope-based light interference surface profiler (ZYGO). A SIMS depth profile was conducted at normal incidence using the same 500eV oxygen primary beam.

4. Results and discussion

A typical bevel in silicon measured using the ZYGO surface optical interferometer is shown below. The lateral uniformity of the bevel is very good (2%) and the bevel surface is smooth with an r.m.s. roughness (AFM) of 1.4nm (the original surface is smooth to 0.7nm r.m.s). The imaged section of the bevel is 585um long and 110nm deep indicating an average bevel magnification of 5320. However, the bevel is curved for the first 25nm below the surface so

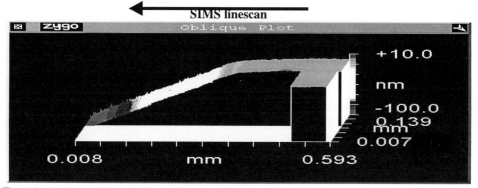

Figure 1. An image of the bevel obtained using a ZYGO Newview optical interferometer

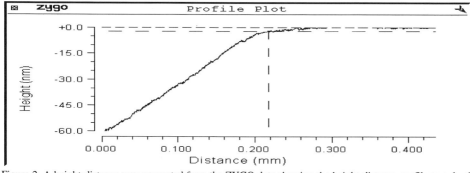

Figure 2. A height-distance map generated from the ZYGO data showing the height-distance profile to a depth of 60nm. This information was used to depth calibrate the SIMS linescan analysis.

588

that the bevel magnification is far higher is this region (the bevel magnification on the surface is infinite) and this curvature must be taken into account when depth calibrating the SIMS linescan data.

The data from the low energy SIMS depth profile and from the bevel and linescan analysis are compared below, using a <u>linear</u> concentration scale. It is clear that there is a good agreement between the two analyses in terms of the general shape of the distributions and the near-surface detail. The bevel and linescan approach suggests a slightly broader distribution on the trailing edge. In that region the broadening of the linescan data due to the W/M term is ~1nm, whilst the contribution due to d_i is unknown but probably similar. The data density of the bevel and linescan approach is high at and near the surface. These data correspond to the time the ion beam spends moving along the surface and down the shallow curving slope of the bevel. Thus the data density is highest at the most important part of the analysis. The bevel and linescan data is somewhat noisier than that from the low energy SIMS depth profile, due to the lower

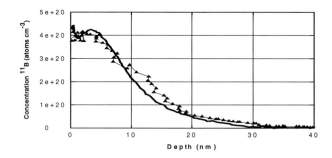

analytical volume and lack of an oxide altered layer. The sensitivity of the analysis will be improved in future experiments by imaging the surface [4] and by irradiating the surface prior to analysis with ultra low energy oxygen ions (<100eV); see [5].

5. Conclusions

The bevel and linescan SIMS analysis procedure has produced a profile shape very similar to that produced by a low energy SIMS depth profile. We will now produce higher magnification bevels in order to improve the resolution of the analysis. We will also investigate methods of increasing the sensitivity of this approach by using a bevel and <u>image</u> approach and by injecting ultra-low energy ions into the bevel surface prior to imaging. We would welcome collaborations especially with groups that can provide delta doped silicon test structures.

References

[1] M.G. Dowsett et al, J. Vac. Sci. Technol. B 16 (1997) 367.

[2] D.P. Chu et al, J. Vac. Sci. Technol. B 16 (1998) 302.

[3] C.M. Hsu et al, Surface and Interface Analysis, 23 (1995) 665

[4] S. Fearn et al, 'High resolution SIMS analysis using a bevel-image technique on shallow boron doped silicon', these Proceedings.

[5] M Hughes et al. 'Useful ion yield enhancement for LMIS-SIMS by oxygen ion implantation: a systematic study', these Proceedings.

A. Benninghoven, P. Bertrand, H.-N. Migeon and H.W. Werner (Editors).
Proceedings of the 12th International Conference on Secondary Ion Mass Spectrometry,
Brussels, Belgium, 5-11 September 1999
© 2000 Elsevier Science B.V. All rights reserved.

SIMS DEPTH PROFILING OF Cu IN GeSi/Si STRUCTURE AND Si MATRIX WITH CAMECA 6F

G. M. Guryanov, R. Loesing, M.O. Aboelfotoh, J. Narayan,
M. A. Borek, and D. P. Griffis
North Carolina State University, Box 7531, Raleigh, NC 27695 USA, Guryanov@unity.ncsu.edu

1. Introduction

Silicon-germanium alloys are important semiconductor materials for many applications including high frequency devices [1]. SIMS depth profile analysis of some elements (Au, Ni, Cu) in Si as well as in GeSi alloys present serious difficulties due to beam-induced segregation (BIS) of impurity atoms. As a result, significant beam induced broadening of the depth profiles of these elements is observed [2-4]. Some approaches that have been proposed to reduce the effect of BIS during Cu depth profiling under oxygen bombardment are: cooling the sample by using a cryogenic sample stage [5], using oblique primary ion angles of incidence [4] and using low energy electrons for charging compensation [6]. In most cases, explanations of BIS of Cu are presented in terms of Gibbsian segregation resulting from oxygen primary ion induced oxide formation while an alternative explanation involves electric field-induced migration [6]. Since ion yields [7] and thus detection limits of Cu in Si are similar for both oxygen and cesium primary ion bombardment, it may be that use of Cs primary ions will result in decreased BIS (if primarily oxygen induced) while still achieving useful detection limits.

In this work, results of SIMS depth profile analysis of Cu in Si and in GeSi/Si structures are compared for Cs$^+$ and O$_2^+$ primary ion bombardment. Positive and negative Cu$^\pm$ and positive molecular CuCs$^+$ secondary ions were monitored. Possible mechanisms of observed BIS effects are discussed.

2. Experimental

All SIMS measurements were performed using a CAMECA 6F instrument. Experiments were carried out with 10keV Cs$^+$ while monitoring 4.5 kV negative Cu$^-$ or posi-tive CuCs$^+$ secondary ions and with 10 and 6.75keV O$_2^+$ beams, recording 4.5kV positive Cu$^+$ ions (Table 1). Angles of incidence in Table 1 were calculated as described in Wilson et al [8].

Table 1

SIMS Conditions	Primary ions	Beam Energy (keV)	Sample potential (kV)	Secondary ions	Normal impact energy/atom (keV)	Incident angle (degree)
1	Cs$^+$	10	-4.5	Cu$^-$	13.2	24.5
2	Cs$^+$	10	+4.5	CuCs$^+$	4.1	42.4
3	O$_2^+$	10	+4.5	Cu$^+$	2.05	42.4
4	O$_2^+$	6.75	+4.5	Cu$^+$	0.55	60.7

In all cases the primary ion beam was scanned over 150 by 150µm square area and secondary ions were extracted from a 60µm diameter circle centered on rastered area. 1800M/ΔM mass resolution was used to acquire both positive and negative atomic Cu ions while 300M/ΔM resolution was used for molecular CuCs$^+$ ions. The samples analyzed were an Si wafer implanted with 150keV Cu^{63} at dose 5x10^{14} at/cm^2 and an epitaxially grown Ge$_{0.5}$Si$_{0.5}$/Si structure upon which a Cu layer was deposited and annealed at 150°C for times varying from 15 minutes to 60 minutes. After annealing samples were etched in nitric acid to remove any remaining Cu on the surface. Primary beam densities were chosen to produce similar Si sputter rates (about 0.8 nm/s) for the differing SIMS conditions. Sputter rates for GeSi and Si were determined using depth measurements on a Tencor P-10 long scan profilometer.

3. Results and Discussion

3.1 Cu in Si

Figure1 shows depth profiles of Cu in Si acquired under SIMS conditions 1 – 3 as listed in Table 1. The Cu depth profile in Si acquired using 10keV O_2^+, while not significantly broadened, showed a small but reproducible 10nm shift of the entire Cu profile away from the surface. A possible explanation for this shift is a small BIS effect under SIMS conditions used (42° incident angle). The Cu depth profile acquired using 6.75keV O_2^+ (Condition 4, not shown in Fig. 1) was identical to the profiles obtained for Cs+ bombardment. Detection limits for Cu in Si varied as expected with poorest detection limit observed for $CuCs^+$ ions (~$1x10^{18}$ at/cm3) and the best (~$8x10^{15}$ at/cm^3) for Cu^- or Cu^+ using 10keV Cs^+ or O_2^+ respectively. The detection limit for 6.75keV O_2^+ was approximately 3 times poorer than that provided by 10keV O_2^+.

3.2 Cu in GeSi/Si

To study the evolution of Cu profile in GeSi/Si structure after annealing, MCs^+ detection was chosen from among the conditions listed in Table 1 since this mode of analysis has been shown to be less sensitive to matrix variation in many cases [9] and since this condition resulted in the least apparent profile distortion. Figure 2 shows the Cu profiles obtained from sample which had been annealed for 15, 30 and 60 minutes. Since no noticeable ion yield change was observed for the Cu at the interface for the 60 minute annealing time, the RSF obtained from Cu in Si ($CuCs^+$ detection) was used for quantification. The data presented in Fig.2 appear to be consistent with increasing annealing time showing migration of Cu with increasing accumulation of Cu in the GeSi. For the lowest annealing time (15 min), Cu accumulation at GeSi/Si interface was observed which can possibly be attributed to trapping of Cu at the interface. For the 30 and 60 minute annealing times, the Cu concentration in the SiGe greatly exceeds the $1x10^{16}$ at/cm^3 solubility limit for Cu in this material. It is postulated that Cu reacted with the $Ge_{0.5}Si_{0.5}$ alloy to form $Cu_3Ge_xSi_{1-x}$ [10] greatly increasing the ability of the GeSi to accommodate Cu.

Figure 3 shows the as measured Cu, Ge and Si secondary ion intensities versus sputter time obtained from the GeSi/Si sample (annealed for 60 minutes at 150°C) acquired using SIMS conditions 1 through 3 (Table 1). Results obtained using Condition 4 are not presented and are considered unreliable for the measurement of Cu distribution both due to increased spreading of the Cu and Ge observed in the depth profiles and due to unexplained problems with depth profile reproducibility. The Cu depth profile obtained using Condition 1, detection of Cu^-, exhibited apparent impurity segregation at hetero structure interface. The apparent Cu redistribution obtained under these analytical conditions, i.e. data acquired using negative sample bias, may be attributable to surface charging which resulted in a strong field induced migration of the Cu into the Si substrate. Cu profiles obtained using conditions 2 and 3 differed significantly from that obtained from condition 1. These profiles, both obtained using positive sample bias, exhibit very similar Cu profile shapes with no obvious change of the Cu ion yield at the GeSi/Si interface.

While the Cu profile shapes obtained for conditions 2 and 3 were similar , a definite increase in broadening of the Cu profile was observed for oxygen beam (condition 3) compared to Cs beam (condition 2). This spreading of the Cu may be attributable to oxygen induced Cu BIS in the presence of Ge. Change in surface morphology due to roughening during oxygen ion beam sputtering was also considered as a possible cause for the Cu spreading. To determine if sputtering induced roughness contributed to the Cu spreading, AFM measurements of a crater bottom roughness were performed at the GeSi/Si interface for

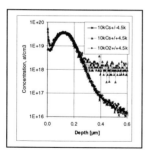

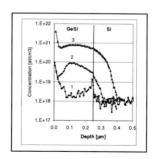

Fig. 1. Ion implanted Cu depth profiles in Si matrix measured for (1-3) SIMS conditions listed in Table 1.

Fig. 2. Cu profiles in GeSi/Si structure taken after annealing at 150°C for: 1-15min, 2-30min, 3-60min measured using SIMS condition 2 listed in Table1.

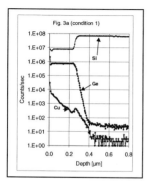

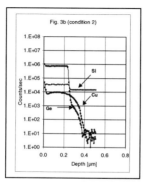

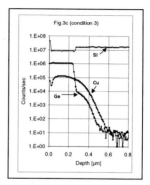

Fig. 3. As measured Cu, Si and Ge profiles in GeSi/Si structure obtained using various SIMS conditions. 3a and 3b: 10keV Cs+ ion beam and secondary Cu⁻ and CsCu⁺ ions respectively. 3c: 10kev O₂⁺ ion beam and secondary Cu⁺ ions

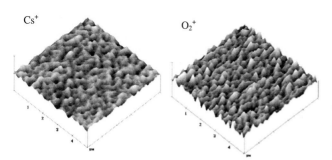

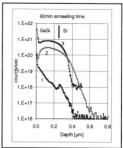

Fig. 4. 5x5μm AFM micrographs of crater bottom at the interface in $Ge_{0.5}Si_{0.5}$/Si structure obtained for Cs^+ (condition 2) and O_2^+ (condition 3) beams z-scale: 40nm/division

Fig. 5. Cu profiles in $Ge_{0.5}Si_{0.5}$/Si structure measured for (1-3) SIMS conditions listed in Table 1 (curve number corresponds conditions number).

conditions 2 and 3 (Figure 4). Maximum peak to valley heights obtained from the AFM micrographs were 8nm for Cs beam and 20nm for oxygen beam. This level of roughness is probably not sufficient to cause the profile spreading observed in Fig.3b and 3c. For further confirmation that beam induced roughness was not the cause of the Cu profile spreading, Cu profiles were obtained using condition 3 and with and without sample rotation. Although, AFM measurements confirmed that sample rotation reduced crater bottom roughness, no difference in Cu distribution was observed.

Ge also appears to be more broadened in the depth profile generated using the oxygen beam (Fig. 3c, condition 3) versus the Cs beam (Fig. 3b, condition 2). The Ge interface decay lengths (nm/decade), obtained using the instrumental conditions 2 and 3 (Table1), 6.4nm and 15.5nm respectively, show the influence of the primary ion species on Ge broadening at the GeSi/Si interface. In addition to the increased decay length observed with the use of the oxygen beam (condition 3), there is also evidence of additional spreading of the Ge into the Si substrate apparently proportional to the spreading of the Cu. This proportional spreading may be evidence of the influence of Ge on the migration of Cu in the $Ge_{0.5}Si_{0.5}/Si$ structure, perhaps via the formation of a Cu_3Ge complex [10]. Finally, for both O_2^+ energies used, the $^{28}Si^+$ ion intensity in the GeSi was half that obtained from the Si in direct proportion to the relative abundance of the Si. This apparent proportionality may be useful for stoichiometric characterization of GeSi alloys.

4. Conclusions

Depth profiling of Cu in Si using a Cs^+ ion beam resulted in no obvious beam induced segregation affects for detection of either Cu^- or $CsCu^+$. Detection limit of Cu in Si is strongly influenced by the SIMS conditions used and, for sputter rate 0.8 nm/s, background concentration levels for Cu in Si of ~$8x10^{15}$ at/cm^3 were obtained for both 10keV Cs^+ and O_2^+ beams while monitoring 4.5kV Cu^- or Cu^+ secondary ions respectively.

Strong beam induced migration of Cu in GeSi/Si structure during SIMS profiling was observed. Minimum profile broadening was observed using a 10keV Cs^+ primary ion beam and detecting $CsCu^+$ secondary ions although the detection limit is rather poor under these conditions (approximately $1x10^{18}$at/cm^3). Evidence of the importance of Ge in the beam induced migration effect of Cu in GeSi/Si sample matrix was observed. Using positive secondary ion detection, no obvious change of Cu ion yield at GeSi/Si interface was obtained when either O_2^+ or Cs^+ primary ions were used.

Acknowledgements: Funding provided by Analytical Instrumentation Facility, NSF and NSF Center for Advanced Materials and Smart Structures.

References

[1] K.L.Wang and R.P.G.Karunasiri, J.Vac. Sci. Technol. B11 (1993) 1159.
[2] K.Wittmaack and N.Menzel, Appl. Phys. Lett. 50 (1987) 815.
[3] C.J.Vriezema, K.T.F.Janssen and P.R.Boudewijn, Appl. Phys. Lett. 54 (1989) 1981.
[4] M.Petravic, B.G.Svensson, J.S.Williams and J.M.Glasko, Nucl. Instr. And Meth. B118 (1996) 151.
[5] S.F.Corcoran, S.K.Hofmeister, D.P.Griffis and R.W.Linton, in Secondary Ion Mass Spectrometry SIMS VII, A.Benninghoven, et al (Eds), Jonh Wiley & Sons, Chichester, 1990, p.643.
[6] C.J.Vriezema and P.C.Zalm, Surf. Interface Anal. 17 (1991) 875.
[7] R.G.Wilson, Int. J. Mass Spec. and Ion Proc. 143 (1995) 43.
[8] R.G.Wilson, F.A.Stevie and C.W.Magee, Secondary Ion Mass Spectrometry. Wiley, New York, 1989, p1.3-2.
[9] Y.Gao, Y.Marie, F.Saldi, H.-N.Migeon, Int. J. Mass Spec. and Ion Proc. 143 (1995) 11
[10] M.O.Aboelfotoh, M.A.Borek and J.Narayan, Appl. Phys. Lett. 75 (1999) 1739
[11] M.O.Aboelfotoh, M.A.Borek and J.Narayan, Appl. Phys. Lett. 78 (1999)

A. Benninghoven, P. Bertrand, H.-N. Migeon and H.W. Werner (Editors).
Proceedings of the 12th International Conference on Secondary Ion Mass Spectrometry,
Brussels, Belgium, 5-11 September 1999
© 2000 Elsevier Science B.V. All rights reserved.

MIGRATION BEHAVIOR OF SODIUM IN SILICON OXIDE DURING SIMS ANALYSIS AT VARIOUS SAMPLE TEMPERATURES

R. Saito[a,c], S. Hayashi[b] and M. Kudo[c]

[a]Corporate Manufacturing Engineering Center, Toshiba Corporation,
33, Shin-isogo-cho, Isogo-ku, Yokohama, Kanagawa 235-0017, Japan
e-mail address: reiko.saito@toshiba.co.jp
[b]Advanced Technology Research Laboratories, Nippon Steel Corporation,
Shintomi 20-1, Futtu, Chiba 293-8511, Japan
[c]Department of Applied Physics, Faculty of Engineering, Seikei University,
3-3-1, Kitamachi, Kichijoji, Musashino, Tokyo 180-8633, Japan

1. Introduction

SiO_2 films are widely used as insulating layers in electronic devices. The accurate evaluation of impurity distribution in the SiO_2 film is important in the manufacturing process because impurities in these films significantly influence their electrical characteristics. However, it is well established that alkali metals, especially Na, easily migrate in SiO_2 films due to the electric field induced by charged particle bombardment. This phenomenon makes it difficult to precisely evaluate the distribution of an element using SIMS. Although several techniques[1-4] have been developed to solve this problem and have proved to be effective from a practical point of view, the detailed mechanisms of alkali metal migration have not been clarified yet.

In this study, in order to obtain information for clarifying the Na migration during SIMS analysis, we characterized the behavior of Na in SiO_2 films during SIMS depth profiling by varying the sample temperature under the condition of self-compensation of charges[5]. The structural property of the SiO_2 film was also analyzed using FT-IR to obtain the distribution of defects in the SiO_2 film, which was caused by ion implantation. Then influence of the defects on Na behavior during SIMS analysis was examined.

2. Experimental

The sample used in this study was a thermally-grown SiO_2 film which was ion implanted with Na at an energy of 100keV and a dose of 1E15 ions/cm^2. The expected Na depth profile and ion implantation damage were simulated using TRIM-92. SIMS depth profiling was performed using the Cameca ims4f instrument equipped with a temperature-variable sample stage which consists of a liquid nitrogen flow and a sample heating system. Using this system, the depth profile was obtained at the sample temperatures of 154K, 203K, 228K, 248K, 278K and 303K. Because the self-charge compensation method was applied, Cs+(14.5keV, 10nA) primary ions were used in all the experiments to detect negative secondary ions.

Additionally, we prepared samples of various thicknesses, removed layers with HF solution and analyzed the stretching vibrations of Si-O bonds using FT-IR in order to obtain the information about the depth distribution of defects in the film.

3. Results and discussions

Figure 1 shows the examples of Na depth profiles in the SiO$_2$ film, which are obtained by SIMS at the sample temperatures of 154K and 278K. The profiles of Na showed "Gaussian-like" distributions, which is common for conventional ion-implanted samples, at all the temperatures by using the self-charge compensation method. However, Na was detected at the SiO$_2$/Si interface in all experiments. The Na$^-$ secondary ion quantity detected in the peak that the interface was approximately 2-3% of the ion quantity detected from the main peak, regardless of the sample temperature. In the case of analyzing the sample for which the Na implanted layer was removed with HF solution (to the depth

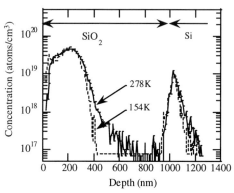

Fig.1 SIMS depth profiles of Na obtained at the sample temperature of 154K and 278K

of 60nm from the surface), the Na secondary ion quantity detected at the SiO$_2$/Si interface was approximately 1/10 of that shown in Fig.1. From this result it can be concluded that almost all the Na detected at the interface shown in Fig. 1 had migrated from the implanted layer during SIMS analysis.

The SIMS profiles around the ion-implanted layer for various sample temperatures are compared with the simulated Na distribution as shown in Figure 2. From the measurements at the sample temperatures of 154K and 203K shown in Fig.2(a), both the peak depth and width approximately fit the simulation result, despite the presence of a small peak around 50nm in depth, which is about 1/4 of the peak depth. The profiles in Fig.2(b) for the sample temperatures of 228K and 248K show that the peak depths and the distributions on the deeper side of the peaks are almost unchanged. However, the profiles on the surface side of the peaks show an increase in the Na secondary ion intensity. The profiles for the sample temperatures of 278K and 303K in Fig.2(c) show that the peaks are slightly shifted toward the interface and the profiles are widened toward the interface. From the results, the apparent differences in the Na profiles indicate that Na migration is accelerated with increasing temperature. Comparing the Na profiles obtained at each temperature using the profile at the lowest temperature of 154K as the reference, it is clear that, with increasing temperature during SIMS analysis, migration occurs toward the surface first, then develops toward the interface with further increase in temperature.

It is considered that defects formed during ion implantation in the SiO$_2$ film have a significant influence on Na migration during SIMS analysis. It seems that positron sensitive defects exist around 50nm in depth [7]. The depth distribution of ion implantation damage was calculated by TRIM to have a peak around 120-140nm in depth, which is closer to the surface than those of the simulated distribution of Na (with a peak depth of 210nm). Furthermore, using the samples of varying thickness of SiO$_2$ layer, the stretching vibration of Si-O bonds was analyzed by FT-IR. The intensity ratio between the side lobe (1200cm^{-1}) and main peak (1100cm^{-1}) was calculated for each depth, and plotted on Figure 3. The peak at

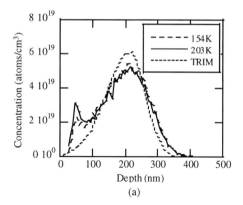

(a)

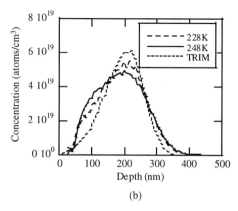

(b)

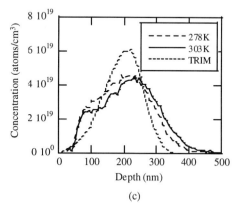

(c)

Fig.2 SIMS depth profiles of Na in SiO2 obtained at the various sample temperatures

$1200cm^{-1}$ is known to arise from porous oxide, i.e., Si-O in a large void [6]. From the results, it is considered that the distribution of defects such as voids has its peak at the depth of 110-180nm, which is closer to the surface than the Na peak depth. This result roughly agrees with the defect distribution obtained by TRIM and it is considered that the voids are formed by the cleavage of the Si-O bonds during ion implantation. On the other hand, at the deeper and un-implanted layer, the ratio is still larger than that of usual thermally-grown SiO_2 film. it is also expected that the structural distortion extends to considerably deep areas in which no Na exists.

Comparing the depth distribution of defects and the Na behavior during SIMS measurement, it is considered that the Na migrations occur due to the influence of the defects on Na during the sputter mixing in the SIMS analysis. Namely, it is considered that the Na migration toward the surface is influenced by the defects such as voids caused by cleavage of Si-O bonds, and the migration toward the interface is influenced by the defects caused by structural distortion. Because migration toward the surface is observed at low temperatures, it is considered that migration into regions with defects, such as voids, caused by the cleavage of Si-O bonds, is more likely to occur.

On the other hand, there exists the possibility that the contribution term from the electric field induced migration is not entirely removed during the SIMS measurement, since there is no method of verifying the actual quantity of charging during the measurement. Therefore, the migration toward the interface could be induced by the slight residual charging. For instance, the existence of Na detected at the interface, which is independent of the temperature or shift of peak position at the higher temperature, might be affected by charging.

596

4. Conclusions

Under the conditions of self-charge compensation, the behavior of Na in SiO_2 films during SIMS depth profiling was characterized by changing the sample temperature. The depth distributions of the defects in the films were also analyzed using FT-IR. The influence of the defects on Na behavior during SIMS analysis was examined by comparing the results.

It is confirmed that the distribution of defects such as voids has its peak at a shallower depth than the depth of the implanted Na distribution. In addition, the structural distortion may reach a considerably deeper layer where no Na exists. At the lower temperatures, the SIMS profiles fit that of a simulated Na distribution (except at the depth of 50nm) and then Na distributions are hardly affected by the defects in the film. However, with increasing temperature, the Na distributions obtained by SIMS analysis were found to be affected by the defects in the film.

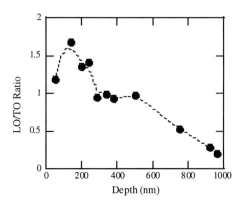

Fig.3 Depth profile of LO/TO peak ratio of the Si-O streching vibration obtained by FT-IR

It is clarified that even with the self-charge compensation method, Na migration in the SiO_2 film is caused by the ion beam during SIMS analysis and is affected by the defects in the films.

Acknowledgements

We would like to thank Dr. N. Nagai of Toray Research Center Inc. for his cooperation and suggestions about the structural analysis of Si oxide films.

References

[1] C. W. Magee and W. L. Harrington, Appl. Phys. Lett., 33 (1978) 193.
[2] S. Nagayama, S. Makinouchi, A. Takano and M. Kudo, in Proceeding of SIMS VII, 1989, p655.
[3] R. Saito and M. Kudo, in Proceeding of SIMS XI, 1997, p379.
[4] J. J. Vajo, Surf. Interface Anal., 25 (1997) 295.
[5] H. N. Migeon, M. Schuhmacher and G. Slodzian, Surf. Interface Anal., 16,(1990)9.
[6] J. S. Chou and S. C. Lee, J. App. Phys., 77(4), (1995) 1805.
[7] S. Hayashi, R. Saito, M. Kudo and H. Kitajima in these proceedings.

A. Benninghoven, P. Bertrand, H.-N. Migeon and H.W. Werner (Editors).
Proceedings of the 12th International Conference on Secondary Ion Mass Spectrometry,
Brussels, Belgium, 5-11 September 1999

OBSERVATION OF SODIUM MIGRATION OF SiO2/Si INTERFACE DURING SIMS ANALYSIS

S. Hayashi [a] , R. Saito [b,c], M. Kudo [c] and H. Kitajima[d]

[a] Advanced Technology Research Labs., Nippon Steel Corporation

20-1 Shintomi, Futtsu,293-8511, Chiba, JAPANe-mail: shun@re.nsc.co.jp

[b] Corporate Manufacturing Engineering Center, Toshiba Corporation,

33 Shin-isogo-cho, Isogo-ku, Yokohama, 235-0017, JAPAN

[c]Department of Applied Physics, Faculty of Engineering, Seikei University,

3-3-1 Kitamachi, Kichijoji, Tokyo, 180-8633, JAPAN

[d]H&S Technology Corporation,

123-10 Kurokawa, Asao-ku, Kawasaki, 211-0035, JAPAN

1. Introduction

It has been reported that negative ion detection mode using self-charge compensation in the CAMECA instruments has been able to provide the electron-migration free depth profile [1,2]. However, the detailed mechanisms of migration of metallic elements, especially Na in SiO_2, during SIMS analysis have not been clearly understood yet. In this study, we developed the temperature variable sample stage, which consists of a liquid nitrogen flow and sample heating. And then influences of the intrinsic defects in SiO_2 film by ion implantation on Na migration were investigated. We discussed the dependence of Na depth profile changes on the disappearance of the implanted defects by post-annealing.

2. Experimental

2.1 Temperature variable sample stage

The temperature variable sample stage consists of the 3 parts , which are a liquid nitrogen circulating system using a liquid nitrogen vessel and a diaphragm pump, a sample heating system in front of the sapphire plate in order to isolate from the sample high voltage(Fig.1). We can do SIMS analysis under the sample temperature from 154 K to 303K.

2.2 Samples

The samples used in this study were 1 μm thick- thermally grown SiO_2 films on Si substrates

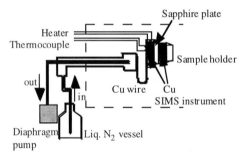

Fig.1 *Schematic diagram of temperature variable sample stage system*

which were implanted with Na$^+$ at the energy of 100 keV (Sample 1) with a dose of 1E15 ions/cm^2 . And then they were annealed at the temperatures of 573K, 873K and 1173K for 30min. The surfaces of all samples were finally coated with 20nm thick gold films.

2.3 Experimental conditions

SIMS depth profiling was performed using the CAMECA ims-4f instrument using a normal incidence electron gun for charge compensation. Cs$^+$ primary ion which had a 14.5 keV impact energy with a current of 10 nA was raster-scanned a 100 µm square area and the analyzed area was settled with 60 µm in diameter at the center of the crater. Negative secondary ions, such as Na$^-$,O$^-$, were detected in order to be able to do charge compensation automatically. The sample was cooled down to the temperature we had previously set during SIMS analysis. We also monitored the intrinsic defects in SiO$_2$ film by ion implantation using ESR.

3. Results and discussion

It was proved that the defects formed by ion implantation in the SiO$_2$ film have a significant influence on Na migration during SIMS analysis in the other contribution [3]. Fig.3 showsthe Na$^-$ SIMS depth profiles in SiO$_2$ films with 203K, 248K and 303K at the sample temperature. During SIMS analysis under room temperature or higher, the electric field migration definitely occurs in direction to the SiO$_2$/Si interface due to the surface charge pile-up. During SIMS analysis with 203K and 248K at the temperature of the sample, the electric field migration does not take place at all.

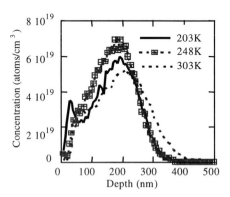

Fig.2 *Na$^-$ depth profiles in SiO$_2$ films with 203K, 248K and 303K*

We can monitor the different kind of migration paths and trapping sites of Na in SiO₂, which the damage was introduced by ion implantation. The one distributes around 50nm in depth from the surface (Defect A) and the other (Defect B), which corresponds to the maximum peak of the vacancy introduced by ion implantation, distributes around 150nm in depth. This suggests the possibility that Defect A is more stable than Defect B as the Na trapping site.

This is because Na⁻ signals - where Defect A mainly exists - can be monitored by SIMS analysis only with 203K. And Na⁻ signals- where Defect B exists - is detected much more with 248K than that with 203K.

The changes of Na depth profiles due to the anneal temperature rise was investigated in order to explain the effects of ion implantation induced damages.

The ESR spectra in Fig.3 show the paramagnetic defects in SiO₂ after anneal. The E' center which is assigned 337 mT decreases after 573K anneal and completely disappears after 873K anneal.

On the other hand, Fujinami *et. al.* reported that the positron sensitive defect remains after above 573K anneal and disappears after above 873K anneal[4]. Fig. 4 shows Na⁻ SIMS depth profiles of the samples after various temperatures anneal. These SIMS analyses were done under room temperature.

Na⁻ profile of the sample annealed at 573K has almost the same profile as the one of as-implanted sample. On the other hands, Na⁻ profile of the sample annealed at 873K has the different shape, which has two peaks and one locates at 50 nm in depth from the surface and the other at Rp region, from Gaussian distribution. After 1173K anneal, Na seems to diffuse to top surface and SiO₂/Si interface because the defects are annealed out of SiO₂. The distortion of Na⁻ profile after 873K anneal suggests the new kind of defect. To confirm it experimentally, SIMS analyses with various sample temperatures have done.

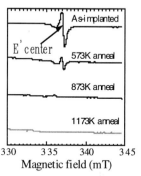

Fig.3 *ESR spectra of Na implanted changes of SiO₂/Si after various temperature anneal*

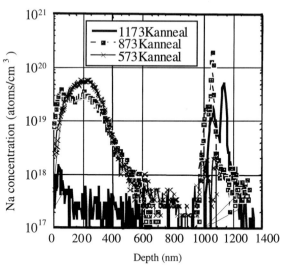

Fig.4 *Na SIMS depth profiles of Na implanted SiO₂/Si after various temperature anneal.*

600

Fig.5 shows the Na depth profiles of the sample annealed at 873K taken by SIMS 154, 209, 251 and 299K. Under 154K analysis, Na profile is close to the Gaussian distribution. However, SIMS analysis under 209K gives Na migration to the shallower region. And SIMS analysis under 251K gives Na segregation around 50 nm drastically from Rp region. This phenomenon is further enhanced at the sample temperature of 299K. As the results, the other kind of the defect which have never been reported is still remined at 50 nm depth from the surface in SiO_2 even after 873K anneal .

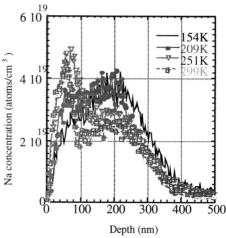

Fig.5 *Dependence of Na SIMS depth profile under the sample temperatures of changes on sample cooling temperatures.*

4. Conclusion

It was proved that the influences of the intrinsic defects in SiO_2 film by ion implantation on Na migration were investigated. The dependence of Na depth profile changes on the disappearance of the implanted defects by post-annealing was investigated. As the results, it is obvious that there are two different kinds of defects in SiO_2 introduced by ion implantation. All defects work as the migration path and trapping site of Na at different temperature of the sample during SIMS analysis. The defect around 150 nm in depth can be assigned as E' center , which disappears after 573K anneal, and the one around 50 nm in depth, which can change from positron trpping defect into Na preferential trpping site through 873K anneal.

References

[1] H. N. Migeon , M. Schuhmacher and G. Slodzian, Surface and Interface Anal.,16,(1990)9.

[2] S. Nagayama, S. Makinouchi, A. Takano and M. Kudo , SIMS VII, 1989,p655.

[3] R. Saito, S. Hayashi, and M. Kudo, in these proceedings.

[4] M. Fujinami and N. Chilton, Applied Phys. Lett.,62(1993)1133.

SECTION 12 :
SEMICONDUCTORS /
MICROELECTRONICS

A. Benninghoven, P. Bertrand, H.-N. Migeon and H.W. Werner (Editors).
Proceedings of the 12th International Conference on Secondary Ion Mass Spectrometry,
Brussels, Belgium, 5-11 September 1999

QUANTITATIVE CHARACTERISATION OF CONTAMINANTS AND OXIDE ON GaAs WAFER SURFACES WITH TOF-SIMS/SNMS AND ARXPS

B. Burkhardt[1], O.Brox[1], F. Kollmer[1], R. Kamischke[1], W. Fliegel[2], L. Wiedmann[1],
A. Kleinwechter[2], A. Benninghoven[1]

[1]Physikalisches Institut der Universität Münster, D-48149 Münster, Germany
[2]Freiberger Compound Materials GmbH, D-09599 Freiberg, Germany,
e-mail : bennial@uni-muenster.de

1. Introduction

Molecular beam epitaxy (MBE) on GaAs requires a very clean substrate surface and a thermally removable oxide. Residual oxides or surface contaminations lead to MBE growth failure or affects their electrical properties. Therefore reliable techniques are needed to control oxide and impurities on the GaAs wafer surfaces during the production process. For the quantitative analysis of surface contaminations we will show that TOF-SIMS and -SNMS are the methods of choice, whereas the quantitative oxide characterisation (thickness and stoichiometry) can presently only be achieved by angle resolved X-ray spectroscopy (ARXPS). In this paper we report on a TOF-SIMS application for both the contaminants and the oxide layer after ARXPS calibration.

2. Instrumentation

SIMS experiments: reflectron based TOF instrument; manipulator for macroscanning on an 8" wafer; dual beam source for depth profiling (sputter beam: 500eV Cs^+, analysis beam: 10kV Ar^+,SF_5^+,...). SNMS TOF instrument: Bergmann analyser, Ga LM Source (25 keV); He/Ne laser (193nm, 248nm). ARXPS: spherical electron analyzer with multichannel detector and monochromator X-ray source (Al K_α: 1486,6 eV) was employed with an energy resolution of $\Delta E = 0,2eV$ on Ag 3d.

3. Samples

Quantification of metal trace contaminants on wafer surfaces requires the use of standards. Our standards were prepared by sputter deposition and afterwards calibrated by Total X-Ray Reflection (TXRF). For the oxide characterisation Epi-ready cleaned GaAs wafers* were stored for different periods of time (one day to three years) after production. This leads to surface oxides varying in thickness and composition.

4. Results and Discussion
4.1 Surface Contaminants

Metals are critical surface contaminations affecting the electrical properties of MBE structures. To monitor them during the production process the SIMS spectra have to be made comparable. Therefore a well defined pretreatment and spectra normalisation is needed. A 10 min UV/ozone treatment leads to a reproducible and well defined surface oxidation, increasing and stabilising the sensitivity for metal contaminations. Using this pretreatment and normalisation (bulk, ^{71}Ga peak integral), the TOF-SIMS signal of each metal species shows a linear dependence on the primary ion dose (N_{PI}). This dose can be transformed into a

---

* Supplier: Freiberger Compound Materials GmbH, Am Junger Löwe Schacht 5, D-09599 Freiberg

theoretical coverage n(Me), if Yield Y, geometry factor G and target concentration c are known (Fig. 1), [1]: $N(Me) = N_{PI} \cdot c(Me) \cdot Y(Me, \varphi, E_p) \cdot G(v, r, d\Omega)$ Calibrating our theoretical results with TXRF determined surface concentration $\vartheta(Me)$ enables us to establish *specific* relative sensitivity factors (RSF*=S*) for positive TOF-SIMS on UV/ozone treated GaAs (100) (Eq. 1). The detection limits were derived by eq. 2 following the usal definition that the detection limit is reached when the signal falls below three times the standard deviation of the noise level. The results are shown in table 1.

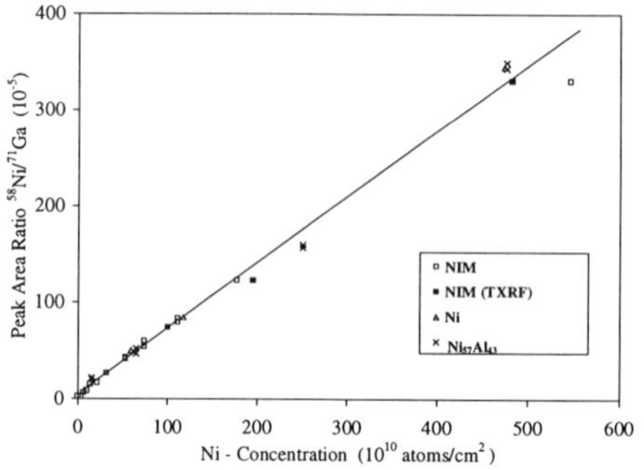

Fig. 1. Linear correlation between the normalized Cr+ TOF-SIMS signal and the Cr surface coverage on a GaAs Wafer

	Rel. Sens.Factors* $\left[10^{-15} \frac{cts(M^{+/\oplus})}{cts(^{71}Ga^{+/\oplus})} \frac{cm^2}{atoms} \right]$		Detection Limits $\left[10^{10} \frac{atoms}{cm^2} \right]$	
Me	SIMS	SNMS	SIMS	SNMS
Mg	0,33	0,32	10	0,2
Al	1,21	0,79	3	0,083
Si	0,65	1,9	6	0,034
Ca	2,38	4,0	2	0,016
Cr	1,14		3	
Fe	0,56	2,0	6	0,033
Co	1,10		3	
Ni	0,70	1,4	5	0,0014
Cu	0,49	1,9	7	0,035
Zn	0,08	0,66	50	0,1

Table 1: Sensitivity factors and detection limits for TOF-SIMS and SNMS (Ion beam diameter: $\varnothing = 50$ µm², PIDD = 10^{13} PI/cm²)

$$S^*_{Me,^{71}Ga} = \frac{S_{Me,^{71}Ga}}{\vartheta_{Ga}} = \frac{I_{Me}}{I_{^{71}Ga}} \vartheta(Me)^{-1}$$

Equ. 1.: Specific relative sensitivity factor

$$n_{Me,min} = \frac{3 \cdot \sigma}{I(^{71}Ga)} \cdot S^*(Me)^{-1}$$

Equ. 2: Detection limit

The same experiments have been performed with TOF-SNMS using non resonant photoionisation. The results are also shown in table 1. In case of no signal interference the detection limits for SNMS are about 100× better than for SIMS.

4.2 Surface oxides

For the native oxide on GaAs (100) wafer surfaces Schröder [2] et al. established the 4-layer oxide model. It contains two different oxide states, an interface and the bulk region (Fig. 2). The layer characteristics like thickness d_i of layer i, the concentrations c_i of As and Ga or the products $d_i \cdot c_i(As)$ and $d_i \cdot c_i(As)$ are going to be determined in the following with AR-XPS, SIMS depth profiling and SIMS cluster analysis.

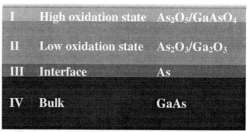

Fig.2: 4 – Layer oxide model with AR-XPS results

X- Ray Photoelectron Spectroscopy (XPS) allows us to distinguish between different binding states of elements due to its chemical shift[2]. Hence the As 3d signal can be separated into the binding states GaAs(0 eV), As(-0,8 eV), As_2O_3 (-3,0 eV) and As_2O_5/GaAsO$_4$(-3,8 eV), whereas the Ga 3d contains the binding states GaAs(0 eV), Ga$_2$O$_3$(-1,1 eV), GaAsO$_4$(-1,8 eV). Taking XPS spectra at various electron take-off angles, one can assign them to different surface layers. By evaluation of the AR-XPS data with the assumption of a 4-layer system, it is possible to estimate the thickness d_i of each layer i (Fig. 3) as well as the atomic concentration c_i of As and Ga within this layer. For comparison with SIMS it is also essential to estimate their product $c_i(As) \cdot d_i$ and $c_i(Ga) \cdot d_i$ in each layer i which is proportional to the total number of atoms $n_i(Ga)$ and $n_i(As)$ within this layer (Fig. 5).

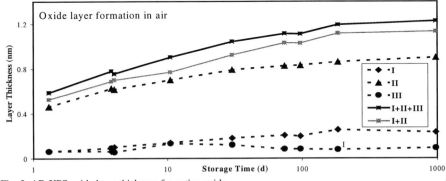

Fig. 3: AR-XPS oxide layer thickness for native oxide

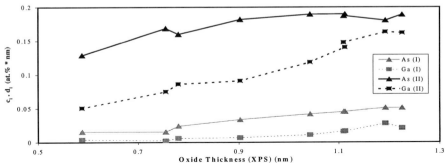

Fig 4: AR-XPS: concentration * thickness for Ga and As in layer I and II

Shallow depth profiling of GaAs oxide layers was used to characterise the oxide thickness and stoichiometry with TOF-SIMS. For evaluation each depth profile has been normalised in two ways. First the signal intensity is normalised by the GaAs intensity at its sputter equilibrium in the bulk region (IV). Secondly since the thickness of the As interface layer is almost independent of the oxide thickness (see Fig. 3), the composition of this interface region (Oxide/ As/ Bulk)

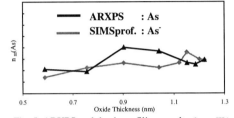

Fig. 5: ARXPS and depth profiling results (layer III)

606

always remains the same. Therefore we assume that the GaAs⁻ bulk signal dependence on depth and especially ist slope at the interface is constant for all profiles of native oxide layers. The thickness within a multilayer system is in general correlated to the full width half maximum (FWHM) of the depth profile signal. Regarding the depth resolution of Cs^+ depth profing at 500 eV, this does not work with layers thinner than 1nm. Instead of the FWHM the integrals of the secondary ions As⁻, AsO_2^-, AsO_3^-, GaO_2^- and $GaAsO_3^-$ are used within the half maximum region of the depth profile. These integrals are assumed to be proportional to the total numer (n_i) of these molecules (see Fig.5-7).

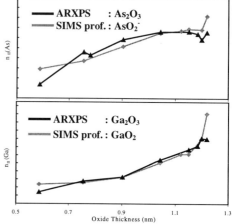

Fig. 6 :ARXPS and depth profiling results (layer II)

Using SF_5^+ primary ions $Ga_mAs_nO_o^\pm$ **clusters** with m+n+o > 40 could be detected. The main clusters could be separated into groups with $(m+n) \cdot (+3) + o \cdot (-2) = \pm 1$ for $Ga_mAs_nO_o^\pm$. Within these cluster groups the center of signals changes with storage time and can be taken as a measure for surface stoichiometry. Normalising the intensity of surface ions $As_2O_2^+$ and $GaAs_2O_4^+$ by the sum of ion clusters allows to compare them to the surface signals of ARXPS ($As_2O_3^-$/$GaAsO_3^-$) and SIMS depth profiles (AsO_3^-/$GaAsO_3^-$) (see Fig. 7). The following clusters are used for normalisation: $GaAs_2O_4^+$:
$(Ga_mAs_nO_o^\pm$ (m+n,o)=(3,4); (5,7); (7,10))
and $As_2O_2^+$: $(Ga_mAs_nO_o^\pm$ (m+n,o)=(2,2); (2,3); (3,2); (3,4); (5,7); (7,10))

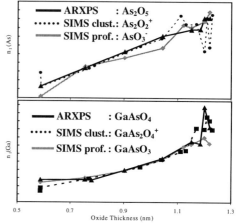

Fig. 7: ARXPS, depth pr. and cluster results (layer I)

5. Summary

TOF-SIMS is a powerful technique to control both the surface contamination and the native oxide on GaAs wafer. We established RSF* (SIMS and Laser-SNMS) for various metals on GaAs (100) wafer surfaces and showed that it is possible to estimate the stoichiometry of native oxides on GaAs wafers with TOF-SIMS after calibration with ARXPS.

References

[1] A.Schnieders, F. Schröder-Oeynhausen, B. Burkhardt, F. Kötter, R. Möllers, L. Wiedmann, A. Benninghoven *Secondary Ion Mass Spectroscopy SIMS X*, Wiley & Sons, Chichester, 1995, 647

[2] F. Schröder-Oeynhausen, B. Burkhardt, T. Fladung, L. Wiedmann, A. Benninghoven *Secondary Ion Mass Spectroscopy SIMS X*, Wiley & Sons, Chichester, 1995, 351

A. Benninghoven, P. Bertrand, H.-N. Migeon and H.W. Werner (Editors).
Proceedings of the 12th International Conference on Secondary Ion Mass Spectrometry,
Brussels, Belgium, 5-11 September 1999
© 2000 Elsevier Science B.V. All rights reserved.

ANALYSIS OF LOW-K DIELECTRICS USING A MAGNETIC SECTOR SIMS INSTRUMENT

J. M. McKinley, F.A. Stevie, and C.N. Granger

Lucent Technologies, 9333 S. John Young Parkway, Orlando, FL 32819 USA
mckinley@lucent.com

1. Introduction

There are many materials considerations and production issues that semiconductor manufacturers must face as they continue to improve aluminum processes and explore copper processes. As device dimensions continue to shrink, new materials are often needed because materials in current use cannot satisfy new device requirements. Using materials with a low dielectric constant ("low-k dielectrics") for intermetal dielectrics should reduce interaction between metal lines for high speed devices. In order to improve device performance, replacements such as copper and low-k dielectrics are needed for the aluminum wiring and silicon dioxide intermetal dielectrics that have been typically used in the industry.

Because there are several design, development, and implementation routes that can be explored, various materials for low-k dielectrics are being examined simultaneously, and probably no single material will dominate. These materials include fluorinated oxides, inorganic polymers, organic polymers, and porous aerogel and xerogel materials. There are a great variety of materials under development, and analysts must be prepared to examine whatever materials are chosen for integration. The electrical, chemical, mechanical, and thermal properties of many of these materials have been determined [1], although information about compositional uniformity and contamination levels, which can drastically affect the performance of these materials, has not been widely reported. This information is best determined by SIMS depth profiling.

Several issues must be addressed when performing SIMS analysis of these materials on a magnetic sector instrument. First, insulator analysis on this type of instrument has traditionally been difficult, and analysis conditions must be chosen so that neutralization is adequate. Additionally, although many of the materials are similar to silicon dioxide, some layers are not at all oxide-like, and quantification of contamination within these materials is not straightforward. Finally, the samples appear to be severely affected by the electron beam used for charge neutralization, and this must be closely examined to assure that accurate depth profiles are obtained. To address these issues, this paper focuses on analysis conditions, quantification issues, and degradation of the materials during depth profiling of low-k dielectric materials.

2. Experimental

Materials examined in this study are listed in Table 1. These materials can be categorized as doped oxide, organic, highly fluorinated, and porous [2].

Table 1. List of low-k dielectric materials examined in this study

Low-k material	Type of material
FSG (fluorinated silicate glass)	Fluorine doped oxide
a-FC (amorphous fluorocarbon)	Fluorinated organic
BCB (bisbenzocylcobutene)	Organic
Parylene (di-para-xylylene)	Fluorinated organic
HSQ (hydrogen silsesquioxane)	Hydrogen doped oxide
SiLK	Organic
HOSP	Carbon doped oxide
Black diamond	Organic
Nanoglass aerogels	Porous

These materials were analyzed using a CAMECA IMS-6f with O_2^+ beam at 5.5 keV impact energy, electron gun flooding at 4.5 keV (9 keV total electron impact energy), and no sample coating. Other studies [3] have used both O_2^+ and Cs^+ beams and either used coating or no coating for polymer and low-k dielectric analyses, and some of these conditions were examined. The conditions listed above were chosen because the authors have most frequently used these conditions for analysis of insulators with successful results [4].

Compositional uniformity of all materials for Si, C, N, F, and H was examined by SIMS, and bulk species compositions at the surface were confirmed with Auger analysis. Trace metals contamination (Na, K, Fe, Cu) for HSQ, SiLK, and HOSP was checked with SIMS. Confirmation of material degradation was examined by SEM and stylus profilometry with a Tencor P-10 stylus profilometer.

3. Results and Discussion

The most important factor that had to be established for these materials was choice of appropriate analysis conditions to achieve good neutralization. For the samples analyzed, the conditions chosen provided excellent neutralization. Figures 1 and 2 show example profiles of selected low-k dielectrics.

Quantification was not determined for many of the bulk species like C or Si, but F, N, or H could be quantified if an appropriate standard existed. For example, in the highly fluorinated samples, quantification of fluorine (a non-dilute species) was determined by a fluorine implant into SiO_2. The choice of the appropriate implanted dose of the reference standard is critical to the quantification of non-dilute species in SIMS [5]. For samples that have both high and low concentrations of a particular species, a solution may be to calculate concentration based on a calibration curve generated by analysis of several implants at various doses.

For metals analysis, quantification could be estimated by implants into SiO_2 for those samples that were the most SiO_2-like. For other samples, quantification could not be easily established. Implant standards are required into each of the low-k dielectric materials for quantification to be accurately determined.

Sample degradation was noted for most samples analyzed using the conditions chosen. Some samples showed bubbling if the electron gun current was too high (above 30 µA), and the depth profile was distorted. The electron current had to be reduced in order to prevent bubbling, and analysis conditions of raster size and ion current had to be altered so that the same neutralization could be achieved for the fluorinated dielectrics as for the rest of the samples. Figure 3 shows an example of a surface of a low-k dielectric sample after irradiation by an electron beam higher than 30 µA.

For all samples except FSG, the films collapsed during analysis in areas that had been exposed in the sample chamber and in areas impacted by the electron beam. Figure 4 shows a profilometer trace of the degraded area. The collapse within the areas exposed in the sample chamber was as much as 100 nm, and the collapse within the area exposed to the electron beam is as much as 30 nm in the figure shown. A profilometer measurement of only the sputtered crater and nearby area will not give an accurate depth calibration for the SIMS profile. This depth scale can be corrected if the portion of the sample covered by the sample holder is profiled along with the crater and used as the surface reference. If the craters are sputtered close to the edge of the sample holder window edge, then the unexposed area can then be easily profiled along with the SIMS crater. SEM cross-sections confirmed layer thicknesses before and after SIMS analysis.

4. Conclusions

Analysis of low-k dielectrics poses several issues that must be addressed in order to provide accurate quantitative compositional information and thickness of the film layers. First, good neutralization must be achieved, and the results of the analyses for many types of low-k materials show that this is possible. Next, quantification can only be determined if reference implants into low-k materials are analyzed. The dose of the reference implants must be chosen such that they closely match the expected concentration of the species analyzed (i.e. dilute or non-dilute species). Additionally, electron beam irradiation can severely affect the sample during analysis, and precautions must be taken during these analyses. Collapse of the sample does not appear to have a significant effect on the profile, but the depth scale must be corrected by profiling a region of the sample that has not been exposed to the electron beam or in the sample holder. Although there are several issues that must be taken into consideration for SIMS analysis of low-k dielectrics, depth profiling for high concentration as well as trace contamination species is possible and should continue to be closely examined as these materials are integrated into semiconductor processes.

5. Acknowledgements

The authors wish to thank the Lucent Technologies Analytical and Diagnostic Laboratories in Orlando, Florida for support analyses and discussions of analytical techniques for low-k dielectrics. The authors also wish to thank analysts Charles Hitzman and Scott Bryan of Charles Evans & Associates for discussion of electron beam damage in polymers and low-k dielectrics. The authors also acknowledge the support of Daniel Vitkavage, Huili Shoa, Mary Roby, and Kurt Steiner of Lucent Technologies Bell Laboratories for supply of the low-k dielectric samples and related informative discussions.

610

References

[1] W.W. Lee, P.S. Ho, *MRS Bulletin*, October (1997) 19.
[2] I. Morey, A. Asthana, *Solid State Technology*, June (1999) 71.
[3] C.C. Parks, *J. Vac. Sci. Technol.*, 15 (1997) 1328.
[4] J. M. McKinley, F.A. Stevie, C.N. Granger, and D. Renard, *J. Vac. Sci. Technol. accepted for publication.*
[5] R.G. Wilson, F.A. Stevie, C.W. Magee, Secondary Ion Mass Spectrometry, John Wiley and Sons, New York, 1989.

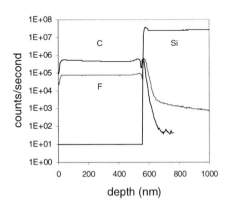

Figure 1. SIMS profile of a-FC.   Figure 2. SIMS profile of HOSP.

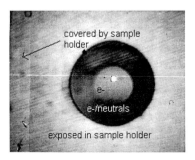

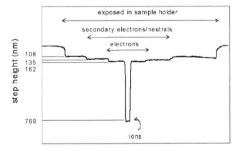

Figure 3. Example of a low-k dielectric sample surface after SIMS analysis with O_2^+ beam and electron gun bombardment.

Figure 4. Example profilometer trace of a low-k surface after SIMS analysis with O_2^+ beam and electron gun bombardment.

A. Benninghoven, P. Bertrand, H.-N. Migeon and H.W. Werner (Editors).
Proceedings of the 12th International Conference on Secondary Ion Mass Spectrometry,
Brussels, Belgium, 5-11 September 1999

611

STUDY OF OXYNITRIDES WITH DUAL BEAM TOF-SIMS

H. De Witte[1,2,*], T. Conard[1], W. Vandervorst[1,3] and R. Gijbels[2]
[1]IMEC, Kapeldreef 75, B-3001 Leuven, Belgium
[2]University of Antwerp, Universiteitsplein 1, B-2610 Antwerp, Belgium
[3]INSYS, University of Leuven, Kardinaal Mercierlaan 92, B-3001 Leuven, Belgium
*Aspirant of the Fund for Scientific Research - Flanders (Belgium)
e-mail: dewitte@imec.be

1. Introduction

As the reliability of thin gate oxides based on silicon dioxide no longer fulfils the technological requirements, intensive research is performed towards replacement by silicon oxynitride [1]. In the characterization of these materials one of the main questions is the location of nitrogen relative to the position of the oxide – silicon interface, as this strongly influences the material characteristics.

SIMS is a sufficiently sensitive technique to detect very low N concentrations and the high mass resolution of the Time Of Flight (TOF) analyzer allows good mass separation. Combined with the off-line data treatment and the profile reconstruction option on the IONTOF IV a detailed study of Si, O and N cluster-ions was performed on both ultrathin SiO_2 films and nitrided SiO_2 films.

2. Sample description and instrumentation

In order to study the influence of decreasing oxide thickness on the matrix signals at the interface a series of pure thermally grown silicon dioxides on silicon (8.8 down to 1.0 nm) were used. The oxynitride sample under study consisted of a 2.54 nm oxide layer, prepared under the following process conditions: 23 min. 10% O_2 at 750 °C and 15 min. 100% NO at 850 °C. The first part of the process determined the oxide thickness, while the second was responsible for the N incorporation in the oxide.

All depth profiling experiments were performed on the IONTOF IV, a dual beam TOF-SIMS instrument. The EI analysis gun (10 keV Ar^+, 1 pA and 30x30 μm^2) was combined with one of the sputter guns (Cs or EI (Ar^+)). These were operated at 0.5 keV, ± 2.5 nA, 300x300 μm^2 raster and negative or positive secondary ion detection mode was used.

3. Selection of N clusters

For the different possible profiling conditions, we examined and selected different N clusters with regard to mass interference and intensity. The aim was to find the best possible analysis conditions for this kind of samples on the IONTOF IV and to retrieve reliable information on the N distribution in the oxide layer and at the interface.

The selected clusters needed to represent sample information. Therefore clusters containing C and H have not been considered suitable, because of possible interference with surface contamination components and thus perturbed evolution in the near surface region.

For Ar^+ bombardment a summary of the most important N clusters is given in Table 1, for positive as well as negative secondary ion detection. Based on mass resolution (MR) and interference, we therefore selected Si_2N in the positive mode and SiN in the negative mode.

	Cluster	Interference	MR	corr. area ratio
Pos.	Si_2N	SiCNO	7000	3:1
	SiN	CNO	5000	1:2
	Si_2NO	$Si_2{}^{30}Si$	4000	1:1
Neg.	SiN	CNO	4000	14:1

Table 1: N clusters for Ar^+ bombardment with positive or negative secondary ion detection (MR: mass resolution, $\Delta mu = 0.02$: mass distance between cluster and nearest interference, corr. area ratio: corrected intensity ratio between cluster and interference)

For Cs^+ bombardment and negative ion detection, the following series of N clusters has been detected with a reasonable intensity: NH, SiNO, SiN and Si_2N. Here none of the clusters seemed especially perturbed by surface contamination. Looking at the profile distribution in the oxide layer, all seemed to have a slightly different peak maximum position. Which of the clusters has the highest reliability can not readily be decided.

From the previous discussion, it has become clear that the choice of one good measurement condition and one significant and informative N cluster is far from trivial. For all conditions, the different selected clusters showed a different evolution through and different peak maximum position in the oxide layer. Mainly for practical reasons, we have focussed further on Ar^+ bombardment and positive secondary ion detection.

4. Study of Si_xO_y clusters at the oxide-silicon interface

To study the influence of the shrinking oxide thickness the evolution of different Si and O clusters in the oxide and at the oxide-silicon interface was considered. The aim was to gain better insight in how to evaluate the position of the interface and the location of the N relative to this interface.

4.1. Selection of matrix clusters

For the different analysis conditions we selected those matrix clusters, which gave a sufficiently high intensity, no (significant) mass interference, no saturation, ... To determine the interface, we looked at the intensity difference dI between the stationary levels in the oxide layer and in the Si substrate. We also derived the slope of the signal between both intensity plateaus because this is a measure for the reaction of the cluster on the changing oxygen concentration. For Ar^+ and positive secondary ion mode, we found the largest dI and slope for SiO and ^{30}Si. In the negative mode the SiO_2 cluster showed the largest dI and slope. For Cs^+ and negative ion detection the largest dI was found for SiO_3 and Si_2, where the steepest slope was attributed to SiO_3.

4.2 Determination of the interface

In [2] Wittmaack described a relation between the oxygen concentration and the Si intensity for Ar^+ profiling of oxygen implanted samples. For O concentrations above 10 at% he found that $\Delta I(Si^+) \sim c_0{}^m$, with m=3.7±0.2. We now applied this relation to determine the oxide-silicon interface corresponding to SiO or an oxygen concentration of 50 at%. In addition to this relation, we also relied on the following assumptions: 1) the stable intensity in the oxide layer corresponds to SiO_2, 2) extrapolation of this power law to SiO_2 (C(O)= 67 at%) and 3) validity at low energy conditions (0.5 keV instead of the 3 keV). The thus determined

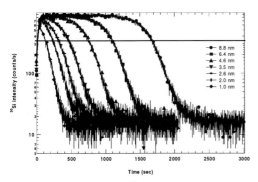

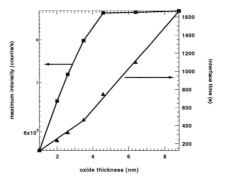

Figure 1: Maximum ^{30}Si signals decreases with decreasing oxide thickness

Figure 2: Maximum intensity and interface time determined with 50% method for the different oxide thickness

interface point corresponds to 34% decrease of the ^{30}Si signal. Figure 1 shows the effect of decreasing oxide thickness on the shape and maximum of the ^{30}Si intensity.

Therefore, we used the full line, corresponding to 34% of the dI of the thickest sample, to determine the interface for all samples. The time-depth relation established by applying this method is shown in Figure 2. The best approximation seemed to correspond to a two line fitting, where the connection point is related to the strong decrease in the maximum ^{30}Si intensity. TRIM calculations showed that for the thinnest samples the collision cascade was not only determined by the oxide layer, but also by the underlying Si substrate. This indicated severe interpretation problems for the applications under study, sub-3 nm oxynitride films! The whole depth of interest fell in the non-stabilized region or altered layer

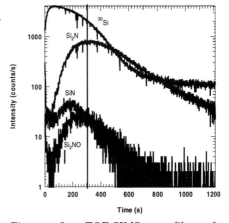

Figure 3: TOF-SIMS profile of oxynitride sample under Ar^+ bombardment and positive ion detection

induced by the ion bombardment! The oxynitride sample (Figure 3) was also analyzed in a small round robin study with different techniques: low energy dynamic SIMS, XPS, HRBS, HERD, ... [3, 4, 5]. From the combined study we were tempted to rely most on the Si_2N signal in our profile, which corresponded to the observation of HERD where N was found at the interface. This cluster was also used for quantification purposes in a combined TOF-SIMS and XPS study [4], where it seemed very reliable and reproducible over different processing conditions.

5. Diffusion of N in oxynitrides

Another issue was the possible migration of N in the oxide layer [6]. In an attempt to clarify this, the following experiment was performed.

An oxynitride sample was first profiled under Ar^+ bombardment (0.5 keV, 45°) with oxygen bleed-in and positive secondary ion detection. A slight decrease in O containing cluster intensities was observed at the original oxide – silicon interface. When all signals had reached a new plateau in the (due to oxygen flooding oxidized) silicon substrate, the oxygen leak valve was closed and the profile was continued through the beam induced oxide until steady state was reached in the silicon substrate. Concentrating on the evolution of the N containing signals, N was not only observed in the original oxide layer, but also at the second interface between the synthesized oxide and the silicon substrate. At the moment this could only be explained by beam induced diffusion, indicating another difficulty in the interpretation of the results to answer the question whether or not the processing gives rise to N diffusion in the underlying substrate.

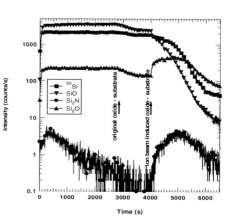

Figure 4: Experiment on ion beam induced N diffusion in oxynitrides. Even with oxygen flooding the original oxide – substrate interface is detected. Once in the substrate ("second interface") the leak valve is closed.

6. Conclusions

For the analysis of thin oxynitrides, SIMS was pushed to its limits. Nitrogen was not one of the easiest elements to detect, therefore all possible analysis conditions on the dual beam TOF-SIMS were explored to find N clusters which retrieved the most useful sample information. These were Ar^+ bombardment with positive secondary ion detection and in this case the most interesting N cluster seemed Si_2N. Also Cs^+ bombardment in the negative mode seemed useful. Based on intensity considerations, we might choose here to follow the SiN cluster.

As the thickness of the layers decreased in the order of a native oxide, attention was paid to the evolution of matrix signals at the interface in pure oxide on silicon layers with decreasing oxide thickness. In the case of Ar^+ bombardment, we saw a decrease in the maximum intensity of the ^{30}Si signal indicating that our analysis fell completely in the disturbed region. This made all attempts to depth scale calibration and location of N relative to the interface very speculative.

An additional issue in the analysis and interpretation formed the diffusion problem: with SIMS we were unable to distinguish between diffusion of N induced during processing or during ion beam bombardment.

As experiments showed, further insight in the characterization of these new materials demands combined multi-technique studies.

References

[1] S. Singhvi and C.G. Takoudis, J. Appl. Phys. 82 (1) (1997) 442
[2] K. Wittmaack, Surface Science, 112 (1981) 168-180
[3] W. Vandervorst, T. Conard, H. De Witte, G.A. Cooke, these Proceedings
[4] T. Conard, H. De Witte, M. Schaeckers, W. Vandervorst, these Proceedings
[5] B. Brijs, J. Deleu, T. Conard, H. De Witte and W. Vandervorst, K. Kimura, G. Dollinger, M. Dobeli, Characterization of Ultra thin Oxynitrydes, a general approach, IBA-14, Dresden, Germany, July 26-30 (1999)
[6] I. Barnerjee and D. Kuzminov, Appl. Phys. Lett. 62 (13) (1993) 1541

A. Benninghoven, P. Bertrand, H.-N. Migeon and H.W. Werner (Editors).
Proceedings of the 12th International Conference on Secondary Ion Mass Spectrometry,
Brussels, Belgium, 5-11 September 1999

615

SIMS MEASUREMENT OF INSULATOR: FROM PLANAR WAVE-GUIDE TO OPTICAL FIBER

Peixiong Shi

Mikroelektronik Centret, Technical University of Denmark, Building 345 east,
Lyngby, DK-2800, Denmark, E-mail: pxshi@mic.dtu.dk

1.Introduction

At present, research in telecommunication is very active, due to the strong demanding for fast Internet. Adopting the manufacturing method of integrated circuits to fabricate planar waveguides can produce the devices with new features and achieve better cost-effectiveness. The planar waveguide functions similar to an optical fiber. Light propagates along the high refractive index media (core layer), which is sandwiched between two layers of low refractive index media (cladding layer). This structure can be realized in many ways. We use thermally grown SiO_2 (silica) as the bottom cladding layer, Ge doped (sometimes co-doped with B) PECVD (Plasma Enhanced Chemical Vapor Deposition) SiO_2 as the core layer, P and B doped PECVD SiO_2 as the top cladding layer. To produce the glass with stable refractive index, annealing is applied in the process to release hydrogen in the waveguide, which is trapped during the PECVD deposition. Annealing enhances the diffusion. This needs be controlled within a certain limit. SIMS is an ideal tool to monitor the diffusion and examine the composition of the planar waveguides. As primary ions impact the insulator, the sample surface gets charged up. Charge compensation is essential for measuring insulators. A quadrupole SIMS, ATOMIKA 4000 [1] is applied for the measurements. It uses a low extraction voltage for collecting secondary ions. This makes the low energy electron beam easy to strike the desired place. The charge compensation is relative easy for the quadrupole SIMS.

2.Experiment

For depth profiling the planar waveguide, the main interest is the distribution of the major elements. The compositions of these elements are not in the trace level. Sensitivities of using MCs^+ molecules in a quadrupole SIMS are high enough. To reduce the matrix effect [2], these molecular species are chosen as secondary ions to detect.

In normal conditions, SiO_2 based glasses are amorphous. They can be sputtered evenly during depth profiling. Excellent depth resolution can be achieved with a low energy ion beam and glancing incidence. Figure 1 displays a depth profile of a sample prepared by doping Al in a layer 20nm thick in the middle of 1.9μm PECVD SiO_2. We define the depth resolution as the depth difference from 16% to 84% of maximum intensity. With a 2KeV Cs^+

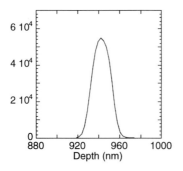

Figure 1. Depth profile of a 20nm Al doping layer in the middle of 1.96μm PECVD SiO₂, measured by a 2KeV Cs⁺ beam at 60° impact angle from normal incidence.

beam at the impact ngle of 60° from normal incidence, depth resolutions of 9nm at the rising and 8nm at falling slop of the Al peak are achieved (Figure1).

SIMS is used routinely to check the compositions of the planar waveguides. The total SiO_2 layer thickness of 33.3μm requires a fast sputtering rate. With an 8KeV 100nA Cs^+ beam, at the impact angle of 60° from normal incidence, 200μm raster scanning size, one single measurement will take around 5 hours for such a structure (Figure2). Three samples can be depth profiled within an automatic overnight measurement. The depth resolution is around 1μm at a depth of 14μm, which is the interface between the top cladding layer and the core of the waveguide.

Figure 2 clearly indicates that the depth resolution degenerates as the crater becomes

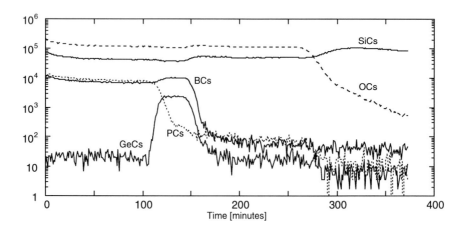

Figure 2. *Depth profile of 33μm thick waveguide, measured by an 8KeV Cs⁺ beam at 60° impact angle from normal incidence.*

Figure 3. SEM picture of the crater bottom of a 33µm thick planar waveguide structure. The crater is produced with an 8KeV Cs⁺ beam at 60° impact angle from normal incidence (from upper right side). The crater depth is 29µm.

deeper. As mentioned previously, SiO_2 based glasses are normally in an amorphous form, and can be sputtered evenly through the depth profiling. This is only partially true. If the crater exceeds a critical depth (around 1µm), under some conditions, the roughness of the crater bottom grows dramatically. During the waveguide SIMS measurement, with an 8KeV Cs^+ beam at 60° incident angle, at a depth of 5µm, the grain size is around 1µm transversely and 0.1µm vertically. At a depth of 29µm, the grain size grows to around 8µm transversely and 1µm vertically (Figure 3). For the 8KeV Cs^+ beam, even with 70° incident angle, the bottom of the crater is still rough. With an 8KeV O^+_2 beam, similar roughness has been observed at 60° incident angle, but by using the incident angle of 70°, the crater bottom is smooth and a depth resolution of better than 0.3µm is achieved for the entire 33.3µm SiO_2 layer (Figure 4).

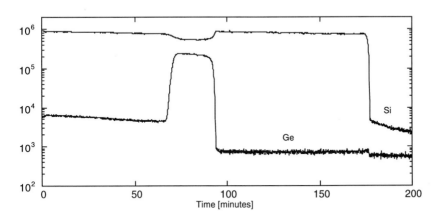

Figure 4. Depth profile of 33µm thick waveguide, measured by an 8KeV, 390nA O^+_2 beam at 70° impact angle from normal incidence. The raster scanning size is 200µm.

618

   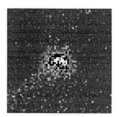

Figure 5. *Cross section of a special single mode optical fiber. This fiber has a cladding diameter of 150μm, and core diameter of 7μm. Starting from left, the first frame is a SEM picture of the entire fiber cross section. Second to fourth are the Si, Al, and Ge SIMS images for the middle section of the fiber in the frame size of 50μm. The SIMS measurement was made with a 3KeV, 50pA O^+_2 beam at normal incidence. The raster scanning size is 100μm.*

Beside the measurement of the depth profiling, in some cases, the information from a small size structure is demanded. Figure 5 illustrates the capability of the quadrupole SIMS by measuring a special shape single mode optical fiber. The core area of this fiber is doped with Al and Ge. With such a small structure, good transverse resolution can also be achieved by applying charge compensation.

3.Conclusion
By using quadrupole SIMS, ATOMIKA 4000, in the charge compensation mode, good depth resolution is achievable with a low energy beam for SiO_2 based glass. Thick structures can be measured with good depth resolution and fast erosion rate. Sputtering conditions need to be chosen carefully to prevent degeneration of the depth resolution due to roughening for such a measurement. High transverse resolution image profiles can be achieved in a glass structure.

Acknowledgement
The author would like to thank Lars Ulrik Andersen, Mickael Svalgaard, Soren Therkelsen for providing the planar waveguide samples, and Martin Kristensen for providing the optical fiber.

References
[1]   K. Wittmaack, in Secondary Ion Mass Spectrometry (SIMS VIII), edited by A. Benninghoven, K.T.F. Janssen, J. Tümpner, and H.W. Werner (John Wiley & Sons, Chichester, 1992) pp. 211-214
[2]   K. Wittmaack, Nuclear Instruments and Methods in Physics Research B64 (1992) pp. 621-625

A. Benninghoven, P. Bertrand, H.-N. Migeon and H.W. Werner (Editors).
Proceedings of the 12th International Conference on Secondary Ion Mass Spectrometry,
Brussels, Belgium, 5-11 September 1999
© 2000 Elsevier Science B.V. All rights reserved.

COMPOSITION AND THICKNESS DISTRIBUTION IN COMPACT AND POROUS ANODIC FILMS GROWN ON TITANIUM AND TA6V

V. Grand-Clément Zwilling[1], A. Boutry-Forveille[2], E. Darque-Ceretti[1], M. Aucouturier[3]

[1] Ecole des Mines de Paris, CEMEF (UMR CNRS 7635), BP 207, F-06904 Sophia-Antipolis
[2] CNRS-Bellevue, Service d'analyse ionique, 1 Pl. A. Briand, F-92205 Meudon Cedex
[3] Université Paris-Sud, Lab. Métallurgie (URA CNRS 1107), Bât. 410, F-91405 Orsay Cedex
e-mail : Marc.Aucouturier@metal.u-psud.fr

1. Introduction

In-depth analysis of thin films is well known to be a preferential field of SIMS application, but quantitative interpretation of the profiles may be disturbed by factors as the occurrence of the transitory step of primary beam implantation and variations of the material density across the analysed layers. In the present study, films grown on titanium or Ti-6% Al-4% V (TA6V) alloy by anodisation in chromic media containing or no fluoride ions are investigated.

Anodic oxidation of metals is a commonly developed surface treatment [1,2,3] for several applications. Depending on substrate and electrochemical conditions, the anodic films may be compact or porous. Each structure has its own advantages : a compact structure is necessary for electrical application ; porous oxides are used to improve environmental behaviour (Al alloys [2], but also Ti alloys [1,3] or stainless steels [4]). In the case of Ti alloy, a previous study [1] has shown that the structure of the films is compact when the elaboration is done in chromic acid solution, or constituted of a compact layer surmounted by a columnar porous layer when grown in a fluoride-containing chromic acid electrolyte.

The purpose of this study is to describe physicochemical features of the films, at different scales, from extreme surface to bulk, and from nanometer pore size to macroscopic composition. Methods used are : high resolution scanning electron microscopy (HR-SEM) and grazing high energy electron diffraction (RHEED) for structure ; X ray-induced photoelectron spectroscopy (XPS), secondary ion mass spectrometry (SIMS), for composition analysis.

2. Experimental details

The substrate composition, thickness, and microstructure are summarised in table I.

Table I : Substrate description

Substrate	Composition	Thickness	Microstructure (phases)	Grain size
Ti 40	Ti	0.8 mm	equiaxial α (HCP)	30 μm
TA6V	Ti, 6% Al, 4% V	2 mm	α (HCP) + β (BCC)	α : 10 μm ; β : 2 μm

Specimens (3 x 1.5 cm^2) are polished until 1/4 μm diamond and ultrasonically rinsed with Methyl Ethyl Ketone. Anodic films are grown in chromic acid solution (0.5 mol.l^{-1}) with

(CA/HF) or without (CA) HF addition ($9.5.10^{-2}$ mol.l^{-1}) under potentiostatic conditions (1 to 10 V between the specimen and the Ti counter-electrode). Growing mechanisms are discussed in another paper through a full electrochemical study [5].

SIMS profiling is performed in a Cameca IMS 4F equipment using Cs$^+$ primary beam (14.5 keV, 5 or 20 nA, 250x250 μm² raster) and negative secondary ion detection. XPS analysis is done in a Riber instrument (Mg Kα irradiation) ; semi-quantitative analysis uses XPS peak reconstruction through standard procedures ; sample charging is compensated by calibrating with regards to the C(1s) binding energy (284,5 eV). Specimens are observed by a Leo field-ion gun HR-SEM. RHEED patterns are obtained in a 120 kV Philips transmission electron microscope (TEM), configured for grazing electron diffraction. Extractive replicas of the surface (carbon + platinum separated in bromine solution) are done and observed by TEM..

3. Results

3.1 Structure

From the SEM observation, the oxide film appears compact when grown in chromic acid and porous when HF is added to the electrolyte. Figure 1 shows the microstructure of the porous film. The size of the pores depends on the elaboration potential : the higher the final voltage, the larger is the pore diameter. The pores are smaller on the titanium substrate than on TA6V alloy substrate, whatever the applied voltage. On the TA6V alloy, the size of the pores depends furthermore on the underlying substrate structure and composition : it is smaller on the top of the V-enriched β phase than on top of the α phase (e.g. : 15 nm on the β phase and 25 nm on the α phase after anodisation at 5 V).

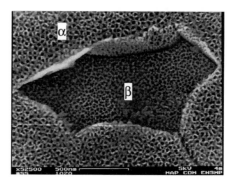

Fig. 1 : HR-SEM observation of the porous anodic film on TA6V on the α (a) and β (b) phase

RHEED measurements prove that the compact films (grown in CA solution) are amorphous, even for high elaboration voltage (10 V.) ; the porous films (grown in CA/HF solution) are partially crystalline with the TiO$_2$ rutile structure, at least on their surface. The fact that the compact film remains amorphous for high forming voltage is in disagreement with observations by Leach [6], showing a crystallisation for voltage higher than the break-down voltage. Indeed, in the present case, appearance of break-down pits shows that the break-down voltage lies below 5 V.

Structure in-depth distribution is difficult to infer from direct SEM. TEM observation of extractive replicas shows that the pores are columnar, with a depth smaller than the total film thickness (see following section).

3.2 Composition and depth distribution

Film composition given by XPS analysis is illustrated in table II. The hydrogen content is neglected (splitting of the O(1s) peak suggests the presence of hydroxylated species). Ti is only on the oxidised (IV) form.

Table II : Average atomic composition of porous anodic films, measured by XPS analysis

	C	Ti	Al	O(1)	O(2)	Cr	F
Binding energies (eV)	284,5	458,5	74,0	530,0	531,0	577,0	684,0
TA6V substrate (ref.)	0,62	0,05	0,03	0,11	0,19		
TA6V, in CA 5V, 20 min.	0,36	0,16	0,03	0,37	0,07	0,01	
TA6V in CA/HF, 5V, 20 min	0,42	0,13	0,04	0,32	0,05		0,04

The surface composition does not depend on anodisation voltage and time for high voltages (5 to 10 V) and long times (more than a few minutes). For short times, a significant amount of chromium is present, whose binding energy (577,0 eV) corresponds to Cr^{VI}, indicating direct incorporation from the solution. That incorporation disappears for longer times. Fluorine is always incorporated in the porous films. The overall composition corresponds to $TiO_2 + Al_2O_3$ with Ti/Al = 5. Vanadium is never detected.

SIMS profiling is illustrated in Figure 2 for compact films on Ti and TA6V, and in figure 3 for porous film on TA6V. Recorded signals are : $^1H^-$, $^{16}O^-$, $^{19}F^-$, $^{27}Al^-$, $^{52}(Cr^- + VH^- + VH_2^-)$, $^{64}(TiO^-)$. On pure titanium (fig. 2a), Cr (amu 52) is present in the compact film. For the TA6V alloy (fig. 2b), it is impossible to separate in the 52 amu signal the contribution of Cr from that of $VH^- + VH_2^-$ (visible in the substrate) ; Cr is also present in the film (confirmed by XPS).

In porous films (Fig. 3) on TA6V, the parallel evolution of signals 1 and 52 and comparison with the profiles on Ti in the same conditions have shown that the 52 amu signal corresponds only to $VH^- + VH_2^-$ species, proving that vanadium contributes to the growing mechanism [1,5]. The $^{64}(TiO^-)$ signal is used as an indicator of the position of the substrate/film interface (Fig. 4). The total thickness can be measured by microprofilometry of the crater. It lies between 95 nm (5 V 6 min.) and 155 nm (10 V 20 min.).

The particular shape of the 64 amu signal is interpreted by the succession of 4 steps (Fig. 5) : (I) = surface pre-coated Au-Pd layer ; (II) = very low density layer (protrusions) ; (III) = porous part of the film ; (IV) = compact part of the film. Existence of protrusions (layer II) at the extreme surface is indeed proved by HR-SEM observation (Fig. 1).

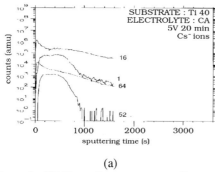 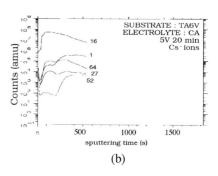

(a)   (b)

Figure 2 : SIMS profiles on compact films grown on (a) Ti, and (b) TA6V in CA, 5V, 20 min.

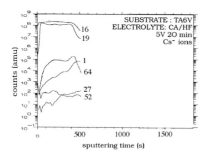 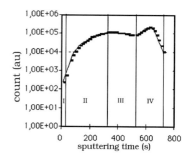

Figure 3 : SIMS profile on a porous film.   Figure 4: Interpretation of the TA6V
                                              in CA/HF, 10V 20min.

4. Conclusion

This study shows how the combination of microstructural and physicochemical investigation method is able to bring complete information on the structure, microchemistry and space arrangement of the very complex anodic films grown on titanium alloys. SIMS is the only way to evidence quantitatively the succession of porous and compact layers.

References

[1] V. Zwilling, E. Darque-Ceretti, A. Boutry-Forveille, D. David, M.Y. Perrin, M. Aucouturier, Surf. Interface Analysis, to be published (1999).
[2] L. Young, Anodic Oxide Films, Academic Press, London and New-York, 1961.
[3] M.E. Sibert, J. Electrochem. Soc., 25, n°1 (1963) 65.
[4] T.E. Evans, Corrosion Science, 17 (1977) 105.
[5] V. Zwilling, M. Aucouturier, E. Darque-Ceretti, Electrochimica Acta, to be published (1999).
[6] J.S.L. Leach, Reviews in Coating and Corrosion, 6, n°1 (1984) 2.

A. Benninghoven, P. Bertrand, H.-N. Migeon and H.W. Werner (Editors).
Proceedings of the 12th International Conference on Secondary Ion Mass Spectrometry,
Brussels, Belgium, 5-11 September 1999

HIGH RESOLUTION DEPTH PROFILING 3-D STRUCTURES WITH QUADRUPOLE SIMS

Peixiong Shi

Mikroelektronik Centret, Technical University of Denmark, Building 345east,
Lyngby, DK-2800, Denmark, E-mail: pxshi@mic.dtu.dk

Wenbin Jiang

E2O Communications Inc., 6320 Canoga Ave. Suite 1500, Woodland Hills,
CA 91367, U.S.A., E-mail: wbjiang@e2oinc.com

1.Introduction

Shrinking of component dimensions sets more critical demand on SIMS instrumentation, such as smaller beam size, higher sensitivity and better stability. In the following presentation, we demonstrate these abilities on a quadrupole SIMS, ATOMIKA 4000 [1], by measuring material characteristics of a Vertical Cavity Surface Emitting Laser (VCSEL).

2.Experiment

The VCSEL (Figure 1) structure under study is grown by MOCVD (Molecular Organic Chemical Vapor Deposition) [2]. Starting from GaAs wafer, an n-type (doped with $1*10^{18}$ atoms/cm^3 Silicon) bottom DBR (distributed Bragg reflector) mirror is composed of 40.5 pairs of $\lambda/4$ thick $Al_{0.8}Ga_{0.2}As/Al_{0.15}Ga_{0.85}As$ layers, where λ is the laser wavelength in the media. The active region with its cladding layer is grown on the bottom DBR with a thickness of one λ. The p-type (doped with $2*10^{18}$ atoms/cm^3 Carbon) top DBR mirror is composed of 31 pairs of $\lambda/4$ thick $Al_{0.8}Ga_{0.2}As/Al_{0.15}Ga_{0.85}As$. SiN layer claps the device for protection.

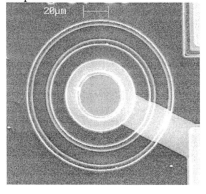

Figure 1. SEM pictures of the VCSEL structure. Left side: view from the top. Right side: view from the side with a titled angle.

624

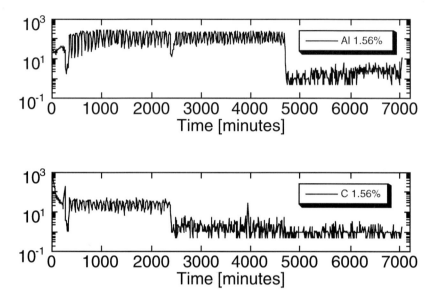

Figure 2. *SIMS depth profiles of Al and C in a VCSEL, measured by a 2.5KeV, 260pA Cs⁺ beam at normal incidence. The data gating area is a square in the middle of the crater, which is 1.56% of the crater area.*

VCSEL is a deep structure (9μm thick from the bottom DBR to top DBR) for the SIMS profiling. The demand for high depth and lateral resolution requires low beam energy and small beam size, leading to low beam current and long measurement time. A 2.5KeV Cs⁺ beam at normal incidence is chosen for the measurement. During the several thousand minutes of data collecting period, the beam current fluctuation is within 5% and the beam pointing stability is within a few micrometers.

To collect detailed information on the doping distribution in both transverse and longitudinal dimensions, image mode [1] is applied during the depth profiling. In each frame of the scanning, the count of an element is collected as a 128*128 pixel image. The data are stored separately in these 128*128 channels. Depth profile can be post processed after the measurement to extract the information from any place within the crater by using data gating technique.

Figure 2 displays the Al and C depth profile of a VCSEL structure. It is taken by gating the data from a center square, which is 1.54% of the total crater area. The depth resolution is good enough to distinguish the entire 70 layer structure. Even with a data gating area of 40μm² (1.54% of the 50μm*50μm), doping profile of $2*10^{18}$ atoms/cm³ C can be resolved clearly.

Since the data is collected in the image mode, we have the flexibility of post processing these data to get a better signal to noise ratio. The laser beam is emitted from a circular area in the middle of the VCSEL with a diameter of 30μm (Figure1). We are

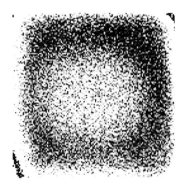

Figure 3. *SEM picture of the VCSEL after SIMS measurement. The crater size is 50μm*50μm, and the depth is over 15μm.*

Figure 4. *C image near the active region, produced by adding the signals in a 2μm thick layer.*

mainly interested on the element distribution within this area. After SIMS measurement, the circular area left in the middle of the crater only has a diameter of 6μm (Figure 3). Since we were not aware of this before the measurement, it is difficult to pre-determine the optimum data gating area for the depth profiling. The image mode offers a path to determine the data gating area after the measurement. Figure 4 displays the image of C signal by adding 100 frames (2μm in thickness) of C signal near the active region. Together with the images of other elements, it tells us that the cross section of laser emitting area is gradually decreased during the sputtering. Since the C doped area has a diameter much large than 6μm near the active region (between p-type and n-type DBR), we gated data from a little larger circle, which is 12% of the total crater area. This produces a C depth profile with a better signal to noise ratio in the doped region, the top DBR mirror (Figure5).

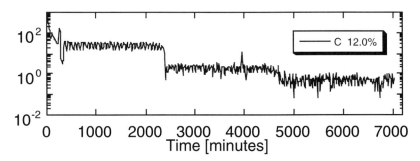

Figure 5. *Depth profile of C in a VCSEL, measured by a 2.5KeV, 260pA Cs+ beam at normal incidence. The data gating area is a circular area in the middle of the crater, which is 12% of the crater area.*

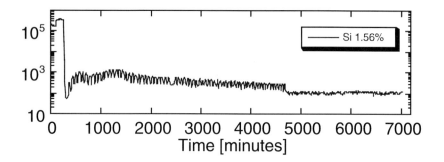

Figure 6. *Depth profile of Si in a VCSEL, measured by a 2.5KeV, 260pA Cs⁺ beam at normal incidence. The data gating area is a square in the middle of the crater, which is 1.56% of the crater area.*

If one is only interested in the depth profile, a 2.5KeV, 1nA Cs⁺ beam can be used with a rather large beam size. The measurement time can be reduced from 80 hours to 25 hours.

Through profiling an element of a 3-D structure, a high concentration of the same element in the surrounding area sometimes produces interference. In a VCSEL, SiN is used as an encapsulating layer. There is no Si doping in the top DBR, only the bottom DBR is doped with Si. The depth profile of Si (Figure 6) displays a high intensity of Si signal also in the top DBR. To get a real Si doping profile through the VCSEL, the top SiN layer should be removed before the SIMS measurement.

3.Conclusion

By measuring a true three-dimensional (3D) structure sample, Vertical Cavity Surface Emitting Laser (VCSEL), the superb performance of a quadrupole SIMS has been demonstrated. A depth resolution better than 20nm has been achieved through a depth of 9μm with a transverse resolution better than 6μm. Long term stability is crucial for this type of measurement. Image data acquisition proves to be a feasible tool for component SIMS probing.

References

[1]   K. Wittmaack, in Secondary Ion Mass Spectrometry (SIMS VIII), edited by A. Benninghoven, K.T.F. Janssen, J. Tümpner, and H.W. Werner (John Wiley & Sons, Chichester, 1992) pp. 211-214

[2]   P.R. Claisse, W. Jiang, P.A. Kiely, B. Gable and B. Koonse, Electronics Letters, 1998, Vol.34, No.7, pp. 681-682

A. Benninghoven, P. Bertrand, H.-N. Migeon and H.W. Werner (Editors).
Proceedings of the 12th International Conference on Secondary Ion Mass Spectrometry,
Brussels, Belgium, 5-11 September 1999

627

UV–OZONE CLEANING OF SURFACE HYDROCARBON CONTAMINATION FOR ACCURATE SHALLOW CARBON MEASUREMENTS BY SIMS

J.W. Marino, T.H. Büyüklimanli and C.W. Magee

Evans East
104 Windsor Center, Suite 101, East Windsor NJ, 08520-1407 U.S.A.

1. Introduction

The impurity concentration measurements of semiconductor materials have been as important as measuring the dopant concentrations. Secondary ion mass spectrometry (SIMS) has been the technique of choice to determine these levels with respect to depth. The main sources of contaminants in ion implanted samples are cross contamination from previous implants and from implanter apparatus parts. Thus, measurement of energetic and surface metal contaminants has become a routine SIMS analysis in ion implanted wafers [1]. Metal contaminants often are due to the sputtering of the metallic chamber walls and parts. Sometimes these contaminants can become ionized, accelerated and implanted in the wafer to levels that counter dope the intended dopant. Some ion implant manufactures have coated the parts exposed to the ion beam with graphite to avoid metallic contamination. However, this can also become a source for both surface and energetic carbon contamination in the implanted wafers. Thus, we must be able to measure carbon in Si using SIMS.

The presence of adventitious hydrocarbons on every surface exposed to the atmosphere makes it difficult to measure the C contamination that arises from ion implantation, especially for ultra-low energy (ULE) ion implants. It is almost impossible to distinguish the graphitic carbon impurity from adventitious hydrocarbon during a depth profile. Furthermore, atomic mixing of the surface C by the primary ion beam makes it harder to determine the amount of energetic C in the near-surface region of a ULE implant. Therefore, in order to be able to measure contamination due to ion implantation, the adventitious C on the surface and atomic mixing have to be minimized.

Several methods of removing the adventitious carbon are available, from solution cleaning to sample heating. Sample heating cannot be used because it may alter the distribution of the implanted species. Solution cleaning may remove carbon in forms other than just hydrocarbons. A third alternative is Ultraviolet Ozone Cleaning (UVOC) [2]. This treatment preferentially attacks the hydrocarbon leaving C in carbonate or graphite forms intact. The source in the UVOC apparatus produces UV light mainly in two separate wavelengths. One of the wavelengths generates highly reactive O_3 near the light source and the other causes a dissociation of the C-H bonds creating radicals. The recombination of the radicals' forms CO_2 and H_2O gas molecules, leaving the surface hydrocarbon free. The surface will then be terminated by O creating at least a monolayer of oxide.

2. Experimental

Virgin, un-implanted (control) and a shallow arsenic-implanted Si wafer ($5E15$ atoms/cm^2) were used for this study. The sample cleaning with UVOC was performed using UVOCS Inc. model #10X10/0ES. Cleaning for durations of 1, 5, 10, 15 and 30 minutes showed that almost all of the C is removed after 10 minutes of UVOC. The samples were introduced to the SIMS analytical chamber within 5 minutes of cleaning.

The SIMS depth profiles were acquired using a Physical Electronics 6600 Quadrupole SIMS instrument. The analyses were carried out using Cs$^+$ or O$_2^+$ primary ion beams, both operated at 1keV impact energy with and without oxygen flooding. Both atomic and molecular ions with positive and negative polarities were measured. The C secondary ion intensities were quantified using a 3% C doped Si film, calibrated by Auger electron spectroscopy.

3. Results and discussion

Figure 1 shows superimposed C profiles of the un-implanted Si wafer (control) using 1keV Cs$^+$ and O$_2^+$ (with O$_2$ flooding), presumably having only adventitious carbon present on the surface. It is clear that the Cs$^+$ bombardment analysis mixes the surface C into much greater depth than the O$_2^+$ bombardment. Furthermore, the pre-equilibrium region with the Cs$^+$ analyses introduces additional complications to the data quantification. Therefore, 1keV O$_2^+$ bombardment with O$_2$ flooding was used for the remainder of the analyses.

The oxide growth during the UVOC treatment for 10 minutes appears to be too thin to be detected. This was unexpected because UVOC is known to grow an oxide on Si. It seems that the native oxide already present before the treatment stopped further oxidation. Therefore, no complication from the growth an oxide had to be dealt with.

The comparison of the C profiles between the un-implanted virgin Si wafer and the arsenic-implanted Si wafer without UVOC cleaning shows similar surface concentrations (Figure 2). This makes it difficult to determine the amount of C incorporation in the wafer due to ion implantation. Therefore, it is necessary to remove the adventitious hydrocarbons prior to performing the SIMS measurements.

Figure 3 shows that the UVOC treatment of the un-implanted wafer to produce an order of magnitude reduction in the surface C concentration as compared to the un-cleaned un-implanted wafer. This suggests that all of the surface C was in hydrocarbon form.

Figure 4 is a comparison of the C profiles acquired from the UVOC treated un-implanted and implanted Si wafers. The profiles clearly show the presence of sub-surface C contamination in the arsenic-implanted wafer. This carbon could be the result of an energetic C impurity in the implant beam, or it could be the result of recoil implantation of the adventitious C by the high fluence As implant. In either case, it is clear that without prior UVOC treatment of the control and implanted wafers, an unambiguous determination of the presence of sub-surface C would not have been possible.

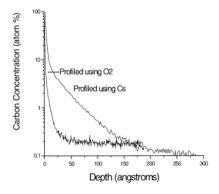

Fig. 1. Comparison of Cs and O₂ profiling of control wafer.

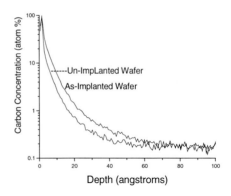

Fig. 2. Implanted vs. un-implanted wafer without UV ozone cleaning.

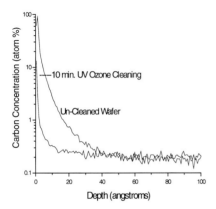

Fig. 3. Un-implanted wafer with and without UV ozone cleaning.

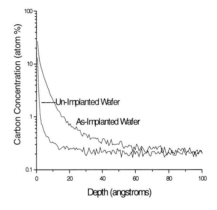

Fig. 4. Comparison of un-implanted & implanted wafers with 10 min. cleaning

The repeated measurements of the control sample in the analytical chamber show detectable re-growth of carbon only after 1 hour in UHV. This suggests that UVOC creates a relatively non-reactive surface, which allows several samples to be cleaned at once prior to analysis and then analyzed sequentially without breaking vacuum.

The biggest disadvantage of the C measurement after surface cleaning is a higher than normal instrumental background, or detection limit (~1E20 atoms/cc ~0.2 atom %). The necessity to start profiling before adequate chamber pumping takes place makes the high background unavoidable. Nevertheless, all of the C contamination measured in the ULE implants into Si wafers has been at least an order of magnitude higher than our detection limit. Therefore, the determination of total *true* C concentration has been possible so far.

4. Conclusion

The measurement of true carbon cross-contamination in Si wafers with ULE implantation has been challenging due to the presence of the adventitious hydrocarbons on the surface. The use of UV-Ozone cleaning preferentially removes the hydrocarbon contamination caused by atmospheric exposure. During the UVOC treatment minimal or no alteration was detected in the sample. The reduced adventitious hydrocarbon permits the determination of the true C implanted during the ion implantation of other species

The usual Cs^+ bombardment negative secondary ion analysis results in heavy atomic mixing of the surface C making it almost impossible to measure the energetic carbon present below the surface. However, O_2^+ bombardment positive ion detection with O2 flooding reduces the atomic mixing allowing the measurement of the deeper component of the carbon incorporated during the ion implantation.

Acknowledgments

The authors would like to thank Genise Bonacorsi of Varian Semiconductor Equipment Association for preparing the wafers used in this experiment.

References

[1] C.W. Magee and M.R. Frost, International Journal of Mass Spectrometry and Ion Processes, 143 (1995) pp. 29-41.
[2] J.R. Vig, UV/Ozone Cleaning of Surfaces in: Treatise on Clean Surface Technology, Vol. 1, (K.L.. Mittal, ed), pp. 1-26, Plenum Press, NY (1987).

A. Benninghoven, P. Bertrand, H.-N. Migeon and H.W. Werner (Editors).
Proceedings of the 12th International Conference on Secondary Ion Mass Spectrometry,
Brussels, Belgium, 5-11 September 1999
631

TOF-SIMS EVALUATION OF THE REMOVAL OF RESISTS ON SILICON BY OZONE-BASED CLEANING

T. Conard[+], C. Kenens[+], S. De Gendt[+], M. Claes[+], S. Lagrange[++], W. WorthA[⊥], S.Jassal[⊥⊥], W. Vandervorst[+, ⊥⊥⊥]
[+] IMEC, 75 Kapeldreef, 3001 Leuven, Belgium, [++] Semitool resident at IMEC, [⊥]International SEMATECH, [⊥⊥]formerly with International SEMATECH, [⊥⊥⊥]also at INSYS, KU Leuven, Belgium, email: tconard@workmail.com

1. Introduction

Resist removal is an important process step in IC manufacturing (silicon processing) and is often done using sulfuric acid based SPM or SPM/APM chemistries. These processes face however numerous environmental issues. The use of ozone could overcome these issues but was hampered up to now by the fact that there was no sufficiently effective processes available. We propose here an evaluation by Time of Flight Secondary Ion Mass Spectrometry (TOFSIMS) of the resist removal using ozone-based chemistries [1]. We show that theses processes can be as efficient as the sulfuric acid based chemistries in terms of removing organics.

2. Experimental

We investigated DUV and I-line resists with or without ion implantation.

For unimplanted resists, four different DUV and one I-line resists were evaluated: TOK022 (Tokyo Ohka), applied on an anti-reflective coating AR2 (Shipley), APEX/E2408 (Shipley), UV6 (Shipley) and PEK150A7 (Sumitomo) for DUV resists and IX845 (JSR electronics) for I-line. This last resist was always applied in combination with HMDS surface priming. Two different post-treatments, softbake or hardbake were investigated.

Two types of resist were used for the evaluation of implanted resists, i.e. IX845 (I-line) and UV6 (DUV) resist. Low dose implanted wafers (LDI), with doses up to $1*10^{14}$ at/cm^2 were processed with and without ashing the resist. High dose implanted wafers (HDI), with doses above $1*10^{14}$ at/cm^2, were given a short ash treatment to break-up the hardened crust layer.

The ozonated cleans (HydrOzone with / without subsequent APM clean) were also evaluated for resist removal on blanket, patterned and/or etched wafers. Two different patterning processes were evaluated, i.e. wafers with active area definition (both with LDI and HDI) and pelox (nitride etching) wafers. All these wafers were exposed either directly to ozonated chemistries or after a suitable ashing treatment. Additionally, wafers were also processed with standard sulfuric and ammonia based processes.

Time-of-flight secondary ion mass spectrometry (ToF-SIMS) measurements were made with an IONTOF-IV instrument using a 10 keV Ar$^+$ electron impact primary ion source. An ion dose of ~6E10 ions/cm^2 was used for each spectrum.

Each wafer was measured in positive and negative ions detection, both at the center and at the edge of the wafer. Ion clusters specific from typical organic contaminants on Si wafers and ions clusters from remains of photoresists were chosen in order to perform a detailed analysis of the TOFSIMS spectra. When the center and the edge spectra did not differ significantly, intensities were added for further comparison.

All intensities were reported after normalization towards $^{30}Si^+$ or $^{28}Si^-$ intensities for positive and negative ion spectra respectively. Further analysis was done by comparing the significant peaks on a one-by-one comparison of the high mass resolution display of the spectra.

3. Results

For most wafers, significant differences were found concerning the S-related peaks. This was related to the fact that the ozone process evaluation was performed in a tank that is routinely used for sulfuric acid processing. Although thoroughly rinsed, the sulfur peak signature remained visible. Also, for most samples (including the SPM reference samples), a peak in the negative ion spectra at 93.04 amu (tentatively attributed to the $C_6H_5O^-$ ion) has a significant higher intensity at the center of the wafer compared to the edge. This ion could come from contaminants containing phenyl groups and related to the cleanroom atmosphere.

3.0 Reference wafers

All cleaning procedures were evaluated by comparison with reference wafers. As a reference, a standard pre-gate cleaned wafer (SPM-dHF/DHCl-O₃/HCl-Marangoni Dry) was prepared and stored in a clean-room wafer box for a length of time equal to the storage time until TOFSIMS analysis for the resist cleaned wafers. A distinction can thus be made between organic residues that originate from the cleanroom background, and organic residues remaining after the various resist cleans. Five reference wafers and 2 points per wafers were measured (center and edge). No significant differences were found, neither in the positive, nor in the negative ion spectra. The intensities of all standard clean spectra were hence averaged to improve the statistical bases of the further comparisons.

3.1 I-line resist

The I-line resist clean was evaluated for SPM, SPM-APM, Hydrozone™ and Hydrozone™-APM clean.

Figure 1 displays the relative intensities of several peaks for the positive spectra representative of different compounds. Equivalent figures were obtained for the negative ion spectra. Very little differences exist between the various splits and all wafers should be considered equally clean or cleaner than the reference cleaned wafer. The exceptions are: (1) sulfate peak is much more

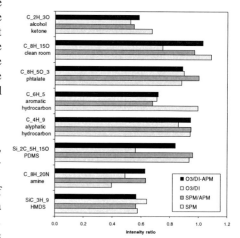

Figure 1: Positive ion normalized intensities after different cleaning processes of the IX845 I line photoresist. The normalization is made with respect to the clean stored wafers

intense after an SPM clean, which is straightforward, (2) Na intensities are higher for the SPM based cleans, (3) Mg and Al intensities are higher for the APM based cleans

Neither of the organic clusters (and compound classes) are thus more intense than on the reference cleaned wafer, nor is the cleanliness after any of the ozone processes worse than after any of the sulfuric based cleans. The efficiency of the ozone process is thus well demonstrated for this I-line unimplanted resist.

3.3. DUV resist unimplanted

An identical comparison was performed for the DUV resists. Three different blanket DUV resists (APEX/E2403, PEK150A7, UV6) were exposed to an ozone clean and processed until cleanliness (2 * 4' process).

Little or no differences in cleanliness between the three types of resist are observed, while also the intensity ratio is typically smaller than one, indicating that the wafers are overall cleaner in appearance than the reference wafers, as can be observed on Figure 2.

Also blanket TOK022 DUV wafers on an anti-reflective coating AR2 were processed. After the ozone clean (2 * 4' process) it can be visually observed that the resist has been removed, but that the anti-reflective coating is still largely intact in the center of the wafer ('delaminating' from the edges out). However, after an extended HydrOzoneTM treatment (with additive spiking) wafers are visually clean. This is also confirmed from the comparison of the ToF-SIMS spectra.

3.4. HDI wafers

High dose phosphorous implanted I-line (IX845) resist, both on blanket $(4*10^{15}$ at/cm^2) and patterned (active area definition, $5*10^{15}$ at/cm^2) wafers was exposed to a partial (incomplete) ash and subsequently stripped until cleanliness using an ozone process (2 * 6' process).

The observation of the TOFSIMS spectra of the HDI implanted wafers and the reference cleaned wafers reveals that even after high dose implantation, and an incomplete ash to quench the hardened crust layer, wafers can be considered clean using an ozone process.

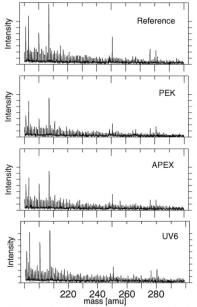

Figure 2: TOFSIMS spectra of the ozone cleaned DUV unimplanted resists. (identical intensity scale)

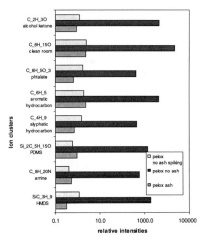

Figure 3: Relative intensities of typical clusters in the positive ion TOFSIMS spectra for different nitride wafers.

634

3.5. DUV pelox wafers

Patterned pelox (nitride etch) wafers were evaluated after ozone processing. The resist used for wafer patterning involved an anti-reflective coating (TOK022 on AR2). It was seen before that this anti-reflective coating is hard to remove by a regular ozone process. Three wafers were considered. The reference clean wafer for these comparisons received a dry ash treatment after the etch process step. The other wafers were ozone based, either an 8' ozone process clean-up, or a modified ozone clean (additive spiking).

Figure 3 shoes that all peaks related to C, C-H, C-N, C-O and combinations of these groups were much more intense on the ozone processed wafer compared to the reference wafer, indicating the presence of organic material with oxygen and nitrogen bonds.

However, after the modified ozone process with additive spiking, wafers are considerably cleaner, comparable to the reference clean wafer. A similar result is obtained when a dry ash is performed before ozone cleaning. This is clearly observed in Figure 4.

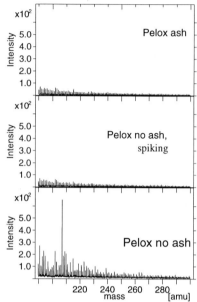

Figure 4: TOFSIMS spectra of pelox wafer with and without ashing. (identical intensity axe)

4. Conclusion

The cleanliness of ozonated chemistries for resist removal has been evaluated. In general, for all the resists under consideration, process times between 6 minutes and 12 minutes are required, the long process being required for high dose implanted, partially ashed resist wafers. The total resist removal time is thus competitive with sulfuric based chemistries. Also the removal of surface prime layers (HMDS) poses little or no difference for the ozone process. The anti-reflective coating however, is resistant to the ozone process. As a solution, a modified ozone process was demonstrated to be successful for this application. The modified ozone process involves spiking of the DI water with additives.

Generally, it can be concluded that the process performance of HydrOzoneTM processes for front-end-of-line processes (FEOL) is comparable in performance to the standard SPM processes. The process can be considered as a viable alternative for sulfuric based cleans.

Acknowledgements

This work was performed in partial fulfillment of the International SEMATECH ESHB009 and LIFE Bolaro project.

References

[1] S.De Gendt,P.Snee, I.Cornelissen, M.Lux, R.Vos, P.W.Mertens, M.Knotter, M.Heyns, 1998 Symp. On VLSI Technol. Digest of Technical papers p168.

A. Benninghoven, P. Bertrand, H.-N. Migeon and H.W. Werner (Editors).
Proceedings of the 12th International Conference on Secondary Ion Mass Spectrometry,
Brussels, Belgium, 5-11 September 1999

CHEMICAL NATURE OF IMPURITIES AND INTERFACE CONCENTRATION ENHANCEMENT IN SIMS PROFILES

Anuradha Dhaul, R.K. Sharma, B.B. Sharma
Solid State Physics Laboratory, Delhi-110054, INDIA, e-mail: bbs@drsspl.ren.nic.in

1. Introduction

Mercury Cadmium Telluride (MCT) epilayers grown from Te or Hg-rich solutions on CdTe or CdZnTe (CZT) substrates have been used over the years for fabricating advanced IR detector structures for various applications in 8-14 μ atmospheric window. Several studies have been focused on the investigation of background and doped impurities in these layers using Secondary Ion Mass Spectrometry (SIMS) and other techniques [1-3]. The sources of background impurities have been traced to the contamination of the substrate surface, substrate holder, quartz container and the starting materials. In case of the epigrowth from Hg-rich solutions, because of the high Hg-vapour pressure (~9 atm.) at the growth temperature (~500°C), the growth reactor is fabricated using Hg-resistant metallic alloys.These alloys, however, could be potential sources of background impurities. This aspect of the epigrowth process has not been discussed in detail in the literature. In the present study, MCT epilayers grown from Hg-rich solutions were analysed for background impurities using SIMS depth profiles. Apart from the impurities like Li, Na & Si commonly reported as showing strong ICE at the MCT/CdTe/CZT interface the SIMS profiles showed unusually high levels of Fe (~10^{18}/cm^3) in some epilayers but without showing ICE. A link rod attached to a graphite substrate holder was found to be the source of the Fe impurity seen in SIMS profiles. This rod was made of a special Hg-resistant alloy which contained Fe as a constituent. Certain sections of the growth reactor contained some brazed/welded joints. These sections were generally held at room temperature and were not exposed to Hg vapours which got condensed in a cooled reflux section. It was, however, found that minute amounts of Hg-vapours do escape beyond this reflux section and the brazing materials were also exposed to Hg vapours albeit very feebly. These portions, therefore, could also be the potential contaminants of the growth melt.

2. Experimental

2.1 Epigrowth the equipment used was similar to the ones described in [4] & [5]. The growth reactor was fabricated using Hg resistant alloys (Ni & Fe based compositions) [6] keeping high temperature and pressure requirements in view. About 5 Kg charge of 7 N pure Hg with appropriate amounts of CdTe & Te was used for growing epilayers with composition Hg$_{.8}$Cd$_{.2}$Te. A specially designed graphite substrate holder with a floating shutter was used in this work. A special steel rod was used for attaching this substrate holder to an externally controlled vertical drive for moving the substrate holder in and out of the growth melt.Although most part of this link rod stayed outside the hot zone of the reactor most of the time, during the actual growth period of about 1 hour a small portion of this rod came very close to the region where Hg/Te vapour density was significant. The rod material did not show significant corrosion in the presence of pure Hg vapours but the presence of Te resulted in substantially increased corrosion levels. This is expected since Fe reacts with Te forming FeTe which is not very resistant to Hg. Since the evaporation & condensation of Hg vapours take place in the reactor continuously, the condensing vapours dissolve the metallic elements present in the link rod and in other parts of the reactor that come into contact with these vapours. The level of these impurities is, therefore, expected to rise in the growth melt with each successive growth run as the same melt is used a number of times for growing epilayers.

2.2. We have used a CAMECA IMS-4F instrument (focused O_2^+ primary beam, ion impact energy of 8 KeV, beam current ~1µA; rastered area of 250 µm x 250 µm nominal extraction 4.5 KV. A fraction of the secondary ions was accepted for analysis from a circular area centered in the rastered region. The stability of the primary beam was about 1.5% during the course of each depth profile. For determining the sputtering rate (sputtered depth vs time) profilometric measurements were carried out, corrected for the dependence of sputtered depth on the compositional variable 'x' in $Hg_{1-x}Cd_xTe$ [7,8]. The quantification was carried out using relative sensitivity factors (RSFs) for [9].

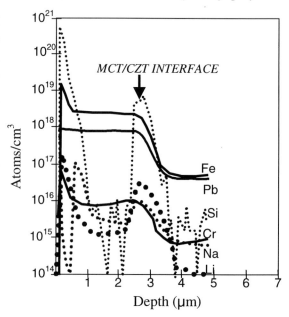

Fig.1   Depth profiles of selected impurities as seen across the MCT/CdTe interface.

3. Results & Discussion

The profiles for Li, Na & Si (fig.1) are similar to the ones reported in literature [2, 3]. The concentration enhancement of impurities at the interface and surface is quite pronounced for Li, Na & Si. The Fe-profile is, however, free from the ICE feature. The surface contamination of the substrate or substrate holder is the possible cause for impurities like Li & Na ; Si possibly gets incorporated due to leaching of quartz containers used for handling of the growth melt. The likely source of Fe-impurity are the high pressure growth chamber and the metallic components used therein as already discussed. The accumulation of some of these impurities at the surface/interface sites is similar to the phenomena of impurity gettering at defect sites commonly observed in semiconductor crystals. Here it is useful to differentiate between isovalent and heterovalent impurities. The gettering effect is pronounced only for the heterovalent impurities and is often used to drive them out of the active device region. The impurity accumulation at the defect sites in crystals is usually attributed to the attractive interaction of strain fields around these sites. However, an important consideration in case of semiconductors is that the defect sites also possess electric fields around them unlike in metallic systems. The charged impurities, therefore, get accumulated around these sites. The lattice-neutral (isovalent) impurities do not show any such tendency. In case of epilayers the substrate-epilayer interface could obviously be an extended defect site depending on the lattice mismatch and growth conditions. The epilayer surface could also have substantial surface charge density and the consequent electric field can also lead to impurity ac-cumulation. Fig. (1) shows ICE but no such feature is seen in Fe - profile. This indicates that Fe behaves as an isovalent impurity in MCT matrix. Being a transition metal atom with an incomplete d-shell $(3d^6 4s^2)$ it displays variable valency (Fe^{2+}, Fe^{3+}) in its compounds, the lower oxidation state (Fe^{2+}) being preferred in compounds with heavier anions (in lower periods of the periodic table). For example while combining

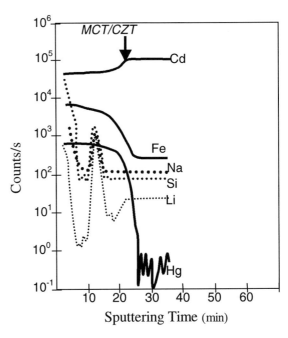

Fig.2   SIMS profiles showing impurity pile up around a growth fault away from MCT/ CdTe interface.

with oxygen the Fe^{3+} state is preferred as in Fe_2O_3 but with Te only FeTe is the stable compound where Fe is in 2+ state. This is a general trend in chemical compounds - a lower oxidation state (lower valency) getting stabilized with increasing atomic number (lower periods). The chemical similarity of FeTe with CdTe & HgTe (bivalent cation) results in a limited but significant solubility of FeTe in CdTe & HgTe [10] although Fe is virtually insoluble in Hg or Cd. In fact $Hg_{1-x}Fe_x$ Te composition with x = 0.016 has been synthesized as a single phase [11]. The lattice-neutral (isovalent with cations) behaviour of Fe in MCT matrix is thus expected on chemical considerations also. A similar argument applies to the incorporation of impurities like Mn, Cr, Pb, etc. since compounds MnTe, CrTe and PbTe are also stable. Depth profiles of Cr and Pb studied in the present work also do not show any ICE feature although these impurities show substantially higher levels in the epilayers than in the substrate (fig.1). Mn, however, was not examined in the present study. A significant observation was accidentally made in an MCT epilayer where significant concentration enhancement of Li, Na & Si was seen at a site within the epilayer but away from the interface (fig 2). This must have been a site of some accidental growth fault. Here also no enhancement in Fe concentration is seen.

4. Conclusions

The heterovalent (with respect to matrix) impurities show concentration enhancement on the defect sites (interfaces, surfaces, extended defects) apparently driven by built-in electric fields around these sites. Isovalent impurities behave like matrix elements showing no concentration enhancement around such sites.

Acknowledgment

Thanks are due to Prof. Vikram Kumar, Director - SSPL, Dr. Pran Kishan and Dr. R.K. Bagai.

References

[1] P.Capper; in Properties of Narrow Gap Cadmium Based Compounds, EMIS Data Review Series No. 10, ed. P. Capper (INSPEC, 1994) p. 163.

[2] M.H. Kalisher, Journal of Crystal Growth 70 (1984) 365.

[3] M.G. Astles, H. Hill, G. Blackmore, S. Courtney and N. Shaw, Journal of Crystal Growth 91 (1988) 1.

[4] P.E. Herning, J. Electron. Mater. 13 (1984)1.

[5] B.B. Sharma, R.K. Sharma, F.R. Chavda, A.K. Garg and S. Kumar, Technical Report No. SPL-042-U-92 (Dec. 1992).

[6] J.F. Nijedlik & E.J. Vargo, Electrochem. Technol. 3(1965) 250.

[7] Anuradha Dhaul, S.K.Sharma,R.K.Sharma and B.B.Sharma, Technical Report No. SSPL- 125 - U – 99

[8] J. Sheng, L. Wang and G.E.Lux and Y.Gao; J. Electronic Materials 27 (1997) 588

[9] R.G.Wilson ; J. Crystal Growth, 86 (1988) 735

[10] R. Triboulet, in Semimagnetic Semiconductors and Diluted magnetic semiconductors, Ed. Michel Averous & Minko Balkanski, (Plenum Press, New York-1991) p 23.

[11] Y. Guldner, C. Rigause and M. Menant, Solid State Commun. 33(1980) 133

A. Benninghoven, P. Bertrand, H.-N. Migeon and H.W. Werner (Editors).
Proceedings of the 12th International Conference on Secondary Ion Mass Spectrometry,
Brussels, Belgium, 5-11 September 1999
© 2000 Elsevier Science B.V. All rights reserved.

SIMS DEPTH PROFILING OF SiGe STRUCTURES USING BOTH OXYGEN AND CESIUM PRIMARY ION BOMBARDMENT: A COMPARISON

Mark S. Denker*, Temel Buyuklimanli, and Jeffrey T. Mayer
Evans East, 104 Windsor Center, Suite 101, East Windsor NJ 08520

1. Introduction

The tremendous growth in the electronics industry, and specifically in communication technologies and optoelectronics, has led to the development of SiGe semiconductor devices that include HBT's, BiCMOS devices, photonic devices, and many others [1]. SiGe devices are faster than Si devices, and because SiGe can be integrated with the mature silicon processing technology, they have significant appeal for use in electronic device technology [2]. This growth in SiGe technology has led to the demand for characterization of these materials, and of course the necessity for those in materials characterization to produce the most accurate data possible.

Much previous work [3-7] has been done on the SIMS of SiGe. Several authors have reported fairly small errors in quantification from matrix effects. References 4 and 5 used oxygen bombardment and stated that the ratio of sensitivities of Si and Ge are independent of the Ge concentration up to 78%. Reference 7, which also used predominantly oxygen bombardment, reported an absence of significant matrix effects up to 40% Ge for both the quantification of impurities and the determination of the Ge composition. Reference 6 presented results, also obtained with oxygen bombardment, which reported significant errors when quantifying relaxed SiGe layers using relative sensitivity factors (RSF's) obtained from a strained SiGe sample. Only reference 3 reports significant quantification errors caused by matrix effects, and stated that they "must be taken into account for a correct SIMS quantification of Ge in SiGe alloys bombarded either by O_2^+ or Cs^+ at oblique incidence."

However, all of the above references used magnetic sector SIMS, almost exclusively oxygen bombardment, and no negative ion detection. They avoided cesium bombardment and negative ion detection because the high positive surface potential gives the cesium ion beam an impact energy of 14.5keV, which seriously degrades depth resolution. Cesium bombardment with negative ion detection is, however, the best way to do analyses of SiGe because it allows the detection of all of the species of interest during one profile: C, O, N, B, P, Ge, and the halogens. This combination on a quadrupole, which also allows the use of cesium as the primary ion beam with significantly better depth resolution compared to magnetic sector instruments, has not been previously described in the literature.

2. Experimental

Samples were prepared with Ge concentrations ranging from 6-45 atomic percent (6, 10, 15, 20, 24, 28, and 45%), and implanted with C, O, P, and B. The Ge concentrations were determined by both Rutherford Backscattering Spectrometry (RBS) and Auger Electron Spectroscopy (AES). The SIMS instruments used were Physical Electronics (PHI) quadrupole-based model 6300 and 6600 instruments, with both cesium and oxygen primary ion guns. Cesium bombardment at 3.0 keV was used with negative ion detection of both atomic and molecular ions. Oxygen bombardment at 1.5keV and 3.0 keV was used with positive ion detection of atomic ions. Crater depths were determined using a Tencor Alphastep 200 stylus profilometer.

3. Results and Discussion

3.1 Cesium Primary Ion Bombardment

Figure 1 shows the relative sensitivity factors (RSF's) of boron implanted into the series of SiGe standards listed above. The samples were sputtered with 3.0 keV cesium at an incidence angle of 60°. The boron was detected as the negative molecular ion, $^{28}Si^{11}B$, and normalized to the Si_2 molecular matrix ion in the SiGe layer. The boron RSF decreases with increasing Ge composition. The boron RSF is 3.2E21 for the pure Si standard, and decreases to 2.1E21 for the 45% SiGe standard, a decrease of approximately 34%. This change in the RSF indicates that the secondary ion yields of the $^{28}Si^{11}B$ and Si_2 molecular ions are changing at different rates. This is contrary to what is assumed when quantifying the boron in samples of unknown boron concentration , and therefore introduces error into the quantification. However, dividing the boron RSF's by the silicon mole fraction in the sample (1-X, where X is the Ge mole fraction) leads to a fairly constant boron RSF as a function of the changing Ge concentration.

Figure 2 compares the percent error in the calculation of the RSF's both with and without the 1-X correction. The data for the other implanted species, C, O, and P, also show RSF's that are not constant as a function of the Ge composition. The carbon RSF's vary differently, depending on which species is being monitored. The RSF's of carbon followed as SiC decrease with increasing Ge composition, similar to boron followed as SiB. The RSF's of carbon followed as the atomic ion C *increase* with increasing Ge composition. Because of the different dependence on Ge composition, the correction is different. The SiC RSF's are corrected by dividing by the mole fraction of the silicon, as with SiB, but the C RSF's are corrected by *multiplying* by the silicon mole fraction.

The phosphorus RSF's show the following behavior. The RSF's of phosphorus followed as SiP increase with increasing Ge composition, in contrast to SiB and SiC. The RSF's of phosphorus followed as atomic P increase slightly with increasing Ge composition, but not nearly to the same degree as the SiP RSF's. Both sets of RSF's show a much more linear behavior when multiplied by the Si mole fraction (1-X). The oxygen RSF's are more constant with changing Ge composition than the other species that were studied. They change only ~7% over the Ge composition range studied here.

The germanium RSF's, followed as the molecular ion SiGe, show behavior similar to SiB and SiC. The RSF's decrease as a function of the Ge composition, and this nonlinear behavior is corrected by dividing them by 1-X.

3.2 Oxygen Primary Ion Bombardment

Sputtering of SiGe samples with 1.5keV oxygen provides better depth resolution, although only B and Ge can be detected. They are followed as positive atomic ions. Carbon cannot be followed under this protocol because it makes a very poor positive ion, resulting in a detection limit of $1E19/cm^3$ or higher. Oxygen of course cannot be followed accurately with oxygen primary ion bombardment.

Figure 3 shows a comparison of an SiGe sample sputtered with both oxygen and cesium bombardment at various energies. The 1.5keV and 3.0keV oxygen-sputtered data both show a significant improvement in depth resolution over the 3.0keV cesium-sputtered data. The cesium-sputtered data erroneously show that some of the boron has diffused out the backside of the SiGe layer, which is an important piece of information for SiGe-based structures. The oxygen-sputtered data shows that, in fact, the boron is contained within the SiGe layer.

For the determination of RSF's using positive atomic ions, the Si atomic ion in the substrate was initially used as the matrix species for normalization. This was done because it was assumed that the B and Ge secondary ion yields would remain fairly constant with Ge composition. Since the B and Ge are followed as atomic ions, and not as molecular ions which depend on combination with matrix atoms for creation, it was expected that their sensitivity would be much less dependent on the matrix composition. The data in fact bear this out. When calculating the RSF's using the Si matrix current in the SiGe layers, the RSF's show the same decrease with increasing Ge composition as several of the cesium-sputtered species did . However, when the RSF's are calculated using the Si matrix current in the substrate, the RSF's are more constant, particularly for Ge compositions below 30%. Similar results were observed for the Ge RSF's.

3.3 Sputter Rate as a Function of Ge Composition

The sputter rate of SiGe layers was observed to increase with increasing Ge composition. If the depth scale is determined by a stylus profilometer, as it usually is, the thickness of the Si and SiGe layers will be somewhat inaccurate. This is because the profilometer measures the total crater depth, and the sputter rate is determined from this assuming a constant sputter rate. The use of this average sputter rate will cause the depth scale to display the Si layers slightly thicker than they actually are, and the SiGe layers slightly thinner than they actually are. The data collected for this study show the difference in sputter rate with Ge composition to be fairly small. The sputter rate for the cesium-sputtering of the samples increases linearly with Ge composition, to a value for the 45% SiGe sample that is ~13% higher than the pure Si sample. The percent change is only 10% for the 25% SiGe sample. The sputter rate for the oxygen-sputtering of the samples increases less; the 45% SiGe sample sputters at a rate ~8% higher than the pure Si sample, and the 25% SiGe sample increases by 6%.

4. Conclusions

Significant ion yield changes of B, C, P and Ge as a function of Ge concentration during cesium bombardment and negative ion detection were observed. These changes lead to errors in quantification, which can be corrected by suitable procedures. During *oxygen* bombardment and positive ion detection, ion yield changes of B and Ge are much smaller than those of cesium bombardment if the RSF's are calculated with reference the atomic Si ion in the substrate, rather than to Si in the SiGe layer. *Cesium* bombardment (3keV) allows the simultaneous detection of C, P, B, Ge and O (and other electronegative elements such as As, S, and the halogens), although it results in poorer depth resolution than oxygen bombardment at 1.5keV. Using *oxygen* bombardment, the trade–off is that only B and Ge can be quantified with good detection limits

References

[1] R.Soref, *MRS Bulletin,* April 1998, p.20.

[2] B.S.Myerson, *Scientific American*, March 1994, pp. 62-67.

[3] G.Prudon, et. al., *Thin Solid Films,* 294 (1997) pp. 54-58.

[4] U.Zastrow, et.al., *Secondary Ion Mass Spectrometry, SIMS X,*
    ed. by A. Benninghoven, et. al., Wiley & Sons (1997), pp. 541.

[5] U.Zastrow, et al., *SIMS IX,,* ed. by A. Benninghoven, et. al., Wiley & Sons (1994), p. 702.

[6] J.P.Newey, et. al., , *SIMS XI,,* ed. by G. Gillen, et. al., Wiley & Sons (1998), p. 979.

[7] P.C.Zalm, et. al., *Surface and Interface Analysis*, Vol. 17, 556-566 (1991).

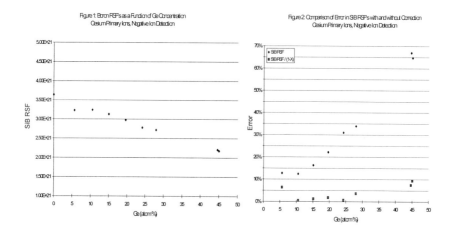

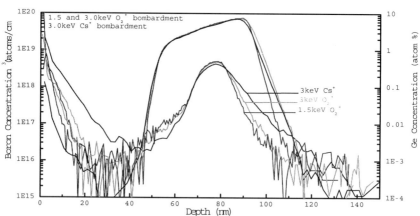

Figure 3: Comparison of B and Ge Profiles Sputtered with Oxygen and Cesium Bombardment

A. Benninghoven, P. Bertrand, H.-N. Migeon and H.W. Werner (Editors).
Proceedings of the 12th International Conference on Secondary Ion Mass Spectrometry,
Brussels, Belgium, 5-11 September 1999

643

DEPTH PROFILING OF ION IMPLANTED SiC

M.K. Linnarsson, A. Hallén and B.G. Svensson

Royal Institute of Technology, Solid State Electronics, P.O. Box Electrum 229, SE-164 40
Kista-Stockholm Sweden
marga@ele.kth.se

1. Introduction

The wide bandgap semiconductor silicon carbide (SiC) has gained an increasing interest as a material for power and high-speed devices, operating at high temperatures or in aggressive media. A large number of SiC polytypes can form but so far only three have been of practical interest; 3C, 4H and 6H with an energy bandgap at room temperature of 2.2, 3.3 and 2.9 eV, respectively [1]. At room temperature SiC shows many similarities with insulators caused by the wide bandgap. Due to the low diffusivity of commonly used dopants (Al, N...) in SiC [2], the main technique for incorporation is during growth or by ion implantation. Together with the implanted species a large amount of damage is introduced and at high doses amorphization will occur [3-6]. For SiC applications reproducible control of incorporation and distribution of dopants is crucial and accurate secondary ion mass spectrometry (SIMS) measurements are essential.

In this study, we have investigated the effect of damage introduced during ion implantation on erosion rate and secondary ion signal intensity in SIMS measurements. A comparison is made between amorphous and crystalline material, and a higher erosion rate is obtained in amorphous material caused by a lower atomic density.

2. Experimental

Samples were prepared at room temperature by ion implantation of ^{75}As using doses of 1×10^{14} and 5×10^{15} ions/cm^2 with energies of 200 and 280 keV respectively. Bulk SiC samples of 4H and 6H polytypes have been investigated. The doping level in n-type (nitrogen doped) material was 8.6×10^{18} cm^{-3} and in p-type (aluminum doped) 1.5×10^{18} cm^{-3}. Furthermore undoped material, previously used in Rutherford backscattering spectrometry (RBS) studies, has also been employed. In this case the implanted species is 2.4 MeV He ions and the helium dose is typically 1×10^{15} cm^{-2}.

The SIMS analyses were carried out using a Cameca ims 4f instrument. Cs$^+$ and O$_2^+$ ions were employed with a net impact energy of 13.5 and 8.2 keV respectively. During the study of effects on the secondary ion signal intensity by the ion induced damage, electron flooding using a normal incidence e-gun was employed or calibration of the sample high voltage (4.5 kV) with respect to maximum intensity of a matrix signal was undertaken. The primary sputter beam was rastered over an area 200x200 $\square m^2$ and secondary ions were collected from the central region of crater (diameter of analyzed area ~60 $\square m$). Crater depths were determined by an Alpha Step-200 stylus profilometer. The pressure in the sample chamber was $<5x10^{-9}$ Torr during analysis.

3. Result and discussion

Fig. 1 shows crater depth versus time for sputtering with Cs^+ ions of two As implanted SiC samples and one unimplanted sample. One sample is implanted with a high dose, $5x10^{15}$ cm^{-2} (280 keV) to obtain an amorphous layer and in the other case a low dose, $1x10^{14}$ cm^{-2} (200 keV) is employed to preserve the crystal structure. When the crystal structure becomes strongly disordered an expansion of the lattice occurs, mainly in the direction of the surface normal. The erosion rate can be estimated from the slope of the curves. For the high dose ($5x10^{15}$ cm^{-2}) sample the curve has two slopes due to a change in erosion rate when passing through the amorphous layer. A 17% higher erosion rate is extracted from the slope in the amorphous SiC which is primarily attributed to a lower density compared to the crystalline material [3-5]. Being so in samples with a varying density the change in erosion rate has to be carefully considered when converting time to depth scale in SIMS measurements. No change in erosion rate with depth is observed for the low dose ($1x10^{14}$ cm^{-2}) sample. The erosion rates for low dose sample and below the amorphous layer in the high dose sample are the same, and curves a and b+c in fig. 1 are parallel within the experimental accuracy. Measurements with oxygen primary ions give similar results as for cesium.

Monte Carlo simulations using the transport of ions in matter code (TRIM, version -90) [7] are performed to determine in which depth interval amorphization takes place and to relate the amorphous layer to the implanted As profile. As criterion for amorphization a value of 0.25 displacements per lattice atom is employed [3]. In fig. 2 the As distribution measured by SIMS is displayed for 280 keV ions and a dose of $5x10^{15}$ cm^{-2} together with an estimation of the thickness of the amorphous layer. The extension of the amorphous zone is based on TRIM calculations in combination with the measured As concentration. The defect distribution generated by ion implantation is slightly closer to the surface and exhibits a larger tail towards the surface compared to the implantation profile. By assuming that the ration between the implanted profile and the damage profile is correctly predicted by TRIM we have used the measured As-profile to estimate the corresponding damage profile. A good agreement is obtained between the layer thickness in fig. 2 and the depth where the erosion rate changes in fig. 1.

Matrix signals in SiC; C, Si or combinations thereof will be affected to a different extent by ion implantation of a sample. Fig. 3 illustrates the effect on SIMS data caused by defects introduced during RBS measurements where the same region is utilized for both RBS and SIMS. During the RBS analysis the sample has been bombarded with high energetic He ions.

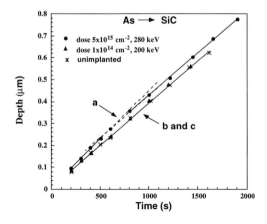

Fig.1. Crater depth versus time for sputtering of SiC using Cs^+ primary ions. Three samples are analyzed, a) as implanted with an As dose of $5x10^{15}$ cm^{-2} (280 keV), b) with an As dose of $1x10^{14}$ cm^{-2} (200 keV) and c) unimplanted.

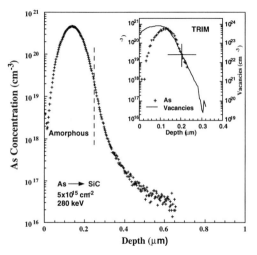

Fig.2. Depth profile of a 280 keV As implantation, dose $5x10^{15}$ cm^{-2}. The region of amorphization is determined from TRIM calculations (se inserted figure). Cs^+ primary ions have been utilized.

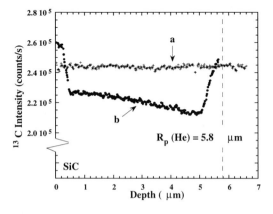

Fig.3. SIMS measurement of a matrix signal versus depth for a SiC sample. The sample has previous been measured by RBS. a) outside and b) inside the area of RBS measurement. The projected range, obtained from TRIM, for 2.4 MeV He ions is indicated in the figure (dotted line). O_2^+ primary ions have been employed.

Hence, a change in the intensity of the matrix signal measured by SIMS is seen, indicating the projected range of 2.4 MeV He ions, the energy used in the RBS measurements. Despite a low density of elastic energy deposition in the tail towards the surface defects introduced during the He implantation, in this case RBS measurements, alter the conductivity in SiC and affect the SIMS measurements. The influence of high defect concentration on signal intensities can be minimized by charge compensation. Gold coating, electron flooding or cyclical calibration of the sample high voltage (4.5 kV) with respect to maximum intensity of the matrix signal will improve the measurements. However a total recovery of signal intensity is not yet possible to obtain in low doped SiC ($\leq 10^{15}$ cm^{-3}). In highly doped SiC the influence on signal intensities caused by defects introduction during ion implantation is less pronounced and can be accounted for.

Acknowledgments

Financial support was partly received from the Swedish Foundation for Strategic research (SSF), SiCEP program. Fruitful discussions with M.S. Janson are greatly appreciated.

References

[1]   E. Janzén, O. Kordina, A. Henry et al., Physica Scripta, **T54** (1998) 283 and references therein.
[2]   Y.A. Vodakov and E.N. Mokov, in Proc. 3rd Int. Conf. on Silicon Carbide, eds. R.C. Marshall, J.W. Faust, Jr. and C.E. Ryan (Univ. of South Caroline Press Columbia, SC, 1973) p508.
[3]   E. Wendler, A. Heft and W. Wesch, Nucl. Instr. Meth., **B141** (1998) 105.
[4]   V. Heera, J. Stoemenos, R. Kögler and W, Skorupa, J. Appl. Phys. **77** (1995) 2999.
[5]   C.J. McHargue and J.M. Williams, Nucl. Instr. Meth., **B80/81** (1993) 889.
[6]   H. Hobert, H. Dunken, F. Seifert et al., Nucl. Instr. Meth. **B129** (1997) 244.
[7]   J.P. Biersack and L.G. Haggmark, Nucl. Instr. Meth., **174** (1980) 257.

A. Benninghoven, P. Bertrand, H.-N. Migeon and H.W. Werner (Editors).
Proceedings of the 12th International Conference on Secondary Ion Mass Spectrometry,
Brussels, Belgium, 5-11 September 1999
647

SIMS AND SNMS INVESTIGATIONS CONCERNING THE SEGREGATION OF Ni IN Al DURING DEPTH PROFILING WITH NORMAL INCIDENCE OXYGEN BOMBARDMENT

U. Breuer[1], U. Zastrow[2] and H. Holzbrecher[1]

[1] Central Department for Analytical Chemistry
[2] Institute of Thin Film and Ion Technology
Research Centre Jülich GmbH, D-52425 Jülich, Germany
(email:UWE.BREUER@FZ-JUELICH.DE)

1. Introduction

SIMS depth profiles of complex multilayer structures principally can be affected by artifacts as isobaric interferences, matrix effects, changing sputter rates and redistribution of elements during sputtering (segregation, preferential sputtering). For example;

Use of near normal oxygen bombardment of Si can cause segregation of elements deeper into the sample (such observations are reported since more than 15 years[1-3]). Due to the fact that Aluminum oxide has a similar heat of formation (8.7 eV/metal atom) as SiO_2 (9.4 eV/metal atom) there is a potential for segregation effects in Al during near normal oxygen bombardment. Oxygen bombardment is preferred since it provides high ion yields and reduces roughening during sputtering.

Since SNMS and MCs-SIMS are much less affected by matrix effects it is possible to investigate the reason for the oxygen sputtering profile distortions in SIMS using SNMS and MCs-SIMS. Aluminum is examined since widely used as part of contact layers in semiconductor devices.

2. Experimental

A part of a layer structure of a solar cell device was investigated using depth profiling with SIMS, SNMS and MCs-SIMS. The structure is used as the backside contact of the solar cell and consists of ZnO(100nm) deposited on amorphous Silicon. On top of the ZnO is a layer of Al(150nm) which is then coated with Ni(150nm). Depth profile measurements were carried out using an ATOMIKA 4000 with O_2^+ and Cs^+ bombardment. The impact angle of O_2^+ was varied from 0° to 30° both for depth profiling and the generation of an oxide in the Al layer. MCs-SIMS was applied in situ to the oxygen presputtered samples. In a CAMECA ims 4f depth profiles were measured with O_2^+ and Cs^+ bombardment. For SNMS a FISONS SIMSLAB 410 was used Ar or Ga primary beams (45°) were employed.

3. Results and Discussion

For depth profiling of the Ni:V/Al/ZnO/a-Si layered structure care has to be taken about mass interferences. Ni has interferences with Zn, Si_2 and SiO_2 and Zn with Ni and VO so it is most likely to monitor more than one isotope of these elements. For clarity not all isotopes measured will be depicted in the following depth profiles and we want to focus on the interplay of Ni, Al and ZnO. The Zn profile in the Ni layer is distorted by the isobaric interferences of $^{64}Ni/^{64}Zn$ and $^{50}VO/^{66}Zn$.

At near normal oxygen bombardment the SIMS depth profiles of the layer structure Ni/Al/ZnO/a-Si showed the expected profiles except for Ni. The Ni depth profile exhibited a large peak at the interface between Al and ZnO (Fig.1) which reaches a countrate of 10% of the metallic Ni-layer value. This interface peak was suspected to be a SIMS-artifact because no Ni should be present in this part of the structure.

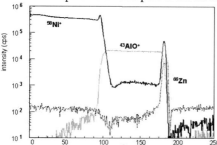

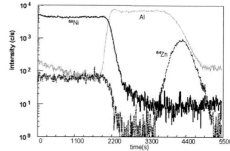

Fig. 1 SIMS depth profile (2.5 keV O_2^+ at normal incidence). Ni pile up at the Al/ZnO interface appears to be present.

Fig. 2: SNMS depth profile (10keV Ar^+ at 45°). No Ni accumulation at the Al/ZnO interface was observed.

The SNMS depth profile of this structure is depicted in Fig. 2. No Ni accumulation is found at the interface between Al and ZnO. The oxide formation in the Al layer due to the near normal oxygen bombardment used in the SIMS analyses must therefore be responsible for the Ni transport across the Al layer. Because the ZnO is an oxide itself it can be expected that this will act as a barrier for Ni transport. The Ni is expected to be trapped between the Aluminum-oxide and the Zinc-oxide. This could explain the Ni peak observed at the Al/ZnO interface.

Increasing the angle of incidence for the oxygen beam will reduce the degree of oxidation and therefore reduces the pile up of Ni at the interface. Under an impact angle of 30° the Ni peak disappears in the ATOMIKA instrument. In the CAMECA where the angle of incidence is about 39° for 8keV [4] the Ni peak is also absent as shown in Fig.3.

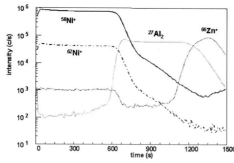

Fig. 3: SIMS depth profile 8keV O_2^+ at 39° in the CAMECA ims 4f. No Ni accumulation is found at the Al/ZnO interface.

To study the dynamic of the Ni transport in the Al layer we stopped the oxygen bombardment at different depths in the Al layer and analyzed the altered layer using SNMS and MCs-SIMS.

The SNMS depth profiles of two presputtered areas are shown in Fig 4a,b. Presputtering was stopped after removal of about 30% (Fig 4a) and 90% (Fig. 4b) of the Al layer respectively.

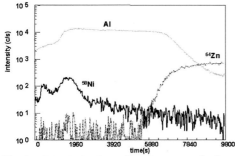
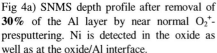

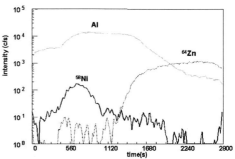

Fig 4a) SNMS depth profile after removal of 30% of the Al layer by near normal O_2^+-presputtering. Ni is detected in the oxide as well as at the oxide/Al interface.

Fig 4b) SNMS depth profile after removal of **90%** of the Al layer by near normal O_2^+-presputtering. The Ni from the oxide was removed but the oxide/Al Ni is still present.

The Ni depth profile in Fig 4a) exhibits two localized Ni maxima one in the oxide and a second at the interface between oxide and the remaining metallic Al layer. Comparing this with the Ni profile in Fig 4b) at least two mechanisms of the Ni transport must be present. The Ni content in the sputter induced oxide is reduced with longer oxygen sputtering this might be due to a coexistence of oxidized Ni and oxidized Al with a certain probability for Ni to be sputtered. At the oxide/Al interface Ni is present in a metallic form and due to the difference in the heat of formation between Al-oxide (8.7eV/metal atom) and Ni-oxide (2.5eV/metal atom) the formation of Al-oxide is energetically preferred. Metallic Ni remains at the metal side of this interface and segregates during further sputtering. Therefore this Ni will not be sputtered and the Ni-concentration remains quite constant. To quantify the Ni content in the Al layer we used a $Ni_{0.5}Al_{0.5}$ glass to establish the relative sensitivity factors (RSF) for SNMS. Using these RSFs the Ni content in the Al after removal of 30% of the Al layer is 4.9% (Fig 4a) and 4.5% after removal of 90% of the Al layer (Fig 4.b) respectively.

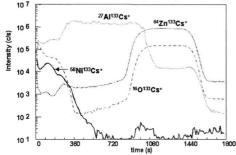

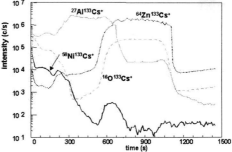

Fig 5a) MCs-SIMS depth profile after removal of **25%** of the Al layer by near normal O_2^+-presputtering. Ni is detected in the oxide as well as at the oxide/Al interface. A small Ni accumulation is found at the Al/ZnO interface.

Fig 5b) MCs-SIMS depth profile after removal of **90%** of the Al layer by near normal O_2^+-presputtering. The Ni in the oxide is reduced but the oxide/Al Ni is still present. A strong Ni accumulation is detected at the Al/ZnO interface

The MCs⁺-SIMS depth profiles of the altered layer after presputtering 25% and 90% of the Al layer respectively are depicted in Fig 5a,b. At the surface an oxide was formed which is shown by a reduction of Al compared to the metallic layer and the presence of oxygen.

The NiCs profile shows similar as for SNMS the presence of Ni in the oxide layer. At the interface between the oxide and the remaining Al a plateau is visible for the short presputtering and even a maximum of Ni is found in the deeper presputtered case. In the case of removing 90% of the Al layer by near normal oxygen bombardment the Ni content in the oxide layer is markedly reduced while the Ni at the interface between Al-oxide and Al stays on the similar level. This is in agreement with the results from the SNMS. Remarkably is the case of 90% Al removal for the Ni-profile at the interface between Al and ZnO because the MCs-SIMS indicates an accumulation of Ni at that interface similar to that found for near normal oxygen bombardment. It is not clear so far whether remaining oxygen during the MCs-SIMS measurement is sufficient for initiating the segregation of Ni or a long term transport mechanism as radiation enhanced diffusion is responsible for Ni transport towards the Al/ZnO interface. The MCs-SIMS depth profile of the structure without presputtering, however, shows no Ni accumulation at the Al/ZnO interface as depicted in Fig 6.

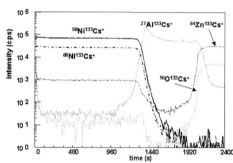

Fig. 6: MCs-SIMS depth profile. No Ni accumulation is found at the Al/ZnO interface.

4. Conclusions

Under near normal oxygen bombardment Ni segregation was observed in Al. For Ni segregation in Al two regimes can be described: 1) The bombardment induced oxide contains a certain amount of Ni which is consumed during further sputter removal. 2) At the interface between the oxide and the remaining Al is a Ni accumulation. This stays fairly constant (about 5% Ni) and moves during sputtering into greater depths. This was confirmed by MCs-SIMS measurements. In addition for MCs-SIMS a Ni transport to the Al/ZnO interface was observed which is stronger the closer the distance between the presputtered oxide and the ZnO is. It is not clear so far whether this is due to a long range transport during oxygen bombardment or initiated during Cs bombardment. Increasing the angle of incidence reduces the oxide formation and the segregation is also reduced.

References

[1] P. R. Boudewijn, H. W. P. Akerboom, M, N, C Kempeners, Spectrochimica Acta 39B, No 12, (1984) 1567
[2] C. Tian, G.B. Beyer, W. Vandervorst, K. Maex, J.A. Killner in SIMS X, ed. By Benninghoven et. Al., John Wiley & Sons Chichester (1997) p383
[3] J. S. Williams, K. T. Short, A. E. White, Appl. Phys. Lett. 70(4) (1997) 426
[4] M. Meuris, P. De Bisschop, J. F. Leclair, W. Vandervorst, Surf. Interface. Anal. 14, (1989) 739

A. Benninghoven, P. Bertrand, H.-N. Migeon and H.W. Werner (Editors).
Proceedings of the 12th International Conference on Secondary Ion Mass Spectrometry,
Brussels, Belgium, 5-11 September 1999

A STUDY OF ION BEAM INDUCED ROUGHENING IN TiN AND AT TiN/Si INTERFACE

A. V. Li-Fatou, G. R. Mount and K. -J. Chao

Charles Evans and Associates, 301 Chesapeake Drive, Redwood City, CA 94063

1. Introduction

Ion beam induced roughening (or ripple formation) in metals, Si, and a few other materials has been under extensive investigation [1] due to its substantial effect on ultimate depth resolution in Secondary Ion Mass Spectrometry (SIMS). However, the effect is far from being well-understood. Recent needs for accurate ultra-shallow implant profile characterization revitalized interest in the mechanisms leading to the sputter induced roughness [2]. As the benefits of further reduction of the primary beam energy are exhausted, the roughening effect becomes the most important factor limiting depth resolution in SIMS measurements. Recent studies are, however, heavily concentrated on the effect of rapid onset of ripple formation in silicon [3].

Thin films of titanium nitride (TiN) have numerous applications in the processing of integrated circuit (IC) devices. The potential of titanium (Ti) and titanium nitride (TiN) films as an effective diffusion barrier for Cu metallization technology creates an additional interest to the mechanism of the interaction of the TiN/Ti adhesion/barrier layer with the underlying silicon of the transistor and with the metal layer forming the contact to the circuit.

In this study we investigated the topography changes that occur in TiN films and in the underlying Si substrate under oxygen ion bombardment. The influence of various SIMS primary ion bombardment conditions on the crater bottom roughening was investigated using Atomic Force Microscopy (AFM).

2. Experimental

The samples used in this study were CVD titanium nitride films grown on Si (001) substrates. The initial sample has a nominal film thickness of approximately 150Å. For one of the samples the deposition was followed by a plasma treatment to reduce carbon content and shrink the film thickness to 100Å. The films' compositions were characterized by Rutherford Backscattering Spectrometry (RBS) and found to be within ±5% of stiochiometric TiN for both initial and plasma treated samples. Prior to SIMS measurements both samples were characterized by X-ray Photoelectron Spectroscopy (XPS) using a PHI-5500 instrument to determine their chemical compositions. The XPS analysis revealed the presence of titanium oxide at the near surface region (~20Å) of the initial "as grown" film [4]. The "plasma treated" sample, on the other hand, did not show a significant oxidation at the surface.

SIMS studies were performed using a PHI-6650 quadrupole-based mass-spectrometer and IMS-4f CAMECA magnetic sector instrument. All measurements were performed using an O_2^+ primary beam and detecting positive secondary ions. A variety of beam energies (0.5keV to 8keV) and impact angles have been examined to determine their influence on roughness formation. The effect of oxygen flooding has also been studied. Secondary ion intensities of ^{30}Si and ^{50}Ti were recorded from the central 10-30% of the rastered area.

Atomic Force Microscopy (AFM) measurements were performed in a tapping mode using NanoScope III Dimension 5000. Several 2x2 µm areas were scanned on the top surface for each sample for the initial surface roughness. For SIMS craters two locations were scanned near the center and near the edge of the crater and results were averaged.

3. Results and Discussion

Figure 1 shows SIMS depth profiles of the "as grown" (solid curves) and "after treatment" (dashed curves) samples performed at 3keV and 8keV beam impact energy using magnetic sector instrument (figs. 1(a) and (b)) and using 0.5keV bombardment energy at 40° and 60° incidence (figs. 1 (c) and (d)) using the quadrupole instrument. The profiles were normalized to the silicon secondary ion intensity in the substrate.

SIMS profiles for the "as grown" sample performed without oxygen flood (fig. 1 (a, b) solid curves) showed much less surface transient width than "treated" sample (dashed

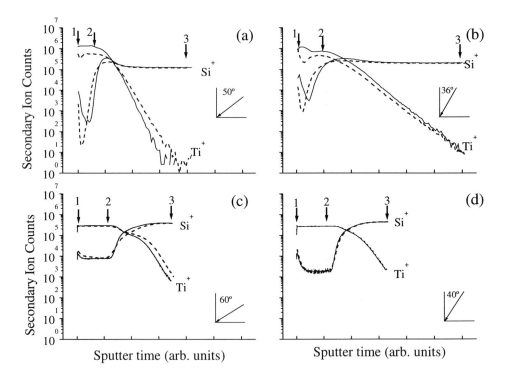

Figure 1. SIMS depth profiles of "as grown" (solid curves) and "after treatment" (dashed curves) samples under various analytical conditions: (a) magnetic sector 3keV net impact energy; (b) magnetic sector 8keV; (c) quadrupole 500eV with oxygen leak at 60° incidence; (d) quadrupole 500eV with oxygen leak at 40° incidence.

curves). This is consistent with the XPS results showing that "as grown" TiN film is oxidized at the surface.

Arrows indicate the positions where ion bombardment was interrupted to perform AFM roughness measurements: top surface (1), middle of the film (2) and in the silicon substrate (3). The roughness measurements are summarized in the Table 1. The surface of the "as grown" TiN film is found to be about 30% rougher than after the plasma treatment.

Table 1. Results of AFM roughness measurements (RMS, Å) of the SIMS crater bottoms.

Impact Energy	Impact Angle	Oxygen Flood	"As grown" sample			"Plasma treated" sample		
			Surface (1)	TiN (2)	Si (3)	Surface (1)	TiN (2)	Si (3)
3.0 keV	50°	No	9.5	6.2	8.4	6.1	11.0	11.5
8.0 keV	36°	No	8.1	4.4	2.8	5.5	13.4	3.9
0.5 keV	60°	Yes	6.1	4.9	6.5	4.6	4.6	7.5
0.5 keV	40°	Yes	6.1	3.2	2.6	4.6	2.4	4.5

The surface topography developed in the middle of the TiN film after 3.0 or 8.0 keV bombardment is found to be significantly less for the "as grown" sample than for the "treated" sample. Furthermore, for the "as grown" TiN film the crater bottom was actually smoother than the initial TiN film surface. On the other hand, the "plasma treated" sample showed rapid ripple formation that was more pronounced for the higher bombardment energy. This dramatic difference in the roughness formation is attributed to the presence of oxide on the surface of "as grown" TiN film.

Unfortunately, the improvement in depth resolution that might be expected from the substantial roughness reduction observed at 8.0 keV is hardly noticeable in the depth profile (fig.1. (a, b)) since the depth resolution is dominated by the increased cascade and recoil mixing at high bombardment energy. The bottom set of SIMS profiles (figs.1(c, d)) was obtained using low primary beam energy (500eV) at different impact angles. Because of the significant reduction in the sputter yield at low bombardment energy the emitting surface is expected to be heavily enriched with oxygen [5]. In addition, oxygen flooding was used to ensure an identical surface condition during ion bombardment for both initially oxidized ("as grown") and unoxidized ("plasma treated") TiN samples. As expected, nearly instantaneous ion yield equilibrium at the surface is observed for both samples. AFM roughness data in Table 1 demonstrates that for this bombardment condition no initial surface oxide is needed to reduce ripples formation. Instead, a smoother crater bottom in the TiN film is observed for both samples.

It should also be noted that both "as grown" and "treated" films appear to have the same thickness under the sub-keV bombardment condition. This is, probably, due to the fact that under oxygen flooding surface oxide layer sputters substantially faster that the remaining nitride film. The profiles for both films look almost identical when primary beam incident angle is decreased (fig.1 (d)). In this case, further reduction in sputter-induced roughening was also observed. However, once the Si substrate is reached, the topography develops faster in the "plasma treated" sample without initial surface oxide (Table 1). Thus even when the analytical conditions ensure complete oxidation of the emitting layer, presence of the thin oxide layer on initial surface plays an important role in resulted sputter roughening.

Therefore, SIMS profiles (fig.1 (d)) obtained using sub-kev ion bombardment at near normal incidence are found to provide the best depth resolution among the investigated analytical conditions.

4. Conclusions

It is shown that initial roughness of the TiN film determines neither the rapidness nor the magnitude of the resulting sputter-induced roughness developed in the TiN film as well as in the Si substrate. Instead, the ripple formation tends to be greatly affected by the ion bombardment conditions as well as the initial chemical state of the film surface. A TiN film with an oxidized surface layer has shown reduced roughness in the middle of the layer by as much as a factor of two (RMS). Furthermore, a film with no initial surface oxide layer has shown a rapid increase in roughness due to ripple formation by a factor of two as compared to the initial surface.

It is found that topography developed in the TiN film has a tendency to be carried over into the Si substrate. This effect was also observed in SIMS depth profiles as a substantial interface broadening. The actual depths at which the AFM data for Si substrate were taken are somewhat different among experiments. Therefore, the roughness data in the Si could not be compared accurately for different analytical conditions. However, the fact that the roughness in the Si substrate is actually less for deeper craters (Table 1, 8.0keV) may indicate that the resulting roughness in Si is determined by the TiN film properties and bombardment condition, and not dependent on the sputter depth.

The effect of oxygen flooding on the roughness development was also studied. Oxygen flooding significantly reduced roughening in the TiN film with no surface oxide. While slowing down the ripple formation in both types of TiN film and improving depth resolution at the TiN/Si interface, oxygen flooding under the conditions used here resulted in greatly increased measured roughness after further sputtering 300-500Å into the Si substrate.

This implies that the initial chemical state of the surface, not its topography plays a determining role in ultimate depth resolution achievable in SIMS measurements of TiN films. The study suggests that extreme caution should be applied when choosing optimal conditions for SIMS profiling of ultra thin TiN films.

Acknowledgment

Authors would like to thank Stephen P. Smith of Charles Evans and Associates and Mauro R. Sardela, Jr. of Materials Research Laboratory of University of Illinois for their helpful comments and discussion.

References

[1] F.A. Stevie and P.M. Kahora, J. Vac. Sci. Technol. A(6), 1988
[2] Z.X. Jiang and P.F.A. Alkemade, J. Vac. Sci. Technol. B16 (4), 1971 (1998)
[3] Proceedings of the Fifth International Workshop on the Measurements and Characterization of Ultra-Shallow Profiles in Semiconductors, Research Triangle Park, NC, USA (1999)
[4] A. Li-Fatou, G.R. Mount and E. Principe, this proceedings
[5] K. Wittmaack, J. Vac. Sci. Technol. B16 (5), 2776 (1998)

A. Benninghoven, P. Bertrand, H.-N. Migeon and H.W. Werner (Editors).
Proceedings of the 12th International Conference on Secondary Ion Mass Spectrometry,
Brussels, Belgium, 5-11 September 1999
© 2000 Elsevier Science B.V. All rights reserved.

QUADRUPOLE-BASED SIMS AS AN ALTERNATIVE TO MAGNETIC SECTOR-BASED SIMS FOR THE PROFILING OF SHALLOW PHOSPHORUS IMPLANTS IN SILICON

I.M. Abdelrehim[1], T.H. Büyüklimanli[1], S.P. Smith[2] and C.W. Magee[1]

[1]Evans East, 104 Windsor Center, Suite 101, East Windsor, New Jersey, 08520, U.S.A.
[2]Charles Evans & Associates, Redwood City, CA 94063, U.S.A.
iabdelrehim@evanseast.com

1. Introduction

Shallow boron and arsenic implants in Si have been investigated with quadrupole-based SIMS for several years using low energy oxygen bombardment under oxygen flood conditions [1-5]. Recently, ultra shallow phosphorus implants have been of interest [6]. These may be used as an n-dopant to form source/drain shallow junctions for deep sub-micron Si device. To date, the accepted method of obtaining profiles of such shallow P in-depth distributions has been based on the use of magnetic sector-based SIMS instruments [7] because of their ability to resolve $^{30}Si^1H$ interference from the desired ^{31}P ions. However, a disadvantage for the majority of magnetic sector instruments is their difficulty to achieve primary beam energies below 3.0 keV. Quadrupole-based SIMS instruments can readily achieve primary ion beam energies less than 3 keV, but their inability to resolve $^{30}Si^1H$ interference from ^{31}P ions was thought to make their use for shallow P depth profiling impractical. In this study, the concerns of SiH interference with P using quadrupole-based SIMS have been carefully addressed. Of equal importance, we have investigated the effect of primary ion energy on the measured shape of low energy P implants in Si.

A novel oxygen leak protocol has been developed to study ultra-low energy phosphorus implants using quadrupole-based SIMS. The P implant energies that are being investigated for this application range from 0.25 keV - 2.0 keV.

2. Instrumental

Quadrupole SIMS analyses were carried out using a Physical Electronics model 6600 instrument. Oxygen bombardment analyses were performed using beam energies ranging from 1.0 keV to 3.0 keV at 60° incidence and 1.0 keV to 1.5 keV at 45° incidence and positive ion detection. The magnetic sector analysis was performed on a double-focusing CAMECA IMS-4f. A 3.0 keV O_2^+ primary ion beam was used during the magnetic sector analysis. During the analyses a constant pressure of high purity oxygen (99.99% pure) was bled into the chamber using a sapphire sealed leak valve until the ^{30}Si signal saturates in order to maximize sensitivity and minimize transient ion yield variations near the surface. The quadrupole conditions used are known [5] to cause roughening of the Si during sputtering. However, the sputter-induced roughening will not affect the degree of SiH interference with P. In addition, any affects of primary ion energy that are observed under these roughening-producing conditions will be even more pronounced in the absence of roughening, which could be obtained if the primary ion angle of incidence would be increased to 45°-50°.

Quantification of the profiles was accomplished using a relative sensitivity factor (RSF) obtained by analyzing a P-doped Si consensus standard with a uniform dopant level of 3.59E19 atoms/cm^3. The precision of the concentrations can be expected to be within 5% as determined by repeat analyses. All quadrupole analyses were performed after the samples were pumped overnight. In addition, all quadrupole SIMS data are background subtracted.

The depth scales were determined by measuring the time required to sputter through a Ge spike in Si, buried 312 Å beneath the surface. The accuracy of the depth scales is within 5-10% at 312 Å.

3. Results and discussion

Figure 1 shows the 0.25 keV and 1.0 keV P as-implanted Si samples with an expected dose of 1E15 atoms/cm^2. The profiles were acquired on both a quadrupole-based and magnetic sector-based SIMS instrument using an O_2^+ beam with a net impact energy of 3.0keV. The profiles obtained for the 0.25 keV and 1.0 keV sample performed on the magnetic sector and quadrupole-based instruments are comparable with the junction depths (X_j) at 5E18 atoms/cm^3 having a 2% difference (Figure 1a and 1b, respectively). However, the measured dose using the quadrupole was 7.40E14 atoms/cm^2 and the magnetic sector was observed at 4.54E14 atoms/cm^2, indicating an error of ~40% between the measurements (Figure 1a). The measured error occurs from a decrease in data point density, as well as the form of data manipulation for the magnetic sector data. The difference between the measured doses decreases to 5% for the 1.0 keV implant when comparing the magnetic sector and the quadrupole-based SIMS data (Figure 1b). Decreased surface P concentrations due to deeper implantation (i.e. 1.0 keV), results in comparable dose determination as opposed to the shallower 0.25 keV implant which has ~30% of the total P dose in the first 10 Å (~2E14 atoms/cm^2).

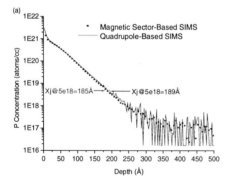 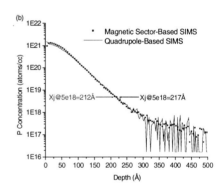

Figure 1. SIMS profiles acquired on a magnetic sector-based instrument and a quadrupole-based instrument. Processed data plots performed on (a) 0.25 keV and (b) 1.0 keV P as-implanted Si wafers.

One important aspect of ultra shallow junction phosphorus (USJ-P) measurements is data point density. It is often overlooked that increased sputter rates, as a result of higher ion energy, can reduce the accuracy of dose measurements for shallow implants. For instance, in Figures 2a-c, the number of data points in the first 10 Å is 16, 5, and 3 for the 1.0 keV, 1.5 keV, and 3.0 keV primary ion energies, respectively, for the same raster size. Using a larger raster easily remedies this problem. However, as expected for all the analyses the junction depth decreases as a function of decreasing primary beam energy resulting from the reduction of atomic mixing. A 2.0 keV P implanted sample (not shown) was analyzed using a 1.0 and 1.5 keV O_2^+ beam under oxygen leak conditions in order to determine whether atomic mixing effects the backside of the profile significantly as seen with the 0.25-1.0 keV P implanted samples (Figure 2). The results show no difference in the backside of the 2.0 keV P implanted profiles when analyzed with a 1.0 keV and 1.5 keV O_2^+ beam.

The issue of $^{30}Si^1H$ interference with ^{31}P was addressed by using a hydrogen-implanted Si standard. During the analysis of the H-implanted standard the H/SiH ratio was determined. Using this ratio the H intensity was subtracted from the P implant in order to remove the $^{30}Si^1H$ interference. The measured dose after the subtraction decreased by 4-6%. Furthermore, the $^{30}Si^1H$ was observed to parallel the ^1H profile when the H-implanted standard was analyzed. Therefore, using ^1H as a guide in tracking the $^{30}Si^1H$, we observe that the ^1H signal drops by a factor of ~10 while the mass 31 signal drops by a factor of 1.5 from the first to the second data point (approx. a 2-3Å depth) in the 0.25 keV - 1.0 keV P implanted samples. Because the H signal drops by a factor of 10 and the mass 31 signal does not, then the mass 31 signal is clearly dominated by phosphorus beyond the first data point. This indicates that the phosphorus concentrations at the surface are so high for the 0.25 keV, 0.55 keV, and 1.0 keV P implanted samples that the $^{30}Si^1H$ interference is inconsequential. Therefore, both the factor used to subtract the SiH interference, calculated from the H-implanted standard, along with the high surface P concentrations (implant dose = 1E15 atoms/cm^2), indicate that the SiH does not interfere with P.

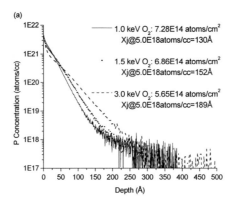

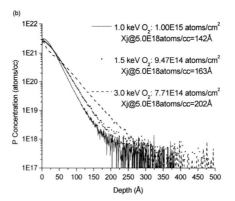

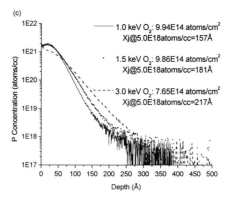

Figure 2. Comparison of various oxygen primary ion beam energies on (a) 0.25 keV (b) 0.55 keV (c) 1.0 keV phosphorus as-implanted Si samples. The analyses were acquired on a quadrupole-based instrument.

Figure 3 shows the profiles acquired at 45° and 60° for the 0.55 keV and 1.0 keV as-implanted P samples. The data shows a slight shift of the 60° profiles towards the surface. This is in agreement with the data in Reference 5 that show the effect of the increased sputter rate in the initial regions of the profile made at 60°. The profiles in Figure 3, however, show that the effect of roughening in the 60° profiles is not significant. Therefore, intercomparison of the data in Figure 2 can be performed since the shift in the profiles (Figures 3a and 3b) resulting from the sputter yield transient is small (~5% difference between the 45° and 60° analyses).

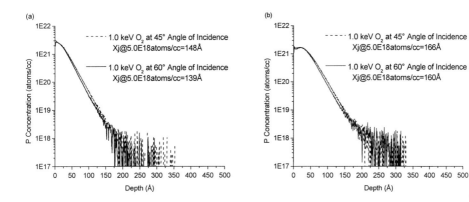

Figure 3. Comparison of 45° and 60° angles of incidence using 1.0 keV primary ion beam energies on (a) 0.55 keV and (b) 1.0 keV phosphorus as-implanted Si samples. The analyses were acquired on a quadrupole-based instrument.

4. Conclusion

It has been shown that the use of quadrupole-based SIMS on samples with high P concentrations is not influenced by $^{30}Si^{1}H$ interference. In addition, we have investigated the effect of primary ion energy on 0.25 keV - 2.0 keV P implants using a primary oxygen beam having a net impact energy of 1.0 keV - 3.0 keV with an impact angle of 60° and 1.0 keV - 1.5 keV with an impact angle of 45° with respect to the surface normal using a quadrupole-based SIMS instrument. Although the 60° conditions cause increased roughening of the Si surface during analysis, this has little effect on the observed results as seen with 45° incidence. For the 1.0 keV P implant energy, the data show that the higher energy O_2^+ beam (1.5 and 3.0 keV) used with quadrupole-based SIMS, as well as with the magnetic sector instrument, causes knock-on resulting in incorrect P junction depths (X_j). By using lower primary beam energies (≤ 1.0 keV) with quadrupole-based SIMS more accurate X_j values are obtained. This would indicate that profiles of low energy P implants in Si should be measured using a quadrupole-based SIMS instrument with primary ion beam energies of 1.0 keV - 1.5keV or less at a 45° angle of incidence with respect to the surface normal.

5. Acknowledgements

Thanks are due to Steven W. Novak of Evans East for his invaluable discussions and assistance with the manuscript.

References

[1] K. Wittmaack and S.F. Corcoran, Proceeding of USJ-97, 1997, 5.1-5.5.
[2] C.W. Magee, S. Smith, G. Mount, H.-J. Gossman, and B. Herner, Proceeding of the XIIth International Conference on Ion Implantation Technology, 1998.
[3] C.W. Magee, D. Jacobson, and H.-J. Gossman, Proceeding of the XIIth International Conference on Ion Implantation Technology, 1998.
[4] K. Wittmaack and S.F. Corcoran, J, Vac. Sci Technol. B, 16 (1998) 272.
[5] C.W. Magee, G.R. Mount, S.P. Smith, B Herner and H-J Gossmann, J. Vac. Sci. Technol. B 16 (6), 1998, p 3099.
[6] J.W. Chow, D.F. Downey, and S.D. Marcus, Proceedings of the Rapid Thermal Processing Conference, 1998.
[7] R. Loesing, G.M. Guryanov, D.P. Griffis, and J.L. Hunter, Proceedings of USJ-99, 1999, 357-364.

A. Benninghoven, P. Bertrand, H.-N. Migeon and H.W. Werner (Editors).
Proceedings of the 12th International Conference on Secondary Ion Mass Spectrometry,
Brussels, Belgium, 5-11 September 1999

661

SUPERIOR DEPTH RESOLUTION OF INDIUM IN (Al, In, Ga) N STRUCTURES

M. Maier, S. Müller and A. Ramakrishnan

Fraunhofer-Institut für Angewandte Festkörperphysik, D-79108 Freiburg, Germany

maier@iaf.fhg.de

1. Introduction

The (Al, Ga, In) N material system has recently found much interest for microelectronic and optoelectronic devices. Heterostructures of this system have been used to fabricate green to ultraviolet light emitting diodes and lasers. SIMS depth profiling has been indispensible for the analysis of the component profiles to characterize the device structure.[1] Depth profiles of fine InGaN/GaN multilayer structures were recorded by SIMS. [2] In this paper, the energy dependence of the depth resolution of In in InGaN/GaN quantum well (QW) structures is investigated taking roughness effects into account. The depth resolution is compared with the corresponding data in the arsenide material system by investigation of InGaAs/GaAs QWs.

2. Experimental

An $In_xGa_{1-x}N/GaN$ single quantum well (SQW) structure and a multiple quantum well (MQW) structure were grown by metal organic chemical vapor deposition (MOCVD) on (0001) sapphire substrates. The In mole fraction is x=0.14. Table 1 shows the nominal SQW structure with data in brackets referring to the layers in the MQW structure that were repeated ten times. The 3.4 nm GaN layer grown at 770°C is essential to obtain a sharp InGaN/GaN interface. An $In_xGa_{1-x}As/GaAs$ MQW structure was grown on (100) oriented undoped semiinsulating LEC GaAs substrate by molecular beam epitaxy (MBE) at a substrate temperature of 480°C. The In mole fraction is x=0.2. The nominal composition is shown in Table 2.

SIMS depth profiles of the structures were measured with an Atomika spectrometer. Cs primary ions with 1.5 to 15 keV energy at an angle of incidence of 45° were used. $InCs^+$ and NCs^+

Table 1
InGaN/GaN QW structure

Layer	thickness (nm)	growth temperature (°C)
GaN	135	1130
GaN	3.4 (3.4)	770
InGaN	0.9 (1.7)	770
GaN	2700	1130
GaN	25	~500
sapphire		

Table 2
InGaAs/GaAs QW structure

layer	thickness (nm)
GaAs	30
InGaAs	16
GaAs	30
InGaAs	13
GaAs	30
InGaAs	10
GaAs	30
InGaAs	5
GaAs	30
InGaAs	2
buffer	

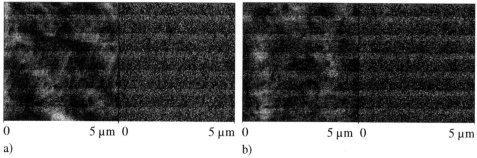

0   5 µm 0   5 µm 0   5 µm 0   5 µm
a)   b)

Fig. 1. AFM micrograph of the InGaN/GaN SQW structure. a) Original surface, b) crater bottom sputtered beyond QW to ~150 nm at 1.5 keV. The left part gives the height information, z range 10 nm. The right part shows the differentiated signal.

(AsCs⁺) secondary ions were chosen for the determination of the In and N (As) reference profiles because MCs⁺ ions show a negligible matrix effect. Calibration of the In profiles was performed by means of the relative sensitivity factors of $InCs^+/NCs^+$ ($InCs^+/AsCs^+$). For depth calibration the crater depth was measured with a surface profilometer yielding an average depth scale. This is justified, since the peak In concentration lowered by ion beam induced broadening is small enough to avoid a significant influence of the In on the erosion rate.

3. Results and Discussion

Fig. 1a and b show atomic force microscope (AFM) images of the surface of the SQW structure determined at the original surface and at the crater bottom of the In depth profile measured at 1.5 keV. The native surface exhibits terraces and a superimposed fine roughness which is only visible in the differentiated image. Almost identical images were determined at the surface of the GaN buffer and the top layer of the MQW structure (both not shown). After ion bombardment the terraces are flattened, whereas the fine roughness is nearly unchanged. Both AFM images and also those taken from craters sputtered at higher energies and to a larger depth far beyond the SQW show a root mean square (RMS) of the roughness of around 0.5 nm. The surface is thus negligibly roughened in the nitride structures. In sharp contrast, in the InGaAs/GaAs structure the RMS is 5 nm at the crater bottom of the 9 keV depth profile though the RMS of the unbombarded surface is 0.25 nm.

Fig. 2 shows the depth profile of the SQW structure determined at an energy of 5 keV. The profile is broadened and the measured In mole fraction is only 3 % as compared to the nominal 14 %. The lines in Fig. 2 represent exponential curve fits at the leading and trailing edges and a Gaussian curve fit to the top decade of the profile. From the curve fits the depth resolution parameters inverse growth slope Λ_g=1.9 nm/decade at the leading edge and inverse decay slope Λ_d=1.5 nm/decade at the trailing edge, following the notation in [3], and full width half maximum FWHM=3.1 nm were derived. The profile is asymmetric. In contrast to usual resolution functions, the profile appears steeper at the trailing than at the leading edge.

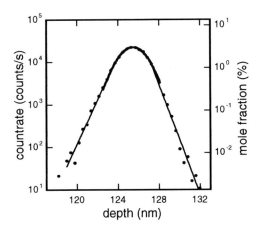

Fig. 2. Indium depth profile of the InGaN/GaN SQW structure. The top order of magnitude is fitted by a Gaussian and the tails by exponential curves.

Fig. 3 shows the depth resolution parameters as a function of the primary ion energy. General trends of the data are indicated by linear fit lines. Λ_g is rather independent of energy and is around 2 nm/decade, a value found for many impurity matrix systems. In contrast to most other systems, Λ_d varies only slightly with energy and is below 2 nm/decade. This remarkably small value is even below Λ_g at small energy. This behavior indicates a large preferential sputtering factor [4] of In in InGaN, possibly correlated with the thermal instability of InN. The FWHM is around 3.5 nm. This rather small width may be caused by the QW width of 0.9 nm and, taking the AFM results into account, the small intrinsic roughness. The width compares with the abruptness of ~2 nm found with a CAMECA instrument at an energy of 1.5 keV (~65°) also using InCs$^+$ secondary ions. [2]

Fig. 4 shows the corresponding behavior of the depth resolution parameters of In in the InGaAs/GaAs QW structure. The FWHM is derived from a Gaussian fit to the 2 nm thick deepest QW (see also Fig. 6). Λ_d was taken from the decay of the deepest QW to the buffer. Both FWHM and Λ_d increase significantly with energy, the FWHM presumably due to surface roughening, and are much larger than the corresponding data of InGaN.

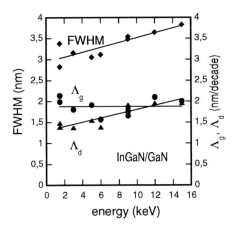

Fig. 3. Depth resolution parameters of In in GaN for Cs primary ions at 45°.

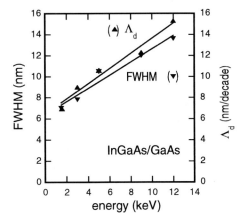

Fig. 4. Depth resolution parameters of In in InGaAs/GaAs QW. Cs primary ions at 45°.

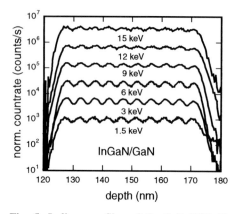

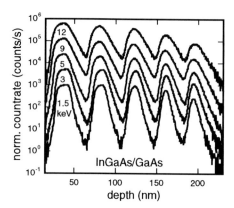

Fig. 5. Indium profiles of the InGaN/GaN MQW structure at different energies.

Fig. 6. Indium profiles of the InGaAs/GaAs MQW structure at different energies.

Figs. 5 and 6, also demonstrate the different depth resolution behaviors. Note the different horizontal scales. The InGaN/GaN MQW with a period of only 5.1 nm is clearly resolved. Additionally, the dynamical range of the oscillating In profile is rather constant up to 6 keV and decreases insignificantly towards 15 keV. In clear contrast, the dynamical range and, correspondingly, the steepness of the In profile in the arsenide decreases significantly with increasing energy. In the InGaN (Fig. 5) the dynamical range does not vary with depth. This indicates the lack of ion beam induced surface roughening in agreement with the AFM results.

4. Summary and conclusions

A significantly different depth resolution behavior has been observed for In in InGaN as compared with InGaAs and most other impurity matrix systems. Whereas the decay parameter at the leading edge behaves similar to other systems, the FWHM and, especially, the decay parameter at the trailing edge are much smaller. In addition, the depth resolution depends only weakly on energy. Consequently, superior depth resolution is achieved such that a MQW structure with a period of only ~5 nm is resolved even at 15 keV. Light emitting devices, which are usually rather thick, can be analyzed conveniently at high energy, i. e. high sputtering rates, without significant loss of depth resolution in the InGaN/GaN QW active region.

References

[1]   Paul K. Chu, Yumin Gao and John W. Erickson, J. Vac. Sci. Technol. B16 (1998) 197.
[2]   M. Koike, S. Yamasaki, S. Nagai, N. Koide, S. Asami, H. Amano and I. Akasaki, Appl. Phys. Lett. 68 (1996) 1403.
[3]   M. G. Dowsett and R. D. Barlow, Anal. Chim. Acta 297 (1994) 253.
[4]   K. Wittmaack in *Practical Surface Analysis*, ed. by D. Briggs and M. P. Seah, Vol. 2, Ion and Neutral Spectroscopy, Wiley, Chichester (1992) p. 142.

A. Benninghoven, P. Bertrand, H.-N. Migeon and H.W. Werner (Editors).
Proceedings of the 12th International Conference on Secondary Ion Mass Spectrometry,
Brussels, Belgium, 5-11 September 1999
© 2000 Elsevier Science B.V. All rights reserved.

665

HIGH ACCURACY SIMS DOPANT PROFILING IN
HETEROJUNCTION SiGe/Si STRUCTURES

Paul K. Chu[1], Salman Mitha[2], and Stephen P. Smith[2]
[1] Dept. of Physics & Materials Science, City University of Hong Kong
83 Tat Chee Avenue, Kowloon, Hong Kong
[2] Charles Evans & Associates
301 Chesapeake Drive, Redwood City, CA 94063, USA

1. Introduction

$Si_{1-x}Ge_x$ heterostructures are found in high-speed and high-frequency microelectronics devices such as heterojunction bipolar transistors (HBT), modulation-doped heterojunction field effect transistors (MODFETs) with high mobility [1]. Typical high-performance SiGe/Si heterostructure devices employ a $Si_{1-x}Ge_x$ alloy layer with thickness below 100 nm and dopant concentrations in the range of 10^{16} to 10^{20} atoms/cm^3. The performance of these devices requires accurate positioning of the dopants with respect to the alloy layers. However, due to dopant segregation during epitaxial growth and other poorly understood dopant incorporation issues that can adversely affect device quality and yield, the empirical determination of the dopant profiles is crucial to device engineering and reliability diagnosis.

Empirical investigation of these structures requires an analytical technique that offers both high depth resolution and sensitivity. Secondary ion mass spectrometry (SIMS) is a widely accepted depth profiling technique for dopants. During a typical SIMS analysis, either oxygen or cesium ion bombardment is used to optimize the secondary ion yields of electropositive (p-type) dopants or electronegative (n-type) dopants. Hence, the dopants are usually measured individually under different conditions [2]. The profiles are then quantified using implant standards and subsequently reconstructed by overlaying the results from the separate analyses. Typically, a matrix marker is used to align the interface. However, due to the differences in sputtering rates and depth resolution under oxygen and cesium ion bombardment, accurate alignment of the p-type and n-type dopants with respect to the alloyed layer is difficult.

In this work, we present a depth profiling technique using SIMS by which boron (p-type dopant), phosphorus (n-type dopant), and germanium (matrix or interface marker) can be monitored simultaneously. A thin $Si_{1-x}Ge_x$ epitaxial film is analyzed using a low energy oxygen ion beam and oxygen backfill. We show that under these conditions, it is possible to achieve excellent depth resolution and detection limits for dopants at the same time. Detection limits on the order of 10^{15} atoms/cm^3 can be achieved for both B and P while simultaneously aligning the dopant profiles relative to the Ge profile with an accuracy of better than 5 nm.

2. Experimental

The analysis was conducted using a CAMECA IMS-4f microanalyzer. The primary O_2^+ primary ions were mass filtered and accelerated to a voltage of 7.5 kV. The $Si_{1-x}Ge_x$/Si sample was biased to +4.5 kV, and so the relative impact energy was 3 kV. Hence, the net bombarding energy of each oxygen particle was 1.5 keV. To remove the surface transient and other related matrix effects, an oxygen leak was used. The oxygen backfill pressure was adjusted until the matrix ion yield was flat at the onset of the depth profile. The use of the oxygen leak also enhanced the positive ion yields of $^{11}B^+$ and $^{31}P^+$, the species monitored in the depth profile [3]. $^{72}Ge^+$ was measured simultaneously to delineate the structure and determine the depth resolution. High mass resolution conditions were employed to eliminate mass interferences such as $^{30}Si^1H^+$ for $^{31}P^+$. The instrumental transmission was maximized. The oxygen ion beam was rastered to an area of 500 μm x 500 μm while the secondary ion signals were acquired from a 400 μm x 400 μm region in the center of the crater using the dynamic transfer optics. As the oxygen ion beam was tightly focused, the crater wall as observed by stylus profilometric measurement was quite steep. No depth resolution degradation due to secondary ions emanating from crater walls and crater edges was observed.

3. Results and discussion

One of the advantages of the technique is that all three elements, B, P, and Ge, are monitored simultaneously using one set of instrumental conditions. Accurate dopant profile alignment can thus be assured. In addition, under the oxygen leak environment, the ion yield of phosphorus can be substantially improved. Fig. 1 depicts the depth profiles of a $Si_{1-x}Ge_x$/Si heterostructure. The B and P profiles are referenced to the left-hand-side concentration scale whereas the Ge composition is plotted versus the right-hand-side atomic % axis. Quantification of the B and P profiles is accomplished by relative sensitivity factors derived from reference implants in SiGe alloy standards. The relationship between the relative sensitivity factors and Si:Ge ratios has been investigated in prior studies [4-6]. The Ge concentration was determined from a separate analysis employing the $CsGe^+$ ion which has been shown to exhibit much less matrix dependence [7]. No RBS (Rutherford backscattering spectrometry) cross referencing is conducted here for the $Si_{1-x}Ge_x$ is quite thin and the continuously varying Ge content in the film makes accurate RBS analysis quite difficult.

The results demonstrate the excellent detection limit of phosphorus under the oxygen leak, high mass resolution conditions. As the typical dopant concentration in SiGe devices ranges from 10^{16} to 10^{20} atoms/cm^3, the detection limits achieved using this experimental protocol is acceptable, thereby obviating the need for a separate analysis for phosphorus using cesium ion bombardment. The oxygen leak also reduces the surface transient effects significantly, and the profile is therefore accurate from the beginning to the end.

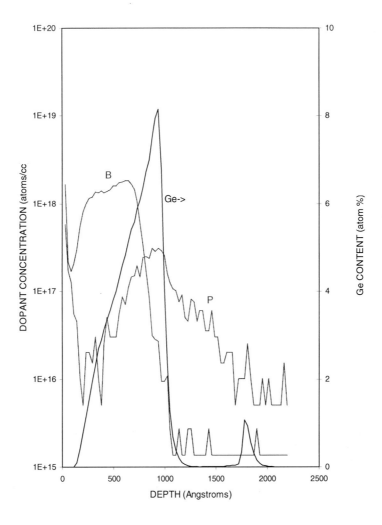

Fig. 1: High sensitivity and depth resolution depth profile of $Si_{1-x}Ge_x/Si$ heterostructure.

The use of low energy primary ion bombardment yields excellent depth resolution, and judging from the trailing edge of the Ge profile, the depth resolution is determined to be better than 5 nm and perhaps as good as a couple of nm. The intersection of the B and P profiles indicates the location of the metallurgical p-n junction. It can also be observed that for this sample, the boron is retained in the SiGe alloy layer whereas phosphorus has diffused into the silicon substrate.

668

In order to assess the day-to-day and instrument-to-instrument variation of the measurement protocol, the sample was analyzed four times using two different CAMECA IMS-4f instruments. The resulting profiles overlay practically on top of each other demonstrating excellent reproducibility.

4. Conclusion

Using a carefully chosen set of conditions incorporating low energy oxygen ion bombardment, high mass resolution, and oxygen leak, boron (p-type dopant), phosphorus (n-type dopant), and germanium (matrix marker) can be profiled simultaneously in a $Si_{1-x}Ge_x$ epitaxial heterostructure with excellent sensitivity and depth resolution. The B and P detection limits are on the order of 10^{15} atoms/cm^3, and the depth resolution is better than 5 nm. The metallurgical junction depth relative to the Ge alloy layer can thus be accurately determined. The analytical protocol is also applicable to other heterostructures such as $Si_{1-x}C_x$ and $Si_xGe_yC_{1-x-y}$.

References
[1] S. C. Jain, *Germanium-Silicon Strained Layers and Heterostructures*, Academic Press, Boston, London (1994).
[2] P. K. Chu, Mat. Chem. Phys., **38**, 203 (1994).
[3] D. Kruger, R. Kurps, E. Bugiel, F. Herzel, and H.P. Zeindl, SIMS X Proceedings, A. Benninghoven, B. Hagenhoff, H. W. Werner (Eds.), John Wiley & Sons, England, 499 (1997).
[4] Vriezema, et al., J. Vac. Sci. Technol. A, **9**, 2402 (1991).
[5] G. Prudon, J. C. dupuy, M. Bonneau, L. Vandroux, C. Dubois, B. Gautier, J. P. Vallard, J. Delmas, P. Warren, and D. Dutartre, SIMS X Proceedings, A. Benninghoven, B. Hagenhoff, H. W. Werner, John Wiley & Sons, England, 689 (1997).
[6] J. P. Newey, D. J. Robbins, and D. Wallis, SIMS XI Proceedings, G. Gillen, R. Lareau, F. Stevie, and J. Bennett (Eds.), 979 (1998).
[7] Y. Gao, J. Appl. Phys., **64**, 3760 (1988).

A. Benninghoven, P. Bertrand, H.-N. Migeon and H.W. Werner (Editors).
Proceedings of the 12th International Conference on Secondary Ion Mass Spectrometry,
Brussels, Belgium, 5-11 September 1999
© 2000 Elsevier Science B.V. All rights reserved.

DETERMINATION OF SURFACE HYDROGEN IN PLASMA IMMERSION IMPLANTED SILICON

Paul K. Chu [1] and Larry X. Wang [2]
[1] Dept. of Physics & Materials Science, City University of Hong Kong
83 Tat Chee Avenue, Kowloon, Hong Kong
[2] Charles Evans & Associates
301 Chesapeake Drive, Redwood City, CA 94063, USA

1. Introduction

Silicon-on-insulator (SOI) is a desirable substrate to fabricate low power, low voltage microelectronics devices [1,2]. Bruel, et al. recently demonstrated that SOI wafers could be produced using a layer transfer technique encompassing hydrogen implantation, wafer bonding, and cleavage [3], and this process has attracted much attention [4,5]. Plasma immersion ion implantation (PIII) has been proposed to be an alternative to conventional beam-line ion implantation in this ion-cut process, especially for thin SOI substrates used in fully depleted CMOS (complementary metal oxide semiconductor) devices [6-10].

In hydrogen PIII, the entire silicon wafer is immersed in a plasma and biased to a pulsing negative high voltage to attain ion implantation. Our previous studies have shown that the amount and distribution of the adsorbed hydrogen affects the yield of the ion-cut method [11-12]. The surface hydrogen can deteriorate the bonding strength, cracked surface uniformity, as well as interfacial quality. If the surface hydrogen concentration is high, it can also impede wafer bonding thereby leaving patches of voids on the SOI or acceptor wafer. Hence, it is important to understand the mechanism of surface hydrogen incorporation. As the entire wafer is immersed in a hydrogen plasma during PIII, hydrogen can adsorb onto the wafer surface during the "off-cycle" of the voltage pulse and subsequently diffuse or can be knocked into the substrate by ion mixing. Another origin of surface hydrogen is the plasma sheath expansion at the beginning of each pulse. When a negative pulse is applied to the wafer, electrons are repelled on the time scale of 10^{-10} s and a plasma sheath is formed. The sheath continues to expand and ions are brought in motion on the time scale of 10^{-7} s. The time to achieve a static Child law sheath state is on the order of 10 μs or longer. Because the sheath propagation is much slower than the ion movement, this period can be described by quasi-static Child law [13]. Although the ions in the quasi-static Child law sheath are implanted at a voltage almost equal to the applied voltage, the ions in the matrix sheath are implanted with lower energy. The lowest energy can be near zero if the initial position of the hydrogen ion is just above the wafer at the beginning of the pulse.

Thus, it is important that this surface hydrogen component be determined accurately to match modeling results. As the concentration of surface hydrogen is quite large (higher than 1×10^{22} atoms/cm^3), the sputtering rate in the surface region will likely be different that that in the bulk of the silicon wafer. In this work, we performed a systematic study on the variation on the sputtering rate in this hydrogen-rich region using high resolution SIMS and crater depth measurement. The correlation between surface hydrogen and the blistering efficiency is also discussed.

2. Experimental

The PIII experiments were conducted in a custom designed PIII machine [14,15] employing five different pulse durations ranging from 5μs to 100μs. P-type, 100-mm, 10-20 Ω-cm, <100> silicon wafers were implanted. The implantation voltage was 20kV. In order to keep the amount of adsorbed hydrogen constant, the implantation time was the same for all samples (1 hour). The pulsing frequency for each run was adjusted to maintain the same integrated current or dose for all samples. The implantation dose was 5×10^{16} atoms/cm^2. After implantation, the samples were annealed at 600°C for 5 minutes. The samples were measured for surface hydrogen by high depth resolution SIMS using a cesium ion beam and a CAMECA IMS-4F. The beam current was 5nA and it was rastered to 70μm. In order to calculate the exact sputtering rates, profiles were conducted to a certain time and the craters were measured by high resolution stylus profilometry and atomic force microscopy.

3. Results and discussion

Our model predicts that a longer pulse width decreases the surface hydrogen to implanted hydrogen ratio [12]. As a proof, we performed a blistering experiment on five wafers implanted using pulsing durations from 5μs to 100μs. When the wafer is heated, the implanted hydrogen coalesce into bubbles or microcavities along the projected range [11]. In the absence of a surface stiffener such as a bonded wafer, the internal pressure build-up causes the surface to blister. The bubble density and size give a quick, albeit indirect, measure of the implanted hydrogen distribution as our previous experiments indicate that a more mono-energetic implant (i.e. more compact) distribution gives rise to denser and bigger bubbles at the same implantation dose. Our results indeed show that blistering is more efficient when the pulse width is longer [12]. The experimental observation is consistent with the cracking temperature observed for the bonded structures. The samples implanted employing 30μs and 60μs pulses were bonded to a silicon wafer with a pre-grown 150nm thermal oxide layer. The bonded structures were then annealed to achieve layer transfer. The cracking temperature could be identified by a clear sound when the structure cleaves. The cracking temperature was 600°C and 500°C for the 30μs and 60μs samples, respectively. The lower cracking temperature of the 60μs sample confirms its more mono-energetic hydrogen distribution.

In order to fit the experimental results to our model, we need to determine the accurate in-depth distribution of this surface hydrogen component. We chose the 60μs sample for this detailed study. Craters were created for different sputtering time and measured. The exact sputtering rate of each region is determined empirically by difference. Table 1 displays the sputtering time of each crater, the measured crater depth, and the sputtering rate of the region (for example, the sputtering rate for 32s represents that between 25s and 32s). To minimize statistical error due to the shallowness of the craters, each crater was measured 8 to 10 times to generate an average.

Table 1: Sputtering rates at different depths in the hydrogen PIII sample

Sputtering Time (s)	Measured Crater Depth (A)	Sputtering Rate (A/s)
15	57	3.7
18	78	4.3
18	74	4.1
24	99	4.1
24	94	3.9
32	166	5.2
40	197	4.9
40	201	5.0
48	242	5.0
56	268	4.8
60	306	5.1
64	328	5.1
72	390	5.2
80	402	5.1
100	553	5.5
100	547	5.5
120	640	5.3
140	767	5.5
150	797	5.3
160	872	5.5
180	980	5.5
200	1095	5.5

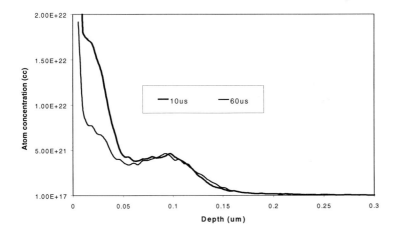

Fig. 1: SIMS depth profiles of the10μs and 60μs pulse width samples.

The calculated sputtering rate is observed to be slower in the near surface region when the hydrogen concentration is highest. Using the empirical results, the depth scale of the SIMS profile can be adjusted. Fig. 1 depicts the adjusted depth profiles of the 10μs and 60μs samples. The results unequivocally illustrate that a higher surface hydrogen component is unfavorable to the ion-cut technique.

4. Conclusion

The sputtering rate in the presence of a large concentration of implanted hydrogen is slower. Our empirical results can be used to calibrate the exact depth scale of the SIMS depth profile. The correction is needed for accurate modeling of the hydrogen plasma immersion ion implantation and ion-cut method.

Acknowledgments

The work was supported by City University of Hong Kong Strategic Research Grants 7000964 and Hong Kong Research Grants Council Earmarked Grants 9040332 and 9040344.

References:

[1]   S. Cristoloveanu and S. S. Li, in "Electrical characterization of silicon-on-Insulator materials and devices", Kluwer Academic Publishers, Boston, 1995.
[2]   J. P. Colinge, in "Silicon-on-insulator technology: materials to VLSI, 2nd Edition", Kluwer, Boston, 1997.
[3]   M. Bruel, B. Aspar, B. Charlet, C. Maleville, T. Poumeyrol, A. Soubie, A. J. Auberton-Herve, J. M. Lamure, T. Barge, F. Metral, and S. Trucchi, Proc. IEEE Int. SOI Conf., p. 178, Tucson, Arizona, 1995.
[4]   Q. Y. Tong, T. H. Lee, K. Gutiahr, S. Hopfe, and U. Gosele, Appl. Phys. Lett., 70, 1390 (1997).
[5]   L. B. Freund, Appl. Phys. Lett., 70, 3519 (1997).
[6]   J. R. Conrad, J. L. Radtke, R. A. Dodd, F. J. Worzala, N. C. Tran, J. Appl. Phys., 62, [4591 (1987).
[7]   P. K. Chu, S. Qin, C. Chan, N. W. Cheung, and L. A. Larson, Mat. Sci. Eng.: Reports, R17, 207 (1996).
[8]   X. Lu, N. W. Cheung, M. D. Strathman, P. K. Chu, and B. Doyle, Appl. Phys. Lett., 71, 1804 (1997).
[9]   X. Lu, S. S. K. Iyer, C. Hu, N. W. Cheung, J. Min, Z. Fan, and P. K. Chu, Appl. Phys. Lett., 71, 2767 (1997).
[10] Z. Fan, "SOI synthesis by plasma immersion ion implantation", PhD Thesis, City University of Hong Kong, Hong Kong, 1998.
[11] P. K. Chu and N. W. Cheung, Mat. Chem. Phys., 57, 1 (1998).
[12] Z. N. Fan, X. C. Zeng, and P. K. Chu, IEEE Trans. Plasma Sci (April 2000).
[13] M. A. Lieberman, J. Appl. Phys., 66, 2926 (1989).
[14] P. K. Chu, S. Qin, C. Chan, N. W. Cheung, and P. K. Ko, IEEE Trans. Plasma Sci., 26(6), 79 (1998).
[15] Z. Fan, Q. Chen, P. K. Chu, and C. Chan, IEEE Trans. Plasma Sci., 26(6), 1661 (1998).

A. Benninghoven, P. Bertrand, H.-N. Migeon and H.W. Werner (Editors).
Proceedings of the 12th International Conference on Secondary Ion Mass Spectrometry,
Brussels, Belgium, 5-11 September 1999
© 2000 Elsevier Science B.V. All rights reserved.

STRUCTURAL TRANSFORMATIONS IN Si AND Si_xGe_{1-x}
DURING SPUTTERING WITH OXYGEN

A.A. Efremov[a], D.Krüger[b], G.Ph. Romanova[a]

[a]Institute of Semiconductor Physics, NAS of Ukraine,
45 Pr. Nauki, 252028 Kiev, Ukraine
E-mail: Lvg@Div9.Semicond.Kiev.UA

[b]Institute for Semiconductor Physics, Frankfurt/Oder, Germany
E-mail: Kruger@IHP-Ffo.DE

1. Introduction

Sputtering of Si and $Si_{1-x}Ge_x$ with oxygen during SIMS measurements is widely used [1]. The most interesting effects are observed at the initial transient stage of sputtering, when both the structure and composition of subsurface layer change from pure semiconductor crystalline matrix to amorphous (sub)oxided film. For silicon we have observed different kinetics for different $Si_nO_m^+$ SI and too long a transient time in comparison with simplest estimations. For $Si_{1-x}Ge_x$ an interesting anomaly in transient behavior of Ge^+ secondary ion yield under near normal incidence of primary oxygen beam has been observed [2]. The effect consists in the appearance (instead of a monotonous increase) of a local minimum on the time dependence of the Ge^+ yield. Besides the position of this minimum is proportional to the projected range of primary ions R_p. In the present paper we consider the effects mentioned in the framework of some unified approach based on computer simulations of oxygen incorporation into sputtered matrix, calculations of the Short-Range Order (SRO) statistics on the surface and modelling of secondary ions formation using the conception of precursors [3]. It will be shown that the secondary ion yield kinetics for Si and SiGe, in particular its anomalous behavior may be successfully explained in the framework of the proposed model and good accordance with the experiment is achieved.

2. Experiments

The ion bombardments of silicon were carried out with mass-filtered O_2^+ primary ions at energy 9 keV at near normal incidence in the SIMS ion microprobe ATOMIKA 6500. So we were able to control in situ the situation at the surface using SIMS measurements. A wide spectrum of secondary ions ($^{30}Si^+$, $^{45}[SiO]^+$, $^{16}O^+$, $^{60}[SiO_2]^+$, $^{76}[Si_2O]^+$, $^{88}[Si_2O_2]^+$, $^{100}[Si_3O]^+$, $^{112}[Si_4]^+$) at the initial stages of near normal $O_2^+ \rightarrow$ Si sputtering was studied. In Fig. 1 the respective $^{60}[SiO_2]^+$ yield kinetics is presented as an example. As for $O_2^+ \rightarrow Si_{1-x}Ge_x$ bombardment we shall analyse quantitatively already published results obtained by U. Zastrow, et al [2] and analyse both peculiarities of transient Ge^+ yield kinetics mentioned.

3. Outline of the physical processes in the subsurface region under low energy oxygen bombardment and approaches

In the case of low energy oxygen implantation and sputtering not only chemical reaction between silicon and oxygen should be taken into account. Such additional processes as *ion-beam mixing* and *atomic relocation* become important. For SiO_x films sputtering the respective models for ion beam induced SRO statistics transformation in the steady-sate sputtering mode were proposed and studied in [4-6]. It should be emphasized also that due to the stress induced phase separation oxygen incorporation into crystalline silicon will proceed via SiO_2 nucleation rather than via random bonding SiO_x phase formation. On the contrary, after ion-beam induced amorphization of subsurface layer just the latter process becomes most probable with quite another kinetics of oxygen accumulation. In the case of $O_2^+ \rightarrow Si_{1-x}Ge_x$ sputtering the situation is more complicate then above. Here two types of suboxides SiO and GeO may be formed at the initial stage of oxygen accumulation. Further they will chemicaly interact not only with incoming oxygen but also each with other due to their different affinity to oxygen [8].

4. Choice of the approaches for the computer simulations of ion beam induced processes and models

In order to handle the processes outlined above we have written several versions of codes **"OXYBEAM"**, and **"SiGeOX"** which consider the problem of ion beam induced new phase formation in the framework of *the phenomenological quasichemical description*. The code, based on mathematical technique of finite differences, calculates the solution of a set of differential equations describing the diffusion, surface recession due to sputtering and reactions for all components of a system which behaviour is important for the process studied. In order to describe the evolution of SRO statistics in the case of $O_2^+ \rightarrow Si$ sputtering we have considered behaviour of the system consisting of tetrahedral $Si\text{-}Si_{4-p}O_p$ [4,5] configurations (p=0,1,2,3,4), defects and oxygen. After some preliminar simulations and tests we have taken into account such physical processes (besides diffusion, and sputtering) as (i) the reactions between implanted oxygen and different short-range order configurations:

$Si\text{-}Si_{4-p}O_p + O \rightarrow Si\text{-}Si_{4-p-1} O_{p+1}$ (ii) ion beam mixing and relocaton: $Si\text{-}Si_{4-p}O_p$ +Displacement $\rightarrow Si\text{-}Si_{4-p+1} O_{p-1} + O$ (iii) phase separation: $2Si\text{-}Si_{4-p} O_p \rightarrow Si\text{-}Si_{4-p-1}$ $O_{p+1} + Si\text{-}Si_{4-p+1} O_{p-1}$ The detailed discussion of rate constants for (i)-(iii) reactions will be done elsewhere [7]. In the case of $O_2^+ \rightarrow Si_{1-x}Ge_x$ sputtering we have considered more crude model describing the behaviour of suboxides SiO, GeO and complete oxides SiO_2, GeO_2 in the presence of implanted oxygen and displacements.

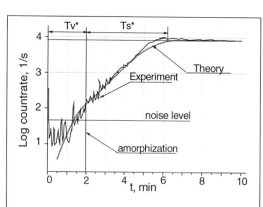

Fig.1 SiO_2^+ yield kinetics. In calculations it is assumed that $A_0: A_1 A_2: A_3: A_4 = 0:1:10:10:100$ in eq.(4)

5. Discussion

According to the conception of *precursors* [3-6] it was assumed that mechanism of SI formation is determined only by the local atomic arrangement (or SRO) of an emitted particle. We calculated the observed yields as the sum of contributions from different atomic configurations [4,5]: $Y^+(t) = \Sigma_p A_p W_p(z, t)|_{z=0}$ Here $W_p(z, t)|_{z=0}$ is a statistical weight of p-th configuration on the surface *under sputtering,* A_p is the partial yield i.e. the contribution of the p-th local atomic configuration (*precursor*) or oxygen containing phase to the total observed one. The relative values A_p were estimated from data processing for SiO_x films. The best accordance with the experiment for several different SI have been achieved when following suppositions were assumed:

$O_2^+ \rightarrow Si$ (i) Up to dose of Si amorphization oxygen atoms are incorporated through the formation of small SiO_2 inclusions. The excess oxygen in a form of weakly bonded interstitials quickly leaves the subsurface layer due to out-diffusion. (ii) After amorphization the solubility of oxygen increased sufficiently and amorphous SiO_x layer (obeying by random bonding model) with increasing x begins to form. The SiO_2 inclusions grown at previous stage are dissolved due to the ion beam mixing. As a result quick exponential ramp up of $Si_nO_m^+$ (m>n) is realized (Fig.1). Good accordance between theory and experiment is observed both for the slope of transient yield kinetics (within about 1.5-2 order of magnitude) and for characteristic time of transient stage. At the end of transient stage SiO_2^+ yield is about 10%

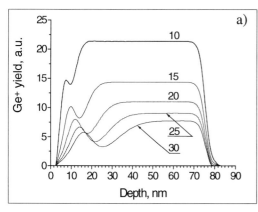

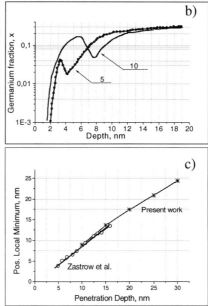

Fig. 2. Ge$^+$ SI yield kinetics at different penetration depth R_p: (a) simulation in the present work; (b)Experiment from [2]. Values on the curves correspond to R_p for primary ions (nm); (c) Comparison of theoretical and experimental [2] dependences "Local minimum position" vs. "Penetration depth"

higher then predicted. The last may be caused by enhancing role of dangling bonds $\equiv$Si-O...-Si$\equiv$ (i.e. some lack of oxygen in SiO$_x$ phase) in formation of large secondary Si$_n$O$_m^+$ clusters. On the other hand, the yield of SI Si$^+$ being not so sensitive to local content of oxygen increase more slowly obeying similar to 1-exp(-t/τ) law. (iii) When oxygen concentration achieves the limit maximum value ~J$_p$/V$_s$, where J$_p$ is a primary beam density and V$_s$ is a sputtering rate such SI as Si$^+$, SiO$^+$, SiO$^+_2$ etc. achieve the steady state but Si$_4^+$ SI yield drops drastically.

$O_2^+ \rightarrow Si_{1-x}Ge_x$ In order to simulate only the Ge$^+$ yield a rather simple model for phase transformations proves to be enough: The important assumption is that Ge$^+$ yield (as well as Si$^+$ from SiO$_x$) depends not only on germanium content but on *oxygen in the local atomic environment of emitted atom*. (i) At the initial stage suboxides SiO and GeO are formed, besides SiO content is sufficiently higher than GeO. (ii) More metastable and active SiO [8] being sufficiently excessive (x<0.2) reduces small quantity of GeO to pure germanium: SiO + GeO $\rightarrow$ SiO$_2$ + Ge. This is the reason *for Ge$^+$ yield drop.* (iii) After this point, due to further oxygen accumulation, GeO and Ge are oxidated and Ge$^+$ yield increases again. Simultaneously SiO transforms to complete oxide and at the later stage of bombardment the previous reaction becomes impossible. Fig. 2,a shows the dependence of yield kinetics on the R$_p$ of primary ions. Simulations reproduce well the experimental kinetics (Fig. 2,b), as well as the relation between local minimum position and R$_p$ (Fig.2,c) [2].

6. Conclusion

Computer modeling is used to describe the secondary ions kinetics and to simulate the *in situ* phase and compositional changes in subsurface silicon region. The model takes into account a detailed mechanism of oxidation and allows us to obtain the oxides and suboxides statistics evolution under the Si and Si$_{1-x-y}$Ge$_x$ (x<0.2) surface. Such processes as ion beam mixing, diffusion, sputtering and phase segregation are considered in the framework of phenomenological quasi chemical approach. The model predicts the important role of chemical interaction between suboxides and reproduce some key peculiarities of the experiment. The results presented above allow us to conclude that mechanisms based on oxygen segregation in Si$_{1-x-y}$Ge$_x$O$_y$ for O$_2^+$ $\rightarrow$Si$_{1-x}$Ge$_x$ system and amorphisation of silicon for O$_2^+$ $\rightarrow$Si one give reasonable explanation of yield kinetics behavior. Further development of the former model in direction of taking into account ion-beam induced amorphisation of Si$_{1-x}$Ge$_x$, and phase separation in SiO$_y$ and GeO$_z$ is worthwhile.

References

[1] K. Wittmaak, in Quantitative microbeam analysis (ed by A.G. Fitzgerald et al) Edinburh, Institute of Physics Publ. ltd (1993).
[2] U. Zastrow, L. Vescan, R. Butz, K. Schmidt, and Diekker. SIMS-IX, Proceeding (1993)702.
[3] A. Benninghoven, SIMS-III, Proceedings (1981)438.
[4] V.G. Litovchenko, A.A. Efremov, and G.Ph Romanova, SIMS-X Proceeding (1996) 701.
[5] V.G. Litovchenko, A.A. Efremov, and G.Ph. Romanova, SIMS-X, Proceeding,(1996) 439.
[6] G.Ph. Romanova, A.A. Efremov, and P.I. Didenko, SIMS-VI, Proceeding (1988) 335.
[7] A.A. Efremov and D. Kruger, to be published.
[8] CRC Handbook of Chemistry and Physics, 58th Edition, CRC Press (1978) F222

A. Benninghoven, P. Bertrand, H.-N. Migeon and H.W. Werner (Editors).
Proceedings of the 12th International Conference on Secondary Ion Mass Spectrometry,
Brussels, Belgium, 5-11 September 1999

677

DEPTHS AND LOCAL ANALYSIS OF IMPURITIES IN GALLIUM NITRIDE AT THE SILICON CARBIDE SUBSTRATE

A.P.Kovarsky, A.E.Nikolaev[1], M.A.Jagovkina

Regional Analytical Center "Mekhanobr-Analyt", Surface Diagnostic Lab.,
8a, 21 liniya V.O., St. Petersburg, 199026 Russia.
[1]Ioffe Physico-Technical Institute of the RAS, St.Petersburg, 194021 Russia.

1. Introduction

Gallium nitride is a semiconductor material with application to high power transistors and optoelectronics devices. Methods of GaN films fabrication include hydride vapor phase epitaxy (HVPE) and metal organic chemical vapor deposition (MOCVD) [1]. The gaseous impurities introduce into films during the growth process to determine the high background carrier concentration of GaN layers [2,3]. This problem is one of tasks of the work.

It is known that GaN films have intrinsic stresses because of lack of a suitable substrate [4]. The reason for these stresses is the second task of the work.

2. Experimental

The analyzed samples were prepared as ascribed in the references [5,6]. The support was a silicon carbide in all cases. The determination of the background concentration was make with help implantation the gaseous impurities in the same samples. The dose and the energy of implantation were H - 50keV, 3e15cm^{-2}; C - 200keV, 3e15cm^{-2}; O - 200keV, 3e15cm^{-2} [7].

The measurements were carried out by secondary ion mass spectrometry (CAMECA IMS4f instrument). The electronegative impurities such as H,C,O and the them complexes ions was measured with Cs$^+$ primary beam and negative secondary ions. The same regime was used for the ion image analyses of these elements. The primary ion current was 120 nA, the raster - 250*250μ^2, the energy - 14,5 keV, a diameter of the analyzing area is 60μ (in-depth analysis) and 150μ (imaging analysis).

3.Results and discussion

The high level of the detection limit of gaseous impurities can have volume and surface origin. The analyzing impurity implantation into the sample allows determination of the detection limit value (equal to the background signal). But the origin of this value (volume or surface) is unknown. The high detection limit of gaseous impurities for the GaN samples prepared by HVPE and MOCVD was found to be about 10^{19} at.cm^{-3}. The implanted carbon depth profile in a GaN film prepared by the MOCVD method is shown in Fig.1. The steady-state level of analytical signal is appropriate to the carbon detection limit in these samples. In this case an analytical signal was ^{26}CN$^-$ whose ion yield is higher than ^{12}C$^-$ by a factor of 10. The ion image at 26 amu "rays" is shown as inset in Fig.1. This picture has been measured at a depth equal to ten times the range straggling. As illustrated (inset in Fig.1) the impurity is concentrated at block boundaries and the high detection limit is a result of the volume pollution of the GaN film.

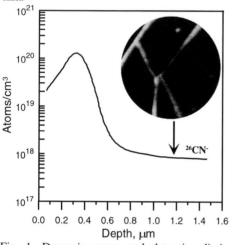

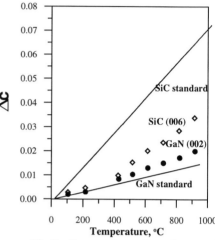

Fig. 1. Dynamic range and detection limit of carbon impurity implanted into GaN. Ion image is inclusions of carbon in analyzed sample on "tail" of the implanted profile.

Fig.2. Temperature dependence of lattice parameter deviation.

The same pattern of the concentration of H and O impurities is observed at the same site of the sample (don't show). This means that they are also volume impurities. It is conceivable that the true values of the background concentration of gaseous impurities is uncertain, because the influence of the ion yield superposition is unknown.

Accumulation of impurities at block boundaries can accounts for a intrinsic stress in gallium nitride films [iii]. We are investigated the influence of thermal treating of a HVPE-grown GaN sample. Using high temperature (20-1000° C) X-ray diffraction in air the changing of the C-axis parameter for <002> GaN and <006> SiC substrate was determinate. As seen in Fig.2 the dependence of the C-parameter on temperature has disruption at $300 \pm 50°C$. This means that the reflections go away from their positions. Microstress relieving may be responsible for this phenomenon.

The same samples were studied by SIMS ion imaging mode before and after annealing at 300°C. Like the MOCVD-grown samples, these have line defects (block boundaries) which are decorated by segregated impurities such as H, C and O. Fig.3 presents the ion images of the same sample before (Fig.3a,b,c) and after (Fig.3d,e,f) annealing at 300°C (from different sites on the sample). The ion images in 'rays' ^1H, $^{12}C^-$, $^{16}O^-$, $^{24}C_2^-$ are identically with that in fig.3a and fig.3d ($^{26}CN^-$) and don't show. The comparison of Fig.3a and Fig.3b shows the difference of the block boundaries decoration: at low part Fig.3b no line defect, which can be seen on Fig.3a. We attribute ion image in 42 amu 'rays' as CNO but not SiN, because the $^{28}Si^-$ image doesn't show line defects. Only dot defects (the inclusions at dislocation tubes) are presented on $^{28}Si^-$ image.

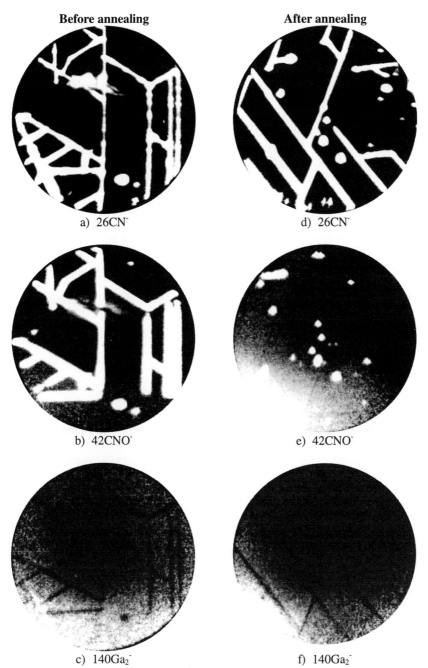

Before annealing

After annealing

a) 26CN⁻

d) 26CN⁻

b) 42CNO⁻

e) 42CNO⁻

c) 140Ga₂⁻

f) 140Ga₂⁻

Fig. 3. Ion images of block boundaries decoration. (a, b, c) – initial sample; (d, e, f) – the same sample after annealing (300° C).

The matrix ion images $^{140}Ga_2^-$ (fig.3c and fig.3f) show line defects as black lines. It is clearly seen that those block boundaries showing enhanced ion yield of matrix Ga_2^- ions (white lines at fig.3c) have no contrast in CNO^-. After annealing, the pattern in CNO^- 'rays' was changed drastically. The decoration of block boundaries disappeared and the image of the inclusions at dislocation tubes only. Also high ion yield of matrix Ga_2^- ions on block boundaries is not observed (fig.3f).

The enhanced ion yield of Ga_2^- can be connected with availability at block boundaries of more electropositive element than oxygen and nitrogen. This can be carbon which can form a chemical phase of Ga_xC_y type. This phase decomposes on annealing and the decoration of block boundaries at 'rays' CNO disappears.

The decomposition of this phase concentrated at certain of block boundaries can account for microstrain relaxation.

4.Conclusion

We have shown that the concentration of gaseous impurities at block boundaries is the reason of the high detection limit of H, C and O elements in HVPE- and MOCVD-grown GaN films on silicon carbide substrates. Combined X-ray and image SIMS data show that the mickostresses are broken at 300°C and line block boundary decoration CNO^- 'rays' disappears at this temperature. Microstrain relief is connected to decomposition of the chemical phase of Ga_xC_y type at GaN block boundaries.

Acknowledgments

The authors would like to acknowledge partial support for this work from INTAS grant 96-1031.

References

[1] H. Morkoc, S. Strite, G.B. Gao, M.E. Lin, B. Sverdlov, M. Burns, J.Appl.Phys. 76, 1363 (1994)

[2] Chris G. Van de Walle, Catherine Stamp, Jorg Neugebauer J. of Crystal Growth 189/190 (1998) 505-510

[3] Jorg Neugebauer and Chris G. Van de Walle, Appl. Phys. Lett. 68 (13), 1829

[4] A.Usikov, V.V.Ratnicov, R.Kyutt, W.V.Lundin, B.Pushnyi, N.M.Shmidt, M.P.Scheglov //Macro- and microstrains in MOCVD-grown GaN. MRS Internet J., Nitride Semicond. Res. 3, 46, p.195-200 (1998).

[5] Yu.Melnik, A.Nikolaev, S.Stepanov, I.Nikitina, K.Vasilevski, A.Ankudinov, Yu.Musikhin, V.A.Dmitriev //Silicon Carbide, III-Nitrides and Related Materials (Materials Science Forum, Vols.264-268), ed. G.Pensl et al., Trans. Tech. Publication Ltd. Switzerland, 1998, 1121-1124.

[6] V.Dmitriev, K.Irvine, G.Bulman, J.Edmond, A.Zubrilov, V.Nikolaev, I.Nikitina, D.Tsvetkov, A.Babanin, A.Sitnikova, Yu.Musikhin, N.Bert. J. Crystal Growth 166 (1996) 601-606

[7] A.P.Kovarsky, Yu.A.Kudryavtsev, V.S.Strykanov, M.P.Vatnik, Eleven Intern. Conf. SIMS XI 7-12 Sept. 1997, Orlando, Florida, Abstract Book p.37.

A. Benninghoven, P. Bertrand, H.-N. Migeon and H.W. Werner (Editors).
Proceedings of the 12th International Conference on Secondary Ion Mass Spectrometry,
Brussels, Belgium, 5-11 September 1999
© 2000 Elsevier Science B.V. All rights reserved.

SIMS ANALYSIS OF DEUTERIUM INCORPORATION IN CMOS TRANSISTORS DURING THE DEUTERIUM SINTERING PROCESS

Jinju Lee, Judith E. Baker[1], Kangguo Cheng, Karl Hess, and Joseph W. Lyding

Beckman Institute, University of Illinois, Urbana, IL 61801, lee18@uiuc.edu
[1]Frederick Seitz Materials Research Laboratory, University of Illinois, Urbana, IL 61801

1. Introduction

The deuterium (D) isotope effect has been found to be very effective in reducing hot carrier induced degradation in CMOS transistors of numerous technologies [1]-[4]. The magnitude of lifetime improvement (10x to 100x) varies from one technology to the other, but it directly correlates with D incorporation at the gate SiO_2/Si interface. Secondary ion mass spectrometry (SIMS) depth profiling has been used to make this determination.

The relative sensitivity factors for H and D in different device layers were calculated using calibration standards [5]. The SIMS analysis indicates that more aggressive sintering conditions are necessary to achieve the maximum D incorporation for devices with diffusion barriers. SIMS depth profiles have also allowed us to correlate the D incorporation at the interfaces with electrically measured lifetime improvement. We will present a summary of these characterizations for devices from several different manufacturers.

We have recently implemented high pressure D annealing to increase the D incorporation at the interface. Lower temperatures and shorter anneal times give the same or better levels of improvement when compared to ambient pressure anneals. We will present data showing the increased incorporation of D at the interface as a function of pressure.

2. Experimental

Three different transistor structures from three different manufacturers went through D processing and were characterized. Some transistors used oxide sidewall structures, while others used nitride sidewalls and nitride caps. Some were sintered at the first metallization (M1) step while others were sintered as a fully processed wafer. The sintering temperatures varied from 400°C - 480 °C and the D concentration inside the furnace ranged from 10% (in ultra-high purity nitrogen, N_2) to 100%. The sintering times ranged between 0.5 to 3 hours while the pressure varied from the ambient to 15 atm.

There was no change in the pre-stress electrical characteristics for all devices sintered in deuterium. The device lifetimes were compared with the lifetimes of the samples that were annealed in a hydrogen environment. The SIMS depth profiles were obtained with a Cs^+ primary ion beam and negative secondary ion detection in a CAMECA ims-5f system. The Cs^+ source was operated at 10 keV and the sample voltage was - 4.5 keV. For the dielectric layer characterizations, sample charging was controlled with an electron gun, Au coating, and Mo cover grid. SIMS analyses were performed on test pads on each device. A 150 μm square area was sputtered with data taken from the center 30 μm. The secondary ion counts were converted to concentrations by calculating the relative sensitivity factors for H and D using calibration standards in every matrix employed in the CMOS transistors [5]. The background at mass 2 before processing was less than 10^{17} cm^{-3}.

Texas Instruments (TI) 0.3 μm channel length CMOS transistors (t_{ox} = 6 nm) with nitride sidewall spacers were sintered right after the M1 step. To investigate the effect of deuterium passivation at different steps of CMOS processing, two sets of nominally identical devices, fabricated using Digital Semiconductor (DEC)'s 0.25 μm 2.0V CMOS technology

(t_{ox} = 4.5 nm), were processed to the M1 step and to the fourth (fully processed) metallization (M4) step, respectively. To investigate the effect of the high pressure D sintering, Samsung Electronics' 0.35 μm 3.3 V CMOS technology (t_{ox} = 5.5 nm) with nitride sidewall spacers and SiON capping layers were used. These wafers were subjected to 100% D sintering at 450 °C at several pressures (2, 6 and 15 atm). The annealing times varied from 10 min to 3 hours.

3. Results and Discussion

Contrary to the previous results for oxide sidewall devices, we found only a slight lifetime improvement by a factor of 1.5 to 2 for Texas Instruments devices. This suggests that D did not reach a significant accumulation level at the interface, indicating that a more rigorous sintering is necessary for D to overcome the Si_3N_4 sidewall diffusion barrier. In reference [6], we have done the SIMS depth profiles for the TI devices and correlated the ratio of D/H concentrations near the interfaces with the mean lifetime improvement as a function of the processing parameters.

For DEC samples processed to M4, hot carrier lifetime improved by a maximum factor of ~4.5 for the most aggressive sintering condition. For the same sintering conditions, a smaller improvement is observed for the fully processed samples due to the larger diffusion barrier. The lifetime improvements are due solely to the presence of deuterium. This was confirmed by the SIMS. A large increase in the concentration of deuterium at the oxide/silicon interface is observed for M1. For the profiles for M4 samples, the majority of the 5.0 μm thick interlevel dielectric was removed. The profile of the M4 device, shown in reference [7] was obtained after all the interlevel dielectric was removed. Figure 2 in reference [7] compares the deuterium incorporation for M1 and M4` devices. As expected from the electrical data, the deuterium incorporation is greater for the M1 device.

With higher pressure processing, shorter annealing times were required to achieve the same improvement for devices with substantially greater diffusion barriers. As expected, a longer annealing time at a specific pressure gives better lifetime improvement. These factors highlight the correlation between D incorporation at the interface and lifetime improvement. Figure 1 shows SIMS profiles comparing the deuterium incorporation for sintering at 2 atm for 1 and 3 hours and at 6 atm for 20 min. The profiles clearly show that for both pressures, deuterium is incorporated at the SiO_2/Si interface and that pressure increases the D incorporation at the interface and throughout the SiO_2 layer. Note that there is more D incorporation for a 20 min anneal at 6 atm than for a 3 hour anneal at 2 atm. All of the processing was done at 450 °C. High pressure processing not only increases the magnitude of improvement but also shortens the annealing time. Even though the wafer structures were highly resistant to D incorporation, 90x improvement was possible due to the increased D incorporation rate [8].

Figure 2 and Figure 3 show actual D incorporations in the fully processed (4 metallizations) Samsung devices. Figure 2 compares the D incorporation in a device that was sintered at 1 atm for 3 hours with a device that was sintered at 6 atm for an hour. The D incorporations are about the same. Figure 3 compares the incorporation at 15 atm for 3 hours with 1 atm for 3 hours. As expected, the D concentration is higher at the interface with the higher pressure sintering. The H background in the Si bulk region is due to the instrumental background. Hydrogen is present in the dielectric layers and remains about the same throughout D processing. The H profiles shown are for the unannealed samples.

4. Conclusions

The effectiveness of deuterium in improving the reliability of CMOS devices of various technologies, even when introduced after multiple metallization steps on devices with nitride sidewall spacers, has been demonstrated. Lifetime improvements ranging from ~5 to more than 90 were observed across this broad range of technologies from TI, DEC and Samsung. SIMS analysis shows that increased annealing temperatures and pressures increase the D/H ratio at the SiO_2/Si interface. This study clearly shows that improvements in device lifetimes correlate directly to deuterium incorporation at the SiO_2/Si interface.

Acknowledgments

This work was supported by the Office of Naval Research under Grants N00014-92-J-1519 and N00014-98-I-0604 and by the Beckman Institute for Advanced Science and Technology at the University of Illinois. The use of the SIMS facility is supported by the U.S. Department of Energy under Grant DEFG02-96-ER45439.

References

[1] J.W. Lyding, K. Hess and I.C. Kizilyalli, Appl.Phys. Lett. 68 (1996) 2526.
[2] I.C. Kizilyalli, J.W. Lyding, and K. Hess, IEEE Elec. Dev. Ltr. 18 (1997) 81-83.
[3] S. Krishnan, S. Rangan, S. Hattangady, G. Xing, K. Brennan, M. Rodder, and S. Ashok, IEDM. Tech. Dig. (1997) 445.
[4] T.G. Ference, J.S. Burnham, W.F. Clark, T.B. Hook, S.W. Mittl, K.M. Watson, and L-K K. Han, IEEE Trans. Elec. Dev. 46(4) (1999) 747.
[5] J. Lee, J. Baker, R. Wilson, and J.W. Lyding in Secondary Ion Mass Spectrometry, edited by G. Gillen, R. Lareau, J. Bennett, and F. Stevie, SIMS XI Proc. (1997) 205.
[6] J. Lee, S. Aur, R. Eklund, K. Hess, and J.W. Lyding, J. Vac. Sci. Technol. A 16(3), (1998) 1762.
[7] J. Lee, Y. Epstein, A. Berti, J. Huber, K. Hess, and J.W. Lyding, IEEE Trans. Elec. Dev. 46(8) (1999) 1.
[8] Submitted for a publication in Elec. Dev. Lett. April, 1999.

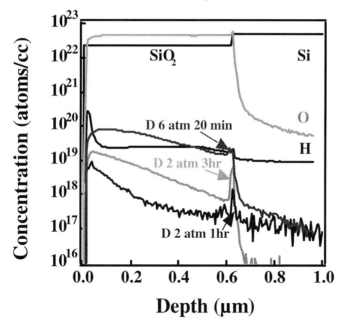

Fig. 1. SIMS profiles of 6000 Å SiO_2/Si using 14.5keV Cs^+ with negative secondary ion detection. The deuterium concentration profiles for the structures that were sintered at 2 atm D for 1 and 3 hrs and at 6 atm D for 20 mins are shown. All were annealed at 450 °C [8].

684

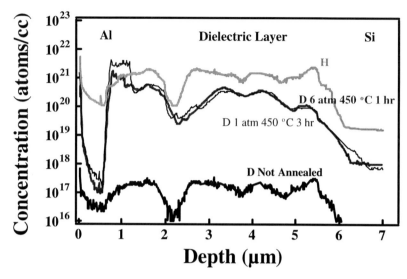

Fig. 2. SIMS profiles of fully processed Samsung devices using 14.5keV Cs$^+$ with negative secondary ion detection. The deuterium concentration profiles for the devices that were not processed, sintered at 1 atm for 3 hrs and at 6 atm for 1hr are shown.

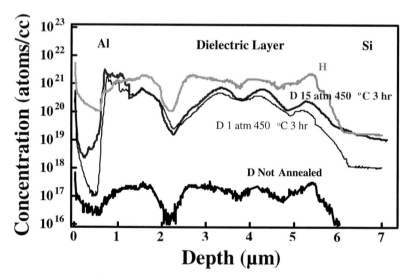

Fig. 3. SIMS profiles of fully processed Samsung devices using 14.5keV Cs$^+$ with negative secondary ion detection. The deuterium concentration profiles for the devices that were not processed, sintered at 1 atm for 3 hrs and at 15 atm for 3hr are shown.

A. Benninghoven, P. Bertrand, H.-N. Migeon and H.W. Werner (Editors).
Proceedings of the 12th International Conference on Secondary Ion Mass Spectrometry,
Brussels, Belgium, 5-11 September 1999

DIFFUSION OF ARSENIC IN GERMANIUM

J. Likonen[a,*], E. Vainonen-Ahlgren[b], T. Ahlgren[b], S. Lehto[a] , W. Li[c], and J. Haapamaa[c]

[a]Technical Research Centre of Finland, Chemical Technology, P.O. Box 1404, FIN-02044
VTT, Finland
*corresponding author, e-mail: Jari.Likonen@vtt.fi
[b]University of Helsinki, Accelerator Laboratory, P.O. Box 43, FIN-00014 University of
Helsinki, Finland
[c] Tampere University of Technology, Optoelectronics Research Centre,
P.O. Box 692, FIN-33101 Tampere, Finland

1. Introduction

The understanding of the diffusion mechanisms of dopant impurities in elemental solids is of great interest, both for technical and for scientific reasons. As semiconductor device dimensions decrease, understanding and controlling diffusion related phenomena become increasingly important. Despite this emphasis, diffusion mechanisms of various dopant elements in Ge are not well understood. The increasing importance of Ge for applications such as $Si_{1-x}Ge_x$ devices and multi-junction GaAs/Ge [1] and GaInP/GaAs/Ge [2] solar cells necessitates further study of diffusion mechanisms in Ge. Wojtczuk *et al.* [1] have made use of arsenic diffusion to create a n-type layer in Ge. During GaAs layer growth by MOCVD, a junction was created through Ga and As in-diffusion, resulting in a two-junction tandem cell.

2. Experimental

Commercially prepared samples of p-type <001>-oriented single-crystal germanium were used as substrates. At first, a thin GaAs layer was grown using migration-enhanced epitaxy (MEE), i.e. alternating exposure to Ga and As fluxes. The MEE layer consisted of 10 monolayers of GaAs deposited at 350 °C, followed by a nucleation layer of 100 nm deposited at 450 °C using a slow growth rate (0.1 µm/hour). After growing a thin layer of GaAs under these conditions, the growth rate and the growth temperature were increased to 1 µm/hour and 490 °C, respectively. Annealings were carried out using rapid thermal annealing (RTA) technique *ex situ* in 100 % N_2 . The GaAs layer was then etched using a solution containing H_2SO_4, H_2O_2 and H_2O in a volumetric ratio of 1:1:1.

Depth profiling of gallium and arsenic was carried out by secondary ion mass spectrometry (SIMS) utilising a double focusing magnetic sector SIMS (VG Ionex IX70S). The negative secondary ions $^{151}AsGe^-$ and $^{152}Ge_2^-$ were analysed using 12 keV Cs^+ primary ions. The ion beam current was 100 nA and the rastered area was 330 x 350 µm^2. The positive secondary ions $^{69}Ga^+$ and $^{70}Ge^+$ were depth profiled using 5 keV O_2^+ primary ion beam with the ion current at 100 nA. In this case the ion beam was raster-scanned over an area of 270 x 470 µm^2.

In both cases crater wall effects were eliminated using a 10% electronic gate and an 1 mm optical gate. The depth of the craters was measured by a Dektak 3030ST profilometer after SIMS analyses. The uncertainty of the crater depth was estimated to be 5 %. The SIMS instrument was calibrated using ion implanted standard samples for As and Ga with an implantation dose of 10^{15} ions/cm^2.

3. Diffusion model

The basic principles of the diffusion model used in this work have been published elsewhere [3-4]. The model was developed for Si diffusion in GaAs and it is based on the model developed by Yu et al. [5]. Here we have modified the diffusion model for GaAs in order to simulate As diffusion in Ge.

In our model we have assumed that As occupies Ge lattice sites and diffuses through Ge vacancies. Our calculations show that vacancies V_{Ge}^0 and V_{Ge}^{2-} need to be taken into account, giving the effective diffusion coefficient of substitutional As atoms as

$$D_{As}^{eff} = D_{As}^0 + D_{As}^{2-}\left(\frac{n}{n_i}\right)^2 \tag{1}$$

where D_{As}^0 and D_{As}^{2-} are diffusion constants through vacancies V_{Ge}^0 and V_{Ge}^{2-}, respectively. n_i is the intrinsic and n is the extrinsic electron concentration. Using the charge neutrality equation $n + [Ga_{Ge}^-] = p + [As_{Ge}^+]$ and the semiconductor equation $pn = n_i^2$, we can calculate the electron concentration as

$$n = \frac{[As_{Ge}^+] - [Ga_{Ge}^-] + \sqrt{([As_{Ge}^+] - [Ga_{Ge}^-])^2 + 4n_i^2}}{2} \tag{2}$$

where the brackets denote concentrations and p is the hole concentration. The general concentration dependent diffusion equation is

$$\frac{\partial C_{As}}{\partial t} = \frac{\partial}{\partial x}\left(D_{As}^{eff}\left[\frac{\partial C_{As}}{\partial x} + \frac{C_{As}}{n}\frac{\partial n}{\partial x}\right]\right) \tag{3}$$

where C_{As} is the total dopant concentration and D_{As}^{eff} is the corresponding effective diffusion coefficient. The second term is due to the electric field produced by electrons. Diffusion equation (3) is numerically solved and fitted to the experimental SIMS profiles as described in Ref. [3]. The fitting parameters are the two diffusion coefficients in Eq. (1) and the solid solubility limit of As in Ge (see Fig. 1). The intrinsic carrier concentration n_i is taken from Ref. [6].

4. Results

Figure 1 shows SIMS profiles of As (a) and Ga (b) in Ge and the numerical fits for annealing temperatures 600, 700 and 800 °C. The arsenic diffusion profiles consist of two regions. In the first region near the surface the As and Ga profiles behave in a similar way but in the second region the Ga concentration has decreased to a doping level of 2×10^{17} cm^{-3}, while

As has diffused deeper into the sample. The model was fitted to the As profiles in the second region. In Fig. 1 (a) the complementary error function fit is also shown, which is the solution of the diffusion equation (3) in the case of a constant diffusion coefficient. It can be observed that the complementary error function cannot be fitted to the steep diffusion front in the SIMS profile indicating that diffusion of As in Ge is concentration dependent. However, the theoretical model fits well in all cases. Furthermore, some test calculations where vacancies V_{Ge}^{0} and V_{Ge}^{1-} were taken into account in Eq. (1), were also made by replacing the term D_{As}^{2-} $(n/n_i)^2$ with $D_{As}^{-}(n/n_i)$. In this case the agreement between the SIMS profiles and the model was rather poor. The best agreement was obtained with Ge vacancy charge states 0 and –2. The diffusion of As and Ga in the first region will be discussed elsewhere.

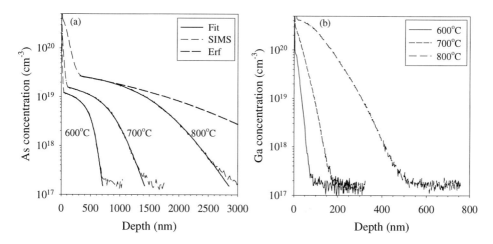

Figure 1. As (a) and Ga (b) SIMS profiles of samples annealed at 600, 700 and 800 °C. Annealing times were 5, 2 and 1 min, respectively. The complementary error function (erf) fit is also given.

In Fig. 2 the Arrhenius plots for the intrinsic diffusion coefficients in Eq. (1) are presented. These are well described by the Arrhenius equation $D = D_0 \exp(-E_a/kT)$ where D_0 is the pre-exponential factor, E_a is the activation energy and k is Boltzmann's constant. When our value for activation energy of D_{As}^{0}, 1.8 eV, is compared to an average value of 2.5±0.2 eV calculated from literature values [7], it can be observed that our value is somewhat lower. One reason for the differences is that concentration independent model was used in the literature [7]. Södervall et al. [8] have pointed out that for group V elements (P, As, Sb and Bi) the activation energy is 2.4 ± 0.3 eV. They obtained a value of 2.1 eV for the activation energy in the case of P diffusion in Ge. This value is close to our value for the activation energy of D_{As}^{0}.

5. Conclusions

We have studied the diffusion of As in Ge. Prior to rapid thermal annealing in the temperature range of 500 – 800 °C, a GaAs layer was deposited on a Ge substrate using MEE and MBE techniques. The concentration dependent diffusion model was fitted to the experimental SIMS profiles. This model is based on the assumption that As occupies Ge lattice sites and diffuses through Ge vacancies. The charge states of Ge vacancies were calculated to be 0 and −2 in order to best fit the experimental SIMS profiles.

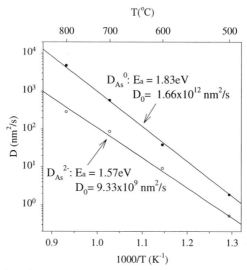

Figure 2. The Arrhenius plots with the corresponding activation energies and pre-exponential factors for As diffusion via Ge vacancies.

Acknowledgements

This work has been supported by the Academy of Finland (EPI-2 project). Dr. J. Campbell (Helsinki University of Technology) is greatly acknowledged for comments on the manuscript.

References

[1] S.J. Wojtczuk, S.P. Tobin, C.J. Keavney, C. Bajgar, M.M. Sanfacon, J.D. Scofield and D.S. Ruby, IEEE Trans. Electron Devices 37 (1990) 455.

[2] P.K. Chiang, J.H. Ermer, W.T. Nishikawa, D.D. Krut, D.E. Joslin, J.W. Eldredge, B.T. Cavicchi and J.M. Olson, Proc. of 25th IEEE Photovoltaic Specialists Conference, 1996, p. 183-186.

[3] T. Ahlgren, J. Likonen, J. Slotte, J. Räisänen, M. Rajatora and J. Keinonen, Phys. Rev. B56 (1997) 4597.

[4] T. Ahlgren, Phys. Rev. Lett. 81 (1998) 842.

[5] S. Yu, U. M. Gösele and T. Y. Tan, J. Appl. Phys. 66 (1989) 2952.

[6] O. Madelung (ed.), Semiconductors, Group IV Elements and III-V Compounds, Springer, Berlin, 1991, p. 28 - 42.

[7] M. Scultz (ed.), Landolt-Börnstein, New Series, III/22b, Springer, Berlin, 1989, p. 457 - 458.

[8] U. Södervall and M. Friesel, Defect and Diffusion Forum 143-147 (1997) 1053.

A. Benninghoven, P. Bertrand, H.-N. Migeon and H.W. Werner (Editors).
Proceedings of the 12th International Conference on Secondary Ion Mass Spectrometry,
Brussels, Belgium, 5-11 September 1999

689

SIMS DEPTH PROFILE ANALYSIS OF OXYGEN CONTAMINATION IN HYDROGENATED AMORPHOUS AND MICROCRYSTALLINE SILICON

A. Mück, U. Zastrow, O. Vetterl and B. Rech

Institut für Schicht- und Ionentechnik, Forschungszentrum Jülich GmbH
D-52425 Jülich, Germany, E-mail: a.mueck@fz-juelich.de

1. Introduction

Thin films of hydrogenated amorphous silicon (a-Si:H) and/or microcrystalline silicon (μc-Si:H) deposited by plasma enhanced chemical vapour deposition (PECVD) are used in opto-electronic devices such as solar cells and color sensors. Previous work has shown that oxygen contamination influences the electronic properties of both materials [1-3].

In this paper we report on the influence of different PECVD conditions on the oxygen contamination of a-Si:H and μc-Si:H films. SIMS depth profiles of layered structures grown with various hydrogen (H_2) dilution of silane (SiH_4) as well as of sandwich structures alternately grown with and without commercial gas purifier are discussed. Furthermore, detailed results concerning the uptake of oxygen in μc-Si:H stored in air atmosphere [1] are presented.

2. Experimental

The samples were grown by PECVD in multichamber deposition systems on Czochralski (CZ) and float zone (FZ) Si-wafers. The residual gas pressure in the deposition chambers was $< 2 \times 10^{-8}$ torr. The deposition feed gas was silane (SiH_4) diluted in hydrogen (H_2). Here, the hydrogen (H_2) dilution is defined as the SiH_4 to H_2 gas flow ratio. The a-Si:H and μc-Si:H films were deposited with excitation frequencies of 13.56 and 95 MHz, respectively, both at a substrate temperature of ~200°C. In case of μc-Si:H the plasma power was varied between 5 and 50 W leading to deposition rates between ~1.5 and ~5 Å/s, respectively [4].

SIMS depth profiles were performed using a quadrupole instrument (Atomika 4000). The residual gas pressure in the SIMS analysis chamber was $< 1 \times 10^{-10}$ torr. Primary Cs^+ ions at near-normal incidence with energies of 6 and 9 keV were used and negative secondary ions were detected. The sputtering rate was > 0.75 nm/s. Applying these conditions we obtain in FZ-Si the oxygen detection limit $< 5 \times 10^{17} cm^{-3}$. Stylus surface profilometer (Dektak 3030) was used to measure the sputtered crater depths.

3. Results and Discussion

The hydrogen (H_2) dilution of silane (SiH_4), which is generally used for PECVD of μc-Si:H, is also known to improve the material properties of a-Si:H [3]. Fig. 1 shows the oxygen depth profile of an a-Si:H sandwich structure alternately grown with two different H_2 dilutions. In the region less than ~200 nm and also between ~400 and ~600 nm the H_2 dilution was 1:1 and the oxygen concentration is about 5×10^{18} cm^{-3}. The increase by a factor of about 8 is observed for H_2 dilution of 1:30, which is used for deposition of the middle layer. The interface between a-Si:H film and substrate is indicated by the sharp oxygen peak at about 600 nm. Fig. 2 shows a similar sandwich structure as discussed in Fig. 1, but here a commercial gas purifier was used during the deposition of the middle layer between ~130 and ~270 nm. Within this layer the oxygen concentration is $< 2 \times 10^{18}$ cm^{-3}. This reduction compared to the layered structure shown in Fig. 1 demonstrates that the main contribution of incorporated oxygen in a-Si:H originates from contamination of the process gas supply.

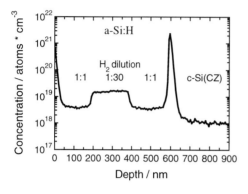

Fig. 1: Oxygen depth profile in layered structure of a-Si:H films grown with two different hydrogen (H$_2$) dilutions of silane (SiH$_4$).

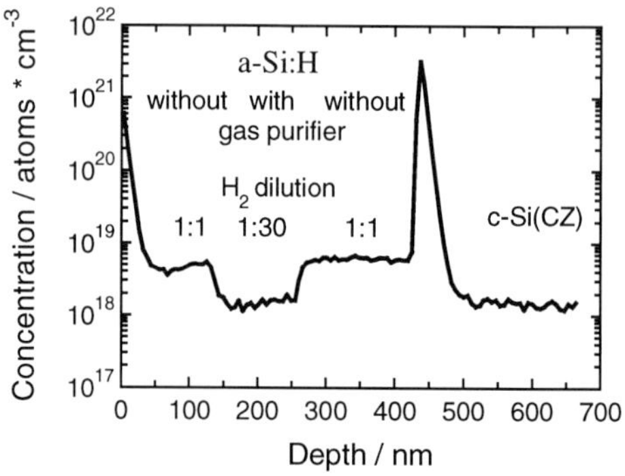

Fig. 2: Oxygen depth profile in similar structure as shown in Fig. 1 but grown with and without the use of a gas purifier.

To study the influence of the residual gas pressure in the PECVD process, the deposition chamber was equipped with a controllable air leak. The gas purifier is used to minimize the oxygen contamination introduced by the gas supply system. Fig. 3 illustrates the oxygen contamination in a-Si:H films as detected by SIMS measurements versus residual gas pressure in the deposition chamber. The oxygen concentration in a-Si:H as function of the residual gas pressure is found to result in a power law dependance.

Turning the attention to the μc-Si:H films, Fig. 4 shows the oxygen depth profile of a sandwich structure of μc-Si:H films alternately grown with and without the use of the gas purifier, but constant H$_2$ dilution. The top layer with a thickness of ~150 nm as well as the bottom layer between ~350 and ~600 nm were grown without gas purifier. Here the oxygen concentration is ~8 $\times$ 10^{18} cm^{-3}. The

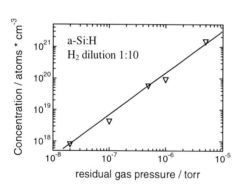

Fig. 3: Oxygen concentration in a-Si:H films as detected by SIMS analysis versus residual gas pressure in the deposition chamber.

middle layer was grown with the gas purifier and shows the oxygen concentration of about 1 $\times$ 10^{18} cm^{-3}. This decrease in the oxygen content demonstrates that the use of the gas purifier shows similar beneficial effect in both, μc-Si:H and a-Si:H.

In order to get information about changes in the oxygen content after deposition, we investigated the oxygen uptake during storage of the materials at air atmosphere. State of the art a-Si:H does not show any change in the oxygen concentration even for long storage times. Different behavior can occur in μc-Si:H. Fig. 5(a-c) shows the oxygen concentrations of differently prepared μc-Si:H films stored in air atmosphere at room temperature for various storage times. Additionally the carbon concentrations are plotted, which do not show any change during storage. The interface between the film and substrate is indicated by the sharp oxygen and carbon peaks at about 700-800 nm. Figure 5a shows the results for a μc-Si:H film grown at the low deposition rate of ~2 Å/s. The oxygen concentration is near to the SIMS detection limit and does not change during exposure to the air atmosphere. This indicates a compact structure of this material. Fig. 5b and 5c

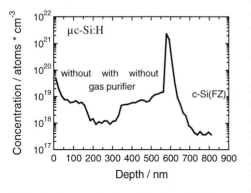

Fig. 4: Oxygen depth profile in sandwich structure of μc-Si:H films alternately grown with and without gas purifier, but constant H$_2$ dilution of 1:20.

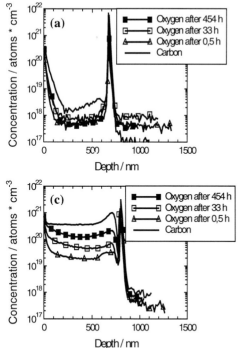

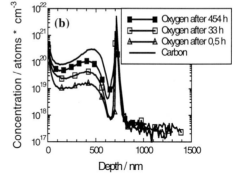

Fig. 5: Oxygen concentrations in μc-Si:H films stored in air atmosphere at room temperature for various storage times. The carbon concentrations do not show any change during the storage. Deposition powers of 10 W (**a**), 20 W (**b**) and 50 W (**c**) were used.

692

illustrate the oxygen uptake in films grown using higher plasma powers up to 50 W. The change in the plasma power results in deposition rates up to 5 Ⓐ/s. The oxygen concentration in these films increases with rising storage times. These results indicate a porous structure of the material which allows the indiffusion of H_2O and/or O_2. While the compact µc-Si:H investigated in this study shows carbon bulk concentrations of $< 3 \times 10^{18}$ cm^{-3} (see Fig. 5a), carbon contents up to 1×10^{21} cm^{-3} are detected in material with a porous structure. The plots in Figs. 5b and 5c illustrate that the long-term oxygen uptake profiles show similar depth distributions as the carbon depth profiles, the latter detected after short-term exposure to the atmosphere for some minutes. Turning the attention to the species penetrating into the porous material, we add D_2O to the air atmosphere. A porous µc-Si:H film, similar to that investigated in Fig. 5b, was stored for 127 hours in this atmosphere at room temperature. Fig. 6 shows the resulting oxygen and the deuterium concentrations prior and after storage. The concentration depth profiles indicate the increase in the oxygen and deuterium (D_2) concentrations of $\sim 4 \times 10^{19}$ and $\sim 8 \times 10^{18}$ cm^{-3}, respectively. These results suggest that a large fraction of the oxygen uptake originates from the humidity of the atmosphere. The penetrated D_2O may react with inner-surfaces in the porous material following the reaction $D_2O + Si \rightarrow SiO + D_2$. While oxygen binds to silicon, small part of the released deuterium substitutes hydrogen, the latter passivating Si dangling bonds at inner-surfaces.

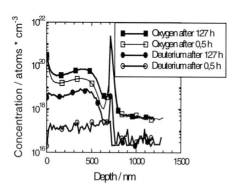

Fig. 6: Oxygen and deuterium concentration of a µc-Si:H film stored in D_2O containing atmosphere at room temperature.

4. Conclusions

The oxygen concentration in a-Si:H is found to increase significantly if the deposition feed gas SiH_4 is diluted in H_2. Our investigations show that the main contribution of incorporated oxygen originates from contamination of the process gas supply. This contamination is strongly reduced by the use of a gas purifier. With purified deposition feed gases the oxygen concentration in a-Si:H is found to increase with rising residual gas pressure in the deposition chamber following a power law dependance. State of the art a-Si:H and compact µc-Si:H do not show any change in the oxygen concentration caused by storage in air atmosphere. In the case of µc-Si:H grown with deposition rates ≥ 3.5 Å/s the uptake of oxygen from the surrounding atmosphere is observed. Depth profiles of deuterium and oxygen in µc-Si:H films stored in D_2O containing air atmosphere indicate a significant indiffusion of water into the porous material.

References

[1]   S. Veprek et. al., J. Phys. C: Solid State Phys,. 16 (1983), 6241
[2]   P. Torres et. al., Appl. Phys. Lett. 69 (1996), 1373
[3]   B. Rech et. al. in: J. Schmid et. al. (eds.), Proc. 2nd World Conf. on Photovoltaic Solar Energy Conversion, Volume I, European Commission, Ispra, 1998, p. 391
[4]   O. Vetterl et al., Solid State Phen., 67-68 (1999), 101

A. Benninghoven, P. Bertrand, H.-N. Migeon and H.W. Werner (Editors).
Proceedings of the 12th International Conference on Secondary Ion Mass Spectrometry,
Brussels, Belgium, 5-11 September 1999

SIMS STUDY OF C AND Al CO-IMPLANTATION IN GaAs

M. A. A. Pudenzi[a], I. Danilov[a], A. Mück[b] and U. Zastrow[b]

[a]Instituto de Física "Gleb Wataghin", C.P. 6165, Universidade Estadual de Campinas,
13083-970, Campinas, São Paulo, Brazil
E-mail: pudenzi@ifi.unicamp.br
[b]Institut für Schicht-und Ionentechnik, Forschungszentrum Jülich
GmbH D-52425 Jülich, Germany

1. Introduction

Carbon is an acceptor impurity when it occupies the As site in GaAs, and it has, also, a low diffusion coefficient in this material. For these reasons, carbon implantation into GaAs is an attractive technique for device fabrication, particularly for buried p-type layers. However, the main problem is the low activation efficiency of C implantation, less than 2%, at high doses ($>10^{13}$ cm^{-2}) [1]. Co-implantation of group III elements has been shown to increase the electrical activation of implanted C in GaAs, due to damage and stoichiometry effects [1].

To the best of our knowledge, there is no SIMS report in the literature about depth profiling of co-implanted C and Al. This kind of measurement is very important for the understanding of damage and stoichiometry effects. In this work, SIMS depth profiling was used to investigate deep (> 1 μm) carbon and aluminum co-implantation in GaAs.

2. Experimental

Aluminum, with energy of 1.4 MeV, was co-implanted in n-type and semi-insulating GaAs substrates, after the 1 MeV carbon implantation. In order to minimize ion channeling effect, all implantation were performed with the sample surface normal tilted by 15° to the ion beam incidence direction.

The energy of the Al^{+} ions was selected in order to obtain the atomic distribution peaks of C and Al close to each other, as calculated by TRIM code [2]. The C implanted dose was kept constant at 5×10^{14} cm^{-2} and the Al dose was varied from 1 to 5×10^{14} cm^{-2}. The substrate temperature during implantation was 80 K because, under this condition and after annealing at 950°C for 10s, higher activation is reached for high C dose.

Rapid thermal annealing (RTA) was performed at 950°C for 10 s, with the sample facing down a silicon wafer. In order to avoid compensation due to the presence of n-type dopant, the implanted n-type substrates were not annealed and they were used only for SIMS reference purpose. That is, only the implanted semi-insulating GaAs substrates were annealed at the conditions above mentioned.

Hall effect measurements, with Van der Pauw geometry, provided the sheet resistance, sheet carrier concentration and effective mobility values. The value of the electrical activity is the ratio of the sheet hole concentration to the carbon implantation dose.

SIMS measurements of the depth distribution of C and Al ions were performed using cesium and oxygen beams, respectively, on Atomika 4000 and MIQ-256 quadrupole microprobes. On the Atomika, the Cs^+ beam parameters were 6 keV at 20° incidence angle and, for the O_2^+ beam, 6 keV at normal incidence. On MIQ-256, Cs^+: 10 keV at 45° incidence angle and O_2^+: 10 keV at normal incidence.

The craters depth was measured using a Dektak 3030.

3. Results and Discussion

Figure 1 shows the electrical activity of C implanted and Al co-implanted samples, as a function of the total dose (C + Al doses) and the implantation temperature, after annealing at 950°C for 10s. The higher activation was obtained for C and Al co-implantation at 80 K (Fig.1, curve d).

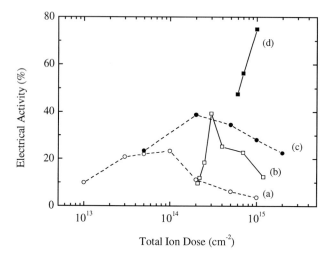

Fig. 1. Electrical activity of C implanted and Al co-implanted samples, as a function of the total dose (C + Al), after annealing at 950°C/10s. (a) only C implantation at room temperature (RT), (b) C and Al implantation at RT, (c) only C implantation at 80 K and (d) C and Al implantation at 80 K.

Figures 2.a and 2.b show the carbon and aluminum depth profiles, respectively, of the annealed and not annealed samples, which have been co-implanted with the aluminum dose equal to the carbon dose ($5x10^{14}$ cm^{-2}). In Fig.2.a, the annealed sample shows the C peak at a distance of 1.35 μm from the surface. Comparing with the not annealed sample, this is a shift of, roughly, 50 nm towards the surface. This apparent shift corresponds to less than 4% of the peak position and it could be attributed to uncertainties in the craters depth measurements.

The C depth distribution of the annealed samples co-implanted with lower Al dose has a profile similar to the one shown in Fig.2.a.

Despite of the expected large amount of defects introduced during implantation at such low temperature, SIMS measurements have shown no out diffusion of carbon after annealing, within the uncertainty in depth scaling (4%).

For the Al dose of 5×10^{14} cm^{-2}, SIMS measurements of the Al profile in the annealed sample have shown a depletion in the Al concentration close to the peak and an accumulation around 0.6 μm (Fig.2.b). This Al diffusion into the damaged region is not well understood at the moment. Aluminum atoms being a group III element occupy, preferentially, Ga sites. One possible explanation for the effect that we have observed is that Ga vacancies, moving from the highest damaged region towards the surface, could drive the Al out-diffusion. The effect depends on the Al dose because we could not observe the shoulder in the Al profile for lower Al implantation dose.

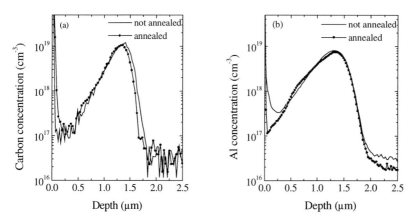

Fig.2. (a) Carbon and (b) aluminum depth profiles of the samples co-implanted with C and Al doses of 5×10^{14} cm^{-2}, before (solid line) and after (circles) annealing at 950°C for10s.

Carbon atoms usually occupy As sites working as acceptors in GaAs. Whereas arsenic vacancy has a diffusion coefficient lower than Ga vacancy [3], Ga vacancy diffusion during annealing will leave an excess of As vacancies in the implanted region, helping C incorporation in As sites. This would explain the high C activation in Al co-implanted samples (Fig.1.d), and why the C profile does not change due to annealing at 950°C/10s even for high Al dose.

4. Conclusions

SIMS measurements have shown that, within the uncertainty in depth scaling (4%), no out diffusion of carbon has occurred after annealing at 950°C for 10 s. This result reinforces the use of C as a suitable acceptor for buried p-type layer in GaAs device technology.

Aluminum out-diffusion was observed for an Al dose of $5x10^{14}$ cm^{-2} and its cause is, presently, not well understood.

Acknowledgments

One of us (M.A.A.P.) would like to thank the support of Fundação de Amparo à Pesquisa do Estado de São Paulo (FAPESP) and Conselho Nacional de Pesquisa (CNPq - Brazil). I.D. would like to thank, also, FAPESP and FAPERGS (Fundação de Amparo à Pesquisa do Estado de Rio Grande do Sul).

References

1. A. J. Moll, K. M. Yu, W. Walukiewicz, W. L. Hansen and E. E. Haller, Appl. Phys. Lett. **60** (1992) 2383.

2. J. F. Ziegler, J. P. Biersack and U. Littmark, The Stopping and Range of Ions in Solids, Pergamon Press, New York, 1985.

3. S. Y. Chiang and G. L. Pearson, J. Appl. Phys. **46** (1975) 2986.

A. Benninghoven, P. Bertrand, H.-N. Migeon and H.W. Werner (Editors).
Proceedings of the 12th International Conference on Secondary Ion Mass Spectrometry,
Brussels, Belgium, 5-11 September 1999

697

A PREPARATION METHOD FOR THE
REMOVAL OF PARTICULATES FROM CLEAVED SEMICONDUCTOR
SAMPLES

D. F. Reich

Physical Electronics, 575 Chesapeake Dr., Redwood City, CA 94063, U.S.A.
freich@phi.com

1. Introduction

Although manufacturers of surface analytical instruments now offer whole wafer capability, the majority of secondary ion mass spectrometers in use today are restricted to small sample holders. The required cleaving of wafers inevitably creates particles on the surface of interest. The presence of these particles is deleterious to subsequent SIMS analysis, and analysts try to identify them in the instrument's optical microscope to avoid profiling in these areas. In the field of optical astronomy it is known that a collodion film (cellulose nitrate) can be applied to, and remove tenacious dust particles from, a telescope's primary mirror or lens [1]. In order to assess whether this method might be appropriate as a preparation step prior to surface analysis, two questions are addressed in this paper. Firstly, is the collodion cleaning method effective in removing particulate material, and secondly, what organic residue, if any, is left behind on the surface to be analyzed, and to what extent does this affect any subsequent surface analysis?

2. Experimental

To generate surfaces with a sufficient number of particles for adequate statistical analysis, samples approximately 10mm x 10mm in size were created by deliberately scribing and then breaking a 150mm silicon wafer. This generates considerably more particles than a typical cleaving action, but served the purposes of the experiment. On each sample, two randomly chosen areas were photographed at high magnification using a metallurgical microscope. All the particles visible in an area of 250µm x 250µm were counted. The optical resolution was approximately 1µm. Particles were graded into three categories: >5µm; 2-5µm; and <2µm.

The following three methods of particle removal were assessed:

(1) Pressurized air 'jetting' from a compressed air canister, employing twenty jets of half-second duration with ~20 p.s.i. force at a distance of ~5cm from the sample surface.
(2) 2 minutes ultrasonic rinsing in acetone, followed by compressed air evaporation.
(3) Collodion cleaning: U.S.P. collodion (cellulose nitrate, or 'pyroxylin') from the J.T. Baker company was diluted 1:1 with methanol to reduce its viscosity, and then applied as

a 50μl droplet from a clean micro pipette. Once on the silicon surface, and while still liquid, a short length of polethylene tubing, 1mm in diameter, was contacted onto the droplet. Once the collodion had dried (5-10 minutes), it was lifted from the sample surface by pulling on the polyethylene.

Three randomly chosen samples were cleaned by each method, re-photographed and a fresh particle count made. The efficiency of particle removal was then quantified. A film of collodion prepared on a silicon substrate as described above was analyzed by TOF-SIMS to determine the characteristic mass spectral fragments of this compound. To assess whether a significant residue of the collodion is imparted to sample surfaces following film removal, samples with and without the collodion cleaning were also analyzed. A Physical Electronics TRIFT II instrument was used, operating at high mass resolution with a 15keV Ga^+ primary probe delivering a primary ion dose of less than 4×10^{12} ions/cm^2.

Finally, to determine if the application of the nitrogen-containing collodion has any measurable effect on the subsequent determination of nitrogen-containing oxide films, silicon samples with thin nitrided oxide films approximately 8nm thick were analyzed with low energy Cs^+ bombardment in a quadrupole SIMS instrument using the MCs^+ protocol. Samples with and without the collodion treatment were analyzed using a Physical Electronics ADEPT 1010 quadrupole SIMS instrument, using a 750eV Cs^+ beam at 55°incidence.

3. Results

The efficiency of particle removal by the three methods is shown in the table below, expressed as a percentage of particles removed in each size category. Each entry in the table is the combined result of two field counts for each of three samples. The actual number of particles remaining following each cleaning method is expressed over the original number of particles counted, and is shown in parentheses next to the percentage values.

Cleaning Method	>5μm	2-5μm	<2μm
Compressed Air	95% (3/61)	50% (73/146)	7% (413/443)
Ultrasonic/Acetone	100% (0/22)	98% (2/111)	98% (4/273)
Collodion Clean	100% (0/22)	98% (2/120)	99% (2/317)

TOF-SIMS mass spectra are shown below. Figure 1 shows the +SIMS mass spectrum in the mass range 0-100 m/z, taken from a freshly cast collodion thick film. The film was stable in vacuo and did not affect the 1×10^{-9} torr pressure reading. Figures 2 and 3 show +SIMS mass spectra plotted on a narrow mass range around mass 46, acquired from a control wafer sample and a collodion-treated sample, respectively. This particular mass range display was chosen because mass 46 (NO_2^+) is seen to be the base peak in the +SIMS spectrum of the collodion compound.

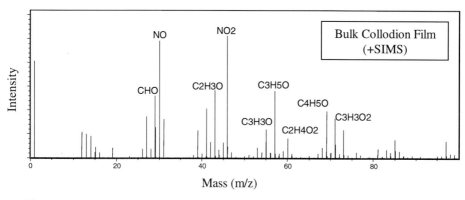

Figure 1. +SIMS mass spectrum acquired from a collodion thin film.

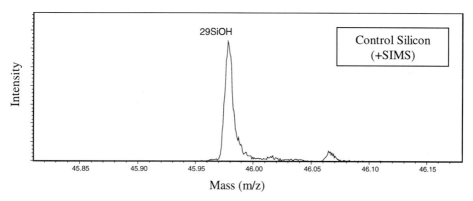

Figure 2. Narrow mass range +SIMS spectrum around mass 46, from a control (untreated) silicon sample.

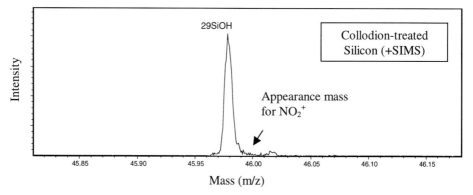

Figure 3. Narrow mass range +SIMS mass spectrum around mass 46, from a collodion-treated silicon sample.

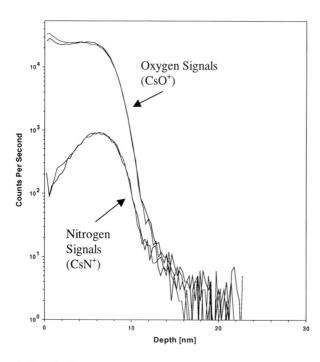

Figure 4. Comparison of oxygen (CsO$^+$) and nitrogen (CsN$^+$) depth profiles obtained from a thin (8nm) nitrided oxide, *with* collodion treatment (dashed lines) and *without* collodion (solid lines). Primary beam conditions: 750eV Cs$^+$ at 55° incidence, 50nA, 500µm x 500µm raster size, 10% area gate.

The peak of the nitrogen signal corresponds to a concentration of approximately 3 atomic percent within the oxide.

4. Conclusions

Compressed air removal of particles may appear to be the logical choice, since it is a non-contact method, but the data suggests that it is very inefficient at removing particles <5µm in size. Within the statistics of the number of particles measured, the collodion treatment described is equivalent to ultrasonic cleaning in acetone. Both methods are extremely efficient at removing particles, including those <2µm in size. Despite one's intuition, the collodion treatment is extremely clean, and leaves no detectable residue in a UHV system as measured by TOF-SIMS, a technique known for it's sub-monolayer surface sensitivity. The most intense characteristic fragment for the collodion, NO$_2^+$ at mass 46, could not be detected on the sample following collodion removal, nor could other characteristic fragment ions. Not surprisingly, since no residue was detected by TOF-SIMS following collodion treatment, there was no measurable effect either on the nitrogen content of ultra-thin nitrided oxide films of approximately 8nm thickness (see figure 4 above), as measured by quadrupole SIMS. By contrast, some care must be taken to avoid film formation following solvent cleaning. Forced air drying is typically required. For samples where an ultrasonic solvent rinse may be unacceptable, the collodion treatment is an inexpensive and effective alternative for particle removal.

References
[1] R.Ariail, J. Antique Telescope Soc., Spring/Summer 1995

A. Benninghoven, P. Bertrand, H.-N. Migeon and H.W. Werner (Editors).
Proceedings of the 12th International Conference on Secondary Ion Mass Spectrometry,
Brussels, Belgium, 5-11 September 1999
© 2000 Elsevier Science B.V. All rights reserved.

INCORPORATION CONTROL OF LIGHT ELEMENTS FOR HIGH - QUALITY SEMICONDUCTING DIAMOND

I. Sakaguchi, H. Haneda, T. Ando, H. Kanda
NIRIM
1-1 Namiki Tsukuba, Ibaraki 305-0044, Japan.

1.Introduction.

The research of new property by trace element in the material is one of the important studies in scientific and technological field. We have been studing on the defect chemistry in ceramic materials using secondary ion mass spectrometry (SIMS) [1,2]. For two years, we have focused on elemental control in microwave assisted chemical vapor deposited (MWCVD) diamond. This CVD technique is firstly reported from NIRIM [3]. However, there is no report on the systematic study of impurity (hydrogen and silicon) and dopant (boron) incorporation in CVD diamond. Our diamond studies are confirmed as follows :

I) the control of hydrogen and silicon incorporation by oxygen addition [4,5],

II) the improvement of boron doping by oxygen addition [6].

III)a discovery of sulfur donor for the real n-type homoepitaxial diamond [7].

The important point in our diamond research using SIMS is a discovery of sulfur donor in CVD diamond. In this paper, we show the results of p-type and the real n-type semiconductor.

2.Experimental.

Homoepitaxial diamond films were grown on the diamond (100) and (111) substrates by using MWCVD. The growth parameters were: microwave power, 350-400 W; total pressure, 40 Torr; total gas flow, 200 ml/min; substrate temperature (monitored by an optical pyrometer), 840 degC. Methane concentration was fixed at 1.0 %. The diborane (B_2H_6) and H_2S were used as dopant sources for producing p- and n-type semiconducting diamond. The homoepitaxial samples having multi-layered structure deposited different gas condition were analyzed by SIMS with sample cooling system. The electrical property of the (100) homoepitaxial diamond was measured. The film was treated in heated solution of mixture of H_2SO_4 and HNO_3. Ohmic contacts were formed by evaporating Ti and annealing, and then Au was coated onto the corners of the sample. The conductivity, Hall coefficient, mobility were measured by means of the van der Pauw method. Finally, cathodoluminescence spectrum of n-type sample was measured.

3.Results and discussion.

3.1 Hydrogen and silicon.

The (100) homoepitaxial diamond contained silicon of 2×10^{18} atoms/cm^3 from the reactor materials and hydrogen of below the detection limit of current analysis. The (111) homoepitaxial diamond contained much hydrogen and silicon. Hydrogen incorporation originated to the surface terminated species. These impurities can be completely controlled by the oxygen addition into the feed gas. The key feature of oxygen addition is the low probability of oxygen incorporation in diamond.

3.2. Boron doping for p-type diamond.

Figure 1 illustrates the depth profiles obtained by SIMS in five layered (111) diamond films synthesized by sequentially introducing diborane in increasing concentration fashion into H_2-CH_4-(O_2) mixture during CVD. The depth profiles of

702

boron shows that boron concentration in CVD diamond can be controlled by the diborane concentration. The hydrogen incorporation is detected in (111) homoepitaxial diamond. Hydrogen incorporation increasing diborane concentration shows the different behaviour, indicating that the source of hydrogen is the surface terminated hydrogen and B-related species. The increase of hydrogen with increasing B concentration, giving evidence for the predicted B-H interactions, was usually observed in (111) diamond films with low hydrogen concentration by oxygen addition (> 0.3 %) into the feed gas. Si concentration decreases with increasing B concentration in (111) diamond. The same behaviour of Si incorporation was also deteced in (100) diamond. It is noted that the silicon concentration in (100) homoepitaxial diamond deposited with the addition of diborane of 0.5 ppm is comparable to that of boron. The suppression of silicon incorporation becomes an important process for high-quality semiconducting diamond. The effect of oxygen on Si incorporation is indicated in Fig. 1 (b). Si concentration indicates a constant value in CVD diamond layers, indicating

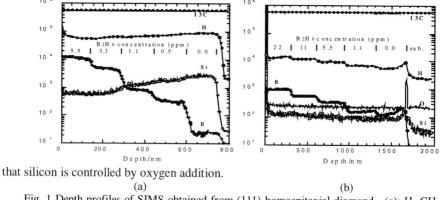

that silicon is controlled by oxygen addition.

(a) (b)

Fig. 1 Depth profiles of SIMS obtained from (111) homoepitaxial diamond. (a): H₂-CH₄-B₂H₆, (b): H₂-CH₄-O₂-B₂H₆.

The calibration curves of boron determined in (100) and (111) diamond films are shown in Fig. 2. The preferential incorporation of B in (111) diamond was considered to be due to the growth property of diamond.

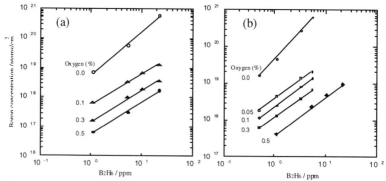

Fig. 2 Calibration of boron in (100) and (111) homoepitaxial diamond. (a) and (b) show the results in (100) and (111) diamond.

The boron concentration in (100) and (111) diamond deposited without oxygen was proportional to the 1.5 and 1.7 power of the diborane concentration. This is an evidence that B in excess incorporates in diamond.The increase of B in excess may arise the reduction of diamond quality.

B concentration in (100) and (111) diamond decreases with increasing the amount of oxygen addition. Boron concentration is proportional to the 1.0 power of the diborane concentration, indicating that oxygen suppresses B in excess. Moreover, the electrical property of (100) homoepitaxial diamond tends to improve by oxygen addition.

3.3. A discovery of sulfur donor in diamond. Figure 3 shows the depth profile in three layered (100) homoepitaxial diamond synthesized with three different H2S concentration from substrate. This reveals that sulfur intensities in the (100) homoepitaxial films increase from 4×10^{-5} to 9×10^{-5} in $^{32}S/^{13}C$ with increasing H_2S concentration. Sulfur concentration in (100) homoepitaxial diamond is estimated to be about 10^{17} atoms/cm^3. The hydrogen intensity was a constant in these layers and substrate, indicating the hydrogen background in this measurement. Si concentration decreased from 2×10^{18} to 4×10^{16} atoms/cm^3 by the increase in the H_2S addition from 0 to 100 ppm.

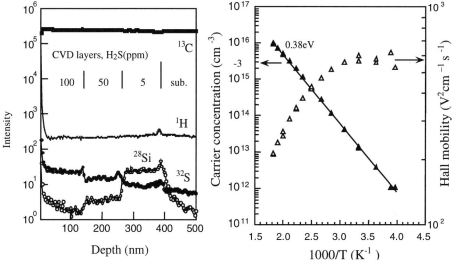

Fig. 3 Depth profile of S-doped (100) homoepitaxial diamond. C and H intensities were measured for 1 s. Si and S showed intensities for 10 s.

Fig. 4 Carrier concentration and Hall mobility as a function of reciprocal temperature.

The Hall effect measurements were carried out using the (100) homoepitaxial diamond films with the 1-μm-thick. The S-doped (100) homoepitaxial diamond films showed n-type conduction. Figure 4 indicates the carrier concentration and resistivity as a function of reciprocal temperature. The impurity level by sulfur in the film was estimated to be 0.38 eV below the conduction band minimum. The carrier concentration and resistivity at room temperature are 4×10^{13} cm^{-3} and 766 Ωcm. The Hall mobility of this film is 597 cm^{2}V^{-1}s^{-1} at room temperature. The mobility decreased with increasing temperature approximately with the relationship of $T^{-1.5}$ in the range of 350 - 450 K. In the temperature over 450 K, the Hall motilies show the departure from above relationship.

Figure 5 shows the near band-gap CL spectra of same diamond films in Fig. 4. The free (FE) and bound (BE, excitons bound to S donor) exciton peaks are observed. These peaks are the evidence of the reasonable quality of S-doped (100) diamond.

Nitrogen is well known impurity in diamond to make the donor level of 1.7 eV below the conduction band minimum[8]. The donor levels of 0.38 eV by sulfur in diamond are shallow compared with that of nitrogen. The Hall mobility decreases with increasing temperature by the phonon scattering mechanism [9], and this is another evidence of the reasonable quality of S-doped (100) homoepitaxial diamond. It is concluded that sulfur occupies the substitutional sites in diamond and makes a donor level below the conduction band minimum. There are a few reports on n-type (111) homoepitaxial diamond doped with phosphorus. Koizumi et al. [10] reported n-type conduction of phosphorus doped (111) homoepitaxial diamond deposited extremely low methane concentration and high substrate temperature and high total pressure. Saito et al. [12] shows the first report of n-type conduction in P-doped (111) homoepitaxial diamond with

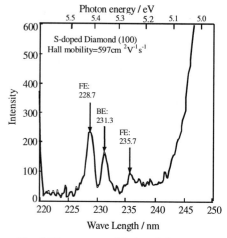

Fig. 5 CL spectrum of S-doped diamond.

negative temperature dependence of Hall mobility. However, the Hall mobility is very low (3.5 $cm^2V^{-1}s^{-1}$) at room temperature. We have synthesized the (100) and (111) homoepitaxial diamond films with H_2-CH_4-O_2-PH_3 gas system. Both homoepitaxial films contained phosphorus of about 2×10^{17} atoms/cm^3 and hydrogen and silicon impurities below their detection limits. These films are the good insulator.

References

[1] H. Haneda and C. Monty, J. Am. Ceram. Soc., 72, 1153 (1989).
[2] I. Sakaguchi, V. Srikanth, T. Ikegami, and H. Haneda, J. Am. Ceram, Soc., 78, 2557 (1995).
[3] M. Kamo, Y. Sato, S. Matsumoto and N. Setaka, J. Cryst. Growth, 62, 642, (1983).
[4] I. Sakaguchi, M. N.-Gamo, K. P. Loh, H. Haneda, S. Hishita, T. Ando, Appl. Phys. Lett., 71, 629 (1997).
[5] I. Sakaguchi, M. N.-Gamo, K. P. Loh, H. Haneda, S. Hishita, T. Ando, Appl. Phys. Lett., 73, 2675 (1998).
[6] I. Sakaguchi, M. N.-Gamo, K. P. Loh, H. Haneda, K. Yamamoto and T. Ando, Diamond. Relat. Mater., 7, 1144 (1998).
[7] I. Sakaguchi, M. N.-Gamo, K. Ushizawa, H. Haneda, E. Yasu, T. Suzuki, and T. Ando, submitted to Appl. Phys. Lett.
[8] R.G. Farrer, Solid State Commun., 7, 685 (1969).
[9] A. T. Collins, The properties of diamond, ed. J. E. Field (Academic Press, London, 1979) Chap. 3.
[10] S. Koizumi, M. Kamo, Y. Sato, H. Ozaki and T. Inuzuka, Appl. Phys. Lett. 71, 1065 (1997).
[11] S. Bohr, R. Haubner, and B. Lux, Diamond Relat. Mater., 4, 133 (1995).
[12] T. Saito, M. Kameta, K. Kusakabe, H. Maeda, Y. Hayashi and T. Asano, Jpn. J. Appl. Phys. 37, L543 (1998).

A. Benninghoven, P. Bertrand, H.-N. Migeon and H.W. Werner (Editors).
Proceedings of the 12th International Conference on Secondary Ion Mass Spectrometry,
Brussels, Belgium, 5-11 September 1999
© 2000 Elsevier Science B.V. All rights reserved.

SIMS INVESTIGATION OF THE DISSOCIATION OF Al$_2$O$_3$(0001) SUBSTRATES DURING MBE GROWTH OF GaN THIN SOLID FILMS

J. S. Solomon*
University of Dayton Research Institute
Dayton, OH 45504-0167, USA,
JAMES.SOLOMON@ML.AFRL.AF.MIL
J. E. Van Nostrand
Air Force Research Laboratory, Materials and Manufacturing Directorate
Wright-Patterson AFB, OH 45433-7322, USA

1. Introduction

There is considerable interest in GaN based optoelectronic devices as photodetectors, light emitting diodes and high temperature electronics. Despite the rapid developmental successes with GaN, many problems remain that hinder further progress. Among them is a lack of understanding of the nature of and mechanisms contributing to impurity incorporation.

Currently, the substrate of choice for GaN growth is Al$_2$O$_3$ (0001) or sapphire. This is because it has a reasonably low cost and wide availability. One nearly universal aspect of unintentionally doped GaN films grown on sapphire by any technique is an n-type background carrier concentration, the source of which has been attributed to impurities such as silicon or oxygen, or to native defects such as N vacancies. The role of Ga and N vacancies in doping, as well as the incorporation mechanisms of impurities must be clearly understood if progress in wide-bandgap semiconductor devices is to continue at its current pace.

In this paper SIMS is used to investigate autodoping in gas source MBE grown GaN on Al$_2$O$_3$ (0001). Oxygen and aluminum doping is shown to emanate from the substrate. Various growth parameters, including intentional doping, are shown to affect oxygen and aluminum levels and distribution.

2. Experimental

A highly modified Varian 360 molecular beam epitaxy system was used to grow the III-nitride films using ammonia as the nitrogen source. Prior to growth, the sapphire surface is exposed to ammonia for one minute. Following the one minute ammonia exposure, a 20nm AlN buffer layer is deposited at 800 °C, followed by 2.0 μm of GaN and 0.5 μm of Al$_x$Ga$_{(1-x)}$N. From cross-sectional transmission electron microscopy on several samples, we estimate the dislocation density to consistently be ~10^9 cm^{-2} near the GaN/AlN interface, but only 3-5×10^8 cm^{-2} at the surface of the 2 μm thick GaN film. Doping with Si occurred in the GaN layer at the level of 1.0×10^{17} cm^{-3}.

The SIMS analyses were performed with a quadrupole-based instrument using 5keV cesium at normal incidence. Sensitivity factors for aluminum, carbon, oxygen, and silicon were obtained from implanted, undoped epitaxial GaN grown on sapphire. Table 1 lists the sensitivity factors for the implanted standards referenced to GaN$^-$.

Table 1. Relative sensitivity factors in GaN with 10keV cesium using GaN⁻ as reference.

Implant Specie	RSF(cm^{-3})
Aluminum	4.7×10^{22}
Carbon	2.1×10^{19}
Oxygen	5.6×10^{18}
Silicon	7.4×10^{19}

3. Results and Discussion

SIMS depth profiles of aluminum and oxygen in Figure 1 show that with a growth temperature of 800°C both aluminum and oxygen out-diffuse from the sapphire substrate to a depth of about one micron with aluminum and oxygen levels from 10^{18}/cm^3 to 10^{19}/cm^3. For thicker films the aluminum and oxygen concentrations remain fairly constant at these levels throughout the remaining GaN layer. Figure 1 also shows that success in suppressing aluminum and oxygen autodoping is achieved by intentionally doping with 4×10^{17}/cm^3. Furthermore, a silicon doping level of approximately 1×10^{17}/cm^3 is sufficient to completely suppress aluminum and oxygen out-diffusion.

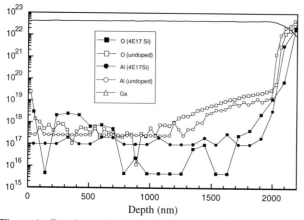

concentration (atoms/cm^3)	Hall Mobility (cm^2/Vs)
undoped	25
5.0×10^{17}	152
7.0×10^{17}	176
1.3×10^{18}	147
1.0×10^{20}	121

Table 2. Hall mobility vs. silicon concentration in silicon doped MBE grown GaN on sapphire substrates.

Figure 1. Depth profiles of aluminum, gallium and oxygen from MBE grown GaN on sapphire, with and without intentional silicon doping.

Table 2 lists the Hall mobility as a function of silicon concentration in the silicon doped MBE grown GaN. The mobility peaks at 7×10^{17} Si atoms/cm^3.

4. Conclusion

The increase in mobility with the presence of silicon confirms that the cause of low mobility is the presence of oxygen due to autodoping from the substrate during growth. The decrease in mobility with silicon concentrations above 1×10^{18} atoms/cm^3 is most likely due to scattering from ionized Si. Another possibility for decreased mobility is lattice dislocations. However, the mobility would have a constant upper limit when influenced by dislocations. As shown in Table 2, this was not the case.

* Corresponding author.

* Work supported by the Materials Directorate, Air Force Research Laboratory, United States Air Force, Wright-Patterson AFB, OH 45433.

TOF-SIMS ANALYSES ON CONTAMINATION INDUCED BY PLASMA ETCHING OF SILICON OXIDE

F. Zanderigo[#], A. Losavio[#], G. Pavia[#], L. Vanzetti[§], S. Ferrari[&] and G.Queirolo[#]

[#] STMicroelectronics, Via Olivetti 2, 20041 Agrate Brianza, Milan, Italy

E-mail: Federica.Zanderigo@st.com

[&] Laboratorio MDM-INFM, Via Olivetti 2, 20041 Agrate Brianza, Milan, Italy

[§] ITC-irst, 38050 Povo-Trento, Italy

1. Introduction

Reactive ion etching (RIE) of SiO_2 is widely used in semiconductor industry to satisfy the requirements of anisotropy and selectivity versus silicon. Usually based on CF_4 plasma, it can induce surface and sub-surface modifications, which depend on the competition between the Si etch rate and the deposition of a polymeric material [1].

An example of its impact on the electrical behavior of devices was provided by trend charts of sheet resistance values measured on low doped silicon layers, which displayed significant variations correlated with specific RIE processes. Post-oxidation treatments performed just after the SiO_2 dry etching proved the same dependence, confirming that this step was introducing detrimental side effects on the properties of the silicon substrate.

TOF-SIMS depth profiles were performed on test samples in order to compare the contaminating film left by different RIE processes. XPS analyses supplied information on the chemical structure of the polymer and TEM observations showed the corresponding morphological characteristics.

2. Experimental

A tunnel oxide of 7 nm was grown on p-type <100> Si wafers and removed with a RIE apparatus used in different conditions. In one case (process "A") an Ar, CHF_3, CF_4 gas mixture was applied with a radiofrequency power of 700 W at a pressure of 175 mT. In another case (process "B"), only CF_4 was used at a radiofrequency power of 50 W at a pressure of 400 mT.

Dual beam depth profiles were acquired by means of CAMECA TOF-SIMS IV [2] with the following experimental conditions: sputtering with Ar^+ 1kV 10 nA; analysis with Ga 25 kV 2.5 pA (mass resolution of 8500 at 28 amu). The sputtered and analyzed areas were respectively 300 x 300 μm^2 and 100 x 100 μm^2.

XPS measurements were performed using a Scienta Esca-200 system equipped with a monochromatized Al Kalfa (1486.6 eV) source and characterized by an overall energy resolution of 0.4 eV.

TEM observations have been performed using a LEO 922 OMEGA (in-column energy-filtered TEM, operating at 200 kV). The cross sections have been prepared via mechanical thinning down to 20 μm followed by ion milling.

3. Results and discussion

Figures 1 and 2 show the TOF-SIMS depth profiles acquired on samples "A" and "B".

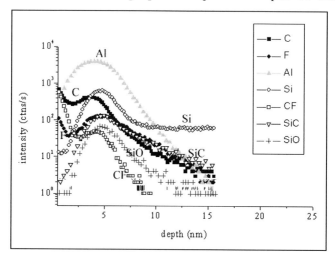

Fig. 1: TOF-SIMS depth profile performed on sample "A" (RIE with Ar, CHF_3, CF_4)

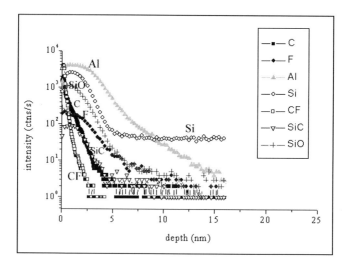

Fig. 2: TOF-SIMS depth profile performed on sample "B" (RIE with CF_4)

Both processes leave on the silicon surface a contaminating layer rich in C and F, but the corresponding thickness and the abundance of the various species are quite different. This result can be mainly ascribed to the different chemistry involved in the two RIE treatments. The presence of CHF_3 in the process "A" enhances the production rate of CF_2 and CF radicals, which are responsible for the fluorocarbon polymer deposition [1] [3], and causes the formation of a thicker layer. Though the contaminating film on the sample "B" grows slower, it cannot be completely removed during the process due to the low rf power and the low etch rate.

The comparison between the surface composition of the two samples could be misleading, because every semi-quantitative evaluation needs to be referred to the same matrix signal, but in this case the matrix itself seems to be different (a polymeric coverage in sample "A", contaminated silicon in sample "B").

Both profiles show a layer of SiO_2 at the interface with silicon. In the sample "A" the SiO signal is buried by C and F, as expected because of the air exposure and the oxygen permeation of the polymer [3]. In addition, the SiC signal, particularly deep in sample "A", may explain the slow down effect of the RIE process on the subsequent post-oxidation. Besides the presence of the fluorocarbon polymer, TOF-SIMS profiles underlined a strong Al contamination, which can be explained by the sputtering of reactive ions against the walls of the reactor [4].

Figures 3 and 4 report the XPS data showing the C 1s binding energy region of samples "A" and "B".

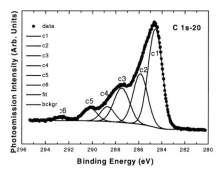

Fig. 3: C 1s core level from sample "A". At least six different components can be recognized to fit the whole

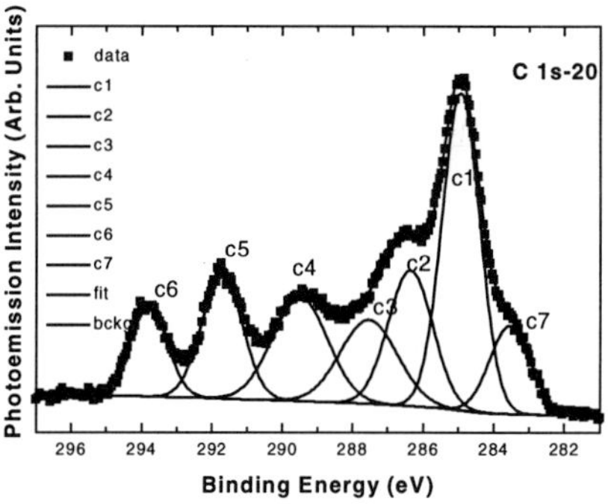

Fig. 4: C 1s core level from sample "B". Seven different components can be be used for the deconvolution of the whole signal.

The C core level was detected with an emission angle of 20°. Several components can be recognized to fit the whole signal, and precisely C_1 : C-C, C_2 : CH_x, C_3 : C-OH, C_4 : O=C-OH, C_5 : CHF, C_6 : CF_x, and C_7 : C-Si. The structure of sample "A" is more C-like than the structure of sample "B", at the expense of CF_x and CHF components. That is expected from the literature [3], because at high energy F atoms can be preferentially sputtered, leaving a "diamond-like" C deposit. The C-Si type bonding of sample "A" becomes comparable to the signal of sample "B" as soon as the emission angle is increased, because the sampling is deeper and the interface of the thicker film can be detected.

The thickness of the contaminating film can be evaluated by considering the attenuation of the elemental Si 2p signal detected at 90° with respect to a reference sample (clean silicon). By assuming an escape depth λ_{layer} of 3 nm and by using the formula $d_{layer} = \lambda_{layer} \cdot \ln(I_0/I)$, where I_0 and I correspond to the reference and to the samples "A" and "B", d_{layer} is respectively 8,1 and 2,3 nm. This estimation confirms the values obtained by means of TOF-SIMS by assuming the same sputter rate of a clean silicon dioxide. Actually, both these techniques need an assumption and can provide only indirect estimations.

710

TEM analyses have been performed in order to investigate directly the morphological properties so far suggested. As shown by the cross sections reported in figure 5 and 6, the film of sample "A" has a double structure corresponding to the polymer and the silicon oxide, whereas the layer of sample "B" is much thinner and doesn't show any internal interface. The measured thicknesses, respectively 6 and 2,3 nm, were used to calibrate the depth scale of the TOF-SIMS profiles.

Fig.: 5 TEM cross section on sample "A"   Fig.: 6: TEM cross section on sample "B"

4. Conclusion

Two different RIE processes were characterized by means of TOF-SIMS, XPS and TEM analyses. A fluorocarbon polymer was detected on the samples prepared with the two dry etching treatments. The main differences between them were discussed and the chemical structure as well as the thickness of the layer was investigated.

TOF-SIMS technique is a powerful tool to detect such a contamination and can be used to monitor any possible impact of the RIE process on electrical properties of devices.

References

[1] E. Kay, Surf. Sci., 1984
[2] E. Niehiuis, T. Heller, C. Bendel and J. Zehnpfenning, Proceedings of the 11th Intl. Conference, John Wiley & Sons, 1997, p 779
[3] Gottlieb, S. Oehrlein and Young H. Lee, J. Vac. Sci. Technol. A 5 (4), 1987, 1585
[4] G. S.Oehrlein, R. G. Schad and M. A. Jaso, Surf. Interface. Anal 8, 243, 1986

A. Benninghoven, P. Bertrand, H.-N. Migeon and H.W. Werner (Editors).
Proceedings of the 12th International Conference on Secondary Ion Mass Spectrometry,
Brussels, Belgium, 5-11 September 1999
© 2000 Elsevier Science B.V. All rights reserved.

SIMS DEPTH PROFILING OF Si$_{1-x}$Ge$_x$/Si HETEROSTRUCTURES[*]

Gui Dong [1]   Qin Chao [1]   Zhu Yizheng [1]   Cha Liangzhen [1]   F. Desse [2]   M. Schuhmacher [2]

[1] Department of Electronic Engineering, Tsinghua University, Beijing 100084, P. R. China
chalz@mail.tsinghua.edu.cn
[2] CAMECA, 103, Boulevard Saint Denis 92400 Courbevoie, France

1. Introduction

Si$_{1-x}$Ge$_x$ alloys attract more and more attention due to their high performance and potential application in optoelectronics and microelectronics. SIMS has been used to determine the composition of Si$_{1-x}$Ge$_x$ [1]. Most of the results published were concentrated on the germanium fraction less than 0.4 [1-3]. The matrix effects in Si$_{1-x}$Ge$_x$ alloys are reported to be small when x<0.3 [3, 4]. But in the case of large Ge fraction, the SIMS experimental results about matrix effects are meager and large discrepancies were observed by different authors. J. A. Jackman *et al* reported that the ion yield of Si$^+$ and Ge$^+$ increased significantly with a small dependence on the energy of primary O$_2^+$ beam when Ge fraction is greater than 0.3. It was found by P. C. Zalm *et al*[3] that the ion yield of Ge$^+$ was always reduced and the reduction became more pronounced with increasing x and O$_2^+$ primary ion energy. Both of the above investigations were carried out on CAMECA IMS 4f instruments.

The purpose of this study is to expand the research of the matrix effects in Si$_{1-x}$Ge$_x$ to high germanium composition fraction (x>0.5). Quantitative depth profiles of matrix elements in the Si$_{1-x}$Ge$_x$ multilayers are expected to be obtained by SIMS.

2. Experimental

The samples were grown by low temperature MBE (<500°C), by which one can obtain arbitrary dopant profiles and precisely control thickness and composition of the alloy layer. Furthermore, it reduces the adatom diffusion, which suppresses roughening consequently. Atomically-smooth surfaces can be obtained with large Ge fraction (>0.5) in low temperature growth[5]. Both samples 980317 and 980318 have four B-doped Si$_{1-x}$Ge$_x$ layers (0.5< x <0.78) with decreasing germanium fraction grown on the silicon substrate, as shown in Fig.1. The Ge fractions are 0.78, 0.76, 0.72, 0.69 and 0.65, 0.61, 0.55, 0.5 for 980317 and 980318 respectively. Sample 980612 has only one Si$_{1-x}$Ge$_x$ layer with x = 0.3 grown on the Si substrate. The compositions of the samples have been pre-calibrated by RBS and AES.

The SIMS experiments were performed on an IMS 6f instrument in CAMECA Application Lab. The samples were bombarded by an O$_2^+$ primary beam with oxygen flooding. The net impact energy of the primary beam was 1 keV only, which is a state-of-the-art

---

[*] This work is supported by the Doctoral Dissertation Foundation of Graduate school, Tsinghua University

technique of CAMECA instruments[6]. Thanks to the improvement of low impact energy technique, good depth resolution can be obtained with reasonable sputtering rate. The real impact angle was 56°. The primary beam was raster-scanned across an area of 180×180 μm^2 and the positive secondary ions were collected in the center of scanned area within a diameter of 3 μm.

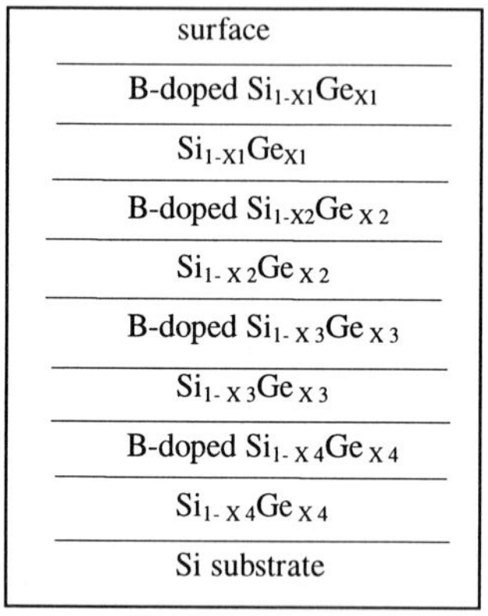

surface
B-doped Si1-X1GeX1
Si1-X1GeX1
B-doped Si1-X2GeX2
Si1-X2GeX2
B-doped Si1-X3GeX3
Si1-X3GeX3
B-doped Si1-X4GeX4
Si1-X4GeX4
Si substrate

Fig.1 The schematic structure of the samples 980317 and 980318.

Intensity (cps)
sputter time (s)
30Si+
11B+
70Ge+
0
500
1000
1500
2000

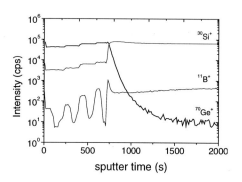

Fig.2 Depth profiles of sample 980317

3. Results and discussion

Fig.2 shows the depth profiles of sample 980317. Note that the intensity of $^{70}Ge^+$ increases with decreasing Ge fraction in the four $Si_{1-x}Ge_x$ layers. To highlight the matrix effects occurring in SiGe alloys, the intensities of secondary $^{30}Si^+$ and $^{70}Ge^+$ are normalized with respect to the intensity of $^{30}Si^+$ in the silicon substrate, as shown in Fig.3. The normalized $^{30}Si^+$ intensity $^{30}I_N^+$ decreases from 92% to 5% when silicon fraction decreases from 70% to 22%. In the range of interest (x > 0.5), $^{30}I_N^+$ is much less than its composition fractions. It's notable that the normalized $^{70}Ge^+$ intensity $^{70}I_N^+$ has different behavior from $^{30}I_N^+$. When x is

CAMECA 6f 1keV O2+
30IN+
70IN+
Normalized Intensity
Ge Fraction x
0.0
0.4
0.8
1.2
1.6
2.0
2.4
0.3
0.4
0.5
0.6
0.7
0.8

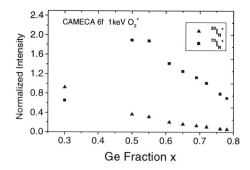

Fig.3 Normalized intensities of $^{30}Si^+$ and $^{70}Ge^+$ in $Si_{1-x}Ge_x$ layers versus different Ge fraction.

less than 0.5, $^{70}I_N^+$ increases with x. Then $^{70}I_N^+$ decreases with increasing x after reaching the maximum around x = 0.5. The results show that the determination of matrix elements is subject to very strong matrix effects when analyzing $Si_{1-x}Ge_x$ multilayers with larger Ge fraction.

Fig.4 shows the useful secondary ion yield of Si and Ge versus the germanium fraction x. The useful secondary ion yield Y_{UA}^+ is the product of the secondary ion yield[7] and the overall transmission, which can be given by the following equation:

$$Y_{UA}^+ = I_A^+ / I_P \, \alpha_A C_A$$

where Y_{UA}^+, I_A^+, I_P, α_A and C_A are useful secondary ion yield, secondary ion intensity, primary beam intensity, isotope abundance and concentration, respectively.

The decrease of Y_{USi}^+ and Y_{UGe}^+ in larger Ge fraction range can be partly explained by the oxygen enhancement effect on positive secondary ion emission. The incorporated oxygen concentration on the surface decreases with increasing Ge fraction. This is due to that the affinity towards oxygen is lower for Ge than Si and the sputtering yield of $Si_{1-x}Ge_x$ alloys increases with x. As a result, both of Y_{USi}^+ and Y_{UGe}^+ decrease with increasing Ge fraction when x greater than 0.5.

However, Y_{USi}^+ and Y_{UGe}^+ decrease in a similar way when x is larger than 0.5. Therefore, it is possible to quantify the concentration ratio $C_{Ge}/C_{Si} = x/(1-x)$ from the intensity ratio $^{70}I_{Ge}^+/^{30}I_{Si}^+$, as shown in Fig.5. The good linearity of this curve means that it can serve as a calibration curve.

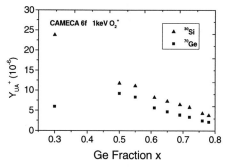
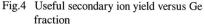

Fig.4   Useful secondary ion yield versus Ge fraction

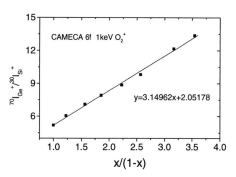

Fig.5   Calibration curve of intensity ratio versus concentration ratio

Fig.6 shows the quantitative depth profiles of the two $Si_{1-x}Ge_x$ multilayers. The depth profiles of the matrix elements were quantified by using the calibration curve aforementioned. The Ge concentrations determined in this way are coincident with the results obtained by RBS.

The depth profiles of boron were calibrated by a ^{11}B-implanted reference material with a dose of 1×10^{13} atom/cm^2. For depth calibration, the crater depth was measured by profile

714

stylus after the depth profiling finished. Accurate calibration of the boron concentration and depth scale will be presented elsewhere.

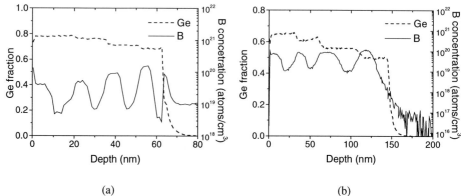

(a)   (b)

Fig.6   Quantitative depth profiles of B-doped $Si_{1-x}Ge_x$ heterostructures. (a) Depth profiles of sample 980317. (b) Depth profiles of sample 980318.

4. Conclusion

The strong matrix effects in $Si_{1-x}Ge_x$ multilayers with x greater than 0.5 have been studied in this paper. Both normalized intensity and useful secondary ion yield of Si and Ge decrease with increasing Ge fraction above 0.5. The evolution of the useful secondary ion yield of Si versus Ge fraction is similar to that of Ge when Ge fraction is greater than 0.5. The good linearity of the calibration curve of intensity ratio versus composition ratio provides a practical way to determine the composition of $Si_{1-x}Ge_x$ alloys. Quantitative depth profiles of matrix elements in $Si_{1-x}Ge_x$ multilayers have been obtained.

Acknowledgements

The authors would like to thank Dr. Liu Jinping for growing the SiGe samples and Mr. Ding Ming for RBS analysis.

References:
[1] G. Prudon, B. Gautier and J. C. Dupuy et al, Thin Solid Films, 294(1997) 54
[2] U. Zastrow, L. Vescan and R. Butz et al, Proceedings of SIMS IX, ed. by A. Benninghoven, Y. Nihei and R. Shimizu et al, John Wiley & Sons, (1994) 702
[3] P. C. Zalm, C. J. Vriezema and D. J. Gravesteijn et al, Surf. Interf. Anal., 17(1991) 556
[4] J. A. Jackman, L. Dignard-Bailley and R. S. Storey et al, Nucl. Instru. Meth. Phys. Res. B45(1990) 592
[5] J. P. Liu, M. Y. Kong and J. P. Li et al, J. Cryt. Grow., 193(1998) 535
[6] CAMECA Technical Note, Shallow Depth Profiling with the CAMECA IMS 6f, (1998)
[7] ISO STANDARD: Surface Chemical Analysis - Vocabulary (Draft), (1997) 18

A. Benninghoven, P. Bertrand, H.-N. Migeon and H.W. Werner (Editors).
Proceedings of the 12th International Conference on Secondary Ion Mass Spectrometry,
Brussels, Belgium, 5-11 September 1999
© 2000 Elsevier Science B.V. All rights reserved.

715

SIMS STUDY OF Si/SiGe MULTIPLE QUANTUM WELLS

R.Liu* [1], S.L.Lim[1], A.T.S. Wee[1],
E.S. Tok[2], W.C. Tjiu[2], J. Zhang[3]
1. Department of Physics, National University of Singapore,
Kent Ridge, Singapore 119260
2. Department of Materials Science, National University of Singapore,
Kent Ridge, Singapore 119260
3. Department of Physics and Centre for Electronic Materials and Devices,
The Blackett Laboratory, Imperial College
Prince Consort Road London SW& 2BZ, UK,s *email: phyliur@nus.edu.sg

1. Introduction

The development of materials growth technologies [1-4] has largely improved the fabrication of semiconductor heterostructures with very abrupt interfaces. Silicon-germanium heterostructures have been of growing interest due to their attractive physical and potentially useful device properties. The gas source epitaxial deposition methods of SiGe layers on Si has recently led to single and multiple quantum wells (QWs) with promising structural and opto-electronic properties.[5] Among other analytical methods secondary ion mass spectrometry (SIMS) has been extensively used to characterize Si/SiGe structures. Low energy primary beams have been shown to give good depth resolution of a few nanometers. In TOF-SIMS depth profiling (dual-beam mode), using a low energy (0.5-3 keV) sputter gun operating with different sputter gases (Ar, O_2, SF_6), a decay length below 2.5 nm was achieved.[6] With a deceleration /extraction electrode in primary beam line of a magnetic-sector SIMS instrument, primary beams with net energy well below 1 keV can produced. For the APCVD grown Si(Ge δ doping) sample, Z.X. Jiang et al attained the decay lengths (distance over which the intensity drops by a factor of e) of 2.5, 1.1, and 0.9 nm using 2.0, 1.0, 0.7 keV beams respectively.[7] This depth resolution can be severely degraded by a number of factors, one of the more important being the development of topography in the crater bottom during analysis.[8-10]

In this letter, we use the steepness of the leading/trailing edge of a QW profile (i.e. λ_u λ_d – the upslope and downslope decay length) to quantify the depth resolution. Si_{1-x} Ge_x / Si, (x < 0.3) single and multiple quantum well (MQW) structures grown by Gas Source Molecular Beam Epitaxy (GSMBE) have been investigated by SIMS using O_2^+ primary beams. This study focuses on the depth resolution attainable by a CAMECA IMS-6f under a variety of experimental conditions such as primary beam energy and incident angle.

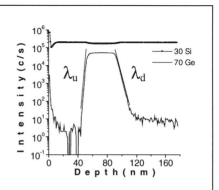

Fig 1. SIMS depth profile for a single QW structure A using a O_2^+ Primary beam of 2.5 keV at 60° incidence

2. Experimental

The structures examined in this work have been grown by GS-MBE, and include a single quantum well structure (A) and three multiple quantum wells structures(B, C and D). The single SiGe quantum well (A) has a composition of 8% Ge with a structure: Si cap (60 nm) / SiGe (40 nm) / Si buffer / Si substrate. The multiple quantum well samples (B, C, D) have the following structures: [Si barrier (30nm) /SiGe well (15nm)] ×10 periods / Si buffer /Si substrate. The well compositions examined in this work were x = 0.10(B), 0.20 (C), 0.28 (D). [11]

A 1 keV O_2^+ primary beam at 60° and 45° off-normal, as well as different impact energies at 60° off-normal were used. Sputter crater profiles were measured with a mechanical stylus Tencor alpha-step 500 profilometer.

Impact Energy (keV)	E_p (keV)	E_s (keV)	λ_u (nm)	λ_d (nm)
1.0	3.0	2.0	**0.8**	**1.8**
1.5	4.5	3.0	**0.9**	**2.2**
2.5	7.5	5.0	**1.0**	**2.5**

Table 1. The λ_u , λ_d of single QW structure A for O_2^+ primary beam at 60° with different impact energies

3. Results and Discusion

Quantum wells are ideal structures to study depth resolution at interfaces because of their sharp transition regions. First, we analysed the single QW A and MQWs B, C, D at 60° to normal incidence using 1 keV, 1.5 keV, 2.5 keV impact energy (Fig 1 and Fig 2). These impact energies were obtained with different combinations of primary and secondary ion energies, namely E_p= 3 keV, E_s=2 keV; E_p= 4.5 keV, E_s=3 keV; and E_p=7.5 keV E_s=5 keV, respectively, since the nominal angle of incidence between the primary column and the sample normal is fixed at 30° in the IMS series of SIMS instruments.[12]

Table 1 shows the decay length λ_u and λ_d of the single QW structure A obtained under O_2^+ primary beam bombarded at 60° with different impact energies. As the impact energy increases, the decay length λ_d increase more rapidly than λ_u. Table 2 shows the decay lengths λ_u and λ_d of the MQW structure C ($Si_{1-x}Ge_x$ x=0.20) obtained under 2.5 keV O_2^+ primary beam bombarded at 60° incident angle. From the 1st QW to 10th QW, λ_u, λ_d are nearly same.

Second, we have analysed the single QW A and MQWs B using 1 keV impact energy at 60° and 45° off-normal in Fig 3. The decay lengths obtained at 60° (1keV) are shorter than those in Table 2 (2.5keV), but similarly constant in depth.

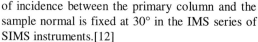

Fig 2. SIMS depth profile for MQW structure C using a O_2^+ primary beam of 2.5 keV at 60° incident angle

The No. of QW	λ_u (nm)	λ_d (nm)
1st	1.1	2.5
2nd	1.1	2.5
3rd	1.3	2.7
4th	1.1	2.6
5th	1.2	2.5
6th	1.2	2.5
7th	1.1	2.5
8th	1.1	2.5
9th	1.2	2.5
10th	1.1	2.4
Average	1.1	2.5

Table 2. The λ_u , λ_d of MQW C using 2.5 keV O_2^+ primary beam at 60° incident angle

Table 3 shows the decay length λ_u and λ_d of the MQWs B ($Si_{1-x}Ge_x$ x=0.10) obtained under 1.0 keV O_2^+ primary beam bombardment at 45° off-normal. From the 1st QW to 10th QW, the decay length λ_u, λ_d are very different to those in Table 2. They increase by between 2 to 4 times from the 4th QW to 10th QW. λ_u appears to be larger than λ_d for the 9th and 10th QW. This anomaly is due to the poor depth resolution causing at this depth adjacent peaks to overlap.

Fig. 4 shows AFM images obtained for MQWs B after 1 keV O_2^+ sputtering at 45° and 60° was stopped at the tenth QW layers as indicated. The images show an obvious change in surface roughness with incident angle. The root-mean-square (R_{rms}) roughness values for the two craters were determined to be: (a) 8.49 nm (45°), (b) 0.43 nm (60°). This shows that under 1 keV O_2^+ primary beam bombardment SiGe MQWs, the λ_u,λ_d strongly infected by primary beam incident angle. The model by Elst et al. [13] suggests that no roughening occurs beyond 60° because of the low concentration of incorporated oxygen. This work shows that good depth resolution can be achieved at 60° incident angle with λ_u, λ_d remaining nearly constant till a depth of at least 500 nm. At 45 ° incidence, λ_u, λ_d increase 2 to 4 times from 100 nm to 500 nm due to the onset of ripple formation. Jiang et al.[14] observed that the roughness reaches a minimum at θ = 60° under 0.5-2.0 keV O_2^+ bombardment at incident angles between 45° and 80°. They postulated

The No. of QW	λ_u (nm)	λ_d (nm)
1st	1.0	2.8
2nd	1.0	2.8
3rd	1.0	2.9
4th	1.3	3.0
5th	1.5	3.6
6th	2.3	3.6
7th	3.2	4.0
8th	4.5	4.6
9th	5.1	4.9
10th	5.9	4.5

Table 3. The λ_u , λ_d of MQW structure B using a 1.0 keV O_2^+ primary beam at 45° incident angle

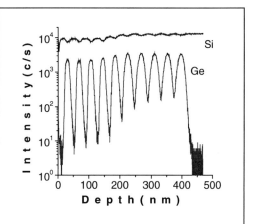

Fig 3. SIMS depth profile for MQW structure B using a O_2^+ primary beam of 1.0 keV at 45° incident angle

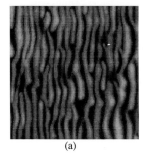

(a)

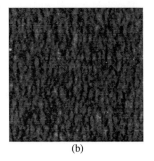

(b)

Figure 4. 2.0 x 2.0 μm² AFM images of (a) 45° and (b) 60° after 1 keV O_2^+ sputtering to the tenth QW layers respectively

that the inhomogeneous incorporation of oxygen combined with the sputtering rate dependence on surface topography and oxygen content play dominant roles in surface roughening.

4. Conclusion

High resolution SIMS depth profiles were obtained for the characterization of Si/SiGe QWs. To attain smaller decay lengths (i.e good depth resolution), the primary ion energy is less critical in the energy range 1 keV to 2.5 keV, but a 60° incident angle is necessary. This minimizes the degradation of depth resolution due to surface roughening. To obtain a decay length (λ_d) in the range of 2-3 nm, we can use 2.5 keV impact energy instead of 1 keV at 60° incident angle to increase the sensitivity to dopants. However to attain a decay length better than 2 nm, it is necessary to use less than 1 keV impact energy. For 1 keV O_2^+ primary beam at 60° incidence angle, we achieved a profile decay length $\lambda_d = 1.8$ nm for SiGe QW structure.

References

[1] D.A. Grutzmacher,T.O. Sedgwick, A. Powell, Appl. Phys. Lett. 63 (1993) 2531

[2] R.T. Carline, C. Pickering, Superlattices and Microstructures 14 (1993) 157

[3] B.S. Meyerson, Appl. Phys. Lett. (1986) 797

[4] A. Yamada, M. Tanda, J. Appl. Phys. (1991) 1008

[5] L.Vescan, A. Hartmann, K.Schmidt, Appl. Phys. Lett. 60 (1992) 2182

[6] D. Kruger, K. Iltgen, A. Benninghoven, J. Vac. Sci.Technol. B 16(1998) 292

[7] Z.X. Jiang and P.F.A. Alkemade, Eelke Algra and S.Radelaar, Surf. Interface Anal. 25 (1997) 285

[8] L. Kiong, A.T.S. Wee, R. Liu, S.L. Lim,   in Secondary Ion Mass Spectrometry, SIMS XII (in press)

[9] N. J. Montgomery, D.S. Phail, Mikrochim. Acta [Suppl.] 13 (1996) 419

[10] J.S. Pan, S.T. Tay, C.H.A. Huan and A.T.S. Wee, Surf. Interface Anal. 26 (1998) 930

[11] J.M. Fernandez, L. Hart, X.M. Zhang, J.Zhang, B.A. Joyce, J. Crystal Growth 164 (1996) 241

[12] SIMS-A Practical Handbook for Depth Profiling and Bulk Impurity analysis ed. by R.G. Wilson, F.A. Stevie, C. W. Magee, John Wiley & Sons. U.S.A. (1989) (part 1.3-2)

[13] K.Elst, W. Vandervorst, J. Alay, J. Snauwaert, and L Hellemans, J. Vac. Sci. Technol. B11 (1993) 1968

[14] Z.X. Jiang and P.F.A. Alkemade, Appl. Phys. Lett., 73 (1998) 315

A. Benninghoven, P. Bertrand, H.-N. Migeon and H.W. Werner (Editors).
Proceedings of the 12th International Conference on Secondary Ion Mass Spectrometry,
Brussels, Belgium, 5-11 September 1999

OPTIMISING PRIMER RESIDUE REMOVAL WITH THE AID OF SIMS, PURGE AND TRAP GAS CHROMATOGRAPHY MASS SPECTROMETRY, AND CONTACT ANGLE MEASUREMENTS

S. Lehto[a]*, J. Likonen[a], T. Riihisaari[c], S. Eränen[c], A. Kiviranta[b], J. Virtanen[b] and E. Sandell[b]

[a]Technical Research Centre of Finland, Chemical Technology, P.O. Box 1404, FIN-02044 VTT, Finland
*corresponding author, e-mail sari.lehto@vtt.fi
[b]Technical Research Centre of Finland, Chemical Technology, P.O. Box 1401, FIN-02044 VTT, Finland
[c]Technical Research Centre of Finland, Electronics, P.O. Box 1101, FIN-02044 VTT, Finland

1. Introduction

The requirement for cleaner processes in microelectronics device fabrication has lead to extensive studies on contamination of surfaces at various stages of manufacturing. Much attention has been paid to the detection of organic residues at trace level by using various surface analytical techniques. In our earlier investigation into residue detection in photoresist removal processes [1] it was observed that after the resist stripping step, residues of hexamethyldisilazane (HMDS) used as a primer, could still be found on the surface. This gave an incentive to take a closer look at the effectiveness of the cleaning baths used in the resist stripping procedure, for removing HMDS or rather its reaction product, trimethylsiloxane (TMS), from the wafer surface. The study presented here describes the application of SIMS, Purge and Trap Gas Chromatography Mass Spectrometry (P&T-GC/MS) and contact angle measurements to help selecting a suitable resist stripping procedure.

2. Experimental

Cleaned bare silicon wafers were vapor primed with HMDS at 1330 Pa at 150°C for 5 min to obtain an optimum coverage for resist layer application, and subsequently put through various resist stripping and cleaning cycles. A set of silicon wafers were put through a resist coating and baking step before the stripping and cleaning procedure, while another batch of samples were taken straight to the stripping and cleaning stage. The stripping procedures studied involved an organic remover (Posistrip® EKC830^{TM}) bath at 90°C alone or combined with the classic SC1 ($NH_3+H_2O_2+H_2O$) cleaning step at 65°C, ozone ashing and a Piranha ($H_2SO_4+(NH_4)_2S_2O_8$) bath at 90°C. After each bath wafers were rinsed with deionised water and dried in a centrifugal rinse and dryer. The organic remover and the Piranha bath were also applied on two types of oxidised wafers, 200 nm thick undensified low temperature oxide (LTO) and 100 nm thick thermal oxide (TOX) covered silicon wafers.

Treated wafers were analysed for residues using a VG IX70S double focusing magnetic sector SIMS. The Ga$^+$ primary ion beam of 8 keV energy was rastered over an area of 0.04 cm^2 and all data were collected under static conditions, the primary ion dose density did not exceed 1×10^{12} cm^{-2}. Positive secondary ion spectra at low resolution were acquired to detect the presence of TMS on the wafer surface, and to check for other impurities possibly introduced in the cleansing stage. A more quantitative measure of the TMS coverage was obtained by measuring the signal ratio of peaks at m/z 73 (SiC$_3$H$_9^+$) and 28 (^{28}Si$^+$) at a higher resolution of approximately 1000 (m/Δm at m/z 28) to separate the TMS peak from the interfering Si$_2$OH$^+$. The normalised TMS signal was assumed to be linearly related to the surface coverage as described in the literature [2, 3, 4]. Contact angles were measured using two techniques, a static drop method TIPPA and a dynamic SIGMA70 method, both using pure water as model liquid. Volatile organic compounds adsorbed on the wafer surfaces were identified with P&T-GC/MS. The test wafers were heated to 100°C in He carrier gas, the emanating volatile compounds were trapped at liquid nitrogen temperature and then desorbed into the analytical column of the GC/MS. The procedure and conditions used were optimised mainly for non-polar and slightly polar compounds whose boiling point is <300°C. Trimethylsilanol formed from TMS and HMDS was identified by its main fragment [Si(CH$_3$)$_2$OH]$^+$ at m/z 75.

3. Results and discussion

Examining the SIMS spectra showed that none of the cleaning methods was clearly superior to the others. Organic contamination was found on all treated samples often more abundant than on the non-treated wafers. Nevertheless, looking at the characteristic peaks of TMS differences were evident. After the organic remover treatment the peaks assigned to TMS at m/z 73 and 43 were still high when compared to those on the primed surface and considerably higher than in other samples (Figure 1). On the basis of the normalised TMS signal measured with higher resolution (given in Table 1) approximately 30 % of the TMS bonded in the priming step could still be found on the stripped silicon wafer surface. On the TOX and LTO wafer surfaces 40 % or 20 %, respectively, of the TMS detected on the primed wafer was still found. After the SC1 bath, though, the amount of TMS was in most of the samples reduced to the background level, as was the case also for the Piranha bath and the ozone stripper treatment.

These observations were confirmed by both contact angle measurements and the P&T-GC/MS results. The contact angle values measured for the primed silicon wafers for example, had a mean value of 72° whereas the primed sample stripped with the organic remover had a contact angle of 39° and the other samples approximately 16°. The cosine of the contact angle is linearly related to surface coverage [2] and can be compared to the normalised TMS signals obtained by SIMS. The reduction of TMS coverage after the remover bath for example, as derived from the contact angle measurements, was to 27 % of the coverage on the primed surface, and is in excellent agreement with the result obtained by SIMS. Similar results were obtained for the oxidised wafers.

By P&T-GC/MS the TMS residues, detected as trimethylsilanol formed in hydrolysis during the cleaning baths, were found on the silicon and TOX test wafers that were stripped with the organic remover. In addition, TMS residues were occasionally detected on the other wafers after the SC1 and Piranha baths, or ozone ashing. The analysis of the LTO wafers, however, showed no signs of trimethylsilanol, only other common hydrocarbon contamination was found. Since TMS residues were detected also on the LTO wafers by SIMS, the test wafers were hydrolysed further with sulfuric acid in dichloromethane and the extracts analysed with a GC/MS. The results of this experiment were finally convergent with those obtained by SIMS and the contact angle measurement.

Even though the organic remover bath studied here performs poorly as applied to removing primer residues, selecting a suitable resist stripping procedure depends on many other factors too. For patterned wafers with metal layers exposed, for example, the Piranha and SC1 baths cannot be applied. Plasma ashing treatments, even though efficient in removing photoresist layers, may cause damage of device structures and are slower than chemical baths. Organic removers, like Posistrip® EKC830[TM], normally remove the photoresist material efficiently without harming the structure and can be applied in a batch process. However, the failure in removing the primer residues might become of great significance at some point in the device fabrication process. In such a case both SIMS and P&T-GC/MS analysis, which can be performed on patterned samples as well, can provide useful information for deciding if the resist stripper procedure needs to be combined with an additional cleaning step to remove both the primer and resist residues.

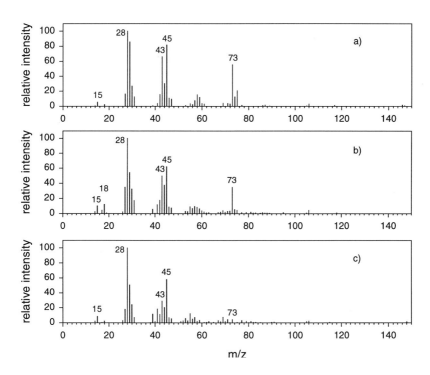

Figure 1. Positive secondary ion mass spectra of a) a primed silicon wafer, b) a primed wafer washed with organic remover and c) a primed and ozone ashed wafer.

Table 1. Normalised TMS signals of the samples measured. The relative standard deviations are derived from replicate measurements on replicate samples.

	Si		LTO		TOX	
	ratio	RSD	ratio	RSD	ratio	RSD
non-treated	0.0098	65%	0.011	94%	0.0036	16%
primed	0.49	17%	0.47	20%	0.40	26%
+ organic remover	0.15	16%	0.097	20%	0.16	19%
+ organic remover + SC1	0.037	123%				
+ Piranha	0.018	53%	0.0051	37%	0.0043	15%
+ ozone ashing	0.012	53%				
primed + resist coated & baked						
+ organic remover	0.062	1%				
+ organic remover + SC1	0.0037	35%				
+ Piranha	0.0064	31%				
+ ozone ashing	0.0030	42%				

4. Conclusions

The efficiency of four resist stripping treatments in removing the primer residues from the wafer surfaces was investigated. An organic solvent based remover bath was found to leave significant amounts of TMS on the surface. When combined with an SC1 cleaning step the residues were reduced to background level. The performance of the Piranha bath and the ozone ashing was significantly better but even then traces of TMS were occasionally found on the treated surfaces, indicating how difficult it is to remove.

Acknowledgements
This work was supported by the National Technology Agency (TEKES), Micro Analog Systems Ltd., Okmetic Ltd., Microchemistry Ltd., VTI Hamlin Ltd., Vaisala Ltd, Planar International Ltd. and Terapixel Ltd. Dr. J. Campbell (Helsinki University of Technology) is thanked for comments on the manuscript.

References
[1] T. Riihisaari, J. Likonen, A. Kiviranta, S. Eränen, S. Lehto, J. Tuominen, T. Lindblom and T. Muukkonen, Solid State Phenomena 65-66 (1999) 215
[2] J.J. Ponjeé, V.B. Marriott, M.C.B.A. Michielsen, F.J. Touwslager, P.N.T. van Velzen and H. van der Wel, J. Vac. Sci. Technol. B 8 (1990) 463
[3] E. Niehuis, P.N.T. van Velzen, J. Lub, T. Heller and A. Benninghoven, Surf. Interface Anal. 14 (1989) 135
[4] P.N.T. van Velzen, J.J. Ponjeé and A. Benninghoven, Appl. Surf. Sci. 37 (1989) 147

A. Benninghoven, P. Bertrand, H.-N. Migeon and H.W. Werner (Editors).
Proceedings of the 12th International Conference on Secondary Ion Mass Spectrometry,
Brussels, Belgium, 5-11 September 1999
© 2000 Elsevier Science B.V. All rights reserved.

SIMS CHARACTERIZATION OF a-Si LAYERS ON Si(001) SUBSTRATES

Anuradha Dhaul, R.K. Sharma, B.B. Sharma
Solid State Physics Laboratory
Lucknow Road, Delhi-110054, INDIA.

1. Introduction

Hydrogenated amorphous/micro-crystalline silicon (a-Si:H/μc-Si:H) layers grown on crystalline Si substrates by Plasma Enhanced Chemical Vapour Deposition (PECVD) Technique [1] are being used for improving the efficiency of solar cells [2]. The thickness of these layers is usually evaluated by optical interferometric/ ellipsometric methods [3]. In an earlier work Smith et al [4] employed Secondary Ion Mass Spectrometry (SIMS) to characterize amorphous regions in ion implanted Si substrates. We tried a similar approach to characterize PECVD grown a- Si:H layers on Si (001) substrates.

In the present work we observe a substantial shift in the secondary ion spectrum of a-Si:H layers compared to the crystalline substrate region and by selecting a suitably narrow energy slit it was possible to distinguish the two regions in the SIMS depth profiles.

2. Experimental

Measurements were performed using a CAMECA IMS4F ion microscope. A 12.5 KeV O_2^+ primary ion beam was employed. The primary ion beam was raster scanned over a specimen area of 250 x 250 μm^2 and positive secondary ions were collected. The primary ion beam current was 400 nA for all the measurements. $^{28}Si^+$ secondary ions were extracted with an accelerating voltage of 4500 volts. The energy spectrum of the secondary ions was recorded with the selection of energy slit from 5eV to 130 eV. An electron multiplier was used to detect the secondary ions. The depth profiles were calibrated by measuring the crater depths by a stylus profilometer after individual SIMS analysis.

The a-Si:H specimens were prepared at SSPL [5]. Heat treatment under Ar atmosphere for one hour at 600°C and 800°C was employed on two pieces from one of the samples to observe the effect of increased microcrystallinity in a-Si:H layers on the SIMS depth profiles.

3. Results and discussion

The energy distribution of secondary ions in the crystalline and amorphous regions is shown in fig. 1. The x-axis indicates the offset in the secondary ion accelerating voltage. The secondary ion accelerating voltage can be varied from 4375V to 4625V. When the energy slit is wide (fully) open (~130eV) the energy spectrums from the amorphous and crystalline regions are quite similar (plots a and b respectively). Although the energy spectrum from amorphous region is slightly shifted towards the high energy side (corresponding to a negative shift in the accelerating voltage) with respect to crystalline region, at 0 V offset, there is not much difference in the secondary ion intensity from the two regions. But, with a narrow energy slit (~ 5eV) there is a marked shift in the peak position of the corresponding energy spectrums (plots c and d) and at zero offset the secondary ion intensity from the amorphous region is negligibly small. It is also evident from this result that the secondary ion intensities from a-Si region would remain negligible upto an energy window ~10 eV. This effect was further utilised to obtain the depth profiles of a-Si:H on Si(001) structures.

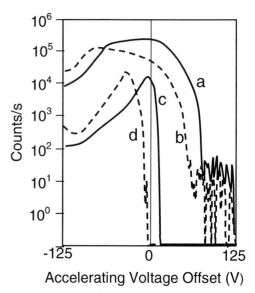

Fig.1 Si$^+$ secondary ion energy distribution for Si(001) (a and c) and a-Si:H (b and d). The energy window for a and b was 130 eV and that for c and d was 5eV.

Fig.2 shows the SIMS depth profiles for two different a-Si:H on Si(001) specimen having thickness of approximately 1500 and 3000 Å as estimated by ellipsometry. Plots a and c are for energy window ~130 eV and, b and d are for that of 10 eV. In these profiles there is a hump in the secondary ion intensity near the interface in all cases. The cause of this hump is not understood at present, but may be a result of interfacial oxygen as also indicated by the results given in [6]. However, an about four orders of magnitude difference in the secondary ion intensity from the two regions (with reduced energy window) makes them clearly distinguishable from each other. Also if the interface is marked approximately halfway between the hump and the mono-Si region, the thickness determined by the SIMS profile matches closely with that obtained from ellipsometry.

The shift in the secondary ion energy spectrum from the amorphous region with respect to the crystalline region can be understood in terms of the charging of the former during SIMS analysis due to its very high resistivity (10^6 Ωcm). Similar explanation was given by Smith et al [4] in case of ion implanted layers. They had shown that the charging effect can be minimized with the help of an electron shower. The conductivity of PECVD grown a-Si:H layers has been found to increase through the incorporation of micro-crystallinity through heat treatments[5] of these layers. The increased micro-crystallinity of these layers is therefore expected to reduce the charging effect. We annealed two pieces of another sample at 600 and 800°C in argon for one hour each. As expected, we observed a very little shift in the energy spectrums of the layers compared to the substrate. Figure 3 shows the SIMS depth profiles of these samples with reduced energy slits (5 eV and 3 eV respectively for 600°C and 800°C annealed samples- plots a and b). For comparison, the SIMS profiles of the un-annealed specimen is also shown (plot c). The difference in the secondary ion intensity from surface to the interface is considerably reduced in case of annealed layers. This is consistent with the assumption of less charging due to increased conductivity. Although the two regions can still be distinguished from each other, the hump at the interface has widened in case of annealed specimens. The exact cause of higher secondary ion intensities from a-Si regions needs further investigation.

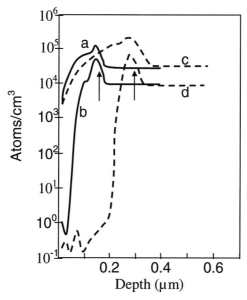

Fig.2 Si$^+$ Depth profiles for two different a-Si:H on Si(001) specimens (a,b and c,d). The energy window for a and c was 130 eV and that for b and d was 5eV. Interfaces marked by arrows.

4. Conclusion

We have observed a marked shift in the secondary ion energy distribution of Si$^+$ in a-Si:H layers as compared to Si(001) substrates. This effect has been attributed to the charging of high resistivity a-Si:H regions during SIMS analysis. Use of a narrow (~5eV) energy window can reduce the secondary ion contribution from the a-Si:H regions and this effect can be utilized for the depth profiling of such structures.

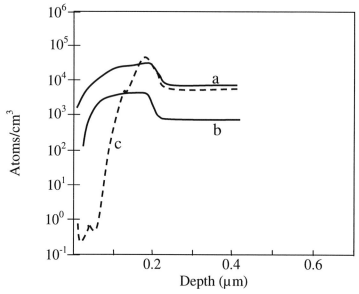

Fig. 3 Si$^+$ Depth profiles for a-Si:H on Si(001) specimens: a and b are
for specimens annealed at 600 and 800°C under Ar for one hour, c
for unannealed sample. The energy window for a and b was 5 eV
and that for c was 3eV

Acknowledgment:

The authors are thankful to Dr. R.A.Singh for providing the a-Si:H layers for the present work
and for many helpful discussions. They also thank Dr. V.K.Jain for his help in the heat
treatment experiments. Thanks are due to Prof. Vikram Kumar, Director, Solid State Physics
Laboratory for his permission to publish this work.

References

[1] Y. Hamakawa and H. Okamoto, Amorphous semiconductor Tech. Devices, 6 (1983) 182.

[2] A process for the manufacture of improved silicon solar cell, Indian Patent No. 180342
(April, 91)

[3] R.W.Collins, J.Vac. Sci. & Technol., A4 (1986) 514

[4] Howard E. Smith, G.H.Morrison and D.T. Hodul, J.Vac. Sci. & Technol. A4 (1986) 2492.

[5] G.C. Dubey, R.A. Singh, S.N. Mukherjee, Surendra Pal & M.G. Rao Bull.Mater.Sci., 8
(1986) 267.

[6] R,G,Wilson, F.A. Stevie and C.W.Magee, *SIMS – a practical hand book for depth
profiling and impurity analysis* (Wiley-Interscience, New York, 1989) p. 2.3-5.

A. Benninghoven, P. Bertrand, H.-N. Migeon and H.W. Werner (Editors).
Proceedings of the 12th International Conference on Secondary Ion Mass Spectrometry,
Brussels, Belgium, 5-11 September 1999
© 2000 Elsevier Science B.V. All rights reserved.

SIMS CHARACTERIZATION OF PHOSPHORUS CONCENTRATIONS IN POLYSILICON USING AN INTERNALLY CALIBRATED BULK DOPED REFERENCE STANDARD

C. Blackmer and W.R. Morinville
Micron Technology, 8000 S. Federal Way, M.S. 632, Boise ID 83707-0006
cblackmer@micron.com, wmorinville@micron.com

1. Introduction

The phosphorus dopant level in the polysilicon layer is crucial in semiconductor processing due to its correlation to the electrical properties of the semiconductor device. The effect of dopant concentration on the resistivity of the polysilicon film is an ongoing study as many factors from choice of heat treatment to changes in deposition can alter the conductive properties of the film [1]. As there is a continuous need for characterization of the dopant profile for both semiconductor process monitoring and research and development, analytical methods such as SRP (Spreading Resistance Profile), ICP (Inductively Coupled Plasma) and SIMS (Secondary Ion Mass Spectrometry) are routinely called upon. SIMS has the unique advantage of being able to provide quantification of the total phosphorus level, not just the activated dopant as in SRP, as well as the shape of the profile throughout the polysilicon layer. SIMS quantification of the phosphorous content in polysilicon is typically determined with an ion implanted standard into monocrystalline silicon or polysilicon/SiO_2 [2]. However, due to the damage caused by implantation, sputter rate changes in the implant region and varying oxygen levels between matrices, there are differences in secondary ion yield between the unknown poly silicon sample and the standard [3]. As is well documented, any change in matrix can alter the relative sensitivity factor (RSF) thus reducing the accuracy of the concentration measurement [4]. In this paper, a straightforward method for creating a bulk SIMS reference standard by correlation with inductively coupled plasma (ICP) is reported. This method provides a standard with a matrix and dopant distribution nearly identical to that of the analyzed polysilicon film. An added benefit to the bulk doped standard being the elimination of the sputter rate measurement in the bulk RSF calculation vs. the implant RSF calculation [5]. The reduced error provides RSF measurements with low standard deviation over time, allowing for an on-going procedure suitable for process monitoring.

2. Experimental Method

Six wafers were prepared by a four-step process of depositing 4 kÅ polysilicon, followed by phosphorus doping, giving a final 16 kÅ of phosphorus doped polysilicon. This method was used to ensure that the phosphorus concentration would be above the detection limits of 30 ppb (3 sigma) for ICP. The phosphorus concentration was assumed to be uniform throughout the polysilicon layer after anneal [6].

Of the six wafers prepared, five were analyzed by ICP. These five wafers were weighed to the nearest 0.1 mg and placed in etching funnels. 1.5 mL of mixed acid etchant (MAE) was selectively delivered onto the wafer surface, and a timer was started. The etching process was stopped after a predetermined time to ensure that the MAE would not etch beyond the doped polysilicon layer. This time was calculated based on the thickness of the doped polysilicon film and the etch rates of the MAE. The wafer was rinsed with a small volume of deionized (DI) water and the solution was captured. The wafers were dried and reweighed, and the weight of the removed film was calculated. The solution was also weighed and run against matrix matched standards by ICP for its phosphorus concentration. The resulting mean phosphorus concentration of 1.33×10^{20} atoms/cm^3 was reported for the subsequent SIMS RSF calculation on the sixth wafer from the set.

SIMS data was obtained using a Perkin Elmer 6300 quadrupole SIMS. A 5 keV, Cs$^+$ source at an incident angle of 60° was rastered over a 500 µm X 500 µm area, with a 150 µm X 150 µm detected area. For quantification the ^{31}P$^-$ species was monitored. To reduce mass interference at m/z 31 from the overlapping species ^{30}Si^{1}H$^-$, the analysis was performed at a base pressure of 5×10^{-10} torr. In addition, the ^{1}H$^-$ species was monitored with suitable mass resolution to allow separation from the "blast-through of ions at mass zero" [7].

3. Results & Discussion

Figure 1 shows the SIMS raw data depth profile obtained from the sixth wafer of the set, which will now be referred to as the "reference standard". Due to the four step deposition process, a thin native oxide layer was present between each polysilicon/polysilicon interface. It should be noted that the phosphorus diffusion into the substrate occurred prior to ICP analysis and therefore does not effect the dose measurement over time.

Due to the low mass resolution obtained on the quadrupole SIMS, it was necessary to account for any hydrogen contribution (^{30}Si^{1}H$^-$) in the peak at 31 m/z as discussed above. Figure 2 provides the hydrogen concentration profile for the reference standard. The hydrogen concentration was approximated to be ~5×10^{18} atoms/cm^3, based on a Charles Evans ^{1}H in Si ion implanted standard. At these levels, it is unlikely that there is appreciable ^{30}Si^{1}H$^-$ contribution to the ^{31}P$^-$ signal. In addition, the uniform distribution of the hydrogen signal in the polysilicon layers and into the substrate supports this conclusion.

A procedure was established to calculate the RSF by choosing the limits within the first poly layer to exclude any contribution due to matrix changes in the oxide layer. Using this method, bulk phosphorus RSF values were calculated. Data taken over a five year time period appears in table 1. The average RSF value from this table is used for process monitoring of the phosphorus levels in polysilicon. As can be noted in table 1, excellent repeatability over time is observed.

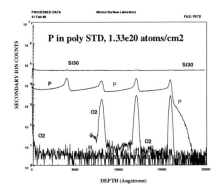

Figure 1: SIMS raw data depth profile of in- house bulk phosphorus doped polysilicon reference standard

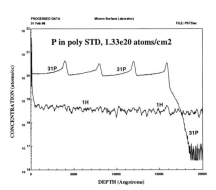

Figure 2: Hydrogen concentration profile from figure 1

Table 1: *Phosphorus RSF values (wrt ^{30}Si) recorded over a five-year span.*

Date of Analysis	Phosphorus RSF
1/12/94	1.08×10^{21}
1/28/94	9.65×10^{20}
2/7/94	1.23×10^{21}
2/8/94	1.12×10^{21}
2/10/94	1.01×10^{21}
2/19/94	1.20×10^{21}
3/1/94	1.13×10^{21}
3/4/94	1.21×10^{21}
5/23/94	1.17×10^{21}
10/21/94	1.15×10^{21}
12/21/94	9.62×10^{20}
1/9/95	1.19×10^{21}
1/30/95	1.02×10^{21}
9/2/95	1.06×10^{21}
9/12/95	1.12×10^{21}
9/20/95	9.54×10^{20}
11/28/95	9.78×10^{20}
12/11/95	9.30×10^{20}
1/27/96	1.10×10^{21}
2/3/96	1.07×10^{21}
2/8/96	1.22×10^{21}
11/19/96	1.07×10^{21}
1/23/97	1.00×10^{21}
6/24/97	1.08×10^{21}
2/28/98	1.08×10^{21}
3/02/98	1.06×10^{21}
4/04/98	1.06×10^{21}
12/15/98	1.07×10^{21}
5/19/99	1.10×10^{21}
Average RSF	1.08×10^{21}
STD Deviation	8.67×10^{19}

4. Conclusion

A procedure has been given for producing a bulk doped internal phosphorus reference standard to provide SIMS quantification of the polysilicon films used in semiconductor processing. The method provides a protocol under which repeatable results can be obtained over an extended time frame. Advantages to this bulk standard over the quintessential ion implanted standard are the reduction of any errors associated with the sputter rate measurement and the option of creating a standard with nearly identical composition to the unknown sample. Further work must be conducted with insitu doped samples in order to resolve the questions of phosphorus uniformity and oxide variations within the sample and their effect on the RSF measurements. This would eliminate the layering process, thus improving the uniformity of the phosphorus profile and providing a more accurate ICP measurement for correlation to the SIMS reference standard.

Acknowledgement

The authors thank Troy Sorensen and the Micron Analytical Chemistry Lab for the ICP work discussed in this paper.

References

[1] S. Wolf and R. N. Tauber, *Silicon Processing for the VLSI Era, Vol. 1- Process, Technology*, Lattice Press, Sunset Beach (1986) p. 182-182.

[2] T.Tanigaki, Y. Kato, and T. Suzuki in *Secondary Ion Mass Spectrometry VII*, ed. by A. Benninghoven, C. A. Evans, K. D. McKeegan, H. A. Storms and H. W. Werner, John Wiley & Sons, Chichester (1990) p. 599.

[3] T. I. Kamins, J. E. Turner, *Oxygen Concentration in LPCVD Polysilicon Films*, Solid State Technology, April (1990), p. 80-82..

[4] *Secondary Ion Mass Spectrometry; Principals and Applications*, ed. By J. C. Vickerman, A. Brown, and N. M. Reed, Clarendon Press, Oxford (1989) p. 108-109.

[5] *Secondary Ion Mass Spectrometry*, ed. by R. G. Wilson, F. A. Stevie, and C. W. Magee, John Wiley & Sons (1989) p. 3.1.5.

[6] S. Batra, K. H. Park, S. K. Banerjee, G. E. Lux, C. L. Kirschbaum, J. C. Norberg, T. C. Smith, J. K. Elliott, B. J. Mulvaney, *Effect of Grain Microstructure on P Diffusion in Polycrystalline-on-Single Crystal Silicon Systems* (1991) p. 1-17.

[7] C. W. Magee and E. M. Botnick, *Hydrogen Depth Profiling Using SIMS-Problems and Their Solutions*, J. Vac. Sci. Technol., 19(1), May/June (1981), p. 47-52.

A. Benninghoven, P. Bertrand, H.-N. Migeon and H.W. Werner (Editors).
Proceedings of the 12th International Conference on Secondary Ion Mass Spectrometry,
Brussels, Belgium, 5-11 September 1999

IN LINE SIMS TOOL FOR OPTOELECTRONIC DEVICE MANUFACTURING

T. Bitner[a], E. De Chambost[b], P. Monsallut[b], B. Rasser[b] and M. Schuhmacher[b]

[a]Lucent Tecnologies, 2525 North 12th Street, Reading, Pennsylvania, 19604, U.S.A.

[b]CAMECA, 103 boulevard Saint Denis, BP6, 92403 Courbevoie Cedex, France

1. Introduction

The manufacture of laser diodes for high-speed transmission of digital and analog information through fiber optic media require careful fabrication of III-V type semiconductor devices. Maintaining acceptable yields for laser devices having geometeries of a few hundred microns necessitate the establishment of viable process control measures capable of routinely characterizing dopant concentration profiles of epitaxial layers. We have found Secondary Ion Mass Spectroscopy (SIMS) to provide relatively fast feedback to the epitaxial manufacturing process while maintaining high degrees of precision.

Epitaxial layers of InP, InGaAs and InGaAsP doped with Zn, Fe and Si are grown on S doped InP substrates using metalorganic chemical vapor deposition (MOCVD) [1] techniques to form various structures of p, i and n type layers. Yields affected by output frequency, threshold currents, laser brightness and overall life are influenced by layer thickness, dopant concentrations and junction integrity. SIMS epitaxial characterizations with rapid feedback are vital to the successful employment of MOCVD epitaxial reactors in the manufacturing process as information is fed directly from the SIMS computer to an online manufacturing database.

The purpose of this paper is to describe techniques which have been applied by our laboratory to optimize turnaround time and enhance precision for SIMS techniques and the advances which are expected by introducing a new SIMS generation into the manufacturing processes control.

2. SIMS analysis of InP Epitaxial layers

A CAMECA IMS4f SIMS equipped with a micro Cesium ion source and its' sample chamber modified to accept two inch wafers was utilized to conduct all of the analysis.

Samples of epitaxial layers were obtained by including InP monitor pieces in reactors, placed adjacent to product wafers during the growth process. The approximately 20mm x 20mm monitor pieces were subsequently subjected to SIMS analysis to determine dopant concentration, layer thickness and interface integrity of the corresponding product wafers. Test-pads incorporated on production wafers, designed to provide SIMS access to epitaxial structures both during the manufacturing process and after the separation of laser devices from two inch product wafers, were also submitted for evaluation. Special sample holders fabricated with apertures to protect in-process product wafers from the primary Cs beam but expose SIMS test pads for analysis were used in the technique.

The location and quantity of Zn in the laser structure has been deemed the most critical and possibly most influential dopant to affect the quality of laser devices. Much effort and many studies[2] [3] [4] have been devoted to the control of Zn concentration and its' inherent diffusion into and through critical areas and junctions.

Ion species $(^{133}Cs^{28}Si)^+$, $(^{133}Cs^{56}Fe)^+$ and $(^{133}Cs^{64}Zn)^+$, accelerated to 4.5kV, were selected to monitor dopant concentrations while$(^{115}In^{75}As)^+$ was chosen to delineate InP/InGaAs and InP/InGaAsP junctions. A 12.5kV Cs+ primary beam having a current ranging between 15nA and 25nA with a diameter, typically, 45-50 um and rastered over an area 125um x 125um to 250um x 250um was chosen for these analysis.

Samples and references were sequenced :

SAMPLE SAMPLE REFERENCE SAMPLE SAMPLE
SAMPLE SAMPLE REFERENCE SAMPLE SAMPLE

so that very little time elapsed between data collection and (re)calibration. Relative sensitivity factors (RSF) were derived from the secondary references and applied to samples within each sequence.

Special sample holders were designed to accommodate two-inch wafers in the SIMS sample chamber. The design included wafer mask covers with 1mm x 2mm apertures exposing SIMS test pads that were incorporated into the wafer fabrication. These holders allowed for in-process profile analysis of epitaxial layers as they were deposited on product wafers while providing protection to the wafer from stray Cs contamination from the primary beam.

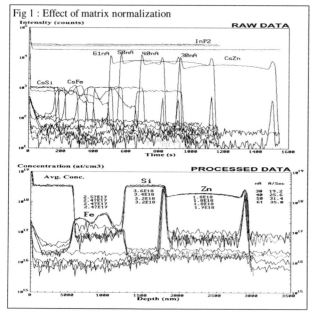

Fig 1 : Effect of matrix normalization

The effect of the matrix normalization process can be seen in Fig. 1. The variation in the secondary ion counts (raw data) of a typical PNIN structure as the primary beam current is varied from 30 to 61 nA is negated after being normalized (processed data) with the $(^{115}In^{31}P_2)^+$ species. Variations in primary beam current do not approach this magnitude even over an eight hour period and can be deemed miniscule in the interval of one calibration sequence. Zn determination in InGaAs has been found to be linear (Fig 2) in the range of 10^{16} to 10^{21} at/cm^3. These limits are well

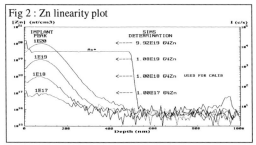

Fig 2 : Zn linearity plot

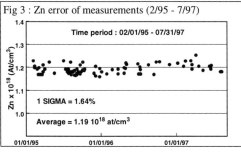

Fig 3 : Zn error of measurements (2/95 - 7/97)

within the range needed to characterize Zn in InP laser devices. Error-of-measurement studies (Fig 3) of Zn in InP conducted along with routine analysis over a two and a half year period with approximately eighty analyses revealed a variation of less than two percent relative standard deviation. Eighteen months later the same experiment, using the same intrinsically doped InP substrate, was randomly repeated for a three month period with twenty additional analyses. The repeated exercise, similarly, exhibited less than two percent relative standard deviation.

Variations exist between results obtained from monitor pieces and their corresponding product wafers. These variations can be attributed to, among other things, wafer/monitor size differences, radial location within reactors and the resulting thermal differences that affect dopant incorporation during epitaxial growth. Steps are being taken to eliminate all monitor piece analysis and focus on total wafer characterization with SIMS. Masks to protect the wafers from unfocused stray Cs ions from the primary beam are being developed.

3. The CAMECA IMS WF: in line SIMS tool for optoelectronic device manufacturing

The aforementioned results demonstrate that the SIMS technique has become a reliable tool for monitoring the manufacture of InP epitaxial layers. The SIMS analysis demand from epitaxial engineers is therefore continuously growing and there is a need for increasing the throughput and the efficiency of SIMS tools.

The analytical throughput of the CAMECA IMS 4f is limited by its analysis chamber which is capable of only accommodating a single 2" wafer per sample load. A new SIMS instrument, the CAMECA IMS Wf, is being incorporated into the manufacturing process in order to overcome this limitation. Its 300 mm sample stage can be loaded with a sample holder containing up to nineteen 2" wafers. Combined with an automation system that includes functions for recognition and access of test-site and wafer pattern codes and the application of appropriate analytical recipes and references, the CAMECA IMS Wf can run overnight analysis in a fully automatic mode.

The IMS Wf primary column accommodates two ion sources (Cs^+ and O_2^+) and a double focusing mass spectrometer. The primary column is of a floating type and provides primary ions with an impact energy ranging from 150 eV up to 10 keV with an incidence angle of $60°$. At 250 eV impact energy, the new secondary ion extraction system can maintain a secondary extraction voltage of 3 kV. Thus, high depth resolution, high transmission and high mass resolution capabilities are combined on the same instrument [5].

734

An example of a profile through an InP epitaxial layers structure is plotted in Fig 4. It has been measured on the CAMECA IMS Wf with 3 keV impact energy Cs^+ primary ions. The results of the continuous primary beam intensity monitoring during analysis is also plotted. This profile illustrates the CAMECA IMS Wf capability for the combination of a good depth resolution (well resolved thin structure) with high sample throughput (less than 20 mn to sputter 3.5 μm).

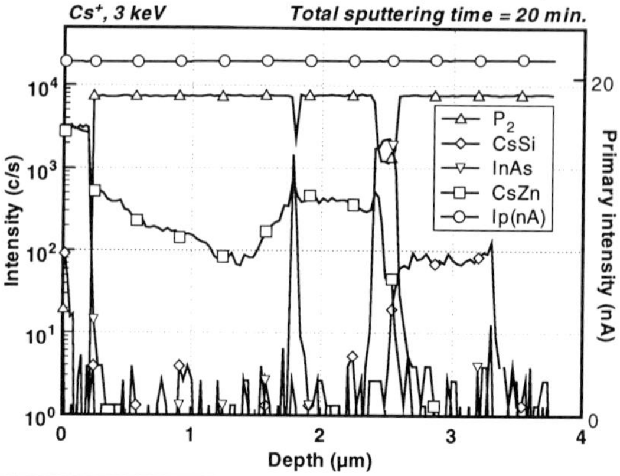

Another important innovation introduced with the CAMECA IMS Wf is real time and absolute "in situ" crater depth measurement during analysis. It will provide a significant improvement for the accuracy of the depth scale calibration of multilayer structures. The principle is based on heterodyne interferometer technique. A single laser beam is split into two beams ($\varnothing = 40$ μm) and both are focused at the sample surface. One beam is focused onto the bottom of the crater and the other onto the sample surface at a distance of 200 μm. After reflection the two beams are sent to the detector of an interferometer. The optical arrangement (patented) is schematically represented in Fig 5. With a laser wave length of 633 nm and a phase resolution of 1/256, the theoretical resolution is 0.62 nm which has been experimentally checked on a bench test. The depth range of this system spreads from nanometers to micrometers. Note that the two beams concept makes the system insensitive to any mechanical vibration and thermal dilatation.

Fig 4 : InP epitaxial profile layer profile measured with Cs^+ at 3 keV impact energy (depth scale calibration by means of crater depth measurements with a surface profilometer)

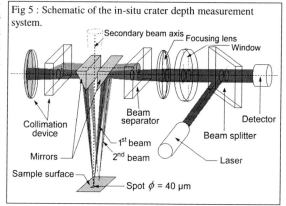

Fig 5 : Schematic of the in-situ crater depth measurement system.

References

[1] Avishay Katz (Artech house, Inc, Norwood, MA, 1992)
[2] V.Swaminathan , C.L.Reynolds , and M.Geva : Electronic Letters, 28th March, 1996, Vol. 32, No. 7
[3] S.J.Taylor , B.Beaumont , and J.C.Guillaume : Semiconductor Science Technology 8 (1993) 2193-2196
[4] C.Blaauw , B.Emmerstorfer , D.Kreller , L.Hobbs , and A.J.Springthorpe : Journal of Electronic Materials, Vol. 21, No. 2, 1992.
[5] E.De Chambost , B.Boyer , M.Brasser and M. Schuhmacher, these proceedings.

A. Benninghoven, P. Bertrand, H.-N. Migeon and H.W. Werner (Editors).
Proceedings of the 12th International Conference on Secondary Ion Mass Spectrometry,
Brussels, Belgium, 5-11 September 1999
© 2000 Elsevier Science B.V. All rights reserved.

EFFECT OF AlN ENCAPSULATION IN HIGH-TEMPERATURE ANNEALING ON ION-IMPLANTED SIC AS CHARACTERIZED BY SIMS

Peter H. Chi [a], Evan M. Handy [b] and Mulpuri V. Rao [b]

[a]National Institute of Standards and Technology, Gaithersburg, MD 20899-8371
[b]Department of Electrical and Computer Engineering, George Mason University
Fairfax, VA 22030

1. Introduction

Silicon carbide has been intensively studied due to its chemical and thermal stability and its wide band-gap characteristics. These characteristics make this material attractive for high power, high speed, and high temperature device applications. At one time, the doping of the silicon carbide crystals was restricted to the in-situ method. Recently, the ion implantation technique has been used to introduce the dopants into silicon carbide crystals at room temperature. Post-implantation annealing is needed to repair the crystalline damage and to activate the implanted species. However, the high temperature annealing also causes the implant to redistribute. To minimize the implant diffusion, several materials, such as SiO_2 and Si_3N_4, have been used to encapsulate the III-V samples prior to high temperature annealing. There has been little success in preventing some implant diffusion in the SiC sample, since these materials become volatile and useless at temperatures higher than $1300°C$, a temperature necessary to process the SiC substrate. In this work, AlN was used as an encapsulating layer for B-, As-, and Sb-implanted 6H-SiC samples before high temperature annealing. These samples were annealed at 1600 °C for 15-30 minutes, and the profiles were characterized by secondary ion mass spectrometry (SIMS) to verify the effectiveness of AlN encapsulating layers.

2. Experiment

Boron was implanted with an energy of 50 keV at a dose of 8.8×10^{14} cm^{-2} into a 2-5 µm thick n-type 6H-SiC substrate. A 2-4 µm thick p-type epitaxial layer of 2×10^{15} to 1×10^{16} cm^{-3} carrier grown on a Si-face, off-axis p-type ($1-2 \times 10^{18}$ cm^{-3}) 6H-SiC was prepared for arsenic and antimony implantation. As and Sb were implanted at multiple energies of 200, 140, 80, 40, and 20 keV. The total dose for As was 1.2×10^{14} cm^{-2} while that for Sb was 7×10^{13} cm^{-2}. After implantation, a 0.17-0.18 µm thick AlN layer was deposited on these SiC samples by a pulsed laser deposition (PLD) technique.

All implanted samples were subject to annealing at $1600°C$ for 30 minutes. The AlN encapsulating layer was removed in KOH solution at $75°C$. Implant characterizations were made in a Cameca IMS-3F* instrument operating with an 8.0 keV net impact energy O_2^+ primary ion beam with positive secondary ion detection for profiling B^+ and Si^+ and a 14.5 keV Cs^+ beam with negative secondary ion detection for profiling As^- and Sb^-. Quantification of annealed profiles was based on the relative sensitivity factors (RSFs) that were generated from the as-implanted samples. For depth calibration, each individual crater depth was measured with stylus profilometry.

3. Results and Discussion
Si in AlN/SiC

To test for thermal stability, two approximately 0.15 μm thick layers of AlN on SiC samples were prepared for annealing at 1600°C for 15 and 30 minutes. Figure 1 shows an overlay of Si profiles before and after annealing at 1600°C for 15 and 30 minutes. The Si profile in unannealed and 15 min annealed samples were similar, and both showed a steep decrease of silicon toward the AlN/SiC interface. The similarity of these two profiles suggests that Si was stable for the 15-minute annealing. However, the AlN/SiC sample that was annealed for 30 minutes showed a gradual shift of Si toward the AlN interface, an indication of silicon out-diffusion into the AlN encapsulating layer. The Al profile (not shown) was stable in all three cases. Jones et al. have found that there was little AlN diffusion into SiC at 1600°C for up to 30 minutes of annealing [1]. In addition, atomic force microscopy (AFM) was performed on these samples with the removal of the AlN layer. AFM revealed very little change of the SiC surface between the unannealed and the 15-minute annealed samples. The 30-minute annealed sample, however, showed pits and spikes on the SiC surface once the AlN layer was removed [2].

As, Sb, and B implant

Figure 2 shows the arsenic depth profiles in the samples that were as-implanted and annealed to 1600°C for 15 min with and without the AlN encapsulating layer. The main features of the arsenic profile before and after annealing with the AlN cap were that both samples showed a flat peak and a trailing profile tail which were the result of multiple energy implants and ion channeling during ion implantation. The similarity of the arsenic profiles in the as-implanted and annealed samples with AlN cap revealed the effectiveness of the AlN encapsulating layer in preventing arsenic diffusion under these conditions. For SiC implanted with arsenic and annealed without the AlN cap, arsenic diffused toward the surface, and more than 60 % of the arsenic dose was lost to diffusion.

The antimony profiles in SiC annealed with and without the AlN protective cap are shown in Figure 3. As observed for the arsenic-implanted SiC sample, the Sb concentration peak was quite stable at 1600°C when annealed for 15 min with the AlN encapsulating layer. Although the Sb tail was slightly broadened compared to the Sb profile before annealing, overall there was no major Sb redistribution in the annealed sample with the AlN cap. For Sb-implanted SiC annealed at 1600°C for 15 min without the AlN encapsulating layer, Sb diffused toward the surface, with more than 90% of the original Sb dose lost to annealing. The dopant loss mechanism can be understood by comparing the As and Sb SIMS profiles of the annealed samples with those of the samples annealed without the AlN encapsulating layer. The As and Sb losses were accounted for by sublimation loss of ~ 0.08 μm of the SiC surface in the 1600°C/15 minute annealing. As the layer of SiC sublimed, it carried with it the dopant within the layer. An AlN cap during annealing served to prevent the sublimation of SiC, and hence the loss of the dopant.

Because of its light atomic mass, B is becoming an attractive acceptor dopant to create deep p-type regions required for making dual implanted n-p junctions and p-wells of complementary field-effect transistors. An overlay of 50 keV/ 8.8×10^{14} cm^{-2} B-implanted SiC before and after annealing at 1600°C for 15 min with and without an AlN cap is shown in Figure 4. The boron profile was redistributed in both annealed samples with or without the AlN protective layer. The use of AlN did not help to contain the out-diffusion of the boron profile because boron redistribution was caused by the stoichiometric disturbances induced in SiC during ion implantation [3].

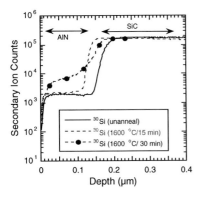

Fig. 1: Si profiles in unannealed and annealed
samples with AlN encapsulating layer

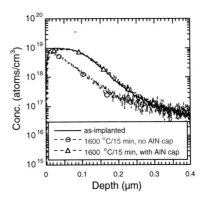

Fig. 2: As profiles as-implanted and annealed
with or without AlN encapsulate layer

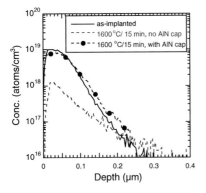

Fig. 3: SIMS depth profiles of Sb as-implanted
and annealed with and without an AlN layer

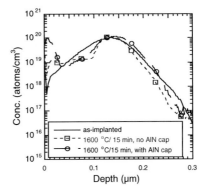

Fig. 4: B profiles unannealed and annealed
at 1600°C with and without an AlN layer

The redistribution was associated with the implant-generated defects and not with the defects
created at the surface during annealing. Thus, the AlN cap could not stop the redistribution of
the boron implant. The only difference in the B out-diffusion behavior due to the presence or
absence of the AlN during annealing was the accumulation of B at the SiC surface with the
AlN encapsulant, due to the prevention of B evaporation by the cap.

4. Conclusion

AlN encapsulation has been shown to prevent As- and Sb-implanted SiC diffusion at
temperatures up to 1600°C for an annealing time of 15 minutes. However, it was not effective
in preventing the boron out-diffusion at this annealing temperature because of the implantation-
generated defects in the boron implant. The AlN encapsulating layer was effective at the

738

1600°C/15 min annealing for SiC. However, after annealing at this temperature for a longer duration (30 minutes), the SiC surface began to deteriorate and Si was out-diffused into the AlN layer.

*Certain commercial equipment, instruments, or materials are identified in this paper to specify adequately the experimental procedure. Such identification does not imply recommendation or endorsement by the National Institute of Standards and Technology, nor does it imply that the materials or equipment identified are necessarily the best available for the purpose.

References

[1] K. A. Jones, K. Xie, D. W. Eckart, M. C. Wood, V. Talyansky, R. D. Vispute, T. Venkatesan, K. Wongchotigul, and M. Spencer, J. Appl. Phys., 83, 8010 (1998).

[2] E. Handy, M. V. Rao, K. A. Jones, M. A. Derenge, P. H. Chi, R. D. Vispute, T. Venkatesan, N. A. Panpanicolaou, and J. Mittereder, J. Appl. Phys., 86, 746 , (1999).

[3] L. A. Christel and J. F. Gibbons, J. Appl. Phys., 52, 5050 (1981).

ORGANIC MATERIALS / POLYMERS

A. Benninghoven, P. Bertrand, H.-N. Migeon and H.W. Werner (Editors).
Proceedings of the 12th International Conference on Secondary Ion Mass Spectrometry,
Brussels, Belgium, 5-11 September 1999

CHARACTERISATION OF PERFLUOROPOLYETHER-URETHANE COATINGS BY TOF-SIMS AND XPS.

R. Canteri[1], G. Speranza[1], M. Anderle[1], S. Turri[2], S. Radice[2], T. Trombetta[2]

[1] ITC-irst, Centro per la Ricerca Scientifica e Tecnologica
Via Sommarive 18, 38050 Povo (TN), Italy, e-mail: canteri@itc.it
[2] Ausimont S.p.A., Research & Development Center
Via S. Pietro 50, 20021 Bollate (MI), Italy

1. Introduction

The introduction of perfluoropolyether (PFPE) macromers in polyurethane coatings [1,2] has led to a substantial improvement of the durability characteristics and surface properties of the material, while it has maintained the advantage of an easy application technology in a variety of environmental conditions and temperatures. In particular the presence of fluorine imparts the coated surface a superior chemical resistance, photoxidative stability and stain release performance [3]. Hydroxy terminated bi-functional PFPE have the following general formula:

$$HOCH_2CF_2(OCF_2CF_2)_p(OCF_2)_qOCF_2CH_2OH \qquad p/q=0.5\text{-}2$$

Recently, cross-linked (three-dimensional) polyurethane coatings based on PFPE have been described and analysed in terms of their surface characteristics by using different techniques [4]. Results have shown that the surface of these coatings were predominantly fluorinated. TOF-SIMS analyses showed in fact the presence of exclusively fluorinated fragments, while XPS confirmed the surface composition with a clear enrichment of fluorine components with respect to the bulk composition of the material. Since these coatings are applied and cross-linked from solvent solutions, it is very interesting to explore the feasibility of producing polyurethane PFPE containing coatings from waterborne dispersions, which would be much more environmentally compatible and friendly.

The aim of this work is to investigate the surface composition of these novel waterborne coatings based on PFPE, and to compare it with the known characteristics of solvent-borne systems.

2. Experimental

The model waterborne polyurethanes (Polymers B and C) were prepared by pre-polymerisation of the PFPE diol macromer (Mn 2000), eventually blended with a hydrogenated polyether PTMEG (polytetramethyleneglycol Mn 1000 – [$HO(CH_2CH_2CH_2CH_2O)_nH$]), with isophorone diisocyanate (IPDI), to form a NCO terminated pre-polymer, followed by chain extension adding with N-methyldiethanolamine (NMDEA). The NMDEA monomer contains a tertiary amine group that allows the ionomeric polymer to be dispersed in water after salification with acid or alkyl halides. Polymers B and C differ for the PFPE concentration. The compositional data, reported in Table 1, as well as the strong difference in the contributions of hydrogenated and fluorinated components between polymer B and polymer C, were confirmed by FT-IR (ATR) investigations. The reference solvent-borne crosslinked coating (Polymer A), obtained by casting from solvent, was described in details elsewhere [5].

Table 1: Concentration data for the Polymers B and C

	Polymer B				Polymer C			
	% Tot.	C	O	N	F	% Tot.	C	O	N	F
PFPE	9,7%	2,0%	1,8%	0,0%	5,9%	78,6%	16,1%	14,5%	0,0%	48%
IPDI	25,4%	17,9%	4,0%	3,5%	0,0%	16,9%	11,9%	2,7%	2,3%	0,0%
NMDEA	7,0%	4,0%	2,1%	0,9%	0,0%	4,5%	2,5%	1,4%	0,6%	0,0%
PTMEG	57,9%	42,6%	15,3%	0,0%	0,0%	0,0%	0,0%	0,0%	0,0%	0,0%

TOF-SSIMS spectra were acquired using a CAMECA TOF-SIMS IV reflectron type instrument equipped with a 25KeV Ga^+ primary ion source. A current of 1.1nA DC was used to generate a 20ns width pulse of primary ions at 5KHz repetition rate. The secondary ions were accelerated into a TOF analyser with 2KV extraction voltage in both positive and negative ion polarity mode. All the spectra were acquired for 1000s and a 0.03 mm^2 analysis area was sampled. Thus SIMS operating conditions were maintained within the static regime. Charge neutralisation was achieved with a pulsed low-energy electron flooding.

XPS spectra were obtained using a Scienta 200 instrument equipped with a 200mm hemispherical analyser and a monochromatized AlK_α radiation (1486.6eV) operated at 500W. The pass energy was 500eV during survey acquisition and it was 150eV during core level acquisition, that implies a ~0.4eV energy resolution. The position of hydrocarbon at 285eV was taken as a reference for binding energy (BE) corrections. The polymer's chemical and structural compositions were measured at different thickness by tilting the sample: 90° (surface sample is normal to the analyser lenses axis, sampling depth ≈7-8nm) and 165° for higher surface sensitivity (sampling depth ≈2-3nm).

3. Results and discussion

TOF-SSIMS spectra (polarities + and -) for both the polymers B and C are dominated by PFPE chain fragments. Anyway there are important differences between polymer B and C. In particular the negative spectra of the polymer C shows a larger contribution due to fragments as NCO; they could be assigned to the IPDI and PFPE bond. This contribution is larger even if the concentration content of IPDI is greater in the polymer B as shown in Table 1.

Figure 1 shows positive TOF spectra regions relative to four important fragments. The positive spectra show many fragments from PFPE macromers; those due to the end-groups of the PFPE macromers, (e.g.: $OCFCH_2$, OCF_2CH_2, CF_2CH_2OH ....), are mainly present in the spectra relative to the polymer B as shown in Fig.1a. In addition positive spectra show contributions of molecular fragment like ($C_nH_{2n-1}O$) [n=1,8] that could be assigned to the PTMEG macromers; these components are present only in the polymer B (Fig1.b). The fragment due to the PFPE macromers like (OCF$_2$) and (OCF$_2$CF$_2$) are comparable in intensity, as reported in Figs.1c and 1d, as well as their combinations. All these features could suggest a different surface conformation between the polymers B and C.

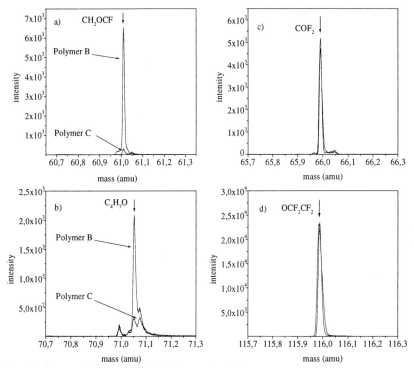

Figure 1: Four positive regions for the Polymers B and C

The XPS concentration measurements confirm the presence of fluorine at the surface as shown by TOF-SSIMS analyses.

The Table 2 reports the concentration calculated by XPS for the different components and angles.

Table 2: XPS elemental concentrations for the Polymers B and C at the different tilting angle.

	Polymer B		Polymer C	
	Tilt 90°	Tilt 165°	Tilt 90°	Tilt 165°
C1s	33%	29%	38%	31%
O1s	18%	18%	18%	18%
N1s	1%	1%	3%	1%
F1s	48%	52%	41%	50%

The fluorine concentration difference between the surface and layers beneath it, for the solvent-borne polymer A previously mentioned, was about 40% (30% at 90° and 54% at 165°); for the polymers B and C it is less evident and their surface fluorine concentrations are similar. For polymer C the XPS atomic concentrations are close to the bulk values, while the values for polymer B differ from them. By considering the sampling depths of XPS, we could make the following considerations: for the polymer C, there is a small difference in concentration of fluorine between the two sampling depths. This fact suggests a weaker stratification between the two macromers (as expected by the polymer composition). The polymer B shows a huge difference in fluorine concentrations between the XPS measures (Table. 2) and the bulk concentration (Table. 1), suggesting a stratification layer thicker than the XPS sampling depth at 90°.

4. Conclusions

The analysed waterborne polyurethane are linear polymers that should allows a higher molecular mobility than the solvent-borne polymer A formed by shorter cross-linked segments. For this polymer a large stratification for the fluorine compound was revealed. TOF-SSIMS analyses show a dominant presence of fluorine compound at the surface for both the polymers B and C and a remarkable concentration of hydrogenated species for the polymer B. These results are confirmed also by XPS data at 165°. In the case of polymer B, the difference between the XPS measurements at 165° and 90° are not remarkable but the concentrations are very different compared with the bulk values. This means that the sample is very stratified and that the layer thickness, with high fluorine concentration, is greater than the sampling depth of XPS at 90°. In the case of polymer C, the XPS analyses show it is more homogenous.

In conclusion the TOF-SIMS and XPS characterisation of polymers B and C show that the fluorine components are dominant at the surface also in these waterborne polymers. In addition these analyses showed that the stratification of the fluorine components is astonishing in the case of polymer B. These characteristics allow to combine the performance of fluorine macromolecules system with the use of aqueous dispersion.

References

[1] G. Simeone, S. Turri, M. Scicchitano, C. Tonelli, Angew. Makromol. Chem. 236 (1996) 111.
[2] S. Turri, M. Scicchitano, G. Simeone, C. Tonelli, Progr. Org. Coat. 32 (1997) 205
[3] J. Scheirs, S. Burks, A. Locaspi, Trends Polym. Sci. 3 (1995) 74
[4] S. Turri, S. Radice, R. Canteri, G. Speranza and M. Anderle, submitted to Macromolecules.
[5] S. Turri, M. Scicchitano, R. Marchetti, A. Sanguineti and S. Radice, "Fuoropolymers: Synthesis and Properties", G. Hougham et al., eds vol. II, Plenum Press, New York 1999.

A. Benninghoven, P. Bertrand, H.-N. Migeon and H.W. Werner (Editors).
Proceedings of the 12th International Conference on Secondary Ion Mass Spectrometry,
Brussels, Belgium, 5-11 September 1999

OPTIMUM MONOLAYER OXIDATION PARAMETERS FOR IMPROVED MASS ANALYSIS

R. D. English, M. J. Van Stipdonk and E. A. Schweikert
Department of Chemistry, Texas A&M University, PO Box 30012, College Station, TX,
77843-3144 U.S.A., rde7754@venus.tamu.edu

1. Introduction

Self-assembled monolayers (SAMs) are used as model surfaces in studies of corrosion, wetting, and adhesion. SAMs are attractive because they spontaneously form well-ordered films that can be functionalized to control and change surface properties. Studies of SAM stability have shown that they are susceptible to oxidation, which causes a conversion of the thiolate moiety to a sulfonate [1]. The $Au-SO_3$ bond of the oxidized monolayer is weaker than the Au-S bond present in the unoxidized molecule, and is therefore easier to desorb and ionize in SIMS [2]. Our study dealt with the sputtering of unoxidized and oxidized SAM substrates by SIMS with atomic and polyatomic projectiles, and spontaneous desorption mass spectrometry. The goal was to optimize the experimental conditions to improve monolayer characterization by SIMS by using controlled photooxidation prior to analysis.

Using static-SIMS, Cooper and Leggett have shown that the oxidation time and rate for various SAM systems depend on the chain lengths and terminal group functionalities [3]. We have investigated the oxidation of various alkanethiol monolayers as a function of UV exposure time and dose. We too have observed that the oxidation conditions are dependent on the UV light source conditions used to oxidize the monolayers.

2. Experimental

Experiments were performed in a dual-ToF SIMS instrument equipped with a polyatomic projectile source, event-by-event bombardment/detection, and coincidence counting. The instrument has been described in detail previously [4-5]. Briefly, +20 keV mono and polyatomic projectiles are generated by fission fragments passing through a Mylar^{TM} foil coated with CsI. The projectiles impact a negatively biased target surface whereupon secondary electrons are steered by a weak magnetic field to signal the arrival of a primary ion. Secondary ions are accelerated into a field-free region, mass separated, and detected. The experiments were performed in the event-by-event mode. The coincidence counting protocol allows for secondary ion spectra to be generated for multiple primary ions under the same experimental conditions. Yield measurements, therefore, can be obtained for different primary ion impacts in the same experiment.

Alkanethiol monolayers included 1-propanethiol, 1-octanethiol and 1-hexadecanethiol. Oxidation of alkanethiol monolayers was performed with a Hg(Ar) Spectral Calibration Lamp. The most intense wavelength emitted by the lamp is 253.7 nm. All oxidation experiments were performed by positioning the wafer (attached to the stainless steel cube) under the lamp at the appropriate distance after the lamp had warmed up for approximately 30 minutes. Oxidation times ranged from 15, 25, and 45 to 65 minutes. The sample-lamp distances varied from 2, 4, 6, and 8 to 10 cm.

3. Results

Our data show that the secondary ion (SI) yields from a 1-propanethiol oxidized monolayer are greatest at short oxidation times such as 15-25 minutes (Fig. 1). Oxidation times of 0 and 5 minutes produced little to negligible SI yields from the monolayers (data not shown). Longer exposure times lead to removal of the monolayer surface by photodesorption and produce spectra similar to Au blanks (spectra not shown). All spectra were obtained with the distance from lamp to sample at 4 cm because this produced optimum SI yields relative to distances of 2, 6, 8 and 10 cm (data not shown).

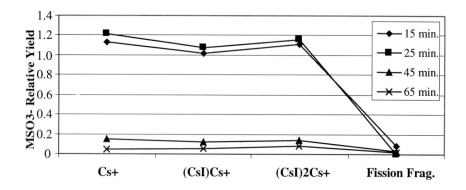

Fig. 1 Oxidized 1-propanethiol monolayer yields (relative to the number of primary ions) at oxidation distance of 4 cm. Oxidation times include 15, 25, 45 and 65 minutes. Primary ions include Cs^+, $(CsI)Cs^+$, $(CsI)_2Cs^+$ and fission fragments.

Fig. 1 illustrates two additional points. First, there is no yield enhancement with cluster projectiles for 1-propanethiol. This is attributed to the fact that it is unlikely that two or more primary ion collision cascades will overlap in space and time in the small area where each SAM molecule stands. It is more likely for collision cascades to cause yield enhancements with cluster projectiles on "thick" organic targets because the energy is deposited into the organic material where multi-layers exist [2].

Second, the SI yield from fission fragments impacting oxidized 1-propanethiol monolayer is small to negligible. This may be due to the manner of energy deposition whereby fission fragments transfer MeV energy by electronic excitation rather than by nuclear stopping as with keV projectiles. Clearly, fission fragments are not adequate for characterizing oxidized monolayers, whereas Cs^+ primary ions produce the quickest spectrum and give similar yields as the CsI clusters.

Similar results were obtained when analyzing oxidized 1-octanethiol monolayers (Fig. 2). Cs^+ is the primary ion of choice because a shorter acquistion time is needed to obtain a statistically meaningful mass spectrum while still producing comparable oxidized 1-octanethiol monolayer yields relative to the CsI cluster projectiles, and fission fragments again produce little to no SIs from the oxidized monolayer. The optimum oxidation time in this study is 25 minutes.

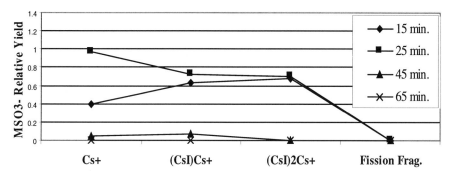

Fig. 2 Oxidized 1-octanethiol monolayer yields (relative to the number of primary ions) at oxidation distance of 4 cm. Oxidation times include 15, 25, 45 and 65 minutes. Primary ions include Cs^+, $(CsI)Cs^+$, $(CsI)_2Cs^+$ and fission fragments.

Similar results were obtained for 1-hexadecanethiol monolayers (data not shown). The best primary ion to use is Cs^+, and the best oxidation time for optimum SI yield is 15 minutes.

4. Conclusions

When ToF-SIMS is applied on alkanethiol monolayers, the yields of representative SIs are enhanced if the monolayer is oxidized prior to analysis. For 1-propanethiol, 1-octanethiol and 1-hexadecanethiol monolayers, short oxidation times between 15 and 25 minutes, sample-lamp distance of 4 cm, and 20 keV Cs^+ primary ions are optimum parameters for maximizing SI yields.

References

[1] J. Huang and J. C. Hemminger, J. Am. Chem. Soc., 115 (1993) 3342.
[2] R. D. Harris, W. S. Baker, M. J. Van Stipdonk, E. A Schweikert and R. M. Crooks, Rapid Comm. Mass Spectrom., in press (1999).
[3] E. Cooper and G. J. Leggett, Langmuir, 14 (1998) 4795-4801.
[4] M. J. Van Stipdonk, R. D. Harris and E. A. Schweikert, Rapid Comm. Mass Spectrom., 11 (1997) 1794-1798.
[5] M. J. Van Stipdonk, E. A. Schweikert and M. A. Park, J. Mass Spectrom., 32 (1997) 1151-1161.

* This work is supported by the National Science Foundation (CHE – 9727474).

A. Benninghoven, P. Bertrand, H.-N. Migeon and H.W. Werner (Editors).
Proceedings of the 12th International Conference on Secondary Ion Mass Spectrometry,
Brussels, Belgium, 5-11 September 1999

749

A NEW TYPE OF SUPPORT BASED ON ION-CONTAINING POLYMERS FOR SELECTIVE GENERATION OF CATIONIZED SPECIES IN TOF-SIMS SPECTRA

B.A. Keller and P. Hug, Swiss Federal Laboratories for Materials Testing and Research
CH-8600 Duebendorf, Switzerland, e-mail: beat.keller@empa.ch

1. Introduction

The formation of cationized pseudo-molecular species of the type $[M+Me]^+$ is a common phenomenon in TOF-SIMS spectra. It has been recognized that very high secondary ion yields of cationized species can be obtained after deposition of soluble organic material on noble metal substrates [1] with the possibility to obtain quantitative data [2]. However, the formation of very stable metal-molecule complexes is responsible for corrugated TOF-SIMS spectra due to competitive cationization processes. If the wish exists to benefit from the analytical possibilities of cationization, control over the formation of cationized quasimolecular ions would be a prerequisite under such conditions.

The conflicting problem of competitive cationization due to complex formation in histidine containing peptides has been addressed in a recent study [3]. In order to avoid spectrum corrugation due to unspecific cationization by trace impurities (usually Na^+ or K^+), a new type of support, based on cation-exchanged ion-containing polymers has been developed for specific cationization of organic species in TOF-SIMS spectra.

2. Experimental

Some classes of ionomers that generally consist of a hydrophobic backbone and a small amount of an acid group carrying side chain or copolymer unit can easily undergo cation exchange on the carboxyl group. A commercial (purchased from Sigma/Aldrich) water/alcoholic solution of Nafion® 117 (DuPont), the chemical structure of which is shown in Figure 1, was diluted and heated under refluxing conditions together either with AgNO₃ or RbOH for two hours. Since Nafion® is known as so-called superacid, almost 100% ion-exchange could be achieved. The superacidity is attributed to the electron-withdrawing, effect of the perfluoro-carbon

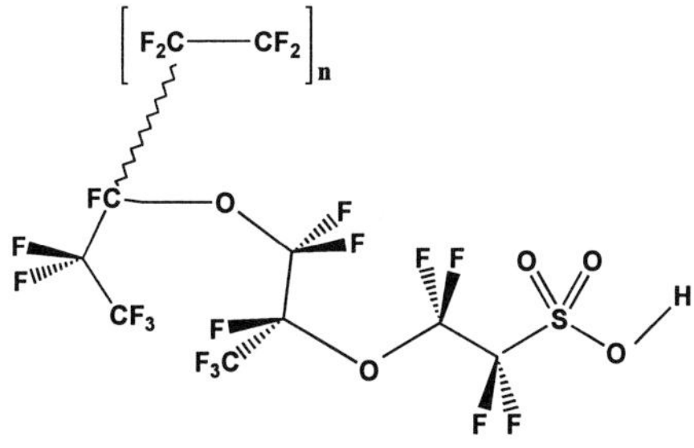

Figure 1. Chemical structure of Nafion 117 (® DuPont).

chain acting on the sulfonic acid group. Furthermore the polymer is water soluble and chemically inert. The final solution was then applied by spin coating onto a gold plated steel substrate to produce ion-exchanged matrices for the TOF-SIMS study. The analyte solution was subsequently spread onto the thin Nafion® film and analyzed in a Physical-Electronics model 7200 TOF-SIMS spectrometer under static (SSIMS) operating condition described elsewhere [3].

Reagent grade nileblue A and cholesterol were purchased from Fluka Chemie and Merck, respectively. Both materials were used as received. Solutions (10^{-4} M) of nileblue in ethanol and cholesterol in benzene (shown in Figure 2) were used in this study to confirm the possibilities to obtain characteristic signal patterns that would strongly reflect the chemical nature of the analyte and the bondig state at the surface.

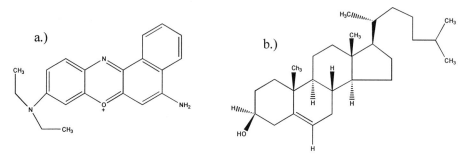

Figure 2. Chemical structures of a.) nileblue A and b.) cholesterol

3. Results

a.) Positive-ion TOF-SIMS spectrum of nileblue A

Nileblue A is a common cationic dye that exhibits distinctive acid-base properties. In absence of proton donators, the molecule is found in its cation form. Nileblue has been chosen in our investigation to confirm the existence of a preformed cationized species on the surface of ion

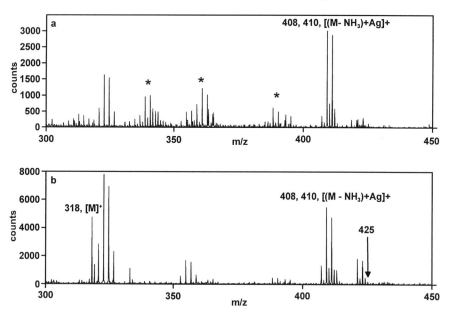

Figure 3. Positive-ion TOF-SIMS spectra of nileblue A on a) Ag$^+$-exchanged Nafion and b) etched metallic silver. Nafion matrix signals are denoted with asterix.

exchanged Nafion matrices. Figure 3 shows static (ion dose $\cong 10^{11}$ ions/cm^2) positive ion TOF-SIMS spectra of nileblue A on a Ag$^+$-exchanged Nafion matrix (a) and on an etched metallic silver substrate (b) in the mass range between m/z = 300 and 450. Both spectra exhibit strong signals at m/z = 408 and 410 that can be assigned to species of formal type [(M-NH$_3$) + Ag]$^+$. The emission of a NH$_3^+$ fragment indicates that nileblue A undergoes a tautomerism on the surface of both, the cation exchanged matrix and the etched metal. However, the detection of a signal at m/z = 318 on the silver surface further suggests that nileblue A is also sputtered from the surface as non-cationized charged species. Since this signal is completely absent in spectrum a of Figure 3, it is most likely due to very different sticking coefficients of nileblue A on the two substrates that lead to different sputtering coefficients. No species of type [(M - H) + Ag]$^+$ is found in both TOF-SIMS spectra, leading to the conclusion that forming a precursor molecule on the surface involves a more complex rearrangement within the nileblue molecule.

b.) Positive-ion TOF-SIMS spectrum of cholesterol

Since cholesterol is only soluble in non-polar solvents, it is deposited on the substrate as neutral particle. Therefore, cationization and sputtering processes are completely controlled by the state of surface adsorption. Figure 4 shows the positive-ion static TOF-SIMS spectra of cholesterol on a) etched silver, b) Ag$^+$-exchanged Nafion and c) Rb$^+$-exchanged Nafion. The dominant signal in the mass range between m/z = 300 and 550 is found in all spectra at m/z = 369, corresponding to [M -OH]$^+$. A signal at m/z = 387 that can be assigned to [M + H]$^+$ is also observed in spectra a), b) and c). However, signals attributed to cationized quasimolecular ions (i.e. [M + Ag]$^+$) are only observed in spectra a) (intense) and b) (weak).

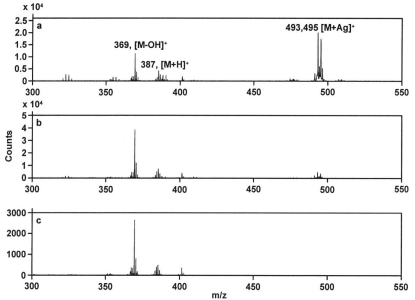

Figure 4. Positive-ion TOF-SIMS spectra of cholesterol on a) etched silver, b) Ag$^+$-exchanged Nafion and c) Rb$^+$-exchanged Nafion.

752

A species of type $[M + Rb]^+$, as expected in spectrum c) at m/z = 471 and 473, respectively is not observed, leading to the conclusion, that Rb^+ has a lower potential than silver to form cationized species. Although absolute signal intensities on Ag^+-exchanged Nafion and etched silver are comparable, cationization seems to be a much more favorable process on the metal substrate.

4. Discussion

Secondary ion formation in TOF-SIMS spectra of a nileblue A, a molecular cation and cholesterol, a non-polar alcohol on metallic and cation exchanged substrates reflects the bonding state at the surface and the ability of different cations to form stable precursor molecules on the surface. A rather complex secondary ion formation process that yields to the complete absence of silver cationized quasimolecular ions is expected in the case of nileblue A. An intact molecular ion is sputtered from the surface of metallic silver, reflecting the extremely weak bonding of the nileblue cation to the surface. Generally, in cases of relatively weak bonding, fast energy transfer from the excited area of primary ion impact to the precursor molecule produces significant amounts of cationized secondary quasimolecular ions. The value of complex formation constants is responsible for the relative number of precursors on the surface. Consequently a cation like Rb^+ with a Kr orbital shell does not exhibit the same ability to form complexes as Ag^+ with a highly hybridized d^{10} electron shell. The absence of cationized quasimolecular secondary ions in the TOF-SIMS spectra shown in Figure 4 is due to this fact. On the other hand, the much weaker signal intensity for $[M + Ag]^+$ species on Ag^+-exchanged Nafion compared to etched metallic silver probably reflects the higher number of rotational and vibrational states into which the kinetic energy can be dissipated in the case of the polymer. Furthermore it is a rather complex question to which amount Ag^+ cations are available for cationization at the near surface region in the case of exchanged ionomers. The question of surface reconstruction has been addressed in a recent study and found to be strongly dependent on type and valence state of the cations [4]. This fact might also be important for the comparison of relative signal intensities in TOF-SIMS spectra taken from differently cation exchanged matrices.

5. Conclusion

We have shown in this paper that substrates based on cation exchanged ion-containing polymers can successfully be used as alternative to spreading soluble organic molecules on etched silver plates. Although in most cases relative ion yields are weaker and strongly depending on the ability of the cations and molecular species to form precursor complexes, the technique opens a pathway for selective cationization that often yields to less corrugated spectra. The possibility to control secondary ion formation and fragmentation processes might be a prerequisite for the application of TOF-SIMS to problems with inherently complex signal patterns, e.g. biolocical and biomedical samples.

References

[1] A. Benninghoven, F.G. Ruedenauer and J.W. Werner, in Secondary Ion Mass Spectrometry, J. Wiley and Sons, New York (1987)
[2] U. Seedorf et al., Clin. Chem. 41, (1995) 548
[3] B.A. Keller and P. Hug in Secondary Ion Mass Spectrometry (SIMS XI), G. Gillen, R. Lareau, J. Bennett and F. Stevie, eds., J. Wiley and Sons, New York (1998), p. 101
[4] B.A. Keller and P. Hug, Europhys. Conf. Abstracts, 21B (1997) 271

A. Benninghoven, P. Bertrand, H.-N. Migeon and H.W. Werner (Editors).
Proceedings of the 12th International Conference on Secondary Ion Mass Spectrometry,
Brussels, Belgium, 5-11 September 1999

753

SECONDARY ION EMISSION FROM HETERO-STRUCTURED LANGMUIR-BLODGETT FILMS INVESTIGATED BY TOF-SIMS

M.Kudo[1], N.Ogura[1], Y.Ichinohe[1], S.Yoshida[2], T.Watanabe[2], K.Endo[3] and T.Hosh[4]

[1]Department of Applied Physics, Seikei University, Tokyo, 180 Japan
[2]Institute of Industrial Science, University of Tokyo, Tokyo, 106 Japan
[3] Department of Chemistry, Kanazawa University, Kanazawa, 920-11 Japan
[4]ULVAC-PHI Inc., Chigasaki, Kanagawa, 253 Japan
*Corresponding author's e-mail address:kudo@apm.seikei.ac.jp

1. Introduction

It is widely recognized that TOF-SIMS is a powerful analytical tool to obtain chemical information on the uppermost monolayer of various solid surfaces [1,2]. The qualitative and quantitative analysis of surface chemical species by means of TOF-SIMS, however, still suffers from a great difficulty due to the insufficient knowledge on the mechanisms of secondary ion emission. Among the parameters which govern the quality of quantification with this technique is the information depth (escape depth) of the emitted secondary ions [3]. In this study, we investigated the secondary ion emission from hetero-structured Langmuir-Blodgett (LB) films formed on silver, gold and silicon substrates, which consist of separated layers of cadmium arachidate and stearilamine molecules, respectively, transferred in layer by layer fashion. Using these samples, we measured systematically the secondary ion intensities and interpreted them in relation to the escape depth of the secondary ions as well as the structure of the samples.

2. Experimental

All the samples used in this experiment were made of arachidic acid $(CH_3(CH_2)_{18}COOH)$(Cd arachidate: denoted as A) and stearilamine $(CH_3(CH_2)_{17}NH_2)$ (mixed with stearilalcohol $(CH_3(CH_2)_{17}OH$: denoted as S) LB films which were formed on the mirror polished Si(100) (denoted as Si), Ag or Au covered Si(100) (denoted as Au or Ag) substrates. Two types of samples were prepared. One type consists of only one kind of molecules such as A on Ag(denoted as A/Ag) , S/Si, S/Ag and so on (homogeneous-structured LB films), and the other is hetero-structured LB films which consist of A and S layers in the different orders such as AA/S/Si, AA/S/Ag and so forth. All analyses were performed on a Physical Electronics TFS2000 instrument, with a pulsed 12keV Ga^+ beam rastered over 80~180μm^2. Other details of the experimental conditions were described elsewhere [4].

3. Results and Discussion

In the TOF-SIMS mass spectrum from a hetero-structured LB film (e.g. S/AA/Ag sample), peaks from the substrate, i.e. Ag^+, Ag_2^+ and peaks both from stearilamine and cadmium arachidate molecules were clearly seen both in their quasi molecular forms and silver cationized forms as well as other finger-print fragment secondary ions. On some parts of the hetero-structured samples, weak variations in contrast of the secomdary ion images were observed. However, it was confirmed that the mass spectra from the different contrast areas showed almost negligible difference in the amount of the secondary ions both from the stearilamine and cadmium arachidate molecules. This fact indicates that the hetero-structured LB film is formed almost as was designed, and that the variation in contrast of the ion images may be due to the slight difference in, say, packing density or angle of the oriented molecules. This interpretation was further supported by the observation of the inhomogeneous secondary ion images(e.g. SS/A/Si), which showed more distinct intensity difference due to the two dimensional inhomogeneity. In the following discussion, however, all the data used are from the homogeneously, densely packed parts of the samples.

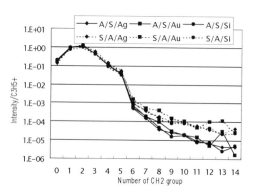

Fig.1 $[CH_3(CH_2)_n]^+$ intensities from hetero-structured LB films on the different substrates as a function of the number of CH₂ groups

The intensity of the hydrocarbon fragment ions from cadmium arachidate LB films formed on the different metal substrates are almost identical. [5] In Figure 1, the fragment intensity variations of $CH_3-(CH_2)_n$ versus n for several hetero-structured LB films formed on the different substrates are found to be almost identical to one another. This result is reasonable since the hydrocarbon chains both in the stearilamine and cadmium arachidete molecules are quite similar.

Using hetero-structured LB films (AA/S/Ag and AA/S/Si with reference samples of S/Ag and S/Si.) the intensity attenuation due to the

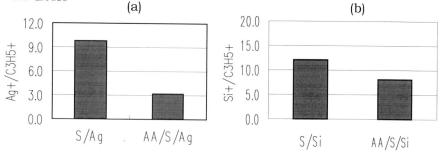

Fig.2 Intensity decrease due to the formation of hetero-structured LB films.

existence of the overlayer (capped layers) was investigated systematically. This may give some insights in the information depth (or escape depth) of the secondary ions formed on the sample surface [3].

Figure 2 shows the intensity change of Ag^+ ions (normalized with the intensity of $C_3H_5^+$) from the stearilamine sample after capped by two layers of cadmium arachidate layers on the Ag (AA/S/Ag) and Si (AA/S/Si) substrates. It is seen that in the case of Ag substrate, the normalized Ag^+ ion intensity dropped to about one third compared with that before capping. In the case of Si substrate, the decrease of Si^+ metal ion intensity was to about two thirds of the non-capped sample.

Similar, but with much more drastic decrease of the secondary ion intensities was observed for quasi-molecular ions such as $[Ms+H]^+$ and $[Ms+Ag]^+$ from samples on Ag substrate(Figure 3(a)), where Ms denotes the stearilamine molecule. In this case the intensities of $[Ms+H]^+$ and $[Ms+Ag]^+$ decreased to as small as less than several percents of that from the uncapped sample. On the Si substrate, the intensity decrease of $[Ms+H]^+$ from SS/A/Si was also observed to be less than one tenth of the uncapped sample, though the $[Ms+Si]^+$ intensity was too low to be evaluated for both S/Si and AA/S/Si samples (Figure 3(b)). Considering these results, it can be presumed that the intensity decrease is much greater for secondary ions which are formed with the intact molecules and have relatively larger number of constituent atoms.This can be understood easily if the intensity decrease occurs due to the escape process of the ions from the location where ionization took place through the overlayers.

The decrease of the secondary ion intensities of the Ag cationized hydrocarbon ions, i.e. AgC_nH_m fragment ions, was also seen after capping the stearilamine LB layer with cadmium arachidate layers on the Ag substrate, as is shown in Figure 4. Since these AgC_nH_m fragment ions are formed with atoms both from the substrate and the covered LB molecules, the intensity change due to the capping of the additional overlayer may give information on the depth where these ions are formed. The fact that these secondary ion intensities decrease drastically after capping indicates that most of these ions are formed near the interface between the substrate and the stearilamine layer. It is noteworthy to mention that the degree of decrease is larger than that of the substrate ion, i.e. Ag^+, but smaller compared with those of the quasi-molecular ions such as $[Ms+H]^+$ and $[Ms+Ag]^+$, which is in good agreement with the interpretation described above.

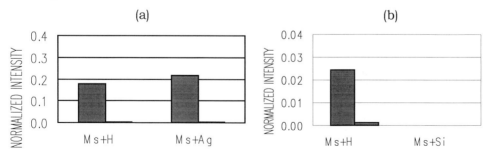

Fig.3 Intensity decrease due to the formation of hetero-structured LB films. The left and right bars in each pair of bargraphs are from samples before and after capping, respectively.

756

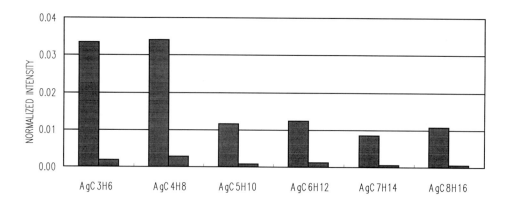

Fig.4 Intensity decrease of Ag cationized ion species due to the formation of hetero-structured LB films.(The same expression as in Fig.3)

4. Conclusion

The secondary ion intensities from hetero-structured LB films, which were formed by transferring stearilamine and cadmium arachidate molecules in layer by layer fashion, were investigated by using a TOF-SIMS instrument. The observed behavior of the $CH_3(CH_2)_n$ intensities versus the number of n showed no dependence on the substrate materials nor sample structures. For the intensity changes of such secondary ions as substrate metals, quasi molecular ions and metal cationized fragment ions from stearilamine layers showed clear decrease after the formation of the hetero-structured LB films capping the stearilamine layers with cadmium arachidate layers. It was found that the degree of intensity decrease caused by the formation of the hetero-structured LB films strongly depend on the kind of secondary ion species, probably on the number of the constituent atoms of the ions under investigation.

References
[1] A. Benninghoven, B. Hagenhoff and E. Niehuis , Anal. Chem. 65(14) ,(1993) 630A.
[2] A. Ishitani, A. Karen, S. Tomita and K. Okuno , SIMSι, (1995) 99.
[3] B. Hagenhoff , M. Deimel , A. Benninghoven , H-U. Siegmund and D. Holtkamp, J. Phys. D: Appl. Phys. 25 (1992) 818.
[4] M. Kudo, N. Ogura, S. Yamada, Y. Ichinohe, S. Yoshida, T. Watanabe T. Hoshi and K.Endo, SIMSXI(1997)471.
[5] T. Hoshi, S. Yoshida, T. Watanabe , Y. Ichinohe and M. Kudo, Appl. Surf. Sci. 142 (1999) 614.

A. Benninghoven, P. Bertrand, H.-N. Migeon and H.W. Werner (Editors).
Proceedings of the 12th International Conference on Secondary Ion Mass Spectrometry,
Brussels, Belgium, 5-11 September 1999

757

ION BEAM PATTERNED POLYMER SURFACES FOR SELECTIVE POLYELECTROLYTE MULTILAYER BUILD-UP

A. Delcorte[1a)], P. Bertrand[1+], E. Wischerhoff[2b)] and A. Laschewsky[2]

[1]Unité de Physico-Chimie et de Physique des Matériaux, [2]Departement de Chimie,
Université catholique de Louvain, 1 pl. Croix du Sud, B-1348 Louvain-la-Neuve, Belgium
e-mail: bertrand@pcpm.ucl.ac.be

1. Introduction

Very thin polymeric coatings can be formed by alternate adsorption of oppositely charged polyelectrolytes onto either a charged [1,2] or an uncharged substrate (polymer[3]), with very thin layer thicknesses (10 Å). Recently, polyelectrolyte assemblies with a lateral structure have been created using the microcontact printing method [4]. In this paper, a new strategy, based on ion beam bombardment of selected substrate areas and subsequent specific polyelectrolyte adsorption, will be presented. Using this method, patterned surfaces of polyelectrolyte multilayers may be built up. Such patterned surfaces are indeed promising for applications in the biological and bio-electronics fields. In addition to the detailed description of the method and its results, the following discussion will address both the influence of the ion beam-induced physico-chemical modifications on the adsorption process and the future developments of the method.

2. Experimental

Substrate preparation. The high molecular weight poly(isobutylene) (PIB) sample was purchased from Aldrich Chemie. It was dissolved in toluene (2 wt % in solution) and spin-coated onto fresh silicon wafers which had been previously cleaned in isopropanol and hexane. The silicon-supported PIB film was then irradiated as described hereafter.

Polyelectrolyte adsorption. The chemical formulae of the polyelectrolytes can be found in Ref. [3]. They were all dissolved in ultrapure water (Millipore), with a concentration of 2×10^{-2} M. The irradiated substrate was first dipped into a poly(ethylene imine) (PEI) solution [5]. After the deposition of this primer layer, the samples were dipped successively into poly(styrene sulfonate) (PSS) and poly(choline methacrylate) (PCM), as described in Ref. [3]. This deposition cycle was repeated three times, i.e. including the primer layer, a total of seven adsorption steps were conducted.

Irradiation, characterization and imaging These three operations were conducted with a Phi-Evans TRIFT1 Time-of-Flight SIMS [6]. The patterning was realized by scanning the 15 keV In[+] beam onto the poly(isobutylene) substrate, up to a fluence of 10^{16} ions/cm^2, in the continuous bombardment mode. The surfaces were characterized at each important step of the process, i.e. before and after ion beam patterning and after polyelectrolyte adsorption, using the ToF-SIMS imaging capabilities in the pulsed beam mode. Images were recorded on 256 x 256 pixels by scanning the pulsed beam (15 keV; 5 kHz) over the pristine and modified areas with a raster size varying in the range 25-200 µm. To confirm the chemical nature of the different areas, spectra were recorded with a raster size smaller than the characteristic size of the inhomogeneities. To avoid polymer degradation during the analysis periods, the ion fluence was kept lower than 5 x 10^{12} ions/cm^2 [7].

3. Results and discussion

In this study, a new method has been developed to elaborate polyelectrolyte multilayers with a lateral pattern by means of ion beam sputtering. The important step of this process is the creation of chemical inhomogeneities on the polymer surface with a good lateral resolution. The newly created surface will have to alternate well-defined areas where a first polyelectrolyte layer adsorbs completely with intermediate regions where the polyelectrolyte adsorption is as poor as possible. To induce chemical inhomogeneities on the surface, we chose the following strategy. First, a polymer known as *bad* support for the polyelectrolyte multilayer build-up was chosen In general, aliphatic polyolefins like poly(ethylene), poly(propylene) or poly(isobutylene) should be adequate if highly polar polyelectrolytes without significantly hydrophobic parts are used. For this study, PIB was chosen because of its very characteristic SIMS fingerprint, allowing us to track easily chemical changes of the surface.

To achieve the local surface modification, the 15 keV In$^+$ beam of our ToF-SIMS was scanned onto predefined areas of 25 x 25 μm^2 with a fluence of 10^{16} ions/cm^2. With the current ToF-SIMS equipment, bombarded areas down to one by one μm^2 and up to several mm^2 should be easily obtained on thin PIB layers. As indicated by previous studies [7], this fluence is high enough to modify strongly the chemical nature of the surface. With 10^{16} ions/cm^2, the surface is no longer characteristic of PIB: the characteristic SIMS peaks disappear, the overall SIMS intensity drops dramatically and only very small unsaturated fragments are detected in the spectra. The evolution of the SIMS intensities with increasing ion fluence demonstrates that an extensive dehydrogenation occurs [7], probably accompanied by cross-linking.

As shown by the results obtained with polymer supports [3], the presence of unsaturation in the substrate favors polyelectrolyte adsorption. Indeed, the adsorption of the PEI/(PSS/PCM)x assembly on poly(styrene) appears successful, whereas the adsorption of the same system on aliphatic polyolefins is inefficient. Therefore, a positive effect of the ion beam modification on the multilayer build-up is expected. Among the structural and chemical modifications induced in the irradiated regions, the numerous bond-scissions and radical creations are likely to induce a higher reactivity of the bombarded surfaces. This might lead to an improved oxidation when returning to air and water, which is also in favor of a better adsorption.

The effects of the surface modification and of the subsequent adsorption sequence, aiming to build-up the PEI/(PSS/PCM)x assembly, are summarized in Fig. 1. The initial pattern (before the multilayer deposition) is revealed by the implanted indium ions (frame a). Concerning the deposition step, frames b-j indicate that the polyelectrolyte adsorption occurs preferentially on the modified areas. Indeed, the intensity related to the ions sputtered from PCM (frames d and g), from PSS (frames i and g) and from the counterions of the PCM last layer (frame h), is at least two times higher in the pre-bombarded areas. The corresponding depletion of intensity in the image of the characteristic PIB ions is mainly due to the beam degradation, rather than to the multilayer deposition (frame c). Therefore, no conclusion can be drawn concerning the layer thickness. The different intensity distribution appearing in the total ion images shows that the contrast observed in the other images is not due to the sample topography, although this topography exists (frames b and f). Finally, the linescans drawn across the PCM and PSS

759

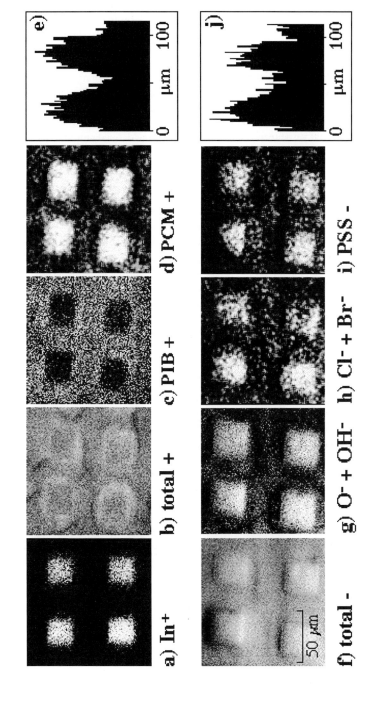

Fig. 1. Multilayer deposition on ion-beam patterned PIB. *Before polyelectrolyte adsorption:* a) Implanted indium. *After polyelectrolyte adsorption, positive ions:* b) total ion image; c) $C_6H_{11}^+$ and $C_7H_{13}^+$ (PIB); d) $C_3H_8N^+$, $C_5H_{12}N^+$, $C_5H_{12}NO^+$ and $C_5H_{14}NO^+$ (PCM); e) horizontal intensity profile through the bottom squares of image d); *negative ions:* f) total ion image; g) oxygen and hydroxyl ions; h) counterions of PEI and PCM; i) SO_2^-, SO_3^- and monomer ion of PSS; j) horizontal intensity profile through the bottom squares of image i).

images confirm the important intensity increase in the pre-bombarded regions (frames e and j). Nevertheless, the intensity threshold corresponding to the PIB areas shows that polyelectrolyte chains adsorb to some extent on the PIB, too. This could be expected from the previous measurements on pristine PIB films [3].

A subsequent test gave us further indications concerning the nature of the surface modification. Indeed, after thorough washing of the sample with hexane, only the bombarded PIB areas remained, and the silicon support reappeared in the intermediate regions. As the ion irradiation is unlikely to modify the silicon-PIB interface due to the short range of the ions in the solid, the increased resistance of the bombarded areas is probably due to extensive cross-linking of the surface layer.

4. Conclusion and outlook

Ion beam-modified PIB surfaces have been created using 12 keV indium ions and they were subsequently dipped into alternate polyelectrolyte solutions to build-up multilayers with a lateral pattern. Chemically resolved ToF-SIMS images of the patterned sample show the preferential adsorption of both polyelectrolytes on the bombarded areas, suggesting the success and reasonable selectivity of the multilayer adsorption step. In the future, this method has to be optimized to obtain a better contrast between the different areas. The polyelectrolyte chains in the intermediate regions, probably weakly anchored to the PIB support, might be washed away after each deposition step using an appropriate procedure. On the other hand, the primary ion fluence used to modify the surface might be changed, to find the best conditions for adsorption. Some preliminary attempts have been made in that direction showing that doses below 5×10^{14} ions/cm^2 do not lead to a significant adsorption contrast. A lateral variation of the ion fluence on a single sample might lead to interesting effects such as a gradient in the absorbed polyelectrolyte amount or in the structure of the deposited layers.

Acknowledgements.

The authors which to thank Gero Decher (University of Strasbourg) for helpful discussion and comments. This work is supported by the *Action de Recherche Concertée* (94/99-173) of the *Communauté Française de Belgique* and by the Belgian Interuniversity Attraction Pole Program (PAI-IUAP P4/10) on Reduced Dimensionality systems. The ToF-SIMS equipment was acquired with the support of the *Région Wallonne and FRFC - Loterie Nationale* of Belgium.

References

[a]   present address : Dep. Chemi., Pennsylvania State Univ., 152 Davey Lab, Univ. Park, PA 16802, USA
[b]   present address : Biotul Bio-Inst., Gollierstrasse 70 / B1, D-80339, Munchen, Germany
[1]   G. Decher, Science 277 (1997) 1232.
[2]   A. Delcorte, P. Bertrand, X. Arys, A. Jonas, E. Wischerhoff, B. Mayer, A. Laschewsky, Surf. Sci. 366 (1996) 149.
[3]   A. Delcorte, P. Bertrand, E. Wischerhoff and A. Laschewsky, Langmuir 13 (1997) 5125-5136
[4]   P. Hammond, G. M. Whitesides, Macromolecules, 28 (1995) 7569.
[5]   Y. M. Lvov, G. Decher, Crystallogr. Rep. 39 (1994) 696.
[6]   B. W. Schueler, Microsc. Microanal. Microstruct. 3 (1992) 119.
[7]   A. Delcorte, L. T. Weng and P. Bertrand, Nucl. Instr. and Meth. B100 (1995) 213.

A. Benninghoven, P. Bertrand, H.-N. Migeon and H.W. Werner (Editors).
Proceedings of the 12th International Conference on Secondary Ion Mass Spectrometry,
Brussels, Belgium, 5-11 September 1999

CHARACTERISATION OF THIN FILMS OF A NON-ORGANOFUNCTIONAL SILANE ON AL-43.4ZN-1.6SI ALLOY COATED STEEL BY ToF-SIMS

U. Bexell, P. Carlsson and M. Olsson

Dalarna University, S-781 88 Borlänge, Sweden, e-mail: ube@du.se

1. Introduction

Organofunctional silanes have shown to be promising candidates for the replacement of currently used chromate and/or phosphate systems in the pretreatment of metal surfaces prior to painting [1]. It has been shown that a two step silane pretreatment process, where the metal surface is treated in sequential rinses with a non-organofunctional silane such as 1,2-bis(triethoxysilyl)ethane (BTSE) and an organofunctional silane such as γ-amino-propyltriethoxysilane (γ-APS), improves the corrosion resistance of the metal and the adhesion of the paint [2]. The purpose of the first step is to form a highly cross-linked siloxane film with covalent metal-oxygen-silicon bonds at the metal surface while the purpose of the second step is to form siloxane bonds between surface Si-OH groups and silanol groups of the organofunctional silane molecule and an outward orientation of the functional group of the molecule. The aim of the present study was to characterise the structure of thin films of the non-organofunctional silane BTSE by ToF-SIMS analysis in the static mode. The influence of deposition conditions and post heat treatment on the film structure when deposited onto mechanically polished Al-43.4Zn-1.6Si alloy coated steel substrates from dilute aqueous solutions was investigated.

2. Experimental

2.1 Instrumentation

All ToF-SIMS analyses were performed with a PHI TRIFT II instrument using a 15 kV pulsed liquid metal ion source of monoisotopic $^{69}Ga^+$ ions. In this system, the secondary ions are accelerated up to ~3 kV before being deflected 270° by three electrostatic hemispherical analysers. Both positive and negative spectra were obtained using a 600 pA d.c. primary ion beam pulsed with a frequency of 10 kHz and rastered over a surface area of 100×100 μm^2. The total integrated primary ion dose was $<10^{12}$ ions/cm^2 ensuring static analysing conditions. The mass resolution $m/\Delta m$ was ~4500 as measured at $m/z = 28$ on a Si wafer. Auger electron spectroscopy (AES) was used to determine the film thickness and the depth distribution of the elements. The AES analyses were performed with a PHI 660 scanning Auger microprobe with an acceleration voltage of 10 kV and a beam current of 300 nA. The analysed area was 300×300 μm^2 for all samples. The thickness of the silane films was measured using depth profiling with 1 kV Ar$^+$ ion sputtering in the Auger system. The sputter rate was 45 Å/min as measured on Ta$_2$O$_5$.

2.2 Sample preparation

Steel strip hot dip coated with a 55.0%Al-43.4%Zn-1.6%Si alloy was supplied by SSAB Tunnplåt AB, Sweden. The samples were punched to a diameter of 20 mm and mechanically polished to a mirror like finish using 1 μm diamond in the final step. Prior to the silane treatment the samples were ultrasonically cleaned with acetone and methanol for 2 minutes. In order to improve the wettability of the substrates by the silane solution, the samples were cleaned with an etching alkaline cleaner, Ytex 4324, supplied by Chemetall Skandinaviska Ytteknik AB, Sweden. The non-functional silane, supplied by Witco Europe S.A., Switzerland, was 1,2-bis(triethoxysilyl)ethane (BTSE) with the following chemical structure:

$$(H_5C_2O)_3\text{-}Si\text{-}CH_2\text{-}CH_2\text{-}Si\text{-}(OC_2H_5)_3$$

The silane solutions were prepared by mixing 5 ml of BTSE, 150 ml of methanol and 25 ml of deionized water. The pH of the methanol plus the deionized water was adjusted to 4.0, using acetic acid, before the BTSE was added. The solutions were then hydrolysed for 1 hour and diluted to 250 ml with deionized water of pH 4.0. The final BTSE concentration of the silane solutions were 2 vol%. The pH-value of the final solutions, 4.0, 6.0, 8.0 and 10.0 (samples 1-4, respectively), were then adjusted by adding different amounts of 1 M NaOH. All solutions were transparent and clear. The samples were alkaline cleaned for 20 s, thoroughly washed in deionized water, dipped in the fresh silane solution for 1 minute and blown dry with nitrogen gas. One sample (5), treated with the pH 4.0 solution, was heated for 1 h at 120 °C. After the treatment the samples were immediately transferred to the instrument.

3. Results and Discussion

Figure 1 shows a typical positive ToF-SIMS spectrum (0-100 amu) obtained from a sample treated with the pH 4.0 silane solution. Table 1 lists the major peaks observed when analysing the five samples with their relative secondary ion yields, i.e. the counts in the corresponding peak area normalised to the total ion count in the mass range 0-1000 amu minus the counts of contaminants such as K and Na [3].

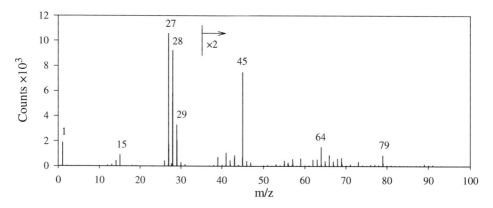

Figure 1. Positive ToF-SIMS spectrum of a silane film (sample 1) deposited on Al-43.4Zn-1.6Si alloy coated steel. See Table 1 for peak identification.

Table 1.   Relative secondary ion yields (in %) of the silane films investigated.

Mass	Ion	Sample				
		1	2	3	4	5
+1	H$^+$	2.228	1.947	3.386	3.080	2.173
+15	CH$_3^+$	0.930	0.857	1.177	0.909	0.887
+27	Al$^+$	16.754	14.324	0.571	0.179	14.044
+28	Si$^+$	17.174	17.577	26.910	27.666	19.773
+29	SiH$^+$	5.798	6.759	10.044	8.859	6.411
	C$_2$H$_5^+$	2.013	2.315	3.078	2.099	1.812
+43	SiCH$_3^+$	0.405	0.567	0.597	0.442	0.481
+45	SiOH$^+$	5.019	3.133	4.716	5.599	4.391
+57	SiC$_2$H$_5^+$	0.045	0.076	0.061	0.037	0.049
+59	SiOCH$_3^+$	0.377	0.144	0.205	0.214	0.299
+62	Si(OH)$_2^+$	0.302	0.289	0.406	0.328	0.219
+63	SiH(OH)$_2^+$	0.356	0.417	0.690	0.387	0.244
+64	Zn$^+$	1.606	0.604	0.364	0.201	1.130
+73	SiOC$_2$H$_5^+$	0.227	0.318	0.516	0.312	0.170
+77	SiO$_2$CH$_5^+$	0.072	0.146	0.155	0.085	0.051
+79	Si(OH)$_3^+$	0.578	0.689	1.036	0.575	0.364
+93	CH$_2$Si(OH)$_3^+$	0.020	0.034	0.031	-	0.013
+105	SiO$_3$SiH$^+$	0.090	0.050	0.130	0.097	0.058
+107	HSiO$_2$SiHOH$^+$	0.064	0.043	0.081	0.074	0.036
	Si(OH)$_2$OC$_2$H$_5^+$	0.031	0.040	0.060	0.035	0.018
+119	CH$_3$CH$_2$SiOHOC$_2$H$_5^+$	0.017	0.064	0.094	0.028	0.026
+123	HSiO$_2$Si(OH)$_2^+$	0.163	0.059	0.155	0.155	0.070
+135	SiOH(OC$_2$H$_5$)$_2^+$	0.014	0.031	0.037	0.017	0.011
+163	Si(OC$_2$H$_5$)$_3^+$	0.095	0.210	0.341	0.189	0.058
+309	Si$_2$O$_5$C$_{12}$H$_{29}^+$	0.014	-	0.022	0.055	0.003

When analysing the relative secondary ion yields in Table 1 the following reflections can be made:

The deposition parameters investigated (pH-value and heat treatment) does not significantly influence on the resulting structure / composition of the silane films.

Comparing the intensity ratio between Si$^+$ (+28 amu) and the major metallic ions Al$^+$ (+27 amu) and Zn$^+$ (+64 amu) can estimate the coverage of the silane films. In the present study, these estimations show that the film coverage increase with increasing pH-value and that the films deposited at pH 8.0 and 10.0 show a significantly higher coverage than the films deposited at pH 4.0 and 6.0. These observations are in good agreement with the AES analyses which show that the film coverage and the film thickness increase with increasing pH-value, see AES depth profiles in Figure 2.

The relatively high secondary ion yields of e.g. the silanol ion SiOH$^+$ (+45 amu) and the silantriol ion Si(OH)$_3^+$ (+79 amu) indicate that all the silane films are largely hydrolysed.

The relatively low secondary ion yields of e.g. Si$_2$O$_3$H$^+$ (+105 amu) and Si$_2$O$_3$H$_3^+$ (+107 amu) indicate that the structure of the silane films is not as highly cross-linked as could be expected. However, complementary studies of samples treated with the pH 10.0 silane solution stored 24 hours in air at room temperature show a high degree of cross-linked silicon polymers. Consequently, the properties of the silane solution will change with time. It should be noted that pH 10.0 silane solution lost its transparency after 24 hours due to polymerisation.

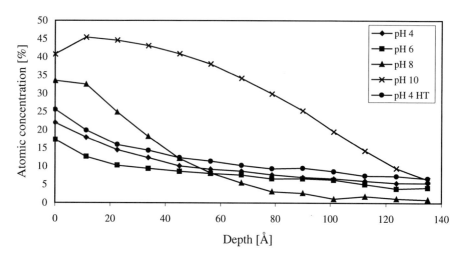

Figure 2. AES depth profiles showing the depth distribution of silicon (Si) in the silane films investigated.

4. Conclusions

In the present study the influence of deposition parameters (pH-value and heat treatment) on the structure of thin films of the non-organofunctional silane BTSE deposited onto Al-43.4Zn-1.6Si alloy coated steel was characterised by ToF-SIMS and AES analysis. The conclusions of the study are:

The deposition parameters investigated (pH-value and heat treatment) do not significantly influence on the resulting intrinsic structure/composition of the silane films.

The silane film coverage and thickness increase with increasing pH-value.

The rather high secondary ion yield of e.g. the silanol ion $SiOH^+$ (+45 amu) and the silantriol ion $Si(OH)_3^+$ (+79 amu) indicate that all the silane films are largely hydrolysed.

The relatively low ion yields of e.g. $Si_2O_3H^+$ (+105 amu), $Si_2O_3H_3^+$ (+107 amu) indicate that the structure of the silane film is not as highly cross-linked as could be expected.

References

[1] T. F. Child and W. J. van Ooij, Trans. of the Institute of Metal Finishing, 77 (1999) 64.
[2] V. Subramanian and W. J.van Ooij, Corrosion, 54 (1998) 204
[3] X. Vanden Eynden, L. T. Weng and P. Bertrand, Surf. and Int. Anal., Vol. 25, (1997) 41.

A. Benninghoven, P. Bertrand, H.-N. Migeon and H.W. Werner (Editors).
Proceedings of the 12th International Conference on Secondary Ion Mass Spectrometry,
Brussels, Belgium, 5-11 September 1999
© 2000 Elsevier Science B.V. All rights reserved.

SECONDARY ION EMISSION FROM ORGANIC MOLECULES ADSORBED ON POLYMER SURFACES

N.Man, A.Karen, A.Shimizu and A.Ishitani
Toray Research Center, Inc.
3-7, Sonoyama 3-chome, Otsu, Shiga, 520-8567, Japan
E-mail: Naoki_Man@trc.toray.co.jp

1. Introduction

TOF-SIMS is a useful technique for the characterization of organic materials, because TOF-SIMS spectra give directly chemical information including molecular structure of the materials. Particularly, characteristic molecular ions from many low molecular weight compounds can be used to identify these compounds. However, yield of the observed molecular ion as well as various fragments depends on the chemical state of the material. TOF-SIMS spectra of a monolayer or multilayers molecular systems (e.g. Langmuir-Blodgett films) on noble metal substrates have been successfully investigated, in order to understand the formation mechanism of secondary ion species generated from organic materials [1][2]. It has been considered that the chemical interaction between adsorbate and the metal substrate influences the TOF-SIMS spectra of those systems. In the case of polymer substrates, however, spectra do not necessarily change very much, because the substrate-adsorbate interaction can be weak compared with the case of metal substrate. Nevertheless, detailed analysis of the spectra can give us information concerning the interaction of functional groups between the substrate and the adsorption molecules. In this work, we have tried to obtain the information related to the polymer-adsorbate interaction from TOF-SIMS spectra. Stearic acid adsorbed polymer materials such as polyethylene(PE), polyacrylicacid (PAA), polytetra-fluoroethylene(PTFE) have been used as a model system.

2. Experimental

PE and PAA were dissolved in heated xylene and water respectively, then cast onto silicon wafers as polymer substrates (0.5-1μm in thickness). The surfaces of PE and PAA were cleaned in xylene and acetone respectively just before the adsorption experiments described later. PTFE tape was used as another substrate without any treatment. Measurements of water contact angle were done to characterize a typical surface property of the prepared three samples. The measured values are 122±0.2° for PE, 54.4±1.3° for PAA and 138.1±1.3° for PTFE in this work. These substrates were exposed to stearic acid vapor saturated at 100°C in a petri dish capped with a glass plate. The exposure time ranged 20 to 300 seconds.

TOF-SIMS measurements in this work were performed in a Physical Electronics TFS-2000 instrument equipped with a low temperature sample stage. The sample stage was cooled with liquid nitrogen to keep a sample temperature of approximately –90°C in order to avoid volatilization of adsorbate during spectrum acquisition [3]. The samples and holder were cooled to about –50°C under a dry nitrogen atmosphere, then introduced into the instrument. TOF-SIMS spectra were acquired with the high mass resolution mode in which the bunched $^{69}Ga^+$ primary beam was operated. The beam energy was 15kV, and total ion dose was around $2 \cdot 10^{12}$ ions/cm^2. Low energy electron ($\perp$15V) was used for charge compensation of the samples.

3. Results and Discussion

Fig.1 shows the reference spectrum of positive secondary ion emitted from stearic acid crystal (bulk material). Characteristic peaks are observed at 267, 285 amu corresponding to molecular like ions of $(M-OH)^+$ and $(M+H)^+$ respectively. The stearic acid dimer peak of $(2M+H)^+$ at 569 amu is also seen with moderate intensity, suggesting that there is a hydrogen bonding interaction between carboxylic groups of two molecules [4]. In the negative ion spectrum, deprotonated $(M-H)^-$ ions is observed at 283 amu which is not included in this paper.

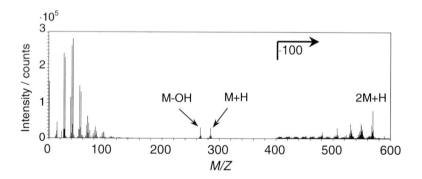

Fig.1 The positive TOF-SIMS spectrum of stearic acid crystal (bulk material).

Fig.2 shows the positive ion spectra of polymer surfaces that have been exposed to stearic acid vapor for 30 (PE, PAA) or 20 (PTFE) seconds. Although fragments containing C and F atoms from PTFE are dominant in the PTFE spectrum, aforementioned peaks from stearic acid are commonly observed on every sample. However, the ratios of those peak intensities [e.g. I(M-OH)$^+$:I(M+H)$^+$, I(2M+H)$^+$:I(M+H)$^+$] are different among three samples as shown in Table 1. In order to distinguish characteristics of spectra in each polymer substrate clearly, peak intensities of $(M-OH)^+$, $(M+H)^+$ and $(M-H)^-$ have been plotted as a function of exposure time of stearic acid vapor in Fig.3. In the case of PTFE spectrum, the ratio of $(M-OH)^+$ and $(M+H)^+$ is approximately 1:1, and a dimer species of $(2M+H)^+$ is also seen clearly. These characteristics are similar to that observed at the spectrum of a stearic acid crystal in which there can be no interaction between a fatty acid molecule and the polymer substrate. The ratio of these peak intensities is almost same during all exposure time. As expected by higher water contact angle of hydrophobic PTFE, the interaction between adsorbed stearic acid molecules and PTFE are so weak that the ionization of preformed dimers might be possible.

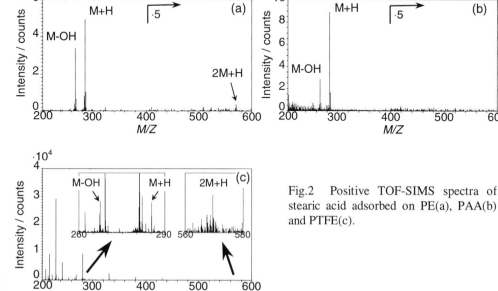

Fig.2 Positive TOF-SIMS spectra of stearic acid adsorbed on PE(a), PAA(b) and PTFE(c).

Table 1 Peak intensities (counts) of the molecular and dimer like ions from stearic acid absorbed on polymers.

	PE	PAA	PTFE	Crystal
$(M-OH)^+$	3.4E+2	2.8E+2	5.2E+2	3.9E+4
$(M+H)^+$	5.1E+2	8.9E+2	5.2E+2	3.9E+4
$(2M+H)^+$	1.0E+1	ND*	5.0E+1	9.1E+2

* not detected

In the spectrum of PAA , on the other hand, the ratio of $(M-OH)^+$ and $(M+H)^+$ is approximately 1:3, without $(2M+H)^+$ being observed at early time of exposure. The large ion yield of $(M+H)^+$ compared to $(M-OH)^+$ may be a result of the protonation of the absorbed molecules by proton donor of PAA substrate. The disappearance of $(2M+H)^+$ may also indicate that the polymer-adsorbate interaction is stronger than the molecular interaction of adsorbates. These characteristic relations of peak intensity appear to be generated by the existence of carboxylic groups on PAA surface. Fig.3(b) shows also that the relations of peak intensity are changing with exposure time, and approach those observed from crystalline stearic acid in which the ion yields of $(M-OH)^+$ and $(M+H)^+$ are almost the same. The spectrum from PE appears to have characteristics between PTFE and PAA at early stage of exposure time. The ratio of $(M-OH)^+$ and $(M+H)^+$ is approximately 2:3 with $(2M+H)^+$ being observed very weakly. These results from three kinds of polymers show that the relative yield of the characteristic ions from stearic acid correlate with the chemical properties of the polymer surface, for example, the hydrophilicity or the proton donating nature depending on the functional groups of polymer substrates.

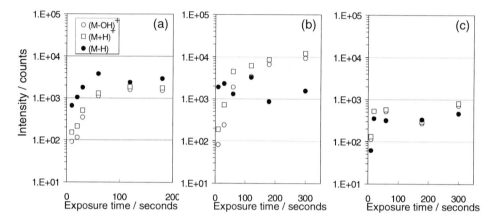

Fig.3 Peak intensities of the $(M-OH)^+$, $(M+H)^+$ and $(M-H)^-$ ions from stearic acid adsorbed on PE(a), PAA(b) and PTFE(c) as a function of exposure time of stearic acid vapor.

4. Conclusion

We have measured the TOF-SIMS spectra of stearic acid adsorbed on polymer substrates with different chemical composition as well as surface properties. Characteristic peaks of $(M-OH)^+$, $(M+H)^+$, $(M-H)^-$, and $(2M+H)^+$ which were typically observed from a bulk sample of stearic acid crystal, were seen on the PE, PAA and PTFE substrates. However, ion yield ratio of $(M+H)^+$ to $(M-OH)^+$ was different depending on the proton donating nature of polymer substrate. The ionization probability of $(2M+H)^+$ might be also affected by the strength of the interaction between molecular adsorbate and the substrate. Although this interaction may be weaker than that of metal-organic layer system, the TOF-SIMS spectra on the polymer systems can be delicately influenced by such interaction. To see this behavior of molecular ion emission may help to understand its mechanism, and to study the surface properties of other kind of industrially developed polymer materials.

References

[1] J.C.Vickerman, *Proceedings of SIMS XI*, John Wiley & Sons, (1998), 19
[2] A.Benninghoven, F.G.Rudenauar and H.W.Werner, *Secondary Ion Mass Spectrometry*, John Wiley & Sons, (1987), 747
[3] G.Strossman, P.Lindley and W.Bowers, *Proceedings of SIMS XI*, John Wiley & Sons, (1998), 699
[4] G.Bolbach and J.C.Blais, *Proceedings of SIMS VI*, John Wiley & Sons, (1988), 655

A. Benninghoven, P. Bertrand, H.-N. Migeon and H.W. Werner (Editors).
Proceedings of the 12th International Conference on Secondary Ion Mass Spectrometry,
Brussels, Belgium, 5-11 September 1999
© 2000 Elsevier Science B.V. All rights reserved.

769

A JOINT SIMS AND AFM STUDY OF THE SURFACE MORPHOLOGY OF POLY(CAPROLACTONE) – POLY(METHYLMETHACRYLATE) BLENDS

M. Ferring[1], R. Gouttebaron[1], V. Cornet[2], Ph. Leclère[2], Ph. Dubois[3],
R. Lazzaroni[2], and M. Hecq[1]

[1] Laboratoire d'Analyse des Surfaces par Spectroscopie d'Ions et d'Electrons (LASSIE),
e-mail: marc.ferring@umh.ac.be
[2] Service de Chimie des Matériaux Nouveaux (SCMN), Centre de Recherche en Electronique
et Photonique Moléculaires
[3] Service des Matériaux Polymères et Composites (SMPC)
Université de Mons-Hainaut, Place du Parc 20, B-7000 Mons (Belgium)

1. Introduction

Polymer blending constitutes the most straightforward approach for obtaining new materials with properties that cannot be found in a single polymer. Because most polymers are immiscible, they tend to phase separate in the solid state and the resulting morphology strongly influences the macroscopic properties of the blend. It is important to notice that the length scale of the phase separation can be controlled via the experimental conditions used for the preparation of the materials. As a consequence, by combining the appropriate polymers and generating the desired morphology, one can tune the properties of the blends.

In this study, we apply this approach to blends of poly(ε-caprolactone), PCL, and poly(methylmethacrylate), PMMA, in order to design new materials with potential biomedical applications. Both polymers are biocompatible, *i.e.*, when put in contact with a living medium, they cause no adverse effect. Moreover, PCL is biodegradable: under certain conditions, numerous chain scissions occur *in vivo* and the resulting short oligomers or monomers are eliminated or re-used by the cell metabolism. In principle, combining these two polymers into a single material can lead to implants, which are partly resorbable, a feature that is expected to favor cell proliferation and tissue regeneration.

$$\left(\!(CH_2)_5 \!-\!\!\!\overset{\displaystyle O}{\overset{\|}{C}}\!-\!O\!\right)_{\!n} \qquad\qquad \left(\!CH_2\!-\!\!\!\underset{\underset{\displaystyle OCH_3}{\overset{\displaystyle C=O}{|}}}{\overset{\displaystyle CH_3}{\underset{|}{\overset{|}{C}}}}\!\right)_{\!n}$$

PCL   PMMA

The material properties critically depend on the microscopic morphology and surface composition of the blends. To investigate these two aspects, we use a combination of complementary techniques: Time-of-flight Secondary Ion Mass Spectrometry (Tof-SIMS) and Atomic Force Microscopy (AFM). Tof-SIMS has become one of the most powerful analytical techniques for polymer surface analysis. Combining high sensitivity, high mass resolution and high spatial resolution, it provides information on surface chemical structures and enables molecule-specific imaging with submicrometer lateral resolution [1,2]. In this work the aim of Tof-SIMS is to examine the surface composition of the polymer blends, and to localize the different components. AFM in tapping mode (TMAFM, [3]) is used to determine the surface morphology of the blends. Compared to the imaging capabilities of SIMS, the lateral resolution of AFM is much higher (on the order of 1nm). However, it provides only qualitative and indirect information on surface composition. Such information is usually obtained by recording the phase of the oscillating cantilever in TMAFM ; it has been shown that the phase signal is very sensitive to the properties of the imaged material and it can thus be used to establish the spatial distribution of the various components [4,5].

2. Experimental

Commercially available PMMA (Polysciences, MW : 75000) was used while PCL (MW : 58800) was synthesized via well-tailored "coordination-insertion" type ring-opening polymerization [6]. Films of blends with varying PMMA/PCL ratios were cast from toluene solutions of appropriate composition in the polymers. The samples were either freestanding films, about 500 µm in thickness, or thin (≈ 400 nm) deposits on mica substrates. Tof-SIMS analyses were performed using an ION-TOF Tof-SIMS IV featuring a 25 KeV Gallium liquid metal ion source and a time-of-flight reflectron mass analyzer. The images were acquired with the Ga gun operated at 25 KeV and rastered over 500x500 µm². The AFM images were recorded with a Nanoscope IIIa microscope operated in tapping mode in air, using commercial Si cantilevers.

3. Results and discussion

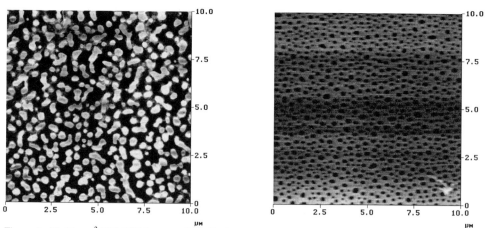

Figure 1: 10x10 µm² TMAFM images of 50:50 (left) and 80:20 (right) PMMA/PCL blends; the vertical grayscale is 20 nm with brighter (darker) areas representing higher (lower) locations in the topographic profile

Figure 1 illustrates the influence of the blend composition on the film morphology. These AFM images correspond to thin deposits prepared from solutions with 50:50 (left) and

80:20 PMMA/PCL ratios. In the 50:50 sample, the surface is made of bright domains of various shape and size in a darker matrix while the 80:20 sample shows a homogeneous dispersion of dark domains (with an average diameter of ≈ 200 nm) in a bright matrix.

Assigning the various morphological features to the two constituents from the AFM images is not straightforward since the technique does not provide direct chemical information. Based on the composition of the system in the right-side image, it is most likely that the domains are made of the minor component (PCL) while the major component (PMMA) forms the continuous matrix. The observed topographic contrast is formed during the early stages of film drying; it is thought to arise from slight differences in solubility between the two polymers [7]. This assignment thus allows for the interpretation of the left-side image of Figure 1: in this case, the bright domains, which are higher in topography, correspond to PMMA and the matrix is made of PCL. It must be noted that the corresponding TMAFM phase images also clearly show phase separation in those samples, consistently with the above interpretation. Nevertheless, it would be most useful to obtain direct information on the surface chemical composition from SIMS in order to: (i) confirm the interpretation of the surface morphology, and (ii) check whether a very thin layer of one component covers the whole surface, without being detected with AFM. For this purpose, we have analyzed thick, freestanding films with 50:50 PMMA/PCL composition. Because complete solvent evaporation is quite slow when preparing thick deposits, phase separation develops on a larger length scale in those samples, compared to thin films. As a result, the AFM images (not presented here) show the formation of PCL domains, with much larger dimensions, *i.e.*, from 5 μm up to over 100 μm.

  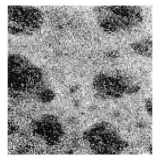

Figure 2: **500x500μm²** positive secondary ion image of 50:50 PMMA/PCL blend, **m/z=57**, number of pixels: 128x128, pulses/pixel: 50, scans: 100, highest signals shown in bright

Figure 3: **500x500μm²** positive secondary ion image of 50:50 PMMA/PCL blend, **m/z=115**, number of pixels: 128x128, pulses/pixel: 50, scans: 100, highest signals shown in bright

Fig. 4: **Normalized** 500x500μm² positive secondary ion image of 50:50 PMMA/PCL blend (image 2 divided by image 3 for contrast magnification)

The nodular morphology shown by the AFM images can also be seen on the Tof-SIMS secondary ion images acquired on the 50:50 PMMA/PCL blend. In order to identify the different domains, reference spectra on single PCL and PMMA homopolymers have been taken. But the similar chemical structure of PCL and PMMA hampers an easy assignment of the different domains to PCL or to PMMA. Indeed the Tof-SIMS spectra taken of PCL and PMMA present mostly the same characteristic fragments.

772

Figures 2 and 3 show secondary ion images at m/z=57 (CHO^+ and $C_4H_9^+$) and at m/z=115 ($C_6H_{11}O_2^+$). In Figure 2, the sample surface presents dark domains in a brighter matrix, whereas Figure 3 shows brighter domains in a dark matrix, giving the "negative" image of Figure 2. Due to the detection of the considered fragments on the surface of both polymers, the contrast of the different phases on the images is rather weak. The magnification of this contrast is achieved by image normalization, as can be seen on Figure 4, obtained by dividing image 2 by image 3.

The identification of the different phases was done by comparing the relative intensities of the fragments m/z=57 and m/z=115 measured on the reference spectra of PCL and PMMA. This ratio (I_{57}/I_{115}) was less important for PCL than for PMMA. Based on these observations, it can be deduced that the dark domains on Figure 4 correspond to PCL. Thus the size and composition of these domains shown on the SIMS images confirm the AFM results, the image size of the SIMS images being $500x500\mu m^2$. Furthermore the SIMS results show that the polymer surface is not covered by a thin layer of either PCL or PMMA.

4. Summary

A joint approach combining Tof-SIMS and atomic force microscopy was used to determine the microscopic surface morphology and composition in biocompatible polymer poly(ε-caprolactone) and poly(methylmethacrylate) blends. These techniques allowed to characterize the length scale of the phase separation process from the 100 μm scale down to the submicron scale. The surface morphology was found to depend strongly on the blend composition and on the experimental conditions used to prepare the polymer films.

Acknowledgements: This work is partly supported by the European Commission and the Government of Région Wallonne (Program FEDER-Objectif 1-Hainaut) and FNRS/FRFC. R.L. is Maître de Recherches du Fonds National de la Recherche Scientifique.

References

[1] K. Stoppek-Langner, J. Grobe, B. Hagenhoff, K. Meyer and A. Benninghoven, *Secondary Ion Mass Spectrometry SIMS X*, 627 (1995)
[2] H. van der Wel, J.M.E. Baken and P.L. Cobben, *Secondary Ion Mass Spectrometry SIMS X*, 631 (1995)
[3] Q. Zhong, D. Iniss, K. Kjoller, V.B. Elings, *Surf. Sci.,* 290, L688 (1993)
[4] Ph. Leclère, R. Lazzaroni, J.L. Brédas, J.M. Yu, Ph. Dubois, R. Jérôme, *Langmuir*, 12, 4317 (1996)
[5] G. Bar, Y. Thomman, R. Brandsch, H.J. Cantow, M.H. Whangbo, *Langmuir,* 13, 3807 (1997)
[6] D. Mecerreyes, R. Jérôme, P. Dubois, *Advances in Polymer Science*, 147, 2-59, (1999)
[7] S. Walheim, M. Ramstein, U. Steiner, *Langmuir*, 15, 4828 (1999)

A. Benninghoven, P. Bertrand, H.-N. Migeon and H.W. Werner (Editors).
Proceedings of the 12th International Conference on Secondary Ion Mass Spectrometry,
Brussels, Belgium, 5-11 September 1999
© 2000 Elsevier Science B.V. All rights reserved.

IDENTIFICATION OF AUTOMOTIVE PAINTS USING TIME-OF-FLIGHT SECONDARY ION MASS SPECTROMETRY

Yeonhee Lee[1]*, Seunghee Han[1], Jung-Hyeon Yoon[1], Young-Man Kim[1], Sung-Kun Shon[2], Sung-Woo Park[2]

[1]Advanced Analysis Center, Korea Institute of Science and Technology, Seoul 136-791, Korea,
[2]Forensic Science Dept., National Institute of Scientific Investigation, Seoul 158-097, Korea, (e-mail: yhlee@kistmail.kist.re.kr)

1. Introduction

Automobile paint samples are frequently submitted to forensic laboratories for identification and comparison in a wide variety of criminal and civil cases. Forensic laboratories analyze paints mainly by microscopic methods, that is, color matching, surface texture, and layer structure.[1,2] Most research groups use a variety of techniques to examine paint samples chemically. The most common techniques include solubility in various solvents and acids, pyrolysis gas chromatography, infrared spectroscopy, x-ray diffraction, emission spectroscopy, and scanning electron microscopy with energy dispersive x-ray analysis.[3-6] Neutron activation analysis has also been used for the analysis of the elemental composition of paints.[7]

Recent studies have demonstrated the use of Time-of-Flight Secondary Ion Mass Spectrometry (TOF-SIMS) for characterizing multi-layer coatings in a paint system.[8] Kaberline et al. have determined the relative photo-oxidation resistance of intact multi-layer polymeric paint systems using TOF-SIMS in combination with cross-sectional microtomy and isotopic labeling techniques. In this work TOF-SIMS was used in order to determine the applicability of SIMS in forensic paint analysis and the specificity of the mass spectra in paint analysis. TOF-SIMS permitted the analysis of very small paint chips and the identification of 73 paint chips of various colors from late model automobiles.

2. Experimental

Paint sample preparation: Blue, red, silver, and white paint chips were collected from late models of domestic automobile companies such as Daewoo, Hyundae, Kia, and Ssangyong. The paint chips were grouped according to the color categories above and the manufacturers. A paint chip of 70 mm^2 was washed with methanol, wrapped with aluminum foil to decrease charging, and mounted on the TOF-SIMS sample holder. If the paint chip contained clearcoat on the top, it was removed with a sharp scalpel blade before analysis.

TOF-SIMS Instrument: The SIMS analyses were performed using the PHI-7200 time-of flight SIMS instrument manufactured by Physical Electronics, Eden Prairie, MN. During analysis the instrument employed an 8 keV Cs^+ ion source. The dc primary ion beam intensity at the sample was 10 nA, and the operating spot size was about 50 μm in diameter. A low energy electron beam was used for charge compensation.

3. Results and Discussion

Survey spectra were employed to determine the relative abundances of elements in the surface layers of the paint chips after removing the clear layers. The depth profiles of paint samples permitted the analysis of very small paint chips, the reproducible results of specific elements, and the identification of individual car paint. An analysis was performed on 73 paint chips of various colors from late model automobiles that were manufactured in Korea. For various paints it was determined by TOF-SIMS data that there were 13 elements which could be used to distinguish the paints. TOF-SIMS results of three different white paint chips from Kia automobile company were obtained. Fig.1 shows the depth profiles of elements such as Al, Ti, Cr, Cu, Ca, Mg, Fe, K, Na, Li, Mn, and Sr. Paints WK5 and WK4 give distinctive Ti distributions and high intensities of Al. Especially, paint WK5 shows intense peaks of Na and K. On the other hand, in the case of paint WK7 very low Ti, Al, and Li distributions are exhibited. From the figure it can be seen that paints WK7, WK5, and WK4 were all distinguishable by their elemental compositions determined by TOF-SIMS data.

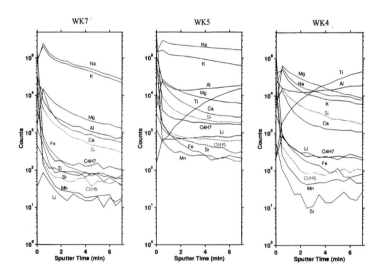

Fig. 1 TOF-SIMS depth profiles of white automobile paints.

Table 1. TOF-SIMS peak intensity ranges for the elements and compounds found in automobile paints.

Element		Range	Element		Range
Al	1	Al < 1.5	K	1	K < 0.1
	2	1.5 < Al < 10.0		2	0.1 < K < 1.0
	3	10.0 < Al < 70.0		3	1.0 < K < 10.0
	4	70.0 < Al		4	10.0 < K < 50.0
Ti	1	Ti < 0.1		5	50.0 < K
	2	0.1 < Ti < 1.2	Na	1	Na < 0.5
	3	1.2 < Ti < 4.0		2	0.5 < Na < 10
	4	4.0 < Ti		3	10.0 < Na
Cr	1	Cr < 0.015	Li	1	Li < 0.01
	2	0.015 < Cr < 0.1		2	0.01 < Li < 0.2
	3	0.1 < Cr		3	0.2 < Li
Cu	1	Cu < 0.01	Mn	1	Mn < 0.04
	2	0.01 < Cu < 0.1		2	0.04 < Mn
	3	0.1 < Cu	Sr	1	Sr < 0.05
Ca	1	Ca < 0.1		2	0.05 < Sr
	2	0.1 < Ca < 1.2	C_4H_7	1	C_4H_7 < 0.1
	3	1.2 < Ca		2	0.1 < C_4H_7
Mg	1	Mg < 0.02	C_6H_5	1	C_6H_5 < 0.1
	2	0.02 < Mg < 0.1		2	0.1 < C_6H_5
	3	0.1 < Mg			
Fe	1	Fe < 0.1			
	2	0.1 < Fe < 2.0			
	3	2.0 < Fe			

The groups of elements indicated in Table 1 represent only the relative intensities of each element in the TOF-SIMS data. In this table, each element was divided into different intensity ranges. The 7 elements Cr, Cu, Ca, Mg, Fe, Na, and Li were divided into 3 different intensity ranges. The elements Al and Ti were divided into 4 different ranges. Arbitrary unit 4 indicates a very high intensity of the element in the TOF-SIMS data; 3 indicates strong intensity; 2 indicates medium intensity; 1 indicates that little trace of the element was detected.

The results of TOF-SIMS analysis of 17 white automobile paints are displayed in Fig. 2. These paints were obtained from Daewoo, HyunDae, Kia, and Ssangyong automobile company. Of the 17 white paints analyzed, WH1 and WK7 were identical and WD2 and WH2 were very similar

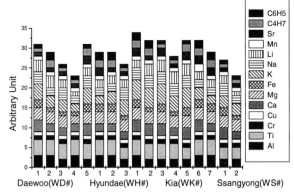

Fig. 2 Classification of white automobile paints using TOF-SIMS

by TOF-SIMS results. The rest of white paints were different in the bar graph and could be distinguished by using the 12 major elements.

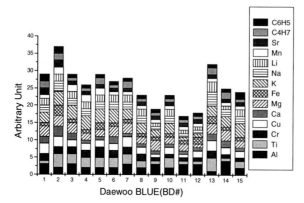

Fig. 3 shows the results of the analysis of 15 blue paints that were from Daewoo automobile company. Of these paints, samples BD8 and BD10 were identical to each other except for the amount of Ti. All the other blue paints were distinguishable by TOF-SIMS.

Fig. 3 Classification of Daewoo blue automobile paints using TOF-SIMS

4. Conclusions

As a result of the analysis of the 73 automobile paint chips, it was concluded that TOF-SIMS is a useful technique for the forensic analysis of automobile paints. TOF-SIMS technique proved to have several advantages in its application to forensic analysis. It enabled the analysis of very small paint chips, that is, chips smaller than 1 mm^2. In the analysis of larger paint chips, the entire paint chip was not destroyed and was, therefore, available for additional analysis and evidence. The method will also be useful in the analysis of paint on cloth and other materials.

References

[1] G. Dabdoub, P. Severin, J. Forensic Sci., 34 (1989) 1395
[2] G.D. Hudson, R.O. Andahl, S.J. Butcher, J. Forensic Sci. Soc. 17 (1977) 27
[3] E.M. Suzuki, J. Forensic Sci., 41 (1996) 393
[4] J.H. Kilbourn, R.B. Marx, Microscope 42 (1994) 167
[5] G.P. Voskertchian, J. Forensic Sci., 40 (1995) 823
[6] P. Burke, C.J. Curry, L.M. Davies, D.R. Cousins, Forensic Sci. International, 28 (1985) 201
[7] K.B. Snow, W.D. Washington, JAOAC, 54 (1971) 917
[8] S.L. Kaberline, T.J. Prater, J.E. deVries, J.L. Gerlock, SIMS X; A. Benninghoven; B. Hagenhoff; H.W. Werner, Eds.; Wiley: Chichester, UK, (1995) 969

A. Benninghoven, P. Bertrand, H.-N. Migeon and H.W. Werner (Editors).
Proceedings of the 12th International Conference on Secondary Ion Mass Spectrometry,
Brussels, Belgium, 5-11 September 1999
© 2000 Elsevier Science B.V. All rights reserved.

DYNAMIC SIMS OF POLYMER FILMS ?

O. Brox, S. Hellweg, and A. Benninghoven

Physikalisches Institut, Universität Münster, D-48149 Münster, Germany

1. Introduction

Static SIMS allows the analysis of all kinds of molecular surfaces including polymers. Using SF_5^+ and other polyatomic primary ions results in remarkable increases in yield Y, damage cross section σ, and efficiency E for characteristic polymer secondary ions [1, 2]. Recently, a PMMA overlayer was found to feature a stable emission of characteristic fragments under high fluence 5.5 keV SF_5^+ bombardment [3].

In this investigation we mainly address two questions:
- Is the stability of PMMA under SF_5^+ bombardment an exception?
- Is the high mass or the polyatomic nature of SF_5^+ the reason for this stability?

For this purpose we investigated a variety of polymer samples, bulk materials as well as spin-coated overlayers, under high fluence Ar^+, Xe^+, SF_5^+, Cs^+ bombardment at different energies. As a result, we found stability under SF_5^+ (and Xe^+) bombardment only for two glycols (PEG and PPG) in addition to PMMA.

2. Instrumentation

We used a TOF-SIMS III reflectron-type instrument built at the University of Münster. For depth profiling it provides an electron impact sputter gun (Ar^+, Xe^+, SF_5^+) and a Cs^+ sputter gun. Sputter depth profiling is done in the dual beam mode. Measurements were done at energies 0.6, 1 and 3 keV at an angle of incidence of 52.5°. The area scanned by the sputter gun was typically $200 \times 200 \mu m^2$. The analysis source was an Ar^+ electron impact ion gun operated at an energy of 10 keV (unrastered, spot size $\varnothing 30$ µm, angle of incidence: 45°). Additionally, the instrument provides an electron flood gun for charge compensation.

3. Samples

We investigated several polymers as bulk (b) and spin coated overlayers (c): PMMA (c), PEG (b,c), PPG (c), PC (b,c), PS (c), PI (b), PE (b), PTFE (b). Polymer overlayer preparation was done by spin coating of polymer solutions on HF dipped and ozonized Si wafers. Reproducible areas of sufficient extension and homogenous layer thickness were achieved that way.

4. Results and Discussion

Characteristic secondary ion intensities show the same behavior in positive and negative mode. A high yield is achieved in the positive mode for Ar^+, Xe^+, SF_5^+ bombardment, and in the negative mode for Cs^+ sputter ions. High and low mass polymer fragment ions show the same behavior for both charge signs. Secondary ion yields are higher for lower masses. So characteristics of secondary ion emission behavior for different polymers can best be evaluated by considering lower mass fragments in the positive mode (Ar^+, Xe^+, SF_5^+) or negative mode (Cs^+), respectively.

The comparison of all investigated polymers shows two kinds of behavior:
- All bulk polymers (except PTFE) show an immediate and rapid decrease in characteristic secondary ion emission for all applied sputter ions. This is in agreement with the known behavior of polymers.
- Polymer overlayers divide into two groups:
  PC, PS, PI, PE show a rapid decrease of fragment ion intensities for all sputter ions.
  PEG, PPG, PMMA show a relative stability of characteristic fragment ion intensities for all sputter ions. The dependence on ion species and energy for these "stable" polymer overlayers is addressed below.
- PTFE bulk polymers show a stable emission of characteristic fragment ions for SF_5^+ sputtering, but not for Ar^+. A possible chemical influence of SF_5^+ bombardment makes it difficult to decide whether steady state PTFE secondary ion signals originate from a stable fragment sputter emission from the original sample material or are due to the generation of new F and C containing surface species under SF_5^+ bombardment.

Cs^+ depth profiling leads to a strong matrix effect and influences "stable" polymer fragment signals. They feature a maximum at the substrate interface and therefore they cannot be compared directly with profiles obtained by other sputter ions.

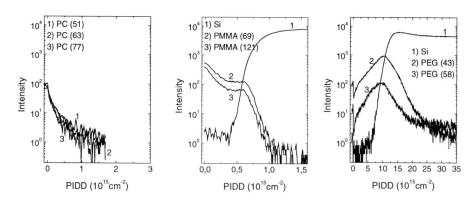

Fig. 1: Depth profiles of polymer overlayers on Si:
PC at 1keV SF_5^+ (left), PMMA at 1keV SF_5^+ (middle), PEG at 1 keV Cs^+ (right)

The dynamic SIMS behavior of stable polymers has been evaluated in more detail for PEG overlayers on Si. Characteristic is a decrease in signal intensity at the beginning of the sputtering process followed by a more or less pronounced stabilization of the characteristic *signals*, until the Si interface is reached. Finally, parallel with an increase of substrate ions, the steady state fragment signals decline.

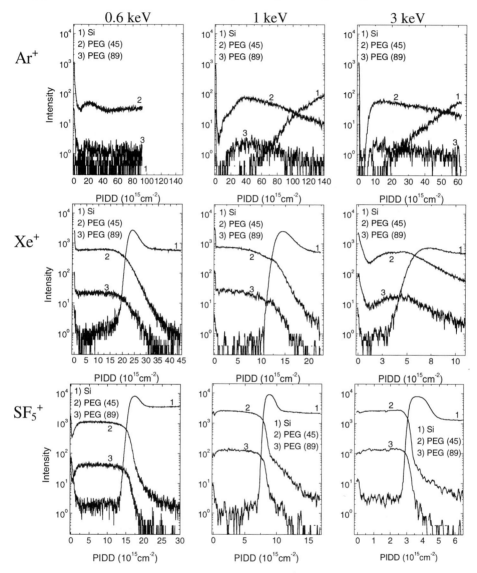

Fig.2:*Depth profiles of PEG overlayers on Si. Sputter ions: Ar^+, Xe^+, SF_5^+; energies: 0.6, 1, 3 keV*

Dynamic SIMS depth profiles with Ar^+, Xe^+, SF_5^+ compared for the same energy show the influence of sputter ion species. The primary ion dose density necessary to reach the interface decreases going from Ar^+ to Xe^+ to SF_5^+ for each energy. As the polymer overlayers are of comparable thickness, the sputter yield evidently increases changing from Ar^+ to Xe^+ and SF_5^+.

Ar^+ bombardment leads to a strong, rapid decrease of polymer ions followed by an increase up to low constant intensities. At the PEG / Si interface only a slow increase of the substrate signal occurs (low depth resolution).

For Xe^+ sputter ions, the decrease of fragment signals is followed by stabilization at a rather high intensity. A sharp increase of the substrate signal indicates the interface.

SF_5^+ sputtering results in a weak decay of characteristic fragment signal followed by an increase to a stable high intensity steady state. The increase of the substrate signal at the interface is very sharp.

Additionally, the energy of the sputter ions was varied between 0.6, 1 and 3 keV. Comparing the depth profiles of one sputter ion species, no influence of sputter energy on the level of fragment signal equilibrium can be observed. With increasing energy Ar^+ sputter ions lead to a faster and stronger decrease of fragment signals at the beginning of sputtering. Xe^+ sputter ions show only minor variations of a fragment signal decrease at different energies. SF_5^+ sputtering results in a nearly contrary behavior, the weak signal decrease at the beginning of sputtering is more pronounced at lower energies.

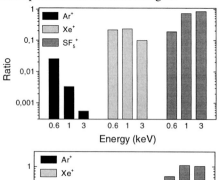

Fig. 3:

Signal decrease at the beginning of PEG sputtering by Ar^+, Xe^+ and SF_5^+ at different energies. Plotted is the ratio between the minimum intensity at the signal decrease and the intensity at the beginning of sputtering (PEG fragment mass 45).

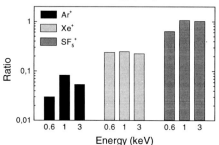

Fig. 4:

Signal stabilization of PEG sputtered by Ar^+, Xe^+ and SF_5^+ at different energies. Plotted is the ratio between the intensity at equilibrium state and the intensity at the beginning of sputtering (PEG fragment mass 45).

5. Conclusion

The stability of polymers under SF_5 bombardment seems to be an exception rather than the rule. Aside from PMMA we found stability only for spin-coated polyglycoles (PEG, PPG) using SF_5^+ as well as heavy atomic primary ions (Xe^+, Cs^+). For high ion fluences all bulk polymers are unstable under any primary ion bombardment.

References

[1] F. Kötter, A. Benninghoven, Appl. Surf. Sci. **133** (1998) 47
[2] D. Stapel, O. Brox, A. Benninghoven, Appl. Surf. Sci. **140** (1999) 156-167
[3] G. Gillen, S. Roberson, Rapid Commun. Mass Spectrom. **12**, 1303-1312 (1998)

A. Benninghoven, P. Bertrand, H.-N. Migeon and H.W. Werner (Editors).
Proceedings of the 12th International Conference on Secondary Ion Mass Spectrometry,
Brussels, Belgium, 5-11 September 1999

SPECTRAL DIFFERENCES AND THEIR INTERPRETATION
FOR THE IDENTIFICATION OF COMMON POLYMERS

A.J. Eccles*(1), T.A. Steele(1) and D. Briggs(2)

(1) Millbrook Instruments Limited, Blackburn Technology Centre, Blackburn, BB1 5QB, UK
* corresponding author   e-mail millbrook@compuserve.com

(2) Siacon Consultants Limited, 21 Woodfarm Road, Malvern, WR14 4PL, UK

1. Introduction

Recent work has shown that it is possible to predict molecular weights in excess of 10,000 using the low mass SIMS peaks arising from the end groups of a molecule [1, 2]. Similarly, it has long been accepted that small fragment secondary ions carry information about the functional groups present in a molecule [3]. There is therefore much to be learned from a static SIMS spectrum below $m/z = 300$, a range which is accessible using either a time-of-flight or a quadrupole instrument.

The Millbrook Chemical Microscope [4] is a low cost, fully automated benchtop SIMS instrument primarily designed for imaging SIMS [4, 5] analysis using a rastered focused beam. However, the operator can choose to run an analysis with the primary beam defocused, allowing the acquisition of full positive and negative spectra within the static SIMS limit of $< 10^{13}$ ions cm^{-2}. The instrument is supplied with a version of the SurfaceSpectra SIMS Library [6] with the data presented so as to simulate acquisition using the Chemical Microscope itself. The operator is thus able directly to compare experimental data with the Library in order to deduce the family of organic compounds to which the unknown species belongs. If this is not sufficiently precise information e.g. to identify the exact origin of a contaminant, it is straightforward to acquire example spectra from the various possible compounds under identical analysis conditions, and hence begin to extend and tailor the Library for a specific application.

This short paper presents two examples (drawn from more extensive studies currently in progress) to illustrate this mode of analysis. In the first case, deliberate modification of a molecular structure is used to generate a variation from the Library spectra, allowing assignment of the characteristic "fingerprint" peaks in the observed spectrum. In the second case no such model samples were available at the time of the analysis, and the experimental spectra are compared with standard Library spectra to deduce the molecular structure.

2. Experimental Conditions

In each case, positive and negative SIMS spectra were acquired using the Millbrook Chemical Microscope in defocused primary beam mode [7]. The primary beam species was 6 keV Ga^+, and the total primary ion dose to acquire each spectrum was 5.6×10^{12} ions cm^{-2}. The spectra were generated by scanning the quadrupole from $m/z = 5$ to $m/z = 260$ in both forward and reverse (i.e. starting at the high mass end) order with no significant variation observed in the

782

relative peak intensities, confirming that ion beam induced damage was negligible. Charge neutralization using the auxiliary indirect electron flood [7] was required for the as received sample discussed in Section 3.2.

3. Results and Discussion

3.1 A Siloxane

Figures 1a and 1b show respectively the positive and negative spectra obtained from a model sample of a siloxane prepared by wiping the viscous liquid on to clean aluminium foil to produce a thin but continuous film. The poly(methylhydrogen siloxane) used differed from the more familiar poly(dimethyl siloxane) (PDMS) included in the Library [6] by the substitution of an H for one of the two methyl side groups attached to the silicon atoms in the main chain of the molecule.

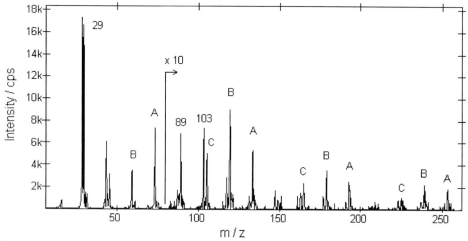

Figure 1a. Positive siloxane spectrum showing sequences of ions separated by 60 mass units

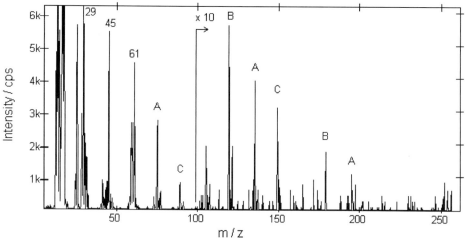

Figure 1b. Negative siloxane spectrum showing sequences of ions separated by 60 mass units

The tri-methyl end group in the model siloxane gives rise to the usual peak at m/z = 73 ($(CH_3)_3Si^+$) in the positive spectrum, instantly identifying it as a member of the siloxane family. However the change in molecular structure is clearly reflected in the positive spectrum by the strong SiH^+ peak at m/z = 29. Similarly, in the negative spectrum, there are strong peaks at m/z = 29 (HSi^-), m/z = 45 ($HSiO^-$) and m/z = 61 ($HSiO_2^-$). Any or all of these peaks could be used as a characteristic feature to identify this specific siloxane.

The other characteristic structures of PDMS peaks are found in the positive and negative spectra, but with the substitution of the appropriate number of methyl groups for H groups. The peak separation is therefore 60 mass units ($OSiHCH_3$) rather than 74 mass units ($OSi(CH_3)_2$). In the positive spectrum, for example, the usual sequence of m/z = 73, 147, 221, 295 peaks is found shifted to m/z = 73, 133, 193, 253, these ions having the generic formula $(CH_3)_3Si(OSiHCH_3)_n^+$. The sequence at m/z = 133, 207, 281 is transposed to m/z = 119, 179, 239 (generic formula $CH_3SiO(SiHCH_3O)_n^+$) and to m/z = 105, 165, 225 (generic formula $HSiO(SiHCH_3O)_n^+$). There is also a sequence at m/z = 89, 103, 117 which are assigned to $HCH_2SiOSi(H)_2^+$, $HCH_2SiOSiHCH_3^+$ and $(CH_3)(CH_2)SiOSiHCH_3^+$, the first two ions having no direct equivalent in PDMS. In the (simpler) negative spectrum, similar sequences are observed at m/z = 75, 135, 195, m/z = 119, 179 and m/z = 89, 149.

3.2 A Fluorocarbon

Figures 2a and 2b show respectively the positive and negative spectra obtained from a hard disk platter of indeterminate origin. The positive spectrum shows a sequence of $C_xF_y^+$ cluster ions, indicating that the surface lubricant is fluorocarbon based. However, the existence of oxygen in the molecule is first indicated by the presence of the O^- peak at m/z = 16 in the negative spectrum. There is a series of peaks in the positive spectrum (m/z = 47, 97, 116, 135, 147, 163, 185, 213) all of which correspond to secondary ions of generic formula $C_xF_yO_z^+$. The negative spectrum is dominated by a similar sequence (m/z = 47, 63, 85, 97, 113, 116, 135, 151, 163, 182, 201, 229, 232) corresponding to secondary ions of generic formula $C_xF_yO_z^-$. This indicates a perfluoroether, and the high intensity of the $C_xF_y^+$ cluster ions at m/z = 50 (CF_2^+) and 100 ($C_2F_4^+$) suggests a co-polymer having the generic formula $X[CF_2O]_m[CF_2CF_2O]_nY$. Utilising both positive and negative mass spectra, an excellent match of relative peak intensities is obtained with the Library spectrum of ZD15 lubricant [6] which identifies the end groups as X = CF_3O and Y = CF_3 (note the strong CF_3^+ peak at m/z = 69 in the positive spectrum).

4. Conclusion

In each case, the positive and negative SIMS spectra acquired using the Chemical Microscope allow direct correlation with molecular structure by reference to the families of compounds included in the Library. This reinforces the value of using a mass spectrometry based technique for the rapid and routine characterisation of organic surfaces.

Acknowledgement

The assistance of Dr Stuart Leadley, Dow Corning Limited, Barry in the provision of the siloxane sample and the interpretation of its spectra is gratefully acknowledged.

784

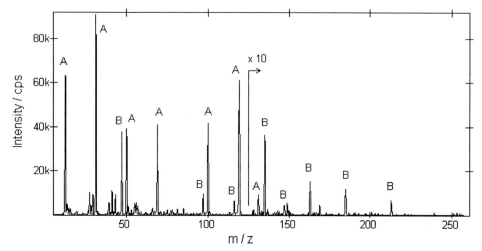

Figure 2a. Positive fluorocarbon spectrum showing sequences of C_xF_y (A) and $C_xF_yO_z$ (B) ions

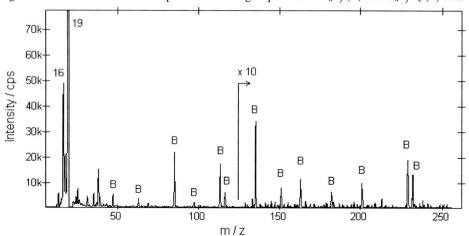

Figure 2b. Negative fluorocarbon spectrum showing sequences of $C_xF_yO_z$ (B) ions

References

[1] A.A. Galuska, Surf. Interface Anal. 25 (1997) 790
[2] X. Van den Eynde, K. Matyjaszewski & P. Bertrand, Surf. Interface. Anal. 26 (1998) 569
[3] D. Briggs, A. Brown & J.C. Vickerman, Handbook of Static SIMS, Wiley, 1989
[4] A.J. Eccles & T.A. Steele, Proc. SIMS XI, G.Gillen et al. (Eds.), Wiley, 1998, pp 775-8
[5] A.J. Eccles & T.A. Steele, Appl. Surf. Science. 144 (1999) 106
[6] The Static SIMS Library, J.C. Vickerman et al. (Eds.), SurfaceSpectra, Manchester, 1999
[7] A.J. Eccles & T.A. Steele, these proceedings

A. Benninghoven, P. Bertrand, H.-N. Migeon and H.W. Werner (Editors).
Proceedings of the 12th International Conference on Secondary Ion Mass Spectrometry,
Brussels, Belgium, 5-11 September 1999
© 2000 Elsevier Science B.V. All rights reserved.

QUANTITATIVE SURFACE ANALYSIS OF STYRENE-BASED COPOLYMERS USING TOF-SIMS

L.T.Weng [1*], S. Liu[2], L. Li[2], K. Ho[1] and C.-M. Chan[2]

[1]Materials Characterization and Preparation Facility
[2]Chemical Engineering Department
The Hong Kong University of Science and Technology
Clear Water Bay, Kowloon, HONG KONG
*E-mail: mcltweng@ust.hk

1. Introduction

Time-of-Flight secondary ion mass spectrometry (ToF-SIMS) has been widely used in the surface characterization of materials owing to its unique advantages compared with other surface techniques. However, the difficulty of ToF-SIMS in quantification has been a major obstacle for extending its applications. For polymer materials, it has been shown that SIMS peak intensity ratios can sometimes be used to evaluate the surface compositions of copolymers or polymer blends but the selection of SIMS peaks needs to be made carefully [1-2]. So far no general guidelines exist for the selection of SIMS peaks for quantitative analysis. It is thus imperative to investigate more polymer systems with controlled structures/compositions so that general guidelines may hopefully be established. The objective of this work is to test the quantitative aspect of ToF-SIMS for two styrene-based copolymers: poly(styrene-*co*-*p*-hexafluorohydroxyisopropyl-α-methyl styrene) (STHFMS) and poly-(styrene-*co*-4-vinyl phenol) (STVPh). The molecular repeat units of these two copolymers are shown below:

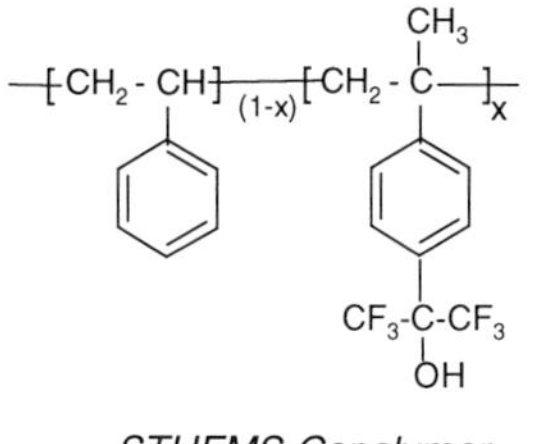

STHFMS Copolymer

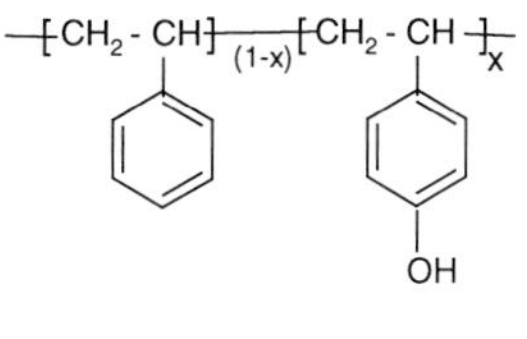

STVPh Copolymer

The similar molecular structures of these two copolymers would allow us to check whether any similarity in terms of ToF-SIMS quantitative analysis exists for these aromatic polymers.

2. Experimental

Copolymers with compositions x varying from 0 to 0.5 for STHFMS and 0 to 1 for STVPh were synthesized. The samples for ToF-SIMS analyses were prepared by spin coating. ToF-SIMS measurements were carried out on a Physical Electronics PHI 7200 ToF SIMS spectrometer. The primary ions were generated from a Cs ion source (8 kV). The scanned area was 200 μm $\times$ 200 μm, and the total ion dose for each spectrum acquisition was $< 4 \times 10^{11}$ ions/cm^2. Charge compensation was realized by low-energy (0-70 eV) flooding electrons. At least three positive and negative spectra were taken for each sample.

3. Results and Discussion

3.1 STHFMS copolymers

Figure 1 displays a positive ToF-SIMS spectrum of a copolymer containing 32-mole % HFMS. It can be observed that except for the characteristic peaks of polystyrene at m/z=77, 91, 103/105, 115, 128, 141, 152, 165, 178, and 193 etc., some peaks appear at high mass range (m/z=257, 271 and 285). These peaks are due to HFMS unit and their molecular structures are summarized below:

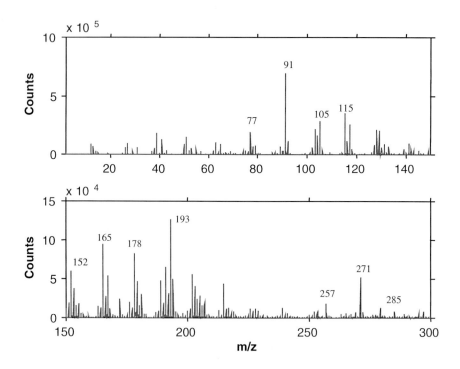

Figure 1: Positive ToF-SIMS spectrum of STHFMS copolymer with 32-mole % HFMS

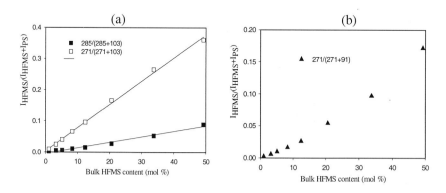

The peak at m/z=285 corresponds to the protonated monomer ($[M+H]^+$) of HFMS. Also some other F-containing peaks such as CF_3 (m/z=69) are observed in low mass range.

As the surface composition of these copolymers is the same as in the bulk (verified by XPS), relative SIMS intensity can be directly compared with the bulk composition. In this work, the relative intensity is expressed in the form of $I_{HFMS}/(I_{HFMS}+I_{PS})$ where I_{HFMS} and I_{PS} are the SIMS intensities of the characteristic peaks representing the HFMS and styrene units. The peaks at m/z= 257, 271, 285 have been identified as the characteristic peaks of HFMS monomer units, while the peaks at m/z=91, 103, and 115 are identified as the main characteristic peaks of polystyrene. Some of the characteristic peaks of PS at m/z=77, 165, and 193 are not used due to their interference with the ions derived from HFMS. As an example, Figure 2 plots the relative SIMS intensity, 285/(285+103), 271/(271+103) and 271/(271+91), as a function of HFMS bulk molar content. It can be seen that 285/(285+103) and 271/(271+103) (Fig. 2a) show a very good linear fit. Similar linear fits are also obtained when the peak m/z=115 is used to represent styrene. However, when the peak m/z=91 is used, non-linear fit is produced (Fig. 2b). These data are in good agreement with the results of Weng *et al.* on the quantification of styrene-butadiene copolymer [1]. The peaks at m/z=103 and 115 are more characteristic of styrene unit while the peak m/z=91 is less characteristic of styrene unit probably because it is produced from multiple pathways.

Figure 2: Relative SIMS intensity, $I_{HFMS}/(I_{HFMS}+I_{PS})$, as a function of bulk HFMS molar content: (a) 285/(285+103) and 271/(271+103); (b) 271/(271+91)

3.2 STVPh copolymers

It has been shown that the positive SIMS spectrum of poly(4-vinyphenol) can be distinguished from that of polystyrene by the presence of a series of oxygen-containing peaks [3]. In particular, the ions $C_7H_7O^+$ (m/z=107), $C_8H_7O^+$ (m/z=119), $C_8H_8O^+$ (m/z=120) and $C_8H_9O^+$ (m/z=121) are the main characteristic peaks of VPh unit. It is worth noting that the last three peaks are respectively the molecular ions of VPh monomer ($[M-H]^+$, M^+ and $[M+H]^+$). Similar to the STHFMS copolymer, the surface composition of the STVPh copolymers is the same as in the bulk (checked by XPS). Figure 3 shows the plots of relative SIMS intensity, $I_{VPh}/(I_{VPh}+I_{PS})$, as a function of the bulk VPh molar content. It can be observed that 119/(119+103) and 119/(119+115) show a good linear fit while 120/(120+91) produces a non-linear fit. This shows that the molecular ions of VPh can be used for quantitative analysis and again confirms that the characteristic peaks of styrene at m/z=103 and 115 are good for quantitative analysis.

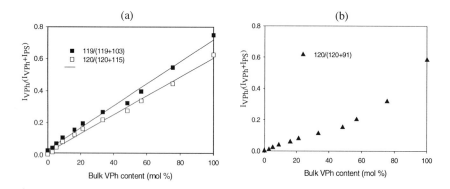

Figure 3: Relative SIMS intensity, $I_{VPh}/(I_{VPh}+I_{PS})$, as a function of bulk VPh molar content: (a) 119/(119+103) and 120/(120+115); (b) 120/(120+91)

4. Conclusions

The relative SIMS intensity, $I_A/(I_A+I_B)$, where A and B represent respectively the most characteristic peaks of each component of the copolymer, has been found to be linearly related to the copolymer composition. However, some other peaks such as m/z=91 of styrene, although very intense, cannot be used for quantitative analysis. It is also interesting to find that the characteristic peaks with the same type of molecular structure behave very similarly for both copolymer systems. In other words, there exists similarity in terms of quantitative analysis for the two copolymer systems.

References

[1] L. T. Weng, P. Bertrand, W. Lauer, R. Zimmer and S. Busetti, Surf. Interface Anal. 23 (1995) 879
[2] D. Briggs and M. C. Davies, Surf. Interface. Anal. 25 (1997) 725
[3] A. Chilkoti, D. G. Castner, B. D. Ratner and D. Briggs, J. Vac. Sci. Technol. **A**, 8 (1990) 2273.

A. Benninghoven, P. Bertrand, H.-N. Migeon and H.W. Werner (Editors).
Proceedings of the 12th International Conference on Secondary Ion Mass Spectrometry,
Brussels, Belgium, 5-11 September 1999
© 2000 Elsevier Science B.V. All rights reserved.

789

SECONDARY ION MASS SPECTROMETRY OF COPOLYMER SYSTEMS

David M. Hercules and John T. Mehl

Chemistry Department, Vanderbilt University, Nashville, Tennessee, USA 37235

1. Introduction. Time-of-flight SIMS (TOF-SIMS) is particularly well suited for surface characterization of polymers because of high sensitivity, high mass resolution, large mass range, and application to insulating surfaces via charge compensation. The number a reports using TOF-SIMS for polymer characterization continues to grow. The majority of TOF-SIMS methods only rely on the low-mass region (< 500 m/z). However, TOF-SIMS can also detect high-mass fragment ions. In a study by Briggs et al., [1] the authors indicate that information about the molecular weight of poly(ethyleneglycol) side chain blocks can be obtained from high-mass TOF-SIMS spectra. Zhuang et al. [2] used the high-mass region to determine the distribution of poly(dimethylsiloxane) (PDMS) segment lengths at the surface of segmented urethane copolymers. Linton et al. [3] used high-mass TOF-SIMS spectra for trace-level determination of polymer additives at the surface. Still, the high- mass region of TOF-SIMS spectra remains under utilized and less understood than the low-mass region. This reflects the difficulty of ionizing and detecting large ions from thick solid polymer films and the necessity of using a TOF-SIMS instrument, versus a quadrupole instrument.

2. Experimental. Samples were dissolved in toluene at concentrations ranging from 1 - 4 mg/mL. 1 μL of polymer solution was solvent cast onto 1 cm dia. silver foil targets and air dried. The silver targets were etched prior to sample deposition using 20% (vol. %) aqueous nitric acid. Spectra were acquired using a TOF-SIMS III instrument manufactured by Ion-Tof GmbH (Münster, Germany). A pulsed Ar^+ primary ion beam was used, maintaining the total ion dose under 1013ions/cm2. All spectra were acquired in positive-ion mode. The PS-PBD and PS-PDMS samples were obtained from Polymer Standards Service (Silver Spring, MD, USA). The PS-PI samples were a generous gift from Dr. Jimmy Mays of the Department of Chemistry, University of Alabama at Birmingham.

3. Results and Discussion. The focus of the present research is to examine the high-mass region of TOF-SIMS copolymer spectra. Particular emphasis is placed on surface segregation to better understand ion formation and fragmentation patterns. Relationships between the ion yield from copolymers and their relevant homopolymers in both the low and high mass region are important to this research.

Di-block copolymer systems can undergo surface segregation. Typically, though not completely understood, the lower surface energy component enriches the surface [4]. In systems where both blocks have similar surface energies, the less crystalline component tends toward the surface. For our initial investigation we choose three di-block copolymer systems which have been previously studied by other groups using a variety of surface techniques, and which have predictable surface behavior. The systems studied are: poly (styrene-co-butadiene), (PS-PBD); poly(styrene-co- isoprene), (PS-PI); and poly(styrene-co-dimethylsiloxane), (PS-PDMS).

Figure 1 shows the TOF-SIMS spectra of two PS-PDMS di-blocks. Only silver cationized PDMS fragment ions, spaced by 74 Da due to the PDMS monomer unit are present in the spectra.

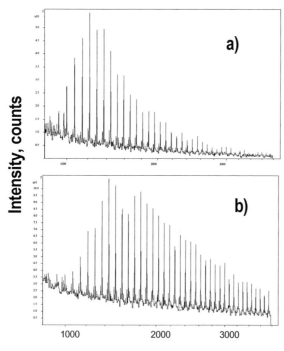

Absolute intensity measurements performed on pure PS and PI homopolymers indicate that PS and PDMS have appro-ximately similar ion yields. PDMS is well known for its low surface energy properties. Sur-face tension values range from 19.8 - 21.2 dyn/cm and 39.3 - 40.7 dyn/cm for PDMS and PS respectively.[5] XPS studies also show that PDMS typically occupies the surface region.[6] It therefore can be concluded that the presence of only PDMS fragment ions in high-mass TOF-SIMS spectra is due to surface enrichment and not selective ionization. Comparison of the two spectra indicates that TOF-SIMS is sensitive to the length of the PDMS block. The presence of longer PDMS blocks increases the probability of forming larger PDMS fragment ions. Also, the peak envelope maximum is

Figure 1 TOF-SIMS spectra of PS-PDMS diblock copolymers cast on etched silver. a) 60K PS-PDMS 91/9 wt%, b) 53K PS-PDMS 79/21 wt%.

shifted to a higher m/z value. PS-PI di-block surfaces have previously been studied using low mass TOF-SIMS. Nicholas et al.[7] found that for samples containing up to 50% PS the surface was enriched with PI. Transmission electron microscopy (TEM) of cross-sections by others also indicates that PI enriches the surface of PS-PI di-blocks [8]. Figure 2 shows the

high-mass region of a PI homopolymer and a symmetrical PS-PI di- block. Consistent with reports mentioned above, the high-mass region contains only PI fragment ions. The spacing of the repeat pattern is 68 Da due to the PI monomer. In the pure PI spectrum, the most intense peak cluster series corresponds to an integral number of repeat monomer units cationized by silver. However, in the PS-PI di-block the most intense peak cluster series corresponds to "oligomeric" ions. A previous TOF-SIMS study of PI homo-polymers reported similar behavior, where oligomeric ions are formed during primary ion impact. [9] Though speculative, this may

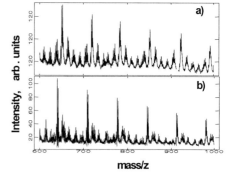

Figure 2 a) Spectrum of 34K PI homopolymer, b) spectrum of 10K PS-PI symmetric diblock.

be due to the presence of terminal groups. Fragmentation could be through a single chain cleavage mechanism in which the terminal group remains in the fragment. As the molecular weight of the block increases the relative concentration of terminal groups decreases leading to reduction of oligomeric ion production.

Figure 3 shows high-mass spectra for a series of PS-PBD di- blocks along with the constituent homopolymers. The %composition was varied while keeping the molecular weight approximately constant. The two homopolymer spectra have characteristic silver catonized fragment ion repeat patterns spaced by the mass of the monomer unit, 104 and 54 Da for PS and PBD, respectively. Characterization of PS and PBD by TOF-SIMS has been described in detail elsewhere [10,11]. The diblocks containing 38% and 49% PBD have both PS and PBD fragment ions.

However, for diblocks containing 58% and greater amounts of PBD, the high-mass spectrum is completely dominated by PBD fragment ions. Segregation of PBD to the surface of PS-PBD diblock surfaces has been previously shown. Henkee et al. [12] using TEM of cross-sectioned PS-PBD films found that the PBD block dominates the surface. We measured the absolute ion yields of pure PS and PBD homopolymers and found that high-mass silver catonized PS fragment ions are approximately 15 times more abundant than the corresponding PBD ions. Therefore, surface enrichment by PBD suppresses PS ion yield in PS- PBD diblocks.

Following a method applied to random PS-PBD copolymers by Weng et al.,[13] the relative intensity of low-mass ions was used to determine surface composition. Figure 4 shows a plot of normalized relative intensity of mass 53 and 103 versus bulk composition. The data indicate that full enrichment of the surface with PBD occurs only for the pure PBD homopolymer. Even with only 10 mol% PS the low-mass

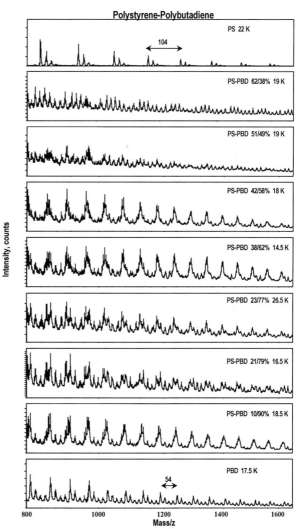

Figure 3 Spectra of PS-PBD diblocks along with spectra of pure PS and pure PBD. Values listed are mole %.

region indicates that a small amount of PS resides at the surface. In contrast, the high-mass spectra suggest that 58 mol% composition has a complete layer of PBD at the surface. More conclusive results are necessary, however the preliminary results discussed here suggest that the high-mass region is more sensitive to surface composition than the low-mass region.

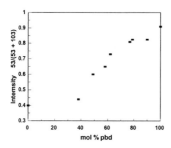

4. Conclusion. The high-mass region of TOF-SIMS copolymer spectra contains valuable information about surface composition. For the systems reported here, the high-mass spectra are dominated by fragment ions originating from the block previously shown by other techniques to enrich the surface. Examination of the PS-PBD diblock system over a range in bulk composition suggests that the high-mass region may be more sensitive to changes in surface composition than the low-mass region.

Figure 4: Low-mass ions from PS-Pbd diblocks. Normalized intensity plotted versus PBD composition

References

[1]   D. Briggs, M.C. Davies *Surf. Interface Anal.* 25 (1997) 725.

[2]   H. Zhuang, J.A. Gardella, Jr., D.M. Hercules *Macromolecules* 30 (1997) 1153.

[3]   R.W. Linton, M.P. Mawn, A.M. Belu, J.M. DeSimone, M.O. Hunt, Y.Z. Menceloglu, H.G. Cramer, A. Benninghoven *Surf. Interface Anal.* 20 (1993) 991.

[4]   F. Garbassi, M. Morra, E. Occhiello "Polymer Surfaces" John Wiley & Sons, Chichester, UK, 1994, pgs. 285-298.

[5]   Wu, S. in Polymer Handbook, 3rd Ed.; Brandup, J. and Immergut, E. H., Eds.; John Wiley & Sons, Inc. New York, p VI/411-483.

[6]   D.T. Clark, J. Peeling, J.M. O'Malley *J. Polm. Sci. Polym. Chem. Ed.* 14 (1976) 543.

[7]   M. Nicholas, C.M. Kassis, Y.Z. Menceloglu, J.M. DeSimone, R.W. Linton *Polymer Preprints* 31, No. 1, (1996) 309.

[8]   H. Hasegawa, T. Hashimoto *Macromolecules* 18 (1985) 589.

[9]   K. Xu, A. Proctor, D.M. Hercules *Mikrochim. Acta* 122 (1996) 1.

[10]   M. P. Chiarelli, A. Proctor, I.V. Bletsos, D.M. Hercules, H. Feld, A. Leute, A. Benninghoven *Macromolecules* 25 (1992) 6970.

[11]   L.R. Hittle, D.M. Hercules *Surf. Interface Anal.* 21 (1994) 217.

[12]   C.S. Henkee, E.L. Thomas, L.J. Fetters *J. Mat. Sci.* 23 (1988) 1685.

[13]   L.T. Weng, P. Bertrand, W. Lauer, R. Zimmer, S. Busetti *Surf. Interface Anal.* 23 (1995) 879.

A. Benninghoven, P. Bertrand, H.-N. Migeon and H.W. Werner (Editors).
Proceedings of the 12th International Conference on Secondary Ion Mass Spectrometry,
Brussels, Belgium, 5-11 September 1999
© 2000 Elsevier Science B.V. All rights reserved.

TOF-SIMS ANALYSIS OF THE MOLECULAR WEIGHT DISTRIBUTION OF POLYACRYLONITRILE SYNTHESIZED BY ELECTROPOLYMERIZATION

C. Poleunis[1], P. Bertrand[1], N. Baute[2] and R. Jérôme[2]

[1] Unité de Physico-Chimie et de Physique des Matériaux (PCPM),
Université Catholique de Louvain (UCL), Place Croix du Sud 1,
B-1348 Louvain-la-Neuve, Belgium
E-mail : poleunis@pcpm.ucl.ac.be

[2] Center for Education and Research on Macromolecules (CERM),
Université de Liège, Sart-Tilman, B6, B-4000 Liège, Belgium

1. Introduction

The electrografting of acrylonitrile (AN) onto Ni cathodes has been reported by Lécayon et al. [1] and confirmed by Mertens et al. [2]. The addition of various amounts of deuterated chloroform ($CDCl_3$) to the electrolytic solution allows the thickness of the films to be controlled [3,4]. $CDCl_3$ is thought to act as a transfer agent, which terminates the electropolymerisation process and end-caps the grafted chains [5]. Moreover, it is also expected to initiate the acrylonitrile polymerisation in solution, in addition to the electrografting onto the cathode. The chains formed in solution are expected to be shorter when the $CDCl_3$ concentration is higher. This general strategy might be of some interest in producing very thin polymer films of different thickness and functionality, and strongly adhering onto a metal surface. Several application fields (optoelectronics, biotechnology...) are currently demanding for this type of films [6].

In this study, very thin and adherent films of polyacrylonitrile (PAN) have been electrografted by electrografting voltammetry onto nickel cathodes in dimethylformamide (DMF), which is a good solvent for the polymer.

Since C_2NHD^+ fragments (41 m/z) which are characteristic of PAN chains end-capped by deuterium, have been observed onto the Ni cathodes by ToF-SIMS [5], further investigation is needed to analyse the composition of the PAN chains formed in the electrochemical bath. For this purpose, this work aimed at investigating the molecular weight distribution of the PAN chains formed in the solution. Indeed, thanks to the ToF-SIMS ability to detect organometallic complex ions formed by cationisation [7], oligomers can be desorbed without fragmentation when they are deposited in very thin layer on noble metal substrates (Ag) [8, 9]. The charge being formed by cationisation with a metal ion $(M + Me)^+$.

2. Experimental

Sample preparation

Solutions were taken from electrochemical bath, where electrografted PAN films were prepared. Then, drops were cast onto freshly silver-metallised (100 nm) silicon wafer and also on clean silicon wafer surface and the solvent was let to evaporate.

Time of Flight-Secondary Ion Mass Spectroscopy

ToF-SIMS measurements were performed with a PHI-Evans TFS-4000MMI (TRIFT) spectrometer. The sample was bombarded with a pulsed $^{69}Ga^+$ ion beam (15 keV, 800 pA DC, 5 kHz frequency and 20 ns unbunched pulse width). The secondary ions were accelerated to ± 3 keV by applying a bias on the sample. The spreading of the initial kinetic energy of the secondary ions was compensated by 270° deflection in three electrostatic analysers. In order to increase the detection efficiency of high-mass ions, a 10 keV post-acceleration was applied at the detector entry. The analysed area was a square of 130 μm x 130 μm. With a 5 min data acquisition time, the fluence was about $9 \cdot 10^{11}$ ions/cm^2, which ensured static conditions. The best mass resolution (m/Δm) obtained with this ToF-SIMS spectrometer is 11000 at m/z = 28 on a Si wafer. For the present samples and analytical conditions, the mass resolution was about 5000 at m/z = 29.

3. Results and discussion
In the negative ToF-SIMS spectra (not shown) of the solutions deposited onto Si wafer surfaces, peaks at 117, 119, 121 and 123 m/z were observed and assigned to CCl_3^- (taking into account ^{35}Cl and ^{37}Cl isotopes). These peaks can not originate from the conducting salt put in

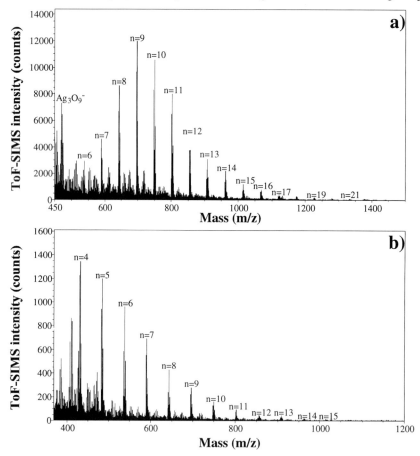

Figure 1. Part of the negative ToF-SIMS spectra obtained from samples taken from electrochemical baths and cast onto Ag-metallised substrates. The bath contents were : DMF, [TEAP] = 0.05 M, [AN] = 1 M :and a) [CDCl$_3$] = 0.2 M and b) [CDCl$_3$] = 0.5 M.

solution (tetraethylammonium perchlorate - TEAP). Indeed, the same fragmentation pattern was observed also when the synthesis was repeated with tetraethylammonium fluoride as conducting salt. No combination of the chlorinated fragment with PAN was found. Thus, there was no experimental evidence that the chlorinated fragment can initiate either the free-radical or the anionic polymerisation of AN in the electrochemical medium.

High mass range negative spectra of the solution cast on Ag are shown in Figs. 1a and 1b for different $CDCl_3$ concentrations. These spectra exhibited the PAN molecular weight distribution. The interval between repetitive units corresponded to AN monomer (53 m/z). This distribution was found to be dependent on the bath initial concentration contents (Table 1). Indeed, when $CDCl_3$ concentration increased, the molecular weight distribution was shifted towards lower masses in agreement with a more rapid chain termination. These results are in good agreement with the PAN-Ni cathode film thickness measured by ellipsometry [10]. In contrast, the positive ToF-SIMS spectra (not shown) did not display any cationisation of PAN with Ag.

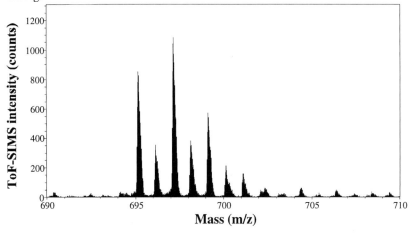

Figure 2. Zoom in the negative ToF-SIMS cluster (n=9) obtained from samples taken from electrochemical baths and cast onto Ag-metallised substrates. The bath contents were : DMF, [TEAP] = 0.05 M, [AN] = 1 M and [$CDCl_3$] = 0.2 M.

Figure 2 shows a detail of the cluster at n = 9. It corresponds to the anionisation of PAN with two Ag. All the clusters correspond to the Ag_2 isotopic distribution of $(Ag_2D_2\text{-}(AN)_n)^-$. The exact mechanism leading to the emission of these negative molecular ions is not yet well understood. However, the detection of two deuterium atoms per PAN macromolecule shows that $CDCl_3$ is a terminating agent for oligomers initiated in solution. This suggests that dianions could be formed by coupling of two AN radical-anions. The detection in SIMS of oligomer anions with two metal atoms is unexpected and new. In the literature, SIMS anonisation results are reported only in the case of alkanethiol on gold [11-14]. Moreover these results do not show molecular weight distributions comparable to the ones observed with metal-cationisation on homopolymers.

Table 1. Number-average molecular weight M_n, Weight-average molecular weight M_w and Polydispersity coefficient $H = M_w/M_n$ for some AN and $CDCl_3$ combinations

[AN] (M)	[$CDCl_3$] (M)	M_n (m/z)	M_w (m/z)	H
1	0.2	736	768	1.04
1	0.5	530	564	1.06
0.2	0.2	778	805	1.03

4. Conclusions

ToF-SIMS allowed us to follow the AN polymerisation in the electrolytic solution baths. The negative spectra showed oligomer anions containing two Ag atoms with $(Ag_2D_2-(AN)_n)^-$ structure. However the positive spectra did not show any cationisation of PAN by Ag. These results allowed us to determine the molecular weight distribution of polymerised PAN in solution. This distribution, as expected, was shown to depend on the $CDCl_3$ concentration in the electrolytic solution, but not on the conducting salt.

The presence of two deuterium atoms in the anionised oligomers per PAN macromolecule detected in SIMS showed that $CDCl_3$ is a terminating agent for oligomers initiated in solution. This suggests a polymerisation mechanism based on dianion formation by the coupling of two AN radical-anions.

Acknowledgements

The financial support of the "Fonds National de la Recherche Scientifique (F.N.R.S.)-Loterie Nationale" (Belgium) and the "Région Wallonne" (Belgium) for the purchase of the TOF-SIMS spectrometer, and the "Services Fédéraux des Affaires Scientifiques, Techniques et Culturelles" under the auspices of the "Pôles d'attraction Interuniversitaires : Chimie et catalyse supramoléculaire", " Reduced Dimensionality Systems" (Belgium) and the program "FIRST n°2585" of the "Région Wallonne" are gratefully acknowledged.

References

[1] G. Deniau, G. Lécayon, P. Viel, G. Hennico and J. Delhalle, Langmuir 8 (1992) 267.

[2] M. Mertens, C. Calberg, L. Martinot, and R. Jérôme, Macromolecules 29 (1996) 4910.

[3] In Encyclopedia of Polymer Science and Engineering, 2nd ed., Wiley-Interscience, Vol. 16, p533.

[4] B. Boutevin, Y. Piétrasanta and M. Taha, Makromol. Chem. 183 (1982) 2977.

[5] C. Poleunis, P. Bertrand, C. Calberg, M. Mertens and R. Jérôme, in J.J. Pireaux, J. Delhalle, P. Rudolf (Eds) Proceedings of the Second International Conference on Polymer-Solid Interfaces : from model to real systems ICPSI-2, Namur, Belgium, August 1996, p.383.

[6] C. Boiziau and G. Lécayon, La Recherche 19 (1988) 890.

[7] B. Hagenhoff in Wiley Static SIMS Library, Wiley, New York, 1996, p.39.

[8] P. Bertrand and L.T. Weng, Mikrochim. Acta [Suppl.] 13 (1996) 167.

[9] I.V. Bletsos, D.M. Hercules, D. Van Leyen, B. Hagenhoff, E. Niehuis and A. Benninghoven, Anal. Chem. 63 (1991) 1953.

[10] C. Calberg, M. Mertens, R. Jérôme, X. Arys, A. Jonas and R. Legras, Thin Solid Films 310 (1998) 148.

[11] M.J. Tarlov and J.G. Newman, Langmuir 8 (1992) 1398.

[12] J.-C. Canry and J.C. Vickerman, in A. Benninghoven, B. Hagenhoff, H.W. Werner (Eds), SIMS X Proceedings, Wiley, New York, 1997, p. 623.

[13] J.-C. Canry and J.C. Vickerman, in H.J. Mathieu, B. Reihl, D. Briggs (Eds), ECASIA95 Proceedings, Wiley, New York, 1996, p. 903.

[14] D.A. Hutt, E. Copper and G.J. Leggett, J. Phys. Chem. B 102 (1998) 174.

A. Benninghoven, P. Bertrand, H.-N. Migeon and H.W. Werner (Editors).
Proceedings of the 12th International Conference on Secondary Ion Mass Spectrometry,
Brussels, Belgium, 5-11 September 1999
© 2000 Elsevier Science B.V. All rights reserved.

TOF-SIMS AND XPS CHARACTERIZATION OF OXYGEN PLASMA TREATED POLYPROPYLENE

Th. Gantenfort, T. Fladung, D. Wolany, L. Wiedmann, A. Benninghoven

Universität Münster, Physikalisches Institut, D-48149 Münster, Germany
e-mail: bennial@uni-muenster.de

1. Introduction

Because of their good mechanical and processing properties, polyolefines are widely used materials. For good adhesion of paint overlayers, the polypropylene surface is usually flame, corona, or plasma treated. This procedure leaves a complex and usually reactive surface, the composition of which is decisive for adhesion, but not yet fully understood. The combination of TOF-SIMS and XPS is particularly suited to monitor the surface changes induced by such modifications. We therefore used these techniques for the analysis of the molecular and chemical surface composition of oxygen plasma treated polypropylene. These investigations were part of a project including adhesion tests as well as other surface analytical methods.

2. Experimental and methodology

The experiments were done in a combined TOF-SIMS/XPS instrument which is coupled on-line to a plasma modification chamber [1]. The SIMS is an ION-TOF module with a 10 keV Ar^+ ion gun. Alternatively, Ga^+ ions from a fine focusing liquid metal ion source could be used as primary ions in a separate TOF-SIMS instrument of the same type. In both cases, charge compensation with low-energy electrons was necessary. The XPS is based on a Leybold EA 11 hemispherical analyser with a monochromated Al $K\alpha$ X-ray source and a standard Mg $K\alpha$ source for charge compensation.

The sample material was isotactic polypropylene with 37 % ethylene-propylene rubber and relatively low concentrations of stabilizing additives. This substrate was modified by a 2.45 GHz microwave oxygen plasma at a process pressure of 0.1 mbar and a flow rate of 5 sccm. Plasma treatment times were varied from pulses ($\approx$ 0.2 s) to 100 s, at 100 W microwave power in the chamber. For all ex-situ measurements, an atmosphere contact time of 24 h between plasma treatment and surface analysis was chosen. Alternatively, the samples could be transferred on-line from the plasma chamber to the TOF-SIMS and XPS chambers. This method of analysis was used to evaluate the influence of the contact to atmosphere.

In order to obtain semi-quantitative information from the TOF-SIMS spectra, we chose a data evaluation procedure as follows: We note that the positive molecular secondary ions are observed in groups only varying in their number of hydrogen atoms (e.g. $C_2H_m^+$, $C_3H_m O^+$, etc.). The most intensive signal of each group was chosen as its representative and is shown in fig. 1 as a single data point. It can be seen that representative ion species with the same number of oxygen atoms form a data set whose signal intensities, within a considerable

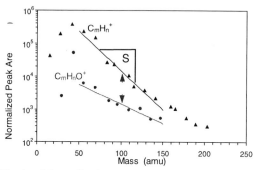

mass range (typically 50–150 amu), decrease exponentially with mass and can be fitted by a straight line in the semilogarithmic plot of fig. 1. The slope S of this line can be considered as a measure for the contribution of molecular ions with higher mass to the spectrum, and hence for the polymer chain length. Furthermore, we define the intensity ratio O/C of the $C_nH_m^+$ and $C_nH_m O^+$ fits at a mass of 100 amu, which is taken as a measure for the amount of oxygen in the uppermost monolayers.

Fig. 1: Normalized peak areas of representative positive secondary ions of polypropylene after 2 s oxygen plasma treatment and 24 h air contact.

3. Oxygen uptake

We first investigated the oxygen uptake by plasma treatment. With increasing plasma exposition time, the oxygen concentration in the near-surface region, as indicated by the O 1s

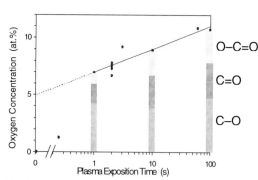

XPS signal (fig. 2), shows a fast increase at small plasma times and a subsequent approximately logarithmic growth. The determination of the nature of the carbon-oxygen bonds by line analysis of the C 1s signal shows that during the logarithmic growth the amount of C–O bonds remains practically constant, whereas the observed increase is due to the higher oxidation states (C=O and O–C=O).

Fig. 2: Oxygen concentration determined by the XPS O 1s signal and distribution of binding states of the XPS C 1s signal after oxygen plasma treatment and 24 h air contact.

In contrast to the XPS results, the value of the O/C parameter, determined according to fig. 1, saturates at about 3 s plasma time, causing the ratio of O/C (SIMS) / c(O) (XPS) to decrease. In view of the different information depths of XPS and SIMS, this is an indication that the fast oxidation at short plasma times is confined to the polymer surface, whereas the subsequent composition changes, as observed by XPS, reveal the in-depth growth of the oxidized region.

These ex-situ results were compared with in-situ XPS and SIMS data, obtained after 2 s plasma treatment without intermediate air contact. The comparison of the ex-situ and in-situ data after 2 s plasma time indicates that without air contact the oxygen concentration in the near-surface region, measured by XPS, is lower by about a factor of 10, whereas the oxygen amount in the top monolayer, indicated by O/C, is as high as after air contact. Thus, the second step of the plasma-induced oxidation, namely the in-depth oxidation, mainly takes place by interaction of atmospheric oxygen with the activated near-surface region.

4. Removal of contamination layer and surface amorphization

The influence of possible surface contaminations on the early stages of plasma interaction with the surface has been investigated by cleaning the polypropylene surface with isopropyl alcohol in an ultrasonic bath for 10 min. The result of this procedure, applied to the as-received surface, is a considerably higher amount of high-molecular species after cleaning, which is indicated by a change of the slope parameter S (see fig. 1) from −0.05 to −0.04. The reason for this is the removal of low-molecular contaminations by the solvent.

Subsequent plasma treatment of the uncleaned and cleaned polypropylene surfaces reveals differences in the O/C parameter (0.1 for the uncleaned and 0.2 for the cleaned surface after 2 s plasma treatment) and hence in the amount of surface oxygen. This difference can be understood by the existence of the contamination layer, which must be removed by the plasma from the uncleaned surface prior to oxidation, whereas the oxygen uptake starts immediately for the cleaned surface, leading to a higher oxygen content for identical treatment times.

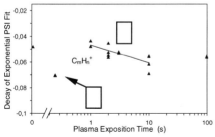

Fig. 3: Slope parameter S after oxygen plasma treatment and 24 h air contact.

The combination of the effects of contamination removal and plasma induced surface amorphization is needed to explain the development of the slope parameter S with plasma treatment time for an uncleaned surface as depicted in fig. 3. The decrease of S with plasma time in region (a) indicates a corresponding disppearance of the high-molecular species at the surface and thus a gradual amorphization of the polymer surface. The very low value of S at data point (b) indicates an early stage of plasma interaction with the surface where the contamination layer has been fragmented prior to its removal.

5. Segregation of additives

The SIMS spectra also indicate that some plasma induced segregation of technical additives to the surface takes place. After plasma treatment, the dominating peaks in the positive secondary ion spectrum at higher masses are the fingerprint lines of the additive Irganox 1010®, which is a frequently used anti-oxidizing agent in technical polypropylene. The lateral distribution of the additive is shown in the TOF-SIMS image in fig. 4. The fingerprint lines of Irganox in the range of 150–300 amu show clusters of enhanced intensity with typically some 10 µm diameter.

800

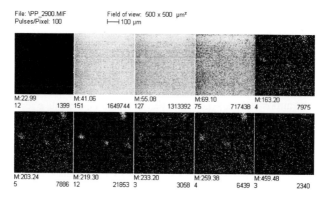

Fig. 4: TOF-SIMS images of a number of characteristic secondary ions from polypropylene with the additive Irganox 1010® after 2 s plasma treatment. The data below each image indicate the mass number, the maximum intensity per pixel, and the total intensity of the line.

6. Conclusion

It has been shown that the analysis of TOF-SIMS spectra, apart from the evaluation of fingerprint signals, can yield valuable semi-quantitative information on the effects of plasma treatment on polymer surfaces, using empirical parameters such as the $C_nH_mO^+$ / $C_nH_m^+$ ratio O/C and the slope of $C_nH_m^+$ signals S. The comparison of SIMS and XPS data provides additional information about oxygen concentration gradients in the near-surface region. As a result, the effect of the plasma is described as a two-step oxidation process involving a fast oxygen uptake at the surface and a slow in-depth growth of the oxidized region, accompanied by the removal of contaminations, the amorphization of the surface and the segregation of additives.

Acknowledgement

This work was supported by the Bundesminister für Bildung und Forschung (grant no. 03 D 0041 D 8).

References

[1] P. W. Jahn, F. M. Petrat, D. Wolany, M. Deimel, T. Gantenfort, C. Schmer-ling, H. Wensing, L. Wiedmann, A. Benninghoven, *J. Vac. Sci. Technol.* **A 12** (1994), 671.

A. Benninghoven, P. Bertrand, H.-N. Migeon and H.W. Werner (Editors).
Proceedings of the 12th International Conference on Secondary Ion Mass Spectrometry,
Brussels, Belgium, 5-11 September 1999   801

STATIC SIMS: TOWARDS UNFRAGMENTED MASS SPECTRA
- THE G-SIMS PROCEDURE

I.S.Gilmore ,M. P. Seah and J. E. Johnstone

National Physical Laboratory, Teddington, Middlesex, UK., e-mail Ian.Gilmore@npl.co.uk

1.Introduction

In this work we study the effects of different primary ion energy densities at surfaces and show how this may be used to lead to the components of the original molecules, before fragmentation in the SIMS process. We alter the energy density by using different primary ion species and energies. Work to understand the effect of primary ion mass and energy was initiated by Briggs *et al* [1] more than a decade ago. More recently, the group in Münster [2] have made detailed studies using time-of-flight SIMS with Ar^+, Xe^+, Ga^+ and SF_5^+ ions.
To identify an unknown material using static SIMS an analyst needs to be able to compare the measured spectrum with those available in libraries [3,4]. The variety of ion sources and energies in use at present makes this task more complex so that the accuracy of matching is reduced. In this work we show the extent of the effects of primary ion mass and energy and how this can be used to aid the uptake of spectral libraries and provide a special simplification of the mass spectrum known as the G(entle)-SIMS procedure.

2.Experimental

The instrument used in this study, a CAMECA TOF SIMS IV, is equipped with a high resolution Ga^+ focused liquid metal ion gun at 45 degrees to the surface normal delivering energies between 12 and 25 keV. A dual source column, also at 45 degrees, allows the use of Ar^+, Xe^+, SF_5^+ or Cs^+. For each analysis the ion beam was rastered over 156 μm by 156 μm with a pulsed beam current of less than a picoamp. Total acquisition times were such that the ion dose did not exceed $1x10^{16}$ ions/m^2. To ensure that the ion dose is even, the spot size was defocused to >3 μm.
Three materials were analysed in this study, a bulk polymer of polytetrafluroethylene (PTFE), and spin cast films of polystyrene (PS) and polycarbonate (PC). A fresh sample was analysed for each ion species with the spectra acquired at the different energies from a 3 by 3 array.

3.Results

For the data reduction, 300 peaks for each material were analysed with intensities above 100 counts. After mass calibration, the peak areas were measured to provide a matrix of intensities, $I_{x,j}$, with x_o mass peaks at j_o energies of mass M_x. To analyse the effects of fragmentation, we proceed as follows. Each spectrum is normalised by dividing by the geometric average intensity of its x_o mass peaks. An average spectrum for all of the ion beam energies, A_x, is then formed from this normalised set using.

$$A_x = \frac{1}{j_o} \sum_j \frac{I_{x,j}}{\prod_x I_{x,j}}$$ (1)

A new matrix of relative intensities, $R_{x,j}$, is produced by dividing each normalised spectrum by A_x. Values of $R_{x,j}$ from the PS spectra for 4 keV and 10 keV argon ions are shown in Figs 1 (a) and (b) respectively. If all of the spectra were identical (ie no effect of beam energy), the plotted points would be at unity. The most striking feature, here, is the sets of parallel groups of points with opposite gradients for the two different energies. The largest fragment in each group is identified as $C_nH_{2n+1}^+$, preceded by ions with the subsequent loss of one hydrogen atom, plotted with a filled circle. Fragments of the form $C_nH_{2n+1}^+$ are more closely related to the polymer backbone whilst those with hydrogen loss are indicative of damaged fragments and contribute little extra information in the original spectrum. The gradient of each of these groups provides a measure on the amount of fragmentation caused by the impacting ion.

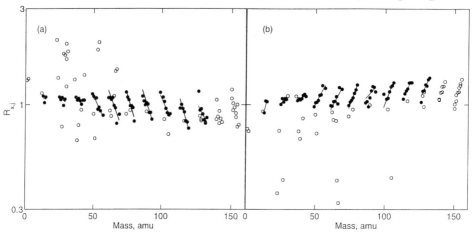

Fig 1　The effect of argon ion energy on relative intensities, $R_{x,j}$, in PS, (a) 10 keV, (b) 4 keV. The solid points are for series of peaks C_nH_{2n-m} with $0<m<8$ and $1<n<10$. The open circles are for other characteristic peaks.

The higher the energy density in the surface region, the more energy is transferred to the emitted fragments and the greater the degree of fragmentation. Thus, the data of Fig 1(a) show the behaviour of a higher energy density at the surface than those of Fig 1(b). Ideally one would like to move from Fig 1(a) to Fig 1(b) and onwards to a state where only the parent fragment is obtained - at the same time one would prefer also to retain some useful intensity. We do this as follows. First, the ratio of the normalised intensities, $R_{x,j}$, for low energy to those at high energy gives a factor, F_x, for each peak which is inversely related to the energy density at the surface or the effective surface plasma temperature [5]. This factor is not far from unity for the small range of ion beam energies we can use. To extrapolate to very low energy densities we use G_x where

$$G_x = M_x.10^{F_x^2} \qquad (2)$$

The mass, M_x, is included to compensate for the loss of intensity of high mass fragments. The new, "gentle-SIMS" or G-SIMS, spectrum which has the reduced fragmentation, is formed by multiplying the normalised spectrum by the factor G_x. The G-SIMS spectrum and the original spectrum for PS are shown in Figs 2 (a) and (b) respectively. These spectra are clearly very different. The predominant peaks in the G-SIMS spectrum are the tropyllium ion followed by ions at nominal mass 105, 117, 131, 161, 193 and 219 amu due to $C_8H_9^+$, $C_9H_9^+$, $C_{10}H_9^+$, $C_{12}H_{17}^+$, $C_{15}H_{13}^+$ and $C_{17}H_{15}^+$. Each of these ions are simply derived from the polystyrene backbone. The pendant phenyl group in their structure makes them easily recognisable as originating from PS. In contrast, the original spectrum has an intense tropyllium ion followed by ions at mass 115, 128, 165 and 178 amu. Structurally, these latter ions have a complex linked cyclic arrangement which exhibits little direct resemblance to the polystyrene structure. Similar results to those of Fig 1 were obtained for the bulk PTFE and spin cast PC samples reported elsewhere [5]. For PTFE the ion fragmentation pattern is already simply related to the polymer structure and so the enhancement is only weak but the behaviour is still correct.

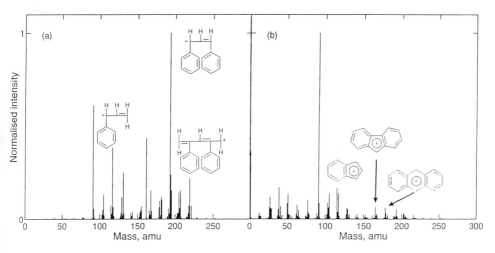

Fig 2   Spectra of polystyrene (a) G-SIMS and (b) 10 keV Ar⁺.

Measurements of the cluster gradients, as shown in Fig 1, provide a framework to build an understanding of the effects of different primary ion masses and energies. To do this, the matrix $R_{x,j}$ is formed with a common overall normalisation based on the average argon energy spectrum $A_{x,Ar}$. An average gradient may be assigned to each material since the gradients in each group are all approximately parallel. These average gradients are plotted in Fig 3 for Ar⁺, Ga⁺,Xe⁺,Cs⁺ and SF₅⁺. This single plot encapsulates all the fragmentation behaviour [5], for the five ion sources as a function of energy on PS.

804

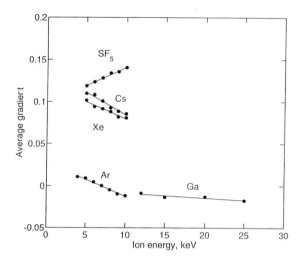

Fig 3   The gradients showing the inverse of the surface energy density or surface plasma temperature for Ar^+, Ga^+, Xe^+, Cs^+ and SF_5^+ ions as a function of energy for measurements on PS.

4. Conclusions

A method to compute a reduced fragmentation SIMS spectrum, G-SIMS, using two spectra at different energies is described. The G-SIMS method simplifies the mass spectrum and so aids the identification of unknown materials. The effects of ion beam mass, energy and species on fragmentation are reduced to one plot for each material. This shows a near linear behaviour with energy with least fragmentation at the lowest energies for monatomic beam ions and the reverse for the polyatomic ion. The fragmentation behaviour for Cs^+ and Xe^+ are very close, indicating the lack of importance of the chemistry of the ion. Increased projectile mass significantly reduces fragmentation. The strength of the G_x term may be increased by taking the ratio of spectra from high to low mass projectiles.

Acknowledgements

This work forms part of the Valid Analytical Measurement programme of the National Measurement System Policy Unit of the Department of Trade and Industry.

References

[1]   D.Briggs and A.B.Wootton, Surf. Interface Anal. 4 (1982) 109.
[2]   F.Kötter, A.Benninghoven, Appl. Surf. Sci. 133 (1998) 47.
[3]   The Static SIMS library, Eds. J.C.Vickerman, D.Briggs and A.Henderson, Surface Spectra, Manchester, (1998).
[4]   The Münster High Mass Resolution Static SIMS Library, B. C. Schwede, T. Heller, D. Rading, E. Niehuis, L. Wiedmann and A. Benninghoven, ION-TOF, Münster (1999).
[5]   I. S. Gilmore and M.P. Seah, to be published.

A. Benninghoven, P. Bertrand, H.-N. Migeon and H.W. Werner (Editors).
Proceedings of the 12th International Conference on Secondary Ion Mass Spectrometry,
Brussels, Belgium, 5-11 September 1999

NEUROSPECTRANET - A SELF-ORGANISING NEURAL NETWORK MECHANISM FOR INTERPRETATION OF COMPLEX SSIMS SPECTRA.

O.D.Sanni, A.Henderson, D.Briggs and J. C.Vickerman

Surface Analysis Research Centre, UMIST, Sackville St, Manchester M60 1QD, UK
email: debo.sanni@stud.umist.ac.uk

1. Introduction

Interpretation of SSIMS spectra requires a great deal of experience and costly expertise. Human experts often support their knowledge by searching a library of known spectra for a suitable match to the unknown spectrum in a process that can be very tedious, time-consuming and uneconomic for industrial surface analysis. To make the power of SSIMS more widely and easily accessible to R&D and Quality Control laboratories, an intelligent automated search engine capable of recognising and classifying SSIMS spectral patterns is required to enhance rapid and efficient interpretation of spectra.

NeuroSpectraNet is a novel and unique neural networks mechanism designed to overcome these difficulties by providing an efficient search engine requiring little or no human assistance for an effective determination of the unknown spectrum.

1.1 Why Neural Networks For SSIMS?

Neural networks are powerful computational software and hardware techniques designed to parallel the operations of the human brain in various tasks of pattern recognition, classification and intelligent data analysis. Currently regarded as the greatest technological advancement since the advent of transistors, neural networks consist of computational processing elements, called neurons, which carry out some specific computational task integral to the overall objective. Unlike classical data analysis, neural networks achieve their objectives by learning the data (which describes the unknown) and inductively reasoning out a solution, rather than being pre-programmed for a specific solution. Each of the various existing neural network paradigms combine the abilities and power of several statistical mechanisms into one powerful algorithm providing robustness against noise and outliers, high speed of operation, adaptive capability and better power of discrimination and prediction.

SSIMS (Static SIMS)spectra are often complex and generally impure in nature. Furthermore, the molecular-ion is not observed in many SSIMS spectra, and ion re-combinations can complicate analysis. For these reasons, neural networks may well become invaluable for intelligent interpretation of SSIMS by fully exploiting the following neural power:

i. Ability to learn, adapt and remember;
ii. Efficiency at modelling non-linearities;
iii. Robustness against inadequate and inconsistent data
iv. Extensive knowledge indexing and automatic data abstraction;
v. Ability to self-organise and readily generalise solutions;
vi. Ability to self-generate own model.

2. NeuroSpectraNet

NeuroSpectraNet was designed to take advantage of both the self-organising and supervised properties of neural networks. The self-organising mechanism enables the network to organise spectral data according to their chemical similarities, while the supervised mechanism supports the ability to interpret a spectrum that is somewhat unique and not directly similar to any spectrum in the database. The supervised mechanism achieves this by detecting some specific chemical properties that the spectrum exhibits in common with some other spectra in the database. Thus, if the self-organising mode fails to find a match for the spectrum, interpretation can be assisted by switching to detection of chemical functionalities that may be evident in the spectrum.

Unlike other methods used for mass spectra analysis including MsNet [1], PCA [2], and STIRS [3], *NeuroSpectraNet* does not require knowledge of the molecular-ion or any specific significant peaks. Instead, it self-generates its own model of significant micro-features (peaks) from the raw composite spectrum of positive-ion and negative-ion spectra of a material.

2.1 Design Principle
The backbone of the design philosophy of *NeuroSpectraNet* is based on a self-organising mechanism similar to the ART2 [4] neural network which is capable of organising input data into categories of similar patterns without *a priori* training. The mechanism is also able to mimic the technique of spectral library searching more as an intelligent search engine. Initially, *NeuroSpectraNet* models various SSIMS patterns into categories of chemical similarities. An unknown spectrum may then be tested for a match with the models of the generated categories. If no match is found, the unknown sets up a new category with its model. The model generated from such a unique spectrum is then analysed to identify any chemical functionalities

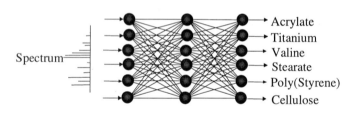

Fig.1. Illustration of NeuroSpectraNet

that may be present in the spectrum. Fig.1 illustrates the principle of this self-organising mechanism.

2.2 Data & Computation
The positive-ion and negative-ion stick spectra of a material are normalised to the total intensities of their respective masses. The normalised positive-ion spectrum is then appended to the negative-ion counterpart to form a composite spectrum used as input to *NeuroSpectraNet* .

2.2.1 Prototype Generation and The Self-Organising Mechanism
The first task is to generate a prototype that contains all the salient features of the original spectrum. The prototype generation is performed by a multi-layer set of neurons. Each of the neurons in a layer is dedicated to computing the spectral information of a mass position. The composite spectrum is modified within the layers by a process that successively re-normalise the composite spectrum and provide contrast enhancements until the prototype generation process stabilises. Since low-intensity peaks at high mass are significant in SSIMS, *NeuroSpectraNet's* contrast enhancement provides a

modified sigmoid function to boost low-intensity peaks at high mass. Automatic bias filteration is also implemented within the mechanism to set a noise-free threshold for each prototype.

The first prototype to be generated is stored as an archetype representing the category of materials the spectrum belongs to. On encountering the second and any subsequent spectrum, the new prototype is compared for a match with the stored archetype of each of the existing categories. *NeuroSpectraNet's* matching process involves several numerical tests of similarity and dissimilarity in which the contribution of each mass in the unknown spectrum is aggregated to produce a unique validation index that is assessed to confirm whether or not the spectra are chemically and structurally similar. The various tests are designed to numerically emphasise the spectral differences between dissimilar materials while similarities of spectra of like materials are enhanced. As a result of the complexity of many SSIMS spectra no single test suffices to cover all the observed spectral differences. Therefore, the various tests operate to produce a joint decision, thus fully utilising the advantage of breaking a complex task into easier sub-tasks that are handled in parallel by different processing elements.

If the archetype of a category is found largely similar to the new spectrum's prototype, it is entered into a pool of potential winners while the archetypes of remaining categories are similarly evaluated for a match. If more than one potential winner exists after all the categories have been tested, the potential winners are then re-assessed in an arbitration module to determine which of them has the best correlation to attract the unknown into it's category's membership. If only one winner exists in the pool, its category automatically becomes the winner.

However, if no match is found, the prototype of the unknown sets up a new category for attracting spectra of materials similar to it. Additional tests are then undertaken to detect pre-defined functionalities that may be present in the new spectrum via a process described in section §2.2.2.

2.2.2 Supervised Training and Functionalities Identification
The prototypes generated from the various spectra are ideal candidates for training a network for detection of some specific functionalities which may be hidden in the spectra of many materials. Through a supervised extension, the self-organising *NeuroSpectraNet* learns via examples, discovers and models the salient characteristics of a functionality. The functionalities present in an unknown spectrum then becomes identifiable through the models thus generated. Thus, *NeuroSpectraNet* is able to utilise collective information available throughout the database to efficiently model functionalities by self-discovery of the characteristics of a functionality, to make it ideal for SSIMS which often contain complex mixture of functionalities.

This added advantage to *NeuroSpectraNet's* self-organising mechanism makes it a powerful tool for providing information on specific chemical functionalities that may be present in the unknown.

3. Results and Discussion

Our exploratory design based on ART2 [4] network correctly grouped closely-related materials together when tested on a small range of materials. However, the classification efficiency degraded over a broader range of materials. The phenomenon of re-grouping was also very evident as membership of categories readjusted when similar spectra of some materials that were previously categorised into some groupings decamped to some more recently-formed categories to which they were indeed closer. This, we found, was due to the original design of ART2 [4] being unsuitable for

SSIMS where there is a very strong commonality amongst spectra of dissimilar materials. With *NeuroSpectraNet*, the re-grouping phenomenon is not observed; efficiency of classification is good over an unlimited range of materials, as the discrimination tests are comprehensive and numerically efficient. A typical classification such as Fig. 2 shows that there is a good correlation between spectra of many materials that have structural similarities.

Poly(2-chloroethyl methacrylate)	1
Poly(methacrylic acid) (ToF)	0.940338
Poly(n-lauryl methacrylate)	0.928526
Poly(n-butyl methacrylate)	0.924523
Poly(methyl methacrylate - co - PEG 1000 methacrylate), (12.5% PEGMA)	0.911585
Poly(methacrylic acid) (Quad)	0.910734
Poly(methyl methacrylate) (ToF)	0.898974
Poly(cyclohexyl methacrylate)	0.898097
Poly(ethyl methacrylate)	0.897175
Poly(2-hydroxyethyl methacrylate)	0.893147
Poly(n-hexyl methacrylate)	0.886860
Poly(2-hydroxypropyl methacrylate)	0.880651
Poly(methyl methacrylate) (Quad)	0.862834
Poly(n-propyl methacrylate) (Quad)	0.794553

Fig.2. A Typical NeuroSpectraNet Grouping of Spectra of Similar Materials, Showing Their Correlation Factors Against Poly(2-chloroethyl methacrylate).

NeuroSpectraNet's classification is fast with an average classification time of 10 sec for a 2x1500 a.m.u spectrum search of 450 spectra in *The Static SIMS Library* [5].

4. Conclusion

NeuroSpectraNet has demonstrated that neural processing power can be harnessed for analysis of SSIMS spectra. If a spectrum similar to an unknown exist in NeuroSpectraNet's database, it would efficiently and correctly identify the unknown in a matter of seconds. If an unknown is so unique that it is completely new to NeuroSpectraNet's self-organising mechanism, NeuroSpectraNet is designed to help the analyst to correctly identify pre-defined functionalities that may be present in the unknown. Because the analysis is fast and reliable, the spectrometrist can focus his attention on more complex tasks better armed.

References

[1] B. Curry and D. E. Rumelhart, Msnet: A Neural Network Which Classifies Mass Spectra, Tetrahedron Computer Methodology, 3 (1990) 213.
[2] K-S. Kwok, R. Venkataraghavan and F. W. McLafferty, J. Am. Chem. Soc. 95 (1973) 4185.
[3] J. Arunachalam and S. Gangadharan, Feature extraction from spectral and other data by principal components and discriminant function techniques, Anal. Chim. Acta 157 (1984) 245.
[4] G.A. Carpenter and S. Grosberg, ART2: Self-Organization of Stable Category Recognition Codes For Analog Input Patterns. IEEE 1st International Conference on Neural Networks, II (1987) II-735.
[5] The Static SIMS Library, Surface Spectra Ltd, Manchester, UK.

A. Benninghoven, P. Bertrand, H.-N. Migeon and H.W. Werner (Editors).
Proceedings of the 12th International Conference on Secondary Ion Mass Spectrometry,
Brussels, Belgium, 5-11 September 1999
© 2000 Elsevier Science B.V. All rights reserved.

ALKYL SULFATES EXCHANGED ONTO SELF-ASSEMBLED MONOLAYER SURFACES: ADSORPTION REVERSIBILITY AND SECONDARY ION YIELD MEASUREMENTS

R. D. English, M. J. Van Stipdonk and E. A. Schweikert

Department of Chemistry, Texas A&M University, PO Box 30012, College Station, TX,
77843-314, U.S.A., rde7754@venus.tamu.edu

1. Introduction

Understanding the interaction of biomolecules with surfaces is of fundamental importance to studies of biocompatibility and medical implant acceptance/rejection. Self-assembled monolayer (SAM) surfaces form highly-organized molecular arrays on surfaces, providing reliable models for the study of adsorption, wetting and adhesion at organic interfaces. The surface properties of SAMs can be altered by the incorporation of terminal functional groups. As a relevant example, Whitesides and coworkers have studied the adsorption of proteins by hydrophobic interactions with self-assembled monolayer surfaces [1].

In this study we investigated the adsorption of model molecules to SAM surfaces via ion-pair formation or ion exchange. The study is relevant to the uptake of charged molecules by surfaces, as well as the use of chemically modified surfaces to improve characterization by ToF-SIMS. We demonstrate here the reversible adsorption of a series of alkyl sulfates by a charged monolayer surface (via ion exchange). In addition, the yields of intact alkyl sulfate secondary ions from the exchanged surfaces sputtered by a series of atomic and polyatomic primary projectiles were measured.

2. Experimental

Mass spectra were collected using a dual ToF-SIMS instrument equipped with a polyatomic projectile source, event-by-event bombardment/detection, and coincidence counting. The instrument has been described in detail elsewhere [2-3]. Briefly, keV atomic and cluster projectiles are generated by fission fragment impacts on a Mylar^{TM} foil coated with the CsI. The projectiles are separated in a primary ToF leg before striking the sample target. Secondary electrons, steered by a weak magnetic field, are used to signal the arrival of a particular primary ion. Secondary ions are accelerated and mass analyzed using a secondary ToF leg. The experiments were performed in the event-by-event bombardment/detection mode. A coincidence counting protocol allowed secondary ion spectra to be generated from multiple primary ions under the same vacuum and experimental conditions. Yield measurements, therefore, can be obtained for different primary ion impacts in the same experiment.

To prepare thick alkyl sulfate targets, 10 µL of 3mM ethanol solutions of sodium tetradecyl sulfate (TDS), octyl sulfate (OS) or dodecyl sulfate (DDS) was deposited onto a stainless steel target cube and allowed to dry at room temperature. Diocyl sulfosuccinate

(DSS) was also used in this study. To prepare the alkyl sulfate exchanged targets Au coated Si wafers (1 cm^2) were soaked in a 1 mM ethanol aminoethanethiol (AET) solution overnight. The monolayer coated wafers were removed, rinsed with ethanol, rinsed with 0.1 M HCl to ensure protonation, rinsed with milli-Q water, and dried under a gentle flux of nitrogen gas. Next, 10 µL of a 3mM ethanol solution of TDS, OS, DDS (data not shown), or DSS was then deposited onto the AET monolayer and allowed to dry. The sample was next rinsed with ethanol and allowed to dry at room temperature.

3. Results

We have shown that aminoethanethiol monolayer surfaces will bind reversibly tetrafluoroborate and tetraphenyl borate anions [4]. The ion yield, per projectile impact, was higher for the exchanged surfaces than from thick targets of the respective Na salts. Figure 1 shows the spectra produced by Cs$^+$ impacts on sodium-TDS (1a) and TDS exchanged onto an AET monolayer (1b). The yield of the TDS anion is improved by a factor of 200 when adsorbed to the monolayer surface.

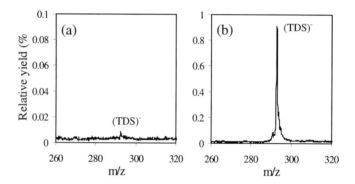

Figure 1. (a) 10 µL ethanol solution of Na-tetradecyl sulfate dried on stainless steel sample support. (b) 10 µL of same solution applied to aminoethanethiol monolayer, allowed to dry and rinsed with ethanol. Both spectra were acquired using 20 keV Cs$^+$ projectiles at a dose of ~1 x 10^6 ions/cm^2.

Non-linear yield enhancements were not observed using polyatomic ion impacts on AET monolayers exchanged with BF$_4^-$ and B(Ph)$_4^-$ [4]. The molecular ion yields (RSO$_4$)$^-$, where R represents the molecular chain specific to each molecule, from TDS exchanged to an AET monolayer produced by (CsI)$_n$Cs$^+$ (n=0-2) projectiles incident at 12 to 24 keV were measured. The RSO$_4^-$ yield, per projectile constituent atom, m, is shown in figure 2. The normalized yields are plotted versus the kinetic energy per mass unit of the primary projectile to facilitate comparison at similar velocities. The yield trends shown in figure 2 demonstrate that no net yield enhancements were observed for the TDS molecule when exchanged to the AET monolayer.

We also studied the reversibility of the exchange of the alkyl sulfates to the AET monolayer. Figure 3 shows the spectrum produced by 20 keV Cs$^+$ projectiles impacts on an exchanged monolayer. In this case, a 10 µL aliquot of a solution containing TDS and OS was applied to an AET monolayer on Au.

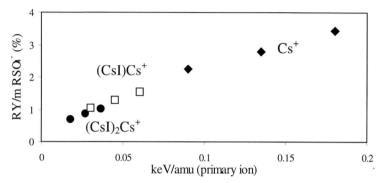

Figure 2. Relative yield (RY) of RSO_4^- sputtered from an AET monolayer, normalized to the number of constituent atoms, m, in the primary projectile.

The surface was allowed to dry, rinsed with ethanol and the wafer subsequently inserted into the mass spectrometer for analysis. Prominent peaks corresponding to the OS and TDS molecular anions were observed.

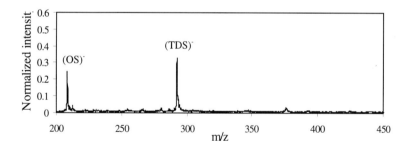

Figure 3. AET monolayer exchanged using mixture of octyl sulfate and tetradecyl sulfate. Projectile: 20 keV Cs^+.

Next, the AET/Au/Si wafer was removed from the instrument, rinsed with ethanol, 0.1 M HCl and deionized water, and then dried with a stream of dry N_2. A 10 µL aliquot of an ethanol solution containing TDS and DSS was then applied to the monolayer and allowed to dry. Finally, the monolayer surface was rinsed with ethanol and dried in air before being placed into the mass spectrometer for analysis. The resulting spectrum is shown in figure 4. A comparison of the spectra in figures 3 and 4 clearly shows that the ethanol / 0.1 M HCl rinse completely removed the OS from the AET monolayer, and a prominent peak corresponding to the DSS molecular anion was observed .

812

Repeated rinse steps and subsequent exchange demonstrated that a single AET monolayer on Au can be used repeated as a sample substrate.

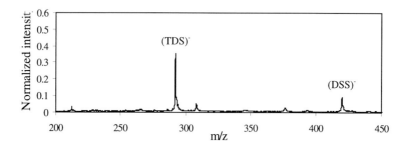

Figure 4. AET monolayer exchanged using mixture of tetradecyl sulfate and dioctyl sulfosuccinate. Projectile: 20 keV Cs^+.

4. Conclusions

Alkyl sulfate anions can be reversibly exchanged to AET monolayers. Our data reveal that the yield of TDS exchanged onto an AET monolayer is 200x greater (using 20 keV Cs^+ projectiles) when compared to a sodium-TDS solution dried on stainless steel. No yield enhancements were observed when cluster projectiles such as $(CsI)Cs^+$ and $(CsI)_2Cs^+$ were used to sputter TDS exchanged AET monolayer surfaces. This is attributed to the fact that it is unlikely that two or more primary ion collision cascades will converge to cooperatively break the same Au-AET or AET-alkylsulfate bond to sputter the exchanged anion.

References

[1] R. R. Seigel, P. Harder, R. Dahint, M. Grunze, F. Josse, M. Mrksich and G. M. Whitesides, Anal Chem., 69 (1997) 3321-3328.
[2] M. J. Van Stipdonk, R. D. Harris and E. A. Schweikert, Rapid Comm. Mass Spectrom., 11 (1997) 1794-1798.
[3] M. J. Van Stipdonk, E. A. Schweikert and M. A. Park, J. Mass Spectrom., 32 (1997) 1151-1161.
[4] M. J. Van Stipdonk, R. D. English and E. A. Schweikert, accepted for publication, J. Phys. Chem. B., (1999).

* This work is supported by the National Science Foundation (CHE – 9727474).

A. Benninghoven, P. Bertrand, H.-N. Migeon and H.W. Werner (Editors).
Proceedings of the 12th International Conference on Secondary Ion Mass Spectrometry,
Brussels, Belgium, 5-11 September 1999

TIME OF FLIGHT SECONDARY ION MASS SPECTROMETRY ANALYSIS OF WASHING-ADDITIVES ON GLASS SURFACES

F. Lang

Alusuisse Technology & Management AG, Technology Center - Surface Technology, CH-8212 Neuhausen am Rheinfall, Switzerland, e-mail: frank.lang@alusuisse.com

1. Introduction

The use of high molecular weight additives as builders, crystal growth inhibitors, etc. in modern high performing detergent formulations has nowadays found a wide application in fabric washing, automatic dishwashing, industrial detergents, etc.[1]. Since these additives are used in application areas with high hygiene standards such as in the food and beverage industry [2], it is important to guaranty cleaning processes which provide clean surfaces with no chemical residues.

TOF-SIMS and PCA (principal component analysis) were used to study ex-situ the glass adsorption and desorption of an industrial additive from an alkaline washing medium.

2. Experimental conditions

The glass substrate material consisting of a Tempax-glass was carefully cleaned using a detergent solution at elevated temperature with subsequent sonication and rinsing with distilled water of MilliQ quality. Three caustic solutions, A, B and C, consisting of 3% NaOH, 0.5% Na_2CO_3 were prepared, where solution B contained in addition 100 ppm and solution C 5% of the additive. Glass samples were stored over night in these solutions to allow the adsorption of the agent. Prior to the TOF-SIMS analysis, the glass-samples were taken out of the solutions, rinsed under various conditions with MilliQ-water and subsequently dried with argon.

TOF-SIMS measurements were carried out on a commercially available TOF-SIMS mass spectrometer from Charles Evans and Associates (described in detail elsewhere [3-4]) equipped with a pulsed $^{69}Ga^+$ ion gun operated at 18 kV in the negative mode. Typical TOF-SIMS spectra were acquired for 5 min using a bunched ion beam with a pulse rate of 5 kHz and a pulse width (unbunched conditions) of about 7 ns. The primary ion current in the DC mode was in the range of 1850 pA. The analyzed area consisted of a $(84 \times 84)\mu m^2$ square, and therefore the total ion dose was estimated to be on the order of 10^{12} ion/cm^2, which is within the so called "static" conditions [5]. To minimize charging effects on the non-conductive substrate material, a 20 eV low energy electron flood gun was operated on the grounded sample in a pulsed mode. Due to charging problems the observed mass resolution at about mass 28 was not higher than 3000 m/Δm. For comparison of different TOF-SIMS spectra, the signal intensity of each mass peak was normalized to the total secondary ion intensity, which was corrected by eliminating the contribution of hydrogen. Furthermore, normalized signal intensities were used for PCA (principal component analysis) [6].

2. Results and discussion

The aim of the present study was to document the adsorption of an industrial additive from a washing-like environment (caustic solution) on a glass surface, as well as to investigate the influence of a subsequent rinsing step.

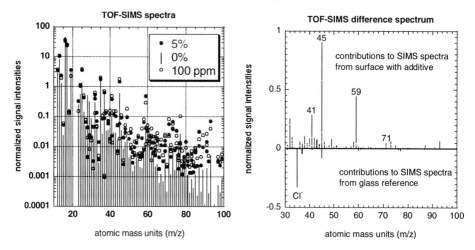

Figure 1. Negative TOF-SIMS mass spectra and a TOF-SIMS difference spectrum calculated from averaged normalized signal intensities. The TOF-SIMS difference spectrum includes spectra obtained from the reference solution A and solution C containing 5% of the additive.

In order to identify the additive on the glass surface, comparative TOF-SIMS measurements with three samples were carried out. The reference sample was prepared from solution A containing no additive; the other samples were obtained from solutions B and C where different amounts of additive had been added. Several mass-spectra were acquired for each sample in the negative SIMS mode. From the normalized signal intensities, averaged mass spectra as well as a TOF-SIMS difference spectrum were calculated as shown in figure 1. No sequence of fragment ions separated by Δm, the mass of the repeat unit, was found for the additive.

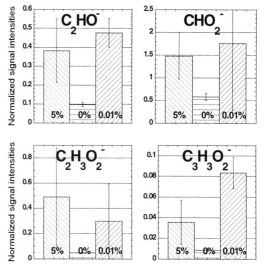

Figure 2. Normalized signal intensities of important contributions (taken from figure 1) obtained from glass surfaces treated with caustic solution containing 5%, 0% and 100 ppm additive.

However, the TOF-SIMS difference spectrum gave evidence of contributions which are more pronounced in the presence of the additive. A closer look at some of these contributions is given in figure 2. The identified fragment ions in figure 2 do represent typical fragment ions one would expect for the additive. The relatively high intensity variation of TOF-SIMS spectra of additive treated surfaces compared to the reference samples might be explained by an inhomogenous distribution of additive or unequal formation of fragment ions.

To answer the question, whether the adsorbed additive can be removed from the surface by pure water, further glass samples from solutions A, B and C had to be rinsed. Typically either a short (ca. 1 sec) or a long (ca. 30 sec) rinsing step with pure Milli-Q water was carried out. Glass slides were basically rinsed on one side. However, to give more statistical weight to the data, for some sample the other side was investigated as well. For all negative TOF-SIMS spectra - including the prior recorded spectra - a principal component analysis (PCA) was carried out. The original matrix contained data of 44 TOF-SIMS spectra including signal intensities from more than 200 mass peaks each. From these data the scores plot in figure 3 was calculated, where each TOF-SIMS spectra is represented in this two dimensional space by one data point. Spectra marked with a big filled square are obtained from surfaces having been in direct contact with the additive solution. These spectra are located in the upper left corner of the scores plot and can be separated by a straight line from reference spectra which are represented by an open circle in the lower part of the plot. It should be noted that this separation occurs along the two principal component vectors PC1 and PC2 which represent with 58% and 18% more than 75% of the total variance. Additional TOF-SIMS spectra obtained from the glass surface which have been rinsed after direct exposure to an additive containing solution are found in or between these two regions.

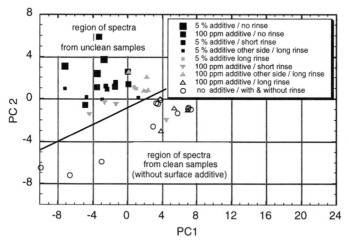

Figure 3. Scores plot of TOF-SIMS spectra obtained from cleaned and uncleaned glass surfaces. Cleaned samples were exposed to solutions containing 5%, 0.01% or 0% of an industrial washing additive and the cleaned in a water rinse prior to the analysis. TOF-SIMS spectra from uncleaned surfaces are located in the upper left corner of the score plot and can be separated by a straight line from spectra obtained from cleaned sample surfaces.

The effect of rinsing can be nicely seen from spectra acquired from surfaces treated with solution B (100 ppm additive). After a long rinse of ca. 30 sec, all these spectra marked with an open triangle are found in the region of reference spectra. However, only one out of four spectra represented by a grey triangle is found in this region after a short rinse. However, when the side opposite to the directly rinsed surface is investigated, no spectra is found in the region of the reference spectra. This is the case even though a long rinse was carried out and some water was able to reach the surface due to the small sample dimensions.

In the case of TOF-SIMS spectra obtained from surfaces treated with solution C (5% additive), no investigated rinsing condition was able to yield spectra which could be compared to the reference. Long rinsing conditions however seem to remove some of the additive since spectra from these surfaces are found closer to the border line separating clean and unclean samples. Also some of the spectra obtained from the insufficiently rinsed backside - marked here with the smallest filled square - are found in this border region, suggesting that some cleaning may have occurred as well.

3. Conclusions

■ TOF-SIMS measurements were able to document ex situ a glass surface treatment with an industrial additive under alkaline washing media conditions.

■ It was shown that the additive can be removed from glass surfaces by a simple rinse with distilled water. A complete removal was achieved after a 30 sec from samples treated with a caustic solution containing 100 ppm additive. However, a shorter rinsing of 1 sec did not completely remove the additive from the glass surface.

■ Principal component analysis (PCA) was a elegant way to study on a visual basis the influence of sample rinsing which causes only small and complex changes to TOF-SIMS signal intensities. In addition, PCA proved to be a fast evaluation method which takes into account the total information content of TOF-SIMS data, provides statistical evidence and does not necessarily require time consuming peak assignments to get valuable information. However, care has to be taken since possible artefacts may well lead to overinterpretation of the data.

4. Acknowledgements

The author wishes to thank his colleagues Peter Angevaare, Roger Dohmen and Freek Schepers for support and valuable discussions. K. Leufgen and D. Léonard from the Ecole Polytechnique de Lausanne are acknowledged for sample preparation and TOF-SIMS measurements.

References

[1] Paolo Zini, Polymeric Additives for high performing detergents, Technomic Publication, Lancaster, 1995, p 251
[2] Paolo Zini, Polymeric Additives for high performing detergents, Technomic Publication, Lancaster, 1995, p 213
[3] B.W. Schüler, Microsc. Microanalysis Microstructure 3 (1992) 119
[4] K. Franzreb, H.J. Mathieu and D. Landolt, Surf. Interface Anal. 23 (1995) 641
[5] D. Briggs in Practical Surface Analysis, Second Edition, Volume 2. Ion and Neutral Spectroscopy, D. Briggs and M. P. Seah (Eds), John Wiley, Chichester, 1992, 367
[6] E. R. Malinowski, Factor Analysis in Chemistry, Second Edition, Wiley, New York 1991

A. Benninghoven, P. Bertrand, H.-N. Migeon and H.W. Werner (Editors).
Proceedings of the 12th International Conference on Secondary Ion Mass Spectrometry,
Brussels, Belgium, 5-11 September 1999
© 2000 Elsevier Science B.V. All rights reserved.

ANALYSIS OF CLEANROOM AIRBORNE MOLECULAR CONTAMINATION BY TOF-SIMS

G. Goodman, P. Schnabel, L. McCaig, P. Lindley, T. Schuerlein, Charles Evans &
Associates, Redwood City, CA 94063 (Tschuerl@cea.com)

1. Introduction

As devices become smaller and technology pushes the physical limit of device size, process parameters and contamination controls must become more stringent. Although the current level of concern of manufactures of semiconductor devices for organic species is typically low, the SEMI roadmap expects the tolerances for organic contamination will become tighter [1]. In this work, the contribution of cleanroom construction materials to the levels of carbon on silicon wafers will be studied. Inorganic airborne contamination also will be investigated.

2. Experimental

A newly installed class 10 cleanroom was used for this study. The cleanroom contained a TXRF instrument. During the experiment the cleanroom was in use, no process chemicals were used. Silicon wafers were stored in open wafer carriers for varying periods of time. Cumulative exposure experiments used wafers that were introduced into the cleanroom at the start of the experiment and removed at prescribed dates. Sequential exposures were performed by introducing the wafer into the cleanroom at a given start date and removing it after three days. All data shown were normalized to the substrate signal, silicon.

Experiments were performed on a Physical Electronics TRIFT I system with a mass resolution of >7000 at m/z 41. All experiments were performed with a cooled sample stage at ~-50° C [2]. The centers of the wafers were analyzed. Three replicates were made for each measurement, the averages were plotted. Typical standard deviations were ~20%.

3. Results and discussion

Figure 1 shows the normalized intensities of boron and phosphorus (measured as B^+ and PO_3^-) as a function of exposure time to the cleanroom ambient. Both of these species show an increase in concentration as a function of exposure time, particularly in the first three days. After this time the levels stabilize, although the phosphite ion signal fluctuates. The P fluctuation may be due to actual changes in the phosphorus concentration in the cleanroom. However, a spectral interference from $^{30}SiO_3H$ increases the uncertainty of the measurement, and may account for the observed fluctuation. Normal B levels in the atmosphere have been used to explain the increase in B intensity on similar samples [3].

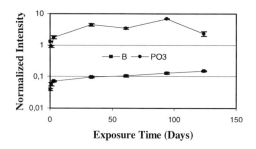

Figure 1: Normalized intensities with error bars of $^{11}B^+$ and PO_3^- as a function of cumulative exposure time.

Figure 2 shows the cumulative and sequential exposures results for silicone and phthalate species. Phthalates (measured as the phthalate cation, $C_8H_5O_3^+$) are plasticizers that outgas from a variety of polymers and are well known to strongly adhere to silicon surfaces [4]. Silicones are common polymers with a wide range of industrial uses. The cumulative exposure data in Figure 2 shows the phthalate signal maximizes after 30 days, while the silicone signal increases in the first three days and then reaches equilibrium. The sequential exposure data shows a decrease in the levels of these species with time, with the phthalate decreasing more rapidly than the silicone signal. The decreased intensities of the sequential exposure experiments indicate the airborne levels of these species are decreasing, as has been observed by previous researchers [5]. These two sets of data also show that the levels of phthalates and silicones on the wafers decrease (measured in the cumulative experiment) as the airborne levels of these materials decrease (as seen in the sequential experiment). This phenomenon is consistent with an equilibrium adsorption process: as the level of atmospheric contamination is reduced, material adsorbed on the wafers is removed to re-establish the equilibrium state.

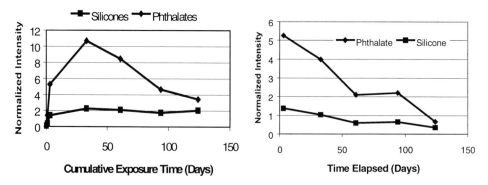

Figure 2: Relative levels of silicones ($C_5H_{15}Si_2O^+$) and phthalates ($C_8H_5O_3^+$) after cumulative (left) and sequential (right) exposures.

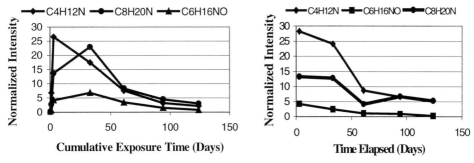

Figure 3: N-containing organic contaminants after cumulative (left) and sequential (right) exposures (positive ion data).

A similar but more pronounced trend is observed for the nitrogen-containing species monitored in Figure 3 ($C_4H_{12}N$, $C_8H_{20}N$ and $C_6H_{16}NO$). The rapid rise and then fall off in these signals in the cumulative experiments is related to the decaying signal observed in the sequential experiments. The initial elevated levels of these species in the cleanroom air lead to the rapid increase in adsorption observed early in the experiment. Over time, the outgassing of these compounds decrease and the equilibrium level of the amine species on the wafers also decreases.

Individually, these species exhibit somewhat different behaviors. For example, the time required to reach a maximum concentration on the wafers is different for $C_8H_{20}N$ and $C_4H_{12}N$. The lower molecular weight amine species ($C_4H_{12}N$) reaches a maximum concentration more quickly in the cumulative exposure data (after three days), while the higher mass ion's intensity increases up to the 30 day measurement. While the chemistry of Figure 4: Normalized intensities of carbon (measured as C_2^-, left) and halogens (right) after cumulative exposures.

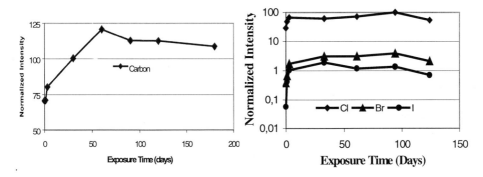

Figure 4: Normalized intensities of carbon (measured as C2-, left) and halogens (right) aftercumulative exposures.

these species is similar, the observed difference is likely due to variations in vapor pressure and outgassing rates based on molecular weight. Figure 4 shows the trend for carbon (measured as C_2^-). This species can be used to track general organic levels of the wafer. The overall carbon signal is seen to increase rapidly initially and then stabilize. In contrast to the other organic species shown, the overall carbon levels do not decrease significantly as a function of time. This is consistent with the expectation that a silicon wafer exposed to the atmosphere will reach a saturation level of contamination, after which the levels will remain relatively constant. Also in Figure 4, halogen levels are seen to increase rapidly in the first three days and then remain relatively constant. This would be expected for species that bind strongly to the wafer surface.

4. Conclusions

Outgassing of a newly constructed cleanroom was investigated by TOF-SIMS. Both organic and inorganic contaminants were detected. Many of the organic contaminants were found to have a higher outgassing rate at the beginning of the experiment and then decreased in intensity later in the experiment. The long-term accumulation of AMC on the wafers showed a relationship with the sequential measurements that is consistent with an equilibrium adsorption process with the atmospheric contamination.

References

[1] Special Report, Cleanrooms, 21-25, (1998).
[2] G. Strossman, P. Lindley and W. Bowers in "Secondary Ion Mass Spectrometry, SIMS XI", G. Gillen, R. Lareau, J. Bennett and F. Stevie Eds., 1997, pp 699-702, John Wiley & Sons, Chichester.
[3] F.Stevie, E Martin, P. Kahora, J. Cargo, A. Nanda, A. Harrus, A. Muller and H. Krautter, J. Vac. Sci. Technol. A 9 (5) 2813-2816, (1991).
[4] Takeda, K., Nonaka, T., Sakamoto, Y., Taira, T., Hirono, K., Fujimoto, T, Suwa, N., and Otsuka, K., IEST Proceedings, Contamination Control, IEST, pp 556-561 (1998).
[5] M. Tamaoki, et. al. IEEE/Semi Adv. Semi. Manuf. Conf. Proceed., pg. 322 (1995).

A. Benninghoven, P. Bertrand, H.-N. Migeon and H.W. Werner (Editors).
Proceedings of the 12th International Conference on Secondary Ion Mass Spectrometry,
Brussels, Belgium, 5-11 September 1999

821

COMBINING TOF-SIMS WITH XPS AND AFM TO QUANTIFY ORGANIC SURFACE COVERAGES

C. Kenens[1], T. Conard[1], L. Hellemans[2], P.Bertrand[3], W. Vandervorst[1]/[4],
[1]IMEC vzw, Kapeldreef 75, Leuven, Belgium, [2]KUL, Celestijnenlaan 200D,
Leuven, Belgium, [3]UCL Place Croix du Sud 1, Louvain-la-Neuve, Belgium
[4]INSYS, KUL Kardinaal Mercierlaan 92, Leuven, Belgium,
e-mail : KENENS@IMEC.BE

1. Introduction

TOF-SIMS is a powerful tool for organic surface characterization due to a combination of advantages: high surface sensitivity, high mass-range, high mass resolution and characteristic fragmentation patterns. [1] Quantitative interpretations of the data however are still at their early stages. Therefore in this work, TOF-SIMS data were combined with XPS measurements, which provides standard quantification methods (overlayer model [2]) to calculate the surface coverage (atoms/cm^2). This number was compared to the (relative) intensity of the molecular peak of the compound under consideration, in the TOF-SIMS spectrum. Furthermore, a linking with AFM via XPS, was realized. By this way, it was possible to reveal more quantitative information from TOF-SIMS spectra.

2. Experimental setup

In this work, Langmuir Blodgett films on silicon surfaces were prepared as being representative for organic surface contamination.

A p-type <100> monitor wafer received first an IMEC clean (SOM (H$_2$SO$_4$/O$_3$) 90°C for 10 min., quick dump rinse 15 min., DHF (0.5%)/DHCl (0.5%) 2 min., DI/HCl/O$_3$ megasoon 10min., Marangoni dryer) and just before the preparation of the organic coating, the wafer was given an HF-dip (2% HF for 5 min. + DI-rinse for 10 min.) to become hydrophobic. Small pieces (± 2 cm^2) were cut out of the wafer before the contamination was realized.

The contaminant under study was stearic acid, a saturated fatty acid with the following formula: CH$_3$-(CH$_2$)$_{16}$-COOH. The polar carboxylic group at one end and the hydrophobic alkyl-chain at the other side of the molecule, makes it amphiphilic and thus suited for Langmuir Blodgett film preparation. As the carboxyl groups will deprotonate at the water surface, their negative loadings were compensated by adding CdCl$_2$ to the water (4.10^{-4} M). This results in a mixture-film of the acid and the Cd-salt of the stearine. At the working pH of 5.6 (measured experimentally), the acid to soap ratio is about 40 to 60%. [3]

The Langmuir Blodgett films (=LB-films) were prepared and extracted onto the Si-substrates, on a KSV Instrument LTD (Finland) model KSV500. The stearic acid was solved in n-hexane (1mg/ml). The water was of Millipore quality. The compression of the subphase and the deposition of the film were performed under the following conditions: a barrier surface-pressure of 30mN/m, compression-speed of 10 mm/min and a dipping speed of 5 mm/min. Two samples with double LB layers were prepared under the same circumstances.

TOF-SIMS analyses were performed on a TRIFT I spectrometer from Charles Evans & ass.(Ga$^+$-source of 800 pA). The XPS instrument was a SSX-100 spectrometer (a monochromatized Al Kα source, 1486.6. eV). The AFM instrument was a Dimension 3000 from Digital Instruments (tapping mode).

As the degradation of LB-films by aging (at room-temperature) is well known [4], the samples were measured each day with both analysis techniques, during four subsequent days. The purpose was to remark a decrease in the signal, representative for the organic surface coverage, with all the techniques and to correlate these data.

3. Results

To evaluate the TOF-SIMS spectra, the most significant peak of the LB film of stearic acid/Cd-stearate, was looked for : the peak at mass 283 amu in the negative mode representing the deprotonated molecular ion. Relative intensities were calculated by normalizing the peak-intensities to the total counts of each spectrum and multiplying this ratio with a factor 100.

The evolution of the intensity with time was decreasing, especially after the first day. The correspondence between the two identical samples was good which confirms the reproducibility of the data. Calculating the averages, which improves the quality of the data, was thus justified. (table 1) A linear combination was fitted through the average values.

XPS data can be used to calculate a surface coverage in a more quantitative approach (atoms per cm^2). The formula (1) which was used, is based on the overlayer model : contaminants in submonolayer coverage on solid surfaces can be regarded as a special case of the simple overlayer model where attenuation by the overlayer can be neglected.[2] In the present case, the situation is not exactly a submonolayer coverage but rather a film of two monolayers with a total thickness of approximately 5 nm when assuming that the molecules are oriented perpendicular to the surface. Since holes of bilayer-depth (average sizes of 5 nm deep and 20 nm broad), are present, substrate information will be measurable as well, originating from these holes. Therefore, the real situation approached the model to a certain degree.

$$N_{overlayer} = (C_{overlayer}/C_{substrate}) . 9.10^{15} \text{ at./cm}^2 \tag{1}$$

with C = I/S : I = measured intensity (normalised to number of scans)

S = Scofield sensitivity factor

$C_{overlayer}$: carbon signal of organic film / $C_{substrate}$: Si signal from the holes

Evaluating the data, the same decreasing trend in surface coverage with time, was found. (table 1) Averages were calculated because of a good agreement between the identical samples. A linear combination was fitted through the average values.

Table 1: Experimental data of TOFSIMS(1) and XPS(2) with averages and stand. deviations

Technique	Day1		Day2		Day3		Day4	
	TOF	XPS	TOF	XPS	TOF	XPS	TOF	XPS
2LB(1)	0.047	1.4×10^{16}	0.03	1.0×10^{16}	0.026	9.9×10^{15}	0.022	6.4×10^{15}
2LB(2)	0.043	1.3×10^{16}	0.023	1.3×10^{16}	0.019	6.5×10^{15}	0.027	5.4×10^{15}
Av.	0.045	1.3×10^{16}	0.027	1.2×10^{16}	0.023	8.2×10^{15}	0.025	5.9×10^{15}
St. Dev.	0.003	1.0×10^{15}	0.005	1.9×10^{15}	0.005	2.4×10^{15}	0.004	7.0×10^{14}

(1) Rel. Int. of molecular peak : (I_{283}/ I_{total}) *100 (%) / (2) Surf. Cov. : atoms/cm^2

The coverage of organic material present on the surface, was decreasing day by day as confirmed by both the analysis techniques : the relative intensity of the molecular peak (negative TOF-SIMS spectrum) as well as the number of atoms per cm^2 (XPS), decreased by a factor two over the four days. This agreement between both techniques, made their linking more justified. Combining the fitted data of TOF-SIMS with these of XPS, gave a more quantitative idea of the decrease in peak-intensities in the TOF-spectra and thus also of the degradation of the film with time. (figure 1A)

To quantify the coverage in terms of percentages of the total surface, calculations were worked out starting from the XPS-data, and compared to the data resulting from a grain-size analysis of the AFM-data. The calculations for the XPS-data are based on a model: the molecules in the film are paired (head to head)(= 36 C-atoms), oriented perpendicular to the surface and an area of 20Å^2 is taken per (bi-)molecule. With these suppositions, the following formula was worked out:

$$\text{Coverage} = [((x \text{ atoms/ cm}^2)/36)* 20\text{Å}^2]/10^{16}\text{ Å}^2 *100 \ (\%) \tag{2}$$

By means of the grain-size analysis performed on the AFM-images, it is possible to calculate the total area taken by the grains (holes in this case) and thus also the complement (total area covered). Linear combinations were fitted through the average values. Combining these data of XPS and AFM, also resulted in a good correlation (figure 1B). The slightly lower coverage from XPS could result from the fact that the number of C-atoms (startpoint for XPS calculations) are an underestimation because not all photo-electrons of the C-atoms down to the surface (5 nm deep) are measurable by XPS. Nevertheless, the agreement between both techniques whereby the AFM data might be regarded as being more reliable (visual observation of grains/holes) in comparison to the XPS-data (model-calculations), implies that the used model approaches the reality. By means of this second correlation, it became possible to link the TOF-SIMS data via XPS with AFM and thus quantify the relative peak-intensities in terms of percentages of the total surface that is covered.[5]

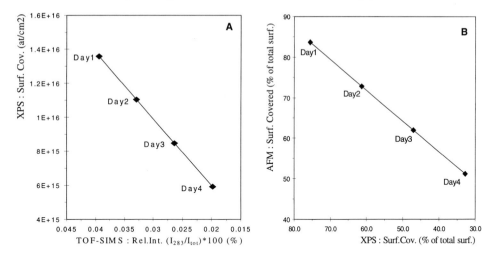

Figure 1 : Combination of the fitted data : (A) TOF-SIMS (reverse axe scale !) and XPS /(B) XPS (reverse axe scale !) and AFM

The cause for the rather fast degradation of the LB-film as compared to the results of B. Pignataro [4] who noticed a degradation process over a period of some weeks at room temperature, might be the ultra-high vacuum conditions inherent to the analysis techniques used here. This was revealed by means of an AFM-analysis, operating at atmospheric pressure. Two samples were taken into account : one 2LB-sample which was stored in a box at room-temperature during the four days and thus did not experienced any vacuum, was compared with a 2LB sample which underwent a TOF-SIMS- and XPS-analysis every day. In figure 2 AFM-images of the samples, measured the first and last day are compared. There are no time-effects seen on the first sample, which has been stored in air. The film-structure of the second sample, which was stored in vacuum during the short time-periods of the analysis, definetely reveals some changes in its structure. Already after 1 hour of vacuum, the density of the holes is increased in comparison with the first sample. Four days later, after 17 hours of vacuum, the film is further degraded : more holes are generated and probably existing holes are enlarged. The average depth of the holes, is 4 to 5 nm which approaches the bilayer-depth of a stearic acid/Cd-stearate film. Therefore, over the four days of measuring, the film was degrading, more and more of the surface coverage was dissappearing and thus the TOF-SIMS- and XPS-signals were decreasing.

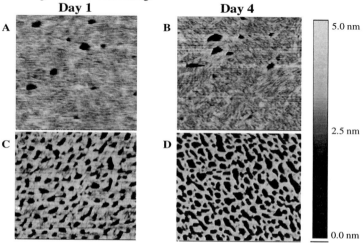

Figure 2: AFM-images of two 2LB samples (0.5x0.5μm^2) taken day 1 and day 4: no vacuum sample (A/B), vacuum sample(C for 1h./D for 17h.)

4. Conclusion

Thus in this work, a principle was worked out to interpret TOF-SIMS spectra from organic surface coverages in a more quantitative way by combining them with XPS-data. Making the correlation of recalculated XPS-data with analysed data of AFM-images, might even enlarge the domain of quantification in terms of percentages of the total surface that is covered. Future intentions are to investigate other organic surface contaminants on silicon by combining TOF-SIMS with XPS to reveal quantitative infromation from the mass-spectra e.g. contamination by silanisation of the silicon-surface.

An important issue noticed in this work, is the fact that LB-films degrade rapidly in UHV-conditions and exposure to it should be limited as much as possible !

References

[1] A. Benninghoven, Angewandte Chemie Int. Ed. Engl. 33 (1994) 1023
[2] A.F. Carley, M.W.Roberts, Proc. R. Soc. London A363 (1978) 403
[3] Daniel K. Schwartz, Surface Science Reports 27 (1997) 241-334
[4] B. Pignataro, C. Consolvo, G. Copagnini, A. Licciardello, Chem. Phys. Letters 299(5) (1999) 430
[5] B. Pignataro, S. Panebianco, C. Consalvo, A. Licciardello, Surf. Interface Anal. 27 (1999), 396-400

A. Benninghoven, P. Bertrand, H.-N. Migeon and H.W. Werner (Editors).
Proceedings of the 12th International Conference on Secondary Ion Mass Spectrometry,
Brussels, Belgium, 5-11 September 1999
© 2000 Elsevier Science B.V. All rights reserved.

CHARACTERIZATION OF POLYMER ADDITIVES BY TIME-OF-FLIGHT SECONDARY ION MASS SPECTROMETRY (TOF-SIMS)

R. Kersting[1], A. P. Pijpers[2], B. Hagenhoff[1], R. Verlaek[2], D. Stapel[3], A. Benninghoven[3],

B.-C. Schwede[4]

[1]TASCON GmbH, Mendelstr. 11, D-48149 Münster, Germany
[2]DSM Research, Box 18, NL-6160 MD Geleen, The Netherlands
[3]University of Münster, Physical Institute, Wilhelm-Klemm-Str. 10,
D-48149 Münster, Germany
[4]ION-TOF GmbH, Mendelstr. 11, D-48149 Münster, Germany

1. Introduction

Modern life is almost non-thinkable without plastic products. The success of plastics in various application fields can be explained by the enormous flexibility of polymers mixed with those materials which are collectively known as additives. Additives are no optional extras but essential ingredients which can make the difference between success and failure of a plastic product. Additive concentrations can be as low as 200 ppm [1]. Whereas the bulk additive composition can be probed by several analytical techniques, a direct analysis of the additives on a polymer surface is more complicated due to the limited number of additive molecules available.

TOF-SIMS is known as an ideally suited analytical technique to characterize surface compositions because it offers molecular information of the uppermost monolayers and a high sensitivity. We therefore started a systematic feasibility study on additives mixed into low density polyethylene (LDPE) with technical relevant concentrations. Some results obtained on stabilizers are presented in this publication.

2. Experimental

The model systems were prepared by mechanically powder mixing of the respective additive into virgin LDPE. Subsequently, the material was heated (180°C) and pressed to thin plates of app. 200µm thickness. The following additives (supplier: Ciba Specialty Chemicals) were used:

Trade name	Molecular weight / u
Irgafos 168 (phosphite)	646.5
Irgafos 168 (phosphate)	662.4
Irganox 1076	530.5
Tinuvin 770	480.4
Irganox 565	589.4

SIMS measurements were performed with a state-of-the-art CAMECA TOF-SIMS IV instrument simultaneously equipped with Ga^+, Ar^+, Cs^+, SF_5^+ primary ion guns. Thus, a variation of the bombardment conditions under identical analytical conditions (analyzer, detector) was possible. Screening of additives in polymeric ambient has been performed with 15 keV Ga in combination with charge compensation. The Münster High Mass Resolution Static SIMS Library [2] software was used to process and store the reference data for future work. Additional Au$^+$ imaging experiments were performed on a second instrument of same type.

3. Results and discussion

3.1 Additive identification

First, the library was filled with spectra of both polarities obtained on 120 additives in LDPE and several additive-free polymers. For this purpose all spectra were transferred into lists with exact peak masses and intensities (peak lists). The library software allows a comparison of the database peak lists to those generated from samples with an unknown chemical composition. With this tool an identification of the chemical surface composition of unknown samples was possible.

3.2 Additive oxidation

The effect of additive oxidation is presented for the phenolic phosphite Irgafos 168. Irgafos belongs to the group of secondary (i.e. preventive) antioxidants which reduce the oxidative degradation of polymer materials. In particular, hydroperoxides are responsible for polymer degradation processes. During the decomposition of peroxides (PD) the Irgafos molecule becomes oxidized to its phosphate form.

TOF-SIMS is well suited to monitor these additive oxidation processes. Figure 1 compares the positive secondary ion spectra acquired on LDPE foils containing Irgafos 168 (phosphite / phosphate). As one can see, TOF-SIMS clearly reflects the chemical state of the Irgafos molecule.

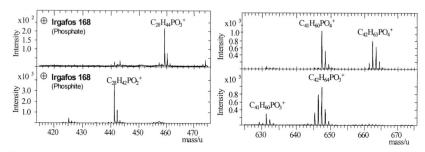

Figure 1: Spectra of Irgafos 168 phosphate (upper row) and phosphite (bottom row). The molecular peak pattern for the phosphite ($645<m/z<651$) is due to the formation of $(M-H)^+$, $(M)^+$ and $(M+H)^+$.

3.3. Additive segregation

Blooming, i.e. an unintentional additive segregation towards the surface is not wanted, as the stabilizer is lost for the polymer. We therefore performed first experiments to study these effects in more detail.

The segregation example presented here was obtained on the surface of an LDPE specimen that contained a relatively high amount of Irgafos 168 (bulk conc. app. 330ppm) and Irganox 1076 (bulk conc. app. 430ppm). The sample (thickness app. 200μm) was leached with CHCl$_3$ in order to remove additive molecules from the surface. Subsequently, the additive molecular peak group intensities were monitored at room temperature as a function of time. For analysis an Ar primary ion gun in combination with the charge compensation system was used. The total ion dose applied for the whole time profile was within the static SIMS limit. The pressure in the vacuum chamber was $2e^{-8}$ mbar.

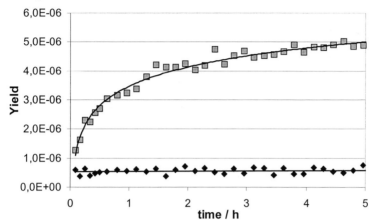

Figure 2:   *Yields of molecular ion distributions of Irganox 1076 (diamonds) and Irgafos 168 (squares) as a function of time.*

Figure 2 shows yields of the complete molecular peak distribution of Irganox 1076 and Irgafos 168 as a function of time. One clearly can see that the intensity of Irgafos increases whereas the Irganox intensity remains constant indicating a segregation of Irgafos to the sample surface. Please note that the end of the leaching procedure defines the starting point of the time scale. The first data were acquired after 5 minutes. At this time the normalized additive intensities are above zero. This might be due to an imperfect leaching procedure or an extremely fast additive segregation. A similar segregation behavior was also found for Tinuvin 770 in LDPE (not shown here).

3.4 Additive imaging using Au^+ primary ions

The useful lateral resolution in imaging SIMS is given by the focus quality of the primary ion gun and the desorption efficiency $E=Y/\sigma$ (Y: secondary ion yield, σ: disappearance cross section) of the used primary ion species in the target material [3]. Good focus quality can only be achieved using liquid metal ion guns. High desorption efficiencies can be expected by use of high mass atomic species or polyatomic ions [4]. In order to combine good focus quality with the possibility to use high masses and polyatomic species we therefore developed a liquid metal ion gun operated with Au^+ and Au-cluster ions.

In figure 3 we present first imaging results obtained with the new Au^+ (197u, 11 keV) gun for the additives Tinuvin 770 and Irganox 565 (bulk conc.: app. 500ppm) in LDPE. We mapped the characteristic molecular ion signals $(M+H)^+$ of both additives. In order to qualitatively compare the obtained imaging results we also recorded images with Ga^+ (69u, 15 keV). To avoid pre-bombardment influences different surface areas of the same sample were imaged. The lateral distribution of Tinuvin can already nicely be seen using Ga^+ bombardment whereas the occurrence of Irganox can only be resolved using Au^+ primary ion bombardment.

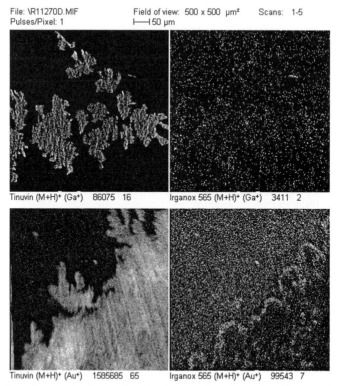

File: \R11270D.MIF   Field of view: 500 x 500 μm²   Scans: 1-5
Pulses/Pixel: 1   ⊢——⊣50 μm

Tinuvin (M+H)⁺ (Ga⁺)   86075   16   Irganox 565 (M+H)⁺ (Ga⁺)   3411   2

Tinuvin (M+H)⁺ (Au⁺)   1585685   65   Irganox 565 (M+H)⁺ (Au⁺)   99543   7

Figure 3:   Mass resolved secondary ion images of a polymer blend material containing Tinuvin 770 and Irganox 565; the upper row was obtained using Ga⁺ (15 keV) primary ions, the lower row using Au⁺ (11 keV); the images were acquired with the same number of primary ions; the numbers below each image refer to the total number of counts and the intensity in the brightest pixel

References

[1] G. Pritchard, Plastics Additives, Polymer Science and Technology, Chapman & Hall, London, UK, 1998
[2] B.-C. Schwede, T. Heller, D. Rading, E. Niehuis, B. Hagenhoff, L. Wiedmann, A. Benninghoven; in: Secondary Ion Mass Spectrometry, Proceedings of the XIth International Meeting, G. Gillen, R. Lareau, J. Bennett, F. Stevie (eds), John Wiley & Sons, Chichester 1998, p. 509
[3] H. Rulle, D. Rading, A. Benninghoven in: Secondary Ion Mass Spectrometry, Proceedings of the Xth International Meeting, A. Benninghoven, B. Hagenhoff, H.W. Werner (eds), John Wiley & Sons, Chichester 1997, p.153
[4] D. Stapel, B. Hagenhoff, A. Benninghoven, these proceedings

A. Benninghoven, P. Bertrand, H.-N. Migeon and H.W. Werner (Editors).
Proceedings of the 12th International Conference on Secondary Ion Mass Spectrometry,
Brussels, Belgium, 5-11 September 1999

829

QUANTITATIVE ANALYSIS OF FUNCTIONAL GROUPS WITH TOF-SIMS

T. Fladung, M. Bültbrune, D. Wolany, Th. Gantenfort, L. Wiedmann, A. Benninghoven

Universität Münster, Physikalisches Institut, D-48149 Münster, Germany
e-mail: bennial@uni-muenster.de

1. Introduction

The plasma treatment of polymer surfaces is a commonly used method for adapting surface properties such as wettability, chemical reactivity, biocompatibility, etc. to specific requirements. For the understanding of the plasma induced surface processes it is necessary to identify the generated functional groups and quantitatively determine their concentration. With XPS, the unique identification of such groups is often difficult, because the line separation of the relevant signals (typically C 1s and/or O 1s) is generally ambiguous due to comparable chemical shifts for different functionalities. Neither does SIMS provide a straightforward one-to-one correspondence between specific secondary ion signals and functional groups. A possible solution to this problem is derivatization, i.e. letting surface functionalities react selectively and quantitatively with a certain marker substance in such a way that the reaction products can be uniquely determined by XPS and SIMS.

Derivatization and subsequent quantitative XPS analysis of the derivatization products is a well-known procedure for a number of important functionalities [1]. We will show in this paper that the analysis of derivatization products with TOF-SIMS can extend the limited sensitivity of XPS by several orders of magnitude and, at the same time, reduce the time needed for data acquisition and evaluation. As an example, we chose the gas phase derivatization of hydroxide groups with trifluoroacetic anhydride (TFAA).

2. Experimental and methodology

TFAA is known as a selective marker substance for the quantitative determination of hydroxide groups [2]. The polymer samples were exposed to an atmosphere saturated with TFAA for up to 3 h and subsequently kept in UHV for 24 h in order to desorb the excess TFAA adsorbed at the surface. Finally, they were analyzed with XPS and TOF-SIMS in our combination instrument [3]. For a systematic analysis of the TOF-SIMS data (as much as 165 positive and 70 negative secondary ion signals per sample) statistical methods were applied. It has been shown that the method of principal component analysis (PCA) [4] can be successfully tailored to this problem [5]. In this case, the individual spectra are considered as columns and the secondary ion species as rows of a two-dimensional data matrix to be evaluated. No scaling of the secondary ion intensities was used.

3. Samples and pretreatment

First, we investigated the development of the TFAA derivatization reaction with time using a model polymer with a monofunctional surface. For this purpose, a polyethylene-polyvinylalcohol copolymer with known hydroxide concentration (Soarnol D 2908®) was used. The samples were stored in an atmosphere saturated with TFAA between 1 min and 3 h. The results of this experiment were used in the derivatization of plasma treated polymer surfaces. The samples in this case were technical polypropylene (Novolen 2900 NC®, manufactured by BASF AG) treated in an oxygen plasma, and bisphenol-A polycarbonate (Bayer AG) treated in an oxygen and argon plasma, respectively.

4. Results and discussion

The TOF-SIMS spectra of the monofunctional Soarnol samples were subjected to principal component analysis and result in a two-dimensional data space. Fig. 1 shows the loadings of the secondary ion signals in the first two principal components. The species with significantly non-zero loadings fall onto two branches, one of which can be represented by the F^- and CF_3^+, the other by the O^-, OH^-, and CH^- signals. The signals represented by the first branch increase, those on the second branch drop with TFAA reaction time.

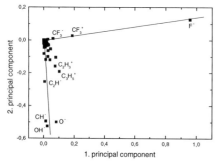

Fig. 1: Loadings of secondary ion species from Soarnol; plot of first vs. second principal component.

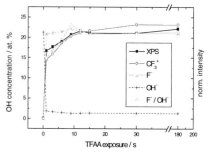

Fig. 2: OH concentration (determined by XPS) and normalized intensity of selected secondary ion signals from Soarnol as a function of TFAA reaction time.

In order to elucidate the significance of these representative ions, Fig. 2 shows that both the F^-/OH^- ratio and the normalized CF_3^+ signal exhibit a similar dependence on reaction time as the concentration of OH groups as determined with XPS. These signals can therefore be used, after calibration with XPS, for the quantitative determination of hydroxide groups. All signals are saturated after a reaction time of about 15–30 min. After this time, XPS and SIMS yield practically identically results despite their different information depths.

For the plasma treated polycarbonate samples, PCA shows that the same ion species as for Soarnol (F^-, CF_3^+ vs. O^-, OH^-, CH^-) represent the main information of the spectra. As a function of plasma treatment time, the F^-/OH^- ratio and the CF_3^+ signal again match the OH concentration as determined with XPS, and can be used for quantitative analysis of the OH content. Comparable results are obtained for polycarbonate treated in an argon and oxygen plasma, respectively, except for the saturation of the signals, which occurs for the oxygen plasma at significantly lower treatment times.

Finally, we compared the spectra of all sample materials in detail by PCA. The result is the existence of four principal components which capture 98 % of the variance. In what follows, we consider the scores of the spectra for these four components. This view emphasizes the similarities and differences of the spectra as revealed by the various principal components. In fig. 3, the scores for the first and second principal component are plotted against each other. The diagram exhibits a linear correlation between these scores. This dependence can easily be explained. The first component represents the fluorine containing secondary ion species, i.e. the OH content of the sample detected *after* the derivatization reaction, whereas the second component represents species such as O$^-$ or OH$^-$, i.e. the oxygen content *not* subjected to the reaction. These two amounts are anticorrelated. The diagram shows that the untreated samples, the plasma treated samples, and the completely derivatized Soarnol samples are well separated from each other.

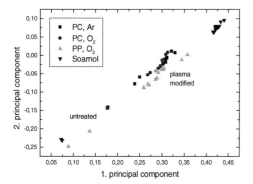

Fig. 3: Two-dimensional plot of the scores for the first and second principal component.

A plot of the first, third and fourth principal component is shown in fig. 4. Each of these components can be interpreted in a straightforward manner. The first component (or, alternatively, the anticorrelated second component) measures the amount of OH which has reacted with TFAA. The third component is inversely correlated with the amount of oxygen before derivatization. Finally, the fourth component, in connection with the first, provides a clear cut between the different sample materials (polypropylene, polycarbonate, and Soarnol), with no distinction between argon and oxygen plasma treatment. The major ions which are represented by these four components are, in this order, F$^-$, OH$^-$, O$^-$ and CH$^-$.

It is illuminating to repeat the analysis for a set of reduced spectra, which contain non-zero intensities only for these four relevant species F$^-$, OH$^-$, O$^-$ and CH$^-$. It is found that the scores for the first three components are practically identical with those of the full set of data, whereas the distinction of the spectra in the direction of the fourth component has been lost. This indicates that the information about the original and reacted amount of OH is fully represented by these four secondary ion species, whereas the identification of the substance under investigation requires additional signals.

832

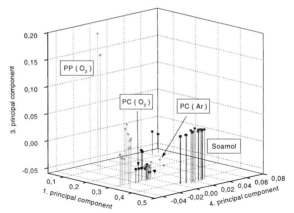

Fig. 4: Three-dimensional plot of the scores for the first, third and fourth principal component.

5. Summary

It has been shown that the derivatization of functional groups is a suitable means for the quantitative detection of these groups on multi-functional surfaces not only by XPS, but also with TOF-SIMS. In the latter case, principal component analysis provides an effective method of data reduction, which reduces the wealth of information contained in the spectra to the intensities of a few significant secondary ion species. After calibration with XPS, these signals can also be used for the quantitative analysis of these functional groups, which provides a fast, sensitive and convenient alternative to the established analytical procedures.

Acknowledgement

This work was supported by the Bundesminister für Bildung und Forschung (grant no. 03 D 0041 D 8).

References

[1] C.D.Batidch, *Appl. Surface Sci.* **32** (1988), 57.

[2] A.Chilkoti, B.Ratner, in: *Surface characterization of advanced polymers*, Weinheim Verlag Chemie 1993, p.221.

[3] P.W.Jahn,F.M.Petrat, D.Wolany, M.Deimel, T.Gantenfort, C.Schmerling, H.Weinsing, L.Wiedmann, A.Benninghoven, *J. Vac. Sci. Tecnol.* **A12** (1994), 671.

[4] K.R.Beebe, B.R.Kowalski, *Anal. Chem.* **59** (1987), 1007A.

[5] B.-C.Schwede, Thesis, University of Münster 1998.

A. Benninghoven, P. Bertrand, H.-N. Migeon and H.W. Werner (Editors).
Proceedings of the 12th International Conference on Secondary Ion Mass Spectrometry,
Brussels, Belgium, 5-11 September 1999
© 2000 Elsevier Science B.V. All rights reserved.

CHARACTERIZATION OF HARD DISK DRIVES BY TIME-OF-FLIGHT SECONDARY ION MASS SPECTROMETRY (TOF-SIMS)

B. Hagenhoff[1], R. Kersting[1], D. Rading[2], S. Kayser[2], E. Niehuis[2]

[1]TASCON GmbH, Mendelstr. 11, 48149 Münster, Germany
[2]ION-TOF GmbH, Mendelstr. 11, 48149 Münster, Germany
Email: Birgit.Hagenhoff@TASCON-GmbH.de

1. Introduction

The layer structure of modern hard disk drives (HDD) consists of elemental as well as molecular components (table 1) [1]. In order to monitor the different production steps and to elucidate failures in production and during use an analytical technique is required which offers both, elemental and molecular information. Time-of-Flight Secondary Ion Mass Spectrometry (TOF-SIMS) is well suited to perform this task, because it offers the required information with high sensitivity. Additionally the lateral and depth distribution of the sample can be probed.

Layer	Function	Materials
Lubricant	Friction control	PFPE (e.g. Fomblins)
Overcoat	Durability Corrosion protection	a-C, a-C:H, N2 doping
Mag. Layer	Information storage	Co alloys (B, Ta, Pt, Cr,...)
Undercoat	Crystallography control	Cr
Substrate	Mechanical stability	NiP, glass, ceramics

Table 1: Typical Layer Structure of a Hard Disk Drive

It already has been shown that TOF-SIMS generally can be used for failure analysis of HDDs [2]. For a routine application in industry, however, an analytical technique additionally must be easy to use and offer high sample throughput. We therefore concentrated on the automation of measurement and data evaluation to address the general surface characterization of NiP substrates, corrosion effects and the contamination of the overcoat layer.

2. Experimental

For the measurements a state of the art CAMECA TOF-SIMS IV instrument was used. For surface spectroscopy and imaging the instrument is equipped with Ar^+ (10 keV) and Ga^+ (25 keV) primary ions. The energy of the Ar^+ ions was additionally lowered to 5 keV in order to investigate the influence of the lower information depth on the obtained spectra. Additionally, a newly developed liquid metal ion gun operated with Au (Au^+, Au_2^+, 10 keV) was used for imaging.

Batch jobs using the TOF-SIMS IV macro language were written allowing the automatic acquisition of spectra and evaluation of the resulting data. The tasks automatically performed included the navigation to the respective measurement position, the spectrum acquisition, the data storage, the reduction of the spectral information to peak lists (peak mass position, peak intensity), the statistical evaluation (mean values, standard deviations) and the transformation to a standard spreadsheet program for graphical visualization of the results.

Mass resolved ion images of a complete HDD could be obtained by using a newly developed stage raster optimized for the HDD's geometry. In this mode images are obtained by combining a radial movement of the sample stage with the electronic raster of the primary ion gun deflection units. Within 25 min acquisition time thus 100 % of the area of the centre, 37% of the area of the middle and 21% of the area of the outer perimeter of the disk can be analyzed.

3. Results and Discussion

3.1 Characterization of NiP substrates

Nine different NiP subsrates which had undergone three different cleaning procedures A-C were analyzed using both, the batch job and the stage raster approach for automation. For each cleaning procedure three samples ("1"-"3") were prepared under identical conditions. The cleaning procedures included dry and wet cleaning techniques. Unfortunately, the exact routines are confidential. The automatic data evaluation focused on elements, aliphatic and aromatic hydrocarbons as well as O and N containing hydrocarbons. Figure 1 shows the results for the elements. Generally, the reproducibility of the data taken at 9 different sample positions was well within 5 %. A larger variation can therefore be attributed to sample inhomogeneities. Note e.g. the distinct variation for Na after cleaning procedure A and the large Ca^+ intensity for procedure C.

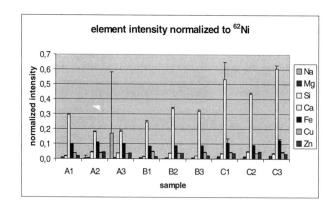

Fig. 1:
Normalized intensity of elemental ions desorbed from differently treated NiP substrates (average over 9 measurement positions; primary ions: Ga^+, 25keV)

Even better impressions on the lateral distribution can be obtained using the stage raster approach. Figure. 2 shows such a stage raster image for selected species of sample C2. Now one can clearly see that Ca$^+$ is homogeneously distributed on this sample whereas C$_2$H$_5$O$^+$ and NO$_x^-$ are not. The samples were stored in boxes with the bottom area corresponding to the right hand side in the images. C$_2$H$_5$O$^+$ is a characteristic fragment of the wet cleaning agent polyethyleneglycol (PEG). It is less intense in the top regions of the sample indicating that this top region was not completely immersed during wet cleaning. The PEG distribution is furthermore complementary to the NO$_x^-$ distribution indicating that these ions are emitted with higher intensities on areas not immersed during cleaning (air contact).

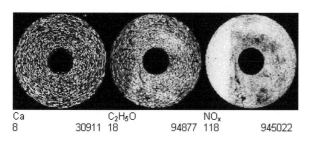

Ca
8   C$_2$H$_5$O
        30911 18   NO$_x$
                      94877 118   945022

Fig. 2:
Stage raster image of sample C2. Ca, and C$_2$H$_5$O are taken in the positive polarity, NO$_x$ is emitted in the negative spectral polarity. Field of view: 9.7 x 9.7 cm^2. Primary ions: Ga$^+$, 25keV

3.2 Corrosion

In HDD industry, corrosion is simulated by applying high relative humidity at elevated temperatures. Figure 3 shows a stage raster scan performed after such a corrosion test. Co from the magnetic layer is visible through the 6 nm carbon overcoat layer. Given the low information depth of SIMS [3] this indicates the existence of corrosion spots on the sample. The appearance of Ni in the images even hints to the existence of pin holes in the magnetic layer itself.

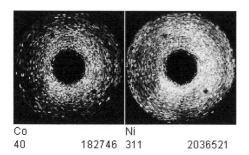

Co
40   Ni
      182746 311   2036521

Fig. 3:
Stage raster image of a HDD after a corrosion test. Field of view: 9.7 x 9.7 cm^2; primary ions: Ar$^+$, 10 keV; the dark spots visible are sputter craters from a XPS investigation performed before the SIMS analysis

3.3 Imaging of Surface Contaminants

The lateral distribution of organic contaminants was investigated using liquid metal ion guns operated with different primary ion species (figure 4). Whereas the low molecular weight fragments of the contaminant silicon oil are easily visible using the monoatomic Ga (69u), the higher mass molecules of the contaminant dimethyldioctylammonia (DODA) are hardly visible. They are distinctly more intense with Au (197u) and best visible using Au dimers (Au_2^+, 394u).

Ga$^+$, 25 keV   Au$^+$, 10 keV   Au$_2^+$, 10 keV

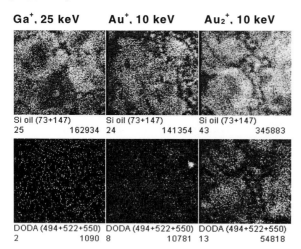

Si oil (73+147)	Si oil (73+147)	Si oil (73+147)
25 162934	24 141354	43 345883

DODA (494+522+550)	DODA (494+522+550)	DODA (494+522+550)
2 1090	8 10781	13 54818

Figure 4: Positive secondary ion images of a contaminated carbon overcoat layer taken with different primary ion species; field of view: 495 x 495 μm^2

Enhancement factors (after normalization of the data to the uncharacteristic low mass hydrocarbon $C_3H_5^+$) for the silicon oil in comparison to Ga$^+$ are 2.2 for Au$^+$ and 3.6 for Au$_2^+$. The values for the DODA molecule are 25 (Au$^+$) and 88 (Au$_2^+$), respectively. The data show that although the mass has a distinct influence on the obtained secondary ion yields, enhancement factors are even larger for polyatomic primary ions. For the here investigated sample the effect was more pronounced for higher secondary ion masses.

Acknowledgement

We wish to thank J. Ziermann (IBM Speichersysteme, Mainz, Germany) and D. Tomcik (Data Storage Institute, University of Singapore) for providing the samples and helpful discussions.

References

[1] M. F. Doerner, R. L. White MRS Bulletin, September 1996, p. 28

[2] T. J. Schuerlein, C. A. Evans, P. M. Lindley, in SIMS, Proceedings of the XIth International Conference, G. Gillen, R. Lareau, J. Bennett, F. Stevie (eds.), John Wiley & Sons, Chichester 1998, p. 616

[3] A. Benninghoven, F.G. Rüdenauer, H.W. Werner Secondary Ion Mass Spectrometry, John Wiley & Sons, New York, 1987, p.874.

SECTION 14 :
MATERIALS SCIENCE

A. Benninghoven, P. Bertrand, H.-N. Migeon and H.W. Werner (Editors).
Proceedings of the 12th International Conference on Secondary Ion Mass Spectrometry,
Brussels, Belgium, 5-11 September 1999
© 2000 Elsevier Science B.V. All rights reserved.

EMISSION OF COMPLEX IONS IN SPUTTERING OF GRAPHITE
AND COPPER BY HYDROGEN IONS

Dzhemilev N.Kh., Maksimov S.E., Solomko V.V.

Arifov Institute of Electronics, 700143, Tashkent, Uzbekistan. E-mail: root@ariel.tashkent.su.

1. Introduction

According to existing models the emission of cluster particles in ion sputtering occurs with a noticable probability sputtering coefficient $Y_{tot}>1$, the condition being fulfilled for heavy bombarding particles with the energies of several keV. However, in our early work [1] it has been shown that light hydrogen ions bombarding Al, Ni and Cu do induce the emission of cluster M_n^+ and molecular $M_nH_m^+$ ions under the conditions, when $Y_{tot} \leq 10^{-1}$ atom/ion. The sputtering of cluster particles by hydrogen ions is out of the scope of the conventional concepts of cluster emission, according to which basic contribution to sputtering of cluster particles is connected with the development of the collision cascade in the zone of ionic hit. In the case of light ions (hydrogen, helium) it is difficult to describe the process of sputtering of heavy elements by the cascade theory because the cascades are so small, that it is difficult to substantiate the proposition about their isotropy [2].

In the present work the results of investigations of mass distributions and spectra of kinetic energies of $M_n^{\pm}$ and $M_nH_m^{\pm}$ ions in sputtering of Cu and C by accelerated hydrogen and Ar^+ ions are given. We attempted to clear up community or distinctions in the regularities of formation of mass spectral distributions and kinetic energies of Cu and C cluster particles under the bombardment by H_2^+ and Ar^+ ions.

2. Experiments

The experiments were carried out by use of double focusing secondary ions mass spectrometer with reverse geometry [3]. Primary ions were generated by an ion source of a duoplasmatron type. Energy of primary ions was 8,5 and 18,5 keV relatively during study of positively and negatively charged secondary ions. Targets were bombarded under the angle of incidence of 45^0. Ions currents were 1-2 μA for H_2^+ and ~1 μA for Ar^+ at the current density of $\approx 3-5*10^3$ A/cm^2. The measurements were carried out at the pressure in the bombardment chamber of $\approx 5*10^{-8}$ Torr by operative gas. The choice of C and Cu polycrystals as the objects of investigation has been stipulated by the fact, that the materials have the different sputtering coefficients, both the ionization potentials and the electron affinities of C and Cu atoms essentially differing. The analyses of kinetic energies of secondary ions were performed by the change of the target's potential. The passband of the tool was changed by the control of the wideness of intermediate and exit slits of the mass spectrometer being ≈ 1.5 eV.

3. Results and discussion

The distributions of intensities for Cu_n^+ and $Cu_nH_m^+$, sputtered from Cu by H_2^+ in dependence on the number of matrix atoms n for the different number of protons m in the cluster are shown in Fig.1. The distribution for Cu_n^+ clusters sputtered by Ar^+ ions is given here for a comparison. Yields of $Cu_nH_m^+$ ions are presented for m=1-3. The numbers of hydrogen atoms depending on the number of atoms in the clusters are given in Table 1.

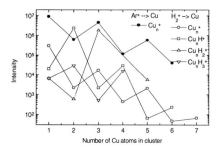

Fig.1. Mass-spectra of cluster ions sputtered by H_2^+ and Ar^+ primary ions from copper surface.

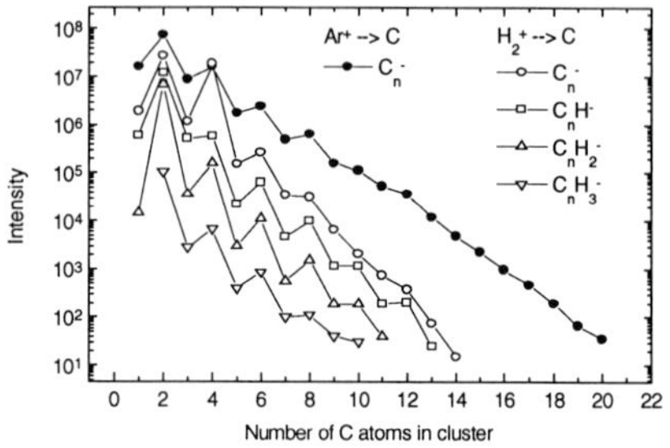

Fig.2. Mass-spectra of cluster ions sputtered by H_2^+ and Ar^+ primary ions from graphite surface.

Table 1.

$Cu_nH_m^+$	n=1	n=2	n=3	n=4	n=5	n=6	n=7
	m=1-5	m=1-6	m=1-6	m=1,3	m=1,2	m=1	-

For both types of primary ions even-odd alternations in the intensities of secondary ions emission take place, the yield increasing at odd n for Cu_n^+, and at odd n+m for $Cu_nH_m^+$. Such even-odd alternations are in good agreement with the results of the calculations of ref.[4], according to which the alternations are explained by the alternative filling of the highest occupied molecular orbital by either one or by two electrons. Clusters Cu_n^+ and $Cu_nH_m^+$ with odd values of n and n+m respectively, have the even number of electrons on the external orbit and therefore the higher value of the bond energy of atoms and the greater intensity in mass spectra. Comparison of yields of molecular and cluster copper atoms with equal n shows, that the presence of hydrogen atoms promote optimal filling of the electron shell of hydrogen containing ions Cu_2H^+, $Cu_3H_2^+$ and Cu_4H^+. This follows from their anomalously high intensity in comparison with Cu_2^+, Cu_3^+ and Cu_4^+.

In Fig.2 the intensity distributions of emitted negatively charged cluster C_n^- and $C_nH_m^-$ molecular ions with m=1-3 are given in dependence on the number of carbon atoms n. In contrast to copper clusters, the character of the C_n^- peaks oscillations coincidences with oscillations of the corresponding molecular ions $C_nH_m^-$. Such a character of the given distributions could be explained from the position of the model [5]. Similary to the case of copper clusters the maximal possible number of protons in the clusters depends on the number of carbon atoms n. For n=1 we have detected the clusters CH_m^- with m=7, for $C_2H_m^-$ the structures with m=6 being found. When n increases the number of hydrogen atoms in the clusters decreases and for $C_{10}H_m^-$ m=3.

Thus, the measurements described above give rise to make the proposition, that the formation of clusters of equal dimensions and charge does not depend on specie, mass and energy of primary ions. It could be assumed, that hydrogen reaching the surface, being a chemically active element, changes chemical and electronic structure of the subsurface layer, that results in the anomalous strong change of the coefficient of ion emission as in the case of the emission under O_2^+ bombardment. For example, the coefficient of Cu sputtering under the bombardment by Ar^+ ions is $Y_{tot} \approx 6$ [6], it is only $Y_{tot} \approx 10^{-1}$ under sputtering by H_2^+. In the same time, the intensities of ions of small series Cu_2H^+, $Cu_3H_2^+$ are comparable with the intensity of Cu^+ atomic ion emission in sputtering by Ar^+.

The spectra measured for Cu_n^+ and C_n^- homogeneous ions in sputtering of copper and graphite by Ar^+ and H_2^+ are shown in Figs. 3 and 4. The energy spectra of Cu_n^+ have been obtained at the energy of primary ions equal to 8,5 keV, in the case of C_n^- the energy was 18,5 keV.

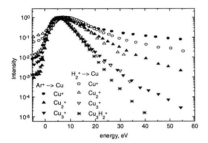

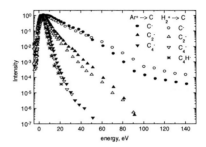

Fig.3. Energy-spectra of cluster ions sputtered by H_2^+ and Ar^+ primary ions from copper surface.

Fig.4. Energy-spectra of cluster ions sputtered by H_2^+ and Ar^+ primary ions from graphite surface.

The main parameters characterising the energy distributions namely the most probable energy E_m, the full width at half maximum of energy distribution $E_{0,5}$, and the exponent k of $N(E) \sim E^{-k}$ exponential law at the energies higher than 10 eV are given in the Table 2.

From the investigated parameters of energy spectra of cluster and molecular ions sputtered from Cu and C a number of features being common for different primary ions (H_2^+ and Ar^+) could be highlighted

Table 2. Parameters of kinetic energy distributions of cluster ions.

Parameter	Primary ions	Species of secondary ions									
		Cu^+	Cu_2^+	Cu_3^+	$Cu_3H_2^+$	C^-	C_2^-	C_3^-	C_4^-	C_2H^-	C_4H^-
E_m, eV	Ar^+	5.7	7	5	-	8	4.2	3.5	3.5	-	-
	H_2^+	8.5	7	5.5	5.5	5.5	3.5	3	3	3.3	2.7
$E_{0,5}$, eV	Ar^+	10.3	9	6.5	-	17	7	5.7	5.5	-	-
	H_2^+	12	9	6.5	6.2	11	5.9	5	4.8	5	4.7
K	Ar^+	-1.3	-3.8	-5.4	-						
	H_2^+	-2.6	-4.1	-5.2	-8.7						

1. Ions Cu_2^+, Cu_3^+, as well as C_2^-, C_3^-, C_4^- have the close values of E_m and $E_{0,5}$ at equal clusters dimensions.
2. Increase of Cu_n^+ и C_n^- dimensions results in relatively monotonous decrease of E_m and $E_{0,5}$. The exception is Cu^+ ion sputtered by Ar^+ for which E_m is significantly shifted to low energies in comparison with Cu_2^+.
3. Molecular ions $Cu_3H_2^+$, C_2H^- and C_4H^- show rather close values of E_m and $E_{0,5}$ in comparison with homogeneous ions at the same n.

842

4. The forms of the energy distributions for Cu^+, Cu_2^+, Cu_3^+ ions in the energy range over 10 eV described by the exponential law (Table 2) are slightly different at equal n. The exception is the energy distribution of Cu^+ under sputtering by H_2^+ falling steeper in comparison with Ar^+ ions.

It should be noted, that the fall of $Cu_3H_2^+$ energy distribution is characterized by significantly higher exponent k in comparison with that typical for Cu_3^+.

Thus, the data of the measurement show, that the parameters describing kinetic energies of cluster ions with the same n, irrespective of their charge state weakly depend on the mass, kind and energy of primary ions. The observable weak differences of these parameters can be connected with both the concrete mechanism of cluster emission and the experimental errors.

On the base of the set of the present studies the following suppositions about a mechanism of cluster sputtering can be stated. Models and mechanisms of cluster emission based on the linear cascade theory of sputtering can not explain the formation of cluster particles under bombardment with hydrogen ions, because the cascades are so small, that for light ions the primary knock-on mechanism contributes mainly to the atom sputtering [2]. Besides considering the formation of molecular $M_nH_m^{\pm}$, ions, owing to the significant differences in masses of hydrogen and metal atoms, any variant of the statistical mechanism it seems to be scarcely possible. The mechanisms of thermal emission [7] and thermodynamic equilibrium [8] can not have essential significance in the cluster emission process under hydrogen bombardment, because in the former case the clusters emission can not be realized for case $Y_{tot}<10^{-1}$, and in the later one the kinetic energy distribution of clusters is supposed to be a thermal one, not confirmed experimentally. The similar conclusion about limitations above mentioned models was made also by authors [9] on the base of the studies of energy distributions of neutral clusters in the high energy region.

4. Conclusion
The emitted cluster particles are low sensitive to the processes occuring within ionic knock-on region but could be caused by surface processes of formation and following repeated sputtering.

The presented results are of especial interest for SIMS analysis of solids, because in the case of sputtering by hydrogen ions at extremely low Y_{tot} ($\sim 10^{-2} - 10^{-1}$ at/ion) high ionicity of sputtered products is observed. Apparently at dense beam SIMS analysis of submonolayers could be carried out in quasistatic regime.

The authors are grateful to INTAS (grant N96-0470) for support of work.

References
[1] N.Kh. Dzhemilev, R.T.Kurbanov, Poverkhnost' N1 (1984) 56 (in Russian).
[2] P. Sigmund, in: Sputtering by Particle Bombardment I, Ed. R. Berisch, Vol.47 of Topics in Applied Physics (Springer, Berlin, 1981) p.9.
[3] A.D. Bekkerman, N.Kh. Dzemilev, V.M. Rotstein, Surf.Interf.Anal. 15 (1990) 587.
[4] P. Joyes, J.Phys. and Chem. Solids 32 (1971) 1269.
[5] K.S. Pitzer, E. Clementi, J. Amer. Chem. Soc. 81 (1959) 4477.
[6] H.H. Andersen and H.L. Bay, in: Particle Bombardment I, Ed. R. Berisch, Vol.47 of Topics in Applied Physics (Springer, Berlin, 1981) p.145.
[7] P. Sigmund and C.Clausse, J.Appl. Phys. 52 (1981) 990.
[8] H.M. Urbassek, Rad. Eff. Def. Solids 109 (1989) 293.
[9] S.R. Coon, W.F. Calaway, M.J. Pellin and J.M. White, Surf. Sci. 298 (1993) 161.

A. Benninghoven, P. Bertrand, H.-N. Migeon and H.W. Werner (Editors).
Proceedings of the 12th International Conference on Secondary Ion Mass Spectrometry,
Brussels, Belgium, 5-11 September 1999

843

A NEW APPLICATION OF SIMS: DISTRIBUTION OF ACTIVE SITES FOR OXYGEN INCORPORATION AT OXIDE CERAMIC INTERFACES

Teruhisa Horita, Katsuhiko Yamaji, Natsuko Sakai, Harumi Yokokawa,
Tatsuya Kawada*, and Tohru Kato**
National Institute of Materials and Chemical Research (NIMC)
1-1 Higashi, Tsukuba, Ibaraki, 305-8565 JAPAN
*: Research Institute for Scientific Measurements (RISM), Tohoku University,
**: Electrotechnical Laboratory (ETL)
Corresponding Author: Teruhisa HORITA, E-mail: horita@home.nimc.go.jp

1. Introduction

At the interfaces of electronic hole conductor / oxide ion conductor ceramics in solid electrochemical devices (such as solid oxide fuel cells (SOFCs)), oxygen can be reduced to O^{2-} and diffuse into the ion-conductive ceramics. The reaction kinetics is closely related to the electrode/electrolyte interface structure, which affects the cell efficiency. To suggest the optimum structure of interface, it is important to investigate the diffusion of oxygen and the distribution of active sites for the oxygen incorporation/reduction. For the investigation of oxygen movements in the solid materials, application of secondary ion mass spectrometry (SIMS) is very powerful because it enables us to measure both the diffusion profiles of isotope oxygen and the distribution of oxygen incorporated points[1-4]. This is a relatively new application field of SIMS: combining the solid state electrochemistry and SIMS analysis. We have demonstrated the application of SIMS technique to investigate the distribution of active sites for oxygen incorporation at the simple interface of $LaMnO_3$ (hole conductor) and Y_2O_3 stabilized ZrO_2 (YSZ, oxide ion conductor) using a stable isotope of oxygen ($^{18}O_2$) [5]. In this paper, the distribution of active sites for oxygen incorporation is investigated on the single crystal YSZ using a similar analytical technique

2. Experimental

2.1 Sample preparation

Strontium doped lanthanum manganite ($La_{0.9}Sr_{0.1}MnO_3$, LSM) was prepared by mixing the appropriate ratio of La_2O_3, $SrCO_3$, and $MnCO_3$. The mixed powders were calcined at 1273 K for 5 h in air. The LSM dense layer was prepared by the RF sputtering technique on the sintered 8 mol% Y_2O_3 stabilized ZrO_2 (YSZ) or single crystal YSZ. The prepared LSM layer was dense without any pin-holes on the surface. The LSM layer was then etched by Ga^+ micro beam shaping the mesh pattern as shown in SEM (Fig.1(a)). The width of the LSM mesh is about 2 μm and the size of the YSZ hole parts is about 9×9 μm^2 with a thickness of about 0.5 μm.

2.2 Isotope oxygen exchange ($^{16}O/^{18}O$ exchange)

To apply the voltage, four electrodes were attached to the LSM/YSZ sample as shown in Fig.1(b). The sample was initially annealed in ^{16}O atmosphere for more than 1 h to saturate ^{16}O in the solids under a potentiostatic condition (cathodic polarization). Then the atmosphere was quickly switched to the ^{18}O (96 vol%) atmosphere under the same potentiostatic conditions. The $^{16}O/^{18}O$ exchanged duration was 600 s at the pressure of about 0.1 bar at 973 K. The samples were rapidly quenched from 973 K to 298 K for 30 s by the flash of N_2.

2.3 SIMS analysis

The SIMS instrument used in this study is magnetic sector type dynamic SIMS (CAMECA, ims5f). Secondary ion images of $^{16}O^-$ and $^{18}O^-$ were collected to determine the active sites for oxygen incorporation. For imaging analysis, a finely focused Cs^+ beam (accelerating voltage of 10 kV and primary beam current of 3-6 nA) sputtered the sample surface with an area of 30×30 μm^2.

3. Results and discussion

3.1 Surface exchange and diffusion of ^{18}O in LaMnO₃

Figure 2 shows $^{18}O^-$ images of the LaMnO₃ mesh/YSZ and YSZ surface after $^{16}O/^{18}O$ exchange under a potentiostatic condition (cathodic overvoltage at –0.336 V). The concentration of $^{18}O^-$ is indicated as the white color parts in these figures. In figure 2(a), the higher $^{18}O^-$ concentration is observed at the LSM mesh part, which indicates the promotion of surface oxygen exchange at the LSM mesh part. This image shows that the surface oxygen exchange of LSM is more active than that of YSZ. In figure 2(b), $^{18}O^-$ image is shown on the YSZ surface after removing the covered LSM mesh. The higher $^{18}O^-$ parts are shown in the shape of mesh, where the LSM was attached. This indicates that the diffused ^{18}O in the LSM mesh directly diffuse into YSZ substrate via the interface of LSM/YSZ. Under the applied voltage condition, the incorporated oxygen can diffuse through the LSM mesh to the interface of LSM/YSZ.

3.2 Distribution of active sites for oxygen incorporation

As shown in Figure 2(b), the active sites for oxygen incorporation are not all the interface of LSM/YSZ but spots on the YSZ surface. To clarify these spots of ^{18}O high concentration, samples of LaMnO₃-layer/YSZ single crystal was used to eliminate the effects of grain boundaries and pores. Figure 3 shows $^{16}O^-$ and $^{18}O^-$ images of YSZ single crystal surface after electrochemical reaction in $^{18}O_2$ and subsequently removing the covered LaMnO₃ layer. While no distribution is observed in $^{16}O^-$ image, many spots of $^{18}O^-$ are observed on the YSZ surface. From these images, not all the interfaces of LaMnO₃/YSZ are active for oxygen incorporation, even though the initial surface of YSZ is smooth enough. One of the possible reasons for these spots is the interdiffusion of elements at the interface of LaMnO₃/YSZ.

4. Conclusion

Distribution of active sites of oxygen incorporation was analyzed by SIMS for electroceramic samples with isotope oxygen exchange under a current flow condition. Diffusion and incorporation of oxygen in the ceramics were investigated at the interface of

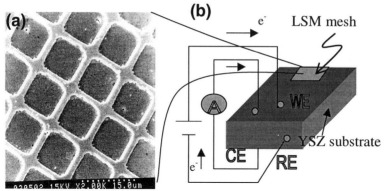

Fig.1 SEM image of LSM mesh/YSZ (a) and schematic
diagram of electrochemical test sample (b).

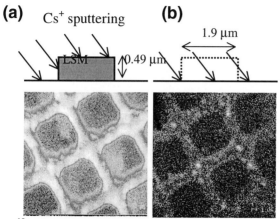

Fig.2 $^{18}O^-$ image of LSM mesh/YSZ (a) and
$^{18}O^-$ image of YSZ surface after removing the LSM mesh (b).

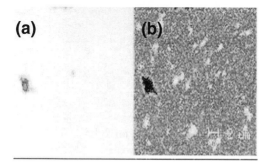

Fig.3 $^{16}O^-$ image of YSZ single crystal surface (a) and
$^{18}O^-$ image of YSZ single crystal surface after removing the LaMnO₃ layer(b).

$LaMnO_3/Y_2O_3$ stabilized ZrO_2. The SIMS imaging analysis enabled us to determine the distribution of active sites for oxygen incorporation as well as oxygen diffusion in the ceramics. This is a new application of SIMS to analyze the active sites at electrode/electrolyte interface in solid state electrochemical devices.

References

[1] R. J. Chater, S. Carter, J. A. Kilner, and B. C. H. Steele, Solid State Ionics, **53-56** (1992) 859-867.

[2] J. A. Kilner, R.A. DeSouza, I. C. Fullarton, Solid State Ionics, **86-88** (1996) 703-709.

[3] T. Kawada, T. Horita, N. Sakai, H. Yokokawa, and M. Dokiya, Solid State Ionics, **79** (1995) 210.

[4] T. Horita, K. Yamaji, N. Sakai, M. Ishikawa, H. Yokokawa, T. Kawada, and M. Dokiya, Electrochemical and Solid-State Letters, **1** No.1 (1998), 4.

[5] T. Horita, K. Yamaji, M. Ishikawa, N. Sakai, H. Yokokawa, T. Kawada, T. Kato, J. Electrochem. Soc. **145** (1998) 3176.

A. Benninghoven, P. Bertrand, H.-N. Migeon and H.W. Werner (Editors).
Proceedings of the 12th International Conference on Secondary Ion Mass Spectrometry,
Brussels, Belgium, 5-11 September 1999
© 2000 Elsevier Science B.V. All rights reserved.

ADSORPTION OF ORGANIC INHIBITORS STUDIED BY TOF-SIMS AND XPS

C-O. A. Olsson[*], D. Léonard, P. Agarwal, H-J. Mathieu and D. Landolt

Laboratoire de Métallurgie Chimique (LMCH), Département des Matériaux, Ecole
Polytechnique Fédérale de Lausanne (EPFL), CH-1015 Lausanne - EPFL, Switzerland
[*]corresponding author: Dr C-O. A. Olsson (email: claes.olsson@epfl.ch)

1. Introduction

A large number of inhibitors have been developed for corrosion protection of mild steels. Recently, environmental concerns have led to the development of water-borne paints, which demand a higher level of corrosion protection due to their inherent sensibility to water exposure. This work concerns carboxylic acid inhibitors investigated on mild steels in near neutral media. To further understand the underlying mechanisms in corrosion inhibition, it is useful to study the steel surface with ToF-SIMS and XPS after different electrochemical treatments. A model for corrosion inhibition was proposed by Agarwal and Landolt [1] for the inhibitors studied in this paper, suggesting a competitive adsorption between inhibitor and anions on the steel surface.

If the inhibitor molecule contains a characteristic atom, quantification of XPS spectra can be straightforward. Studies on DMEA (2-dimethylamino-ethanol) have been performed by Rossi *et al* [2] and Brundle *et al* [3] who both used the nitrogen signal to determine the amount of inhibitor on the surface. Brundle also proved the combination of XPS and ToF-SIMS to be successful in the analysis of inhibitors on iron surfaces. In this study, an inhibitor with Br as a replacement to the normally used Cl or CH_3 functional groups was synthesised to allow for satisfactory XPS quantification.

On the other hand, Time-of-Flight Secondary Ion Mass Spectrometry (ToF-SIMS) was specifically used to identify the presence of the molecules at the steel surface. Moreover, thanks to the high mass molecular information of ToF-SIMS spectra, even the inhibitors intended for practical use could be detected.

2. Experimental Conditions

The inhibitor in this work belongs to the family of ω-benzoyl alcanoic acids, which have the structure indicated in Figure 1. R is a functional group and m indicates the chain length. The molecular structure and inhibiting properties of the family of compounds can be varied by changing R and m. In this paper, R was either a CH_3 group, a Cl or a Br atom; m = 2. The acid group was neutralised with a stoichiometric amount of N-ethyl-morpholine to obtain the corresponding salt.

Samples were made of low carbon steel plates and given a surface finish using a 3µm diamond paste. After polishing, the samples were ultrasonically rinsed in hexane, acetone, iso-propanol and water. The final polishing step and subsequent rinsing was performed immediately before the electrochemical experiments.

Reference samples of dried-up inhibitor, having a thickness in the μm range, were prepared. The electrochemically treated samples were prepared by a cathodic polarisation at -1.6 V (vs. Hg/Hg$_2$SO$_4$) for 2 minutes followed by 1 min at a potential in the active or passive region. At open circuit, the samples were prepared by leaving them in the electrolyte for 5 minutes after cathodic polarisation. The electrolyte used was a 5 mM inhibitor solution. After polarisation experiments, the samples were taken out of the electrochemical cell and then dried and stored for 14-24 hours, before being introduced into UHV, either as-polarised, or as-rinsed in deionised water.

The ToF-SIMS system used in this study was a commercial ToF-SIMS mass spectrometer (described in detail elsewhere [5-6]) from PHI-EVANS (PHI-EVANS Trift 1). The DC 15 keV ^{69}Ga$^+$ ion beam current was pulsed at 5 kHz repetition rate (pulse width of about 7 ns (unbunched)). All spectra were acquired in the high resolution mode (bunched beam). The total ion dose for a 5 min spectrum was below $1 \cdot 10^{12}$ ions/cm^2, which is within the so-called 'static' SIMS conditions.

X-ray Photoelectron Spectroscopy (XPS) measurements were performed with a PHI 5500 XPS system, using a monochromatised Al Kα X-ray source. The analysed area had a diameter of about 800 μm and the spectra were recorded at an analyser angle of 45° to the sample surface. No sputtering was performed prior to analysis. For quantification of the oxide film composition, PHI sensitivity factors supplied with the system were used. The quantification was checked on a thick Br-tagged reference sample. The nominal composition for the inhibitor C$_{10}$O$_3$H$_9$Br, normalised without hydrogen is 71.4 - 21.4 - 7.1 at% for C, O and Br, respectively. The corresponding values obtained with XPS were 71.7 - 21.1 - 7.2 at%.

3. Results and Discussion

There are several mechanisms by which inhibitors decrease the corrosion of steel. An important piece of information when investigating these mechanisms is to estimate the amount of inhibitor adsorbed on the surface. This information is preferably obtained using XPS, since the inhibitor coverage is normally found to be fractions of a monolayer. Moreover, along with the quantification of adsorbed inhibitor, it is also desirable to find out if and how the inhibitor is bound to the surface. This information could be found by studying ToF-SIMS peak relative intensities.

As can be seen in Figure 2, the overall fraction of inhibitor in the surface oxide film is of the order of 2-4 at%. Active polarisations gave larger amounts of inhibitor on the surface. As the electrochemical equivalence between this molecule and those intended for practical use has been established by recording polarisation curves [4], these results are consistent with the competitive adsorption model from Agarwal and Landolt [1]. A more detailed discussion on the XPS results has been done elsewhere [4].

ToF-SIMS also permits a comparison of the Br tagged inhibitor and those intended for practical use. Molecular peaks corresponding to (M-H)$^-$ have been identified for the three molecules (Br tagged and Cl or CH$_3$ containing molecules). Characteristic fragments have also been observed. ToF-SIMS intensity ratios of C$_{10}$H$_8$O$_3$X$^-$ and C$_9$H$_8$OX$^-$ (where X= Br, Cl or CH$_3$) are compared in Figure 3 for the dried-up thick sample and for the surface polarised to open circuit potentials (OCP). For inhibitors containing Br and Cl, there is a marked change in the intensity ratio for the dried-up inhibitors compared to the electrochemically adsorbed inhibitors. For the inhibitor containing the CH$_3$ group, the corresponding difference is hardly

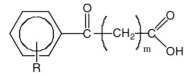

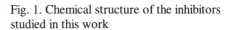

Fig. 1. Chemical structure of the inhibitors studied in this work

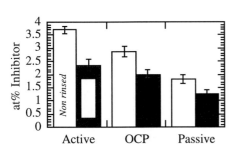

Fig. 2. Inhibitor adsorption on surfaces polarised to active, open circuit and passive potentials. The highest amount of inhibitor is found for active polarisations.

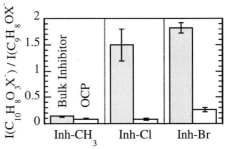

Fig. 3. $C_{10}H_8O_3X^-$ / $C_9H_8OX^-$ (where X= Br, Cl or CH_3) intensity ratios for the dried-up inhibitors and for inhibitors adsorbed from an electrolyte at open circuit potential.

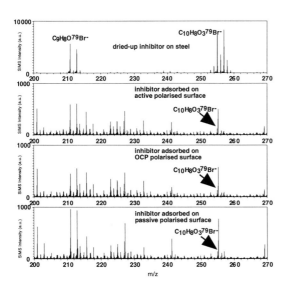

Fig. 4. Negative ion mass spectra for the mass range 200-270 amu. The dried-up inhibitor (top) shows a strong $(M-H)^-$ peak, as opposed to spectra obtained for active, OCP and passive polarisations (top-bottom).

seen. One possible explanation to this difference is that the ionisation cross-section for negative secondary ions is much higher for molecules containing Cl or Br, which both show a high electronegativity. This is confirmed by positive mode results where $C_{10}H_8O_3X^+$ and $C_9H_8OX^+$ are only observed for the inhibitor containing the CH_3 group. Consequently, it seems reasonable to assume that the functional group is not affecting the fragmentation of the inhibitor in ToF-SIMS analysis.

Figure 4 displays the 200-270 amu mass range of the negative ion spectra acquired on the dried-up reference samples and on the various electrochemically treated samples. As already observed in Figure 3, $C_{10}H_8O_3Br^-$, corresponding to the entire inhibitor molecule $(M-H)^-$, shows a strong presence in the mass spectrum from the dried-up inhibitor sample. Figure 4 illustrates that the marked change in the relative peak intensities observed for the surface polarised to open circuit potentials - the intensity corresponding to the intact inhibitor molecule drops significantly - is observed for all electrochemical treatments. This could indicate that the carboxyl group plays a vital role in the adsorption to the iron substrate. Through studies of binding shifts in the IR-spectrum, a chemical bond involving the carboxyl group was suggested by Tejedor-Tejedor et al [7]. Still, it is possible that this effect is caused by oxide deposited during sample transfer from the cell to the solution.

4. Conclusions

Satisfactory quantification results were obtained using XPS. The use of a Br tagged molecule also illustrated the role played by the molecule when in contact with polarised samples. ToF-SIMS relative peak intensities for the entire inhibitor and for fragments proved markedly different for a bulk layer of dried-up inhibitor when compared to electrochemically treated samples. The surface analysis results are not contradictory to a competitive adsorption model.

Acknowledgements

Part of this work was funded by Fonds National Suisse, Bern. The authors are also grateful to Dr M. Frey from CIBA Specialty Chemicals, Basel, for financial support, inhibitor material and useful discussions.

References

[1]   P. Agarwal and D. Landolt, Corr. Sci. 40 (1998) 673
[2]   A. Rossi, B. Elsener, M. Textor and N. D. Spencer, Analusis Magazine 25 (1997) M30
[3]   C. R. Brundle, M. Gunze, U. Mäder and N. Blank, Surf. Interface Anal. 24 (1996) 549
[4]   C-O. A. Olsson, P. Agarwal, M. Frey and D. Landolt, submitted to Corr. Sci.
[5]   B.W. Schueler, Microsc. Microanalysis Microstructure 3 (1992) 119
[6]   K. Franzreb, H.J. Mathieu and D. Landolt, Surf. Interface Anal. 23 (1995) 641
[7]   M. I. Tejedor-Tejedor, E. C. Yost and M. A. Anderson, Langmuir 6 (1990) 979

A. Benninghoven, P. Bertrand, H.-N. Migeon and H.W. Werner (Editors).
Proceedings of the 12th International Conference on Secondary Ion Mass Spectrometry,
Brussels, Belgium, 5-11 September 1999

QUANTITATIVE SIMS OF DIAMOND FILMS AND COATINGS OF DIAMOND-CARBIDE COMPOUND MATERIALS

P.Willich and U.Wischmann
Fraunhofer Institute for Surface Engineering and Thin Films
Bienroder Weg 54E, D-38108 Braunschweig, Germany
e-mail: willich@ist.fhg.de

1. Introduction

SIMS is applied to the chemical characterization of polycrystalline diamond films prepared by CVD processes using thermal [1] or microwave-plasma[2] activation of a gas phase composed of H_2 and hydrocarbons with impurity concentrations of N_2 and O_2. The most important impurities in CVD diamond coatings are therefore H, N and O. In the case of thermal activation by Ta-filaments also Ta may be incorporated into the coating material. Of particular interest would be to study the local distribution of impurity elements, i.e., the possibility of enhancement at grain boundaries. CVD-diamond films can be doped with B by adding suitable metal-organic precursors to the reactive gas mixture [2]. In a similar way diamond-carbide (e.g., TiC) compound materials are deposited, with improved adhesion properties as compared with "pure" diamond.

The advantages of MCs^+-SIMS (Cs^+ primary ions, MCs^+ molecular secondary ions, M stands for the element of interest) in respect of quantification are widely recognized [3,4]. MCs^+-SIMS can be applied to the determination of metal impurities in diamond, e.g., B, Ti and Ta, in the case of metals the MCs^+ ion yields are sufficient to obtain sensities of 10 ppmat (~10^{19} at/cm^3) or even better. However, for typical electronegative elements, e.g., H, N and O, the yields of MCs^+ secondary ions are very low, consequently trace analysis of these elements is not practicable.

This leads to the use of Cs^+ primary ions and M^- secondary ions. For N in a C-matrix the most sensitive way of SIMS analysis is to monitor CN^- molecular ions. The high yields for M^- species enables one to apply high mass resolution in combination with local analysis, at least on the scale of a few microns. For special diamond coatings with large crystallites, it should be possible to separate between intrinsic impurity concentrations and incorporation of certain elements at grain boundaries.

2. Experimental

SIMS-experiments were carried out in a CAMECA IMS5f ion microscope employing a Cs^+ primary ion beam of 6 keV (MCs^+ secondary ions) or 14.5 keV (M^- secondary ions) impact energy. For depth profiling the primary beam (beam current 80 nA) was scanned across an area of 150x150 µm and the secondary ions were accepted from a circular area of 30 µm in diameter. Under these conditions the sputter rates on polycrystalline diamond films are about 1µm/h for 6 keV impact energy and about 2.5 µm/h for 14.5 keV impact energy. For local analysis the primary ion beam (beam current 40 nA) was scanned across an area of 80x80 µm and M^- secondary ions were accepted from a circular area of about 5 µm. M^--SIMS was carried out under conditions of high mass resolution (~7000) to minimize the mass interference of $^{12}C^{14}N$ with $^{12}C^{14}C$ and $^{12}C^{12}CH_2$. For MCs^+-SIMS the mass resolution was about 300. The pressure in the target chamber amounted to 6-8 x 10^{-10} Torr with the Cs-beam in operation.

3. Results and Discussion

Table 1. Relative sensitivity factors (RSF's) for MCs$^+$-SIMS and M$^-$-SIMS derived from standards of modified DLC (diamond-like carbon) coating materials . Quantitative analysis of minor components in CVD-diamond as compared with the results of ERD and EPMA. RSF$_{M/C}$ = (I$_M$ x c$_C$) / (I$_C$ x c$_M$). Reference element is C.

Element	Standard	RSF (MCs$^+$)	RSF (M$^-$)	Diamond-Test Ref. [ppmat]	MCs$^+$ [ppmat]	M$^-$ [ppmat]
H	DLC-15.5 at% H (*)	0.72	0.64	2300(*)	3800	2200
B	DLC+8.7 at% B (**)	5.1	0.07	80(*)	75	90
C		1.0	1.0			
N	DLC+4.5 at% N (**)	0.68	7.2 (CN)	10(*)	40	8
O	DLC+2.2 at% O (**)	0.75	1.2	120(*)	140	110
Ti	DLC+9.7 at% Ti (**)	82		70(**)	65	
Ta	DLC+8.4 at% Ta (**)	35		450(**)	430	

(*) Reference analysis by ERD   (**) Reference analysis by EPMA

3.1 Quantitative Analysis

Table 1 shows relative sensitivity factors for the determination of some trace elements in diamond. Coatings of diamond-like carbon (DLC) containing relatively high concentrations of "additional elements" (Tab.1) were used as standards, the concentrations of B, N, O, Ti and Ta were defined by Electron Probe Microanalysis (EPMA)[5]. A DLC-coating with 15.5 at% H, defined by Elastic Recoil Detection (ERD) was applied to derive RSF's for H [3]. The accuracy of SIMS quantification can be estimated from analysis of diamond coatings for which the impurity concentrations were defined by ERD or EPMA. The concentrations for H, B, N and O obtained by using negative secondary ions (M$^-$ -SIMS) are in good agreement with the results of ERD (Tab.1: diamond-test), including the determination of N (as CN$^-$) at a level of 10 ppmat.

MCs$^+$-SIMS enables reliable analysis of B, O, Ti and Ta (Tab.1: diamond-test).

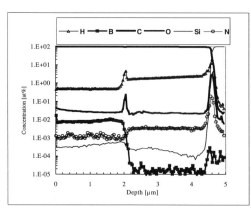

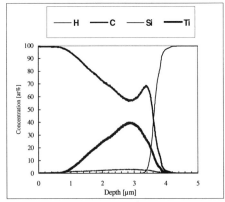

Fig.1. Depth profile (M$^-$ secondary ions) of a diamond double layer deposited on Si. The upper layer is doped with about 100 ppmat of B.

Fig.2. Depth profile (MCs$^+$ secondary ions) of diamond –TiC compound layer on Si-substrate

The concentration for H (3800 ppmat) based on HCs^+ is too high (Tab.1: diamond-test) as compared to M^--SIMS (2200 ppmat) and ERD (2300 ppmat). An explanation may be the influence of the very strong ^{133}Cs mass line, which causes a background intensity for the mass 134 of HCs^+. Also the N-concentration obtained by using NCs^+ (40 ppmat) is too high (ERD: 10 ppmat, M^--SIMS: 8 ppmat), probably this is due to the background intensity caused by the mass interference NCs^+-CH_2Cs^+. The signal intensity of NCs^+ for about 10 ppmat of N in diamond is of the order of 1 cps, whereas CN^- secondary ions provide an intensity of about 1000 cps.

3.2 Depth Profiling

A depth profile (based on M^- secondary ions) of a diamond double layer deposited on Si is given in Fig.1. The surface layer shows a very homogeneous doping with B at a level of 100 ppmat (~$2x10^{19}$ at/cm^3), a similar value (110 ppmat) was obtained by MCs^+ secondary ions. The bottom layer should contain no B, the visible background (Fig.1) in a matrix of diamond corresponds to a concentration of 0.1 ppmat. Typically, polycrystalline diamond coatings exhibit a very rough surface which makes high resolution depth profiling very difficult. Nevertheless, enhancement of H, N and O is visible at the diamond/Si interface and also a narrow enhancement of H and O at the interface between the two diamond coatings. After deposition of the bottom layer and before deposition of the surface layer, the sample was exposed to air for some weeks. This obviously causes oxidation, the oxide interlayer may be a reason for the poor adhesion of the the surface layer to the bottom layer.

Fig.2 exhibits a depth profile (MCs^+-SIMS) of a diamond-TiC compound layer on a substrate of Si. Analysis by X-ray diffraction and Raman-spectroscopy confirms that the coating is a mixture of diamond and TiC, the size of the crystallites is of the order of 1 μm. At the applied growth conditions, the maximum concentration of Ti occurs at a distance of about 1 μm from the substrate.The maximum concentration of Ti (40 at%), which was confirmed by EPMA on a polished cross section, corresponds to a mixture of 80% TiC / 20% diamond. The concept of diamond - metal carbide interlayers, followed by a smooth transition to "pure" diamond results in a significantly improved adhesion to certain substrate materials (e.g. Si or WC).

Fig. 3. SEM-micrograph of diamond coating with large crystallites. Position of SIMS-linescan (Fig.4) is marked.

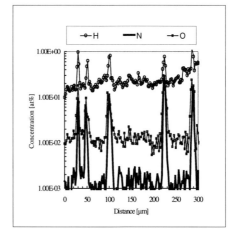

Fig. 4. Linescan (position marked in Fig.3) of elements H, N and O. Enhancement of these elements at grain boundaries is visible.

3.3. Local analysis

Under particular experimental conditions it is possible to grow diamond films with crystallites having a size of 50-200 µm (Fig.3). Such materials offer the possibility to study the local distribution of impurity elements by SIMS. Fig.4 shows a linescan over several large and relatively smooth crystallites, the position of the linescan (total distance 300 µm) is marked in Fig.3. The primary beam was scanned over an area of 80x80 µm, the secondary ions (M-, high mass resolution) were accepted from a central circular area of 5µm in diameter, and the stage was mechanically moved by steps of 2 µm. Before starting data accumulation (counting time 30 s /element), each point of analysis was pre-sputtered by the scanning ion beam for about 30 min, this corresponds to sputter removal of at least 0.5 µm of material. Therefore influence of non-specific surface material can be excluded. The surface was coated with Au, the SEM-micrograph of Fig.3 shows a weak contrast between the non-analyzed surface (Au-coating) and the central region (Au-coating removed) where the scanned area of the ion beam was linearly moved over a distance of 300 µm. There is a clear correlation between the position of grain boundaries (Fig.3) and the relatively sharp local enhancement of the impurity elements (Fig.4), particularly for N, where the intrinsic concentrations are very low (~10 ppmat). The enhancement of N at grain boundaries reaches a level of about 1000 ppmat, this may be an underestimation if one assumes that the dimensions of a grain boundary are probably much smaller than the size of the "probing area" (about 5 µm in diameter). H seems to be mostly located within the grains, the relative enhancement at grain boundaries is fairly weak. Oxygen exhibits concentrations of ~100 ppmat within the crystallites, the enhancement at grain boundaries reaches a level of 1000 ppmat.

4. Conclusions

SIMS based on MCs^+ secondary ions is applied to the determination of metal impurities, e.g.,Ta, in CVD diamond coatings and depth profiling of diamond-TiC compound materials. In the case of non-metal impurities (H, N, O,) quantitative analysis based on MCs^+-SIMS is restricted to relatively high concentrations (>0.5 at% for H, >0.1 at% for N and O) because of the low ion yields and problems of mass interference. Only the use of M⁻ (in the case of N: CN⁻) secondary ions in combination with high mass resolution enables reliable analysis of H (0.1-1at%), N and O (10-500 ppmat%) in diamond coatings. Quantification in the case of M⁻-SIMS is possible with an accuracy of about 20 % rel. when using standards of DLC (diamond-like carbon). The detection limits for B in diamond prove to be 10 ppmat (MCs^+) and 0.1 ppmat (~10^{16} at/cm³) when using B⁻ secondary ions. The high yields for M⁻ species created by Cs primary ions enables one to study the local distribution of H, N and C with a lateral resolution of about 5 µm. It can be shown that concentrations within the diamond crystallites are low (N~10 ppmat, O~100 ppmat) and that significant local enhancement (N,O~1000 ppmat) is clearly correlated with grain boundaries.

5. References

[1] C.-P. Klages and L.Schäfer, in Springer Series in Materials Processing – Low Pressure Synthetic Diamond, ed. by B. Dischler a. C. Wild (Springer, Berlin-Heidelberg, 1998), p.86

[2] X.Jiang, P.Willich, M.Paul, and C.-P. Klages, J.Mater.Res.,Vol.14, No.8 (1999), in print

[3] P.Willich, in Secondary Ion Mass Spectrometry SIMS X, ed. by A.Benninghoven et al. (Wiley,Chichester, 1997), p.609

[4] P.Willich and R.Bethke, in Secondary Ion Mass Spectrometry SIMS XI, ed. by G. Gillen et al. (Wiley,Chichester, 1998), p.991

[5] P.Willich and U.Wischmann, Mikrochim.Acta [Suppl.] 15 (1998), 141

A. Benninghoven, P. Bertrand, H.-N. Migeon and H.W. Werner (Editors).
Proceedings of the 12th International Conference on Secondary Ion Mass Spectrometry,
Brussels, Belgium, 5-11 September 1999
© 2000 Elsevier Science B.V. All rights reserved.

A SIMS AND NRA STUDY OF O DIFFUSION IN YSZ AND EPITAXIAL FILMS OF La$_{0.5}$Sr$_{0.5}$CoO$_{3-x}$ ON YSZ SINGLE CRYSTALS

P.A.W. van der Heide[1], N. Joos[3], C.L. Chen[2], C.W. Chu[2], J.R. Liu[2], W.K. Chu[2], C.A. Mims[3] and A.J. Jacobson[1].

[1]Materials Research Science and Engineering Centre (MRSEC) and
[2]Texas Center for Superconductivity, University of Houston, Houston 77204, Texas, U.S.A
[3]Department of Chemistry, University of Toronto, Toronto, Ontario, M5S 3E5, Canada.

1. Introduction

The power output available from high temperature solid oxide fuel cells operating on natural gas depends on the specific cell design and on a number of factors associated with the material properties[1]. Slow reaction rates for oxygen reduction at the cathode or hydrocarbon oxidation at the anode may cause significant power losses. Rates for bulk transport of oxygen ions through the electrolyte and across electrolyte-electrode interfaces may also limit performance. It is difficult to separate the relative contributions of the various rate processes in practical devices that are based on dense electrolytes and porous electrodes. Consequently, issues such as the relative importance of interfacial transfer and surface reaction rates are unresolved. Model systems based on epitaxial thin dense electrode films grown on single crystal electrolyte substrates provide one approach to develop the understanding of these fundamental questions.

Specifically, we have investigated films of the oxygen electrode material La$_{0.5}$Sr$_{0.5}$CoO$_{3-x}$ grown by laser deposition on <100> oriented single crystals of yttria stabilized zirconia (YSZ) electrolyte (Y$_2$O$_3$ = 9.5 mol%). Infusion of ^{18}O into the sample and subsequent depth profile analysis by Secondary Ion Mass Spectrometry (SIMS) and Nuclear Reaction Analysis (NRA) enabled the simultaneous determination of four transfer coefficients (bulk diffusion coefficients for La$_{0.5}$Sr$_{0.5}$CoO$_{3-x}$ and YSZ and gas-solid and solid-solid interface transfer rate constants). SIMS and NRA analysis of YSZ single crystals was also carried out to compare and extend results from previous studies.

2. Experimental

A series of YSZ samples with and with out La$_{0.5}$Sr$_{0.5}$CoO$_{3-x}$ films infused at T=250°C, 275°C, 300°C, 325°C and 350°C for 15, 30 and 45 minute durations in a 1-20% C^{18}O$_2$/balance argon gas atmosphere were prepared. C^{18}O$_2$ was used since CO$_2$ has a higher surface exchange rate than O$_2$, thus, enabling the measurement of ^{18}O tracer profiles to lower temperatures than previously reported[3,4].

^{18}O infusion was carried out by placing the samples in a quartz tube reactor. This was heated to the required temperature whereupon it was evacuated to 10^{-3} Torr and immediately backfilled with isotope labeled gas to a pressure of 122 kPa. To avoid isotope depletion in the exchange gas a small flow (1.5 mL/min) of preheated isotope labeled gas was maintained over the sample for the duration of the experiment. The quartz reactor tube was then removed from the oven and quenched to room temperature while maintaining the gas flow. Preheating prior to dosing and rapid quenching ensured accurate dosing times to within ±10 seconds. This eliminated the need for anneal time corrections required by other methods[2]. Further details can be found elsewhere[5].

SIMS analysis was performed on a Phi 6600 instrument using a 5 keV Cs$^+$ ion beam rastered over a 250x250 µm area. The incident angel is 60° with respect to sample normal. Positive secondary ions of ^{16}O, ^{18}O, ^{88}Sr, ^{89}Y, and ^{94}Zr, and their associated MCs$^+$ signals, emanating from the central 50% of these craters were recorded. These conditions were used since (a) the positive secondary ions provided sufficient intensities, (b) improved charge stabilization stability was noted, and (c) an O_2^+ primary beam (typically used for Sr, Y, and Zr analysis) would preclude the possibility of oxygen analysis. Charge stabilization was instigated through electron beam co-bombardment of the analyzed region. Sputter rates were defined through stylus profilometry measurements of the SIMS Craters using a Dektak IIA profilometer.

Nuclear Reaction Analysis, which involves bombardment with a proton beam and the detection of α particles produced during the subsequent ^{18}O(p,α)^{15}N nuclear reaction, was carried out using a 2x1.7 MV Tandem accelerator. The main amplifier was a Canberra Spectroscopy Amplifier model 2020 with amplified pulse and pile-up rejection signal to a Nuclear Data ADC 582 in conjunction with a ND 9000 multichannel analyzer. All samples were carbon coated prior to NRA analysis, to avoid sample charging problems. Further details can be found elsewhere[6].

3. Results and discussion

Shown in Fig. 1 is a representative SIMS depth profile of ^{16}O, ^{18}O, and ^{89}Y, and their MCs$^+$ populations from the YSZ substrate exposed to 5 mol% C^{18}O$_2$ for 30 minutes at 250°C. The fact that the M$^+$ and MCs$^+$ track each other reveals that the M$^+$ secondary ions, I, are not perturbed by matrix effects during the analysis of these samples. ^{16}O and ^{18}O concentrations can thus be defined over each cycle of the depth profile via:

$$[^{18}O] = I(^{18}O^+)/(I(^{16}O+) + I(^{18}O+)) \times [O_{tot}]/100 \qquad (1)$$

where [O$_{tot}$] is oxygen concentration in atomic % (the stoichiometry was confirmed via XPS). These ^{18}O concentrations agree well with NRA data as can be seen in Fig. 2.

This data can also be plotted as ^{18}O/^{16}O ratios defined directly from measured intensities, as illustrated in Fig.3. Here, a ~0.3 µm La$_{0.5}$Sr$_{0.5}$CoO$_{3-x}$ film on YSZ exposed to a 15% C^{18}O$_2$ gas atmosphere for 30 minutes at 300°C was analyzed. Again, good agreement is seen between the two techniques. The only difference lies in the superior depth resolution provided by SIMS at greater depths (see the steeper drop off of the ^{18}O signal following the La$_{0.5}$Sr$_{0.5}$CoO$_{3-x}$–YSZ interface in Fig. 3). This steep drop off also reveals that recoil implantation, also active during SIMS analysis, plays a negligible role.

Assuming a constant gas phase isotope concentration throughout the experiment, the rate of ^{18}O transport across the solid/gas interface is directly proportional to the difference between the gas and oxide surface concentrations, C; this is described as:

$$k(C_g - C_s) = -D \left| \partial C(x)/\partial x \right|_{x=0} \qquad (2)$$

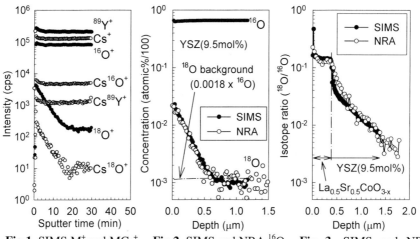

Fig 1. SIMS M⁺ and MCs⁺ depth profile from YSZ (30min at 250°C).

Fig 2. SIMS and NRA ^{16}O and ^{18}O concentration vs depth for YSZ from Fig. 1.

Fig 3. SIMS and NRA $^{18}O/^{16}O$ ratios vs depth for La$_{0.5}$Sr$_{0.5}$CoO$_{3-x}$ on YSZ.

where the first order rate constant, k, is the surface exchange coefficient, and D is the diffusion coefficient. Equation 2 is used as the boundary condition for the overall exchange process which is modeled by one dimensional diffusion into a semi-infinite medium[7]. The resulting profile is given by:

$$C'(x)=(C(x)-C_{bg})/(C_g-C_{bg})=\mathrm{erfc}(x/2(Dt)^{\frac{1}{2}})-\exp(hx+h^2(Dt)^{\frac{1}{2}})\mathrm{erfc}((x/(Dt)^{\frac{1}{2}})+h(Dt)^{\frac{1}{2}}) \quad (3)$$

where $C(x)$ is the isotope fraction, C_{bg} is the natural abundance of ^{18}O in the sample, C_g is the isotope concentration in the gas phase, x is the depth, h is k/D, and t is time. The transport properties (k and D) were calculated by fitting SIMS and NRA diffusion profiles to Equation 3 using MathCad's non-linear least squares regression algorithm.

The diffusion coefficients obtained from SIMS and NRA are shown in Fig. 4 along with previously published diffusion coefficients (triangles and diamonds) for 9.5 mol% YSZ dosed using an $^{18}O_2$ exchange gas[3,4]. The diffusion coefficient was found to have an activation energy of 114 kJ/mol (1.2 eV) compared to 84 kJ/mol (0.9 eV) for Manning's oxygen self-diffusion results[3], 106 kJ/mol (1.1 eV) for Manning's AC impedance results[3] and 114 kJ/mol (1.2 eV) for lower temperature D$_{slow}$ data measured by Solmon[4]. Manning and Solmon both used $^{18}O_2$ as opposed to a C$^{18}O_2$ exchange gas. Extrapolation from this previously published data[4] also indicates that the exchange gas has a negligible effect on the Diffusion coefficient.

Shown in the inset of Fig. 4, are the surface exchange coefficients obtained from samples dosed in 5% C$^{18}O_2$ along with previously published data for 9.5 mol% YSZ infused with $^{18}O_2$[3]. The difference in the two data sets reveals that CO$_2$ has a much faster surface exchange rate than O$_2$ resulting in higher surface concentrations at the same temperature. This is as expected on the basis of the differing exchange mechanisms predicted for these gases on these surfaces. The surface exchange coefficients for C$^{18}O_2$ were defined to be 149 and 154 kJ/mol respectively.

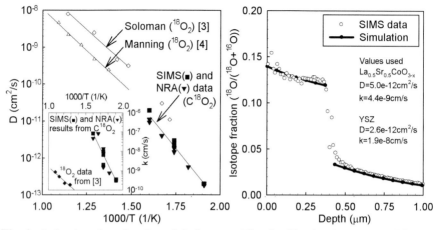

Fig 4. Arrhenius plots for D and k (in inset) in YSZ (9.5 mol%).

Fig 5. Simulated oxygen diffusion profile across $La_{0.5}Sr_{0.5}CoO_{3-x}$ on YSZ.

Simulations of the transport of ^{18}O through epitaxial films of $La_{0.5}Sr_{0.5}CoO_{3-x}$ on YSZ were also carried out. Preliminary results from the data presented in Fig. 3 are shown in Fig. 5 along with the derived k and D values. The value of D for YSZ is in agreement with the data presented in Fig.4. The value of D for $La_{0.5}Sr_{0.5}CoO_{3-x}$ is also in the expected range, but may be underestimated. Significantly, these results reveal a notable transfer resistance (diffusion barrier) at the $La_{0.5}Sr_{0.5}CoO_{3-x}$ –YSZ interface, hence the sharp drop in the ^{18}O profiles following the interface.

4. Conclusions

SIMS analysis of the positive secondary ions of ^{16}O and ^{18}O as a function of depth is shown to be an effective method for extracting D and k values from YSZ and $La_{0.5}Sr_{0.5}CoO_{3-x}$. This was validated via NRA. Use of $C^{18}O_2$ as opposed to an O_2 exchange gas also allowed for the determination of D and k values to lower temperatures than previously possible. Simulations of the transport of oxygen across $La_{0.5}Sr_{0.5}CoO_{3-x}$ on YSZ revealed the presence of a significant interfacial diffusion barrier.

Acknowledgements

This work was funded primarily by the MRSEC program of the National Science Foundation under award number 9632667.

References

[1] S. Kim, Y.L. Yang, A.J. Jacobsen, B. Abelles, *Solid State Ionics*, 121, (1999), 31.
[2] J.A. Kilner, B.C.H. Steele, *Solid State Ionics* **12**, 89 (1984).
[3] P.S. Manning, J.D. Sirman, R.A. DeSouza, and J.A. Kilner, *Solid State Ionics* **100**, 1 (1997).
[4] H. Solmon, *PhD thesis*, Université Paris, 1992.
[5] N. Joos, P.A.W. van der Heide, J.R. Liu, R. Christoffersen, W.K. Chu, C.A. Mims, *MRS proceedings*, in press, (1999).
[6] J.R. Liu, Y.P. Li, Q.Y. Chen, X.T. Cui, R. Christoffersen, A. Jacobson, and W.K. Chu, *Nucl. Instru.& Meth. Phy. Res. B.*, **138**, 1306 (1998).
[7] J. Crank. *The mathematics of diffusion* (Oxford University Press, Oxford, 1975).

A. Benninghoven, P. Bertrand, H.-N. Migeon and H.W. Werner (Editors).
Proceedings of the 12th International Conference on Secondary Ion Mass Spectrometry,
Brussels, Belgium, 5-11 September 1999

CAPABILITIES OF STATIC SIMS FOR INORGANIC SPECIATION

R. Van Ham, A. Adriaens*, L. Van Vaeck and F. Adams
University of Antwerp, Department of Chemistry, Universiteitsplein 1, B-2610
Antwerp, Belgium. *Corresponding author: mieke@uia.ua.ac.be

1. Introduction

A lot of practical problems or questions in health and material science, such as the toxicological impact of given compounds in a tissue, can be solved by knowing the molecular composition of the analyte. In this respect static SIMS (S-SIMS) emerges as a promising tool. The main merit of this technique resides in the capability to perform speciation of inorganic compounds at microscopical level on the surface of solid samples. The term molecular "speciation" refers to the detection of molecule-specific information, not just element ratios. Up to now little has been published on inorganic speciation, this in contrast to the amount of data on organic compounds. Much of the systematic work dates back to the seventies [1,2,3]. Mass spectral libraries have become available recently [4,5] but contain only a selected range of inorganic compounds. The work on inorganic compounds with static SIMS in different fields has been reviewed recently [6,7].

Our research project focuses on the feasibility of S-SIMS for molecular speciation in micro-objects, such as aerosol particles in the μm size range. However success is not obvious because of the trade off between lateral resolution of the primary ion beam, secondary ion yield, detection sensitivity and static ion dose. Therefore, the purpose of this paper is to assess the influence of the primary ion dose on the relative intensity of diagnostic ions to be used for speciation. This has required the elaboration of a suitable preparation method yielding samples that are representative for aerosols. Specifically we will discuss the method of aerosol spraying and cascade impaction as an alternative to pressing pellets.

2. Experimental

2.1 Sample Preparation

The binary salts used for our experiments were LiCl, NaCl, KCl, CuCl, NaBr, KBr, NaI and KI. All were of analytical grade and were used without further purification.

As to the aerosol spraying procedure, solutions of pure compounds (~ 0.2g) were prepared in 50% methanol/ 50% H_2O. The solution was sprayed on a flat substrate (Al-foil and Si-wafer) with an airbrush (Badger, model 200, Illinois) under a nitrogen pressure of approximately 1 bar. The substrate was mounted in a Berner impactor for 10 minutes. The aperture of the airbrush was adjusted for a spray diameter of about 1 cm on a glass at a distance of 5 cm. This avoided a large amount of aerosols on the substrate and ensured that the formed aerosols could dry during the flight time. The aerosol passed first through a flow tube of about 42 cm before they were collected. The airflow was kept constant by mounting a vacuum pump behind the impactor. The vacuum pump had a nominal flow rate of ~ 40 l/min that becomes ~26 l/min with the Berner impactor attached between the flow tube and the pump.

Tests were done with Al-foil and Si-wafer as a substrate. The substrates were chosen because of their flatness and their conductivity so charging of the samples during analysis caused no problem [8]. The substrates were cut into smaller pieces to fit the sample holder. Also the Berner impaction plate was modified so that a Si-wafer could be attached by double-sided tape without disturbing the airflow. The advantage of this sample preparation is that the coverage of aerosols on the Si substrate occurs in small spots, which are relatively flat. In addition the surface coverage can be easily controlled by the spraying time.

A second method to prepare the binary salts consisted of pressing the powders into pellets (die, pressure ~5 tons/cm^2). The pellets were ~ 1 mm thick and had a diameter of ~ 13 mm. In order to avoid the adsorption of water from the air, the pellets were stored in a dessicator under vacuum. Afterwards the pellets were broken. A small piece with a flat surface was mounted into the sample holder. Under these conditions the TOF-SIMS was able to reach a good vacuum of typically 5 x 10^{-6} mbar in a reasonable time.

2.2 TOF-SIMS analysis

The analyses were performed with a TOF-SIMS IV (Cameca, France) instrument, equipped with a Ga$^+$-liquid metal ion gun (Ga$^+$-LMIG). The gun (angle 45°) was operated at 25 keV beam voltage in the bunched mode with a pulse width of 20 ns. The analysed area was typically between 100x100 μm^2 and 300x300 μm^2. Under these conditions, the total primary ion dose for an analysis of 200 s was below 10^{12} ions/cm^2. Measurements were done on the most dense area of the aerosol spots. In the imaging mode the Ga$^+$- LMIG was used in the collimated mode with a pulse width of 200 ns. Sample charge compensation by flooding low energy electrons was only necessary for the pellets.

3. Results and discussion

A full description of the diagnostic ions in mass spectra of comprehensive series of binary salts (MY) is given elsewhere [9]. The qualitative information present in the positive and negative detection mode are found to be very systematic and can be subdivided in fragment ions (Y$^-$ and M$^+$), adduct ions (MY)$_n$.Y$^-$ and (MY)$_n$.M$^+$), molecular ion (MY$^-$ and MY$^+$), cluster ions with less structural specificity (MY.Y$_2^-$) and recombination clusters (Y$_2^-$, M$_2^+$, M$_2$O$^+$, MOH.M$^+$, YO$^-$, M$_3$O$^+$, HY.Y$^-$). Parallel to the analysis of inorganic binary salts, an investigation on oxides is carried out [10].

It was found that normalisation of the diagnostic adduct ion peaks must be done on a adduct instead of an elemental ion to allow identification of the analyte with acceptable certainty. Therefore the relative intensity ratios of these specific ions, e.g. (CuCl)$_2$.Cl$^-$ normalised on CuCl.Cl$^-$, will be used a guiding criterion to optimise sample preparation.

3.1 Optimisation of the sample preparation

As to the aerosol spraying method the substrate must be flat to facilitate the S-SIMS analysis, mechanically stable to allow easy manipulation and chemically inert. Especially the last requirement proved to be important. Specifically Al-foil, In-foil and Si-wafers were compared. All salts except KCl and NaCl readily attacked the Al-foil. Moreover CuCl reacted faster with the Al-foil when sprayed (in solution 50% H2O/50% methanol) on the foil then when deposited in powder form. Black spots (oxidation-reduction reactions) were already formed before the sample preparation was finished. NaI and LiCl only reacted after a few days or weeks. However we considered Al-foil no longer as sufficient inert.

The same problem existed with the In-foil, commonly used as substrate in SIMS experiments. Visible damage rapidly occurred when brought in contact with inorganic salts such as CuCl. According to Groenewold [11], spectra on In-foil contained ion peaks from InCl$_4^-$, InCl$_2^-$, InCl$_3^-$, In$_2$Cl$_7^-$, and In$_2$Cl$_8^-$ because In was transported onto the surface of the salt, either through the gas phase in vacuum, or by diffusion across the surface or through the bulk matrix of the Cu salts. As a result of the rapid visible damage In-foil was rejected as a possible substrate for the aerosol spraying. Therefore we preferred the use of Si-wafers which were not damaged visibly by any of the salts. Questions still remain about possible reactions that can occur between solid and substrate. However no positive nor negative spectra contained signals pointing to analyte-substrate reactions. The reproducibility of the relative peak intensities in mass spectra taken from different impaction spots is typically within 10 %. Note that the diameter of the collected particles was substantially larger than the specified cut off diameter of the impactor at the flow rate used. This pointed to recrystallisation after impaction that is not important for our study. Strikingly, more intense mass spectra were observed when the samples were prepared one day in advance and after preparation were stored in Petri dishes closed with tape.

Spectra taken on a pellet were more intense, maybe due to the absence of solvent residues, which are inevitable with former procedure, but reveal the same qualitative information. Making pellets is less time consuming but sample charging hampers analysis. Therefore, we have measured all samples on Si-wafer.

3.2 Ion dose and relative intensities, damage cross section

In a number of papers [12,13] it is stated that the molecular speciation information of the uppermost layer is lost under bombardment of the surface above the static limit. By increasing the primary ion dose there must therefore be a point where the intensity of the secondary ions gradually decreases, the damage cross section can be calculated.

The first step was to look how the peak intensities relative to a chosen adduct-ion peak were varying as a function of the ion dose. Figure 1 shows the ratios calculated for Cl_2^-,

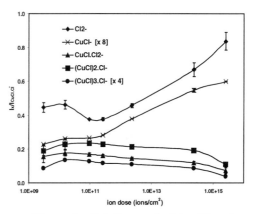

Figure 1. Relative peak intensities for CuCl as a function of primary ion dose with standard error bars

$CuCl^-$, $CuCl.Cl_2^-$, $(CuCl)_2.Cl^-$ and $(CuCl)_3.Cl^-$ over $CuCl.Cl^-$ for ion doses varying from 3.0×10^9 ions/cm^2 up to 2.6×10^{15} ions/cm^2. For the highest ion doses the primary ion current and the measuring time was kept constant and the raster area was changed while the measuring time for the lower ion doses was gradually decreased. Calculated ratios vary between 0.039 for $(CuCl)_3.Cl^-$ and 0.837 for Cl_2^- at the highest ion dose. An ion dose of $\sim 10^{11}$ ions/cm^2 optimises the contribution of structurally relevant adduct ions.

Time profiles of selected adduct ions and fragment ions showed no marked drop in ion intensity at primary ion doses of 10^{17} ions/cm^2. This permits imaging of secondary cluster ions on small areas (like aerosols). As an example a sample was prepared by means of spraying a solution of NaI in 50% H$_2$O/ 50% methanol on a Si-wafer. High-resolution images (Figure 2) were recorded in negative mode not only from the fragment ion I$^-$ but also from the molecular ion NaI$^-$ and the adduct ions NaI.I$^-$ and

862

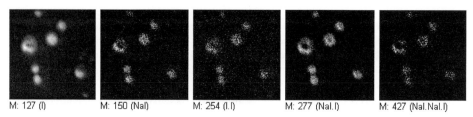

| M: 127 (I) | M: 150 (NaI) | M: 254 (I.I) | M: 277 (NaI.I) | M: 427 (NaI.NaI.I) |

Figure 2. 12.7 x 12.7 μm² images of NaI on Si-wafer

4. Conclusions

A search for the optimal substrate led to the use of Si-wafers for the preparation of the samples because they are not damaged visibly by any of the salts and display no charging effect. The flatness of the sample surface and the conductivity were optimal with spraying solutions on Si-wafer. When Si-wafers were chosen as substrate more cluster information and more intense peaks were recorded.

Both low and high ion doses were used to compare cluster ion formation and differences in secondary ion yields. The cluster ion yield showed to be more dependent on the sample preparation and storage conditions than on the ion dose. Molecular information remains present, even at ion doses of 10^{17} ions/cm². In future experiments, systematic analysis will be performed on mixtures of inorganic salts.

References

[1]   A. Benninghoven and A. Müller, Phys. Lett. 40A (2) (1972) 169.
[2]   A. Benninghoven and A. Müller, Surf. Sci. 39 (1973) 416.
[3]   H. W. Werner, Surf. Sci., 47 (1975) 301.
[4]   D. Briggs, A. Brown and J. C. Vickerman, John Wiley & Sons, Chichester, Handbook of Static Secondary Ion Mass Spectrometry (SIMS), 1989.
[5]   J. C. Vickerman, D. Briggs and A. Henderson, Surfacespectra Ltd, Manchester, The Static SIMS Library, Part 1, 1998.
[6]   L. Van Vaeck, A. Adriaens and R. Gijbels, Mass Spectrom. Rev. in press.
[7]   A. Adriaens, L. Van Vaeck and F. Adams, Mass Spectrom. Rev. in press.
[8]   H. –P. Ewinger, J. Goschnick and H. J. Ache, Fresenius J. Anal. Chem. 341 (1991) 17.
[9]   R.Van Ham, A. Adriaens, L. Van Vaeck, R. Gijbels and F. Adams, Nucl. Instrum. Meth. B, submitted.
[10]   E. Cuynen, L. Van Vaeck, R. Gijbels and P. Van Espen, Rapid. Commun. Mass. Spec. submitted.
[11]   G. S. Groenewold, Int. J. Mass Spectrom. 178 (1998) 19.
[12]   S. Tamaki, W. Sichtermann and A. Benninghoven, Jpn. J. Appl. Phys. 23 (5) (1984) 544.
[13]   D. Rading, R. Kersting and A. Benninghoven, *SIMS XI*, John Wiley & Sons, Chichester (1997), 455.

Acknowledgement

This work was supported in part by the Belgian Office for Scientific, Technical and Cultural Affairs (IUAP 4/10) and by FWO, Brussels, Belgium (research project G.0090.98). A. A. and L. V. V. are indebted to FWO, Belgium.

A. Benninghoven, P. Bertrand, H.-N. Migeon and H.W. Werner (Editors).
Proceedings of the 12th International Conference on Secondary Ion Mass Spectrometry,
Brussels, Belgium, 5-11 September 1999

SIMS ANALYSIS OF TITANIUM NITRIDE LAYER PREPARED BY PLASMA NITRIDING

M. Tamaki[1], Y. Tomii[2], N. Yamamoto[3], and H. Sumiya[4]

[1]Graduate School of Human Environmental Studies, Kyoto University, Kyoto 606-8501,
Japan, tamaki@helios.jinkan.kyoto-u.ac.jp
[2]Graduate School of Energy Science, Kyoto University, Kyoto 606-8501, Japan,
tomii@karma.mtl.kyoto-u.ac.jp
[3]Graduate School of Human Environmental Studies, Kyoto University, Kyoto 606-8501,
Japan, naoichi@helios.jinkan.kyoto-u.ac.jp
[4]Techno Research Laboratory, Hitachi Science Systems, Ltd., Ibaraki 312-8504, Japan,
sumiya_h_hk@cm.naka.hitachi.co.jp

1. Introduction

Plasma nitriding is one of the most effective methods for surface modification of titanium metal [1]. In this process, it is well known that nitrogen-hydrogen plasmas enhance the rate of nitriding. [2]. However, little is investigated on absorbed hydrogen in the specimen because surface analysis based on electron spectroscopy cannot directly detect hydrogen. In contrast, SIMS provides direct detection of hydrogen with high sensitivity. R.Bastasz has developed a method to observe hydrogen in pure titanium, which consists of monitoring the ratio of TiH^+ to Ti^+ using Ar^+ as a primary ion [3]. However, the distinction of titanium hydride ion from atomic titanium ion of the next heavier titanium isotope needs complicated calculation because titanium has five stable isotopes with adjacent masses (^{46}Ti: 8.0%, ^{47}Ti: 7.3%, ^{48}Ti: 73.8%, ^{49}Ti: 5.5%, and ^{50}Ti: 5.4%). In the present work, another approach using SIMS was carried out to obtain hydrogen distribution in the specimen. Our aim was to clarify the behavior of hydrogen in the nitrided titanium microscopically.

2. Experimental

Specimens were sliced into 30 x 30 x 5 mm from a pure titanium ingot prepared from sponge titanium by an electron beam melting. They were mechanically polished with SiC (2000mesh) and Al_2O_3 (1μm) powder. Nitriding was carried out using a plasma jet apparatus. The flow rates for the N_2, H_2, and Ar gas were fixed at 6, 4, and 20 L/min, respectively. Operating pressure was kept at 100 Torr. Titanium specimen was nitrided at 1673 K for 20~32.4ks. After nitriding, XRD (JEOL: JDX-8030W) measurement was conducted with graphite-monochromator using Cu Kα radiation for phase identification.

SIMS (HITACHI, Ltd.: IMA-3000) measurement was carried out to analyze hydrogen in the specimen using the 17.5 kV Cs^+ primary ion and detecting the negative secondary ions. For the measurement on the cross section normal to the reacting surface, the primary ion current was 20 nA and the diameter of each crater was ϕ30μm. For the depth profiling, the primary ion current was 200 nA. The raster size and the analyzed size were 200 x 200 μm^2 and 63 x 63 μm^2, respectively. The base pressure was 10^{-10} Torr, and the operating pressure was 10^{-9} Torr. Crater depth measurement as a function of sputtering time was performed using a DEKTAK stylus profilometer.

3.Results and discussion

Figure 1 shows the hydrogen distribution on the cross section of the specimen nitrided for 32.4ks. ^{1}H$^-$ ion was detected as a secondary ion because it was sensitive and distinguishable from other ions. From the results of monitored ^{1}H$^-$ depth profile, the intensity that has become constant were judged to be bulk value free from the surface effect. Nitrogen content profile obtained by EPMA, described in the previous paper [4], was also plotted in Fig. 1. The results indicated that the hydrogen content in the nitride layer was higher than that in the diffusion layer. In α-Ti(N) layer, hydrogen content seemed to correlate with nitrogen content. K.Neu et al. reported a similar phenomenon that nitrogen implantation caused hydrogen gettering in titanium [5].

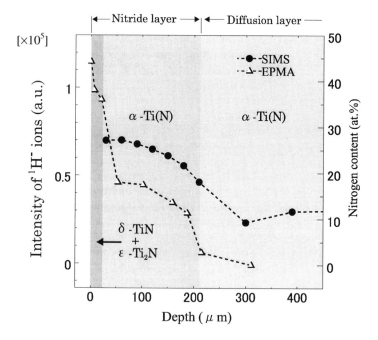

Fig.1 Hydrogen and nitrogen content profiles on the cross section of the nitrided specimen

Hydrogen analysis at the surface region was conducted by the following depth profiling. First of all, we have evaluated the matrix effect that might cause a problem in interpreting the shapes of depth profiles. To examine this, the intensity of $^1H^-$ ion was monitored with that of $^{48}Ti^-$, $^{62}(TiN)^-$, and $^{64}(TiO)^-$ as matrix ions, as shown in Fig.2. The result indicated that all profiles of each ion, especially $^{48}Ti^+$ ion, had an increment at 15μm in depth. That was thought to be due to the interference of $^{48}(TiH)^-$, $^{64}(TiOH)^-$, and $^{62}(TiNH)^-$. As a consequence, the matrix effect on $^1H^-$ ion was considered to be negligible in the analyzed region because the intensity of ions that consist of matrix was constant except at 15μm in depth. Therefore, $^1H^-$ ions were monitored as an objective ion for obtaining a hydrogen depth profile in the nitrided specimen.

From the depth profiling mentioned above, it was confirmed that a hydrogen deficient region was present at the surface. Figures 3 and 4 show the time dependence of hydrogen depth profiles and XRD patterns at the surface region, respectively. Figure 3 indicated that the extent of the hydrogen deficient region has expanded with increasing nitriding time. That is to say, absorbed hydrogen in α-Ti(N) region seemed to be released out of the surface region, as the volume fraction of δ-TiN increased. From the fact that hydrogen deficient region has expanded as nitriding process proceeded, it was considered that δ-TiN has low hydrogen solubility.

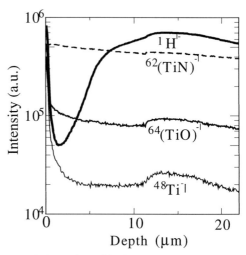

Fig.2 Depth profiles for several secondary ions

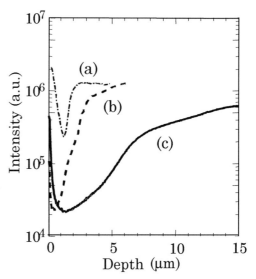

Fig. 3. Hydrogen depth profiles as a function of nitriding time; (a) 20sec, (b) 600sec, and (c) 3600sec

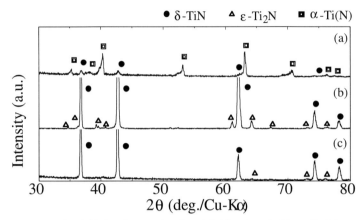

Fig.4 XRD patterns on the nitrided surface as a function of nitriding time; (a) 20sec, (b) 600sec, and (c) 3600sec

4.Conclusion

SIMS measurement was proved to be a useful technique for obtaining the hydrogen distribution in nitrided titanium specimens. From the results of depth profiling, we found that hydrogen deficient region was present at the surface of the nitrided specimen. It was considered that the absorbed hydrogen at the initial stage of nitriding was saturated and released out of the surface region when nitrogen content increased up to the composition of δ-TiN.

Reference

[1] Brading H.J., Morton P.H., Bell T., and Earwaker L.G., Plasma nitriding with nitrogen, hydrogen, and argon gas mixtures: structure and composition of coatings on titanium, Surf. Eng. ,8(1992)206-212.
[2] Tamaki M., Tomii Y., Yamamoto N., Kuwahara H., Nishikawa I., Behavior and role of hydrogen during plasma nitriding, J. Jpn. Powder and Powder Met., 44 (1997) 712-715.
[3] Bastasz R., Determination of hydrogen concentration profiles in titanium using SIMS, J.Vac.Sci.Technol.A, 3(1985)1363-1366
[4] Tamaki M., Kuwahara H., Tomii Y., Yamamoto N., An investigation of titanium nitride prepared by a DC arc plasma jet., J. Mater. Syn.and Proc., 6(1998)215-219
[5] K.Neu, H. Baumann, N. Angert, D. Ruck, K. Bethge, Gettering of hydrogen in titanium caused by nitrogen implantation, Nucl. Instr. And Meth. B, 89(1994)379-381

A. Benninghoven, P. Bertrand, H.-N. Migeon and H.W. Werner (Editors).
Proceedings of the 12th International Conference on Secondary Ion Mass Spectrometry,
Brussels, Belgium, 5-11 September 1999
© 2000 Elsevier Science B.V. All rights reserved.

USE OF ISOTOPIC TRACERS AND SIMS ANALYSIS FOR EVALUATING THE DEGRADATION OF PROTECTIVE COATINGS ON NICKEL BASED SUPERALLOYS

A. Alibhai, D.S. McPhail, B. A. Shollock

Department of Materials, Imperial College of Science, Technology and Medicine, Prince
Consort Road, London, SW7 2BP, UK. E-mail: a.alibhai@ic.ac.uk

1. Introduction

High temperature coatings are used to protect and enhance the service lifetime of superalloy materials, which are primarily used in aerospace and industrial gas turbine applications. The protective coating must meet a number of materials requirements: it must form a compact barrier between the highly corrosive environment and the substrate superalloy, it must have good adherence to the substrate and it must have good thermomechanical compatibility with the substrate [1]. The effectiveness of these coating to protect against environmental attack relies on the mechanism by which the healing oxide layer is formed and replaced during thermal cycling. With increasing engine operating temperatures and efficiency requirements, the high temperature degradation of protective coatings is of significant commercial interest. The use of isotopic tracer experiments and SIMS analysis has extensively been reported for various metal systems [2]. With respect to studies of the transport properties of alumina forming alloys [3-4] much ambiguity remains due to the large number of parameters that affect the oxide growth mechanisms. In the case of protective coatings, such parameters include coating composition, materials processing, oxidation temperature and poisonous gasses in the environment. The complex growth mechanisms may involve inward oxygen diffusion and/or outward cation diffusion and phase transformations. For temperatures lower than 1400°K, fast growing, metastable oxide formation occurs, involving the growth of transient oxides such as γ-Al_2O_3, θ-Al_2O_3 and $NiAl_2O_4$. At higher temperatures stable α-Al_2O_3 growth takes place. Depending on the temperature of oxidation, the diffusion of the oxygen tracer ($^{16}O_2$) during the second anneal treatment can take place at any of these three locations:

- At the gas – oxide interface.
- Within the existing scale, formed during the first anneal.
- At the oxide – coating interface.

Figure 1 below shows a simplified model of the possible concentration profiles for the $^{16}O_2$ tracer.

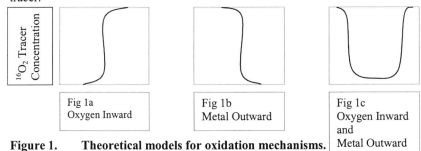

| Fig 1a | Fig 1b | Fig 1c |
| Oxygen Inward | Metal Outward | Oxygen Inward and Metal Outward |

Figure 1.   Theoretical models for oxidation mechanisms.

In this study, isotopic $^{18}O_2$ and $^{16}O_2$ oxidations and SIMS depth profiling analyses were performed in order to investigate the oxide growth mechanism of a silicon aluminide coating.

2. Experimental

Sample Preparation- Small sections with dimensions 8mm×2mm×2mm were cut from an industrial gas turbine blade that had received 2751 hours of service. The samples were mechanically polished to a 3μm finish and cleaned ultrasonically in acetone.

Oxidation- Samples were oxidised for 18 hours in isotopic $^{18}O_2$ (enriched to 97%), followed by 4 hours in unlabelled $^{16}O_2$. The furnace tube was briefly evacuated between anneals. All oxidations took place at 200mbar pressure and samples were oxidised at temperatures between 1060°K and 1363°K.

SIMS- SIMS depth profiling measurements were conducted using the ATOMIKA 6500 Ion Microprobe. A Xenon source (Xe^+) was used and a primary ion beam energy of +15keV was selected to bombard the surface, at near normal incidence. A scan width of 200μm was used and gated to 25%. A steady current of 320nA was maintained during analysis. Charge compensation due to the alumina scale was achieved by flooding the surface with 1.2keV electrons with an electron beam current of 1μA. Secondary ions $^{16}O^-$ and $^{18}O^-$ and $^{27}Al^-$ were detected as negative secondary ions.

Depth Calibration- The SIMS craters were measured for depth calibration using the Zygo interferometric microscope.

3. Results and Discussion

Characteristic depth profiling values, such as profiling time and crater depths are given in table 1 below. An example of a depth profile attained is shown in figure 2 below.

Oxidation Temperature (°K)	SIMS Profiling Time (sec)	Crater Depth (nm)	Total Oxide Depth (nm)
1063	3300	800	600
1118	1800	1140	1000
1158	2100	1850	1460
1258	6000	5330	4030
*1363	3720	2500	-

*This sample was oxidised for 18 hours in $^{16}O_2$, followed by 4 hours in $^{18}O_2$

Table 1. Summary of oxidation experiments and characteristic SIMS depth profile values.

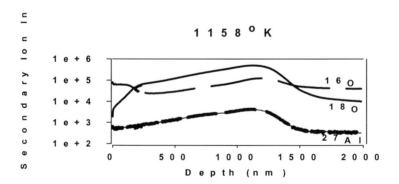

Figure 2.   Depth profile for sample oxidised at 1158°K.

In order to correct for any changes in secondary ion intensities which may occur during charge compensation, the oxygen isotopic ratios $ir_{18} = {}^{18}O^-/({}^{18}O^- + {}^{16}O^-)$ and $ir_{16} = 1 - r_{18}$ were evaluated. Examples of oxygen isotopic ratio curves obtained are given in figures 3-5.

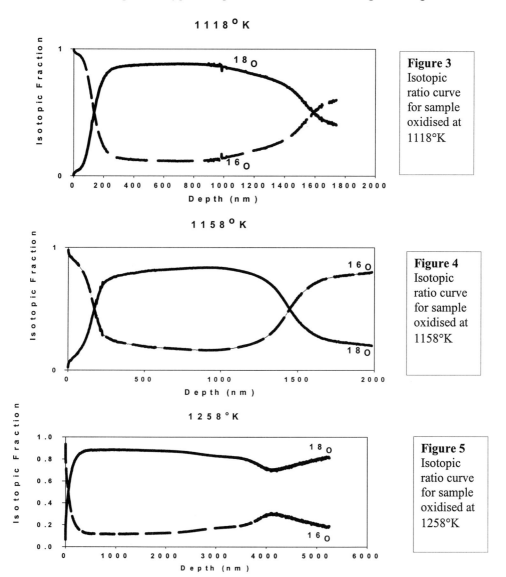

Figure 3
Isotopic ratio curve for sample oxidised at 1118°K

Figure 4
Isotopic ratio curve for sample oxidised at 1158°K

Figure 5
Isotopic ratio curve for sample oxidised at 1258°K

Figures 3-5. Isotopic Ratio curves for samples annealed at temperatures between 1118°K and 1258°K.

The isotopic ratio curves shown in figures 3-4 for temperatures 1118°K and 1158°K show a high tracer concentration ($^{16}O_2$) at the gas/oxide interface indicating partial new oxide growth. This tapers off to a plateau region with a ^{16}O isotopic ratio of 0.18 and represents a region of inward oxygen diffusion via a grain boundary diffusion mechanism. During this region, outward cation diffusion takes place and the cations reaching the surface form the new oxide at the surface. As the $^{16}O_2$ reaches the oxide/coating interface the isotopic fraction for $^{16}O_2$ increases and represents new oxide growth at this back interface.

Figure 6 below illustrates the oxide growth mechanism after the two-stage oxidation treatment for temperatures between 1063°K and 1158°K.

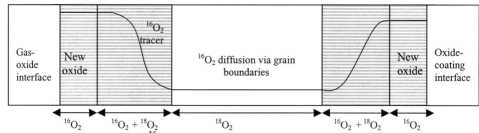

Figure 6. Model illustrating $^{16}O_2$ diffusion through the existing oxide.

This mechanism is altered slightly at 1258°K. In this case, oxide thickness is significantly increased although the growth at the back interface is reduced. This suggests greater outward cation flux and new oxide growth at the surface.

The isotopic profiles show that for temperatures between 1060°K and 1300°K the oxide growth takes place at both the gas-oxide interface and the oxide-coating interface, thus involving both outward cation and inward oxygen diffusion. However, for temperatures higher than 1300°K there is a change in the oxidation mechanism and the oxide scale growth at the gas – oxide interface is less than 20nm. Such obvious changes in oxidation mechanisms have also been observed in previous studies of alumina forming alloys, and relate to the formation of a stable α-Al_2O_3 scale, rather than a fast growing transient oxide, which is observed at lower temperatures

4. Conclusion

The usefulness of isotopic tracers and SIMS analysis in elucidating the high temperature oxidation of protective coatings has been established. Two different oxidation mechanisms have been determined for a commercial silicon aluminide coating. For temperatures below 1300°K, both inward oxygen and outward cation diffusion takes place. At temperatures above 1300°K this mechanism is much reduced and relates to stable α-Al_2O_3.

5. Acknowledgements

The author wishes to thank Engineering and Physical Sciences Research Council for financial funding and Dr.D.Garriga-Majo for his assistance and advise with this study.

References

[1]   C.T. Sims, N.S. Stoloff and W.C Hagel (Editors), Superalloys II, John Wiley & Sons, 1987, p 359-379.

[2]   G. Borchard, J Jedlinski and W. Wegener, In Proc. Secondary Ion Mass Spectroscopy VIII, p737-740.

[3]   G. Borchard, J Jedlinski and S. Mrowec, Solid State Ionics, 50, (1992), p 67-74.

[4]   R. Prescott, D. Mictchell, J Doychak and M Graham, Corr.Sci, 37, no9, (1995), p 1341-1364.

A. Benninghoven, P. Bertrand, H.-N. Migeon and H.W. Werner (Editors).
Proceedings of the 12th International Conference on Secondary Ion Mass Spectrometry,
Brussels, Belgium, 5-11 September 1999
© 2000 Elsevier Science B.V. All rights reserved.

CHARACTERIZATION OF THE TRACE ELEMENT DISTRIBUTION IN RHENIUM POWDERS AND FILMS WITH 3D-SIMS

H. Hutter, S. Musser
Department of Analytical Chemistry, Vienna University of Technology,
Getreidemarkt 9, A-1060 Vienna, Austria, h.hutter@tuwien.ac.at

1. Introduction

Many advanced materials like semiconductors, refractory metals and composites derive their qualities from the three-dimensional distribution of trace elements. Imaging-SIMS exhibits an unique potential for this task: laterally resolved secondary ion signals can be measured during sputter removal of the material, thus yielding signals with n chemical and three spatial dimensions. Imaging SIMS is capable of producing two and three-dimensional spatially resolved information of the element distribution of a significantly and therefore representative volume (150 x 150 x 20 µm^3) in a relatively short time (1 hour) [1].

2. System Description

The system developed in our group is based on a CAMECA IMS 3f. The whole computer interface was replaced, the instrument is controlled by a PC. Several new peripherals were built e.g.: high voltages of the primary column and the channelplate control [1]. In imaging mode the distributions are registered by the use of a CCD camera in combination with a double microchannel-plate fluorescent screen assembly. The camera signal is digitized and stored on hard disk for post processing by an image processor. During the depth profiling, the computer controls the high voltage of the channelplate according to the brightness of the image. This results in a full automatic measurement of the three-dimensional distribution of trace elements, including the case when the signal intensities vary over several orders of magnitude. Increased hard disk capacities allow us now to save 16-bit images of the measured masses. During a depth profile the gain of the channelplate is changing. For visualization and processing this can be corrected by one of the two following methods: Either by the use of a measured calibration curve of the channelplate gain versus the applied high voltage, or by adjustment of the total image brightness according to the total ion signal detected by the electron multiplier. The visualization is done by a own written program based on a free available library (VTK, Visualisation Tool Kit [2]).

3. Sample Description

Rhenium possesses an unique combination of properties which makes it an excellent choice for many demanding high temperature structural (melting point: 3180°C), wear resistant, and corrosion-resistant applications. Rhenium is used as components in long life x-ray tubes, missile propulsion components, temperature measurement instruments, improved jet engine components and heating filaments of mass spectrometers.

Due to the fact that Re is used in extreme environments the purity of the material is essential. Trace elements and inhomogeneities influences the mechanical and physiochemical properties of the material negatively. Especially the quantitative determination of low carbon contents in

Re with GDMS or combustion analysis is problematic due to the low vaporization pressure of the Re_2O_7. For improvement of the high temperature resistance of aircraft components these are increasingly coated with Re. Apart from the well established PVD (Physical vapor deposition) process, the VPS (Vacuum Plasma Spying) is tested for production of thicker films.

For quantitative SIMS measurements generally standards are necessary. Compared to liquid standards the production of solid state standards is complicated. One widespread method of producing solid state standards is ion-implantation. For technical samples this method is not successful in many cases.

The standards used for this investigation were produced by standard addition of carbon to PM (powder metallurgical) rhenium powders. The powders having a grain size of several microns were mixed intensely with soot. To prove the homogeneity of the standards it is necessary to measure the three dimensional distribution of carbon. Further rhenium films produced by VPS as well as by PVD were investigated.

4. Results

4.1 Carbon in Re Powder

For determination of the sensitivity factor for C several Re-powders were mixed with 1000 ppm soot. Fig. 1.a illustrate the distribution of C in one undoped Re-powder, 1.b. in a powder with standard addition. The C-concentration of the undoped powder is calculated to 25 ppm. The mass spectra of the two samples are quite similar, especially the relation of the peaks of C, C_2, ReC and ReC_2. There are no other important C-containing molecules. Due to this fact we think that the carbon is represented in identical chemical phases, either as elemental C or as ReC. To minimize the carbon background due to the residual gas the samples were changed in the evening before measurement. The detection limit is determined by the background signal due to the residual gas and is lower than 0,1 ppm.

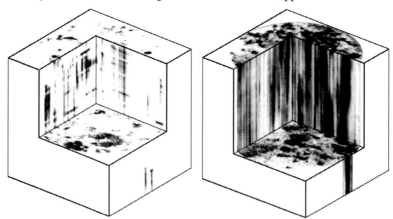

Figure 1. Distribution of C in the Re-powders. Measurement parameters: primary ions: Cs^+, primary energy: 14,5 kV, primary intensity: 150 nA, scanned area: 250*250 µm, analysed area: ⌀150µm, depth: 5 µm, number of cycles: 64, frames per image added: 256 (~10 seconds), image size: 256^2 pixels, pixel depth: 16 bit, for visualization the grey scales were adjusted
Left: "pure" powder, C-content: 25 ppm; Right: with standard addition of 1000 ppm carbon, C-content: 1025 ppm, depth scale is corresponding Fig. 2

In the "pure" sample the carbon is concentrated to inclusions with a diameter of approximately 0,5 μm. In the standard the carbon is distributed comparably.

4.2 Carbon in Re-films

The investigated Re-powders are used as raw material for the production of Re coatings. The carbon content and distribution in these films are of decisive interest. The measurements of the coating were done with the same parameters as those of the standards. The C concentrations are significantly lower than in the powder, obviously there is a reduction of the C content during the coating process. C is also precipitated in impurities with diameters in the sub μm range.

Figure 2. Distribution of C in the Re-films. Same measurement parameters as in Fig. 1.

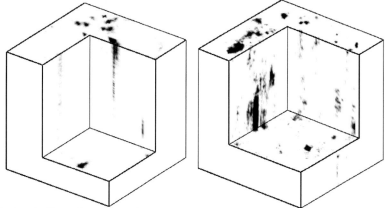

Left: PVD-film, C-content: 8 ppm; Right: VPS-film, C-content: 60 ppm, analysed volume 150x150x5μm (depth scale was determined by a crater depth measurement)

4.3 Metallic impurities

Beside the concentration of carbon the distribution of all trace elements are of interest. The distributions of 16 elements were measured. In this contribution we present only the distributions of Fe and K of the two different films.

In Fig. 3 a iso-surface visualization was used to show both distributions of the VPS film and the K distribution of the PVD film. This kind of visualization shows these areas in the sample with intensities higher than a selectable threshold and is useful to show impurities and precipitates in a sample.

The Fe is solved homogeneously in the PVD film, however the Fe in the VPS film and the K in both films is concentrated to impurities with diameters in the μm range.

5. Conclusion

The quantification of complex systems with unknown chemical phases is not trivial. For the system Re-C the production of solid state standards by mixing of powders and following grinding seems to be possible. 3D-SIMS shows that the deviation is due to the inhomogeneous distribution of C in the samples. The C contents of the coatings are

874

significantly lower than those of the powders. Due to this fact a further reduction of the C-content of the powders is not the only way to reduce the C content of the coatings. An improvement of the coating deposition techniques seems to be a possibility to reduce the C-content of the coatings.

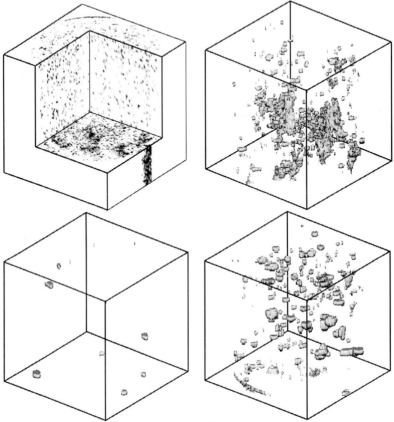

Figure 3. Distribution of Fe and K in the films. Measurement parameters: primary ions: O_2^+, primary energy: 5,5 kV, primary intensity: 2 µA, residual parameter see Fig.:1

Top row: PVD film, bottom row VPS film, left column Fe, right column: K, analysed volume 150x150x50µm

Acknowledgement

The authors thank the Austrian Science Research Council (Project 12053-CHE) and the Jubilaeumsfond of the Oesterreichischen Nationalbank (Projekt 6176) for supporting the research activities this paper is based on.

References

[1]   H. Hutter, M. Grasserbauer: Mikrochim. Acta 107, 137-148 (1992)
[2]   M.G. Wolkenstein, H. Hutter, M. Grasserbauer: Fresenius J. Anal. Chem. (1998)361, 722-24.

A. Benninghoven, P. Bertrand, H.-N. Migeon and H.W. Werner (Editors).
Proceedings of the 12th International Conference on Secondary Ion Mass Spectrometry,
Brussels, Belgium, 5-11 September 1999
© 2000 Elsevier Science B.V. All rights reserved.

A TOF-SIMS STUDY OF THE IRON-ANTIMONY MIXED OXIDE CATALYST SYSTEM

D Briggs[a] and S R Bryan[b]

[a]Siacon Consultants Ltd, 21 Woodfarm Road, Malvern, WR14 4PL, UK
briggs.siacon@dial.pipex.com
[b]Physical Electronics Inc, 6509 Flying Cloud Drive, Eden Prarie, MN 55344, USA

1. Introduction

Iron-Antimony (Fe/Sb) mixed oxides are effective catalysts for the selective oxidation and ammoxidation of olefines (eg the conversion of propene to acrylonitrile). There have been numerous studies of the bulk (microscopy/diffraction methods) and surface (XPS), in order to identify the nature of the catalyst site or active phase - especially for the catalyst with the 1:1 Fe:Sb ratio. The bulk structure corresponds to the stoichiometric compound iron antimonate, rutile-FeSbO$_4$, however XPS data suggest Sb enrichment at the surface. Such results have heavily influenced models of the surface structure and the discussion of catalytic activity [1]. The interpretation of the XPS data is, however, not straightforward. Quantitative analysis is hampered by the direct overlap of the O 1s and Sb 3d$_{5/2}$ peaks and by the complex structure of the Fe 2p level due to shake-up/shake-off transitions. The attenuation length of the Fe 2p electrons (BE ~ 710 eV) is significantly shorter than that of the Sb 3d electrons (BE ~ 530 eV) so the interpretation of the quantitative data in terms of concentration depth profiles is rather uncertain. Analysis of the antimony oxidation state by XPS is also difficult. The Sb 3d chemical shifts between the two oxidation states concerned (Sb^{III} and Sb^{V}) are very small. BE scale referencing is required for these insulating materials; this usually relies on the low intensity C 1s peak from contamination and involves assumptions about the nature of the contamination and its electrical contact with the inorganic particles. Peak shapes may also be distorted by differential charging.

Recent studies of the Pr/Mo oxide system have demonstrated [2,3] the power of ToF-SIMS for the characterisation of surface phases and suggest its usefulness to complement the previous XPS studies of the Fe/Sb mixed oxide catalyst system.

2. Experimental

The antimony oxides Sb$_2$O$_3$, Sb$_2$O$_4$ and Sb$_2$O$_5$ were purchased from Aldrich (>99%) and examined as received except for grinding to a smaller particle size if required. Iron-antiminy mixed oxide catalysts were prepared, by slurry impregnation of Sb$_2$O$_3$ with Fe(NO$_3$)$_3$ as previously described [4], to produce materials with Fe:Sb atomic ratios of 1:1 and 1:2. A few small granules of the catalysts were finely ground for analysis.

The ToF-SIMS experiments were carried out on a PHI TRIFT II™ instrument using a 2 nA, 15 keV In⁺ ion beam. Spectra were aquired from a 100 μm x 100 μm area using a primary ion dose of 4×10^{11} ions cm⁻². Sample charging was controlled by flooding the sample with low energy electrons between ion beam pulses. The powder samples were simply mounted on silicone-free, double-sided, tape.

3. Results and Discussion

Both the positive and negative ion spectra of the three antimony oxides readily allow them to be distinguished. In particular, the negative ion spectra contain clusters $Sb_xO_y(H)$ to high mass (eg $Sb_5O_{10}^-$ m/z ~770) which have different relative intensities from each oxide. Fig 1 shows partial spectra from the single valence oxides Sb_2O_3 and Sb_2O_5 covering the Sb_2O_y and Sb_3O_y clusters (¹²¹Sb:¹²³Sb isotope ratio is 57.3:42.7). To a first approximation the spectrum of Sb_2O_4 (Fig 2), which in the bulk oxide contains equal numbers of Sb^{III} and Sb^V sites, is a superposition

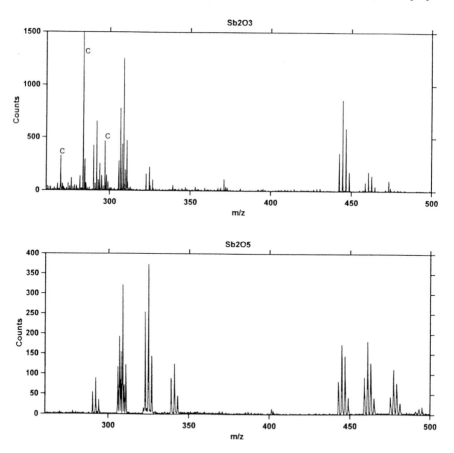

Fig.1. Partial negative ToF-SIMS spectra of Sb_2O_3 and Sb_2O_5 in the region of the clusters Sb_2O_y (y=3-6) and Sb_3O_y (y=5-8). Organic contamination peaks are labelled 'c'.

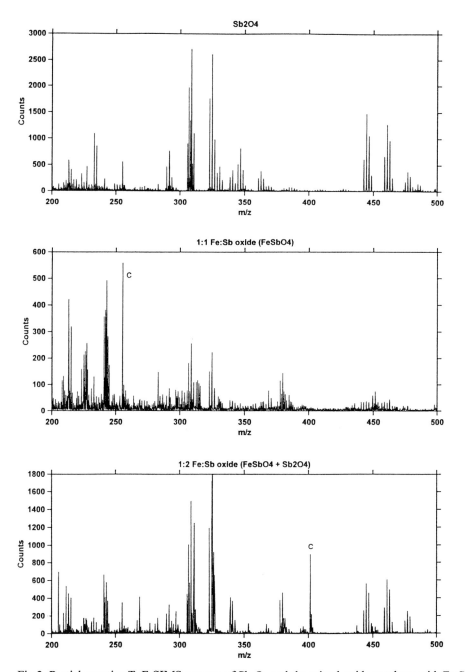

Fig.2. Partial negative ToF-SIMS spectra of Sb_2O_4 and the mixed oxide catalysts with Fe:Sb atomic ratios of 1:1 and 1:2. Peaks labelled 'c' are due to organic contamination.

878

of the spectra from the single valence oxides. XPS shows the Sb_2O_4 sample surface to contain a significant level of sodium and the ToF-SIMS spectra of this oxide contain a number of Na containing clusters, including $Sb_4O_yNa^-$ (y>6).

By contrast the 1:1 Fe/Sb oxide spectra have little in common with these spectra, with $Sb_xO_y^-$ clusters only up to x=2. Both positive and negative ion spectra include clusters containing both Fe and Sb, eg $FeSbO^+$(193), $Fe_2SbO_3^+$(281), $FeSbO_2H_4^-$(213), $FeSbO_3^-$(225), $FeSbO_4^-$(241), and $FeSb_2O_5^-$(378) where masses are for the ^{121}Sb isotope. The mass resolution is sufficiently high to resolve these inorganic cluster ions from organic contaminant interferences and to provide the mass accuracy required for empirical structural determination. The negative ion spectra from Sb_2O_4 and the 1:1 catalyst are compared in Fig 2 over the range m/z 200-500. In this region the above mentioned clusters are observed, often accompanied by peaks from the clusters plus one or two H atoms. These data do not support a description of the primary catalyst particle structure in which Sb enrichment at the surface leads to a thin 'skin' of Sb_2O_4 [5], although they do not rule out a more gradual concentration profile [1]. The spectra appear to best represent a surface which is a termination of the bulk structure of crystalline rutile-$FeSbO_4$. Further confirmation for this comes from the spectra of the 1:2 Fe/Sb catalyst which in the bulk is a mixture of $FeSbO_4$ and α-Sb_2O_4 phases [4]. The negative ion spectrum is also shown in Fig 2 and this can be seen to be a superposition of the other two spectra (ie it represents exactly the spectrum expected from the bulk composition). These results confirm the power of ToF-SIMS for inorganic phase determination.

The $FeSbO_4$ sample was subjected to a series of increasing primary ion doses prior to obtaining static SIMS spectra. Below 1E13 ions cm^{-2} the spectra remained virtually unchanged. Between 1E13 and 1E14 peaks due to organic contamination were progressively eliminated but inorganic clusters were little changed. Between 1E14 and 1E15 most peaks due to OH containing inorganic clusters were eliminated. Above 1E15 the relative intensities of the oxide clusters begin to change significantly and peaks due to alkali ions reduced in intensity relative to those of the mixed oxide elements. Surface cleaning by sputtering without noticeable damage to the mixed oxide is therefore possible in this system.

4. Acknowledgement

We thank Prof M Bowker, Reading University (UK) for providing the samples used in this work.

References

[1] M.D. Allen and M. Bowker, Catal. Lett., 33 (1995) 269
[2] F. de Smet, M. Devillers, C. Poleunis and P. Bertrand, J. Chem. Soc. Farad. Trans. 94 (1998) 941
[3] F. de Smet, M. Devillers, E. Ferain, C. Poleunis and P. Bertrand, Chem. Mater. 11 (1999) 324
[4] M.D. Allen, S. Poulston, E.G. Bithell, M.J. Goringe and M. Bowker, J. Catal. 163 (1996) 204
[5] R.G. Teller, J.F. Brazdil and R.K. Grasselli, J. Chem. Soc. Farad. Trans. I 81 (1985) 1693

A. Benninghoven, P. Bertrand, H.-N. Migeon and H.W. Werner (Editors).
Proceedings of the 12th International Conference on Secondary Ion Mass Spectrometry,
Brussels, Belgium, 5-11 September 1999
© 2000 Elsevier Science B.V. All rights reserved.

GRAIN BOUNDARY DIFFUSION OF OXIDE IONS IN ZINC OXIDE CERAMICS MEASURED WITH SIMS

H. Haneda, I. Sakaguchi, A. Watanabe, M. Komatsu and S. Tanaka*
National Institute for Research in Inorganic Materials.
1-1 Namiki, Tsukuba, Ibaraki 305-0044 JAPAN., haneda@nirim.go.jp
*Hitachi Research Laboratory, Hitachi Ltd., 3-1-1 Saiwai-cho, Hitachi, Ibaraki Japan.

1. Introduction

Metal-oxide varistors used in surge arresters are ZnO-based ceramic semiconductor devices with highly nonlinear current-voltage characteristics similar to back-to-back Zener diodes, but with much greater current-, voltage-, and energy-handling capabilities[1-2]. Such materials are characterized by non-uniform grain size, porosity, second phase distribution, impurity segregation and grain-grain structure. The electric properties of ZnO varistors are, furthermore, known to be greatly influenced by the defect chemistry of ceramics.

The intrinsic stoichiometric deviation exists with lattice defects in ZnO. In the case of zinc excess these point defects can be zinc interstitials or oxygen vacancies. In general, diffusion coefficients, and their temperature and dopant dependence permit conclusions with respect to the transport mechanism and thus to the kind of defect structure. If the oxygen vacancy is the dominant defect in zinc excess ZnO, the oxygen diffuses through the oxygen vacancy. In this paper, we focus our attention on attempts to investigate diffusion of oxygen ions in various ZnO-based ceramics. Furthermore, we also examined the oxygen diffusivity along grain boundaries.

2. Experimental procedure

ZnO based ceramics prepared by a hot-isostatic-pressing (HIP) technique were used for oxygen diffusion experiment[3]. Precursor powders were 4N-grade(Hakusui Chem. Co. LTD). To clarify the doping effect on the oxygen diffusion, Co-, Mn-, Al- and Li-doped samples were used. These powdered were pressed at 30MPa in to discs 12mm in diameter and 6 mm in thickness, and then cold-isostatic-pressed at 160MPa at the room temperature. Thereafter they were pre sintered in O2 for 5h at 1250°C. Pores in samples were closed after pre sintering. These discs were HIPed at 1250°C under a pressure of 130MPa in Ar atmosphere without any capsule because of no open pore, and then annealed in O2 at 1000°C for 5h. After hipping and annealing, all samples have the porosity under 0.2%, and no-doped sample has a transparent characteristic, which is very favorable to eliminate effects of pore during diffusion experiments. Samples were cut from ceramics into disks shape. The doping amounts were fixed to 0.3 at.%. One side of the large faces was polished to optical flatness with diamond paste of decreasing particle size (10, 3, 1, 0.5μm). Diffusion coefficient was determined by a solid-gas exchange technique[4]. After being cleaned with water, ethanol, acetone, and ethanol, the samples were placed inside a platinum crucible with platinum susceptor in a vessel of a RF furnace. The system was evacuated, and the ^{18}O-enriched oxygen gas with 5kPa pressure was introduced into vessel that was closed from the gas line. The sample crucible was firstly heated at 800°C for 15 minutes to maintain the constant concentration at sample surface, and then the temperature was elevated to a desired temperature for isotope exchange. The temperature was monitored by an optical pyrometer. Although the temperature accuracy of pyrometer is in 10K, the temperature variation among samples in a same experimental cycle is believed to be less than few degrees. After isotopic exchange of oxygen between the gaseous phase and the samples during a given time, the furnace was cooled down by switching off the power and ^{18}O-enriched gas was reabsorbed back into zeolite storage flask by sold trapping with liquid nitrogen. The [18]O diffusion profiles (concentration versus depth) were measured using a Cameca magnetic sector secondary ion mass spectrometer (SIMS, MS-4f) with [133]Cs[+] as the primary ions, an accelerating voltage 10kV, and beam current of 5 to 20nA. The samples were coated with Au films of 20nm thickness to maintain the sample surface at constant potential during the SIMS analysis. An electron gun was used as a supplemental neutralizing source. The primary beam scanned over a 100x100μm² area, and signals of secondary ions were detected in a 40% central square of the sputtered crater. Intensities for the negative ions [16]O and [18]O were measured as a function of time. The crater depths were measured using a Dektak 3000 profilometer. After a predetermined time of sputtering to eliminate locally the Au film, the concentrations of [18]O are converted as a function of depth. The concentration (c(x,t)) of [18]O at any sample depth was determined from the ion intensities:

$$c(x,t) = \frac{I(^{18}O)}{I(^{18}O) + I(^{16}O)} \qquad (1)$$

If the surface is maintained at a constant concentration of ^{18}O, C_g, which is the same concentration as in the gaseous phase, and if the concentration in the solid is initially uniform(C(x,0)=C0, natural abundance, 0.204%), the following relation can be used to calculate the diffusion coefficients, D [5]:

$$\frac{c(x,t) - c_0}{c_g - c_0} = \text{erfc}\left(\frac{x}{2 \cdot \sqrt{D \cdot t}}\right) \qquad (2)$$

Where x is the penetration, t the duration of diffusion annealing, and erfc=1-erf (erf the Gaussian error function). In the polycrystalline samples, the tracer diffuses deeper inside than expected from the volume diffusion. This is due to the effect of grain boundary diffusion. Le Claire(4) have proposed the relation between the grain boundary diffusion coefficient and concentration at large depth, which is useful in present case. The value of $(Dt)^{1/2}$ was smaller than the grain size, so a product of oxygen grainboundary coefficient, D' and grainboundary width, δ, is evaluated as follows [6]:

$$D' \cdot \delta = 0.66 \left(4D/t\right)^{1/2} \left[- \frac{\partial \log (c(x))}{\partial x^{6/5}}\right]^{-5/3} \qquad (3)$$

3. Results and discussion

Figure 1 shows a typical depth profile of [18]O in a ZnO samples. Lattice diffusion coefficients were obtained, using data near surface(<1000nm) with the Eq.(2). The profile had a long tail. The long tail at deeper depth was not due to the lattice diffusion but might be caused by the diffusion along grain boundaries, seen in Fig.2. The lattice diffusion coefficients of oxygen ions depended on dopants. The lattice diffusion coefficients were greater in Al-doped samples than in the Li-doped. According to this fact it might be believed that the oxygen ions diffuse with an interstitialcy mechanism as follows,

Interstitialcy model:
$$Li_2O + O_i^{''} \rightarrow 2Li_{Zn}^{'} + 2O_i^{x} \qquad (4)$$
$$Al_2O_3 \rightarrow 2\,Al_{Zn}^{'} + 2O_O^{x} + O_i^{''}$$

If the oxide ions had diffused through the oxygen vacancies, the Al-doped samples had greater diffusion coefficients than Li-doped ones.

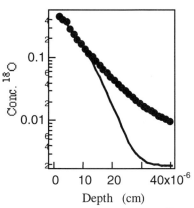

Fig.1. Typical depth profile of ^{18}O in Co-doped ZnO (1330K, 3120s) $D=1.31\times10^{-14}$ cm^2s^{-1}. Closed circles: obsd. data and solid line: calcd. values.

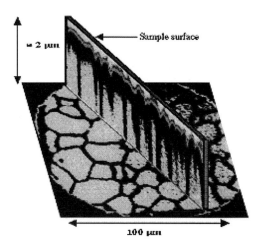

Fig.2. Oxygen 18 3-D distribution in non-doped ZnO after oxygen diffusion annealing at 1243K for 5h.

The activation energies of oxide ion diffusion are of the order of 200kJ/mol as a mean value in polycrystalline samples. On the contrary the diffusion coefficients in single crystal are lower than those of the present studies, and the activation energies are around 571kJ/mol[7]. The difference of mechanism caused the discrepancy, and the oxide ions are believed to diffuse through oxygen vacancies. The mechanism depends on the impurity level of samples in this temperature range.

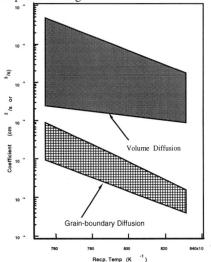

Fig.3. Temperature dependences of grain boundary diffusion coefficients and the volume diffusion coefficients.

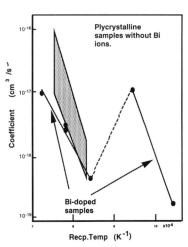

Fig.4. Comparison between the grain boundary diffusion in the samples without Bi ions and that with Bi ions.

882

As seen in figure 2 of ^{18}O ion image at 2mm depth, the grain boundary network could be observed in pure ZnO. It is considered to be an evidence of contribution of grain boundary diffusion to the long tail of diffusion profiles. Same high diffusivities paths along grain boundary were appeared in all samples. Using the tail parts of the curves, one can calculate the products of D'δ with Eq.(3). The range of D'δ is shown in Fig.3., including the range of the volume diffusion coefficients. The variation range of the grain boundary diffusion coefficients was narrower than that for the lattice diffusion, which indicates that the structure of grain boundaries and mechanism for grain boundary diffusion of oxygen ions little depend on the characteristics of the dopants, suggesting that the grain boundary diffusion is mainly controlled by the structure of grain boundaries..

The varistor characteristics are very sensitive to the type of dopant, and then is believed to be related with the preferential oxidation at grain boundary. Bi-dopant is well known to give a high non-linearity of V-I characteristics[8], which is caused by the existence of some excess oxygen ions. In the present study, the grain boundary diffusivity drastically changed at a temperature above which the electrical non-linearity was lost. We concluded that the grain boundary structure change to a state without grain boundary electric state above this temperature and the grain boundary diffusion drastically decreased. We believe that this phenomenon is an evidence of structural transition at grain boundaries.

References
[1] G.D.Mahan, L.M.Levinson, and H.R.Philipp, Appl.Phys.Lett., 33, 80 (1978).
[2] T.K.Gupta, J.Am.Cerm.Soc., 73, 1817 (1990).
[3] A.Watanabe, H.Haneda, T.Ikegami, J.Tanaka, Y.Moriyoshi, S.Shirasaki, and T.Yamamoto, in "Hot isostatic pressing: theory and applicatons,' ed. by M.Koizumi (Els.Sci.Pub. Essex, 1992), p.105.
[4] Y.Oishi and W.D.Kingery, J.Chem.Phys., 33, 905 (1960).
[5] J. Crank, in "The mathematics of diffusion,"(Oxford University Press, London, 1957) P.30.
[6] A.D.Le Claire, Brit. J. Appl. Phys., 14, 351-6 (1963).
[7] H. Haneda, I. Sakaguchi, A. Watanabe and J. Tanaka, Diffusion and Defect Forum, 143-147, 1219-24 (1997).
[8] K.Kostic, O.Milosevic, and D.Uskokovic, Sinter'85 (1985) p.301.

A. Benninghoven, P. Bertrand, H.-N. Migeon and H.W. Werner (Editors).
Proceedings of the 12th International Conference on Secondary Ion Mass Spectrometry,
Brussels, Belgium, 5-11 September 1999

CATIONIZATION IN TOF-SIMS SPECTRA OF BIOLOGICALLY ACTIVE PEPTIDES USING MODIFIED ION-CONTAINING POLYMERS AS SUPPORT

B.A. Keller and P. Hug, Swiss Federal Laboratories for Materials Testing and Research
CH-8600 Duebendorf, Switzerland, e-mail: beat.keller@empa.ch

1. Introduction

Cationization of soluble organic material after thin film deposition onto noble metal substrates has been developed into a versatile method for identification and quantification of biologically active molecules using time-of-fight secondary ion mass spectrometry (TOF-SIMS) [1]. However, in a recent study [2] we addressed the topic of competitive cationization in TOF-SIMS spectra of small histidine containing peptides on silver substrates in presence Cu(II) ions. In order to prevent this type of signal corrugation, a new type of cation exchanged ionomer matrix was used to optimize the formation of cationized quasimolecular ions. Our earlier investigations led to the conclusion that the strong affinity of copper ions to gly-gly-his was due to the formation of a very stable complex of the cation with the histidine residue and the adjacent glycine groups.

2. Experimental

Nafion (® DuPont) was purchased from Aldrich in its hydrogen ion form (equiv. wt. 1100) as 5 wt % solution in a mixture of lower aliphatic alcohols and water. Known since the 1960s, Nafion is a perfluorinated superacid ion-containing polymer that contains small proportions of sulfonic or carboxylic ionic functional groups. Its chemical structure is shown in Figure 1. The superacidity is attributed to the electron-withdrawing effect of the perfluorocarbon chain acting on the sulfonic acid group. Due to this property, almost 100 % ion-exchange could be achieved by adding aequimolar quantities of metal salts to an aquatic solution of the polymer. The mixture was heated under refluxing conditions for 2 hours. Thin films of the ion-exchanged

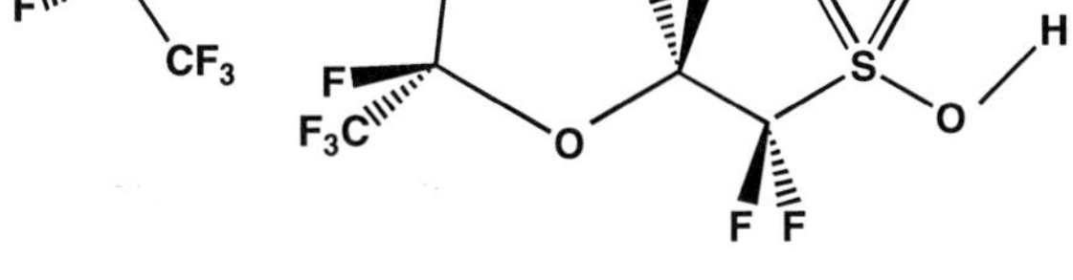

Figure 1. Chemical structure of Nafion 117 (®DuPont).

Nafion were produced by spin coating gold plated stainless steel supports with the cold mixture. The hexapeptide his-leu-gly-leu-ala-arg (C3a) has been found to express C3a-like anaphylatoxin reactivity in both, the classical and alternative complement pathway (causing TXB$_2$ release) [3].

His-leu-gly-leu-ala-arg, purity 99%) was purchased from Sigma-Aldrich and used without further treatment. Figure 2 shows the chemical structure of the hexapeptide in its zwitterionic form. The solubility in water was approximately 1 mg/ml. A 1.5 x 10^{-3} M solution was prepared by dissolving 1 mg of the peptide in 1 ml water (pH = 6.8). Samples were prepared by spin coating after depositing microliter quantities of the peptide solution onto freshly coated ion-containing Nafion substrates.

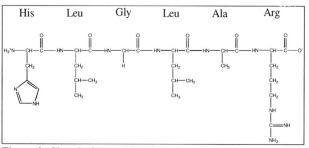

Figure 2. Chemical structure of C3a active peptide (72-77, His-Leu-Gly-Leu-Ala-Arg).

TOF-SIMS spectra were recorded using a Physical Electronics 7200 system, equipped with a 8 keV Cs^+ primary ion gun and a reflectron-type mass analyzer. Under standard operation conditions the instrument produced 1 ns FWHM primary ion pulses, yielding a mass resolution $M/\Delta M > 7000$ at m/z = 28. The band pass energy of the reflectron was set to 70 eV. During data acquisition, the ion dose was kept in the range of 10^{11} ions/cm^2, well below the static SIMS limit of 10^{13} ions/cm^2.

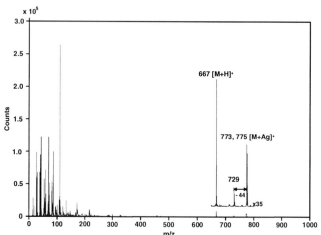

TOF-SIMS spectra of C3a peptide applied to neat Nafion (i.e. without cation exchange) showed only unspecific low-mass signals, indicating a rapid hydrolization of the material due to the high pH-value of the support.

Figure 3 shows the positive ion TOF-SIMS spectrum of C3a on an Ag^+-exchanged Nafion matrix. The spectrum contains intense signals at masses belonging to cationized quasi-molecular ions of types $[M+H]^+$ (m/z = 667) and

Figure 3. Positive ion TOF-SIMS spectrum of C3a peptide. The insert shows an enlarged view of the quasimolecular ion mass region.

$[M+Ag]^+$ (m/z = 773 and 775). The most intense signal, however, was found at mass m/z = 110. This fragment corresponds to $C_8H_5N_3^+$ and can easily be assigned to the structure of histidine. As outlined in an earlier work [4], thin films (approx. 10 nm in this work) of ion-exchanged ionomers provide a quasi-conducting surface that does not require additional charge compensation during spectrum acquisition.

The formation of cationized species in absence of a solid metallic silver substrate is clearly supporting the precursor model of Benninghoven et al. [6] as dominant mechanism for cationization in TOF-SIMS spectra. This mechanistic approach has been subject to further investigation by analyzing TOF-SIMS spectra of organic molecules measured after deposition of the material onto matrices providing other types of cations for the process [6].

4. Discussion

The fragmentation pattern in mass spectra of peptides using the nomenclature of Roepstorff [7] would predict three major series of distinct fragment ions, corresponding to breaking between amino acid C-C bonds (A-series), C-N amide bonds (B-series) and amino acid N-C bonds (C-series). The observed signal at m/z = 110 can be assigned to fragment A_1. However, all other signals of the expected series are missing, or small. The strong preference for the formation of $C_8H_5N_3^+$ fragments can not be explained by simply applying the fragmentation rules of Roepsdorff and Fohlmann.

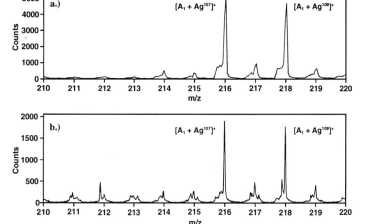

Figure 4. Positive ion TOF-SIMS spectra of a.) C3a and b.) Gly-Gly-His on a silver exchanged Nafion matrix in the mass range of the cationized A_1-fragment. Spectrum b.) was recorded with higher mass resolution

Figure 4 shows the mass range of silver cationized histidine (A_1) fragment species of C3a and gly-gly-his, respectively. Although weaker by factor of 50, the detection of cationized A_1-fragment signals indicates that a preformed species was present on the surface of the polymer matrix. The formation of a precursor, however, is most likely facilitated by the strong affinity of Ag^+ to the histidine residue. This theory is further supported by the fact that cationized species of type $[A_1 + Ag]^+$ are found in the TOF-SIMS spectra of both, C3a and the small peptide gly-gly-his. Strong complex formation between silver and copper ions that yields competitive cationization in TOF-SIMS spectra of gly-gly-his was discussed recently [2]. The absence of other signals that can be assigned to cationized fragments of the Roepsdorff series suggests that the preferred cationizing site in the case of histidine containing molecules is located on the imidazole ring of the amino acid. Due to the small energy gap between 4d and 5s orbitals, Ag (I) ions ($4d^{10}$ configuration) tend occur as highly hybridized species that easily undergo complex formation. On the other hand, the

888

emission of a stable preformed positively charged quasimolecular ion is expected to influence subsequent fragmentation processes.

No cationized species were found in the negative ion TOF-SIMS (not shown) spectra of the peptides, supporting the postulate of charge sign conservation. A parentlike secondary species can leave the surface either as a neutral particle or as an ion, depending on the surface-particle bond strength. For a cationized species present on the polymeric Nafion matrix, this bond strength is expected to be low. Therefore, the small amount of kinetic energy that is available after momentum and energy transfer following the impact of a primary ion [8] is sufficient to initiate the emission of the precursor complex. TOF-SIMS spectra from histidine containing peptides on Ag$^+$-exchanged Nafion substrates strongly support the theory that cationized species are preformed on the Nafion surface prior to emission as quasimolecular secondary ion, with the substrate acting as ion reservoir.

5. Conclusions

Cation exchanged Nafion can be used as substrate for controlled formation of quasimolecular ions in TOF-SIMS spectra of small histidine containing peptides. In cases where strongly directing cationizing sites influence secondary ion yields, classical models for peptide fragmentation can no longer be applied to fully describe fragentation in mass spectra of simple peptides. The presence of [M + Ag]$^+$ ions in the TOF-SIMS spectra of his-leu-gly-leu-ala-arg is a consequence of the precursor model of Benninghoven. The formation of a very stable preformed complex on the surface of the ionomer substrate might therefore also be responsible for the dominant A$_1$ fragment signal in the spectrum of the peptide. This theory is supported by the detection of signals belonging to [A$_1$ + Ag]$^+$, indicating that the imidazole part of the histidine residue plays an important role as preferred complexion site within the quasimolecular ion.

Due to the fact that cation exchanged Nafion substrates can be prepared via simple chemical modification steps and because a wide variety of different cation species can be incorporated in the Nafion matrix, the possibility to gain control over quasimolecular ion formation via cation exchanged ionomers can be used to enhance the selectivity for certain species in TOF-SIMS spectrometry. Matrix controlled quasimolecular ion formation allows the application of the high detection sensitivity of TOF-SIMS instruments to the analysis of trace components in mixtures. Using polyatomic primary ion sources might further improve secondary ion yields in the future.

References

[1] U. Seedorf et al., Clin. Chem. 41 (1995) 548
[2] B.A. Keller and P. Hug in Secondary Ion Mass Spectrometry (SIMS XI), G. Gillen, R. Lareau, J. Bennett and F. Stevie, eds., J. Wiley and Sons, New York, 1998, p. 101
[3] H. P. Hartung, D. Bitter-Suermann and U. Hadding, Agents and Actions, 15 (1984) 14
[4] B. A. Keller in Secondary Ion Mass Spectrometry (SIMS X), A. Benninghoven, B. Hagenhoff and J. W. Werner, eds., J. Wiley and Sons, Chichester, 1997, p. 747
[5] A. Benninghoven, F.G. Ruedenauer and J.W. Werner, in Secondary Ion Mass Spectrometry, J. Wiley and Sons, New York ,1987, p. 753 ff.
[6] B. A. Keller and P. Hug, to be published
[7] P. Roepstorff and J. Fohlmann, Biomed. Mass Spectrometry, 11 (1984) 601
[8] A. Benninghoven, Springer Series in Cemical Physics, 9A (1979) 116

A. Benninghoven, P. Bertrand, H.-N. Migeon and H.W. Werner (Editors).
Proceedings of the 12th International Conference on Secondary Ion Mass Spectrometry,
Brussels, Belgium, 5-11 September 1999
© 2000 Elsevier Science B.V. All rights reserved.

TOF-SIMS STUDY OF THE CHEMICAL STRUCTURE OF AGED ION-IRRADIATED POLYSILOXANE SURFACES

A.Licciardello, C.Satriano, G.Marletta

Dipartimento di Scienze Chimiche, Universita' di Catania – V. A.Doria, 6 - 95125 Catania, Italy
e-mail: alicciardello@dipchi.unict.it

1. Introduction

Ion beam induced modification of polymer surfaces has been shown to be able to promote the dramatic increase of biocompatibility, in terms of enhanced cell and protein adhesion [1-3]. These effects are of great potential interest for the development of new strategies of preparation of new bio-active surfaces. It is well known that the increase of biocompatibility for the ion-irradiated surfaces is basically linked to the properties of the uppermost layers, so that surface characterization is needed in order to understand the mechanisms underlying the modification of the biocompatibility.

In the present paper we study the property and structure modification for 5 keV Ar-irradiated surfaces of polyhydroxymethylsiloxane (PHMS) films:

Indeed, it has been shown that ion-irradiation treatment of such surfaces is able to promote fibroblast adhesion with a well-defined fluence-dependent trend, i.e., whilst no cell adhesion is observed for the unirradiated surfaces, a complete cell confluence is obtained already at ~5×10^{14} ions/cm^2 [4]. The beam-enhanced cell adhesion has been related mainly to the more or less pronounced increase of the hydrophilic character of the irradiated surfaces.

However, the cell adhesion experiments imply the exposure of the irradiated surfaces to atmosphere, so that a rearrangement of the chemical structure of the uppermost layers can occur. Hence, the aim of the present work is to investigate the structure and the relevant chemical features of the PHMS irradiated layers induced by aging in air. In this respect it is to be noted that XPS measurements have been shown to be not sufficiently informative to allow – alone- the unambiguous identification of the top-surface modifications [5]. Then, the characterization at molecular level of the uppermost layers was performed by using TOF-SIMS, in order to get a more detailed picture of the changes induced by ion irradiation and subsequent aging process in atmosphere. The unique information provided by TOF-SIMS allowed to establish a clear correlation between the surface energy of the aged samples and their chemical structure.

2. Experimental

PHMS films (0.5 μm thick) have been prepared by spin coating technique on silicon wafers from a chloroform/acetone/methanol solution. Several series of samples have been ion-irradiated at fluence in the range $1 \times 10^{13} \div 1 \times 10^{16}$ ions cm^{-2} with 5 keV Ar$^+$ in the XPS and TOF-SIMS apparatus (see below). Some series were analyzed in situ by XPS or TOF-SIMS, immediately after ion-irradiation, meanwhile other series, prepared in identical

890

condition, were aged in air for 48 hours before XPS, TOF-SIMS or contact angle measurements. We have chosen an aging period of 48 hours because preliminary results show that after such period the surface composition is stabilized enough; the same aging period has been used in the cell adhesion experiments [4]. TOF-SIMS measurements have been performed in a CAMECA TOFSIMS IV. A 25 keV pulsed Ga^+ beam has been used in high mass resolution mode for static SIMS measurements (primary ion fluence $<2x10^{12}$ ions cm^{-2}), whilst an EI gas source has been used for Ar^+ irradiation. XPS spectra have been obtained in a KRATOS ES 300B apparatus, equipped, for ion bombardment, with a rastered VG AG61 ion source. Contact angle measurements have been performed with a Kernco apparatus.

3. Results and Discussion

TOF-SIMS, XPS and contact angle measurements have been performed in order to obtain composition, detailed chemical structure and free energy of the surfaces after irradiation at different fluence. TOF-SIMS and XPS have been performed both *in situ* and after aging in air, whilst contact angle data are obtained only after exposure of sample to atmosphere.

As to XPS, the quantitative data obtained from Si2p, C1s and O1s total peak areas show that the irradiation induces compositional changes mainly consisting in the decrease of C-containing species. Indeed, the atomic percentage of C changes from 22% (unirradiated) to about 10%. The beam induced compositional changes for C, O and Si are reported in fig.1 for samples analyzed both *in situ* and after aging. The compositional changes, as observed by XPS, follow the cell adhesion trend for aged samples (threshold at about $5x10^{14}$ ions/cm^2) [4]. To date, the threshold in cell adhesion appears closely related to the surface free energy, as obtained from contact angle measurements [4]. However due to the lack of a distinct -OH signal in the XPS O1s band, the XPS results do not justify the strong increase of hydrophilic character of the irradiated surfaces, as described in details elsewhere [5,6]. Moreover, the similarity of XPS results for "aged" and "*in situ*"

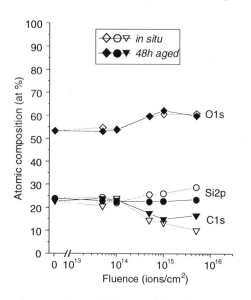

Fig. 1. Compositional changes of PHMS vs irradiation fluence, as determined by XPS both *in situ* and after aging.

results illustrates that XPS fails in identifying possible surface rearrangements due to aging.

Static SIMS spectra were obtained both in situ and after aging of PHMS surfaces irradiated with $1x10^{13}$, $5x10^{13}$, $1x10^{14}$, $5x10^{14}$, $1x10^{15}$, $5x10^{15}$ and $1x10^{16}$ Ar ions/cm^2. The spectra showed a progressive modification of the original structure of the surface.Figure 2 reports the low-mass region of the TOF-SIMS spectra obtained before irradiation (Fig.2a) and at the threshold dose for complete cell confluence (i.e., $5x10^{14}$ ions/cm^2)(Fig.2b). Spectra have been acquired at high resolution so that, as shown in the insets in figure, different

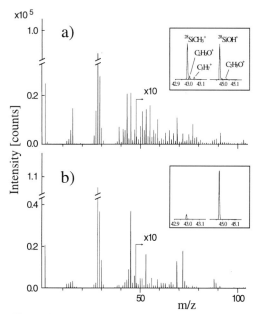

Fig. 2. TOF-SIMS spectra of PHMS surfaces: a) unirradiated; b) after 5x10¹⁴ Ar⁺ ions/cm² (analyzed in situ, immediately after irradiation)

species having the same nominal mass are easily separated. From the TOF-SIMS spectra it turns out that irradiation induces large intensity changes in some peaks, namely CH_x^+ ($0 \leq x \leq 3$), m/z 43.000 ($SiCH_3^+$), 44.980 ($SiOH^+$), 71.949 (Si_2O^+); 87.944 (Si_2O_2). The TOF-SIMS data show the depletion of C-containing surface species, confirming the XPS results. This appears to be accomplished mainly at expenses of Si-C bonds, and seems to be consistent with a surface composed by a mixture of highly cross-linked carbon-containing islands and a SiO_x-rich matrix. Indeed a closer analysis of the relative intensities clearly shows that [CH_3]- and [$Si-CH_x$]-related peaks decrease with ion irradiation, while peaks due to SiOH and [SiO_x]-related species simultaneously increase. Also the modification of the relative intensity pattern of the [CH_x] peak cluster (increase of C^+/CH_3 and CH/CH_3 ratios) is in agreement with a progressive dehydrogenation and cross-linking. The intensity modification of some relevant peaks is plotted for all the studied fluences in figure 3

(solid symbols for the *in situ* analyzed samples). The reported intensities are normalized to the total ion current. Other normalization criteria, and even no normalization, do not affect significantly the observed trends that, anyway, cannot be interpreted in a quantitative way since both composition and nature of the surface are altered by ion irradiation, so that a matrix effect cannot be excluded. However, it appears that the observed trends reflect, at least qualitatively, real changes in the surface composition. Such statement is justified by the good correlation found with surface properties of the film (see also fig.4).

Together with the data for the *in situ* analysis after irradiation, figure 3 reports also the corresponding data for samples that have been exposed to atmosphere for 48 hours after irradiation (open symbols). The comparison of the two sets of data gives, at variance of XPS results (see fig.1), an immediate evidence of the effect of aging on the surface composition of the irradiated PHMS. Indeed

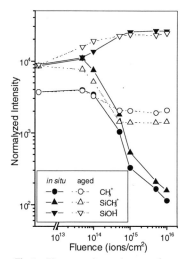

Fig.3. Fluence dependence of some relevant peak intensities, measured immediately after irradiation (*in situ*) and after aging in air.

892

air exposition for 48 hours results in a partial recovery of the surface CH_3's, as shown both by m/z 15.023 (CH_3^+) and m/z 43.000 ($SiCH_3^+$). In spite of such recovery of the surface, the – OH enrichment with respect to the non irradiated samples is confirmed. It is to note that the intensity variation of m/z 44.980 with irradiation fluence could be taken as a measure of the relative variation of Si-OH groups at the surface. Indeed the SiOH intensity varies with irradiation fluence in a parallel way to the measured contact angle values, and this gives a strong indication that the increase of surface SiOH groups is largely responsible for the increased hydrophilic character of the surface. The strong correlation of the SIMS data with the surface energy measurements is shown by the plot shown in figure 4. Up to a fluence of 5×10^{15} ions cm^{-2} a linear relationship is found between the SiOH yield and the measured contact angles, which are known to be related with the composition of the uppermost layer of the surface, approximately the same sampled by static SIMS.

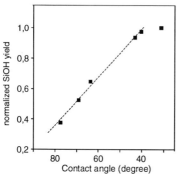

Fig.4. SiOH yield (normalized to the highest observed value) *vs* contac angle value for irradiated surfaces after 48 hours of air exposure. Decreasing angle corresponds to increasing ion fluence.

4. Conclusions

TOF-SIMS allows to obtain a realistic picture of the real irradiated surfaces and to characterize the aging process. First, SIMS allows to get the demonstration of a possible phase separation effect related to the elimination of the Si-C species and to the increase of SiO_x phases, supporting the picture of formation of speciated carbonaceous and silica-like phases. Second, TOF-SIMS allowed to demonstrate the presence on the surface of the hydrophilic –OH groups needed to explain the dramatic decrease of contact angle, which could not be justified by mere XPS analysis. Finally, it appears from the SIMS data that, upon aging, a partial recovering of the surface occurs, that anyway preserves the hydrophilic character induced by ion irradiation.

Acknowledgements
Work supported by U.E. through the Italian Network of Mass Spectrometry. MURST and CNR (Rome) are acknowledged for partial support.

References
[1] Y. Suzuki, M. Kusakabe, M. Iwaki, and M. Suzuki "Ion Beam Modification of Silicone Rubber" in *Interfaces between Polymers, Metals and Ceramics, Mater. Res. Soc. Symp. Proceed*, **153**, B.M. Dekoven, R. Rosenberg and A.J. Gellman (Ed.) 1989, pp.223-228.
[2] H. Tsuji, H. Satoh, S. Ikeda, N. Ikemoto, Y. Gotoh and Junzo Ishokawa, Surface and Coatings Technology, **103-104** (1998) 124-128.
[3] B.Pignataro, E.Conte, A.Scandurra and G.Marletta, Biomaterials, **18**, 1461-1470 (1997).
[4] C. Satriano, G. Marletta and E. Conte, NIMB **148** (1999), 1079-1084.
[5] A. Toth, I. Bertoti, G. Marletta, G.G.Ferenczy and M.Mohai, NIMB **116** (1996), 299-304.
[6] C.Satriano, A.Licciardello, G. Marletta, submitted.

A. Benninghoven, P. Bertrand, H.-N. Migeon and H.W. Werner (Editors).
Proceedings of the 12th International Conference on Secondary Ion Mass Spectrometry,
Brussels, Belgium, 5-11 September 1999
© 2000 Elsevier Science B.V. All rights reserved.

ANALYSIS OF BUPRENORPHINE IN URINE, SERUM AND HEMOLYZED BLOOD BY TIME OF FLIGHT SECONDARY ION MASS SPECTROMETRY (TOF-SIMS)

F. Saldi[1], S. Schneider[2], C. Marson[2], R. Wennig[2] and H.N. Migeon[1]

[1]Laboratoire d'Analyse des Matériaux (LAM),
Centre de Recherche Public-Gabriel Lippmann (saldi@crpgl.lu)
[2]Laboratoire National de Santé, Division de Toxicologie, Centre Universitaire
162a, av. de la Faïencerie, L-1511 Luxembourg, G.D. Luxembourg

1. Introduction

In the last few years Time-of-Flight Secondary Ion Mass Spectrometry (ToF-SIMS), one of the most sensitive analytical techniques in surface science, has become a potential alternative tool for analysing biomolecules and drugs after adsorption on a noble metal [1-4]. As the analysis of buprenorphine, a semi-synthetic opioid having both analgesic and opioid antagonist properties [5] remains difficult in routine clinical and forensic analytical toxicology because of its thermal instability and its low therapeutic range (0.5 - 5 ng/mL) [6], it seemed an interesting analyte to investigate further.

Previous investigations [7] have demonstrated that ToF-SIMS allows detection and quantification of buprenorphine in urine. To extend these studies, the present work is concentrated on the performance of ToF-SIMS for the detection and quantification of buprenorphine in serum and hemolyzed blood. Comparative investigations of the nature of the metal surface (Ag or Au) used to adsorb the analyte, as well as the extraction methods will be discussed.

2. Methods

2.1 Instrumental

Static ToF-SIMS measurements were conducted on a ToF-SIMS III (ION-ToF of Münster, Germany) instrument. A pulsed 10 kV Ar$^+$ primary ion beam was used with a pulse length less than 1 ns. During the measurement, the sample was bombarded over an area of 200x200 μm^2 with an average current of 0.2 pA for 200 seconds. In these conditions, the total primary ion doses were < 10^{12} ions/cm^2. Secondary ions generated by the primary ion pulse were accelerated by a 3 kV extraction lens into the flight tube operated in the reflecting mode. After post-acceleration at 10 kV, the secondary ions were subsequently detected by a channel-plate-scintillator-photomultiplier combination detector.

2.2 Sample preparation

Liquid-liquid extraction of buprenorphine (LLE): To 0.5 ml of serum, hemolyzed blood and urine was added 50 ng of buprenorphine-d_4 as internal standard, 0.5 ml of ammonium buffer, pH 9.5, 0.5 mL of a saturated solution of ammonium sulfate and 5 mL of n-hexane/CH_2Cl_2/2-propanol (60:40:2, v/v/v). After agitation (5 min) and centrifugation (3 min at 3,500 rpm), the organic layer was isolated. 3 mL H_2O were added and the pH was adjusted to 1 by adding conc. HCl. The mixture was agitated and centrifuged as before. After phase separation the aqueous layer was neutralized by addition of 12 M NaOH. 1 mL of ammonium buffer, pH 9.5, and 5 mL of hexane/CH_2Cl_2/2-propanol (60:40:2, v/v/v) were added. After a final agitation and centrifugation, the organic layer was evaporated and the residue dissolved in 0.5 mL of acetonitrile.

Solid phase extraction of buprenorphine (SPE): To 0.5 mL of serum/hemolyzed blood was added 50 ng of buprenorphine-d_4 as internal standard and 1 mL of 0.1 M phosphate buffer, pH 6.0. The mixture was vortexed for 10 sec. and poured onto a Clean-Screen extraction column, previously conditioned with 3 mL methanol, 3 mL de-ionized H_2O and 1 mL of phosphate buffer, pH 6.0. The column was rinsed with 3 mL H_2O, 1 mL 1 M acetic acid and 3 mL methanol. After drying the column under reduced pressure for 5 minutes, buprenorphine was eluted with 3 mL of CH_2Cl_2/2-propanol/NH_3 (85:15:2, v/v/v). The eluate was evaporated under nitrogen then dissolved in 6 mL of diethylether/toluene (1:1, v/v) and 1.5 mL of phosphoric acid (50 mM) was added. The mixture was agitated for 10 min and centrifuged 5 min at 4,000 rpm. The aqueous layer was alkalinized by addition of 1.5 mL of a saturated borate buffer, pH 9.0 and extracted by 5 mL of diethylether for 10 min. After centrifugation (5 min), the organic layer was evaporated under a flux of nitrogen and the residue dissolved in 0.5 mL of acetonitrile.

For ToF-SIMS analysis, 2 microliters of the serum or blood extract were placed on Ag or Au substrate. Ag was etched in 20% nitric acid and Au in *aqua regina*.

3. Results and discussion

Figure 1 shows the mass spectra of serum extract solutions (buprenorphine 1μg/mL) deposited on the Ag and Au etched targets. The silver substrate shows the emission of the buprenorphine molecular ions $(M+H)^+$ and $(M-H)^+$ with the highest intensity for the protonated molecular cluster. For the Au target, we clearly observe with a high intensity, the isotopic ratio corresponding to the depronated $(M-H)^+$ secondary ions of buprenorphine. The integral intensity of $(M-H)^+$ obtained on Au is 680000 counts and about 62000 counts for $(M+H)^+$ on the Ag substrate. An other disadvantage of the Ag substrate is an important emission of organic, metallic (Ag_x) and cationized $(M+Ag)$ ions, limiting considerably the identification of buprenorphine molecular ions $(M+H)^+$ or $(M-H)^+$ when the concentrations

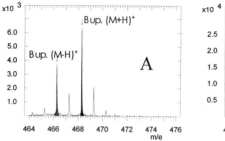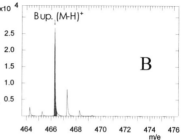

Figure 1. Positive secondary ion mass spectra of serum samples containing buprenorphine (1μg/mL),A : on Ag, B : on Au.

are below 10 ng/mL [7]. The difference between Ag and Au may be explained in terms of surface chemistry as acid-basic interactions between the substrate and the analyte [8], which is certainly the single most important parameter of the molecular ion formation on the metal surface. It seems that Au etched surface favors the pre-formed deprotonated molecular ion but further measurements are necessary to understand the phenomena.

For the quantification of buprenorphine in serum and hemolyzed blood, we analysed 5 samples containing 0.1 µg/mL of buprenorphine-d_4 and 1, 0.1, 0.01, 0.001, 0.0001 µg/mL of buprenorphine. Figure 2 shows secondary ion mass spectra of serum extract spiked respectively with 50 ng (A) and 5 ng (B) of buprenorphine and 50 ng of buprenorphine-d_4 as an internal standard. For the concentrations below 5ng/mL, background peaks due to endogenous species limits detection of the analyte.

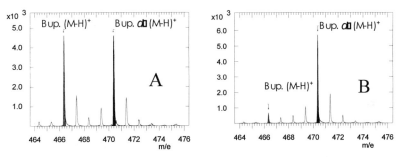

Figure 2 . Positive secondary ion mass spectra on Au of serum samples (LLE) containing buprenorphine and buprenorphine-d_4. A :50 ng buprenorphine and 50 ng buprenorphine-d_4, B : 5 ng buprenorphine and 50 ng buprenorphine-d_4.

The influence of the extraction method used for hemolyzed blood is illustrated in figure 3. In the case of liquid-liquid extraction (A), the spectrum shows unusual organic clusters certainly co-extracted from the organic layer. This contamination decreases the secondary ion yield of buprenorphine. For the SPE, spectrum B shows relatively clearly the analyte peaks and that the sensitivity is close to the one obtained for serum (LLE).

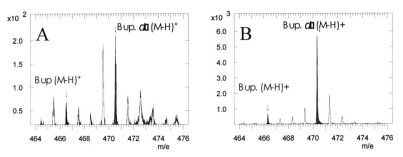

Figure 3 . Positive secondary ion mass spectra on Au of hemolyzed blood samples containing buprenorphine (5 ng) and buprenorphine-d_4 (50ng) :liquid-liquid extraction (A), solid phase extraction (B).

Table 2: LOD and LOQ obtained for urine (LLE), serum (LLE) and hemolyzed blood (SPE).

	Urine [6]	Serum	Hemolyzed blood
LOD	0.1 ng/mL	0.6 ng/mL	1.5 ng/mL
LOQ	0.4 ng/mL	2 ng/mL	5 ng/mL
RSD %	6	8	11

The table 2 shows the estimation of limit of detection (LOD) and limit of quantification (LOQ) using the best extraction method for urine [7], serum and hemolyzed blood. The LOD and LOQ were calculated from the signal-to-noise ratio (S/N) and defined as 3 times the S/N for the LOD and 10 times for the LOQ. These values are better in the case of urine because of less endogenous material in this matrix. The co-extraction of endogenous molecules with the analyte increases the surface coverage of the metal target and thus decrease the secondary ion yield of the molecules of interest [9].

4. Conclusions

The results of the present study show that ToF-SIMS can be used as a new technique for detection and quantification of buprenorphine in serum and hemolyzed blood after suitable extraction. Buprenorphine deposited on Au targets gave clean spectra; interference with matrix compounds remains the main problem in obtaining low LOD and LOQ results, especially in hemolyzed blood. Further work will focus on the optimization of the extraction techniques and the application of ToF-SIMS, to the quantification of buprenorphine in real cases and the analysis of other drugs will be investigated.

Acknowledgments

The authors like to thank Dr. Michel Yegles from LNS-Toxicology, Luxembourg, for helpful discussions.

References

[1] D.C. Muddiman, A.I. Gusev, L.B. Martin, and D.M. Hercules, *Fresenius Z. Anal. Chem.* 354, 103-110 (1996).
[2] K. Meyer, A. Benninghoven, M. Fobker, M. Erren, A. Assmann, U. Christians, and K.-F. Sewing, *Proceedings of SIMS X*, Eds. A. Benninghoven, B. Hagenhoff, H.W. Werner, pp 851-854 (1995).
[3] B. Hagenhoff, R. Kock, M. Deimel, and A. Benninghoven, *Proceedings of SIMS VIII*, Eds A. Benninghoven, K.T.F. Janssen, J. Tümpner, H.W. Werner, pp 831-834 (1992).
[4] A. J. Nicola, D.C. Muddiman and D.M. Hercules, *J. Am. Soc. Mass Spectrom. 1996, 7, 467-472.*
[5] T. Reisine and G. Pasternak. Opioid analgesics and antagonists. In *Goodman & Gilman's The Pharmacological Basis of Therapeutics*, 9th ed. J.G. Hardman and L.E. Limbird, Eds. McGraw Hill, New York, NY, 1996, pp 521-55.
[6] M. Schulz and A.Schmoldt, Anaesthesist 43, 835-844 (1996).
[7] R. Wennig, F. Saldi, C. Marson, S. Schneider, H.-N. Migeon, *Proceedings* SOFT-TIAFT Meeting, Albuquerque Oct. 1998 (in press).
[8] A. I. Gusev, B. K. Choi and D. M. Hercules, *Proceedings of SIMS XI*, Eds G. Gillen, R. Lareau, J. Bennett, F. Stevie, pp 575-578 (1998).
[9] D.C. Muddiman, A. J. Nicola, A. Proctor and D.M. Hercules, *J. of Applied Spectroscopy Volume 50, Number 2, 161-166 (1996).*

A. Benninghoven, P. Bertrand, H.-N. Migeon and H.W. Werner (Editors).
Proceedings of the 12th International Conference on Secondary Ion Mass Spectrometry,
Brussels, Belgium, 5-11 September 1999
© 2000 Elsevier Science B.V. All rights reserved.

QUANTITATIVE TIME - OF -FLIGHT SECONDARY ION MASS SPECTROMETRY OF LIPIDS FOR THE IDENTIFICATION OF HUMAN METABOLIC DISEASES

M. Fobker[1], R. Voß[1,2], M. Erren [2], F. Kannenberg[2], H. Assad[4],
A.Benninghoven[3], G. Assmann[1,2]

[1] Institut für Klinische Chemie und Laboratoriumsmedizin,
[2] Institut für Arteriosklerose-forschung,
[3] Physikalisches Institut, Universität Münster, Germany,
[4] Department of Biochemistry, Al-Baath University, Homs, Syria.

1. Introduction

For many human metabolic diseases, the accumulation of biomolecules provides a clue to the basic biochemical defect. A number of analytic methods have been published for quantifying accumulated molecules. These include thin layer chromatography, gas liquid chromatography and high performance liquid chromatography alone or in combination with mass spectrometry. These analytical methods have expanded the spectrum of separable compounds, in part by allowing the detection of lower abundance components. These developments have markedly improved current understanding of metabolic bases of inherited diseases. Lipid compounds have generally been difficult to quantify in human materials because current analytical techniques have limited ranges and sensitivities, and require large blood samples not readily available from newborn patients. In an attempt to overcome these difficulties, we tested TOF-SIMS for lipid compound analysis in combination with internal standards. The TOF-SIMS method has been developed in the last decade and has been applied in many analytical questions [1]. For the quantification of biomolecules in clinical chemistry only a few data have been published [3-5]. We describe here a simple, novel and sensitive method for the measurement of blood and tissue samples from patients having an unidentified lipid storage disease.

2. Materials and Methods

All reagents were of analytical grade and were obtained from Sigma-Aldrich Chemie GmbH (Deisenhofen, FRG). All solvents were of HPLC grade and were purchased from Baker GmbH (Gross-Gerau, FRG). Mass spectrometry was performed on a TOF-SIMS II (ION-TOF Münster, Germany) [1]. 20 µL of (whole) blood or a 1 cm^2 blot paper with dried blood was given into a glass vial. After addition of a 20 µL internal standard mix (1 g/L stigmasterol, 1g/L cholesteryl heptadecanoate, 0.162 g/L heneicosanoic acid, 1g/L dilauroylphosphytidylethanolamine) to the samples, 50 µL of freshly prepared ethanolic KOH (150 g/L) was added, followed by brief vortexing and incubation for 10 min at 40°C. This saponification step was only done by analysis of total phytanic acid, cholesterol and 7-dehydrocholesterol. After extraction of the serum lipids with 500 µL n-hexane/isopropanol (3:2 v/v) and 500 µL water, 2 µL of the upper phase was applied to a silver target (galvanic deposited silver layers on a platinum substrate). After evaporation of the solvent, the resulting submonolayer was analyzed by TOF-SIMS (Primary ion current 10^{11} $^{40}Ar^+$ ions/cm^2 (11 keV), mass resolution m/Δm $\approx$ 3000 (m= peak mass; Δm =peak widths at half-widths of full maximum), typical acquisition time 90 s. Gaschromatography was done according to Seedorf et al.[3] and Cullen et al. [5].

3. Theoretical Aspects

Quantitation was carried out by determining relative sensitivity factors (*RSF* or S_r) from linear calibration curves. When analyte and internal standard are present in a sample with concentration c_A and c_S, respectively, their peak height ratio I_A/I_S in the SIMS-spectrum can be expressed by the "fundamental" SIMS formula (2)

$$\frac{I_A}{I_S} = \frac{c_A}{c_S}\frac{a_A}{a_S}\frac{\alpha_A T_A Y_{tot}}{\alpha_S T_S Y_{tot}}$$

(1),

where Y_{tot} is the total secondary ion yield, α_A and α_S are the degree of ionization, a_A and a_S are the isotopic dependence factors and T_A and T_S are the transmission of the analyzer system for analyte and standard molecules. The last four factors in eq. 1 are combined into the "relative sensitivity factor" of the analyte A with respect to the internal standard S

$$S_r(A) = \frac{a_A}{a_S}\frac{\alpha_A T_A Y_{tot}}{\alpha_S T_S Y_{tot}}$$

(2).

The link from the physical model (calculation of S_r or isotope frequencies a) to the more practically orientated demands of clinical chemistry can be made by calculating relative sensitivity factors (S_r) from linear calibration curve regression analysis. To determine an unknown amount of analyte in a sample, we used the formula (from eq. 1 and 2)

$$m_A = \frac{1}{S_r}(\frac{I_A}{I_S} - a_c)m_S$$

(3),

where m_S is the known amount of the internal standard, a_c is the intercept of the linear calibration curve and represents a nonvanishing systematic error (minor analytical specificity) of this method. This can occur if TOF-SIMS cannot distinguish between two masses, e.g. the peaks of phytanic acid and of the endogenous arachidic acid appear at the same mass in the spectra of normal patients. In this case we used a mean value calculated from controls to correct this problem.

4. Results and Conclusions

The TOF-SIMS-method described here is a rapid and sensitive method for a specific diagnosis of human metabolic diseases. Direct and simultaneous detection of the clinically important lipid parameters triglycerides, steroids, fatty acids, phospholipids and sphingolipids was achieved. Using synthetic nonendogenous internal standards we identified and quantified the disease-specific lipids in patients with familiar hypercholesterolemia (cholesterol), Smith-Lemli-Opitz syndrome (7-dehydrocholesterol) and Refsum-syndrome (phytanic acid) (Fig 1.).

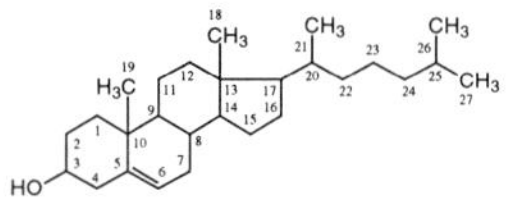

cholesterol
(5-cholesten-3ß-ol)
$C_{27}H_{46}O$, MW 386.64 g/mol

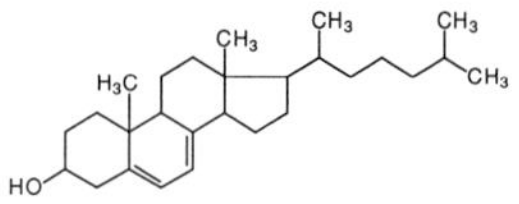

7-dehydrocholesterol
(5,7-cholestadien-3ß-ol)
$C_{27}H_{44}O$, MW 384.6 g/mol

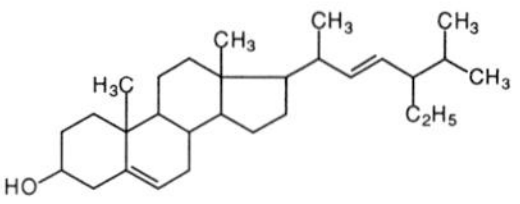

Stigmasterol
(3ß-hydroxy-24-ethyl-
5,22-cholestadien)
$C_{29}H_{48}O$, MW 412.67 g/mol

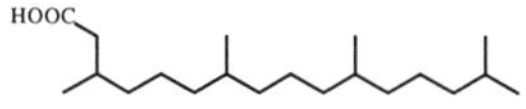

phytanic acid
(3,7,11,15 Tetramethylhexade-
canoic acid) $C_{20}H_{40}O_2$
MW=312.5 g/mol

heneicosanoic acid
$C_{21}H_{42}O_2$
MW 326,5 g/mol

Fig.1. Analytes and Internal Standards.

Data for identification of wolman's disease (cholesterol ester) and metachromatic leukodystrophy (sulfogalactosylsphingosine) are not shown.

We used an internal standard mix to correct for any variations due to variable yields after extraction or to variable counting efficiencies in the analysis. Thus, the method allowed the detection and quantification of all studied lipid components in an organic extract indicating it may also be suitable for multi-component analysis of different classes of parameters in clinical chemistry.

The dynamic range of calibration is three orders of magnitude for each internal standard control (Fig 2).

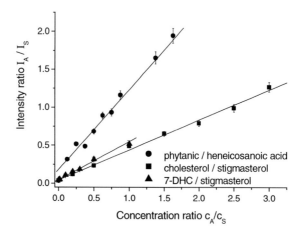

Fig. 2. Serum calibration curves obtained from: phytanic acid (●, analyte A) with heneicosanoic acid (internal standard S), linear regression data (y = a+bx) with a = 0,16±0,03, b = 1,09 ± 0,04 (cv = 7%), Sylx = 0,05, r = 0,996 (n = 9, 3 replicates), P = 2*10-8; for cholesterol (■) with stigmasterol (internal standard S), with a = 0,037±0,021, b = 0,396 ± 0,012 (cv = 3,3%), Sylx = 0,037, r = 0,996 (n = 8, 3 replicates), P = 8,168*10-8. and for 7-DHC (▲) with stigmasterol (internal standard S): a = - 0.00565 ± 0.01171, b = 0.22429 ± 0.02219 (cv = 9.9%); r = 0.97639 ± 0.0192 (n = 7); p = 0.00016. I (7-DHC) was corrected for cholesterol interference at 491.3 mass units as described in the Methods section.

A TOF-SIMS spectrum obtained from a patient with hypercholesterolemia and Smith-Lemli-Opitz syndrome is shown in Fig. 3. For the quantitation of these sterols, stigmasterol was used as internal standard. Another lipid storage disease called Refsum syndrome is characterized by accumulation of phytanic acid (C20:0-fatty acid) in serum and tissues. The nonphysiological heneicosanoic acid (C21:0) was used as internal standard (Fig. 4).

Due to the high sensitivity (in the range of 10^{-15} - 10^{-16} mol) TOF-SIMS is particularly useful whenever only small sample volumes from newborn patients are available. One droplet of blood (~ 20 µL) on a paper is sufficient for a correct identification of the diseases. This underlines the future potential of this technique for postnatal screening and for monitoring dietary or drug treatment. Furthermore, the method can be applied to stored material from biopsy or cultured cell samples obtained from patients with known storage diseases and should therefore be suitable for human serum or tissue samples from patients having an unidentified lipid storage disease.

As shown in Table 1, quantification of lipids with the TOF-SIMS method displayed a good agreement with the results of gas-chromatography. The good precision (< 3,5 %) of the technique in combination with internal standards described in this work may allow TOF-SIMS to be developed as an alternative reference method for the measurement of biological samples.

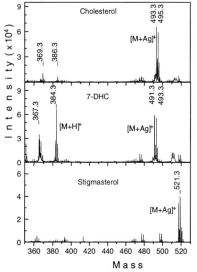

Fig. 3. TOF-SIMS spectra of cholesterol, 7-DHC and stigmasterol. The mass range 350 to 530 mass units is shown. 1 μL of standard solutions (1 g/L) dissolved in ethanol were applied to a silver target. After evaporation of the solvent the resulting submonolayer was bombarded by 10^{11} ^{40}Ar$^+$ ions/cm^2 (11 keV), the acquisition time was 100 seconds. Intensity represents counts/channel.

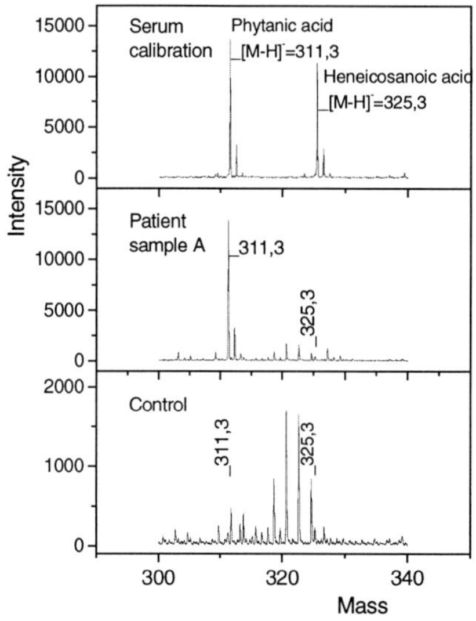

Fig. 4. TOF-SIMS spectra of phytanic acid and heneicosanoic acid on a silver target in the mass range of 300 - 340 amu (500 μmol/L in n-hexane, primary ion current: 10^{11} ^{40}Ar$^+$ ions/cm^2, 11 keV, acquisition time: 90 s)

Table 1. Concentration of Lipids in Patients and Controls-
Intercomparison of two analytical methods

Analyte	Disease	Method	Patients (n=5)	Controls (n=10)
7-dehydrocholesterol (mmol/L)	Smith-Lemli-Opitz-syndrome	TOF-SIMS	1.04 ± 0.13	< 0.001
		GC	0.99 ± 0.05	< 0.001
cholesterol (mmol/L)	hypercholesterole-mia	TOF-SIMS	7.26 ± 0.22	6.1 ± 1.37
		GC	7.12 ± 0.41	6.11 ± 1.23
phytanic acid (g/L)	Refsum-syndrome	TOF-SIMS	1.09 ± 0.07	0.14 ± 0.01
		GC	1.02 ± 0.05	non detectable

Measurements performed in triplicate. Values given as mean ± SD.

902

References

[1] A. Benninghoven, B. Hagenhoff, E. Niehuis. Anal. Chem. 65 (1993) 630
[2] F. Rüdenauer, W. Steiger Anal. Chem. 57 (1985) 1636
[3] Seedorf U, Fobker M, Voss R, Meyer K, Kannenberg F, Meschede D. Clin. Chem. 41 (1995) 548
[4] K. Meyer, M. Fobker, U. Christians, M. Erren, K.F. Sewing, G. Assmann, A. Benninghoven Drug Metabol. and Disp. 24 (1996) 1151
[5] P. Cullen, M. Fobker, K. Tegelkamp; K. Meyer, F. Kannenberg, A. Cignarella. J Lipid Res. 38 (1997) 401

A. Benninghoven, P. Bertrand, H.-N. Migeon and H.W. Werner (Editors).
Proceedings of the 12th International Conference on Secondary Ion Mass Spectrometry,
Brussels, Belgium, 5-11 September 1999

903

PHYSIOLOGICAL APPLICATION OF THE NANOSIMS 50 ION MICROSCOPE: LOCALIZATION AT SUBCELLULAR LEVEL OF ^{15}N LABELLING IN *ARABIDOPSIS THALIANA.*

N. Grignon[a], J.J. Vidmar[a], F. Hillion[b] and B. Jaillard[c]

[a]Biochimie et Physiologie Moléculaire des Plantes, Agro-M, INRA, CNRS (URA 2133), UM2 34060 Montpellier cedex 1, France. [b]CAMECA, 103 bd Saint Denis, 92400 Courbevoie, France. [c]Science du Sol, Agro-M, INRA, 34060 Montpellier cedex 1, France

1. Introduction

The NANOSIMS 50 ion microscope [1, 2] meets the challenge of accessing elemental subcellular compartmentalization (around 100 nm lateral resolution). Such a resolution is necessary for physiological analyses, since metabolism is highly compartimentalized between various interacting organelles inside the cell. Higher plant cells display an heterogeneous structure made up of three main compartments, namely the cell wall, the cytoplasm and a large unstructured central vacuole. This first study concerns the location of the nitrogen tracer ^{15}N, detected simultaneously to ^{14}N, in subcellular compartments in leaves of intact plants.

Nitrogen is mainly acquired as nitrate by plant roots in the soil, and translocated to leaves through specialized vessels by the transpiration stream (a convective flow driven by evaporation at the leaf surface). After reaching the leaves, nitrate is absorbed by leaf cells and reduced to NH_3, which is incorporated into amino acids. In this paper we describe the pathway followed by nitrate imported into the leaf. A relative quantification was possible comparing cells in the samples with biological standards.

2. Materials and methods

The experiments were performed on whole plants (*Arabidopsis thaliana*) in normal physiological conditions (low nitrate concentration in the culture medium) [3]. The plants were grown for 3 weeks in 2 mM $^{14}NO_3K$ medium, then transferred to 10 mM $^{15}NO_3K$ medium (99.5 % enrichment) for 5 min. Thereafter, they were transferred to ^{14}N medium for either 5 min or 60 min. Leaf samples were cryoprocessed, embedded, and dry-cut as described elsewhere [4]. Since nitrate is a diffusible ion, the preparation procedure was devised to optimize preservation of compartmentalization in plant cells. Normal physiological compartmentalization of highly diffusible solutes (K, Ca, Na, Mg) was verified by SIMS (data not shown). For quantification, biological standards were prepared as described in [5]. Isotopic ratios in standards were measured by SIMS and gazeous mass spectrometry of whole leaves. The results of the two methods were in agreement. Imaging and analysis with the NANOSIMS 50 ion probe were performed with as a Cs^+ primary ion beam at 8 keV energy used to sputter the sample. Probe size was 100 nm carrying 2 pA. Negative secondary ions at 8 keV energy were collected and detected in multicollection mode (up to 4 detectors

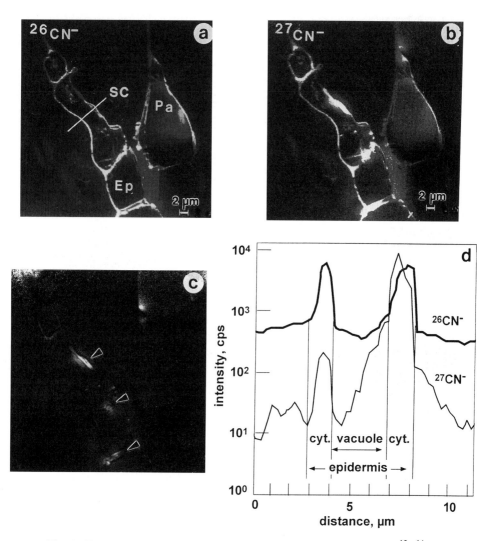

Fig. 1. Short time of transport inside the leaf (10 min). Images of (a) $^{12}C^{14}N^-$, (b) $^{12}C^{15}N^-$, and (c) $^{14}N/^{15}N$ calculated ratio (Ep: epidermal cell; Pa: parenchyma cell). (d) Scanline on ^{14}N and ^{15}N images (cyt.: cytoplasm). The $^{15}N/^{14}N$ ratio in some internal and intercellular regions of the epidermal cells was 20–fold higher than the natural ratio (arrowheads on c). Light regions correspond to ^{15}N enrichment.

905

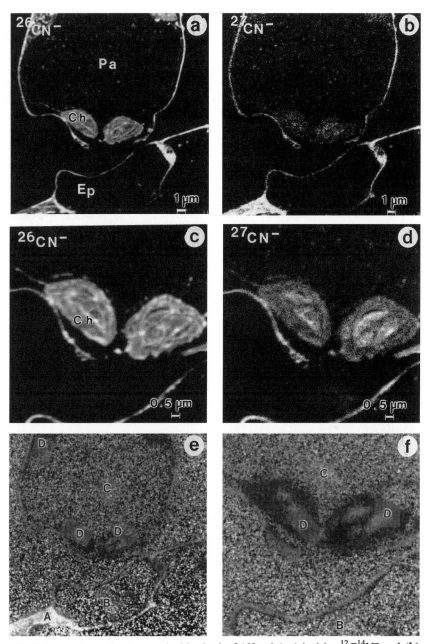

Fig. 2. Long time of transport inside the leaf (60 min). (a), (c) : $^{12}C^{14}N^-$ and (b), (d) : $^{12}C^{15}N^-$. (e), (f) : $^{14}N/^{15}N$ image ratios. (Ep: epidermal cell; Pa: parenchyma cell; Ch: chloroplast). In (e) and (f): A, B, C, D, E et F are regions where mean ratios were calculated. Light regions correspond to ^{15}N enrichment.

simultaneously). To separate the $^{12}C^{15}N^-$ and $^{13}C^{14}N^-$ polyatomic ions at mass number 27, the mass spectrometer was tuned to achieve a mass resolution of 5000 [6,7]. The $^{15}N/^{14}N$ ratio images were calculated using $^{12}C^{14}N^-$ images smoothed with a volume conservative filter [8]. Mean ratios on image areas were compared using GLM procedure of SAS software [9]: italic letters indicate values significantly different at 0.001 probability.

3. Results and discussion

The different tissues of the leaf were recognized. The sites of water and solute import (xylem vessels) are located at the centre of the leaf width, approximately 100 µm distant from the farthest tissue (epidermis) where water is evaporated. After the short ^{14}N chase (5 min) (Fig. 1 a, b), the $^{15}N/^{14}N$ ratio in the epidermis was 20–fold higher than the natural ratio, while in other tissues the $^{15}N/^{14}N$ ratio was close to the natural ratio (Fig. 1 c, d). That means that nitrate entering the leaf was primarily transported to the epidermis. After the longer ^{14}N chase (60 min) (Fig. 2 a, b), the $^{15}N/^{14}N$ ratio decreased in the epidermis. The tracer ^{15}N was observed in the cytoplasm of the epidermis (Figs. 2 b and 2 e; isotopic ratio at spot A in Fig. 2 e : 0.0215*a*) and to a lesser extent in the vacuole of the epidermis (0.0093*b* at spot B in Fig. 2 e). By contrast with the short time, the parenchyma cell displayed an increased labelling, indicating a redistribution of ^{15}N from the epidermis to the inner tissues: the tracer appeared in the vacuoles (Fig 2 d and 2 e; 0.0085*b* at spot C in Fig. 2 e) and in chloroplasts (0.0055*c* at spot D in Fig. 2 e). With a greater magnification, scanlines (data not shown) and image analysis showed that ^{15}N enrichment in chloroplasts can locally reach 3-fold the natural ratio (0.0098*b* at spot E in Fig 2 f). The chloroplasts are known as the sites of first steps of nitrate assimilation [10]. These results suggest that nitrate, after being delivered to the leaf by the xylem vessels, was directly transported to the epidermis by evaporation stream (bulk water movement), then diffused back to the inner tissues. The role of epidermis as a first step in the nitrate translocation pathway has only been observed by SIMS microanalysis techniques [4].

4. Conclusion

The unique features of the NANOSIMS 50 Ion probe, *i.e.* high lateral resolution, simultaneous acquisition of two different signals, and high mass resolving power, has demonstrated the unsuspected role of the epidermis in the distribution of N in plant leaves. We were able to follow the fate of newly acquired N within the plant leaf and to demonstrate nitrogen (^{15}N) localization at the suborganelle level for the analysis of N assimilation.

References
[1] F. Hillion, B. Daigne, F. Girard and G. Slodzian, SIMS IX Proc., Yokohama (1993) 254.
[2] F. Hillion, B. Daigne, F. Girard and G. Slodzian, SIMS X Proc., Münster (1995) 979.
[3] Touraine B., Glass ADM., Plant Physiol., 114 (1997) 137.
[4] N. Grignon, S. Halpern, J. Jeusset, C. Briançon and P. Fragu, J. Microsc., 186 (1997) 51.
[5] N. Grignon, S. Halpern, J. Jeusset, E. Lebeau, C. Moro, A. Gojon and P. Fragu, J. Trace Microprobe Tech., 4 (1999) in press.
[6] L. Schaumann, P. Galle, W. Ulrich and M. Thellier, C. R. Acad. Sci. Paris, Life Sci. 302 (1986) 109.
[7] N. Grignon, S. Halpern, A. Gojon and P. Fragu, Biol. Cell, 74 (1992) 143.
[8] R. Deriche, Inter. J. Computer Vision, 1 (1987) 167.
[9] SAS Institute, Cary, North Carolina (1987).
[10] N.M. Crawford and A.D.M. Glass. Trends Plant Sci., 3 (1998) 389.

A. Benninghoven, P. Bertrand, H.-N. Migeon and H.W. Werner (Editors).
Proceedings of the 12th International Conference on Secondary Ion Mass Spectrometry,
Brussels, Belgium, 5-11 September 1999

ALBUMIN ADSORPTION ON POLYCARBONATE : CORRELATION BETWEEN XPS AND TOF-SIMS ANALYSES

L.Rouxhet and P.Bertrand
Unité de Physico-Chimie et de Physique des Matériaux
Croix du Sud1 B-1348 Louvain-la-Neuve Belgium
e-mail : bertrand@pcpm.ucl.ac.be

1. Introduction

The implantation of a biomaterial often induces an inflammatory response. When it comes in contact with biological fluids, the implant surface is reconditioned by proteins which will direct the subsequent interactions with cells and eventually lead to a granulation tissue and/or to thrombus formation. The biocompatibility is thus highly dependent on the interactions between proteins and the surface and is directed by the surface properties. Among plasma proteins, albumin is the most abundant one and a major candidate for adsorption at the implant surface. Polycarbonate, a potential biomaterial for artificial organs, has been selected for this study.

XPS is well known for its ability of quantification of protein adsorption. In this work, it has been attempted to evaluate the performances of ToF-SIMS for this quantification by comparison with XPS.

2. Materials and methods

The polymer substrates consisted either of bisphenol A polycarbonate PC (Lexan 8800) 15 μm thick films from General Electric (Brussels, Belgium), hydrophilic PC 10 μm thick membranes with a pore size of 0,4 μm or Argon plasma (50 W, 10 min) treated hydrophilic PC 10 μm thick membranes dipped into polyvinylpyrrolidone (PVP) after the plasma treatment. All the membranes were purchased from Whatman S.A. (Louvain-la-Neuve, Belgium) and had a pore density of 6.10^8 pores/cm^2. The films were washed in *n*-hexane to remove the PDMS contamination detected in preliminary experiments.

Protein adsorption

After incubation for 2h at 37°C in 2 ml of the bovine serum albumin (Sigma, St Louis, MI) solutions at selected concentrations (varying from 0 to 10 mg/ml), each sample (disk of 13 mm diameter) was rinsed 3 times with PBS (phosphate buffer saline) and 3 times with ultrapure water while shaking for 5 minutes. The samples were then flushed with a nitrogen flow and stored in a dessicator containing P_2O_5. PBS was adjusted at pH 7.4 and consists of NaCl 137 mM, KCl 2.68 mM, KH_2PO_4 6.44 mM and $Na_2HPO_4.2H_2O$ 8.00 mM. Ultrapure water (resistivity $\geq$ 18 mΩ) was prepared with a Milli-Q system (Millipore, Bedford, MA).

X-ray Photoelectron Spectroscopy (XPS)

XPS measurements were performed with a SSX100/206 spectrometer (Fisons) equipped with an aluminum anode (10kV) and a quartz monochromator. The direction of photoelectron collection made angles of 55° and 71° with the surface normal of the sample and with the incident X-ray beam, respectively. The electron flood gun was set at 6 eV. For each sample, the O_{1s}, N_{1s} and C_{1s} bands were recorded with a 1000 μm spot, an emission current of 12 mA and a pass energy of 50 eV, followed by a wide scan (0-1100 eV) collected with an emission current of 20 mA and a pass energy of 150 eV. The binding energies of the analyzed peaks were determined by fixing the C_{1s} component due to carbon only bound to carbon and hydrogen at 284.8 eV. The peak area was determined using a linear background and a Gaussian/Lorentzian (85/15) function . The atomic percentages were calculated from the peak area corrected by the corresponding sensitivity factor (C_{1s} : 1.0, O_{1s} : 2.49, N_{1s} : 1.68)

Time-of-flight secondary ion mass spectrometry (ToF-SIMS)

Positive ToF-SIMS spectra were recorded with a PHI-Evans TFS-4000MMI (TRIFT) spectrometer. A pulsed 15keV Gallium ion beam (15 keV, 800 pA DC, 11kHz frequency and 20 ns unbunched pulse width) was rastered over a 130 μm x 130 μm area for an acquisition time of 300s. The fluence was about 2.10^{12} ions/cm^2, which ensured static conditions. The secondary ions were accelerated to ± 3 keV by applying a bias on the sample. The spreading of the initial kinetic energy of the secondary ions was compensated by 270° deflection in three electrostatic analyzers. To increase the detection efficiency of high-mass ions, a 7 keV post-acceleration was applied at the detector entry. The best mass-resolution (m/Δm) obtained with this ToF-SIMS spectrometer is 11000 at m/z = 28 on a Si wafer. For the present samples and analytical conditions, the mass resolution was about 2500 at m/z = 29.

3. Results and discussion
XPS

The amount of albumin adsorbed on the surface of the different substrates studied has been evaluated by calculating the N/C ratio from the decomposition of the C_{1s}, O_{1s} and N_{1s} individual spectra as reported in the literature [1]. The results obtained for each substrate are reported in figure 1. The N/C ratios of the film reported are the mean between 5 independent experiments whereas the ratios of the hydrophobic membrane were calculated for two independent experiments.

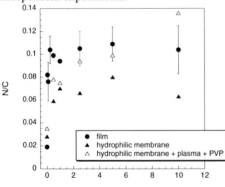

Figure 1 : Evolution of the N/C ratio determined by XPS as a function of the albumin concentration

A nitrogen contamination from the atmosphere was detected on all the samples. Actually, the N/C ratio of the native substrates varied between 0.018 and 0.037. Saturation of the surface appeared very rapidly. Roughly, the surface was saturated when any of the sample was incubated with solutions containing at least 250 μg/ml of albumin. According to these results, protein adsorption was slightly higher on the film and on the hydrophilic membrane which went through a plasma treatment and was dipped into PVP than on the other membrane. These are however preliminary results and duplicates should be performed on the membranes to examine the reproducibility of the measurements.

The maximal N/C ratio was approximately 0.1. Theoretical calculations from the aminoacid composition of the protein showed that the N/C ratio of albumin is 0.286. Conformation changes upon adsorption most probably appeared and could result in lower N/C values than the theoretical one. Nevertheless, the very low N/C values obtained are probably pointing out that either the protein does not entirely cover the surface or the protein layer is so thin that the substrate contributes to the C signal. Albumin is an ellipsoid 14 x 3.8 x 3.8 nm protein [2]. If the protein adsorbed in a 'vertical' position, it would form a layer about 14 nm thick. The substrate would thus not contribute to the C signal and the results obtained would mean that only part of the surface is covered by the protein. However, albumin is well-known as a highly deformable protein and therefore it would maximize its interactions with the substrate. It would thus adsorb in an 'horizontal' or intermediary position and the results might be explained by the second proposition.

ToF-SIMS

Two different methods have been used to evaluate the protein adsorption from the ToF-SIMS results. The first one consisted of comparing the evolution of one peak characteristic of the protein and one of the polymer situated at close m/z to minimize any bias resulting from the charge effect. A careful analysis of spectra of the native polymer and protein brought the choice to the peak at m/z = 120 (characteristic of $C_8H_{10}N^+$ ion) for albumin and the one at m/z = 135 (characteristic of $C_9H_{11}O^+$) for PC [3]. The second one consisted of summing the intensity of the nitrogen containing peaks at m/z up to 120 and dividing the sum by the total intensity of the spectrum without the inorganic contaminants. The results obtained for each substrate are reported in figures 2 and 3. The results reported for the membranes are the mean for 4 different areas of the same sample. Those reported for the film are the mean of 5 independent experiments. For each experiment, the spectra of 4 different areas of the sample have been taken.

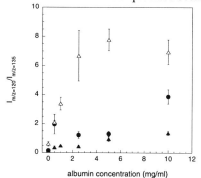

Figure 2 : Evolution of the ratio of the peak intensities at m/z = 120 and m/z = 135 as a function of the albumin concentration

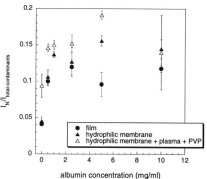

Figure 3 : Evolution of the relative intensity of N-containing peaks as a function of the albumin concentration

Results obtained with the second method revealed, like the XPS results, that the surface was saturated with the protein at low concentration. It is obvious that the sum of the N-containing peaks present at the surface of the plasma treated membrane dipped into PVP before adsorption was higher than on the other substrates. Actually, PVP is a N-containing polymer. The hydrophilic membrane had also been dipped into PVP but it appears clearly

910

here that the plasma pre-treatment modified the surface in such a way that much more PVP is fixed on the surface. The first method confirmed these observations. According to these preliminary results, I_{120}/I_{135} was much higher on the plasma treated membrane than on the other one and on the film. It was difficult to highlight a net difference in protein adsorption on the different substrates by the second method. The differences observed between the two data analyses might indicate changes in protein conformation or segregation, but this needs further investigations to be confirmed.

The fast decrease of the relative intensity of one peak characteristic of the substrate (m/z = 135) upon adsorption revealed, as reported in figure 4, that the protein dispersion was quite homogeneous at the extreme surface according to the analysis depth [4]. These results favour the second hypothesis from the XPS results about the protein dispersion. Nevertheless, since the residual relative intensity was different from zero, it suggests that the substrate was not completely covered with the protein. Eventhough XPS and ToF-SIMS present differences, SIMS brings complementary pieces of evidence to the XPS analyses.

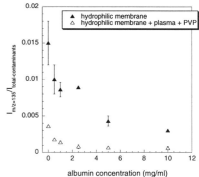

Figure 4 : Evolution of the relative intensity of the peak at m/z = 135 as a function of the albumin concentration

4. Conclusion

Discrepancies have been noted between the comparative behaviour of the different substrates obtained by XPS and by ToF-SIMS data analysis. Nevertheless, it was possible to follow protein adsorption by ToF-SIMS and to detect specific peaks of the protein. A confirmation of the ToF-SIMS results would be necessary before going deeper into the interpretation. However, ToF-SIMS seems to enhance the differences between substrates due to the lower analysis depth. This technique brings complementary informations to XPS. However, it is currently difficult to make a precise quantification of the amount of adsorbed protein. Two different types of data analysis have been used in this work and led to different results. It will thus be necessary to optimize the data treatment by finding a reproducible way to estimate protein adsorption by taking into account possible matrix effects. Quantification of the adsorption of radiolabelled albumin would provide a precise amount of protein adsorbed and would help define the contributions of each technique.

Acknowledgment

L.Rouxhet and this work are financially supported by the European Commission CRAFT-BARP project # BMH4-CT98-9516

References

[1] Y. Dufrêne, T.G. Marchal and P.G. Rouxhet, Appl. Surface Sci., 144-145 (1999) 638
[2] J.Y. Yoon, H.Y. Park, J.H. Kim and W.S. Kim, J.Colloid Interface Sci., 177 (1996) 613
[3] J.C. Vickerman, D. Briggs and A. Henderson, The Wiley Static SIMS Library, Wiley and Sons Publishers, England, 1977, p.3:3.23
[4] A. Delcorte, P. Bertrand, E. Wischerhoff and A. Laschewsky, Langmuir, 13 (1997) 5125

A. Benninghoven, P. Bertrand, H.-N. Migeon and H.W. Werner (Editors).
Proceedings of the 12th International Conference on Secondary Ion Mass Spectrometry,
Brussels, Belgium, 5-11 September 1999
© 2000 Elsevier Science B.V. All rights reserved.

TOF-SIMS CHARACTERISATION OF SIMPLE AND COMPLEX CARBOHYDRATE CONTAINING PHOTOACTIVATABLE REAGENTS FOR SURFACE GLYCOENGINEERING

D. Léonard[a]*, F. Heger[a], Y. Chevolot[a], J. Martins[b], D.H.G. Crout[b], H. Sigrist[c] and H.J. Mathieu[a]

[a]Laboratoire de Métallurgie Chimique (LMCH), Département des Matériaux, Ecole Polytechnique Fédérale de Lausanne (EPFL), CH-1015 Lausanne - EPFL, Switzerland
*corresponding author: Dr Didier Léonard (email: didier.leonard@epfl.ch)
[b]Department of Chemistry, University of Warwick, CV4 5AL Coventry, UK
[c]Centre Suisse d'Electronique et de Microtechnique (CSEM), 2007 Neuchâtel, Switzerland

1. Introduction

Controlled surface glycoengineering is of crucial importance in biosensing, cell guidance and biomedical applications. Our route to surface glycoengineering is based on photochemistry through derivatisation of carbohydrates with a photoactivatable group (i.e. diazirines). Previous studies using X-ray Photoelectron Spectroscopy (XPS) and Time-of-Flight Secondary Ion Mass Spectrometry (ToF-SIMS) have demonstrated the surface photoimmobilisation of a newly synthesised aryldiazirine derivatised galactose, MAD-Gal ((N-[m-[3-(trifluoromethyl) diazirin-3-yl] phenyl]-4-(-3-thio(-1-D-galactopyranosyl)-succinimidyl)butyramide)) (Figure 1a) [1]. The next step is the application of the strategy to more complex carbohydrates. This study focuses on the ToF-SIMS characterisation of the photoimmobilised molecule containing a more complex carbohydrate (lactose aryl diazirine : 5-carboxamidopentyl N-[m-[3-(trifluoromethyl)diazirin-3-yl] phenyl β-D-galactopyranosyl)-(1->4)-1-thio-β-D-glucopyranoside - Figure 1b). Of particular interest is also the ability of the technique to differentiate the synthesised molecules because their spectral differences could be related to differences observed in biological assays of the surface immobilised carbohydrates.

2. Experimental Conditions

MAD-Gal was synthesised following the protocol of Chevolot et al [1]. Details about the synthesis of lactose aryl diazirine are given elsewhere [2]. Diamond deposited on a Si/Si_3N_4 wafer served as substrate for photoimmobilisation of both molecules. Pristine diamond samples were washed (5 min, ultrasonic treatment in hexane then in ethanol) and dried for 2 hours at room temperature under vacuum (6 mbar). Then a MAD-Gal or lactose aryl diazirine solution (0.25 mM in ethanol, 10 µl) was deposited and the samples were dried for 2 hours at room temperature under vacuum (30-40 mbar). For photobonding, the samples were irradiated for 20 min using the Stratalinker 350 nm light source with an irradiance of 0.95 mW/cm^2 and washed again. The investigated samples were referenced as: **A** (pristine surface), **B** (washed surface), **C** (after deposition), **D** (C illuminated), **E** (C not illuminated but washed) and **F** (C illuminated then washed).

The ToF-SIMS system used in this study was a commercial ToF-SIMS mass spectrometer (described in detail elsewhere [3-4]) from PHI-EVANS (PHI-EVANS Trift 1). The DC 15 keV ^{69}Ga$^+$ ion beam current was pulsed at 5 kHz repetition rate (pulse width of about 7 ns (unbunched)). Spectra acquisition was performed in high mass resolution conditions (bunched ion beam) without any charge compensation. The analysed area was estimated to be a square of 84 x 84 µm^2. The total ion dose for a 5 min spectrum was below $1 \cdot 10^{12}$ ions/cm^2, which is within the so-called 'static' SIMS conditions [5].

ToF-SIMS spectra were recorded for each sample on four different sample spots for both positive and negative ions. Values presented (in Figure 2 and Table 1) are mean values and standard deviations. ToF-SIMS peak values were normalised by dividing the absolute peak intensity of secondary ions by the corrected total intensity, i.e. the total intensity from which intensities of H$^{+/-}$ (because of their low reproducibility), of some inorganic peaks, and of the main peaks of ubiquitous contaminants such as PDMS were subtracted.

3. Results and Discussion

Several low mass characteristic signatures have been identified for MAD-Gal (Figure 1a) [1]. They are similar to those observed for the basic diazirine containing photoreagent MAD [1] and are related to the diazirine group (CN$_2^-$), the CF$_3$ group (F$^-$ and CF$_3^-$) and to the succinimidyl group (CN$^-$, CNO$^-$ and C$_4$H$_4$NO$_2^-$, characteristic peak of the whole group) [1].

In the case of the lactose aryl diazirine molecule (Figure 1b), the succinimidyl group is no longer present, there is a different spacer and a different carbohydrate, lactose. A different efficiency of the surface immobilised carbohydrate is expected for semi-synthesis with α 2-6 sialyl transferase [2]. Photoimmobilised MAD-Gal on polystyrene has led to very good biological responses with galactose specific (Allo A) lectins and primary rat hepatocytes [2]. However, semi-synthesis was not be very efficient with this molecule because of the presence of the succinimidyl group in the structure. Moreover, for the semi-synthesis application, lactose appears to be the most suitable carbohydrate.

Figure 2 displays for MAD-Gal and lactose aryl diazirine the variation in relative intensity for F$^-$ and CN$_2^-$ detected at the various photoimmobilisation steps. The results illustrate that the same conclusions can be drawn for the two molecules: when illuminated, the diazirine functions are lost as exhibited by the difference in CN$_2^-$ relative intensity between samples **C** and **D**. They lead to carbenes which then react at the surface. On the other hand, molecules are still present at the surface only if the illumination was performed before the final washing as illustrated by the difference in F$^-$ relative intensity between samples **E** and **F**.

Table 1 displays the normalised values of selected negative and positive ions for surfaces before (samples **B**) and after (samples **C**) molecule solution deposition. The most significant differences are related to the absence of the succinimidyl group in the structure of the lactose aryl diazirine molecule (see CNO$^-$ and mostly C$_4$H$_4$NO$_2^-$ which is characteristic of the succinimidyl group). The same information is given in the positive ion spectra by among others C$_4$H$_8$NO$^+$. Concerning the expected difference between the two carbohydrates, only limited information can be obtained from the low mass range of positive and negative ion spectra. Numerous low mass oxygen containing peaks exhibit very similar normalised intensities (data not shown). Even those for which a difference is observed like C$_2$H$_3$O$_2^+$ (Table 1) are probably not specific as they are also observed for samples **B** and thus could be related to contamination.

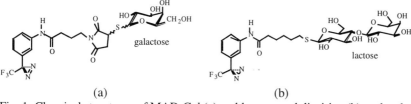

(a)   (b)

Fig. 1. Chemical structures of MAD-Gal (a) and lactose aryl diazirine (b) molecules

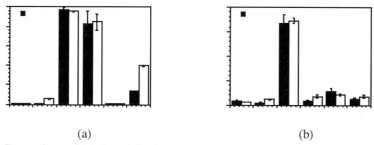

(a)   (b)

Fig. 2. Comparison of (a) F⁻ and (b) CN_2^- normalised intensities (‰) for the various steps of the process of MAD-Gal and lactose aryl diazirine (LACTO) immobilisation on diamond.

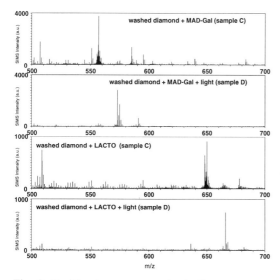

Fig. 3. Positive ion mass spectra in the mass range 500-700 amu for the **C** and **D** steps of the process of MAD-Gal and lactose aryl diazirine (LACTO) immobilisation on diamond.

914

It is the high mass range in the positive ion spectra which definitively exhibits the most characteristic difference between ToF-SIMS spectra of the two molecules. As illustrated in Figure 3, a high mass peak at 557 m/z is observed in the case of MAD-Gal when the molecule is deposited (sample **C**) and another high mass fragment is observed at 573 m/z after illumination (sample **D**). The difference corresponds to an oxygen atom and this is consistent with previous observation [1] of reaction of the photoreactive part with a surface O atom. However, it has not been clear how to relate these peaks to MAD-Gal (the molecular peak should be detected at 562 m/z). Here, the observation of corresponding peaks for the lactose aryl diazirine molecule (at 650 and 666 m/z - Figure 3), consistent with the expected difference in mass of both molecules, indicates that all these peaks must be characteristic fragments of the molecules and are not related to contamination. It is proposed that peaks at 557 and 650 m/z correspond to $(M-2N+Na)^+$. The cationisation with Na^+ is consistent with high levels observed for Na^+ (data not shown) and previous observations of such effects for carbohydrates [6]. The only difference is that the cationised ion is not $(M+Na)^+$ but involves the loss of the diazirine even when not illuminated. This was not observed in the negative ion mass spectra of the basic photoreagent MAD [1] and illustrates a clear difference in the creation of positive and negative ions for molecules containing the reactive diazirine function.

Acknowledgements
Financial support by the Swiss Priority Program on Materials Research is gratefully acknowledged.

References
[1]   D. Léonard, Y. Chevolot, O. Bucher, H. Sigrist and H. J. Mathieu, Surf. Interface Anal. 26 (1998) 783; Y. Chevolot, O. Bucher, D. Léonard, H. J. Mathieu and H. Sigrist, Bioconjug. Chem. 10 (1999) 169; D. Léonard, Y. Chevolot, O. Bucher, W. Haenni, H. Sigrist and H.J. Mathieu, Surf. Interface Anal. 26 (1998) 793.
[2]   Y. Chevolot, PhD thesis, EPFL, Lausanne (1999)
[3]   B.W. Schueler, Microsc. Microanalysis Microstructure 3 (1992) 119
[4]   K. Franzreb, H.J. Mathieu and D. Landolt, Surf. Interface Anal. 23 (1995) 641
[5]   D. Briggs in Practical Surface Analysis, Second Edition, Volume 2. Ion and Neutral Spectroscopy, D. Briggs and M. P. Seah (Eds), John Wiley, Chichester, 1992, p 367
[6]   M.C. Davies, R.A.P. Lynn, S.S. Davis, J. Hearn, J.F. Watts, J.C. Vickerman and A.J. Paul, Langmuir 9 (1993) 1637.

Table 1
Normalised ToF-SIMS intensities (‰) for surfaces before (**B**) and after (**C**) MAD-Gal and lactose aryl diazirine (LACTO) immobilisation on diamond. 98^- refers to $C_4H_4NO_2^-$, 59^- refers to $C_2H_3O_2^-$, 61^+ refers to $C_2H_5O_2^+$ and 86^+ refers to $C_4H_8NO^+$.

	MAD-Gal **B**	MAD-Gal **C**	LACTO **B**	LACTO **C**
CN^-	7.28 ± 0.91	131.4 ± 1.2	2.97 ± 0.18	135.2 ± 5.6
CNO^-	4.66 ± 0.71	8.61 ± 0.32	2.19 ± 0.15	4.77 ± 1.02
98^-	0.07 ± 0.01	0.61 ± 0.01	0.04 ± 0.00	0.10 ± 0.05
59^-	3.89 ± 0.33	0.48 ± 0.02	3.95 ± 3.77	2.05 ± 0.50
61^+	0.42 ± 0.02	1.80 ± 0.05	0.21 ± 0.02	3.53 ± 0.86
86^+	0.29 ± 0.05	7.15 ± 0.09	0.21 ± 0.02	0.27 ± 0.03

A. Benninghoven, P. Bertrand, H.-N. Migeon and H.W. Werner (Editors).
Proceedings of the 12th International Conference on Secondary Ion Mass Spectrometry,
Brussels, Belgium, 5-11 September 1999
© 2000 Elsevier Science B.V. All rights reserved.

INVESTIGATION OF THE IMMOBILIZATION PROCESS OF NUCLEIC ACID

C. Höppener, J. Drexler, M. Ostrop, and H. F. Arlinghaus

Physikalisches Institut der Universität Münster, Wilhelm-Klemm-Str. 10,
D-48149 Münster, Germany, Email: arlinghaus@uni-muenster.de

1. Introduction

In recent years, DNA chip technology has been a subject of growing interest for DNA sequencing as well as for clinical diagnostics and forensics. DNA-chips are based on the method of sequencing by hybridization (SBH), where unknown DNA sequences, which are typically labeled with radioactive or fluorescent markers, are hybridized to known complementary short DNA sequences called oligodeoxynucleotides (ODN), which have been immobilized on a solid surface [1-3]. The hybridization depends on the development of hydrogen bonds between the different nucleic bases following the Watson-Crick-rules that allow only AT and GC base pair combinations between DNA strands. The main variables in SBH are the attachment of the nucleic acid sequences to the solid surface, the conditions for hybridization, and the detection of the hybridized DNA sequences.

We have used TOF-SIMS and temperature-programmed SIMS (TP-SIMS) to examine the process of immobilizing ODN to either silanized silicon wafers or directly to Au-coated glass surfaces by thiol-linkers. The silanization process and the influence of ODN concentration and immobilization time on the immobilization process are discussed in this paper.

2. Experiment

The experiments were performed with a Poschenrieder-type TOF (Münster TOF-I) and a high-resolution TOF-SIMS (Münster TOF-II) instrument. The Poschenrieder instrument was equipped with a combined cooling and heating device which controled the sample temperature with an adjustable temperature rate in the range of 150-700 K [4]. The primary ion beam of 11 keV Ar^+ ions was focussed to a beam width of approximately 70 µm. The acquisition time was typically 100 s with a primary ion current of 0.3 pA, a bombarded raster area of 200x200 µm² resulting in a total ion dose of $5x10^{11}$ ions/cm².

3. Sample Preparation

ODN was immobilized to either silanized silicon wafers (5x5 mm²) or directly to Au-coated glass surfaces (6x6 mm²) by thiol-linkers.

Silanization: For destroying the oxide layer and creating a hydrophobic surface, the Si wafers were etched in a 1% aqueous solution of HF for 2 minutes, rinsed with deionized H_2O and then UV/ozone-treated to ensure that the surface was completely covered with OH-groups.

Subsequently, the Si wafers were silanized with either 3-Glycidoxypropyltrimethoxysilane or 2-3-4-Epoxycyclohexylethylsilane by immersing them in a 1:1000 diluted silane:hexane solution for approximately 25 minutes at 25°C under separation of methanol. The silanized samples were rinsed with hexane four times to remove molecules that were not covalently bonded to the surface and then air dried.

Immobilization to silanized Si wafers: ODNs were solved in deionized H_2O obtaining concentrations between 1 μM and 1 mM. About 1 μl of the solution was pipetted onto the silanized silicon wafer (drop diameter of about 1 mm) and left there for several hours for immobilization. During that time, the epoxygroup of the silane breaks open and allows the formation of covalent bonds to the NH_2–linker of the ODNs. Subsequently, the wafers were washed with H_2O to remove ODN that was not covalently bonded.

Immobilization to Au surfaces: ODNs, modified with thiol-linkers, e.g., H-S-$(CH_2)_6$-AAAAAAAAAA, were dissolved in an aqueous solution, obtaining concentrations between 1 μM and 1 mM. An Au-coated glass sample was put in the solution for approximately 24 hours to allow the formation of self-assembled monolayers. During that time, the thiol-linker of the ODN forms a covalent bond to the Au surface. Subsequently, the samples were rinsed for several minutes with deionized water to remove ODN that was not covalently bonded.

4. Results and Discussion

The conditions for silanizing the silicon wafers with either 3-Glycidoxy-propyltrimethoxysilane or 2-3-4-Epoxycyclohexylethylsilane were investigated by varying concentration and self-assembly time. This resulted in an optimum self-assembly time of approximately 25 min for 1 mM solution. Figure 1 depicts TOF-SIMS spectra of the two silanes and Figure 2 the silane signals as a function of silane concentration for 25 minutes self-assembly time. The highest signal is obtained at 1 mM solution. Notable is the difference in maximum signal

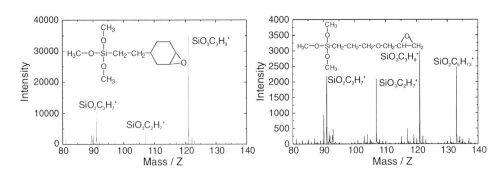

Fig. 1 TOF-SIMS spectra of 2-3-4-Epoxycyclohexylethylsilane (left) and (b) 3-Glycidoxypropyltrimethoxysilane (right).

between the two silanes. TP-SIMS measurements were used to investigate the thermal stability. The data in Figure 3 show that the two types of silane evaporate at slightly different temperatures, indicating a difference in binding energies.

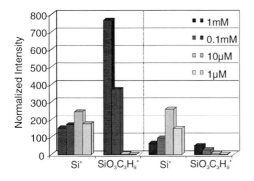

Fig. 2 Dependence of silane signal on concentration.

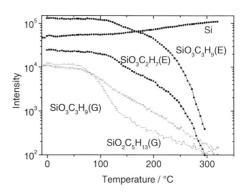

Fig. 3 TP-SIMS measurements of 3-Glycidoxypropyltrimethoxysilane and 2-3-4-Epoxycyclohexylethylsilane.

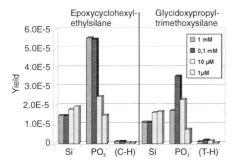

Fig. 4 Dependence of ODN yield on ODN concentration on a silanized Si-wafer with 18 h immobilization time.

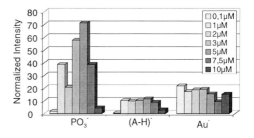

Fig. 5 Dependence of ODN signal on ODN concentration on Au with 24 h immobilization time.

The conditions for immobilizing ODN on Si wafers silanized with 3-Glycidoxypropyltrimethoxysilane and 2-3-4-Epoxycyclohexylethylsilane were investigated by varying concentration and immobilization time. Masses corresponding to PO_2^-, PO_3^- and $H_2PO_4^-$ and the protonated $(M_b+H)^+$ and deprotonated $(M_b-H)^-$ signals of the bases were used to identify the presence of ODN. The data indicate that for both silanes the surface is well covered with ODN after 9 h immobilization. Shown at 18 h immobilization time is the ODN signal as a function of ODN concentration and type of silane (Figure 4). The maximum yield for the two wafers varies by less than a factor of two between the maximum signal, indicating that under saturated conditions the two variables are less critical for the immobilization process, and does not show the noticeable difference between the maximum signals as was seen for the silanes in Figure 2. TP-SIMS measurements for ODN on silanes show the bases starting to evaporate at 150 °C.

The conditions for immobilizing thiol-linked ODN directly to Au surfaces were also investigated by varying concentration and immobilization time.

918

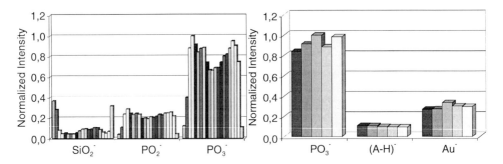

Fig. 6 Dependence of ODN signal on ion beam position on immobilized droplet on a silanized Si wafer (left) and on a Au surface (right). Linescan approximately 1.2 mm.
ODN on Si: c = 0.1 mM, t = 18 h, ODN on Au: c = 1 µM, t = 24 h

In contrast to the ODN data on silanized Si wafers, the data showed that the surface is only completely covered after 24 h immobilization time. Figure 5 depicts the ODN signal as a function of ODN concentration for 24 h self-assembly time. The highest signal is obtained with a 3 µM solution. TP-SIMS measurements showed, as expected, similar thermal characteristics as seen for ODN immobilized on silanized Si wafers, with the onset of signal decrease for $(M_b\text{-}H)^-$ at 150 °C.

The homogeneity of the immobilized DNA distribution was examined for both ODN on silanized Si-wafers and ODN on Au surfaces. As shown in Figure 6, ODN on Au was more evenly distributed than ODN on silanized silicon oxides, which exhibits the typical donut shape of droplet preparation. The pipetted and dried ODN droplet distribution was likely affected by the ionic strength of the aqueous DNA solution. Adding salt to the ODN solution such as $MgCl_2$ resulted in a decrease of the DNA charge and a better homogeneity. Measurements of how surface structure affects the process of immobilization on Au-surfaces showed a higher intensity of the characteristic ODN signals and a less homogeneous ODN layer with increasing surface roughness.

5. Conclusion

We have shown that both TOF-SIMS and TP-SIMS are valuable tools for studying the complexity of the silanization and immobilization processes on SiO_2- and Au-surfaces. ODN can readily be identified by either monitoring the phosphate ions or the corresponding protonated or deprotonated bases. In future experiments, we will use both techniques for studying the complexity of the hybridization process which has a significantly higher number of variables than those of the immobilization process.

References
[1] E.M. Southern, U. Maskos, and J.K. Elder, Genomics **13**, 1008 (1992).
[2] H.F. Arlinghaus, M.N. Kwoka, and K.B. Jacobson, Analy. Chem. **69**, 3747 (1997).
[3] H. F. Arlinghaus, C. Höppener, and J. Drexler, this conference.
[4] M. Deimel, D. Rading, G. Egbers, E. Göcke, and A. Benninghoven, in: *SIMS X Proceedings,* ed. A. Benninghoven et al., J. Wiley & Sons, New York (1997), p 507.

A. Benninghoven, P. Bertrand, H.-N. Migeon and H.W. Werner (Editors).
Proceedings of the 12th International Conference on Secondary Ion Mass Spectrometry,
Brussels, Belgium, 5-11 September 1999
© 2000 Elsevier Science B.V. All rights reserved.

CHARACTERIZATION OF PHARMACEUTICALS BY TOF-SIMS

A. Belu*, S. Bryan*, M.C. Davies^, N. Patel[†]
*Physical Electronics, 6509 Flying Cloud Drive, Eden Prairie MN 55344 USA
e-mail: abelu@phi.com
^School of Pharmaceutical Sciences, University of Nottingham,
Nottingham NG7 2RD U.K.
[†]Molecular Profiles Ltd, University Park, Nottingham NG7 2RD U.K.

1. Introduction

The use of controlled release drug delivery systems has increased in popularity in the last decade. Many associated advantages include reduced fluctuations of plasma drug concentration, sustained drug effects with reduced side effects, and increased patient compliance [1]. The reservoir controlled release system in which a drug core is enclosed with one or more polymeric layers is a popular controlled release method. The release of drug depends on the physicochemical properties of these polymers used to coat the core particle. Often, a number of different polymer layers are used to form a multi-layer system with each layer designed for a specific purpose, for example, to release the drug at a specific rate or at a specific pH. The coating system must be easy to manufacture, must be stable over an extended shelf life and must deliver the appropriate drug dosage to the target area over the desired time period. Since the fabrication of these systems can be technically difficult compared with conventional dosage forms, evaluation and analysis of the final product is vital. Dissolution studies have the capability to monitor the rate of drug release, however, any unwanted effects observed by these methods cannot be readily associated with specific defects in the structure or composition of the controlled release system. To overcome this, an analytical technique is required which can probe the interior or probe cross-sections of the device for the detection and distribution of various ingredients. Vibrational spectroscopy techniques such as Raman microprobe and FT-IR microscopy are options, however, these techniques to not have sufficient spatial resolution for analyzing the distribution of ingredients or excipient within a system. Time-of-flight secondary ion mass spectrometry (TOF-SIMS) is a powerful method of analyzing and imaging components within cross-sections of drug dosage forms with a sufficiently high level of resolution.

To date, the use of TOF-SIMS within the pharmaceutical industry has centered on the analysis of bulk polymeric films intended for use as either biomaterial coatings or as drug delivery vehicles [2]. In this study we report on the use of TOF-SIMS for analyzing entire drug dosage forms. This information aids in not only the development of drug delivery systems, but also in defending a patented position against infringement and counterfeiting. Here, TOF-SIMS spectroscopy and imaging have been employed to investigate the distribution of excipient, drug and polymer layers within multilayer controlled release pellets.

2. Experimental

Two pellets were analyzed in this study. Each pellet was mounted on a silicon substrate and sectioned in half with a sharp blade. The resultant inner surface (cross-section) was analyzed using a TRIFT II TOF-SIMS (Physical Electronics, Eden Prairie MN USA). During analysis, the instrument employed a 15 keV Ga+ ion source. The 600 pA DC primary ion beam was pulsed at 11 kHz frequency with a pulse width of 12 ns. Under these conditions mass resolution of 9,000 is typical at 28 Da on a silicon substrate. The data was collected using an ion dose below the static SIMS limit of 10^{13} ions/cm^2. A low energy electron beam was used for charge compensation.

3. Results

3.1 Evaluation of Full Drug Pellet Cross-Sections by Imaging

A 500 μm diameter drug pellet was analyzed by TOF-SIMS. The pellet contains a ~100 μm wide silica core, a ~100 μm wide metoprolol drug layer, and a ~50 μm wide outer coating of ethylcellulose. The results shown in Figure 1 are 600 x 600 μm^2 images of the full pellet cross-section. Mapping of specific species allows evaluation of their distribution in each of the layers.

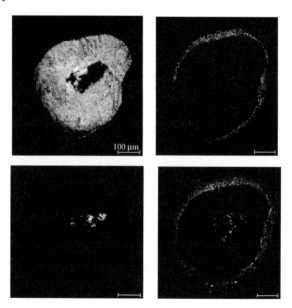

Figure 1. TOF-SIMS images (positive ion mode, 600x600 μm^2) show the distribution of specific species in the drug pellet. The drug metoprolol (molecular ion, 268 Da) is shown in the upper left, the ethylcellulose coating (fragment ion C_3H_7O, 59 Da) is shown in upper right, the silica core (Si, 28 Da) is shown in lower left, and Na (23 Da) is shown in lower right.

3.2 Evaluation of Molecular and Chemical Information Through Spectroscopy

The TOF-SIMS data collection method allows an entire mass spectrum to be collected at each pixel in the image (256 x 256). As a result mass spectra can be extracted from specific regions of interest. The spectra can be analyzed to obtain molecular and chemical information. Figure 2 shows mass spectra extracted from the outer coating, the drug layer and the core of the drug pellet. In the spectrum of the drug layer, the largest signal (268 Da) is representative of the intact molecular ion of metoprolol (not shown). The signals at 58, 72 and 116 Da (labeled with *) reflect the structure of the molecule, as they represent fragments along the backbone. The spectra from the core and from the outer coating show minimal signals at these masses. The spectrum of the outer coating shows a strong signal at 23 Da (Na) and at 59 Da (C_3H_7O, characteristic cellulose fragment). The spectrum of the core shows a strong signal at mass 28 Da (Si), as would be expected for a silica core. However, an unexpected series of signals representative of fluorocarbon species is also observed (12, 31, 69, 100, 119, and 131 Da, labeled with ^). The spectra allow full chemical characterization of each of the layers.

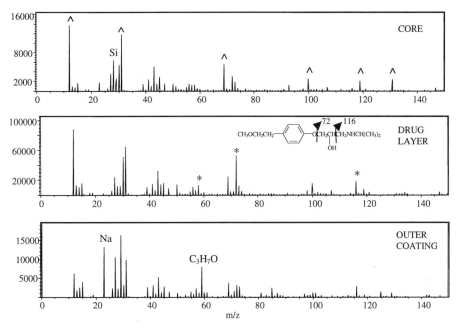

Figure 2. Positive ion mass spectra show that each layer of the drug pellet cross-section has a unique chemical composition. The significant chemical components in each layer are identified. The * represents characteristic metoprolol drug fragment species. The ^ identifies characteristic fluorocarbon species.

3.3 Evaluation of Pellet Components by Imaging

Figure 3 shows 250 x 250 μm^2 images of the edge of a cross-section of a different drug pellet system. This pellet also contains an outer coating of ethylcellulose. The inner core, however contains a mixture of components including a steroid, Avicel (microcrystalline cellulose) and lactose. The image of a characteristic ethylcellulose fragment (59 Da) shows this component to be present in the outer coating as well as a small specific region in the inner layer (Avicel). The image of the lactose signal (365 Da, lactose+Na) indicates it is present as clusters ranging in size from 1 to 20 μm. The image of the steroid (130 Da) shows it also is present as clusters (1 to 10 μm) but with a different distribution than the lactose. The hydrocarbon species (C_2H_3 at 27 Da) shows a fairly homogeneous distribution in both of the layers. The images show that TOF-SIMS is useful for evaluating the integrity of the coatings of drug pellets as well as investigating the distribution of species within a particular layer.

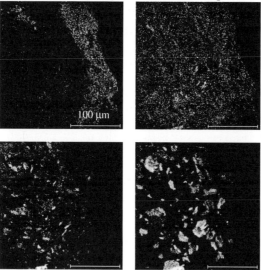

Figure 3. TOF-SIMS images (positive ion mode, 250x250 μm^2) show
the distribution of specific species in the outer layers of a drug pellet.
The ethylcellulose image (fragment ion C_3H_7O, 59 Da) is shown in the
upper left, a common hydrocarbon (C_2H_3, 27 Da) is shown in the
upper right image, the steroid (130 Da) distribution is shown in the
lower left, and the lactose ($C_{12}H_{22}O_{11}Na$ molecular ion, 365 Da)
distribution is shown in the lower right.

4. Summary

TOF-SIMS allows *in situ* analysis of drug pellets. The ability to image molecular ions with submicron spatial resolution makes TOF-SIMS well suited to pharmaceutical analysis. Through imaging of specific species, the integrity of each of the layers can be evaluated. Furthermore, TOF-SIMS is a mass spectral technique, which gives structural and molecular information from each of the layers simultaneously. The chemical composition of each of the layers can then individually be examined.

References

[1] H. Park; K. Park; *Polymers in Pharmaceutical Products* (Chapter 1) in Polymers of Biological and Biomedical Significance, ACS Symposium Series 540, Eds: S.W. Shalaby; Y.
[2] Ikada; R. Langer; J. Williams, 1994.
   D. Briggs; Surface Analysis of Polymers by XPS and Static SIMS, Cambridge Solid State Science Series, Cambridge University Press, 1998.

A. Benninghoven, P. Bertrand, H.-N. Migeon and H.W. Werner (Editors).
Proceedings of the 12th International Conference on Secondary Ion Mass Spectrometry,
Brussels, Belgium, 5-11 September 1999
© 2000 Elsevier Science B.V. All rights reserved.

TOF-SIMS AND LASER-SNMS CHARACTERIZATION OF MULTICOMPONENT PHOSPHOLIPID LANGMUIR-BLODGETT LAYERS

N. Bourdos[†*], F. Kollmer[†], R. Kamischke[†], A. Benninghoven[†], H.-J. Galla[*], M. Sieber[*]

[†] Physikalisches Institut, Wilhelm-Klemm-Str. 10, [*] Institut für Biochemie, Wilhelm-Klemm-Str. 2, both Westfälische Wilhelms-Universität, D-48149 Münster, Germany

1. Introduction

The *lung surfactant* (LS) is a complex mixture of lipids, proteins and carbohydrates, with the phospholipids dipalmitoyl phosphatidylcholine (DPPC) and dipalmitoyl phosphatidylglycerol (DPPG) (fig. 1) as major constituents. A molecular monolayer of the LS lines the air/water interface of the lung alveoli. These are compressed on exhaling and expanded on inhaling. On compression, this surface-active film lowers the interfacial tension considerably, preventing lung collapse. But at end-expiration the interfacial area is too small to preserve the existence of a pure monolayer and material must be excluded into the aqueous subphase. When highly compressed, material must be excluded into the aqueous phase: a *reservoir* develops, from which the molecules re-insert into the monolayer on expansion. For this reversible process the amphipathic surfactant protein C (SP-C) is essential. It is assumed that the LS separates into an SP-C-rich phase comprising the reservoir, and one of almost pure lipid. For this, a model system of DPPC/DPPG (4:1 molar ratio) plus 0.4 mole% SP-C is investigated. We could image the lateral structures formed in such a film with both TOF-SIMS and Laser-SNMS. The latter was applied for the first time to study Langmuir-Blodgett layers to visualize the lateral accumulation of SP-C. Further, by correlating the Laser-SNMS results with those from atomic force- and fluorescence light microscopy (AFM, FLM), it is likely that there are SP-C-rich domains forming the surfactant reservoir. This illustrates the crucial role of this unique peptide in breathing.

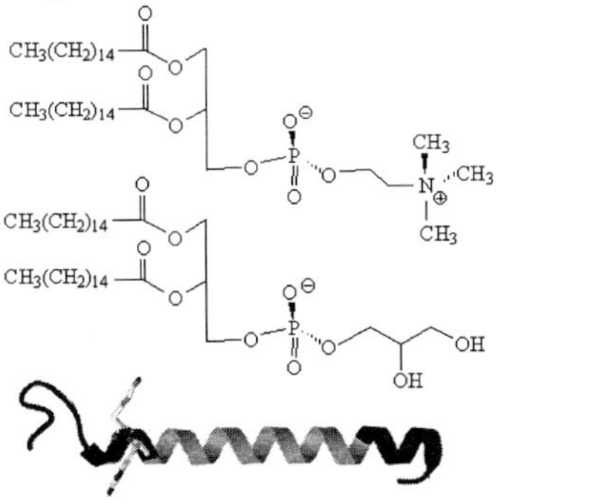

Figure 1: The phospholipids DPPC (M=733.5) and DPPG (M=721.5) and the surfactant protein C (M=4023), with the amino acid sequence GIPCCPVHLK-RLLIVVVVVVLIVVVIVGALLMGL. The SP-C is mostly α-helical. The largest part of the helix mainly consists of valine (M=117) and leucine/isoleucine (M=131) residues, making it extremely hydrophobic. Palmitic acid chains are covalently bound to C4 and C5

Capabilities of TOF-SIMS/SNMS. Domain formation was already imaged in lipid monolayers with TOF-SIMS [1], since the matrix effect allows to distinguish co-existing lyotropic phases, in which the molecules are differently packed, meaning that the chemical environment of a single molecule affects the secondary ion (SI) formation. The analysis of secondary neutrals (SN) yields more quantitative results, since the SN are the majority of the sputterd particles. Thus, if a compound is not homogeneously distributed over a substrate, SN maps should mirror the proportions of its surface concentration. Laser-SNMS can also be used to distinguish co-existing phases, since in the condensed domains the surface concentration is higher than in the liquid ones.

2. Instrumentation

The samples were analyzed using a combined TOF-SIMS/SNMS instrument equipped with a reflectron-type TOF analyzer, a 30 keV Ga$^+$ primary ion source, and an excimer laser for resonantly enhanced multiphoton postionization of neutrals, tuned at λ=193 nm, a wavelength that proved to be adequate for the analysis of amino acids and peptides [2].

3. Sample preparation: the Langmuir-Blodgett (LB) technique

The LB technique is used to prepare overlayers of molecules in a well-defined state on a solid support. Monolayers of the amphipathic substances are prepared on a Langmuir film balance on an aqueous subphase and compressed to a pre-specified lateral film pressure Π. A gold-covered glass slide is then vertically dipped into the film and drawn out slowly, through which the film is transferred onto the surface of the slide. Π corresponds to a defined molecular density or surface concentration.

4. Experimental Results

Figure 2 shows the fingerprint range of the mass spectra of positive SI (+) and SN (⊕) from DPPC, SP-C and the ternary system. Important SI are summarized in the table. Spectra of DPPG mainly contain hydrocarbons and substrate-related peaks, except for P$^{\oplus}$, PO$^{\oplus}$ and DPPG$^-$, and are therefore not shown.

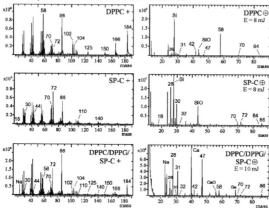

Figure 2:
Mass spectra. Ordinate: total number of counts. The laser pulse energy E is given for the SNMS spectra. In the ternary system, Ca and Na were added for purposes not discussed here.

Figure 3 shows maps of DPPC- and SP-C-specific fragments and others that also give marked contrast. The highly SP-C-specific NH$_4^+$ and C$_5$H$_8$N$_3^+$ yield distinct contrast, C$_5$H$_{12}$N$^+$ is more uniformly distributed. Both the SI and SN species of C$_4$H$_{10}$N give similar images. The neutrals P$^{\oplus}$ and S$^{\oplus}$ mirror the concentration of phospholipids and SP-C, respectively. There are three S per SP-C, located in cysteine and methionine, but no P, which is specific for both DPPC and DPPG. A small amount of P$^{\oplus}$ and S$^{\oplus}$ arises from impurities. The binary systems are not shown here; domains are observable in DPPC/DPPG and DPPG/SP-C, but not in DPPC/SP-C.

In figure 4 images are presented of the state of exclusion along with force- and fluorescence micrographs. The contrast of CH$_4$N is better with SNMS, because in SIMS there is an interference with ^{13}CCH$_5$. Although in SNMS NO$^{\oplus}$ has the same nominal mass, but it does not interfere. The lipid-specific fragments (middle) show opposite contrast, but it is not that sharp, indicating that DPPC might be distributed more homogeneously than SP-C.

m/z	sum formula	Yield/10^{-6} +	Yield/10^{-6} ⊕	Origin DPPC	Origin SP-C
18	NH_4	40	280	–	√
26	CN	–	112000	(√)	√
28	CO	–	278000	√*	√
30	NO	–	109000	–	√
30	CH_4N	220	490	–	√
31	P	–	365000	√*	–
32	S	–	1900	–	√
42	C_2H_4N	–	46100	√	–
44	C_2H_6N	170	940	–	√
47	PO	–	273000	√*	–
58	C_3H_8N	2200	63900	√	–
70	C_4H_8N	550	9200	(√)	√
72	$C_4H_{10}N$	5400	14700	(√)	√
86	$C_5H_{12}N$	8900	19600	√	√
104	$C_5H_{14}NO$	1700	–	√	–
110	$C_5H_8N_3$	90	–	–	√
184	$C_5H_{15}PNO_4$	1850	–	√	–

Table: Characteristic SI and SN of DPPC and SP-C, emerging from an LB overlayer of the ternary system at 5 mN/m lateral pressure, corresponding to $\approx 1.5 \cdot 10^{14}$ molecules/cm^2

* also DPPG

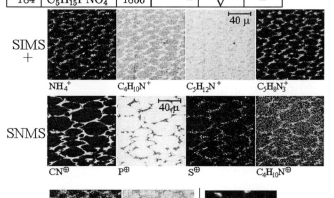

SIMS +

SNMS

Figure 3: SI and SN maps of the ternary system at 30~mN/m lateral pressure. Area: 120 x 120 μm^2, PIDD:†$4.0 \cdot 10^{12}$ (SIMS), $2.3 \cdot 10^{12}$ (SNMS). The domain size may vary, which explains the differences between the SI and the SN maps

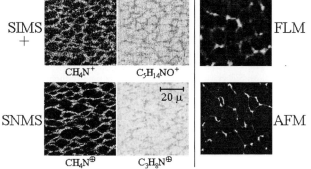

SIMS +

SNMS

FLM

AFM

Figure 4: Mapping of characteristic fragments in the ternary system at the state of exclusion. All images: ≈ 60 x 60 μm^2.†PIDD: $1.6 \cdot 10^{13}$ (SIMS), $8.5 \cdot 10^{12}$ (SNMS)

5. Summary and discussion

TOF-MS results   SI and SN spectra contain fragments characteristic of DPPC or SP-C, but not DPPG; however, there are a few SN emerging from both lipids, like $P^{\oplus}$ and $PO^{\oplus}$. In DPPC intense fragments originate from the hydrophilic head group, whereas peptide-specific ones come from cleavage of COOH (m-45), e.g. valine $\rightarrow$ m/z 72, (iso)leucine $\rightarrow$ m/z 86 [2]. The small $NH_4^{+,\oplus}$ and $CN^{\oplus}$ are common to all amino acids (negative SIMS is not shown here), CN comes from DPPC as well, but is less intense. SP-C can be also imaged by mapping of $S^{\oplus}$, which is part of cysteine and methionine, and with a content of ≈ 3 pmole% in the monolayer is well above the detection limit.

Comparing TOF-MS with AFM and FLM   The lateral structures of the imaged SI and SN fairly correspond with the ones obtained with AFM and FLM (fig. 4, see also [3,4]). In FLM, bright areas mirror high lateral concentrations of a fluorescence dye (in this case a DPPC derivative, but labeled SP-C yields the same contrast [4], whereas in AFM they are elevated, layered domains of the film ("protrusions") — the surfactant reservoir. In the TOF-MS maps, the bright areas are obviously rich in SP-C, which can be derived with greater certainty from SNMS than from SIMS. We may conclude that these SP-C-rich areas comprise the surfactant reservoir; of course, no depth information could be obtained with both TOF-MS techniques. Whether the content of DPPC is indeed lower in the reservoir, is not that clear, because the contrast of DPPC-specific SN is much weaker and yields might be affected by the multilayer nature of the reservoir. LB multilayers have not been studied yet with SNMS.

Further work   The experimental results obtained for multi-component LB layers on Au allow us to determine important data for the SI an SN emission from these variety of samples. For the peptide-specific SNMS signals $CN^{\oplus}$ and $NO^{\oplus}$ we determined yields of approximately 10^{-1} and damage cross sections in the range of 10^{-14} cm^2. These values indicate a very high sensitivity for quantitative peptide detection and for SNMS imaging of peptides a best lateral resolution $\Delta l = \sqrt{\sigma / Y}$ of well below 100 nm. Histogram analysis of SN maps allows us to estimate — and thus to verify — the overall peptide concentration. Along with the AFM and FLM results, SIMS and SNMS supply information on the transmission of the secondary particles originating from the identical substrate through the different domains of the molecular overlayer. A detailed analysis of the experimental results will be published elsewhere.

It can be concluded that Laser-SNMS was successfully introduced to study thin organic films. The lateral distribution of a peptide in lipid matrices could be mapped more readily than with SIMS.

References

[1]   K. M. Leufgen, H. Rulle, A. Benninghoven, M. Sieber, and H.-J. Galla. Imaging time-of-flight secondary ion mass spectrometry allows visualization and analysis of coexisting phases in Langmuir-Blodgett films. *Langmuir*, 12, 1708-1711, 1996.

[2]   M. Terhorst, G. Kampwerth, E. Niehuis, and Benninghoven. Sputtered neutrals mass spectrometry of organic molecules using multiphoton post-ionization. *J. Vac. Sci. Technol.*, A10, 3210-3215, 1992.

[3]   A. von Nahmen, M. Schenk, M. Sieber, and M. Amrein. The phase behaviour of lipid monolayers containing pulmonary surfactant protein C studied by fluorescence light microscopy. *Biophys. J.*, 72, 463-469, 1997.

[4]   A. Nahmen, A. Post, H.-J. Galla and M. Sieber. The structure of a model pulmonary surfactant as revealed by scanning force microscopy. *Eur. Biophys. J.*, 26, 359-369, 1997.

A. Benninghoven, P. Bertrand, H.-N. Migeon and H.W. Werner (Editors).
Proceedings of the 12th International Conference on Secondary Ion Mass Spectrometry,
Brussels, Belgium, 5-11 September 1999
© 2000 Elsevier Science B.V. All rights reserved.

MAPPING OF INTRACELLULAR ORGANELLES IN RELATION TO BORON DISTRIBUTION IN THE SAME HUMAN GLIOBLASTOMA CELL FOR THE EVALUATION OF THE EFFICACY OF ANTICANCER BORONATED DRUGS

S. Chandra[a*], D. R. Lorey, II[a], D. R. Smith[a], M. Miura[b], and G. H. Morrison[a]

[a]Department of Chemistry and Chemical Biology, Baker Laboratory, Cornell University, Ithaca, New York 14853-1301 USA; [*] Corresponding author. E-mail: sc40@cornell.edu
[b]Medical Department, Brookhaven National Laboratory, Upton, New York, USA

1. Introduction

Boron Neutron Capture Therapy (BNCT) of brain cancer critically depends on the incorporation of at least 15-30 ppm boron-10 atoms in tumor cells and not in the adjacent normal brain [1]. The B-10 atoms can then be irradiated by thermal neutrons for achieving the local cell damage/killing effect of BNCT. Ion microscopy, based on dynamic secondary ion mass spectrometry (SIMS), provides an ideal technique for quantitatively imaging boron at a subcellular scale for examining the selectivity and intracellular locations of boron atoms delivered by experimental boronated drugs [2, 3]. However, the ion microscopy boron images showing intracellular gradients need to be correlated with the position of organelles for an unequivocal identification of boron targeting. Many boronated compounds are synthesized to target specific cellular organelles, such as the nucleus and mitochondria, in tumor cells [4]. However, the tagging with boron may alter this characteristic of the parent molecule. In the present study, we analyzed the same cryogenically prepared cell for organelle localization with a laser scanning confocal microscope (LSCM) and boron distribution with a CAMECA IMS-3f ion microscope. This correlation provided the distribution of boron from BNCT drugs in relation to intracellular organelle localization.

2. Experimental

In the first study, T98G human glioblastoma cells were exposed for 48 hr. to nutrient medium containing 22 µg/ml boron equivalent of a new carborane-containing, porphyrin-based BNCT agent, CuTCP-H [5]. For the last 30 min. of the treatment the cells were also exposed to 10 µM rhodamine 123 for fluorescently labeling the mitochondria. The treatments for the second study included the exposure of T98G cells to a mixture of two BNCT drugs, CuTCP-H and p-boronophenylalanine complexed with fructose (BPA-F). The latter drug is currently used in human clinical trials of brain cancer. The mixture of these two drugs provides B-10 atoms from BPA-F and B-11 atoms from CuTCP-H. The exposure of CuTCP-H was for 48 hr., and 110 µg/ml boron equivalent of BPA-F was added to the nutrient medium for the final two hr. of this treatment. For the last 30 min. the cells were also exposed to rhodamine 123.

Following the treatments, the cells were fast frozen, freeze-fractured and freeze-dried with our sandwich fracture technique routinely used for cell culture studies [6]. This method produces well preserved frozen freeze-dried cells fractured at the apical plasma membrane [7]. The frozen freeze-dried cells were analyzed first with LSCM and then with ion microscopy for B-10, B-11, K-39, Na-23 and Ca-40 intracellular distributions. The 0.5 µm spatial resolution of the CAMECA IMS-3f is sufficient for resolving cytoplasmic organelles such as Golgi apparatus, mitochondria, and lysosomes.

3. Results and Discussion

Figure 1 shows correlative LSCM and ion microscopy analyses from the first study. The left panel of the image shows an optical image of fractured freeze-dried cells. The nucleus, nucleolus, and the cytoplasm are discernible in the optical reflected light Nomarski image of

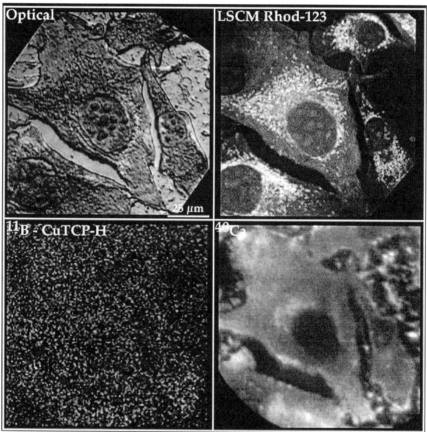

Fig. 1. Correlative optical, laser scanning confocal, and ion microscopy images revealing morphology (optical), mitochondrial localization (LSCM), and ion microscopy images of Boron -11 and Ca-40 in the same frozen freeze-dried cells.

individual T98G human glioblastoma cells. Note that although the cell cytoplasm is clearly discernible in the optical image, the recognition of individual cytoplasmic organelles is not possible. The LSCM image of the rhodamine 123 fluorescence unequivocally reveals brightly labeled mitochondria in the same cells. Correlative ion microscopy images of ^{11}B and ^{40}Ca from the same cells are shown in the designated panels. A characteristic localization of ^{40}Ca is revealed with dark nuclei indicating a lower concentration of total calcium. The ^{11}B image reveals low concentrations of boron with punctate distribution. The localization is not specific to mitochondria or any other discernible compartments. This distribution is in agreement with the anticipated behavior of this drug, which is believed to be mainly confined to the cell surface.

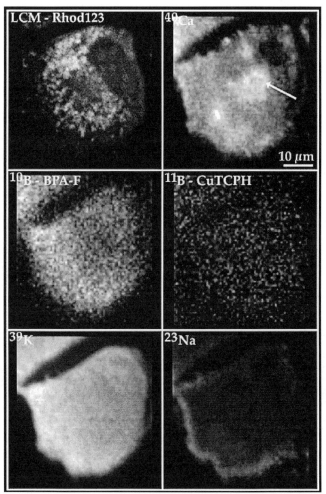

Fig. 2. Correlative laser scanning confocal microscopy and ion microscopy images revealing the distribution of mitochondria (LCM-Rhod 123), Ca-40, B-10 from BPA-F, B-11 from CuTCP-H, K-39, and Na-23 in the same frozen freeze-dried T98G human glioblastoma cell.

Figure 2 shows results from the second study. The left panel of the composite photograph shows the localization of mitochondria in the rhodamine 123 fluorescence image of a single frozen freeze-dried T98G cell revealed by LSCM. The other images, in designated panels, reveal ion microscopy isotopic distributions of ^{40}Ca, ^{10}B (from ^{10}BPA-F), ^{11}B (from CuTCP-H), ^{39}K and ^{23}Na from the same cell. The ^{40}Ca image reveals a low intensity nucleus and a perinuclear region with high concentrations of calcium indicated by an arrow. This perinuclear region also shows lower intensities of ^{10}B delivered from BPA-F (see ^{10}B image). It is remarkable that this is also the same cytoplasmic region where mitochondrial density is low, as revealed in the LSCM image. This region is Golgi apparatus, which resides in the perinuclear location and has been shown previously to sequester calcium [8]. The ^{11}B signals from CuTCP-H, as observed before, are distributed throughout the cell in low intensities. The ^{39}K and ^{23}Na images from the same cell reveal high-K and low-Na signals. The observed K/Na ratio of 12 provides confidence in the reliability of cryogenic sample preparation for preserving the true intracellular distributions of boron as well as the most diffusible intracellular ionic species. Furthermore, the SIMS imaging of two boron isotopes in the same cell, as shown here, provides a powerful approach for studying the synergistic/antagonistic boron delivery behavior of two BNCT drugs mixed together.

This work provides a demonstration for probing boron accumulations in relation to cytoplasmic organelles from BNCT agents. Many new boronated compounds need such evaluations of intracellular boron targeting [1, 4]. Correlative LSCM and ion microscopy provides a unique combination of powerful technologies for revealing boron delivery characteristics of BNCT drugs.

4. Acknowledgment

This work was supported by the United States Department of Energy.

References

[1]   Barth, R. F., Soloway, A. H., Goodman, J. H., Gahbauer, R. A., Gupta, N., Blue, T. E., Yang, W., and Tjarks, W. *Neurosurgery 44: 433-451 (1999)*.
[2]   Smith, D. R., Chandra, S., Coderre, J. A., and Morrison, G. H. *Cancer Res. 56: 4302-4306 (1996)*.
[3]   Zha, X. Ausserer, W.A., Morrison, G.H. *Cancer Res. 52: 5219-5222 (1992)*.
[4]   Soloway, A. H., Tjarks, W., Braum, B. A., Rong, F-G, Barth, R. F., Codogni, I. M., and Wilson, G. *Chem. Rev. 98: 1515-1562 (1998)*.
[5]   Miura, M., Micca, P. L., Fisher, C. D., Gordon, C. R., Heinrichs, J. C., Slatkin, D, N. *British J. Radiol. 71: 773-781 (1998)*.
[6]   Chandra, S., Morrison, G.H., Wolcott, C.C. *J. Microsc. (Oxf.)144: 15-37 (1986)*.
[7]   Chandra, S., and Morrison, G. H. *J. Microsc. (Oxf.), 186:232-245 (1997)*.
[8]   Chandra, S., Kable, E.P.W., Morrison, G.H., and Webb, W.W. *J. Cell Science 100:747-752 (1991)*.

A. Benninghoven, P. Bertrand, H.-N. Migeon and H.W. Werner (Editors).
Proceedings of the 12th International Conference on Secondary Ion Mass Spectrometry,
Brussels, Belgium, 5-11 September 1999

LIPID-SPECIFIC IMAGING OF MEMBRANE DYNAMICS
USING MASS SPECTROMETRY

D. M. Cannon, Jr., M. L. Pacholski, T. P. Roddy, N. Winograd and A. G. Ewing

The Pennsylvania State University, Department of Chemistry,
152 Davey Labs, University Park, PA 16802, USA
corresponding author email: dmc17@psu.edu

1. Introduction

Biological membranes are essential in defining cellular boundaries and sustaining cellular functions [1]. However, a lack of total understanding concerning the vast complexity of membranes still remains, especially at the molecular level. The fluid mosaic model of membranes has been extended to recognize the importance of chemical domains in influencing membrane shape and function [2]. Many cellular functions, such as fusion (i.e. exocytosis) and fission (i.e. cell division and endocytosis), rely on membrane dynamics and are likely to be dependent upon formation of membrane domains. To allow fusion of two cellular membranes, a transient local alteration from the bilayer structure is required. In model systems, the hexagonal (H_{II}) cylinder structure, observable under certain conditions, has been implicated as an intermediate model for localized membrane deformations that result in contact points between two interacting bilayers [3]. Factors that induce H_{II} lipid polymorphism, such as calcium and cholesterol, are also important in dynamic membrane events. Chemical specific domains to create the proper environment for the inducement of the H_{II} intermediate structures have also been proposed. However, it is still unclear whether chemical heterogeneity associated with the two merging or diverging membranes drives these fundamental membrane processes.

Molecule-specific imaging mass spectrometry is uniquely suited for spatially resolving the distribution of native molecular surface species at the micrometer scale. Time-of-flight secondary ion mass spectrometry (TOF-SIMS) molecular imaging has been carried out in our laboratories on model membrane systems [4-6]. Preliminary work suggests that it is feasible to characterize domains of specific lipid molecules [5], to assess their molecular orientation [6] and to monitor dynamic behavior, all at the micrometer spatial dimension [5]. By using rapid freezing and freeze-fracture techniques [7,8], snapshots in time of the spatially resolved membrane chemical compositions during dynamic membrane events have been taken at various time intervals after contact. Frozen-hydrated systems have been studied to preserve the native state of the cell without introducing severe sample preparation artifacts. We have captured each stage of the fusion event between two liposomes and have shown that membrane structure during fusion ranges from specific domains that then migrate across possible contact points to produce a homogeneous, fluid-mosaic membrane. Reported here, H_{II} cylinder aggregates, in the presence of salt, show the inherent SIMS competition in the sputtering and ionization processes. Initial trials have proven the possibility of culturing model neuronal cells (rat pheochromocytoma (PC12)) on coated SIMS targets while still maintaining ability for induced cellular function. Further validation of sample preparation improvements and optimization of analysis conditions described here hold the promise to define the cellular membranes at the molecular level.

2. Experimental

All analyses were performed on a Kratos Prism TOF-SIMS spectrometer equipped with a gallium liquid metal ion gun (LMIG - FEI Co.) with a pulsed 25 kV, 500 pA beam focused to a 45° incident, 200 nm spot. A liquid nitrogen (LN_2) cooled stage was biased at $^+/-$ 2.5 kV, along with an extraction lens biased at $^-/_+$ 4.7 kV. The horizontal TOF reflectron path length was 4.5 m with a microchannel plate detector. Charge compensation involved an electron flood gun pulse of 30 eV electrons for 50 μs after each LMIG pulse. The LMIG was rastered over the surface while collecting the corresponding TOF spectra for each point to generate a pixel image of selected ions. Scanning ion micrographs (SIMs) were taken after TOF-SIMS analysis with a channeltron detecting both electrons and ions.

Multilamellar, micrometer-sized liposomes and H_{II} cylinders were formed in aqueous solutions by a rotary-evaporation technique [1] and characterized by optical microscopy. A small drop (3-10 μL) of suspension was placed on a 5 x 5 mm silicon wafer with a smaller shard of Si placed across the diagonal to form the sample sandwich. This was then immersed into liquid propane for several seconds and then stored in LN_2. Time-resolved analysis was accomplished by fast freezing in liquid propane at given time intervals after an event.

The complete cold-chain freeze-fracture method used in previous studies has been described elsewhere [4] with a newly constructed design presented here (Fig. 1). A two-stage fast-entry port (**A**) was evacuated for sample entry in approximately 1 min. The specimen was transferred onto a pre-cooled (**B**, 100 K) horizontal transfer arm (**C**) and then to another transfer arm (**D**) for positioning the specimen on a freeze-fracture stage (**E**). Once the sample was securely clamped (**F**) the sample temperature was precisely controlled (0.1 K) with LN_2 flow and cartridge heaters. An X, Y, Z manipulated LN_2 cooled knife (**G**) fractured the specimen. After fracturing, the sample was transported into the TOF-SIMS chamber via the horizontal transfer arm (**C**) for imaging. Pressures were typically kept in the 10^{-10} torr range by utilizing a turbo pump (**J**) and a LN_2 cooled cryoshroud (**H**) that encompasses the entire inner surface of the chamber. An IR lamp (**I**) was available for rapid baking after each completed analysis.

PC12 cells were successfully cultured on Si chips that were thinly coated with type I mouse collagen (Sigma). Differentiation was induced in a few days by adding 100 ng / mL nerve growth factor (NGF, Sigma) to the media when the cells were initially plated. Cells were then stained for two hours with DiI (Molecular Probes) for fluorescence imaging verification.

(← to TOF-SIMS analysis chamber)

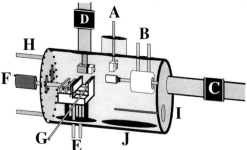

Figure 1. Schematic of freeze-fracture chamber specifically designed for molecular-imaging experiments. (**A**) fast-entry port, (**B**) cold-clamp for (**C**) horizontal transfer rod, (**D**) vertical transfer rod, (**E**) fracturing stage, (**F**) stage clamp feedthrough, (**G**) cryo-knife, (**H**) cryo-shroud (inside vacuum chamber), (**I**) infrared lamp, and (**J**) turbo pump.

3. Results and discussion

Direct molecule-specific TOF-SIMS imaging of cellular membranes requires sample preparation protocols based on proven cryo-microscopy methods, but optimized for measurements of the top molecular layer. Imaging has been achieved by probing the inner portion of a sample, frozen as a sandwich that has been fractured *in vacuo* [5]. Fracturing criteria for preserving chemical distributions have been shown to be much more stringent than for morphological cryo-electron microscopy studies. The act of fracturing is suggested to be intrinsically violent, thus creating high, localized partial pressures of water at the fracture surface. The goal of providing a clean, undisturbed fracture surface *in vacuo* involves rapid equilibration of the surface condensation and sublimation fluxes just <u>after</u> fracturing. To this end, a newly constructed freeze-fracture unit is presently being characterized. A two-stage fast-entry system allows rapid sample introduction into the vacuum to reduce ambient water condensation and sample warming (further minimized along the cold-chain pathway to the fracturing stage). Fracturing temperatures are now more precisely controlled, for better reproducibility. Through the use of an internal cryo-shroud and an internal infrared light source, lower pressures can be maintained. The ability to maintain lower pressures is desired because of decreased residual water, a greater force to rapidly move water away from a freshly exposed surface, a reduction in the contamination of the analysis chamber, and the possibility for a higher throughput of fractured samples.

Molecule-specific TOF-SIMS imaging has directly measured the chemical and spatial distribution of lipid molecules on the surface of single multi-lamellar, micrometer-size liposomes. These studies have suggested that the lipid structure of model membranes during fusion proceeds through a discrete domain stage, where diffusion appears limited through a contact point, to eventually end in a completely homogeneous fused liposome. These segregated areas appear to be similar to what is expected for membrane domains in cellular systems. These studies recently have been extended to include various lipid structures along with high-salt aqueous environments. As discussed earlier, the H_{II} cylinder phase is an interesting model for investigating membrane fusion with the physical structure consisting of minute aqueous-filled hexagonal cylinders embedded in a hydrocarbon environment, thus imparting poor hydration and favored aggregation. Figure 2 shows TOF-SIMS images (A-D) of frozen-hydrated aggregated phosphatidylethanolamine dipalmitoyl (DPPE) H_{II} cylinders in a high NaCl environment. The total ion image (**A**) suggests relative ionization enhancement at

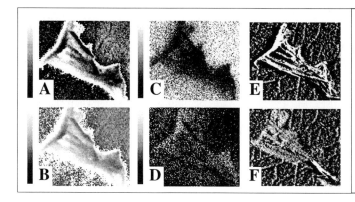

Figure 2. TOF-SIMS images of aggregated DPPE H_{II} cylinders in NaCl (10 mM). (A) total ion, (B) Na^+, (C) H_2O^+ and H_3O^+, (D) C_3 hydrocarbons, (E) SIM after TOF-SIMS analysis and (F) SIM after approximately 1 min of DC beam rastering subsequent to E. Images are ~200 μm wide. A-D were acquired with 2.5 x 10^{11} primary ions / cm^2.

934

the edges of the structure. Furthermore, the Na$^+$ image (**B**) is the dominant signal, not only around the edges as expected with cation stabilized structures, but over the entire analysis area. The water image (**C**) verifies the hydrated nature of the sample surface around the relatively frost-free lipid structure, indicative of a desirable fracture. However, the C$_3$ hydrocarbon image (**D**) illustrates the inability, thus far, of detecting lipid species within a high-salt environment. Comparison of SIMs **E** and **F** exemplifies beam-induced damage (less than 1 min. DC beam exposure) that is seemingly more prevalent in aqueous salt environments. Although these systems have extreme amounts of associated cations like Na$^+$ with high sputter and ionization relative to lipids, these investigations show the possible analysis interferences that need to be minimized through proper sample preparation and experimental design for successful lipid-specific imaging of membrane composition.

4. Summary and future directions

Development and optimization of freeze-fracture methodology specific to static TOF-SIMS molecular imaging of native chemical species of cellular membranes is discussed. It is apparent from the data that salt interferences could present difficulties if not accounted for. As noted above, PC12 cells represent a target model for these investigations. The promise of near-future studies on PC12 cells is shown in Figure 3, by not only the attachment to a substrate, but of the ability to influence membrane function during culturing such as differentiation. The ability to image the heterogeneous molecular spatial distribution of membranes captured during dynamic events represents a unique approach in our development of membrane bioanalytical chemistry.

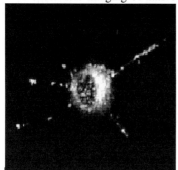

Figure 3. Fluorescence image of a differentiated, as noted by axonal-like growths, PC12 cell on collagen-coated Si wafer. NGF treatment for 3 days Average PC12 diameter is ~ 15 µm.

The authors would thank NIH and NSF for funding support. Thanks also goes to Rosemary Walsh at the PSU EM lab for all her helpful conversations. Thanks also goes to Robert Braun, Dan Lehman, Vasil Vorsa, and Ken Willey for their assistance in design and construction of the new fracturing chamber.

References

[1] *Biochemistry of Lipids, Lipoproteins and Membranes, New Comprehensive Biochemistry,* Vol. 20, Vance, D. E., Vance, J. E., Eds., Elsevier, New York, 1991.

[2] Glaser, M., *Current Opinion in Structural Biology* **1993**, *3*, 475-481.

[3] Van Venetie, R., Verkleij, A. J., *Biochim. Biophys. Acta* **1981**, *645*, 262-269

[4] Colliver T. L., et.al., *Anal. Chem.* **1997**, *69*, 2225-2231.

[5] Cannon, D. M. Jr., Pacholski M. L., Winograd, N., Ewing A. G. *J.Am.Chem.Soc.* (submitted).

[6] Pacholski M. L., Cannon, D. M. Jr., Ewing, A. G., Winograd, N. *J. Am. Chem. Soc.* **1999**, *121*, 4716-4717.

[7] *Rapid Freezing, Freeze-Fracture, and Deep Etching,* Severs, N. and Shotton, D., Eds., Wiley-Liss: New York, 1995.

[8] Chandra, S., Bernius, M. T., Morrison, G. H., *Anal. Chem.* **1986**, *58*, 493-496.

A. Benninghoven, P. Bertrand, H.-N. Migeon and H.W. Werner (Editors).
Proceedings of the 12th International Conference on Secondary Ion Mass Spectrometry,
Brussels, Belgium, 5-11 September 1999
935

DETERMINATION OF THE IDENTITY OF ADSORBED PROTEINS WITH STATIC SIMS

J.-B. Lhoest[1], M. S. Wagner[2], David G.Castner[1,2]
National ESCA and Surface Analysis Center for Biomedical Problems
Departments of Bioengineering[1] and Chemical Engineering[2]
University of Washington, Box 351750 ,Seattle, WA 98195 USA

1. Introduction

Time of Flight Secondary Ion Mass Spectrometry (ToF-SIMS) is ideally suited for the analysis of adsorbed protein films due to its high surface sensitivity and the molecular information it provides about a sample. Previous studies have reported that SIMS is sensitive to the amount and conformation of proteins adsorbed onto different substrates [1, 2].

The nature of the adsorbed protein film on a biomaterial surface has been shown to play an important role in determining the biological response to the material [3]. Protein adsorption is a highly complex phenomenon with many unknowns. Parameters such as the amount and type of protein in the adsorption solution as well as the type of substrate will influence the amount, coverage, composition, and conformation of the adsorbed protein film. Previously, several techniques have been used to examine adsorbed protein films, but they do not provide the specific molecular information generated by ToF-SIMS.

The spectra generated by ToF-SIMS are complex and can be difficult to analyze. For example, the complexity of protein ToF-SIMS spectra make it challenging to compare the spectrum from an unknown protein film to a library of reference spectra. Thus, multivariate analysis methods are required for analysis of protein ToF-SIMS spectra. Several multivariate analysis techniques, such as Principal Component Analysis (PCA), have previously been employed for a range of different spectroscopic data analyses, including ToF-SIMS. We have utilized PCA to categorize reference protein spectra to generate a spectral library to use for analysis of multi-component, adsorbed protein films by ToF-SIMS.

2. Experimental

The protein adsorption onto mica (SPI Supplies, West Chester, PA) and polytetrafluoro-ethylene (PTFE) (Berghof/America, Concord, CA) substrates was done in degassed CPBSzI for two hours at $37^\circ C$ using protein concentrations of 0.1 $^{mg}/_{mL}$. The composition of the CPBSzI buffer was 0.11 M NaCl, 0.01 M NaI, 0.01 M citric acid, 0.01 M sodium phosphate, and 0.2% sodium azide. The pH of the CPBSzI buffer was adjusted to 7.4 using solid NaOH. The substrates were chosen due to their large difference in hydrophobicity. Furthermore, PTFE was chosen due to its high matrix effect. After adsorption, the samples were rinsed twice in stirred buffer solutions to remove loosely bound protein and twice in stirred deionized water to remove buffer salts. The samples were then allowed to dry overnight in a laminar flow hood.

The proteins used in this study were bovine plasma fibronectin (Fn), bovine serum albumin (BSA), bovine plasma fibrinogen type I-S (Fg), and chicken egg white lysozyme

(Ly), all purchased from Sigma (St. Louis, MO). These proteins were selected because of their relevance to biomaterial (i.e. blood and tear contacting) surfaces.

Mass spectra from the adsorbed protein films were acquired using a Model 7200 Physical Electronics ToF-SIMS (PHI, Eden Prairie, MN) with an 8 keV Cs^+ primary ion source. The total ion flux to the surface was maintained below 10^{12} ions/cm^2 to insure static conditions [4]. A low energy pulsed electron flood gun was used for charge neutralization. High mass resolution spectra were acquired with a raster size on 200 μm by 200 μm. At least three spectra were recorded for each sample. A minimum mass resolution of 4500 on the $C_4H_8N^+$ peaks at 70 $^m/_z$ was obtained for all of the spectra. Furthermore, spectra were discarded if the sodium ion intensity from the buffer represented more than 5% of the total spectral intensity since the presence of sodium can affect the secondary ion yields of the other fragments.

PCA was carried out using MATLAB (The Mathworks, Inc., Natick, MA) in conjunction with the PLS Toolbox 2.0 (Eigenvector Research, Inc., Manson, WA).

3. Data Treatment

From each of the mass spectra, peaks were selected that correspond to amino acid fragments. The amino acid fragment peaks had previously been identified in SIMS studies of amino acid homopolymers by Bartiaux and Mantus et al. [5,6]. The intensity of each amino acid fragment peak was normalized to the total intensity of all amino acid peaks in the spectrum and then mean centered and variance scaled to give all the peaks the same weighting in PCA.

Principal component analysis has been described in detail elsewhere [7, 8], so only a short description is presented here. Briefly, PCA is an eigenvector decomposition of the covariance matrix of the original data set. This matrix manipulation decomposes the original data set into a product of scores and loading matrices, given mathematically by:

$$X = TP' + E,$$

where X is the mean centered and variance scaled matrix of sample measurements, T is the matrix of *scores* (which describe the relationship between the samples), P is the matrix of *loadings* (which describe the relationship between the variables), and E is the residual matrix. The power of PCA is the reduction of n correlated variables to a smaller number of j uncorrelated principal components (PCs). These PCs describe the directions of greatest variation in the original data set. Therefore, a few PCs can be used to describe the variation in a complex set of many variables. By applying this technique to the SIMS spectra of adsorbed protein films, the spectra can be readily compared and identified by the type of protein and substrate.

4. Results and Discussion

Figure 1 shows the ToF-SIMS spectra from BSA, Fg, Fn, and Ly adsorbed from a 0.1 $^{mg}/_{ml}$ solution onto mica. Since all proteins are constructed from the same twenty different amino acids, the differences between the spectra reside in the relative intensity of the amino acid peaks rather than the presence or absence of unique identifying peaks.

To identify the differences observed between the protein spectra and test the reproducibility of the data, a multivariate analysis of the data was conducted. Principal component analysis of the pure protein spectra was used to differentiate the pure protein spectra adsorbed onto both mica and PTFE. Figure 2 shows a plot of the PC 1 and 2 scores for BSA, Fg, Fn, and Ly on mica. The first two PCs capture 68% of the variance in the data. The third and fourth PCs, which capture an additional 17.92% of the variance, only enhance the classification of these protein spectra. PCA was easily able to group together the spectra from the same protein and verify the reproducibility of these spectra.

Figure 3 shows a plot of the PC 1 and 2 scores for BSA, Fg, Fn, and Ly spectra on mica and PTFE substrates. The first two principal components capture 56% of the variance in the combined data set. While differences in the spectra for BSA, Fg, and Fn films on mica and PTFE can be distinguished using PCA, the Ly spectra from the two substrates are not clearly distinguished. This may be due to the more rigid conformation of Ly which inhibits denaturation of the protein on the two surfaces.

The ToF-SIMS spectra of pure proteins on both mica and PTFE are complex and difficult to distinguish using univariate analysis methods. While differences in the spectra of one or two pure protein samples may be readily recognized, spectra of several pure protein samples or spectra of complex mixtures are not easily distinguishable. Principal component analysis was used to group the spectra based on the type of adsorbed protein and the type of substrate. Future work will utilize PCA in the classification of several pure protein films in addition to the determination of the relative surface concentration of complex protein mixtures.

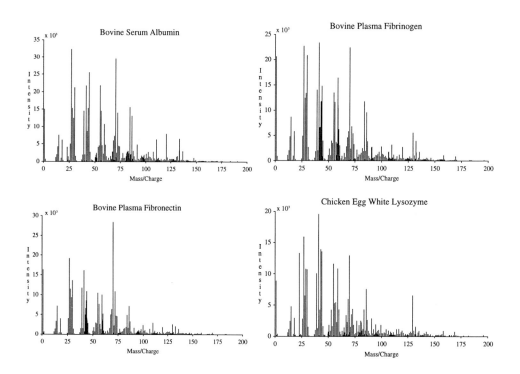

Figure 1. Positive ion ToF-SIMS spectra of BSA, Fg, Fn and Ly adsorbed onto mica from 0.1 $^{mg}/_{mL}$ protein solutions.

938

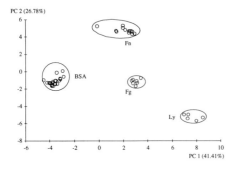
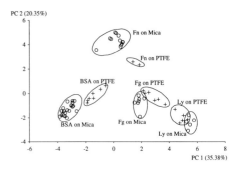

Figure 2. Scores on PCs 1 and 2 for BSA, Fg, Fn and Ly adsorbed onto mica substrates from pure 0.1 $^{mg}/_{mL}$ solutions.

Figure 3. Scores on PCs 1 and 2 for BSA, Fg, Fn and Ly adsorbed onto mica and PTFE substrates from pure 0.1 $^{mg}/_{mL}$ solutions.

5. Conclusions

ToF-SIMS coupled with PCA is a powerful technique for analyzing the composition of adsorbed protein films. The results of this study show that different types of adsorbed protein films can be readily identified with the combination of ToF-SIMS and PCA. It is also possible to use ToF SIMS to determine the relative surface concentration of proteins adsorbed from binary mixtures [9]. Absolute protein surface concentrations can be obtained when radiolabeled protein adsorption experiments are done in conjunction with the ToF-SIMS analysis. The multivariate analysis of additional pure protein spectra and binary (and more complex) protein mixtures will be the subject of future studies.

Acknowledgements

Support from NIH grant RR-01296 (NESAC/BIO) for these experiments is gratefully acknowledged.

References

[1] J.-B.Lhoest, E.Detrait, P.van den Bosch de Aguilar, P.Bertrand, *Journal of Biomedical Materials Research* **41** (1998) 95.
[2] B.D.Ratner, C.D.Tidwell, K.Meyer, D.G.Castner, S.Golledge, B.Hagenhoff, A.Benninghoven, Proceedings of the Fifth World Biomaterials Congress (May 29-June 2, 1996, Toronto, Canada) 577.
[3] J.L.Brash and T.A.Horbett (Eds.), *ACS Symposium Series*, American Chemical Society, Washington, DC, 1987, Vol. 343.
[4] G. Marletta, S.M. Catalano and S. Pignataro, *Surf.& Interf.ce Anal.* **16** (1990) ,407.
[5] S. Bartiaux, undergraduate thesis Universite Catholique de Louvain (Faculte des Sciences Agronomiques, Unite de Chimie des interfaces), Belgium 1995.
[6] D.S.Mantus, B.D.Ratner, B.A.Carlson and J.F.Moulder, *Anal.Chem.* **65,**(1993) 1431.
[7] J.E.Jackson, *Journal of Quality Technology* **12** (1980) 201.
[8] S.Wold, K.Esbensen and P.Geladi, *Chemometrics and Intelligent Laboratory Systems* **2** (1987) 37.
[9] J.-B.Lhoest, M.S.Wagner, and D.G.Castner, manuscript in preparation.

A. Benninghoven, P. Bertrand, H.-N. Migeon and H.W. Werner (Editors).
Proceedings of the 12th International Conference on Secondary Ion Mass Spectrometry,
Brussels, Belgium, 5-11 September 1999
© 2000 Elsevier Science B.V. All rights reserved.

SURFACE CHEMISTRY AND MICROCONTACT PRINTED PATTERNS FOR NEURONAL NETWORK ARCHITECTURES STUDIED BY TOF-SIMS

D. Léonard[a]*, M. Scholl[b, d], Y. Chevolot[a], C. Sprössler[b, c], M.C. Denyer[b], A. Offenhäusser[c], W. Knoll[b, c], A. Maelicke[d], H. Sigrist[e] and H.J. Mathieu[a]

[a]Laboratoire de Métallurgie Chimique (LMCH), Département des Matériaux, Ecole Polytechnique Fédérale de Lausanne (EPFL), CH-1015 Lausanne - EPFL, Switzerland
*corresponding author: Dr Didier Léonard (email: didier.leonard@epfl.ch)
[b]The Institute of Physical and Chemical Research (RIKEN), Japan
[c]Max-Planck-Institute for Polymer Research, 55128 Mainz, Germany
[d]Institute for Physiological Chemistry, Johannes Gutenberg University, Germany
[e]Centre Suisse d'Electronique et de Microtechnique (CSEM), 2007 Neuchâtel, Switzerland

1. Introduction

Receptor-mediated recognition of substrate molecules is one of the key guidance cues which nerve cells use to find their target structures in vivo. Precise targeting is the prerequisite for the formation of correct neuronal connections and networks. In order to study these mechanisms under simplified in vitro conditions, a geometrical grid pattern of a particular substrate, PA22-2, is covalently immobilised via cross-linker chemistry on silicon oxide based and glass substrates using microcontact printing (µCP). PA22-2 is a synthetic peptide matching the corresponding sequence in the A chain of the extracellular matrix protein laminin, except that a cysteine residue was added at the N-terminus.

Imaging Time-of-Flight Secondary Ion Mass Spectrometry (ToF-SIMS) is used to characterise the pattern formation using microcontact printing. ToF-SIMS spectra of the various steps of the surface modification process are compared and data are discussed in terms of efficiency of these steps.

2. Experimental Conditions

Reference samples corresponding to the various steps of the surface modification process leading to covalent binding of the synthetic peptide PA22-2 on the substrates were compared: pristine samples, aminosilanised samples, aminosilanised samples after reaction with sulfo-GMBS (Figure 1 a) and the latter after contact with the PA22-2 solution (Figure 1 b). Patterned glass samples underwent similar surface modifications except for the contact with the peptide solution which was performed using microcontact printing [1]. Note that higher concentrations were used for reference samples to allow better surface analysis identification of some steps of the process (aminosilanisation, reaction with sulfo-GMBS). Details on the experimental conditions for each step of the process are given elsewhere [2].

The ToF-SIMS system used in this study was a commercial ToF-SIMS mass spectrometer (described in detail elsewhere [3-4]) from PHI-EVANS (PHI-EVANS Trift 1). The DC 15 keV ^{69}Ga$^+$ ion beam current was pulsed at 5 kHz repetition rate (pulse width of about 7 ns (unbunched)). Spectra acquisition was performed in high mass resolution conditions (bunched ion beam) using a charge compensation (only for the negative ion acquisition for silicon wafer samples). The analysed area was estimated to be a square of 84 x 84 µm^2. The total ion dose for a 5 min spectrum was below $1 \cdot 10^{12}$ ions/cm^2, which is within the so-called 'static' SIMS conditions [5]. Using these experimental conditions, the mass resolution obtained on a Si wafer was m/Δm > 6000 at mass 28 in the positive mode and > 4000 in the negative mode.

ToF-SIMS spectra were recorded for each sample on four different sample spots for both positive and negative ions. Values presented (in Table 1) are mean values and standard deviations. ToF-SIMS peak values were normalised by dividing the absolute peak intensity of secondary ions by the corrected total intensity, i.e. the total intensity from which intensities of H$^{+/-}$ (because of their low reproducibility), of some inorganic peaks, and of the main peaks of ubiquitous contaminants such as PDMS were subtracted.

Image acquisition was performed in high lateral conditions using an unbunched pulsed 25 keV ^{69}Ga$^+$ beam. The analysed area was estimated to be a square of 126 x 126 µm^2 or 42 x 42 µm^2. The total ion dose for a 10 or 20 min (respectively) acquisition was below or in the order of the so-called 'static' SIMS conditions, respectively.

3. Results and Discussion

Table 1 displays a selection of normalised ToF-SIMS intensities for the following reference samples: surfaces before any surface reaction (naked glass and acid cleaned silicon wafer) and surfaces before and after contact with the PA22-2 peptide solution.

Before any contact with the peptide solution (samples B in Table 1), it was expected that the surface contains a significant amount of sulfo-GBMS functions. Due to the presence of the maleimido group in sulfo-GBMS, characteristic signatures such as CN$^-$ (its relative intensity should increase), CNO$^-$ and C$_4$H$_2$NO$_2$$^-$ (corresponding to the whole maleimido group [6]) were expected. It appears that the maleimido characteristic peak is very weak compared to what was observed in the case of MAD, another maleimido containing molecule which was covalently grafted on diamond [6]. This is confirmed by limited differences observed for the other characteristic peaks (CN$^-$ and CNO$^-$ in Table 1). Thus, it is not clear to which extent the surface modification has been successful. Actually the problem could arise from the first step of the surface modification process because significant differences could not be identified between the surfaces before any modification and those after aminosilanisation (except for contaminants - data not shown).

After contact with the peptide solution (samples C in Table 1), clear differences appear in the ToF-SIMS spectra. All the expected signatures in the negative mode are clearly observed: CN$^-$, CNO$^-$ and S$^-$, the latter is characteristic because it does not follow the same variation as the sulphate contamination characteristic peaks (such as SO$_4$$^-$, also listed in Table 1). On the other hand, all the amino acids are clearly identified (through normalised values of the corresponding positive ions, Table 1): for example, S (Ser) identified by the ion C$_2$H$_6$NO$^+$ at mass 60 and V (Val) specifically identified by the ion C$_4$H$_{10}$N$^+$ at mass 72. Thus, the presence of the peptide at the surface of the final sample is evident but from the discussion above it could rather be due to a physisorption process.

ToF-SIMS imaging was used to characterise patterns of peptide using microcontact printing. As an example of the results obtained with various patterns, Figure 2 illustrates a pattern for which lines are 10µm broad and the size of the pitch is 100µm. The pattern is well defined with sharp edges using the following characteristic masses. In the image of the substrate characteristic ion Si^+ (Figure 2a), the lower intensity in the lines indicates the covering of the substrate with microcontact printed material. The nature of this material is identified in Figure 2b as the peptide on the basis of the peak at mass 72 characteristic of V (Val). However, the contrast is better in Figure 2c where the image from mass 73 is displayed. This is identified in high mass resolution spectra as a PDMS signature ($C_3H_9Si^+$). The presence of this contaminant is not surprising because the stamp is made from this material. At the same time, an image similar to that of Si^+ can be obtained from mass 27 clearly identified here as being mostly Al^+ (not illustrated). Even if its origin is unclear, it appears that this material was introduced during the surface modification process independently from the material used (glass or silicon). Figure 2d confirms that peptide was printed. Indeed, a clear contrast can be obtained with the mass 26 image (identified in high mass resolution spectra as CN^-).

Complementary experiments were performed to clear up the question of chemi- or physisorption of the peptide at the surface of both substrates. As explained above, the surface photoimmobilisation of a maleimido group containing molecule (MAD [6]) has already been shown. It is thus proposed to try to graft the peptide onto photoimmobilised MAD. Figures 3a and 3b illustrate two completely different patterns obtained with F^- (characteristic of MAD) and $C_4H_{10}N^+$ (characteristic of the peptide - CN^- is impractical as it is also characteristic of MAD). Evidently, there is no matching between both imaging results, illustrating that the surface modification process is mostly based on physisorption.

Complementary assays with embryonic hippocampal neurons cultured onto the pattern indicate that the patterned bio-functionalisation of the surface induce the hippocampal neurons to form a neuronal network of the same geometry [2]. Such a result is consistent with the surface analysis results. A still open question is the role of Al that could influence the neuronal network pattern due to its cytotoxicity.

References

[1]   A. Kumar and G.M. Whitesides, Appl. Phys. Lett. 63 (1993) 2002
[2]   M. Scholl, C. Sprössler, M. Krause, M. Denyer, A. Offenhäusser, W. Knoll and A. Maelicke, J. Neurosci. Meth., submitted
[3]   B.W. Schueler, Microsc. Microanalysis Microstructure 3 (1992) 119
[4]   K. Franzreb, H.J. Mathieu and D. Landolt, Surf. Interface Anal. 23 (1995) 641
[5]   D. Briggs in Practical Surface Analysis, Second Edition, Volume 2. Ion and Neutral Spectroscopy, D. Briggs and M. P. Seah (Eds), John Wiley, Chichester, 1992, p 367
[6]   D. Léonard, Y. Chevolot, O. Bucher, H. Sigrist and H. J. Mathieu, Surf. Interface Anal. 26 (1998) 783.

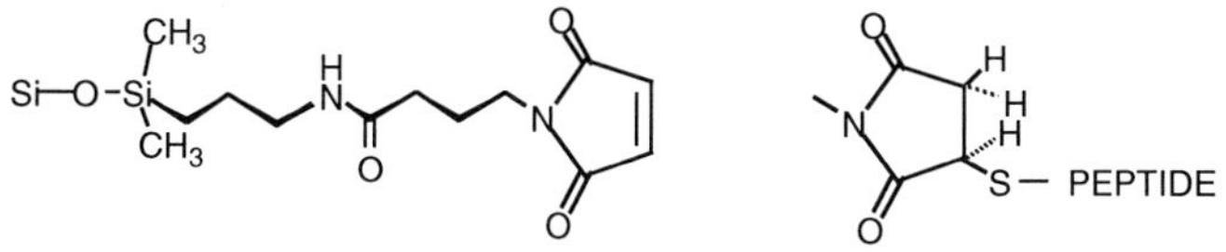

(a)   (b)

Fig. 1. (a) surface chemistry after aminosilanisation and reaction with sulfo-GMBS (b) surface chemistry after reaction of the maleimido group of the sulfo-GMBS with the peptide

942

Table 1
Normalised ToF-SIMS intensities (‰) for surfaces before any surface reaction (A) and surfaces before (B) and after (C) contact with the PA22-2 peptide solution. 96⁻ refers to $C_4H_2NO_2^-$, 60⁺ refers to $C_2H_6NO^+$ and 72⁺ refers to $C_4H_{10}N^+$.

	glass A	glass B	glass C	Si A	Si B	Si C
CN⁻	10.1 ± 4.8	10 ± 0.2	29.6 ± 6	3.06 ± 0.36	6.9 ± 2.1	29.5 ± 1.8
CNO⁻	2.2 ± 0.9	3.7 ± 0.1	7 ± 2	1.02 ± 0.25	2.81 ± 0.97	10.8 ± 0.97
96⁻	0.02 ± 0.01	0.07 ± 0.02	0.05 ± 0.02	0.01 ± 0.00	0.06 ± 0.02	0.06 ± 0.01
S⁻	1.2 ± 0.6	0.5 ± 0.1	3.4 ± 0.6	0.27 ± 0.05	0.29 ± 0.06	3.5 ± 0.2
SO₄⁻	0.08 ± 0.05	0.03 ± 0.01	0.05 ± 0.01	0.03 ± 0.01	0.05 ± 0.01	0.12 ± 0.03
60⁺	0.14 ± 0.05	0.62 ± 0.13	2.58 ± 0.15	0.10 ± 0.01	1.48 ± 0.09	3.40 ± 0.12
72⁺	0.27 ± 0.09	0.27 ± 0.04	3.15 ± 0.22	0.36 ± 0.11	0.33 ± 0.10	2.97 ± 0.07

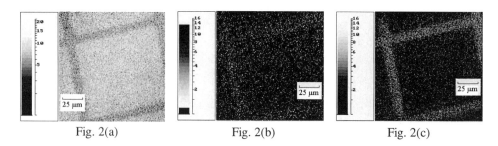

Fig. 2(a)   Fig. 2(b)   Fig. 2(c)

Fig. 2. Si⁺ (a), $C_4H_{10}N^+$ (b), $C_3H_9Si^+$ (c) and CN⁻ (d) images of a microcontact printed pattern of peptide PA22-2 on sulfo-GMBS modified silicon wafer (lines are 10µm broad and the size of the pitch is 100µm). It should be noted that for the CN⁻ image, there is a slight shift in comparison with the three positive ion images.

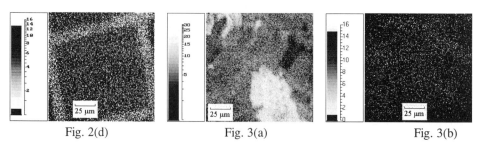

Fig. 2(d)   Fig. 3(a)   Fig. 3(b)

Fig. 3. F⁻ (a) and $C_4H_{10}N^+$ (b) images of a microcontact printed pattern of peptide PA22-2 on MAD modified silicon wafer (lines are 10µm broad and the pitch is 50 µm or 100µm in every direction). It should be noted that there is a slight shift between both images.

A. Benninghoven, P. Bertrand, H.-N. Migeon and H.W. Werner (Editors).
Proceedings of the 12th International Conference on Secondary Ion Mass Spectrometry,
Brussels, Belgium, 5-11 September 1999
943

MULTIVARIATE STATISTICAL APPROACHES FOR INTERPRETING TOF-SIMS SPECTRA OF BACTERIAL AND FUNGAL CELL WALLS

Bonnie J. Tyler, Alan Willse and Hong Shi

Dept. of Chemical Engineering, Montana State University, Bozeman MT

bonniet@coe.montana.edu

Richard E. Peterson

Dept. of Chemistry and Biochemistry, Montana State University, Bozeman MT

1. Introduction

Cell surface molecules play a crucial role in a variety of biological processes including adhesion of cells to both biological and synthetic surfaces. Unfortunately, chemical characterization of biological surfaces is a difficult and time consuming process. Cell surfaces are a complex mosaic of proteins, saccharides and lipids whose orientation and stereochemistry are critical for biological activity. TOF-SIMS has potential for rapid characterization of biological surfaces because of its high information content and exquisite sensitivity. However, interpretation of SIMS spectra from complex mixtures, such as those found in biological samples, is a daunting task. In addition, the relevant environment for cells is always an aqueous medium, not the high vacuum environment necessary for SIMS analysis. If the samples are handled improperly the hydrated surface structure will be destroyed and the resulting spectra will not be reflective of the relevant surface features.

The objective of our work has been to develop methods for preparing biological samples for TOF-SIMS analysis and to explore a variety of multivariate statistical approaches for interpretation of SIMS spectra from these biological samples. Our approach has been to study systems of biological surfaces that vary in some known manner, such as adhesiveness, anti-body binding or elemental composition. The apriory information about the cell surfaces is then used in conjunction with multivariate statistical methods to leverage relevant information from the SIMS spectra. A variety of statistical approaches have been used including Principal Components Analysis (PCA), Partial Least Squares Regression (PLS), and Discriminant Analysis (DA).

For our initial studies we have chosen to work with a gram positive bacteria and fungi because these cells have a rigid cell wall which can withstand rinsing with nanopure water. In addition, these cell types are known to maintain their viability when properly freeze dried. As a result, these cells should be far easier to prepare for SIMS analysis than animal cells, which have only a lipid membrane and no cell wall.

The first cell system considered is the oral bacteria *Streptococcus salivarius.* Four strains of *S. salivarius*, a parent strain and three mutants that show an increasing loss of the proteinaceous fibrillar layer, have been studied with TOF-SIMS. Van der Mei et al have extensively characterized the surfaces of the four strains for antigenic composition, presence or absence of surface appendages, the relative amounts of lipoteichoic acid/teichoic acid exposed at the surface, the surface free energy, adhesive behavior, infrared spectrum, XPS spectrum and zeta potentials. For this cell system we have used the XPS P/C ratio as a lever to extract the spectra of the phosphorus containing molecules from the other components of the SIMS spectra.

The second cell system considered is the dimorphic yeast, *Candida albicans*. It has been demonstrated that changes in growth condition for *C. albicans* result in changes in cell wall structure, as observed by TEM, and changes in the cells' adhesive behavior. For this cell system we have used adhesiveness of the cells and composition of the growth media as levers to extract relevant components from the spectra.

2. Experimental

Samples of the four strains of *S. salivarius* were obtained from Henni Van der Mei as freeze dried powder. The freeze dried powder was mounted on 3M double stick tape for SIMS analysis.

C. albicans was grown in a variety of defined media, including glucose yeast extract peptone broth (GluYEP), galactose yeast extract peptone broth (GalcYEP), glucose yeast nitrogen base (GluYNB) and galactose yeast nitrogen base (GalYNB). The cells were grown in a shaker incubator for 24 hours and then washed in buffer, filtered through alumina filters and rinsed with nanopure water to produce a uniform carpet of cells. The cells were then freeze dried in a specially designed freeze drier. The freeze drier uses a turbo pump and special pumping train to reduce oil contamination of the sample and has a sample holder designed for rapid cooling of a monolayer of cells. The integrity of the freeze drying process was verified by checking for cell viability and by XPS, SEM and TEM characterization.

XPS spectra of the cells were obtained using a PHI 5600 spectrometer with a monochromatic Al Kα source. Frozen hydrated cells were analyzed using a cryostage in both the analytical and introduction chambers. Freeze dried cells and air dried cells were analyzed at ambient temperature to determine whether the drying process caused changes in the cell surface composition. Quantitation of the surface elemental composition was done using spectra collected at 58 eV pass energy and employed the standard PHI quantitation routines C1s spectra were also collected at 23 eV pass energy to determine whether there had been changes in the shape of the C1s peak envelope.

Positive and negative ion SIMS spectra of the freeze dried cells were collected on an PHI TRIFT I Time of Flight Secondary Ion Mass Spectrometer with a Cs ion source. Spectra were obtained for at least 3 replicate samples. Both replicate preparations of the cell surfaces and replicate spectra on a single surface were included in the statistical analysis. The ion dose was kept below 10^{12} ions/cm^2 for all analyses.

The data was prepared for multivariate statistical analysis by combining the spectra into 1 amu bins. All of the mass peaks from 1 to 1000 amu were considered in the analysis of the *S. salivarius* cells. For the analysis of the *C. albicans* cells, all of the mass peaks from 1 to 500 amu were considered. Spectra were normalized for total ion intensity. Since PCA and PLS are sensitive to scaling a variety of scaling methods were investigated. Both autoscaling and log scaling produced results that amplify the noise in very small peaks. However, with no scaling, the value of important high mass peaks was underestimated. To eliminate these problems, a new scaling method was developed. Each peak was scaled to the mean of the highest peak within a 25 m/z window of the peak. This has a similar effect to log scaling the data but reduces the amplification of noise peaks commonly seen with other scaling methods.

3. Results

Sample Preparation XPS, SEM and TEM analysis of the freeze dried cells indicates that the cell walls are well preserved in the drying process. SEM and TEM verified that the cells maintain their shape and cell wall structure. Comparison of the XPS spectra from the freeze dried cells with those of frozen hydrated cells showed no statistically significant changes in the elemental composition or in the C1s peak shape,

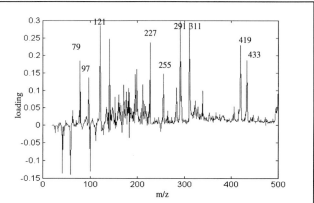

Figure 1: Results of PLS regression of the *S. salivarius* SIMS spectra against the XPS P/C ratio. The graph shows the loadings for the first latent variable. Labeled peaks can be attributed to the presence of Lipoteichoic acid in the bacterial cell wall.

indicating that the cell wall chemistry was well preserved during the drying process. In contrast, air dried cells showed a significant increase in hydrocarbon relative to C-O linkages when compared to the hydrated cells.

S. salivarius   The XPS spectra of the four strains showed the presence of C, O, N, and P on the cell surfaces. Large variations in the P/C ratio were observed between the strains. The SIMS spectra of all four strains showed a high degree of complexity with fragments indicative of the presence of proteins, hydrocarbons, and carbohydrates. In addition, the negative ion spectra showed a large number of peaks containing phosphorus. PCA of SIMS spectra demonstrated that each strain could be uniquely identified by either the positive or negative ion SIMS spectra alone. PLS was used to search for negative SIMS peaks that correlated strongly with the XPS P/C ratio. It was found that the XPS P/C ratio could be accurately predicted using a one latent variable model. Figure 1 shows the loadings for the first PLS latent variable. The PLS model extracts a series of peaks from the complex SIMS spectra that correlate strongly with the phosphorus content in the samples. The peaks labeled in figure 1 are found in the spectrum of pure lipoteichoic acid. The results support the hypothesis that differences in XPS P/C ratio observed in these strains are the result of exposure of lipoteichoic acid at the cell wall surface.

C. albicans

The positive ion SIMS spectra of all cell samples showed a high degree of complexity, with fragments indicative of the presence of proteins and carbohydrates. PCA and Discriminant Analysis (DA) were used to extract the peaks from the

Table 1: Fragments Selected by Discriminant Analysis of SIMS spectra from *C. albicans*

Nominal Mass	Exact Mass	Peak Assignment		Species
m/z	m/z	Functional Group	Mass (amu)	
28	28,019	CH2N+	28,019	Glycine
30	30,034	CH4N+	30,034	Glycine
44	44,053	C2H6N+	44,05	Alanine
72	72,083	C4H10N+	72,081	Valine
86	86,098	C5H12N+	86,081	Leucine

spectra that showed the largest difference between the cells grown in different media. Cells were divided into classes, based first on the sugar present in the growth media (glucose vs galactose) and then by the base growth media (YEP vs YNB). DA showed a statistically significant difference between the different cell classes at a confidence level greater than 99%. Figure 2 shows the spectra projected on the plane described by the two discriminant axes.

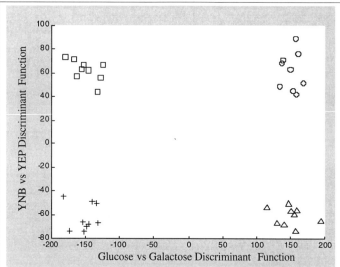

Figure 2: Spectra of *C. albicans* cell s plotted on Discriminant axes. Cell growth media are indicated by symbols. o=GluYNB cells, ▲=GluYEP, □=GluYEP, +=GalcYEP,

The clear separation of all four classes is evident. Cells grown in glucose containing media could be distinguished from those grown in galactose containing media independently of the base media used. Table 1 shows the peaks that contributed most to the separation of the galactose cells from the glucose cells. Each of these peaks can be attributed to a hydrophobic amino acid. The presence of these peaks on the surface was also correlated with adhesion to both Teflon and PVC. Similarly, cells grown in YEP media could be distinguished from cells grown in YNB media independently of the carbohydrate used in the media. The discriminant function for the base media shows a completely different signature from the discriminant function for the carbohydrate, which suggests that while the carbohydrate influences the presence of certain manno-proteins on the cell surface the base media influence the production of another set of surface molecules.

4. Conclusion

Multivariate statistical methods, including PLS, PCA, and DA show considerable utility as an aid for interpreting the SIMS spectra obtained from complex biological surfaces. In the study of *S. salivarius*, PLS was able to aid in the identification of a cell wall component. In the study of *C. albicans*, DA was able to identify amino acids on the cell surface that are associated with the adhesive behavior of the cells.

A. Benninghoven, P. Bertrand, H.-N. Migeon and H.W. Werner (Editors).
Proceedings of the 12th International Conference on Secondary Ion Mass Spectrometry,
Brussels, Belgium, 5-11 September 1999

DYNAMIC AND TOF-SIMS FOR ELEMENTS AND ORGANIC SUBSTANCES IN THE FINE STRUCTURE OF CELLS AND TISSUES

Kenichi Takaya, He Li, Motonori Okabe, Toshiko Yoshida, Jun Murakami, *Miyako Totsu and
*Takahiro Hoshi
Department of Anatomy 2, Toyama Medical & Pharmaceutical University Faculty of Medicine,
2630 Sugitani, Toyama, 930-0194 and *Analytical Division, Ulvac-Phi, Inc., 370 Enzo,
Chigasaki City, 253-0084 Japan

1. Introduction

Ion microscopy (secondary ion mass spectrometry, SIMS) has high detection sensitivity and a spatial resolution comparable better than light microscopy. Its application to cell and tissues to determine the distribution of elements and organic substances at fine structures has given invaluable new information to explore the functions of these elements [1,2]. We report an attempt to apply SIMS (both dynamic and TOF-SIMS) to fresh frozen dried semi-thin sections to examine the element and organic substances distribution by their mass in the ion images [3].

2. Materials and methods

The tongue of five tree frogs, *Hyla arborea* (male and female, 0.8 to 2.4g), the tongue of a ddY mouse (female, 6 week, 36g), the tongue and perirenal adipose tissue of a rat (Wistar, male, 340g) were removed after spinal and ether anesthesia, respectively. Biopsy materials were removed from the skin of six atopic dermatitis patients by local anesthesia with 1% xylocaine and the buffy coat was prepared from the peripheral blood. Tissue pieces were removed and freshly frozen by dipping into propane chilled with liquid nitrogen. The serial ultrathin (100nm) and semi-thin (1-1.5µm) sections were made with an ultracryomicrotome (Leica, FC R) at a cutting speed of 1.8 and 0.7mm/s respectively. The ultrathin sections were attached onto the collodion film covered titanium grids. Both ultrathin and semi-thin sections were attached on the silicon wafer square pieces (7mm x 7mm x 0.5mm) by pressing the sections with the Teflon pieces and freeze-dried by high vacuum in the frozen specimen treatment apparatus (FD-2A). Cryostat sections (10µm) were attached to the slide glass and silicon wafer pieces and air-dried. Prints and smear were also used. Specimens on the slide glass were treated in a new quick procedure, fixed in the Carnoy-Lebrun solution containing mercuric chloride [4] for 30s, stained in undiluted Giemsa solution for 30s observed by light microscopy. Some specimens on the silicon wafer were plasma-coated with gold. Non-coated sections were observed by atomic force microscopy (JSTM-4200).

For ion microscopy, IMS-6f (Cameca) was used for the elements and time-of-flight SIMS, TRIFT II (Physical Electronics) for the elements and organic ions. In dynamic SIMS, O2+, Cs+ and Ga+ were employed for the primary ion beam sources. With the O2+ primary ion source the acceleration voltage was 15kV and the secondary acceleration voltage was 4.5kV. The primary beam size was 0.5µm in diameter. With the Cs+ ion source the acceleration voltage was 10kV and the secondary acceleration voltage was 4.5kV. The primary beam size was approximately 0.4µm in diameter. With the Ga+ ion source the acceleration voltage was

30kV, the extracting voltage was 27kV and the beam current was about 1μA. The minimum size of the primary ion beam was 55nm in diameter. The Ga+ primary ion source was used in TOF-SIMS. For spectrometry, the acceleration voltage was 15kV and for image acquisition 25kV was employed. The primary beam size was about 0.4μm in diameter.

Spectrometry by the IMS-6f was performed also over the tissue sections and cells in the print. The primary beam intensity was approximately 1nA. Image acquisition was made for the mass of the element and organic substances with the peaks in spectrometry in both the positive and negative secondary ions. The primary ion raster size was 250μm x 250μm and 50μm x 50μm, and also 100μm x 100μm . Positive ions of the metal elements were examined. After the analysis with the Cs+ primary ion source, positive ion images for 133Cs56Fe, 133Cs63Cu and 133Cs64Zn were examined with the Ga+ primary ion source. Negative ions 16O, 17HO, 12C14N, 28Si, 31P, 32S, 35Cl, 37Cl, 63Cu, 64Zn and 197Au were investigated. The less abundant isotopes were scanned for a longer period, 10 to 20 fold higher times than for the most abundant isotopes of the elements. TOF-SIMS images for the negative total ions, 35Cl, 63:16O231P, 79:16O331P, 255:palmitic acid (256amu), 283:stearic acid (284amu), 281:oleic acid (282amu) and 279:linoleic acid (289amu) were examined.

3. Results

Positive 39K ion images with the O2+ primary ion source and negative 26CN images with the Cs+ ion source by the IMS-6f and total ion images by the TOF-SIMS gave good histology of the freeze-dried and air-dried cryosections and prints. Histology of the cryosections of the skin biopsy from the atopic dermatitis patients disclosed abundant eosinophils in the connective tissues and mast cells in and around the wall of small vessels. In the buffy coat smear showed a large number of eosinophils and sparse other white blood cells as well as red blood cells and platelets. Sulfur and phosphorus ion images were disclosed in the eosinophils which were shown distinctly by the negative 26CN in the buffy coat smear from the atopic dermatitis patient using the IMS-6f with the Cs+ primary ion beam. Small amounts of zinc and copper were also detected in the eosinophils.

Mast cells of the tree frog tongue on freeze-dried and air-dried cryostat sections were revealed by atomic force microscopy. They had abundant granules in their cytoplasm (Fig. 1). They were also disclosed to have high content of magnesium in their granules in the cytoplasm by TOF-SIMS microscopy. They had stellate appearance with many processes. They were situated among the skeletal muscle fibers, facing and protruding into the lymph sinus. They contained less sodium than the surrounding tissue (Fig. 2). Mast cells in the mouse tongue cryostat sections were identified to contain large amounts of sulfur in their granules of the cytoplasm with the IMS-6f using the Cs+ primary ion source. Very small amounts of silicon, 28Si and zinc, 66Zn were detected in some of them (Fig. 3).

Palmitic, stearic and oleic acids were revealed and localized in the fat droplets of the rat perirenal fat in the negative ion images by TOF-SIMS microscopy using Ga+ as the primary ion source. Chloride, 35Cl was revealed in the margin of the lipid droplet (Fig. 4).

4. Discussion

Elements and organic substances were identified by their mass and their distributions were indicated by ion imaging in the cell and tissue samples.

Dynamic SIMS with the IMS-6f was very effective for detecting elements in the cell and tissues and TOF-SIMS showed the distribution of organic substances in the cell in high resolution ion images. Mast cells of the tree frogs and mammals are known to contain sulfated proteoglycans, including heparin. Mammalian mast cells also contain histamine which aggregate the proteoglycans as a divalent cation. The tree frog mast cells, however, have almost no histamine in their granules [5] and contain large amounts of magnesium. Mast cells and basophils of the other amphibians including toads, common frogs, American bull frogs and newts also contained large amounts of magnesium in their granules, which was shown by a quantitative energy dispersive X-ray microanalysis [6].

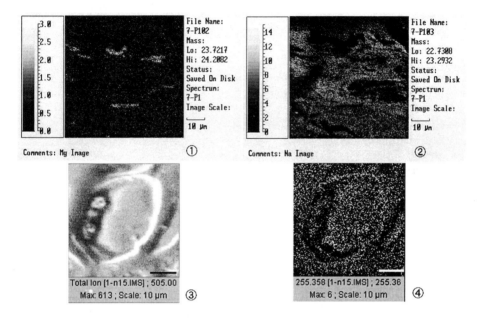

Figures 1 and 2. Tree frog tongue freeze-dried cryostat sections imaged by TOF-SIMS microscopy using Ga+ as the primary ion source.
Figures 3 and 4. The adipose cell air-dried cryostat sections of rat perirenal fat imaged by TOF-SIMS microscopy using Ga+ as the primary ion source.

5. Conclusion

Information on the distribution of fatty acids in the adipose tissues is valuable because the difficulty of the production of antibodies against these substances so far. This approach to make use of the mass for the identification of molecules is expected to provide a new technique to determine the distribution of the substances which are unable to be detected by chemical reactions.

950

References
[1] S. Chandra and G. H. Morrison, Meth. Enzymol. 158(1988) 157.
[2] P. Frague, C. Briancon, C. Fourre, J. Clerc, O. Casiraghi, J. Jeusset, F. Omri and S. Halpern, Biol. Cell. 74(1992) 5.
[3] K. Takaya, Y. Kamisaki and T. Yoshida, SIMS X (1997) 893.
[4] J. B. Carnoy and H. Lebrun, La Cellule 13 (1897) 63.
[5] K. Takaya, T. Fujita and K. Endo, Nature, 215 (1967) 776.
[6] K. Takaya and T. Yoshida, J. Trace Microprobe Techniques, 15 (1997) 669.

A. Benninghoven, P. Bertrand, H.-N. Migeon and H.W. Werner (Editors).
Proceedings of the 12th International Conference on Secondary Ion Mass Spectrometry,
Brussels, Belgium, 5-11 September 1999
951

TOF-SIMS CHARACTERIZATION OF DNA AND PNA BIOSENSOR CHIPS

H. F. Arlinghaus, C. Höppener, and J. Drexler

Physikalisches Institut der Universität Münster, Wilhelm-Klemm-Str. 10,
D-48149 Münster, Germany, Email: arlinghaus@uni-muenster.de

1. Introduction

A novel DNA sequencing method is described that uses peptide nucleic acids (PNA) hybridization biosensor chips [1,2]. PNA is a synthesized DNA analog in which both the phosphate and the deoxyribose of the DNA backbone are replaced by polyamides. These DNA analogs retain the ability to hybridize with complementary DNA or RNA sequences. Thus PNA-chips can be used in the same way as DNA chips for genome diagnostics, the sequencing of cDNAs or the partial sequencing of clones, DNA and RNA sequencing, gene polymorphism studies, and identification of expressed genes. The major advantages of PNA over DNA are the neutral backbone and the increased strength of the PNA/DNA pairing. The lack of charge repulsion improves the hybridization properties in DNA/PNA duplexes compared to DNA/DNA duplexes and the increased binding strength usually leads to a higher sequence discrimination for PNA-DNA hybrids than for DNA-DNA. Because the backbone of DNA contains phosphates and PNA does not, an analysis technique that identifies the presence of the phosphates in a molecular surface layer would, for the first time, allow the use of genomic DNA for hybridization on a biosensor chip, rather than the use of DNA fragments labeled with radioisotopes, stable isotopes or fluorescent substances.

We have employed TOF-SIMS to investigate its ability to detect short fragments of DNA called oligodeoxynucleotides (ODN) and short PNA sequences on Si-surfaces and characterize and compare the immobilization process. Temperature-programmed SIMS (TP-SIMS) was used to examine in detail the thermal stability of the immobilized ODN and PNA. In addition, we have examined the dependency of the secondary ion yield of the phosphate present in the ODN and of the different nucleic acid sequences present in ODN and PNA as a function of primary ion gases.

2. Experiment and Sample Preparation

The experiments were performed with a Poschenrieder-type TOF instrument (Münster TOF-I) equipped with a combined cooling and heating device, allowing the control of the sample temperature in the range of 150-700 K [4]. The increase in the temperature as a function of time can be adjusted on this instrument. A high-resolution TOF-SIMS (Münster TOF-II) was used for spectrum analysis.

Silicon wafers were used to immobilize the ODN. They were cut into pieces of 5x5 mm², etched in a 1% aqueous solution of HF for 2 minutes, rinsed with deionized H_2O, UV/ozone-treated, and subsequently silanized with either 3-Glycidoxypropyltrimethoxysilane or 2-3-4-Epoxycyclohexylethylsilane by immersion in a 1:1000 diluted silane:hexane solution for 25 minutes at 25°C [3]. The silanized probes were rinsed four times with hexane to remove the molecules that were not covalently bonded to the surface. ODN or PNA, dissolved in deionized H_2O with concentrations between 1 µM and 1 mM, were pipetted (1 µl) onto the silanized silicon wafer with a drop diameter of about 1 mm. The wafers were then washed with H_2O to remove ODN or PNA that were not covalently bonded to the silane.

3. Results and Discussion

We immobilized silane self-assembled-layers to UV/ozone-treated silicon wafers [3] and bonded ODN and PNA with different concentrations and immobilization times to these layers. Figure 1 shows the structure of PNA and DNA, and Figure 2 depicts some TOF-SIMS spectra obtained from ODN and PNA. The spectra clearly demonstrate that the masses corresponding to PO_2^-, PO_3^- and $H_2PO_4^-$ provide the best correlation to ODN presence and can be used to precisely distinguish between ODN and PNA. The CF_3^- and $C_2O_2F_3^-$ peaks seen in the PNA spectra are due to trifluoroacetic acid which was part of the PNA solution. Protonated $(M_b+H)^+$ and deprotonated $(M_b-H)^-$ signals of the bases A_b, T_b, C_b, and G_b were observed for both immobilized PNA and ODN sequences, where $(M_b-H)^-$ presented the highest signal. We used the PO_3^- and $(M_b-H)^-$ signal to characterize the immobilized ODNs and only $(M_b-H)^-$ to characterize the immobilized PNA in the following experiments.

Figure 3 shows the ODN and PNA signals as a function of immobilization time. It can be seen that the ODN signal increases with increasing immobilization time and levels off after approximately 6 hours. Comparable behavior was observed with concentration of 10 µM and 1 µM. No significant changes can be detected for PNA immobilization times between 1 h and 24 h, and the data indicate that the signal is already saturated after 1 h. The shorter immobilization time of PNA in comparison to ODN is likely due to the lack of charge repulsion.

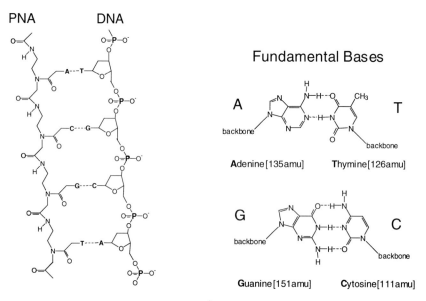

Fig. 1 Structure of PNA and DNA.

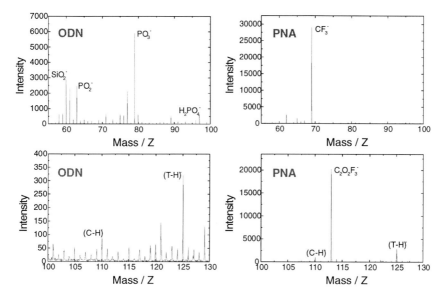

Fig. 2 Negative TOF-SIMS spectra obtained from ODN (left) and PNA (right).

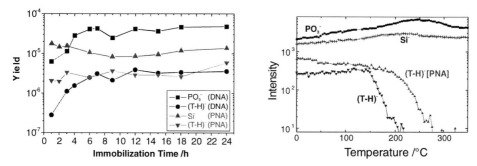

Fig. 3 Dependence of the ODN (c = 0.1 mM) and PNA (c = 0.1 mM) yield on immobilization time.

Fig. 4 TP-SIMS measurements of an ODN (c = 0.1 mM) and PNA (c = 0.1 mM, curve labled as PNA) TTTTCCCTCTCTC-sequence.

TP-SIMS experiments were used to investigate the thermal stability of immobilized ODN and PNA. Figure 4 depicts some characteristic peaks of ODN and PNA as well as the signal from the silicon substrate. The signal for the T- and C-bases starts to decrease at about 150 °C for ODN and about 200 °C for PNA. This variance is caused by the differences in binding strength between the bases and the sugar-phosphate-backbone or the peptide-backbone, respectively.

The homogeneity of the immobilized ODN and PNA distribution was also examined. It was found that PNA is more evenly distributed around the center of the immobilized droplet than ODN which depicts a donut-shaped distribution (see Figure 5). The ODN distribution was likely affected by the ionic strength of the aqueous ODN solution. Adding salt to the ODN solution, such

954

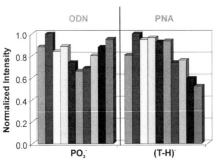

Fig. 5 Dependence of ODN (c = 0.1 mM) and PNA (c = 0.1 mM) signal on ion beam position on immobilized droplet.

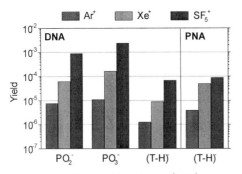

Fig. 6 Dependence of SI yield on Ar^+, Xe^+ and SF_5^+ primary ion bombardment. Sample preparation same as in Figure 5.

as $MgCl_2$, resulted in a decrease of the DNA charge and a better homogeneity.

Figure 6 shows the dependency of the secondary ion yield of phosphate present in the DNA and of the C- and T-bases present in the used ODN and PNAs as a function of Ar^+, Xe^+, and SF_5^+ primary ions. For ODN, the ion yield for both phosphate and C- and T-bases could be increased by a factor of 10 with Xe^+ and even by a factor of 100 with SF_5^+ ion bombardment. In comparison, for the PNA sample a smaller signal increase for the C- and T-bases was observed during SF_5^+ ion bombardment. The results indicate that poly-atomic primary ion bombardment would significantly increase the sensitivity of identifying hybridized DNA on a PNA biosensor chip.

4. Conclusion

We have successfully shown that TOF-SIMS is a useful tool for identifying DNA on a biosensor chip by detecting the phosphorus present in the DNA. TOF-SIMS and TP-SIMS are valuable tools for studying the complexity of the immobilization process. Employing unlabeled DNA has several advantages over using fluorescent and radioactive labeling procedures, such as significantly higher signal-to-noise ratio, higher sensitivity, absence of a labeling procedure, and direct analysis of hybridized genomic DNA. In future experiments, we will use TOF-SIMS and TP-SIMS for studying the complexity of the hybridization process and for evaluating the potential of TOF-SIMS for providing a rapid method for DNA/RNA sequencing and diagnostics.

References

[1] H.F. Arlinghaus, M.N. Kwoka, and K.B. Jacobson, Anal. Chem. **69**, 3747 (1997).
[2] H.F. Arlinghaus and K.B. Jacobson, US Patent 05821060 (1998).
[3] C. Höppener, J. Drexler, M. Ostrop, and H. F. Arlinghaus, this conference.
[4] M. Deimel, D. Rading, G. Egbers, E. Göcke, and A. Benninghoven, in: *SIMS X Proceedings,* ed. A. Benninghoven et al., J. Wiley & Sons, New York (1997), p 507.

SECTION 16 :
ENVIRONMENTAL SCIENCES

A. Benninghoven, P. Bertrand, H.-N. Migeon and H.W. Werner (Editors).
Proceedings of the 12th International Conference on Secondary Ion Mass Spectrometry,
Brussels, Belgium, 5-11 September 1999
© 2000 Elsevier Science B.V. All rights reserved.

SECONDARY ION MASS SPECTROSCOPY IN DENDROANALYSIS

R. R. Martin[*] rrhm@julian.uwo.ca

T. K. Sham[*], G. Wong Won[*], and M.C. Biesinger[**]

[*]Department of Chemistry, [**]Surface Science Western
University of Western Ontario London, ON, Canada N6A 5B7

1. Introduction

The study of the element distribution between the annual growth rings of trees is called dendroanalysis. In principle it can serve as an indicator of environmental element deposition, providing an accurate chronology of significant pollution events and/or show changes in soil metal content [1]. Ideally elemental chronologies derived from dendroanalysis could be combined with known deposition events to establish the kinetics of metal transport in soil and plants. Dendroanalysis may have severe limitations including the possibility of lateral migration of elements within stemwood and the relative ability of different species to regulate metal uptake [2]. The analytical community remains divided on the usefulness of the technique [3, 4]. Surface analytical techniques which are well suited to probing areas about the same size as annual growth rings are well suited to dendroanalysis. SIMS, with its ability to identify virtually all the elements and their isotopes, appears to be particularly well suited to investigate the metal content of tree rings [5, 6, 7]. This paper compares the results obtained by Inductively Coupled Plasma Mass Spectroscopy(ICP/MS) and SIMS in the analysis of the tree rings of Eastern White Pine, <u>Pinus strobus</u>, in the Pinery Provincial Park, Ontario, Canada.

The Pinery Provincial Park is an oak savanna on the shores of Lake Huron. The soil consists of a parallel series of sand dunes deposited by the prevailing wind off the lake. The dunes are composed of approximately equal parts of silica sand, clay, and dolomite ($CaMg(CO_3)_2$). The age of the dunes increases from the lake shore inland so that the shore dunes are still being deposited while the most remote inland dunes have been dated to an age of approximately 5000 B.P (Before Present). Protz and VandenBygaart [8] have carried out an extensive survey of the soils in the Pinery and have established that Mg and Ca are slowly leaching from the dunes so that there is a concentration gradient from the shore to the oldest dunes. In this work both SIMS and ICP/MS are used to monitor the metal concentration in trees from the shore to the oldest dunes. Consistent changes in ring metal content reflecting dune weathering would suggest that dendroanalysis in comparable systems is a useful indicator of metal availability.

2. Experimental

Wood samples were collected from Eastern white pine, <u>Pinus strobus L.</u>, using a HAGLOF A 558 increment borer which removes a cylinder of wood 4mm in diameter and 40 cm in length from the stemwood of the tree. Samples were collected at breast height (1.5 metres) and stored in plastic drinking straws for transport to the laboratory. Four sample cores were obtained at each site, with the sites chosen at the height of each series of dune ridges. The samples were lightly sanded and the rings identified under a low power optical microscope.

The surface was then cleaned using a microtome with a stainless steel blade and sputter coated with a thin layer of gold prior to SIMS analysis.

The SIMS instrument used was the Cameca IMS/3f at Surface Science Western using a 200 nA O⁻ primary ion beam at 15keV net energy in the step scanning mode. The sample was sputtered for 50 seconds prior to analysis at each spot in the step scan to ensure a clean surface. ^{12}C, ^{23}Na, ^{24}Mg, ^{39}K and ^{40}Ca were collected as positive secondary ions. C secondary ions were collected without an offset while a 100 V offset was applied to the sample holder to suppress molecular secondary ions. A counting time of 1 sec was used for C while 2 sec was used for all the other species. The step scan was carried out across the entire ring corresponding to the year 1993. This procedure was used to ensure that the entire growing season was represented in the final result so that any seasonal variations in element uptake would be eliminated. Finally all results are ratioed to the C secondary ion yield, thus carbon is employed as an internal standard. Naturally the results are not quantitative and show only relative changes between samples.

The 1993 tree rings were cut from the core after SIMS analysis using a stainless steel blade. The individual rings were then placed in quartz tubes and ashed at 525 °C for 24 hours. The resulting ash was dissolved in 10% high purity HNO_3. The resulting solution was analysed for Ca, Mg, Na and K using a Finnigan MAT ELEMENT ICP-MS, an ultra-trace instrument.

3. Results and discussion

The SIMS results are shown in table1. A student's t-test shows the differences in secondary ion ratios to be significant at 95% for Ca, with an increase from the youngest to the oldest dune. Significant differences are also noted for Mg which increases from the youngest to the oldest but decreases from the oldest to the middle dune, Na decreases from oldest to youngest and K increases. In summary the SIMS results show no monotonic changes from the shore to the inland dunes. The results which are significant do not show any trends with the exception of Ca which increases from the youngest to the oldest dunes.

Table 1. SIMS Results: Metal/C Ration In Dune System (Standard Deviation)

Ratio	Oldest (4,700 B.P)	Middle (1,750 B.P.)	Youngest (100 B.P.)
Ca/C	0.32 (0.30)	0.29 (0.06)	0.20 (0.19)
Mg/C	0.005 (0.005)	0.006 (0.001)	0.002 (0.001)
Na/C	0.02 (0.01)	0.04 (0.01)	0.03 (0.02)
K/C	0.08 (0.06)	0.18 (0.06)	0.07 (0.09)

Most plant nutrients in this system are introduced by atmospheric deposition, either as particulates or dissolved in rainwater. Accordingly no pattern from shore to inland dunes would be expected for easily leached elements such as Na and K and the results obtained here are consistent with this hypothesis. The results for Ca are more difficult to rationalize. Since there is relatively more leaching in the oldest, inland dune the levels might be expected to be lower. If the SIMS results are a reliable indicator of tree metal content, at least two hypotheses might be advanced to explain the calcium increase in the trees with dune age.

The pH in the first 50 cm of soil falls from the newest to the oldest dune (7.4 to 4.7) which might help mobilize metals. The surface $CaCO_3$ also falls from 15% to 0.2% while the concentration at depth, 100 cm, is essentially constant at about 15% [8]. In addition since this study can not compare the root zones of the trees in different dunes, it is possible that the Ca differences may be explained by local ground water effects. In any case the standard deviation on the measurements is high and additional sampling could well change the results.

The ICP/MS results are shown in table 2. A student's t-test shows no significant difference in any of the metals between any of the sites at 95% confidence.

Table 2. ICP/MS Results: Metal Concentrations, ppm, In Dune System (Standard Deviation)

Metal	Oldest (4,700 B.P)	Middle (1,750 B.P.)	Youngest (100 B.P.)
Ca	552 (146)	532 (157)	670 (202)
Mg	126 (22)	113 (34)	117 (27)
Na	12 (3.8)	9 (8)	44 (52)
K	203 (61)	288 (173)	317 (101)

The different significance levels between the ICP and SIMS results are due to the fact that SIMS interrogates a relatively small volume of wood while ICP/MS is essentially a bulk technique. SIMS is thus less reliable as an indicator of bulk properties while it gives valuable insights into local variations in metal concentration [9].

In summary the results do not show statistically significant, consistent changes in metal content in trees growing in the sand dunes with increasing age of the dunes, even though significant metal leaching has occurred with time in the dune system. The one statistically significant result obtained by SIMS is not confirmed by ICP/MS. The difference in results between instruments is attributed to differences in sampling volume, though matrix effects may affect the SIMS results. We suggest that additional SIMS analysis would both increase the reliability of the SIMS data set and bring it into agreement with the ICP data. More significantly the results do not reflect the changes in the soil Ca content in the first 75 cm of the soil profile. This result suggests that dendroanalysis as a measure of soil metals can be applied only with the utmost caution.

4. Conclusions

SIMS analysis of the metal content of tree rings in a well-defined dune system yields consistent, statistically significant results only for the Ca content, showing a Ca increase with the age of the dune. This result is opposite to that observed in the first 75 cm of the soil profile. If correct the difference may be attributed to changes in soil pH, however the standard deviation of the data is high, and the result is tentative at best.

ICP/MS conducted on the same samples as those used for SIMS shows no statistically significant difference between samples. This casts further doubt on the SIMS data, and since ICP interrogates a larger volume of material, the ICP result should be accepted. SIMS is perhaps a better measure of localized changes in metal content while ICP is better for bulk analysis.

In any case neither technique shows changes in metal content that represent measured changes in the first 75 cm of soil. This, in turn, suggests that dendroanalysis has limited application as a measure of soil metal content, at least in surface soil.

References

[1]   Amato, I. Anal. Chem. 60 (1988)1103.
[2]   Hagenmeyer, J. , Markert, B. in Plants As Biomonitors, VCH-Publisher, Weinheim, New York (1993) 549.
[3]   Qian, J-L, Ke, S-Z, and Xiang, C-X. Pedosphere 3 (1993) 309.
[4]   Trueby, P. Angew. Bot. 69 (1995) 135.
[5]   Watmough S. A., Hutchinson T. C., and Evans R. D. J. Environ. Qual. 27 (1998) 1087.
[6]   Bailey, J.H.E and Reeve, D.W. Journal Of Pulp And Paper Science 20 (1994) 83
[7]   Martin, R. R., Sham, T. K. Wong Won, G., van der Heide, P., Jones, K. W., Song, S-R, Protz, R. Can. J. For. Res. 28 (1998) 1464.
[8]   Protz, R. and VandenBygraat, A. J. Canadian Journal Of Soil Science 74 (1994) 63
[9]   Martin, R. R., Furimsky, E., Jain, J., and Skinner W. M. in Evironmental Biomonitoring, Exposure Assessment and Specimen Banking, ACS Symposium Series 654 (1995)30

A. Benninghoven, P. Bertrand, H.-N. Migeon and H.W. Werner (Editors).
Proceedings of the 12th International Conference on Secondary Ion Mass Spectrometry,
Brussels, Belgium, 5-11 September 1999

961

MS/MS SIMS OF CHEMICAL WARFARE AGENTS ON ENVIRONMENTAL SAMPLES

A. D. Appelhans, G. S. Groenewold, G. L. Gresham, J. E. Olson

Idaho National Engineering and Environmental Laboratory
P. O. Box 1625, Idaho Falls, Idaho, USA 83415-2208, ada2@inel.gov

1. Introduction

The fate and transport of chemicals and biological organisms within the environment is strongly affected by their interaction with surfaces, and understanding these interactions is key to elucidating transport pathways, sequestration, and degradation. Probing the surface region has been a challenge, particularly when the compounds of interest may be present at only a fraction of a monolayer. Compounding the challenge is the presence of a tremendous variety of compounds that populate the surface environment, providing mass spectroscopists spectra with a peak at every unit mass, indeed more often than not, several peaks at most unit masses. Seeing through this high level of background "noise" presents a major challenge to applying secondary ion mass spectrometry to environmental samples [1,2]. We have designed and employed an ion trap secondary ion mass spectrometer (IT-SIMS) with a polyatomic primary beam [3] and the capability to perform collision induced dissociation (CID) and multiple stages of mass spectrometry (MS^n), in order to separate the signal from the noise. In this paper several examples of the application of CID with MS^2 to detect the chemical warfare agent VX (methylphosphonothioic acid, S-[2-[bis(1-methylethyl)amino]ethyl] O-ethyl ester) and its degradation products on concrete are presented to illustrate the power of the approach.

2. Experimental

Measurements were conducted with an ion trap secondary ion mass spectrometer (Figure 1) utilizing a perrhenate primary beam of 4 kV, ~100 pA focused to a 1.5 mm spot [2]. The vacuum housing was located in a fume hood, the instrument control and data system were located outside the hood. Samples were mounted using double-sided tape to a room temperature sample insertion probe tip. During insertion the samples are held for 1 minute at a vacuum of ~100 mTorr, then introduced into the main vacuum chamber at ~3×10^{-5} torr helium (3×10^{-6} base pressure).

Sample Generation. Both neat VX and an analytical reference standard of 1 μg/μl in isopropanol were used. *(VX is a highly lethal compound and should only be handled in approved chemical surety laboratories.)* The reference

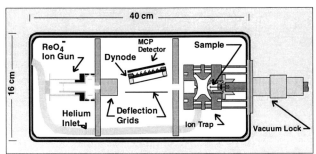

Figure 1. Vacuum chamber of ion trap SIMS.

standard solution was used for serial dilutions which were added to the crushed concrete (~50 mg) to obtain a specific surface coverage. The molecular area of the VX was calculated to be 79 Å^2 assuming the molecule laid flat on the surface. If the molecule is upright or is coiled, then the monolayer coverages will be less. Neat VX was added to small concrete chips (~2x2 mm) in measured microdroplets to simulate conditions typical of an actual dispersal in the environment. The concrete, which had been weathered for several years in an urban environment, was cleaned with an alkylsulfonate soap, distilled water rinse, followed by heating to dryness prior to addition of the VX. The surface area of the crushed concrete was measured at 4.0 m^2/g using N_2 adsorption (BET method) [4]. Following application of the analyte the samples were allowed to dry for approximately 2 hours under ambient conditions, whereupon approximately 1 mg of sample (for the crushed concrete) was attached to a sample holder using double-sided tape. The sample holder was then attached to the direct insertion probe (Figure 1) for analysis.

Mass Spectrometry For a typical MS^1 measurement, the ion trap was operated at a low mass cutoff of 40 amu and the ionization time was ~20 milliseconds. Each spectrum consisted of ten summed scans and typically 30 spectra would be acquired for an analysis. The primary ion dose for a typical analysis was about 2 x 10^{11} ions/cm^2. For MS^2 experiments, the ionization time was longer (100 - 200 milliseconds) resulting in a primary ion beam dose of 1-2 x 10^{12} ions/cm^2. During ionization a filtered noise field was applied to the ion trap which restricted the mass range of the trapped ions to the peak of interest. Following ionization an RF ramp was applied up to the parent ion peak m/z to remove any ions not ejected by the filtered noise field. This results in the trap being filled with essentially only the ions of the targeted m/z (a few m/z in width). These ions were then excited via application of an RF wave form tuned to the ions' natural frequency, which causes the ions to oscillate within the trap, colliding with the helium ions and picking up internal energy leading to fragmentation. The fragment ions were trapped and then scanned out for detection.

3. Results

The positive ion mass spectrum of the 0.05 monolayer of VX on crushed concrete, shortly after spiking, was essentially identical to that for VX on silicate (soil) particles [5], with abundant ions at m/z 268, 128, and 86 (Figure 2). These ions indicate the presence of intact VX on the sample surface, and are not the result of surface decomposition prior to analysis. Specifically, the appearance of m/z 268 (VX + H)$^+$ can be used to indicate the presence of intact VX on the concrete surface if the composition of the m/z ion can be unequivocally determined (using CID-MS^2). As the surface concentration decreases the m/z 268 peak falls into the chemical noise (Figure 3). To unequivocally identify the m/z

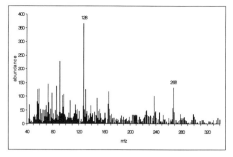

Figure 2. Cation MS^1 of 0.05 monolayer of VX on crushed concrete.

268 as VX and to separate it from the chemical noise, the m/z 268 ions are collisionally dissociated to produce the MS^2 spectrum. An example is shown in Figure 4; a concrete chip

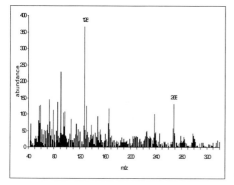

Figure 3. MS^1 of 0.004 monolayer of VX on crushed concrete.

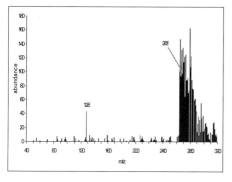

Figure 4. MS^2 of m/z 268 (M+H)$^+$ of 5 ng of VX on concrete chip.

(~2x2 mm) was spiked with 5 ng of neat VX and then analyzed within a few hours after application. All ions below m/z 268 were removed from the trap and the m/z 268 was collisionally dissociated. The m/z 128 is clearly seen, indicating the m/z 268 was intact VX. Figure 5 illustrates the fragmentation reaction.

After one day at room temperature significant degradation of the VX on the crushed concrete had occurred as evidenced by the spectra shown in Figure 6. The degradation occurred through cleaving at the P-S and S-C linkages, resulting in five distinct degradation products. CID-MS^2 was used to determine the structure of the degradation products and the most likely decomposition pathways. An example is shown in Figure 7. Concrete-induced cleavage of the P-S linkage results in the formation of N,N-diisopro-pylaminoethane thiol (DESH) and a resultant ion at m/z 160, which corresponds to [DESH − H]$^+$. This ion was identified using CID-MS^2 by the elimination of CH_2S and C_3H_6 to produce fragment ions at m/z 114 and 118, respectively (Figure 7). It is significant to note that the degradation products could not be detected using a conventional continuous air monitor, and only one was detected via alcohol extraction followed by GCMS.

4. Conclusion

The foregoing illustrates the ability at SIMS to desorb compounds, strongly adsorbed to the surface and the power of CID-MS^2 for determining chemical structure.

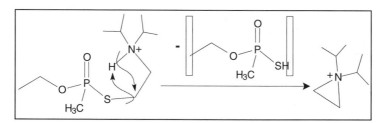

Figure 5. Fragmentation of m/z 268 (VX + H)$^+$ to m/z 128.

964

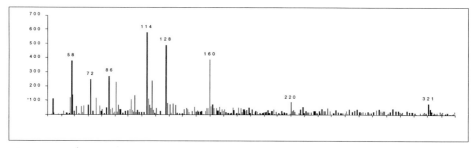

Figure 6. MS^1 spectrum of VX on concrete after one day; note that the molecular ion of VX at m/z 268 is absent.

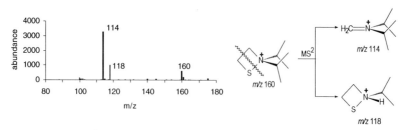

Figure 7. CID-MS^2 of m/z 160, (DESH-H)$^+$ degradation product of VX, showing fragmentation pathways to m/z 114 and 118.

Acknowledgement

Research supported by the US Department of Energy under contract DE-AC07-94ID13223. The assistance of M. Weibel and M. Jeffery is gratefully acknowledged.

References

[1] G. S. Groenewold, A. K. Gianotto, J. C. Ingram, A. D. Appelhans, Current Topics in Anal. Chem. 1 (1998) 73.

[2] A. D. Appelhans, G. S. Groenewold, J. C. Ingram, J. E. Delmore, D. A. Dahl, *Secondary Ion Mass Spectrometry SIMS X,* John Wiley & Sons, New York (1997) p935.

[3] J. E. Delmore, A. D. Appelhans, E. S. Peterson, Intrntl. Jrnl. Mass Spec. & Ion Proc., 178 (1998) 9.

[4] A. W. Adamson, *Physical Chemistry of Surfaces,* John Wiley & Sons, New York, (1990), p 609.

[5] G. S. Groenewold, A. D. Appelhans, G. L. Gresham, J. E. Olson, M. Jeffery, J. B. Wright, Anal. Chem. 71 (1999) 2318.

A. Benninghoven, P. Bertrand, H.-N. Migeon and H.W. Werner (Editors).
Proceedings of the 12th International Conference on Secondary Ion Mass Spectrometry,
Brussels, Belgium, 5-11 September 1999
© 2000 Elsevier Science B.V. All rights reserved.

HIGH SPATIAL RESOLUTION SIMS ANALYSIS OF ICE CRYSTAL FORMVAR REPLICAS

S.H. Ehrman[b] and O. Gebhardt[a,c]

[a] corresponding author
[b] Department of Chemical Engineering, University of Maryland, College Park, MD 20742, USA
[c] Paul Scherrer Institute, CH-5232 Villigen, PSI Switzerland, gebhardt@psi.ch

1. Introduction

In addition to the so-called 'greenhouse gases', aerosols are believed to affect global climate [1]. The magnitude of this aerosol climate forcing is uncertain, particularly the magnitude of the indirect effects associated with cloud formation. To reduce this uncertainty, an improved understanding of the relationship between clouds and aerosols is needed. This information is also useful for reconstructing the composition of past atmospheres based on analysis of glacier ice cores since incorporation into cloud droplets and snow crystals during precipitation events is an important mechanism for deposition of aerosols onto glaciers.

Because of the multiple scavenging processes which can occur, including nucleation, inertial impaction, Brownian motion, accretion of supercooled cloud droplets (riming), and gas phase scavenging, the relationship between the concentrations of pollutants in the atmosphere and in bulk snow or rain is quite complex [2-4]. Differences between in-cloud and below-cloud scavenging mechanisms may additionally obscure the relationship. The most complicated scavenging scenario occurs in mixed-phase clouds; i.e. clouds containing both supercooled cloud droplets and ice crystals.

In order to better understand the scavenging process, analytical techniques are needed which can resolve the composition of particulate matter contained in ice crystals as a function of position within the crystal. Previous efforts have focused on evaporating ice crystals and analysing the residue using scanning electron microscopy coupled with energy dispersive x-ray spectrometry or transmission electron microscopy coupled with electron diffraction [5-7]. In related studies involving secondary ion or neutral mass spectrometry, secondary neutral mass spectrometry (SNMS) and secondary ion mass spectrometry (SIMS) have been used to obtain the depth resolved composition of atmospheric aerosol particles [8-11], and dynamic as well as static secondary ion mass spectrometry have been used to probe the interactions of molecular chlorine, dichlorine monoxide and hypochlorous acid with solid ice films [12-13]. In the following, results are presented for the high spatial resolution analysis of ice crystal replicas as a function of position using static SIMS.

2. Experimental

Sampling was conducted on April 1, 1998 at the Jungfraujoch High-Alpine Research Station (3450 m a.s.l.) located in the Swiss Alps. Crystal replicas were collected onto glass slides using the formvar method developed by Schaefer [14]. A schematic of this process is shown in Figure 1.

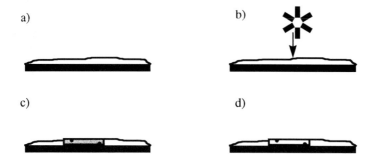

Fig. 1. a) Glass slide is dipped in 2% by mass solution of formvar resin in dichloroethane, b) slide is exposed to falling crystals, c) crystal lands, formvar and dichloroethane diffuse over crystal, d) water and dichloroethane sublime leaving shape and non-aqueous material behind.

The formvar replicas were carefully removed from the glass slides using a scalpel and transferred to a substrate consisting of aluminium foil over a silicon wafer. To minimise contamination, the transfer was conducted in a laminar flow hood. The formvar replicas were sputtered with a layer (less than 15 nm thick) of platinum and imaged using a scanning electron microscope (SEM). An image of one of the crystals analysed is shown in Figure 2.

The SIMS analysis was performed using a S4000 secondary ion mass spectrometer (Atomika Instruments) equipped with a quadrupole mass spectrometer. Analyses were conducted for the following ions: ^{23}Na, ^{27}Al, ^{28}Si, ^{39}K, ^{40}Ca, chemical species which would be expected in the presence of soil-derived aerosol particles. A liquid metal ion source (LMIS) equipped with two lenses (Fei Company) was operated with Gallium ions striking the samples with 25 keV at normal incidence. With a primary ion current of 400 picoamperes the primary ion beam was focused down to a diameter of about 100 nm

For analysis 50 to 1000 micron square areas were scanned by the primary ion beam. Images were recorded 8 seconds per cycle with 256x256 pixels stored. To improve the statistical reliability the data of 10 image scans per mass were superposed to obtain the final results. Composition as a function of the individual image scans did not change significantly over the course of the 10 scans.

a)   b)

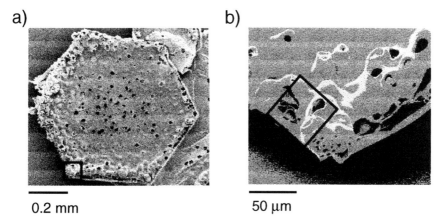

0.2 mm   50 µm

Fig. 2. SEM image of a formvar ice crystal replica, collected April 1, 1998
showing a) the entire ice crystal and the 50 micron square region analysed
with SIMS (marked) and b) a detail of a 50 micron square region,
corresponding to chemical mapping results shown below in Figure 3.

3. Results

At low magnifications sufficient for analysis of entire crystal replicas (500 to 1000 micron
square region) the composition of individual aerosol particles, thought to be 10 microns or
less in diameter, could not be resolved. However, at 50 to 100 micron square regions
analysed, enriched regions were detected, which are believed to correspond to aerosol
particles trapped within the formvar resin. Figure 3 shows the relative intensities for the
following ions, ^{27}Al, ^{28}Si, ^{39}K, and ^{40}Ca, as a function of position for the analysis area shown
above in Figure 2b. The enriched areas are a few microns in diameter, and their spatial
locations suggest some variation in the aerosol particle composition from particle to particle.

Analyses, not presented here, were conducted in the centre of the crystal in an attempt to
determine the composition of the ice nucleating particle. However, as in Figure 3, several
enriched areas were visible, and it was not possible to determine which enriched area
corresponded to the nucleating particle. Future work will include qualitative comparisons of
rimed and unrimed regions of the ice crystal replicas to determine if significant differences in
composition exist.

968

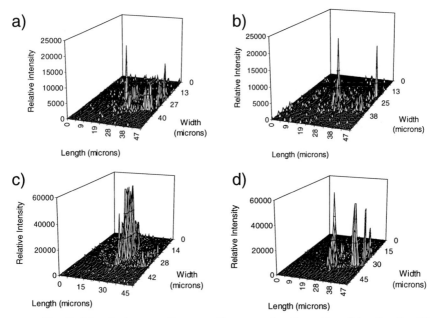

Fig. 3. Chemical maps of composition as a function of position for the 50 micron square region shown in Figure 2b, for the ions: a) ^{27}Al, b) ^{28}Si, c) ^{39}K, and d) ^{40}Ca.

References

[1]   S.E. Schwartz and M.O. Andreae, Science 272 (1996) 1121.
[2]   R.D. Borys, E.E. Hindman and P.J. Demott, J. Atmos. Chem. 7 (1988) 213.
[3]   U. Baltensperger, M. Schwikowski, D.T. Jost, H.W. Gäggeler, and O. Poulida, Atmos. Environ., 32 (1998) 3975.
[4]   O. Poulida, M. Schwikowski, U. Baltensperger, and J. Staehelin, Atmos. Environ. 32 (1998) 3985.
[5]   M. Kumai and K.E. Francis, J. Atmos. Sci. 19 (1962) 474.
[6]   K. Kikuchi, M. Murakami, and S. Sanuki, Mem. Natl. Inst. Polar Res. 24 (1982) 157.
[7]   M. Kumai, J. Atmos. Sci. 33 (1976) 833.
[8]   J. Goschnick, J. Schuricht., and H.J. Ache, Fresenius J. Anal. Chem. 350 (1994) 426.
[9]   J.W.G. Bentz, J. Goschnick, J. Schuricht., and H.J. Ache, Fresenius J. Anal. Chem. 353 (1995) 559.
[10] J. Goschnick, C. Natzeck, and M. Sommer, Appl. Surf. Sci. 145 (1999) 201.
[11] F. Faude and J. Goschnick, Fresenius J. Anal. Chem. 358 (1997) 67.
[12] H.A. Donsig and J.C. Vickerman, J. Chem. Soc. Faraday Trans. 93 (1997) 2755.
[13] H.A. Donsig, D. Herridge, and J.C. Vickerman, J. Phys. Chem. A 102 (1998) 2302.
[14] V.J. Schaefer, Weatherwise, 9 (1956) 132.

A. Benninghoven, P. Bertrand, H.-N. Migeon and H.W. Werner (Editors).
Proceedings of the 12th International Conference on Secondary Ion Mass Spectrometry,
Brussels, Belgium, 5-11 September 1999

APPLICATION OF SIMS TO DUST SAMPLE IN FLUE GAS

S.Oishi [1], M.Shirahase [1], R.Oiwa [2], K.Kusama [3]

[1] National Institute for Resources and Environment, e-mail oishi@nire.go.jp
16-3 Onogawa,Tsukuba, Ibaraki,305-8569
[2] ULVAC-PHI,Inc370 Enzou,Chigasaki, Kanagawa, 253-0084
[3] Sumitomo Metal Technology, Inc,1-8 Fusoucho, Amagasaki, Hyougo, 660-0891

1. Introduction

SPM(suspended particulate matter) is produced in a variety of ways, including artificially by factories, businesses, automobiles, etc., naturally by soil, sea salt, etc., and by secondary particles resulting from photochemical reaction of gaseous substances in the atmosphere. The mechanism of production is very complex. After emission of primary particulates and gaseous substances from fixed sources, secondary particulates are formed by photochemical reactions. Also, we know that immediately after some particles that cannot be detected by current methods are released into the atmosphere from smokestacks, "condensation dust" occurs which forms particles. In addition, as the proportion of this condensation dust ranges from several tenths to several times previous particulate emissions and the dust can be hazardous to human health because of its microscopic size, it has become a serious issue in policies for dealing with floating dust. Furthermore, during normal collection times the amount of condensation dust is very low, and only the major chemical components has been known. Therefore, high-sensitive spectrometers, SIMS and TOF-SIMS were used to measure condensation dust. Previously these spectrometers had been used to measure dust particles [1-3], but not condensation dusts.

2. Experiment
2.1 Collection of samples

Both particulate matter contained in emissions in a JIS-Z8808 gas duct, and condensation dust passing through the gas duct, were collected from an experimental furnace which burns Type A low-sulfur heavy oil. Condensation dust was collected on filter paper, an impactor and a drain using two methods: water-based indirect cooling (Method A) and air-based direct cooling (Method B). In Method A, the samples were cooled by water from the external (double) suction duct. At that time, the aqueous component of the sample gas was condensed into water on the interior wall of the duct, then it ran down into a drain where it was collected. In Method B, filter paper was used on the inside of the gas duct. After separating the dust, the sample gas was mixed with diluted air and cooled. After forming into particulates, the samples were collected using filter paper or an impactor installed further along the passageway.

2.2 Sample preparation

The particulate substances in the dust and condensation dust were stripped away and pressure adhered onto either indium foil or a silver membrane filter. The samples collected with the impactor were measured directly.

3. Results

In the particulate sample we can see aggregates and globules. The condensation dust collected on the filter paper adhered as globules, and as a film on the fibers. Thus we know that the condensation dust collected on the filter paper in mist form. The condensation dust collected in the drain developed cracks during the drying process. EDX measurements showed that the main components of all samples were C,O and S. Carbon was the main component of the particulates, and sulfur was detected despite its existence in only small amounts.

3.1 SIMS

The analytical results of the two types of samples are shown in Figure 1. In both samples, H,C,O,Na,Si,K,Ca,S, etc., were detected. V was found in the particulate samples. As the temperature in the heavy oil furnace was low, significant differences were not found between condensation dusts and other dusts.

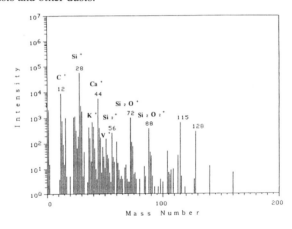

Fig.1 Positive SIMS spectrum of particulate dust

3.2 TOF-SIMS

TOF-SIMS found both aliphatic and aromatic hydrocarbons. In addition to these hydrocarbons, sulfur compounds such as SO, SO , SOH, as well as thionyl chloride, were detected in the condensation dust. Higher alcohols such as CH_7O, C_9H_9O, CH_1O, CH_3O were quite apparent in the condensation dust collected with the impactor. We believe these compounds to be of the Octavcosan-1-ol, Nonacosan-1-ol, Tricontan-1-ol and Hentriacontan-1-ol groups.

For some specimens, polycycloxylens originating from silicone grease, which is often used to lubricate connecting parts of vacuum systems used to collect samples, was apparently responsible for mass spectrum peaks.

A)Particulate dust in flue gas

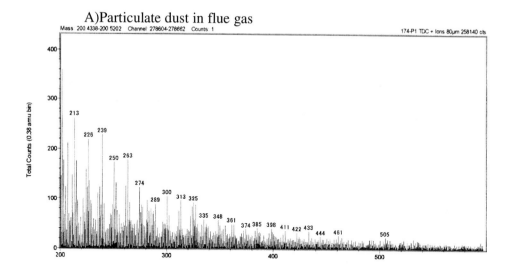

B)Condensation dust

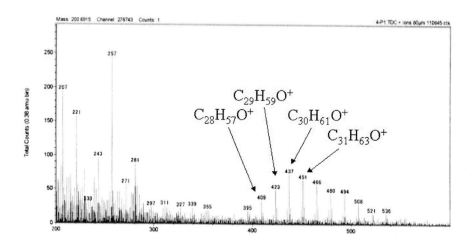

Fig.2 TOF-SIMS spectrum of dust and condensation dust

4. Summary

SIMS and TOF-SIMS were used to analyze the components of regular dusts and condensation dust produced by a furnace burning type A heavy oil. The main component (carbon) and a trace component (sulfur) were detected. Though in SIMS measurement showed no significant differences between regular dusts and condensation dust, TOF-SIMS showed that carbon existed as aliphatic and aromatic hydrocarbons. This result was similar to results from coal-fly ash particles obtained by G.Strossman et al [1,2], which could not be obtained from measurements by SEM-EDX etc. Since the high molecular weight compound (m/z=400-500) detected in the condensation dust could not be detected in dust inside draft, drainage or type-A heavy oil, this compound was thought to be produced in the cooling process. TOF-SIMS appears to be a useful method for investigating true formation mechanism of condensation dust. This is particularly true for comparisons of regular dust and condensation dusts, whose trace materials can now be measured.

References

[1] G.Strossman, T.F.Fister, R.W.Odom, and R.W.Linton, Proc. SIMS X, ed. by Benninghoven, John Wiley (1997) p1061

[2] T.F.Fisher, G.S.Strossman, K.L.Willett, R.W.Odoms, R.W.Linton, Intern. Jr. of Mass and Ion Processes 143(1995) p87

[3] R.W.Linton, A.Loh, D.F.S.Natush, C.A.Evans, Jr., P.Williams, Science, 191, (1976), p394

A. Benninghoven, P. Bertrand, H.-N. Migeon and H.W. Werner (Editors).
Proceedings of the 12th International Conference on Secondary Ion Mass Spectrometry,
Brussels, Belgium, 5-11 September 1999
© 2000 Elsevier Science B.V. All rights reserved.

DEPTH PROFILING OF NATURALLY WEATHERED BIOTITE

H. Seyama[a], M. Soma[b] and M. Nanzyo[c]

[a] National Institute for Environmental Studies, 16-2 Onogawa, Tsukuba, Ibaraki 305-0053, Japan
E-mail: seyamah@nies.go.jp
[b] University of Shizuoka, 52-1 Yada, Shizuoka, Shizuoka 422-8526, Japan
[c] Tohoku University, 1-1 Amamiya-machi, Tsutsumi-dori, Aoba, Sendai, Miyagi 981-8555, Japan

1. Introduction

Rock and mineral weathering is a major process in the geochemical cycle of element on the earth's surface. Surface analytical techniques such as SIMS are useful tools to get clues on the mechanism of chemical weathering, which is essentially a surface process. Surface analysis of some weathered rock-forming minerals has been already reported. Reviews on chemical weathering and surface alteration of silicate minerals have appeared [1, 2]. Most of the studies are concerned with the surface alteration of minerals weathered in laboratory processes such as acid dissolution [3-8], whereas there are several studies on the surface analysis of naturally weathered minerals [9-13]. It is valuable to compare the surface alteration of minerals weathered in the laboratory and in the field for a better understanding of the chemical weathering process. In this study to elucidate the mechanism of silicate mineral weathering, we will report on SIMS depth profiling of naturally weathered biotite and compare the result with that of the laboratory weathering [7].

2. Experimental

Biotite is a common rock-forming aluminosilicate mineral of the mica group comprising SiO_4^{4-} tetrahedra linked to form a flat sheet. Its formal composition is $K(Fe,Mg)_3AlSi_3O_{10}(OH,F)_2$. Potassium ions are held between the aluminosilicate layers. Divalent cations (Fe^{2+}, the major one, and Mg^{2+}) occupy the octahedral site in the alumino-silicate layer. Some of the Si^{4+} ions in the tetrahedral site are replaced with Al^{3+} ions.

Naturally weathered biotite samples were collected from sand at the banks of a river (Arakawa) in Yakushima Island, Japan and from a volcanic ash soil around Mt. Pinatubo, Philippine. Another naturally weathered biotite was peeled from the surface of weathered granite (Inada, Ibaraki, Japan). The biotite samples (thin section) were *ca.* 5 mm (Yakushima), a few mm (Inada) and *ca.* 500 μm (Pinatubo) in size. Unaltered biotites were collected from the inside of granite samples obtained from Yakushima and Inada.

Positive secondary ion depth profiling was performed on a CAMECA IMS4f instrument using a 17 keV O^- primary ion beam with a typical current of 100 nA. The biotite samples were coated with a layer of gold to reduce sample charging. The O⁻ beam was rastered over an area of $250 \times 250\ \mu m^2$. Positive secondary ions were collected from a circular area with a diameter of 60 μm. In order to compensate the negative sample charging due to O⁻ bombardment, the secondary accelerating voltage was automatically adjusted by optimizing $^{28}Si^+$ intensity (10^5 - 10^4 cps) during depth profiling.

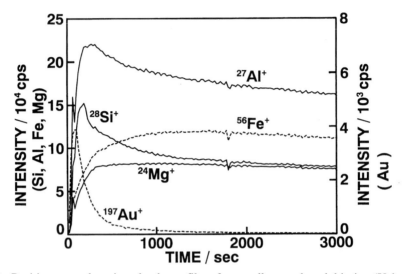

Fig. 1. Positive secondary ion depth profile of naturally weathered biotite (Yakushima Island, Japan).

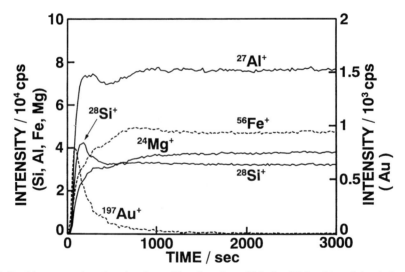

Fig. 2. Positive secondary ion depth profile of unaltered biotite (Yakushima Island, Japan).

3. Result and discussion

A previous study on the surface characterization of acid-leached biotite [7] has demonstrated that Fe, Mg, Al and K are selectively leached during acid dissolution (20 °C, 0.05 mol l^{-1} H_2SO_4), resulting in the formation of an altered layer residually enriched in Si ($SiO_2 \cdot nH_2O$) on the biotite surface. The depth of the Al depletion was less than that of the divalent cations, indicating that Fe^{2+} and Mg^{2+} in the octahedral site are more susceptible to leaching by acid solution than Al^{3+} in the tetrahedral site. After acid dissolution for one week, the thickness of altered surface layer was estimated to be about 100 nm.

The depth profiles of the naturally weathered and unaltered biotite samples (Yakushima) are shown in Figs. 1 and 2, respectively. The depth profile of the unaltered biotite is in agreement with that found for a bulk biotite crystal [7]. Depth profiles similar to Figs. 1 and 2 were observed for other naturally weathered (Inada and Pinatubo) and unaltered (Inada) biotite samples, respectively. There is no drastic difference in depth profile between the weathered and unaltered samples, i. e., a thick altered surface layer depleted of Fe, Mg and Al was not found for the naturally weathered biotite in contrast to the acid-leached biotite. The secondary ion intensities of the constituent elements of biotite increased with decreasing $^{197}Au^+$ intensity at the beginning of the SIMS analysis. The rise of $^{56}Fe^+$ and $^{24}Mg^+$ secondary ion intensities of the naturally weathered biotite was somewhat slower than that of $^{28}Si^+$ and $^{27}Al^+$ secondary ion intensities, suggesting slight depletion of divalent cations (Fe^{2+} and Mg^{2+}) in the surface. A comparable lag in the rise of $^{56}Fe^+$ and $^{24}Mg^+$ secondary ion intensities, however, was also observed in the depth profile of the unaltered biotite. Figure 1 shows that the $^{28}Si^+$ secondary ion intensity of the naturally weathered biotite increased sharply at first and then decreased gradually to a value representative of the bulk, indicating the formation of surface altered layer rich in Si. This result is consistent with the Si depth profile of the acid-leached biotite [7] though the surface layer rich in Si is thinner and less pronounced.

There was a clear difference in $^{27}Al^+$ depth profile between the acid-leached and naturally weathered biotite samples. Depth profiling of the acid-leached biotite indicated that Al^{3+} ions, as well as Fe^{2+} and Mg^{2+} ions, were leached from the surface layer during acid dissolution [7]. On the other hand, the surface depletion of Al was not found and Al was held in the surface layer of naturally weathered biotite. As shown in Fig. 1, it was observed for the naturally weathered samples of Yakushima and Pinatubo that the $^{27}Al^+$ secondary ion intensity of the surface was higher than that of the bulk, suggesting a slight surface enrichment of Al. The surface enrichment of Al has been also observed in previous studies on the surface analysis of naturally weathered feldspar [11-13].

The experimentally determined sputter rate (100 nA O^- primary ion) was 0.07 nm sec^{-1} for a silicate glass. Assuming the same sputter rate for both altered surface layer and bulk phase in the biotite, the thickness of altered surface layer enriched in Al and Si was calculated to be about 60 nm or less.

4. Conclusion

The depth profile of the naturally weathered biotite showed the formation of a thin altered surface layer slightly enriched in Al and Si, and was different from that of the acid-leached biotite in the laboratory. This result indicates that the simple dissolution mechanism in acid solution is inapplicable to the natural weathering of aluminosilicate minerals under the different weathering condition. The mechanism of chemical weathering depends on the weathering solution reacting with minerals. The difference in surface altered layer (thickness and chemical composition) between the acid-leached and naturally weathered biotites is attributable to the temperature, acidity, dissolved components and ionic strength of the weathering solution (soil solution). The surface enrichment of Al and Si may result in the depression of Al leaching (retention of aluminosilicate structure) and/or the precipitation of hydroxide containing Al and Si caused by the weathering solution with a moderate pH value. It is presumed that the weathering solution has an appreciable influence particularly on the behavior of Al (enrichment or depletion on the mineral surface) during natural weathering.

References

[1] S. L. Brantley and Y. Chen, Chemical Weathering Rates of Silicate Minerals (Reviews in Mineralogy Vol. 31), A. F. White and S. L. Brantley, Eds., Miner. Soc. Am., Washington, D. C., 1995, p119.
[2] A. E. Blum and L. L. Stillings, Chemical Weathering Rates of Silicate Minerals (Reviews in Mineralogy Vol. 31), A. F. White and S. L. Brantley, Eds., Miner. Soc. Am., Washington, D. C., 1995, p291.
[3] K. Fujimoto and F. Sakamoto, Water-Rock Interaction (Proceedings of the 8th International Symposium on Water-Rock Interaction), Y. K. Kharaka and O. V. Chudaev, Eds., A. A. Balkema, Rotterdam, 1995, p145.
[4] H. Seyama, M. Soma and A. Tanaka, Chem. Geol., 129 (1996) 209.
[5] I. J. Muir and H. W. Nesbitt, Geochim. Cosmochim. Acta, 61 (1997) 265.
[6] P. Schweda, L. Sjöberg and U. Sdervall, Geochim. Cosmochim. Acta, 61 (1997) 1985.
[7] H. Seyama, A. Tanaka, J. Sato, M. Tsurumi and M. Soma, Water-Rock Interaction (Proceedings of the 9th International Symposium on Water-Rock Interaction), G. B. Arehart and J. R. Hulston, Eds., A. A. Balkema, Rotterdam, 1998, p353.
[8] A. Adriaens, D. Goossens, A. Pijpers G. Van Tendeloo and R. Gijbels, Surf. Interface Anal., 27 (1999) 8.
[9] R. A. Berner and J. Schott, Am. J. Sci., 282 (1982) 1214.
[10] D. W. Mogk and W. W. Locke, III, Geochim. Cosmochim. Acta, 52 (1988) 2537.
[11] H. W. Nesbitt and I. J. Muir, Nature, 334 (1988) 336.
[12] M. Kawano and K. Tomita, Clays Clay Miner, 44 (1996) 672.
[13] M. A. Nugent, S. L. Brantley, C. G. Pantano and P. A. Maurice, Nature, 395 (1998) 588.

A. Benninghoven, P. Bertrand, H.-N. Migeon and H.W. Werner (Editors).
Proceedings of the 12th International Conference on Secondary Ion Mass Spectrometry,
Brussels, Belgium, 5-11 September 1999

CHARACTERIZATION OF INDIVIDUAL PARTICLES CONTAINING LEAD BY COMBINATION OF SIMS AND EPMA

F. Esaka, K. Watanabe, M. Magara, Y. Hanzawa, S. Usuda, K. Gunji, H. Nishimura and
T. Adachi

Department of Environmental Sciences,
Japan Atomic Energy Research Institute,
Tokai-mura, Naka-gun, Ibaraki-ken 319-1195, Japan

1. Introduction

Characterization of individual particles is of relevance in environmental science such as atmospheric processes, air pollution and health hazards [1]. In particular, chemical composition and isotope ratios are closely related to the origin of particles. For example, isotope ratios of lead in aerosol particles depend on lead sources such as coal combustion and leaded gasoline [2]. Thermal ionization mass spectrometry (TIMS) and inductively coupled plasma mass spectrometry (ICP-MS) coupled with decomposition and separation have been used for the isotopic analysis of lead in atmospheric particulate matters to elucidate their transport process [2-4]. Only average values of lead isotope ratio are obtained in such bulk analyses. When particles in the samples are of different origins, microanalysis of individual particles can provide very useful information as a complement to the bulk analysis. The combination of secondary ion mass spectrometry (SIMS) and electron probe microanalysis (EPMA) techniques is desirable for obtaining detailed information on individual particles. In this study, chemical composition, morphology and isotope ratios of individual particles containing lead in coal fly ash and urban particulate matter samples are determined by SIMS and EPMA techniques.

2. Experimental

The particles analyzed were coal fly ash (NIST SRM-2689 and 2690) and urban particulate matter (NIST SRM-1648) samples. These samples were loaded on carbon planchets with copper grids. The copper grids with indicators were used to avoid charge-up and to identify the locations of the particles.

An electron probe microanalyzer CAMECA SX-100 was used for the determination of elemental composition and observation of morphology of particles. An electron beam with an accelerating voltage of 20 keV and a beam current of 100 nA was used to acquire elemental distribution maps and to perform elemental analysis. The secondary electron (SE) image was obtained by using an electron beam with an accelerating energy of 20 keV and a beam current of 1 nA.

A secondary ion mass spectrometer CAMECA IMS-6f was used for lead isotopic measurements. The SIMS analysis was performed using a 12.5 keV O_2^+ focused beam of 200 nA. Mass calibration on the masses 206, 207 and 208 was performed each time before starting measurements. The NIST SRM-981 sample was used as a lead isotope ratio standard.

3. Results and Discussion
3.1 EPMA analysis

In EPMA analysis, we acquired elemental distribution maps of copper and lead for the samples by a wavelength dispersive X-ray (WDX) technique. The primary beam was scanned over a 300×300 µm area (approximately equal to the grid size). Figure 1 shows the elemental distribution maps of the copper and lead in SRM-1648 (urban particulate matter) sample. We can observe four particles containing lead in the area. Figure 2 shows the SE images of a particle (shown by arrow in Fig.1). Its location can be identified by the number on the grid. The particle is estimated to be about 4 µm in diameter. For the particle, the elemental composition was analyzed by using energy dispersive X-ray (EDX) and WDX techniques. As shown in the EDX spectrum (Fig. 3(a)), a strong peak assigned to Pb and/or S is observed, in addition to weak peaks assigned to Si, Cl, Ca, Fe and Cu. The peaks assigned to Pb and S are completely separated in the WDX spectrum (Fig. 3(b)), while those are entirely overlapped in the EDX spectrum. These results suggest that the particle mainly consists of lead sulfate, which is considered to be produced by the reaction of lead particles with ammonium sulfate aerosol present in the urban atmosphere [5].

The particles containing lead in SRM-2689 and 2690 (coal fly ash) samples are spheres with more than 5 µm in diameter. In the EDX and WDX spectra of the particles, a strong peak assigned to Pb is observed, in addition to weak peaks assigned to Si, Al, Ca, Fe, Ti and Cu. No peak attributed to S is detected, which is in contrast to the results of the SRM-1648 sample. This suggests that the particles containing lead in SRM-2689 and 2690 samples mainly consists of lead oxide. The lead oxide is produced by the reaction of lead in coal with oxygen at high temperature.

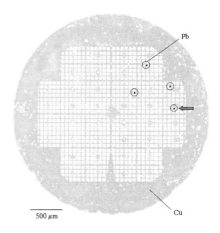

500 µm

Fig.1 : Elemental distribution maps of Cu and Pb in SRM-1648 sample

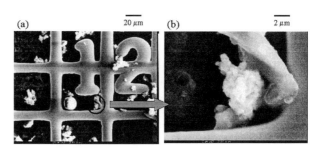

(a) 20 µm (b) 2 µm

Fig.2 : SE images of the particle in SRM-1648 sample. Magnification : (a) ×1,000, (b) ×10,000

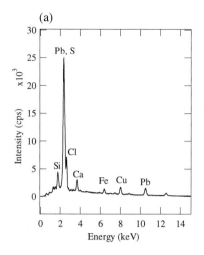
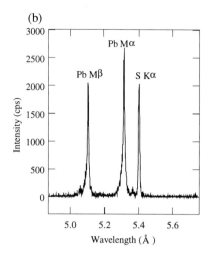

Fig. 3 : (a) EDX and (b) WDX spectra of the particle in SRM-1648 sample.

3.2 SIMS analysis

In SIMS analysis, the rough location of the particle in Fig. 2 was searched with the use of CCD camera installed in SIMS. The exact location was determined by monitoring the intensity of the Pb signal. For the particle, a secondary ion mass spectrum ranging from 203.5 to 209 (amu) was measured by SIMS. The result is shown in Fig. 4. In this analysis, the mass resolving power was set at 3,000. In addition to the Pb^+, peaks related to the Cu grid are observed at about 205 and 207 (amu). These peaks can be assigned to $^{63}Cu_3^{16}O^+$ and $^{63}Cu_2^{65}Cu^{16}O^+$, respectively. It should be noted that the $^{207}Pb^+$ and $^{63}Cu_2^{65}Cu^{16}O^+$ peaks are completely separated in this spectrum. Isotope ratios of $^{207}Pb/^{206}Pb = 0.818 \pm 0.004$ and $^{208}Pb/^{206}Pb = 2.019 \pm 0.002$ (mean ± s.d.) are obtained for the particle. The isotope ratio of $^{207}Pb/^{206}Pb$ is close to that in the US city sample analyzed by ICP-MS (0.824) [6]. All data for the isotope ratios of particles are listed in Table 1. It is clear that the isotope ratios of $^{207}Pb/^{206}Pb$ and $^{208}Pb/^{206}Pb$ in urban particulate matter sample are lower than those in coal fly ash samples.

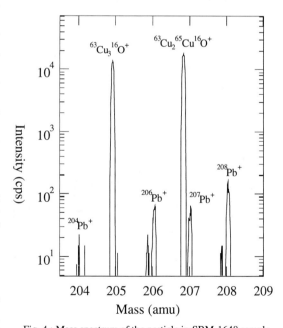

Fig. 4 : Mass spectrum of the particle in SRM-1648 sample.

Based on ICP-MS analysis, Chow et al. reported that the isotope ratios of $^{207}Pb/^{206}Pb$ and $^{208}Pb/^{206}Pb$ were 0.820 and 2.012 in gasoline (Houston, USA) [7]. Although the leaded gasoline in Europe has high isotope ratios (ex. $^{207}Pb/^{206}Pb > 0.89$), that in USA has low isotope ratios due to the different origin of the lead ores [8]. In this study, the measured ratios of the particle in the urban particulate matter sample are very close to those in the gasoline of USA. This suggests that the particle containing lead in the urban particulate matter sample is produced by automobile exhaust emission.

Table 1. : Lead isotope ratios of the particles in the samples

Sample	$^{207}Pb/^{206}Pb$ (Mean ± S.D.)	$^{208}Pb/^{206}Pb$ (Mean ± S.D.)
Coal Fly Ash (SRM-2689)	0.854 ± 0.019	2.105 ± 0.026
Coal Fly Ash (SRM-2690)	0.844 ± 0.023	2.064 ± 0.046
Urban Particulate Matter (SRM-1648)	0.818 ± 0.004	2.019 ± 0.002

4. Conclusion

The chemical composition, morphology and isotope ratios of individual particles containing lead were measured for coal fly ash and urban particulate matter samples with the use of both SIMS and EPMA techniques. Each particle containing lead was found and its location on the planchet was identified by EPMA. Isotope ratios of lead in each particle were measured with SIMS. The EPMA results suggested that the particles containing lead in urban particulate matter and coal fly ash were in the form of lead sulfate and lead oxide, respectively. In addition, the SIMS results revealed that these particles had different isotope ratios of $^{207}Pb/^{206}Pb$ and $^{208}Pb/^{206}Pb$ due to the different origin. The combination of SIMS and EPMA techniques is very useful for obtaining detailed information on individual particles in atmosphere and on their transport.

Acknowledgements

A portion of this work was performed by JAERI under the auspices of the Science and Technology Agency of Japan. The authors wish to thank Mr. T. Onodera for assistance with EPMA analysis.

References

[1] H. M. Ortner, P. Hoffmann, F. J. Stadermann, S. Weinbruch and M. Wentzel, Analyst 123 (1998) 833.
[2] H. Mukai, A. Tanaka and T. Fujii, J. Geophys. Res. 99 (1994) 3717.
[3] J. Wu and E. A. Boyle, Geochim. Cosmochim. Acta 61 (1997) 3279.
[4] A. Véron, P. Flament, M. L. Bertho, L. Alleman, R. Flegal and B. Hamelin, Atmos. Environ. 33 (1999) 3377.
[5] W. Jambers, L. De Bock and R. Van Grieken, Fresenius' J. Anal. Chem. 355 (1996) 521.
[6] W. T. Sturges and L. A. Barrie, Nature 329 (1987) 144.
[7] T. J. Chow, C. B. Snyder and J. L. Earl, in : Modern Isotope Ratio Mass Spectrometry, ed. I. T. Platzner (John Wiley & Sons, New York, 1997) p. 358.
[8] P. Krause, M. Kriews, W. Dannecker, C. –D. Garbe-Schönberg and M. Kersten, Fresenius' J. Anal. Chem. 347 (1993) 324.

A. Benninghoven, P. Bertrand, H.-N. Migeon and H.W. Werner (Editors).
Proceedings of the 12th International Conference on Secondary Ion Mass Spectrometry,
Brussels, Belgium, 5-11 September 1999
© 2000 Elsevier Science B.V. All rights reserved.

APPLICATION OF SAMPLE ROTATION TECHNIQUE IN SIMS ANALYSIS OF MICROPARTICLES*

P. Konarski ** and I. Iwanejko
Institute of Vacuum Technology, Dluga 44/50, 00-241 Warszawa, Poland
E mail: pkonarsk@warman.com.pl

1. Introduction

Monitoring of the environmental contamination requires determination of the concentration, chemical composition and structure of aerosol microparticles. Absolute concentration can be measured by various optical methods. Collecting of the particles allows for measurements of their chemical composition, typically performed in a volume analysis. The appearance of small particles in the atmosphere may result from grinding and rubbing of solid material, wind erosion, various industrial operations or from nucleation process, in which gases condense to initiate particle growth. The layered structure of particles is caused by changes in the gaseous environment during the condensation process.

The ion erosion previously applied in SIMS and SNMS depth profile analyses [1, 2], allowed for a structural examination of microparticles. Here we present a new method of the microparticle depth profile analysis based on the application of a sample rotation technique in SIMS analysis. The sample rotation, i.e. ion sputtering with variable azimuth incidence angle of the primary beam, was performed in order to reduce a shadowing effect in rough surface sputtering and to obtain more uniform erosion of the microparticle atomic layers.

2. Experimental

Analysed microparticles were attached to an indium substrate with a 50% coverage. A special procedure of sample preparation [3] is shown schematically in fig.1. The particles are attached to an indium foil placed on the substrate and the forming element is pressed on top to form a 0.6 mm diameter cylinder covered with the microparticles. The cylinder held by a 0.3 mm diameter tantalum wire is mounted on a transfer holder and introduced into a modified version of the sample rotation manipulator [4] equipped with a step motor. The positioning procedure allows for rotation of the sample along the axis perpendicular to the cylinder face. The sample preparation procedure allows us to use the mini-chip technique [5] if the primary ion beam scanning area is greater than the face of

---

*) This project is part of the National Strategic Programme "Occupational Safety and Health Protection in the Working Environment", supported in 1998-2001 by the State Committee for Scientific Research of Poland. The main co-ordinator is Central Institute for Labour Protection.
**) Corresponding author

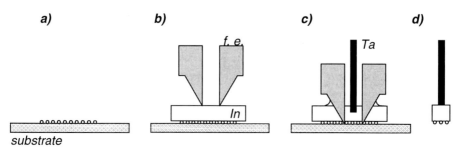

substrate

Fig. 1. Sample preparation procedure shown in steps. a) - Substrate with collected microparticles, b) - indium foil covering microparticles with the forming element above, c) - pressing of the forming element (*f. e.*) through indium foil and attaching of the tantalum wire, d) - indium pastille attached to the tantalum wire.

the indium cylinder covered with microparticles.

The ion sputtering was performed with a 250 nA, 4 keV Ar^+ ion beam in a SAJW-02 SIMS spectrometer equipped with a 16-mm QMA-410 Balzers quadrupole. The primary ion beam angle of incidence with respect to the matrix surface normal is 45°. The beam is digitally spiral scanned, with a frame 1 mm x 1 mm, *i.e.* greater than the sample area, in order to avoid the crater edge effects.

3. Results

Recently, the sample rotation technique has been applied for a depth profile analysis of the planar layered structures [6-8]. Here we present experimental results of the sample rotation technique applied for microparticle sputtering. The rotation and the standard sputtering methods are compared in fig. 2.

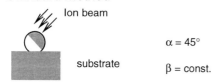

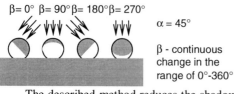

Fig 2. Standard method of ion erosion of microparticles with ion bombardment at an incidence angle α, constant azimuth angle β, and sample rotation method with continuous change of azimuth angle β. Microparticles are shown as spheres, with shaded bombarded area at a given azimuth angle β.

The described method reduces the shadowing effect present in the standard method and also increases the uniformity of atomic layer removal of bombarded microparticles. The rotation technique yields greater bombarded area than that observed using the standard technique.

In order to test the presented method, two microparticle materials of known "core - shell" structure were examined using both the standard and a sample rotation techniques. The analysed materials were: Iriodin 221 Rutile Fine Blue and Iriodin 231 Rutile Fine Green [9]. The particles, sized 5 - 25 μm consist of aluminosilicate (illite) cores covered by rutile titanium dioxide shells. The average thickness of TiO_2 layer is 435 nm in the first, and 500 nm in the second case. An example of the positive secondary ion spectrum of Iriodin microparticles attached to the indium substrate is shown in fig. 3.

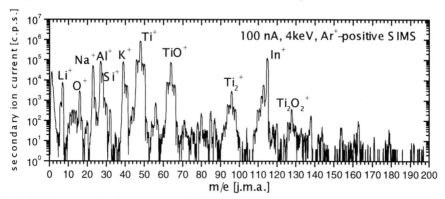

Fig. 3. Positive secondary ion spectrum of TiO_2 covered illite particles attached to the indium substrate.

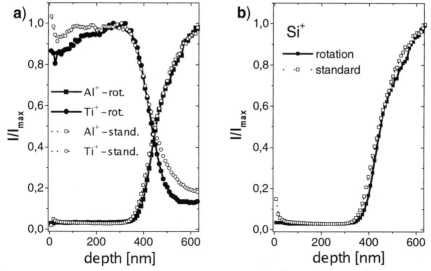

Fig. 4. Depth profiles of positive secondary ions: a) Al^+ and Ti^+, b) Si^+ emitted during ion bombardment of Iriodin 231particles using the sample rotation and standard techniques.

For the depth profile analysis three masses were chosen: Al^+, Si^+ representing illite core and Ti^+ representing titanium dioxide shell. The experimental results of the standard and sample rotation profiles of Iriodin 221 and 231 microparticles, are shown in figs. 4 and 5, respectively. For Iriodin 221 sample, better depth resolution with sample rotation

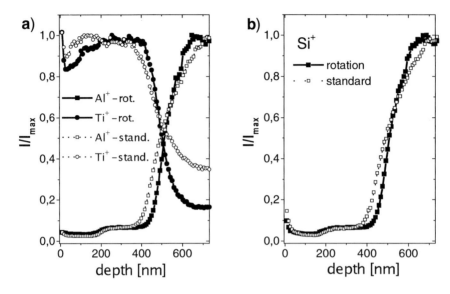

Fig. 5. Depth profiles of: a) Al⁺ and Ti⁺, b) Si⁺ of Iriodin 231particles - the sample rotation and standard techniques.

technique is obtained only for titanium signal. For Iriodin 231 sample all three signals i.e. aluminium, silicon and titanium show significantly better depth resolution using the rotation technique.

4. Conclusions

In the case of constant azimuth angle bombardment, erosion of microparticles is not parallel to the surface. A more uniform erosion is obtained with the variable azimuth ion bombardment. Experimental data show that the sample rotation technique applied in SIMS depth profiling of microparticles gives a more accurate result of depth profile analysis than the standard stationary sample technique. The described technique can be applied in depth profiling of microparticles contaminating the environment.

References
[1] J. Goschnick, and J. Schuricht, *J. Aerosol Sci.*, **27** (1996) S1.
[2] J. Goschnick, M. Lipp, e. al. *J Aerosol Sci.* **22**, (1991) S835.
[3] P. Konarski, I. Iwanejko, A. Sobolewski, E. Kaufman, Patent pending (1999).
[4] P. Konarski, *Rev. Sci. Instrum.* **66** (1995) 4713.
[5] R. v. Criegern et al. „SIMS IV" Ed.: A. Benninghoven, Berlin (1984), p 308.
[6] A. Zalar, *Thin Solid Films*, 124 (1985), 223.
[7] E. H. Cirlin, J.J. Vajo, et al., *J.Vac.Sci.Technol.* A8 (1990) 4101.
[8] P. Konarski, M. Hautala, *Vacuum* **47** (1996) 1111.
[9] Merck KGaA, 64271 Darmstadt, Germany.

A. Benninghoven, P. Bertrand, H.-N. Migeon and H.W. Werner (Editors).
Proceedings of the 12th International Conference on Secondary Ion Mass Spectrometry,
Brussels, Belgium, 5-11 September 1999
© 2000 Elsevier Science B.V. All rights reserved.

SINGLE PARTICLE ANALYSIS OF PARTICULATE POLLUTANTS IN YELLOWSTONE NATIONAL PARK DURING THE WINTER SNOWMOBILE SEASON

Richard E. Peterson* and Bonnie J. Tyler**
* Dept. of Chemistry and Biochemistry
**Dept. of Chemical Engineering
Montana State University, Bozeman, MT 59717, USA, e-mail: bonnie_t@coe.montana.edu

1. Introduction

Particulate, or aerosol, pollution is a complex mixture of organic and inorganic compounds which includes a wide range of sizes and whose composition can vary widely depending on the time of year, geographical location, and both local and long range sources. Aerosol are important because of participation in atmospheric electricity, absorption and scattering of radiation (i.e. sunlight and thus affecting climate and visibility), their role as condensation nuclei for water vapor (and thus affecting precipitation chemistry and pH), and health effects. Particles greater than 2 micrometers in diameter (coarse) are generally formed by mechanical processes while smaller particles (fine) are formed by gas to particle conversion and accumulation/coagulation of these smallest aerosol. Because particles smaller than 2.5 micrometers (USEPA PM2.5) can become trapped deep in the lungs, it is of particular interest to identify toxic substances, such as heavy metals and polyaromatic hydrocarbons, that may be present in particles of this size range. Epidemiological studies have typically used particle size as the metric for identifying adverse health effects of particulate matter (PM), largely because data on PM size is available. Data on particle composition or other characteristics are less well known, if known at all in many cases.

We are evaluating the potential for using Time of Flight Secondary Ion Mass Spectroscopy (TOF-SIMS) to study the composition of single particles from atmospheric aerosol. X-ray analysis has commonly been used to analyze the composition of single particles but it is useful only for elemental analysis and cannot be used to study organic compounds. It offers low sensitivity for light elements (C, O, N) common in particles. Microanalysis SIMS can provide higher sensitivity and molecular information but has lower spatial resolution than SEM [1].

For this study, samples of naturally occurring and anthropogenic atmospheric aerosol were collected at the west entrance to Yellowstone National Park (YNP) during the winter snowmobile season of 1998/99. During the winter snowmobile season, incomplete combustion products from snowmobile exhaust may be a predominant source of airborne particulate matter and carbon monoxide in YNP [2,3]. Two methods were used to collect aerosol. Total suspended particulate (TSP) matter was collected on 47 mm Millipore Fluoropore (PTFE) filters using a vacuum pump system. A Graseby/Anderson 8 stage cascade impactor was used to collect size segregated fractions of the aerosol onto aluminum disks. The cascade impactor separates aerosol according to aerodynamic diameter. Our impactor stages collect particles ranging from 10 to 0.7 micrometers diameter in 8 fractions. Sections of the PTFE filters and aluminum disks have been imaged using a PHI TRIFT I instrument with a Ga primary ion source. A large number of particles could be distinguished on both the filter and impactor surfaces. Multivariate statistical methods have been employed to enhance image resolution and aid in interpretation of the SIMS images. This paper will compare and contrast information obtained from the impactor samples using SEM/X-ray Microanalysis and imaging TOF-SIMS.

2. Experimental

This study was one part of a multi-investigator study of winter transportation and visitation impacts on YNP in winter 1998/1999. A sampling hut was installed at the West Yellowstone entrance to YNP. Our vacuum pump and flowmeter for the 47 mm TSP filters was installed within the hut, and the filter holder assembly was secured to a pole, supported by the hut, 3.2 meters above the ground to minimize problems from blowing ground snow. Samples were taken for intervals of 3 days to one week.

The 8 stage cascade impactor was loaded at MSU with 81 mm diameter aluminum substrates obtained from Anderson Instruments Inc. The impactor was deployed just outside the central kiosk at the West Yellowstone entrance. Location of the impactor close to the ground was intended to allow sampling of emissions from snowmobiles entering YNP. Sampling was typically for 6 to 8 hours.

Sections of the 47 mm Fluoropore filters and the aluminum cascade impactor substrates were imaged and analyzed using a PHI TRIFT I TOF-SIMS. Sections of the aluminum impactor substrates were also examined with a JEOL JSM-6100 Scanning Electron Microscope with a Noran Instrument Tracor Northern Z-Max 30 X-ray detector.

3. Data Analysis

The dark color of the TSP filter samples indicated the presence of elemental, or black, carbon. Particles on the PTFE filters could be clearly visualized as dark areas in the CF^+ SIMS image. Still, the filter sample included a very wide range of particle sizes and showed

many overlapping particles, making data analysis difficult. Hence, we will focus in this paper on the size segregated impactor samples, using stage 6 of the sample taken January 23, 1999 11:25 AM to 5:27 PM, with light snow and moderate snowmobile traffic. The sample was analyzed first with SIMS. Two squares were etched with the Ga beam

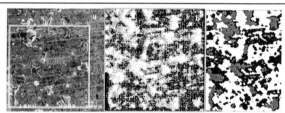

Figure 1: Images of Region A. From left to right: (a) SEM image (box shows area of SIMS analysis), (b) SIMS image of PC1, (c) SIMS image of 3 component latent profile.

just outside the static SIMS analysis regions to serve as registration marks for the subsequent SEM analysis. We will discuss three regions. Region A shows many par-ticles, over-lapping each other. Region B is the etched region. Region C contains an area with relatively few particles and more substrate surface. The SEM images are treated first.

SEM images

The SEM images show several apparently

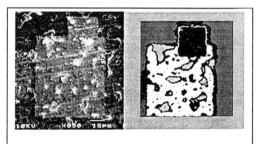

Figure 2: Images from Region B. SEM image shown

different types of particles. Figures 1 and 2 show regions A and B. The individual particles appear to be about 1or 2 micro-meters in diameter, with some larger clumps, especially where there are many particles. Stage 6 is calibrated to collect particles of 0.7 to 1.1 micrometer aerodynamic diameter at unit specific gravity at sea level (our size cut will differ slightly due to elevation, particle specific gravity and particle shape). One type of particle , somewhat "amoeba" shaped, seems to resemble the oil soot shown by McCrone and Delly in The Particle Atlas [4] except that it is covered by a film. X-ray microanalysis showed C, O, S, and a little K. A strong Al signal showed that the beam was penetrating the particle into the substrate. Another type of particle was evidenced only by a very thin black layer, which showed no elements (except background Al) by X-ray microanalysis. It appears that we can see these "black spots" in the SEM solely because they reduce the background Al signal from the substrate. Likely, then, the black spots are made of a light element which gives only a poor X-ray signal. We expect that they are carbon or organic spots. These particles were readily erased by the electron beam.

SIMS images

Figure 3 shows the SIMS spectra of regions A, B and C. Region A shows a strong organic signature, and C a similar signature, though weaker due to lower number of particles. Some high mass peaks were seen, at fair ion yield, at 256.3, 419.4, 435.4, 441.4 and 455.4 amu. Region B, which was etched with the Ga beam, shows little but Al substrate and Ga from the beam. Clearly, etching the sample prior to analysis removes the organic layer from the particles, as does the electron beam in SEM. The raw spectra for region A showed only small peaks for elemental carbon (ions 12, 24, 36, etc.). The etched region B still showed only small amounts of elemental carbon, which could have formed from destruction of organics in the etching process. Clearly, the samples contain far more organic than elemental carbon, despite visual observation of black carbon on the TSP filters.

Several multivariate statistical data analysis methods were used to examine the SIMS data. Principal components analysis (PCA) separates the data into components showing covarying information. These components often reveal chemical information. Figure 1b shows an image of region A using principal component 1, describing 56 % of the variance in the data. Principal component 1 consisted of a strong organic component. The image shows light spots, indicating organic-rich particles, with dark patches of Al substrate. Principal component 2 gave similar information. Principal compo-nents 3 and 4 showed particles richer in Na, K and Ca with less organics. Principal components 5 and 6 correlated well with the SEM dark particles and contained mass spectral ions indicative of organic com-pounds. These included $C_2H_3^+$, $C_2H_5^+$, $C_3H_5^+$, $C_3H_7^+$, $C_4H_7^+$, $C_4H_9^+$, $C_5H_5^+$, $C_5H_7^+$, $C_5H_{11}^+$, $C_6H_5^+$, $C_6H_{11}^+$, $C_7H_{13}^+$, $C_7H_{16}^+$, $C_8H_{17}^+$, $C_{11}H_{23}^+$, $C_{12}H_{25}^+$ and some oxygenated species. Ions 83 ($C_6H_{11}^+$) and 97

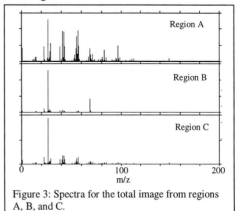

Figure 3: Spectra for the total image from regions A, B, and C.

($C_7H_{13}^+$) were strongly associated with the dark spots, and somewhat less ions 55 and 57 ($C_4H_7^+$, $C_4H_9^+$). These six principal components together described 89.5% of the sample variance. Higher components described less than 1% of variance and look like noise.

The other multivariate method used was Latent Profile Analysis (LPA), a model based statistical method which accounts for the Poisson distribution of low count rate data and allows us to classify each pixel into classes and extract the spectra for each class as described by Willse et al [5]. Figure 1c shows a 3 component latent profile analysis of region A. The image is dramatically clearer than that provided by PCA (Figure 1b) and remarkably resembles the SEM image. The gray-scale latent profile analysis image indicates Al substrate as white, "amoeba" shaped as gray, and the SEM dark spots as black. LPA indicates a somewhat different organic signature for the two particle types. The dark spots, as also indicated by PCA, have more $C_6H_{11}^+$, $C_7H_{13}^+$, $C_4H_7^+$ and $C_4H_9^+$. LPA also indicates enrichment of the dark spots in $C_3H_5^+$, $C_5H_7^+$ and $C_8H_{17}^+$. The "amoebas" have more Na, K, Ca, and a few probably oxygenated organic fragments including 149 (probably $C_8H_5O_3^+$, phthalate).

The two particle components of region A from LPA were examined with discriminant analysis to look for differences. This indicated more 83, 97 and 113 ($C_8H_{17}^+$) for the dark spots (and more Al showing through) and, interestingly, many even numbered ions (possibly indicating the presence of N) for the "amoebas". LPA was also used to examine region B (Figure 2) and region C. Six components were found to describe region B. Two components are etched regions from the marking and are described by Al and Ga (from the beam). Another component describes the much higher organic concentrations outside the etched areas. The top and rims (two components) of the "amoebas" are indicated by Na, K, Ca, CaH and Fe. Finally, a few remaining organic particles in the etched area are described by fragments similar to the organic signatures previously described. Etched particles are somewhat higher in elemental carbon and metals than unetched particles. Region C, with its lower particle numbers, showed the same organic signature as region A. Significantly, the areas with no particles do not show the organic signature, indicating that the organics are indeed part of the particles and were not deposited by vapor phase over the whole substrate.

4. Conclusion

This study indicates that SEM/X-ray microanalysis and SIMS imaging using multivariate data analysis are complementary techniques for single particle analysis. Latent profile analysis is a powerful tool to help resolve SIMS images and allow the elemental and molecular information available from SIMS to be utilized. Clear differences were seen between particle types using LPA, as well as imaging capabilities more similar to SEM.

Analysis showed a great predominance of organic aerosol, with differences in degree of oxidation, in the 1 micrometer size range of West Yellowstone winter air.

Etching of samples prior to SIMS analysis can remove valuable information. In our case, etching prohibited observation of the important organic portion of the aerosol.

References

[1]. Spurny, K.R., Physical and Chemical Characterization of Individual Airborne Particles, John Wiley and Sons, New York, 1986, p. 331.
[2]. White, Jeff J. , James N. Carroll and Howard E. Haines, "Emissions from Snowmobile Engines using Bio-based Fuels and Lubricants", Technical paper, Society of Automotive Engineers of Japan, Inc. , Yokohama, Japan, 1997.
[3]. Fussell, Lori, Park Science, National Park Service, US Dept. of Interior, Vol. 17, No. 1, 1997, pp. 7-10.
[4]. McCrone, Walter and John Gustav Delly, The Particle Atlas, edition 2, vol. III, Ann Arbor Science, Ann Arbor, Michigan, 1973, p. 773.
[5]. Willse, Alan and Bonnie J. Tyler, SIMS XI, 1997, pp. 843-846.

SECTION 17 :
ISOTOPIC RATIO
AND
EARTH SCIENCES

A. Benninghoven, P. Bertrand, H.-N. Migeon and H.W. Werner (Editors).
Proceedings of the 12th International Conference on Secondary Ion Mass Spectrometry,
Brussels, Belgium, 5-11 September 1999

USE OF ^{109}Ag TO ^{107}Ag ISOTOPE RATIO IN NATIVE SILVER FOR CLARIFYING THE FORMATION CONDITIONS OF SILVER DEPOSITS

P.I. Didenko

Center of Environmental Radiogeochemistry, National Academy of Sciences of Ukraine,
34 Pr. Palladin, 252680, Kyiv, Ukraine, e-mail: CENTER@radgeo.freenet.kiev.ua

1. Introduction

The varieties of mineral forms of natural associations of silver (native silver, intermetallides, sulfides, tellurides, selenides), its high mobility in geochemical processes are caused by characteristic crystal chemical and other properties of this element such as valence, electronegativity, effective dimension of atoms, structure of the outer electron shell, a high ability of silver ions for polarization etc. Minerals, grown mostly in hydrothermal conditions, are the main concentrators of silver. We have carried out the investigations of gold-silver and silver ores of the Dukat deposit paying a particular attention for studying a behavior of ^{109}Ag/^{107}Ag isotope ratio in native silver.

2. Experimental

Four groups of samples of the native silver from vertical section of different zones of an ore deposit (from bottom to top) were studied by SIMS: (1) Sp. I is a native silver formed under the influence of metasomatic processes from intrusion granite on primary high-temperature (400 – 600°C) veins which contain argentum sulfide; the dimension of grains varies from 0,1 to 0,3 mm; (2) Sp.II is a native silver in the association with argentum sulfide localized in quartz veins and along their contact with rhodonite-rhodochrosite rocks (the temperature of fluid-inclusions homogenization in quartz is 200-600°C); the dimension of grains is approximately 0,5 mm; (3) Sp.III is a native silver in the association with argentum sulfide and quartz from the productive ore horizon (the temperature of inclusions homogenization in quartz is 290 – 350°C); the dimension of grains is nearly 1 mm; (4) Sp.IV is a native silver from the upper zone characterized by temperature of inclusions homogenization in accompanying quartz of 180 – 220°C; the dimension of grains varies from 1 to 2 mm.

Silver isotopic compositions have been measured with the Cameca IMS 4f ion microprobe on native silver specimens. The primary O_2^+ beam with an energy of 10.5 keV was used for the ion etching. Because of the presence of other mineral segregations (including insulators), which are characterized by different types of conductivity, the charge compensation was used. Chemically pure silver was used as a standard. All studied samples as well as the standard one were mounted in the same holder. The measurement of isotopic ratios was carried out when the plateau conditions were reached [1]. Silver isotope ratios were determined according to techniques described elsewhere [2]. The secondary ion energy distributions of the Ag isotopes were measured both at the beginning and at the end of each analysis to be sure that there was no significant change in the energy distribution. No significant variations in the energy spectra of silver isotopes were observed. On the contrary for the heterogeneous geological samples we have found during layer by layer analysis of the same sample a noticeable change of energy distribution. In particular there is a shift of its maximum and variations of high-energy part of the energy spectrum, these changes being different for different isotopes. The latter causes an error for the determinations of isotope ratios [3]. This factor has been taken into consideration in this work, when analyzing silver isotope ratios in samples containing a number of inclusions including those of argentum sulfide.

3. Results

The results of $^{109}Ag/^{107}Ag$ ratios are shown in Fig. 1. From the Figures it is seen, that for short-term bombardment (0-5 min) the values are almost constant being 0,9090, 0,9100, 0,9202 and 0,9203 for Sps. I, II, III and IV, respectively. For Sps.I to IV (curves f, d, b and a, respectively) the ratios of the yields of $^{109}Ag^+/^{107}Ag^+$ secondary ions do not almost depend on time of sputtering. For Sp.I (curve g) the isotope ratio at t>7 min. rather significantly varies, depending on time of the sputtering that may be connected with presence of relic inclusions of argentum sulfides. In samples taken from the productive zone (Sp.III, curve c) there are also the relics of slightly altered argentum sulfides, that probably cause the strongly «broken» character of the curve at t>2 min. A similarity of the profiles of the isotope ratio for Sps. I and II (curves g and e, respectively) is noticeable. The profiles of $^{109}Ag^+/^{107}Ag^+$ ratios for Sps. I-III are obtained in a process of a few measurements. When the measurements were started to be made in different points of a sample surface, some irreproducibility of the profiles takes place due to the presence of irregularly distributed inclusions of sulfur-containing phase (see Fig. 1: curves b and c, d and e, f and g).

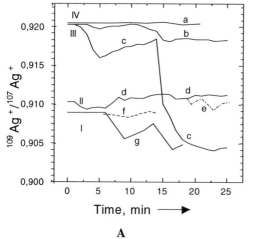
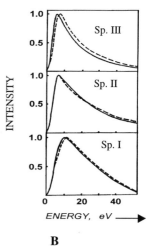

A
                   B

Fig.1 (A) Ratios of intensities for $^{109}Ag^+$ and $^{107}Ag^+$ secondary ions in native silver having conserved relics of high-temperature sulfides (Sp.I), from a transitional zone (Sp.II), from a productive zone (Sp.III), from an upper zone (Sp.IV) and (B) the energy spectra of $^{107}Ag^+$ and $^{109}Ag^+$ secondary ions for the Sps. I-III (curves g, e and c, respectively).

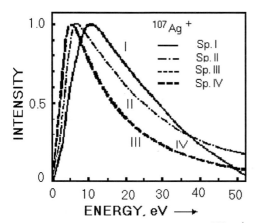

Fig. 2. Energy spectra of secondary ions $^{107}Ag^+$ emitted from various native silver samples

For more precise definition of the nature of the change of the isotope ratios in samples of the type III, additional measurements of the energy spectra of $^{107}Ag^+$ and $^{109}Ag^+$ secondary ions were carried out. It was found that the normalized curves of the energy distributions of $^{107}Ag^+$ ions for the samples from the productive (Sp.III, curve b) and upper (Sp.IV, curve a) zones nearly coincide (Fig. 2). For the samples from the transitional zone (Sp.II, curve e) and, especially, from the deep ore zone having the conserved relics of high-temperature sulfides (I, curve g) a significant change of the energy distribution is observed, namely, a shift of the curve maximum to higher energies and broadening of the curve. The curve II displays a significant broadening and a weak shift of the maximum. Note, that qualitatively the high-energy part of the spectrum is also similar to the respective parts of the spectra of Sps.III and IV. For curve II there take place a noticeable differences from the above spectra, namely, a significant shift of the maximum and broadening and, at the same time, a comparatively fast drop of the high-energy «tail». These indicate subtle differences of chemical composition of Sps. I and II, III and IV, respectively.

On examination of the energy spectra of $^{107}Ag^+$ and $^{109}Ag^+$ secondary ions for Sps. I-III (Fig. I(B)) indicated that: (1) for Sp.II the curves of the energy distribution of the both isotopes of silver almost coincide (there is only a negligible difference in the high-energy parts of the curves); (2) for the energy distributions of Sp.I an insignificant and for Sp.III a significant shift of a spectral maximum to higher energies is characteristic.

Therefore, for the samples of type III there was revealed a change of the secondary ion energy spectra of the Ag isotopes of close masses. The reason of this effect will be discussed further on. Here we only note that the sharp jumps indeed of the curves of the isotope ratios for the samples of group III are caused above all other factors by variations of the energy spectra of the both isotopes, which did not succeed to allow at the automatic measuring of the yield of the secondary ions in the specified energy windows.

4. Discussion

The investigation of native silver originating from the Dukat deposit by SIMS technique allowed to determine a change of silver isotope ratio for the samples belonging to different horizons. Thermal conditions of formation of a sample which promote the appearance of sulfide-bearing inclusions influence on the ratio considerably. While temperature of ore formation increases, the enrichment of native silver by the light isotope ^{107}Ag takes place whereas sulfide-bearing inclusions are enriched by heavier isotope ^{109}Ag. This process is more intensive at elevated temperatures.

For the non-homogeneous samples of native silver the ratio of silver isotopes is characteristic. In the process of formation of mentioned inclusions the diffusion of silver atoms takes place thus increasing the fractionation of the isotopes. Assuming that formation of sulfide inclusions (Ag_2S, for instance) within the body of native silver is accompanied by out-diffusion of surplus Ag atoms, this process occurs easier for the lighter [107]Ag isotope. As a result, the inclusions themselves are enriched with more heavy [109]Ag isotopes while the native silver matrix is enriched with the lighter ones, [107]Ag. Because of that we observed a difference between isotope ratios in native silver for Sps. I and II, and Sps. II and IV. Sps. I and II are enriched with sulfur whereas native silver gives higher yield of the lighter [107]Ag isotope. This assumption is confirmed by direct measurements of the isotope ratios for sulfur-bearing minerals including acantite (argentite). This also explains observed noticeable variations of the isotope ratios at layer by layer analysis of the samples. An additional argument is the direct measurement of a content of sulfur in the samples studied. The direct correlations between fractionation of the silver isotopes, non-homogeneity of the profiles, parameters of the energy spectra and sulfur content takes place. These correlations are explained by the following way. In one assumes that migration of atoms at elevated temperatures results in a preferred bonding of more heavy [109]Ag isotope to sulfur, two factors influencing on the registered value of the isotope ratio in SIMS technique appear: (a) an increase of yield of this isotope which is mainly bound with sulfur (the yield from acantite is two orders higher than from pure silver); (b) emission of Ag^+ from a sulfide-containing phase is accompanied by the break of Ag-S bond ($E^{Ag-S} \sim (2,1-2,6)$ eV) that causes a change in the energy spectrum, first of all, a shift of the maximum in comparison with the spectrum detected from silver ($E^{Ag-Ag} = 1,68$ eV). As a result, the isotope ratio, which is measured from automatically registered mass-spectra of the secondary ions, will also differ from the true one.

Therefore, an analysis of the isotopes in geological samples of a complex composition and intricate thermal prehistory by SIMS technique is complicated by a number of factors, which ought to be taken into consideration, otherwise additional errors, caused by matrix effects, are possible.

5. Summary

The study of native silver originating from the Dukat deposit by SIMS technique allowed to determine the change of silver isotope ratio for the samples belonging to different horizons. Thermal conditions of formation of a sample which promote the appearance of sulfide-bearing inclusions influence on the ratio considerably. When temperature of ore formation increases, the enrichment of native silver by the light isotope [107]Ag takes place whereas sulfide-bearing inclusions are enriched by heavier isotope [109]Ag. This process is more intensive at elevated temperatures. Prevailing bonding of sulfur atoms by one of Ag isotopes leads also to differences in [107]Ag^+ and [109]Ag^+ energy spectra being a reason for additional errors during automatic registration of isotopic ratio for the samples with different content of sulfur.

References

[1] R. Kelly, Nucl. Instr. Methods, 149(1978)553.
[2] P.I. Didenko, Rapid Communications in Mass Spectrometry, 9(1995)583.
[3] N. Shimizu and S. Hart, J. Appl. Phys., 53(1982)1303.

A. Benninghoven, P. Bertrand, H.-N. Migeon and H.W. Werner (Editors).
Proceedings of the 12th International Conference on Secondary Ion Mass Spectrometry,
Brussels, Belgium, 5-11 September 1999

SIMS CHARACTERISATION OF IN–HOUSE MONODISPERSED ISOTOPIC STANDARD URANIUM OXIDE PARTICLES

G. Tamborini, M. Betti, N. Erdmann , O. Stetzer and J. van Geel

European Commission, Joint Research Centre, Institute for Transuranium Elements,
P.O. Box 2340, D-76125 Karlsruhe, Germany.

1. Introduction

The Institute for Transuranium Elements (ITU) provides impartial and independent expertise for the protection of the population against risks associated with handling and storage of highly radioactive transuranium elements. ITU plays an important role in the control of fissile materials supporting the Euratom Safeguards Directorate and the International Atomic Energy Agency (IAEA).

Misappropriated nuclear materials seized by state authorities and environmental samples are sent to ITU for forensic analysis. An important component of forensic analysis at ITU is the determination of the uraniun isotopic composition by Secondary Ion Mass Spectrometry (SIMS). In many cases, the samples for SIMS analysis are individual radioactive particles (often < 1 μm in diameter). To calibrate such SIMS measurements, reference particles with a defined size and enrichment are needed. Monodispersed uranium oxide particles are produced at ITU to supply an in–house particle standard.

2. Experimental parameters

Particle production

To generate particles with a defined enrichment, a uranyl nitrate solution is prepared from certified standard reference uranium oxide powder (NIST). Using a commercial vibrating orifice aerosol generator (TSI, model 3450) small monodispersed droplets are produced from a dilution of this uranyl nitrate solution (adjusted to get particles with a diameter of 1 μm). These droplets are dried by a stream of pressured air. In this process the dissolved uranyl nitrate precipitates as the droplet becomes smaller. Finally solvent free particles of uranyl nitrate are obtained which are then heated up to 800°C in a sequence of three furnaces to induce calcination of the nitrate into uranium oxide. The uranium oxide particles are collected on nucleopore filters.

SIMS technique

At ITU, SIMS has been optimised for the characterisation of single uranium and plutonium microparticles. A Cameca IMS6F is used mostly in the microprobe mode for the analysis of individual particles. The samples are bombarded with a scanned primary O_2^+ beam of 15 keV having a current intensity between 1 and 2 nA and a size of a few micrometers. Positive secondary ions are accelerated through 5 keV. The energy band-pass is between 40 and 50 eV and a mass resolution power of 1000 is sufficient to separate the molecular interferences present in the matrix. Under these conditions, flat top peaks are obtained, which ensure good acquisition statistics during the isotopic analyses.

SEM-EDAX
The particles are characterised using a SEM Philips XL40 coupled to an EDAX detector and a detector for backscattered electrons. The applied voltage is 30 kV. The elemental content of the particle can be analysed with the EDAX detector. The obtained energy spectrum is evaluated by comparing the peaks in the spectrum with known peaks in a source library.

3. Results

Morphology of the particles
A SEM image of several uranium oxide particles on a nucleopore filter and the image of secondary ions recorded with the scanning mode by SIMS are shown in figure 1. The two pictures clearly show that the single particles have a mean diameter of 1 μm in size ($\approx 1 \times 10^{10}$ uranium atoms). The polydispersion effect is very small and can be explained as a consequence of the aerosol generation process. Incompletely dried droplets can stick together and form larger particles.

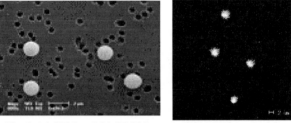

Fig. 1. (a) SEM and (b) SIMS images of the uranium particles

The size distribution of the particles is determined by taking 10 images of different locations on the sample with the SEM at 800x magnification. The images are evaluated with commercial image analysis software (Zeiss Vision, KS 300). The resulting size distribution of the monodispersed particles is shown in figure 2 for four different uranium enrichments.

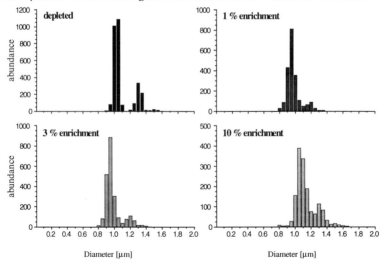

Fig. 2. Size distribution of the uranium particles for four different enrichments

In order to characterise the chemical composition of these particles using SIMS, the primary beam is focused onto the particles and a spectrum is recorded between the masses 230 and 280. This spectrum indicates that the particles are mostly composed of U_3O_8.

Isotopic characterisation
After setting the mass resolution to obtain flat-topped peaks the acquisition for the determination of the isotopic ratio is started. Acquiring secondary ion beam intensities for the uranium isotopes, at the masses 234, 235, 236, 238 and 239 (mass 239 is assumed to be $^{238}UH^+$ and is to correct the 236 peak for $^{235}UH^+$), accuracies of 0.5% for the ratio 235/238 and of 1.0% for the minor isotopes can be obtained.

Samples containing particles with four different enrichments were measured with respect to their isotopic composition. The obtained data are given in table 1. The SIMS results are in good agreement with the certified values.

Table 1. Mean values and relative standard deviation for the 235/238 U ratios

Enrichment	235/238 U ratio	Certified NIST 235/238 U ratio
Depleted	0.00490 (5)	0.00492
1 %	0.01020 (10)	0.01014
3 %	0.03150 (10)	0.03143
10 %	0.1140 (9)	0.1136

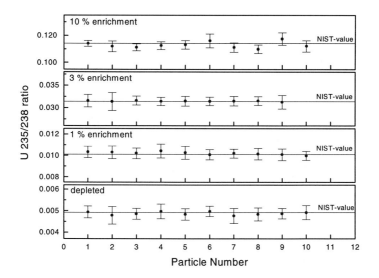

Fig. 3. 235/238 uranium ratio for particles of different enrichment

3. Conclusions

The particles produced at ITU are routinely used for the calibration of the SIMS technique. The distribution size of these particles is centred around 1 μm. As shown by the SEM and SIMS imaging analysis, polydispersion effects are almost negligible. The isotope ratio measurements of 235/238 obtained by SIMS have a typical accuracy of 0.5% for the depleted-U particles and 0.2 % for the 10% enriched particles.

Acknowledgements

The authors acknowledge Dr. Ian Ray, Dr. Thierry Wiss and Mr. Helmut Thiele for the SEM-EDAX measurements.

A. Benninghoven, P. Bertrand, H.-N. Migeon and H.W. Werner (Editors).
Proceedings of the 12th International Conference on Secondary Ion Mass Spectrometry,
Brussels, Belgium, 5-11 September 1999

999

ISOTOPIC RATIO MEASUREMENTS OF PARTICLES BY TOF-SIMS

A. J. Fahey

NIST, 100 Bureau Dr. Stop 8371 Gaithersburg, MD 20899-8371, USA
(albert.fahey@nist.gov)

1. Introduction

A technique has been developed to measure isotopic ratios by Time-of-Flight Secondary Ion Mass Spectrometry (ToF-SIMS). It has been applied to the measurements of Si, and Mg isotopes. These isotopic measurements require high mass resolution so that interferences due to hydrides can be subtracted from the signal of interest. Isotopic measurements of 1 μm to 2 μm particles demand that high spatial resolution accompany the high mass resolution.

Refractory particles separated from primitive meteorites have been discovered to be of presolar origin[1] and have a wide range of isotopic compositions. These presolar particles, that can have significant isotopic perturbations, are typically small (~1μm or less) and can be minerals such as SiC and corundum. The combination of small size and large range in isotopic composition make these particles good candidates for measurements by ToF-SIMS.

2. Experimental

Measurements were made with a CAMECA/IonToF ToF-SIMS IV[2]. In order to achieve high spatial resolution while keeping the mass resolving power high enough to identify interferences, the Ga^+ ion gun is operated in "burst mode". This is a special mode available on the ToF-SIMS IV that uses two sets of blanking plates to produce a series of primary ion pulses spaced at ~250 ns for each analysis cycle (~100 μs period). Figure 1 shows a typical burst-mode spectrum in the region of ^{28}Si. The use of the burst-mode increases the secondary ion signal level by the number of burst pulses, while maintaining a spatial resolution of ~100 nm. In addition to using the burst-mode it was found that using a second ion beam of O_2^+ for sputtering enhanced the secondary ion yield and helped to reduce hydride production.

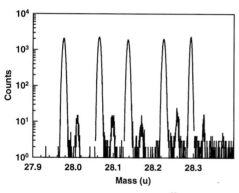

Figure 1. Burst Mode Spectrum near ^{28}Si

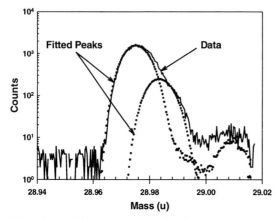

Figure 2. Combine peak with fitted peaks.

A dead time correction was applied to the spectrum before any processing was performed[3]. Since a burst-mode spectrum consists of a string of pulses, an algorithm was developed to find the peak centers and combine the data for individual masses into single peaks. Once a single peak was produced, a fitting and stripping algorithm was developed and applied to remove signals from partially interfering masses such as $^{28}SiH^+$ from the $^{29}Si^+$ signal.

Signals for the hydride were subtracted from the minor isotopes by fitting the data at the minor isotope to the scaled and shifted peak data of the major isotope. Figure 2 shows a plot of the data from a terrestrial SiC particle and the fitted peaks of the ^{29}Si and the ^{28}SiH derived from the ^{28}Si peak. The data from the ^{28}Si peak are fit to the ^{29}Si and the ^{28}SiH data by minimizing the expression:

$$\chi^2 = \sum (S_m^i - Ax_i - By_i)^2 \qquad (1)$$

where i spans the region around the peak to be corrected, S_m^i is the measured spectral data in the region of interest, x_i is the major isotope data (e.g. ^{28}Si) shifted to the position of the isotope data to be fitted, and y_i is the major isotope data shifted to the position of the hydride interference. In practice the isotope data to be fitted (e.g. ^{29}Si) is assumed to be the more intense than the interfering peak, thus its center is easily identified. The interference peak position is then referenced from the center of the peak to be corrected, thus ensuring accurate positioning of the shifted data from the major isotope.
The solution to equation 1 is:

$$B = \frac{\sum S_m^i x_i \sum x_i y_i - \sum S_m^i y_i \sum x_i^2}{\left(\sum x_i y_i\right)^2 - \sum x_i^2 \sum y_i^2} \qquad (2)$$

$$A = \frac{\sum S_m^i y_i \sum x_i y_i - \sum S_m^i x_i \sum y_i^2}{\left(\sum x_i y_i\right)^2 - \sum x_i^2 \sum y_i^2} \qquad (3)$$

Once A and B are computed the hydride contribution, By_i, is subtracted from S_m^i. The peaks are then integrated to the 10% level. If a minor isotope peak has less than 20 counts at it's maximum then a fixed width computed from the major isotope is used for the integration.
Uncertainties are assigned to the peak integrals by vectorially combining the counting statistical uncertainty and an estimated uncertainty in the computation of the integral due to the finite number of channels that span a peak. Typically the uncertainty due to the finite number of

channels is much smaller than counting statistic, however, if the peak is of low intensity it can be a significant factor.

3. Results

Isotopes of Si, and Mg have been measured thus far. A hydride correction was applied to the ^{29}Si signal and the ^{25}Mg signal as described above. Data for Si isotopes from terrestrial SiC particles (Alfa AESAR Stock No. 40155) are shown in Figure 3. The data fit a line consistent with the terrestrial mass fractionation line and have a reasonable value of instrumental fractionation of ~-2.2% (i.e., Δ^{29}Si = -22‰). In addition the fitted line passes within ~1σ of the origin showing that there are no non-linear effects in the data. Such non-linear effects might be present if the dead time correction was not properly applied. Figure 4 shows the Si isotopic data from the Murchison meteorite SiC particles as well as the terrestrial SiC data. Several meteoritic SiC grains have isotopic compositions that differ significantly from terrestrial. These grains are typically called "X-grains"[1]. The Si isotopic compositions of the majority of the meteoritic particles plot to the upper right of the terrestrial mean, showing the enrichment in the heavier isotopes of Si that is characteristic of the "main-stream" SiC particles. The "main-stream" compositions typically plot along a line of slope ~1.34; that trend is reflected in the data presented here as well. It is thought that "main-stream" compositions reflect the chemical evolution of the galaxy over a period of time whereas it has been proposed that the X-grains are of supernova origin.

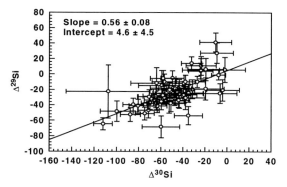

Figure 3. Si isotopic measurements of terrestrial SiC.

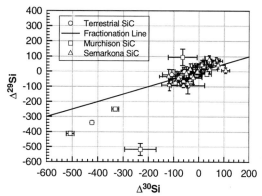

Figure 4. Si isotopic measurements of terrestrial and meteoritic SiC.

The results of measurements of Mg isotopes are shown in Figures 5 and 6. Figure 5 shows measurements of terrestrial Burma spinel (NMNH B12071). The data cluster around the origin and fit a line close to the expected mass fractionation line of slope 1/2. Figure 6 shows the terrestrial data along with the meteoritic data. Mg is present in the meteoritic SiC at measurable trace levels. In addition, it is well known that ^{26}Mg excesses are present in some meteoritic particles due to the decay of ^{26}Al. Data that plot to the right in Figure 6 show excesses of ^{26}Mg. The most extreme values of Δ^{26}Mg correspond the X-grain composition shown in Figure 4.

4. Conclusion

A technique for isotopic ratio measurements by ToF-SIMS has been developed. It's successful application has been demonstrated for terrestrial materials as well as for meteoritic materials. The data exhibit no spurious behavior that could be attributed to instrumental effects. In addition, values of mass bias obtained were similar to those typically measured by dynamic SIMS.

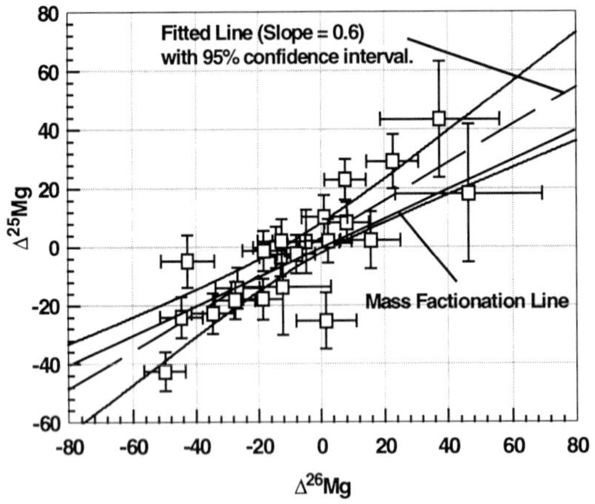

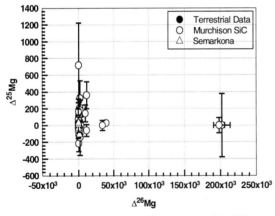

Figure 5. Mg isotopic measurements of a terrestrial spinel

Figure 6. Mg isotopes in standards and meteoritic SiC.

References:
[1] Zinner (1997) Astrophysical Implications of the Laboratory Study of Presolar Materials, AIP, Woodbury, New York, 3-26.
[2] Certain commercial equipment, instruments, or materials are identified in this paper in order to adequately specify the experimental procedure. Such identification does not imply recommendation or endorsement by the National Institute of Standards and Technology, nor does it imply that the materials or equipment identified are necessarily the best available for the purpose.
[3] Stephan T. et al (1994) J. Vac. Sci Technol., 12(2), 405-410.

A. Benninghoven, P. Bertrand, H.-N. Migeon and H.W. Werner (Editors).
Proceedings of the 12th International Conference on Secondary Ion Mass Spectrometry,
Brussels, Belgium, 5-11 September 1999

PRECISE ISOTOPIC ANALYSIS OF SILICON CRYSTALS FOR THE MOLAR MASS DETERMINATION USING THE IMS-1270 SIMS WITH MULTICOLLECTORS

Y. Morishita, N. T. Kita and S. Togashi

Geological Survey of Japan, 1-1-3 Higashi, Tsukuba 305-8567, Japan; yuichi@gsj.go.jp

1. Introduction

Silicon crystals are widely used as density references. They are also recognized as a candidate for the replacement to the kilogram prototype, which is the only SI base unit defined with an artificial material. The way of defining mass using silicon crystals in the future is tracing back the unit of mass to an atomic mass. The kilogram can then be defined as a certain number of atoms. For this, a precise determination of the Avogadro constant N_A is necessary.

A precise determination of N_A requires accurate measurements of the lattice constant, density and molar mass on a very pure and highly perfect crystal (e.g. [1]). The molar mass of silicon, M(Si), depending on the isotopic composition of the silicon crystal is as follows;

$M(Si) = \Sigma$ f(^{i}Si) M(^{i}Si), where f(^{i}Si) is the fraction of each silicon isotope (^{28}Si, ^{29}Si and ^{30}Si) and M(^{i}Si) is the molar mass of each silicon isotope. Since relative atomic mass is accurately determined, the molar mass of each silicon isotope is known. Then, M(Si) can be determined by measuring the isotopic composition of silicon crystals. The molar mass has been determined on SiF_4 gas by mass spectrometry. The mass spectrometer, which was used for the absolute ratio measurements, had been calibrated using synthetic mixture of the three highly enriched isotopes ^{28}Si, ^{29}Si and ^{30}Si (e.g. [2]). The molar mass measurement with precision of 0.1 ppm is necessary to improve the current N_A value. The precision of 0.04 ‰ in ^{30}Si/^{28}Si ratios corresponds to the 0.1 ppm of the molar mass.

An important thing we have to consider is homogeneity of the target silicon crystals. Although variations in silicon isotopic compositions in terrestrial natural samples are small (less than 10 ‰ in δ^{30}Si, e.g. [3]) compared to the case of oxygen or sulfur isotopes, the silicon isotopic compositions of the silicon crystals, which was grown by the floating zone (FZ) method, might depend on the procedure of crystallization and the silicon isotopic compositions of the raw materials. We have to investigate the homogeneities (or heterogeneities) in silicon isotopic compositions of the standard silicon crystals for molar mass determinations as well as their absolute isotopic compositions.

SIMS can analyze silicon isotopic ratios in a very small area of silicon crystals using a reference silicon crystal, and it is suitable to survey the homogeneity in silicon isotopic compositions of any standard silicon samples. Silicon isotopic ratios have been precisely measured using an electron multiplier (e.g. [4]) and using Faraday cup (FC) multicollectors [5]. In this study silicon isotopic ratios have been precisely determined for silicon crystals using the Cameca ims-1270 SIMS with multicollectors at the Geological Survey of Japan.

2. Experimental

2.1 Samples

Table 1 shows the samples analyzed. The sample SiW, which is a commercially distributed silicon wafer, is a working standard at the GSJ lab. IRMM-017 is a silicon isotope reference material. $^{29}Si/^{28}Si$ and $^{30}Si/^{28}Si$ ratios for IRMM-017 were accurately determined by the conventional mass spectrometry, which are 0.0507715 ±0.0000066 (2σ) and 0.0334889 ±0.0000078 (2σ), respectively [6]. M1, M21 and M31 are from a NRLM silicon crystal that was grown by the FZ method.

Two spheres, which are 1 kg in weight, were taken from the same NRLM crystal, and they are used as standard silicon samples for precise measurements of volume, weight, density and mean molar mass. The samples including M1, M21 and M31 for the molar mass measurements were taken near the spheres assuming that the crystal was isotopically homogeneous.

Table 1. Silicon isotopic ratios determined by SIMS for silicon crystals

Sample	Run No.	Description	Primary current	^{28}Si yield (cps)	Measured $^{29}Si/^{28}Si$	2σ mean (‰)	Measured $^{30}Si/^{28}Si$	2σ mean (‰)
SiW	33@14	Working standard	5.22 nA	4.21E+08	0.0502266	0.018	0.0329733	0.021
IRMM-017	33@16	IRMM Reference	5.21 nA	4.25E+08	0.0501793	0.015	0.0329098	0.020
M1	33@20	NRLM ingot	5.20 nA	4.22E+08	0.0501975	0.018	0.0329308	0.022
M21	33@30	NRLM ingot	5.19 nA	4.36E+08	0.0502065	0.017	0.0329443	0.023
M31	33@26	NRLM ingot	5.19 nA	4.31E+08	0.0502037	0.016	0.0329413	0.019

2.2 Experimental conditions

In our preliminary study, silicon isotopic ratios were analyzed using a Cs^+ primary beam and a single FC detector (which is preferable for precise isotopic ratio measurements) under the same conditions for sulfur isotopic measurements [7]. A defocused Cs^+ primary beam was restricted to 40μm in diameter by a circular aperture to obtain a homogeneous primary beam of 5 nA. Negative secondary ions of silicon were uniformly sputtered by the primary beam with a total impact energy of 20kV (a primary accelerating voltage of +10kV and a secondary extraction voltage of -10kV). A rectangular field aperture of 2mm by 2mm was introduced into the secondary ion optics, limiting the analyzed area on the sample surface to a central square measuring 20 μm by 20 μm to avoid the crater wall effect. The centering of the primary beam was ascertained each time by looking at the beam position in the field aperture of 4mm by 4mm. Although silicon is a semiconductor, the electric resistivity of a very pure silicon is higher than a doped silicon. Therefore, a normal-incidence electron gun was used for charge compensation on the sample surface to get a better stability of secondary ions. The secondary ions were detected at a mass resolving power of 3000 without energy filtering by a Faraday cup. An energy window of 60 eV, which is sufficient to pass most of the energy bandpass of the Si^- secondary ions, was chosen each time to make sure that we can always obtain the same energy distribution of Si^- ions.

2.3 Multicollection system

The multicollection system of the ims-1270 SIMS consists of 5 detection units. Each unit has one EM or one FC detector with a slit assembly mounted on a motorized trolley. Among 5 detectors there is one FC detector on the second outer trolley, which collects ^{29}Si ions in this study. An additional FC detector is mounted on the outside of the each innermost and outermost trolley which has an EM. ^{28}Si and ^{30}Si ions are detected using the additional FCs. The secondary ^{28}Si, ^{29}Si and ^{30}Si ions were simultaneously detected without energy filtering using three FCs. The center of each flat top was adjusted by moving each detector trolley accordingly. Silicon isotopic ratios were measured at the center of the silicon peaks at an identical magnetic field. An internal calibration among the three FCs were made by using three kinds of reference voltages (0V, 4.5V and 9V) as input signals. The measurement conditions were the same as the monocollection mode other than the above description on the detection system.

3. Results and discussion

Firstly, silicon isotopic ratios were analyzed using a Cs^+ primary beam and a single FC detector with internal precisions around ±0.3 ‰ in ^{30}Si/^{28}Si ratios (2σ). The reproducibility of the silicon isotopic ratios from several spots on silicon crystals is within the internal errors. Most uncertainties in the isotopic ratio measurements are caused by the instability of the primary beam in the monocollection mode.

The use of FC multicollectors might decrease uncertainty and increase counting efficiency. The influence of the primary beam instability on the secondary ion intensity was cancelled out in the multicollection mode since the secondary ^{28}Si, ^{29}Si and ^{30}Si ions were measured simultaneously. Moreover, simultaneous measurements has the advantage of effective counting of ions sputtered from a certain volume of samples. As a result, the measurement time can be shorten accordingly. The secondary ^{28}Si, ^{29}Si and ^{30}Si ions were simultaneously accumulated for 20 seconds and this cycle was repeated 50 times for a single analysis. A reported value in isotopic ratio is the mean of these 50 cycle measurements. We have analyzed silicon isotopic ratios with internal precisions less than ±0.03 ‰ in ^{30}Si/^{28}Si ratios (2σ) using three FC detectors. The required sample size was 2ng for a single measurement. Since the measured isotopic ratios depends on the ion optics settings (e.g. [4]), we keep the ion optics under the same condition for measuring both standard and unknown samples. Table 1 shows typical examples of SIMS measurements of ^{29}Si/^{28}Si and ^{30}Si/^{28}Si ratios for silicon crystals. A silicon 3-isotope diagram shows that the SIMS measurement data are basically on a mass fractionation line.

The differences in silicon isotopic ratios between SIMS and conventional measurements [6], which may correspond to the instrumental mass fractionation of SIMS, are about -12 ‰ and -17 ‰ for ^{29}Si/^{28}Si ratio and ^{30}Si/^{28}Si ratio, respectively. However, when we take another set of absolute isotopic abundance ratios of silicon [8] as conventional measurement data, the differences in silicon isotopic ratios between SIMS and conventional measurements are about -9 ‰ and -21 ‰ for ^{29}Si/^{28}Si ratio and ^{30}Si/^{28}Si ratio, respectively.

The difference in ^{29}Si/^{28}Si ratios (Δ^{29}Si) between the average NRLM ingot and IRMM-017 measured by SIMS is about +0.4 ‰ whereas it is about +1.4 ‰ by the conventional method [6, 9]. The differences in ^{30}Si/^{28}Si ratios (Δ^{30}Si) between the two samples by SIMS and by the conventional method are about +0.8 ‰ and +2.0 ‰, respectively. The relationship between Δ^{29}Si and Δ^{30}Si measured by SIMS shows mass dependent effects, while that measured by the conventional method [6, 9] does not.

While M1, M21 and M31 were taken from the NRLM crystal, the molar mass was determined for 14 silicon samples from the same NRLM crystal. A slight dependence of the measured values of molar mass on the sample position is observed [9]. The maximum difference among the 14 samples in molar mass was 0.5 ppm [9], which corresponds to about 0.2 ‰ in ^{30}Si/^{28}Si ratios. Table 1 shows that the difference in ^{30}Si/^{28}Si ratios determined by SIMS among M1, M21 and M31 samples (taken from near the 14 samples) is about 0.4 ‰, which exceeds the value of 0.2 ‰ measured by the conventional method. Although the reason is not known so far, there is a possibility of sample heterogeneities.

An advantage of the SIMS analysis, compared with the conventional method, is its high sensitivity and its capability of in situ microanalysis. Therefore a systematic procedure of analyses in ^{30}Si/^{28}Si ratios on a small sample area using SIMS is promising to solve the problem. We can survey the silicon isotopic heterogeneities in silicon specimens by the accurate measurement techniques using multicollectors.

4. Summary

A precise determination of the molar mass of a silicon crystal requires accurate measurements of silicon isotopic ratios of the crystal. In this study we have precisely determined silicon isotopic ratios in silicon crystals using the Cameca ims-1270 SIMS with multicollectors at the Geological Survey of Japan. The internal precisions were less than ±0.03 ‰ in δ^{30}Si (2σ) using a Cs$^+$ primary beam and three Faraday cup detectors.

This level of uncertainty meets the current requirement (±0.04 ‰) for the calculation of the molar mass of silicon crystals. While silicon crystals are considered to be the standard samples for physical properties, an important issue on the homogeneity of the standard silicon crystals is left unsolved. The microanalysis in silicon isotopic ratios using SIMS may contribute to this problem.

References

[1] P. De Bièvre and S. Valkiers, Metrologia, 31, 245 (1994).
[2] R. Gonfiantini, P. De Bièvre, S. Valkiers and P. D.P. Taylor, IEEE Trans. Instrum. Meas., 46, 566 (1997).
[3] T. Ding, S. Jiang, D. Wan, Y. Li, J. Li, H. Song, Z. Liu and X. Yao, Silicon isotope geochemistry, Geological publishing house, Beijing (1996).
[4] G. Slodzian, M. Chaintreau, R. Dennebouy and B. Rasser, Secondary Ion Mass Spectrometry SIMS XI, Wiley, 29 (1998).
[5] E. De Chambost, P. Fercocq, F. Fernandes, E. Deloule and M. Chaussidon, Secondary Ion Mass Spectrometry SIMS XI, Wiley, 727 (1998).
[6] P. De Bièvre, S. Valkiers and H. S. Peiser, J. Res. Natl. Inst. Stand. Technol., 99, 201 (1994).
[7] Y. Morishita, A. Sasaki, N. T. Kita and S. Togashi, Secondary Ion Mass Spectrometry SIMS XI, Wiley, 67 (1998).
[8] I. L. Barnes, L. J. Moore, L. A. Machlan, T. J. Murphy and W. R. Shields, J. Res. Natl. Bur. Stand., 79A, 727 (1975).
[9] K. Fujii, M. Tanaka, Y. Nezu, K. Nakayama, H. Fujimoto, P. De Bièvre and S. Valkiers, Abstr. Seventeenth Japan Symposium Thermophysical Properties, 291 (1996).

A. Benninghoven, P. Bertrand, H.-N. Migeon and H.W. Werner (Editors).
Proceedings of the 12th International Conference on Secondary Ion Mass Spectrometry,
Brussels, Belgium, 5-11 September 1999
© 2000 Elsevier Science B.V. All rights reserved.

INFLUENCE OF ION COUNTING WITH AN ELECTRON MULTIPLIER UPON THE REPEATABILITY OF ISOTOPIC MEASUREMENTS.

G. Slodzian, M. Chaintreau, R. Dennebouy and G. Rousse
Laboratoire de Physique des Solides, Bât 510, Univ. Paris Sud 91405 Orsay France
E-mail: slodzian@lps.u-psud.fr

1. Introduction

It is generally admitted that the isotopic composition of the beam of secondary ions leaving the sample surface is not exactly the same as that of the sample from which those ions have been ejected. In addition, when measurements are made with a multiplier, isotopic discriminations may occur during the "ion to electrons" conversion process so that different isotopes are not counted with the same detection quantum efficiency (DQE). For further studies on isotopic fractionation during secondary ion formation processes, it is of great importance to have an order of magnitude of the multiplier discrimination effects.

2. Experimental conditions

Experimental conditions have already been described in the previous Proceedings [1]. A sample made of a piece of silicon wafer is bombarded with a primary beam of Cs^+ ions and negative Si^- ions are collected. The beam of secondary ions is carefully selected by the entrance and the aperture diaphragms and mass analysed at constant magnetic field with an electrostatic peak switching system. The impact position on the first dynode is adjusted to yield the maximum count rates. The size of the impact area is controlled by rastering the beam over about 800μmx800μm.The three Si isotopes are addressed on the same impact area.

The negative secondary ions are post-accelerated just before entering the multiplier so as to strike the first dynode width 10 keV energy. The bunch of electrons exiting the last dynode is amplified as a voltage pulse before entering a discriminator coupled to electronic devices which fix the dead time at 65ns (in a non-paralysable working mode) and maintain near zero the base line (base line restorer). Count rates are recorded while the threshold S is step-scanned. Thresholds S are measured with a digital voltmeter during acquisition. Count rates versus S curves are locally smoothed before applying the derivation procedure which provides the distribution of pulse height PH as a function of S, the variable S being numerically equal to PH. Distributions are normalised at 10^6 total counts.

3. Modelling the pulse height distribution

The first dynode is characterised by an average effective yield Np (number of electrons being produced per incident ion and collected by the next dynode). It is known that Np depends upon many parameters : (i) energy, incidence angle, mass, charge state and chemical nature of the impinging ion, (ii) surface state of the dynode, position of the ion impact area on the dynode. The other dynodes are characterised by an average effective yield Ne, number of secondary electrons per incident electron and collected by the next dynode.

The production of electrons by one ion impact on the first dynode is assumed to obey a Poisson law with Np as a mean and a similar assumption is made for the electron production by one electron impact on a dynode but this time with Ne as a mean. It can then be demonstrate that the production of electrons resulting from the quasi-simultaneous arrival of n electrons on a given dynode obeys a Poisson law with (n·Ne) as a mean. By combining Poisson laws as the multiplication process is progressing from one dynode to the next, it is possible to calculate the probability P(N) for one ion impact to produce N electrons exiting a given dynode. Calculations have been carried on with a desk-top computer.

The first result which came out was that the shape of the probability distribution P(N) remained practically unchanged after the fourth dynode. This result was part of the justification for dividing the multiplier in two sections, the first one comprising the first five dynodes including the conversion dynode and the second one comprising the eleven other dynodes which provide for the main multiplication gain. There is also a practical reason for that dichotomy which is that the doses received by the dynodes of the first part are much weaker than those in the second. As a consequence, one may guess that the two parts will be ageing at a different pace, the first signs appearing as a mere change of gain mainly due to the second section [2].

The next step is to characterise the probability distribution taken at the exit of the fifth dynode with the aim of comparing it to the experimental distribution. For that purpose it is convenient: (i) to normalise the calculated distribution to 10^6 (probabilities replaced by number of events with an outcome of N electrons when a number of 10^6 ions have struck the first dynode). (ii) to determine the values D and G of S corresponding to the half of the distribution maximum height with D > G. (iii) to calculate the full width at half maximum L = D - G and the ratio D/G as well. Considering the latter ratio, a remarkable result emerged from the calculations: the same D/G values were obtained for different couples of (Np, Ne), a given Np being associated at each Ne. Thus the loci of constant D/G appear as separate curves in a (Np, Ne) representation as shown in figure 1.

4. Comparison between experimental and calculated distributions

The experimental distribution is determined as a function of pulse heights expressed in mV whereas the calculated distribution is determined as a function of N, number of electrons. In addition, the calculated distribution (γ) ends at the exit of the fifth dynode and the gain due to the rest of the multiplier is left as an open parameter. Transformation rules are obviously necessary for comparing the experimental distributions and (γ).

Let us first define the conversion coefficient as K = Lexp / Lcalc, ratio of the FWHMs of the two distributions. To obtain a calculated distribution (Γ) which can be compared with experiment, the abscissa of (γ) are multiplied by K and the ordinates of (γ) are divided by K in order to maintain the proper normalisation. The experimental value of D/G then sets the choice of a specific locus line in figure 1. At last, by using heuristic arguments a final choice can be made for Ne and Np. Indeed, it is easy to see that a small change of Ne produces a very rapid change in the multiplier gain because the gain roughly varies as $(Ne)^{15}$. By crude calculations it is possible to evaluate the average pulse height in mV produced by a bunch of a given number of electrons leaving the last dynode and compare it with the average pulse height of the experimental distribution. For the multiplier being used under the specific conditions of our experiments it came out that Ne should fall within a fairly narrow margin from 2.7 to 2.3, implying a corresponding range for Np from 8 to about 9.

Taking Ne =2.5 for instance and adjusting Np to obtain a D/G ratio equal to that of the experimental distribution (D/G $\cong$ 3.40) gave the result shown in figure 2 with Np $\cong$ 8.55. The fit is quite good considering the experimental uncertainties. Changing Ne within the range given above and taking the appropriate Np did not significantly change the results.

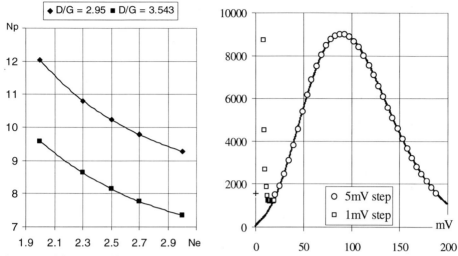

Fig. 1. Loci for two different (D/G) ratios in the (Ne, Np) representation.
Fig. 2. Ordinates: counts/mV for 10^6 total counts. The sharp rise on the left is electronic noise; dynamic noise can be seen near the minimum. "+" : P(0)* 10^6 .

5. Isotopic discriminations of the multiplier

The algorithm presented in the preceding sections allows to calculate the evolution of the DQE with thresholds which makes it possible to determine the isotopic discrimination with the assumption that when one isotope is switched to another the only changing parameter is the yield Np. Let M be the mass of the arriving isotope, Np(M) can be developed in series and approximated by the first terms so that :

$$\frac{\Delta Np}{Np} \cong -\alpha \frac{\Delta M}{M} \quad \text{with} \quad \alpha > 0$$

It is then possible for a given α to calculate the isotopic discriminations δmult defined as:

$$\delta\text{mult}(29/28) = \left(\frac{DQE(S;29)}{DQE(S;28)} - 1\right) \times 1000$$

In Table 1, δmult have been listed as a function of S for $\alpha = 0.5$ since it is generally admitted that Np varies roughly as the velocity of the incoming ion. Np(28) and Ne are here the same as those taken in figure 2. In the 2nd column, (1 –DQE) have been calculated for $^{28}Si^-$.

	S (mV)	(1- DQE) (‰)	δmult (29/28) (‰)	δmult(30/28) (‰)
	10	3.34	-0.39	-0.80
	14	5.97	-0.65	-1.34
Table 1	18	9.81	-1.01	-2.07
	22	15.11	-1.48	-3.01
	26	22.10	-2.05	-4.15
	30	31.04	-2.73	-5.52

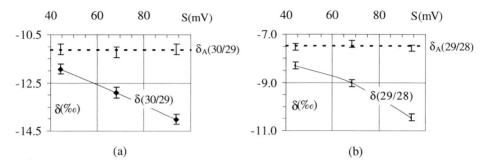

Fig. 3. Measurements at 3 different S. (a): α is adjusted to correct $\delta(30/29)$ and get the true incoming δ_A. (b): corrected $\delta_A(29/30)$ values resulting from the previous fit with $\alpha \cong 0.345$.

The values in Table 1 show that δmult are linear with ΔM to a good approximation which means that δmult are linear with ΔNp. The values in Table 1 can therefore be easily used to recalculate δmult for different values of α when this coefficient is taken as a fitting parameter.

Now, let us consider the unknown isotopic fractionation δ_A of the beam entering the spectrometer. The fractionation δ being measured contains δmult and it can be easily shown that $\delta \cong \delta_A + \delta$mult. When measurements at different thresholds are made, the changes being observed on δ values reflect the variations of δmult with S since δ_A is constant. With $\delta(30/29)$ measured at 3 different settings of S, the parameter α can be adjusted to make the difference $\delta_A = \{\delta(30/29) - \delta mult(30/29)\}$ independent of S. The best fit was obtained for $\alpha \cong 0.345$ (Fig.3a). The corrections applied to $\delta(29/28)$ with this α value yielded a constant value of $\delta_A(29/28)$ well inside experimental uncertainties (Fig. 3b). The same was true of course for $\delta_A(30/28)$. From δ_A one can get $^{29}Si / ^{28}Si \cong 0.050250$ and $^{30}Si / ^{28}S \cong 0.032987$ (± 0.000007). Data reported in figure 3 were obtained after replacing the multiplier with a fresh one.

6. Discussion and conclusion

Using fairly crude models for the emission of the first dynode and the working mode of the multiplier we have built an algorithm able to reconstruct the lost information, ie the δ_A values, which works surprising well. The deeper insight which has been gained will help to improve the working conditions of the multiplier. In addition, although not described here, we should indicated that this approach (i) offered an interpretative framework for ageing effects, (ii) allowed to determine the noise amplitudes with the ion beam on and off and (iii) brought evidence of count rate effects different from dead time. Moreover, pulse height distributions of other ions (not shown here) such as O^-, C^- and various dimers and trimers raise interesting questions about the probability laws followed by Np for negative ions.

From a practical point of view, with appropriate electronics, it will be possible to record, the signal coming from a single ion impact simultaneously at different thresholds leading to an easy way of freeing isotopic measurements from multiplier discriminations.

References

[1] G. Slodzian, M. Chaintreau, R. Dennebouy and R. Rasser. In secondary ion mass spectrometry SIMS XI ed by G. Gillen and al. John Wiley. (1997) pp. 29-34.
[2] A.D. Cutter, K.L. Hunter, R.W. Stresau and P.J.K. Paterson. Communication at the 1994 ASMS conference.

A. Benninghoven, P. Bertrand, H.-N. Migeon and H.W. Werner (Editors).
Proceedings of the 12th International Conference on Secondary Ion Mass Spectrometry,
Brussels, Belgium, 5-11 September 1999

DETERMINATION OF OXYGEN ISOTOPIC RATIOS IN TROPOSPHERIC AEROSOLS BY QUANTITATIVE ISOTOPIC IMAGING

J. Aléon*, M. Chaussidon, B. Marty, M. Champenois, D. Mangin
Centre de Recherches Petrographiques et Geochimiques-CNRS
15 rue Notre-Dame des Pauvres, BP20, 54500 Vandoeuvre les Nancy, France
*corresponding author aleon@crpg.cnrs-nancy.fr

1. Introduction

Aerosol particles play a fundamental role in the transport of elements between ocean, continents and atmosphere. Trace element contents and isotopic ratios of minor and major forming elements are potential indicators of the sources which contribute aerosols to the atmosphere. However, isotope geochemical studies have been drastically limited up to now by the very small (typically micron-sized) dimensions of aerosol particles. We present a new method to measure isotopic ratios of stable elements in individual aerosol microparticles using a high sensitivity ion microprobe. An imaging mode has been preferred to conventional spot analysis because it gives the possibility to analyse several particles at the same time. The development of this method has involved the conception and realisation of the following procedures : separation of the micron-sized particles suitable for isotope analyses from the bulk samples ; handling of these particles before and during ion analysis ; adequate settings of the ion probe.

The isotopic ratio of oxygen in aerosol quartz has been selected as a tracer of source provenance. Indeed, aerosols are sampling quartz particles from different lithologies each having characteristic O isotopic signatures. Previous studies of potential source rock quartz and of aerosol quartz have allowed to identify several poles (fig. 1).

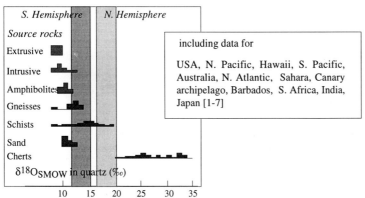

Figure 1 : $\delta^{18}O$ values of quartz in source rocks and mean values in aerosols from the Southern Hemisphere and the Northern Hemisphere. Modified after ref [4].

Rocks crystallized at high temperature i.e. magmatic rocks generally show quartz with low O isotopic values in the range 8-12 ‰, whereas quartz formed at low temperature, e.g. in sedimentary environment present higher oxygen isotopic ratios (25‰ up to 35‰), metamorphic rocks have intermediate values, between 10 and 15‰ [4 e.g.]. These values are given using the delta notation and the Standard Mean Ocean Water as the zero reference value ($\delta^{18}O = [(^{18}O/^{16}O)_{sample} / (^{18}O/^{16}O)_{SMOW} - 1] \times 1000$).

Comparison between the geographical repartition of potentially contributing source rock lithologies and aerosol sampling sites allows to put constraints on atmospheric circulations. Previous studies [1-7] were done on bulk quartz samples by classical mass spectrometry on large quantity of material (around 20 to 40 mg quartz samples representing several billions of grains assuming a size of 1 micron in diameter and a density of 2.7).

2. Method description

In this study standard powder samples of known composition have been used to set the different steps of analysis. A major fraction of continental aerosol is supplied by desert dust. Consequently, the composition of these samples approximates that of the mean desertic dust, 70% to 80% of clay minerals, 10 to 20% of quartz and around 10% of feldspars. Sample powders are prepared by crushing (1 - 10 microns) clays, quartz and feldspars minerals of known oxygen isotopic composition. Quartz grains are separated from the bulk samples by selective chemical treatment following ref [8]. The main steps are potassium pyrosulfate fusion, hydrochloric acid and sodium hydroxide dissolutions and then selective dissolution by hexafluorosilicic acid saturated in silica. The obtained yields are between 55% and 100% for several tests. The bests conditions lead to yields over 85% for samples containing around 1 mg of quartz, which is approximately the quartz fraction in typical aerosol samples. After the chemical treatment, quartz particulate samples are suspended in an ethanol solution and then ultrasonically cleaned and separated from each other.

For ion microprobe analyses, several sample conditions are required. First the sample must be flat and conductive. To ensure such conditions an In foil is pressed to obtain a flat polished and conductive surface. Droplets of the ethanol suspension are then deposited on that surface and evaporated. The samples are checked by optical microscope observations until a good preparation is obtained, where grains are sufficiently concentrated and separated. Then the grains are incrusted in indium by a slight pressure.

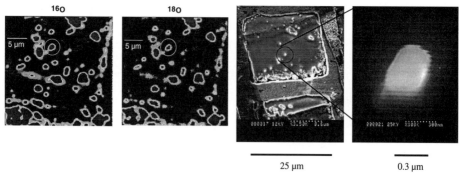

Figure 2 : ^{16}O, ^{18}O and SEM images of an analyzed zone, single grains inferior to 1μm can be easily localized.

The analyses are done in a scanning imaging mode, using a Cs^+ primary beam with the Cameca IMS 1270 ion probe installed at C.R.P.G. in Nancy. The intensity of the beam is around 5 to 10 pA and the resulting size is a very focused beam with a less than 1μm diameter. Both ^{16}O and ^{18}O isotopes are measured on an electron multiplier (EM) for the image acquisition. Acquisition are done during around 1 hour for both isotopes, with counting times of around 100 s for ^{18}O acquisition and 10 s for ^{16}O acquisition. Ion images of Figure 2 show that all particles are well individualized and can be easily mapped by scanning electron microscopy.

Isotopic compositions are determined afterwards by image processing. As both isotopic images have been acquired on the same electron multiplier, each pixel gives directly a number of counts. The first step of image processing consists in applying a threshold in order to extract the grain from the background of the image. Then for each grain a second threshold leads to the determination of a volume of ion counts for each isotope. The signal to noise ratio is then optimized using the ^{16}O signal and this ratio is subsequently applied to both isotopes. These integrated volumes of ^{16}O and ^{18}O represent the ion counts used to calculate the isotopic ratio for each particle. Prior to the calculation of the isotopic ratio the values are corrected for the dead time of the electron multiplier.

3. Results and discussion

The first measurements showed a reproducibility not better than 10 to 20 ‰ for several grains having a similar isotopic composition. To elucidate the causes of this low reproducibility, the whole analytical process has been examined step by step. Since the indium surface is conductive and the grains have small sizes we do not expect to have significant charging effect, we nevertheless avoided this possibility by using a normally incident electron gun. The second step was to check if the rastering could introduce

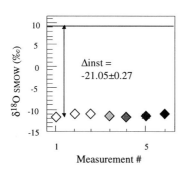

Figure 3 : Measurements made on quartz standards in defocused mode for several rastering conditions symbolized by the differents grey-levels. Error bars are within diamonds, typically around 0.3 ‰. White diamonds : no rastering; black diamonds : same rastering as that used during image acquisition.

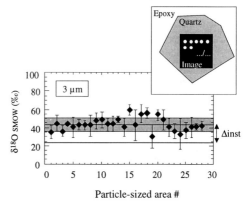

Figure 4 : Oxygen isotopic ratios obtained for aerosol-sized areas within an homogeneous quartz surface. Data show that the reproducibility is only limited by counting statistics.

fractionation. As it is visible on figure 3 there is no fractionation between a classical ponctual mode and a rastering mode on standard grains.

Later on, both isotopes have been counted in rastering mode with dynamical transfer operanding system on the EM. First without imaging and then with imaging. In imaging mode the observed instrumental mass fractionation is +20‰. Due to the similarity of the tuning and analytical conditions between the two modes, we tentatively attribute this fractionation to an electronic problem in the image acquisition process. Finally before measurement, it is necessary to ensure that there is no fractionation inside the image plane. To solve this problem " homogeneous " images were acquired on non-crushed standards and some aerosol-sized points are defined by image processing on the whole surface of the image (fig. 4). The standard deviation between these points was only limited by the counting time.

4. Conclusion

From these tests we believe that it is highly conceivable to analyse the oxygen isotopic ratios of micrometric particles with a precision $\leq$ 5‰. Such precision is sufficient to discriminate among the different aerosol emission sources. In summary to realise these analyses we will use a Cs^+ 5pA micron-focused primary beam, high counting time, normal electron gun and image processing to determine the oxygen isotopic ratios of individual micrometric particles.

References
[1] R.W. Rex, J.K. Syers, M.L. Jackson and R.N. Clayton, Science 163 (1969) 277
[2] J.K. Syers, M.L. Jackson, V.E. Berkheiser, R.N. Clayton and R.W. Rex, Soil Sci. 107 (1969) 421
[3] D.L. Mokma, J.K. Syers, M.L. Jackson, R.N. Clayton and R.W. Rex, J. Soil Sci. 23 (1972) 147
[4] R.N. Clayton, R.W. Rex, J.K. Syers and M.L. Jackson, J. Geophys. Res. 77 (1972) 3907
[5] R.N. Clayton, M.L. Jackson and K. Sridhar, Geochim. Cosmochim. Acta 42 (1978) 1517
[6] J. Le Roux, R.N. Clayton and M.L. Jackson, Geochim. Cosmochim. Acta 44 (1980) 533
[7] C. Misota and Y. Matsuhisa, Geoderma 66 (1995) 313
[8] J.K. Syers, S.L. Chapman, M.L. Jackson, R.W. Rex and R.N. Clayton, Geochim. Cosmochim. Acta 32 (1968) 1022.

A. Benninghoven, P. Bertrand, H.-N. Migeon and H.W. Werner (Editors).
Proceedings of the 12th International Conference on Secondary Ion Mass Spectrometry,
Brussels, Belgium, 5-11 September 1999

MICROMETER SCALE VARIATIONS OF $\delta^{18}O$ IN CORALS

Claire Rollion-Bard[a], Marc Chaussidon[a], Christian France-Lanord[a] and Edouard Bard[b]

[a] CRPG-CNRS, BP 20, 54 501 Vandoeuvre-lès-Nancy Cédex, France,
rollion@crpg.cnrs-nancy.fr

[b] CEREGE, BP 80, 13 545 Aix-en-Provence Cédex, France

1. Introduction

Annual density banding in massive skeletons of scleractinian corals was first discovered almost 30 years ago [1]. This allowed the development of the use of corals as a proxy of paleoenvironmental conditions. Several studies suggested the potential of different geochemical proxies to provide information about paleotemperature like oxygen isotopic composition ($\delta^{18}O \equiv {}^{18}O/{}^{16}O$) [2-3], Sr/Ca [4-6], Mg/Ca [7] and more recently U/Ca [8]. $\delta^{18}O$ values of marine carbonate depend on the temperature of crystallization and the $\delta^{18}O$ value of seawater. However, most biological skeletons have $\delta^{18}O$ lower than predicted by the equilibrium between inorganic carbonate and water. This is due to the so-called « vital effect » which is variable between species. Paleotemperature records therefore depend on emperical corrections factors determined on modern species. In this study, we focus on the $\delta^{18}O$ record at a high spatial resolution (about 20 µm) to reveal the oxygen isotopes behaviour which could not be observable with the conventional technique.

2. Results and discussion

2.1 Coral sample and conventional analysis.

The coral used in this study is a modern coral collected in 1994, species *Porites* and comes from New Caledonia. A 2.2 cm piece was first analysed for $\delta^{18}O$ using a VG 602 spectrometer at one millimeter spatial resolution. 2 - 4 mg samples were crushed and reacted in orthophosphoric acid at 25 °C. The uncertainty on the isotope meaurements is ± 0.1 ‰. Results are reported relative to the SMOW standard. The $\delta^{18}O$ profile is presented in figure 1.

The record displays a strong seasonnality with an amplitude of 1 ‰. It is believed that the principal factors controlling the variations in the coral skeletal oxygen isotopic composition are changes in seawater temperature and changes in seawater isotopic composition by rainfall and evaporation. For the *Porites* 1°C rise in temperature corresponds to a 0.21 ‰ decrease in $\delta^{18}O$ [9]. So this 1 ‰ amplitude represents a variation in temperature of about 4 °C between 22.3 °C and 26.4 °C. This is in good correspondence with the data of this region with an seasonal amplitude of 4.8 °C. We have not recorded the total amplitude of the temperature because the extension rate is smaller in winter and our sampling method is not precise enough to allow this meseaurement. With the $\delta^{18}O$ profile we can also determine the extension rate of this coral ($\approx$ 13 mm/yr).

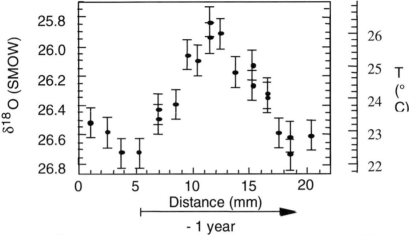

Figure 1 : $\delta^{18}O$ record obtained by the conventional method. On Y-axis, $\delta^{18}O$ versus SMOW and the conversion in temperature with the McConnaughey equation [9] are notified.

2.2 SIMS anaysis of $\delta^{18}O$ on carbonate.

For the ion probe analysis, oxygen isotopic measurements were performed using a Caméca ims 1270. The coral is bombarded with a Cs^+ primary beam accelareted with a 10 kV voltage. The primary beam of 0.5 nA was focused using several electrostatic lenses to a diameter of 20 μm. A mass resolution of 1579 is required to separate ^{18}O from this main interference $H_2^{16}O$. In this study, the mass resolution was generaly about 5000 (figure 2).

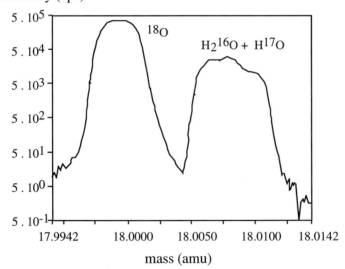

Figure 2 : Peacks of ^{18}O and its main interference $H_2^{16}O$ with a mass resolution of 4500. Note that the two peaks are well separated and that there is no contribution of $H_2^{16}O$ in the measurement of ^{18}O.

[16]O⁻ ions were counted on a faraday cup during 4 s (1.3 x 10^8 cps) and [18]O⁻ on an electron multiplier during 5 s (2.6 x 10^5 cps) sequentially. In this configuration the precision is on the order of ± 0.4 ‰. However, the ims 1270 ion probe allows the measurement simultaneously. There are 5 mobile collectors and 2 fixed collectors which are faraday cups. In this counting mode both oxygen isotopes are counted on faraday cups during 3 s (3 x 10^9 cps for [16]O and 6 x 10^6 cps for ^{18}O). This way, the precision is about ± 0.2 ‰.

Moreover, the oxygen isotopic measurements of several carbonate like aragonite and calcite have shown that the instrumental fractionation is not the same for these two carbonates. Indeed, the instrumental fractionation of aragonite is about 3 ‰ lower than this of calcite.

2.3 $\delta^{18}O$ data on coral.
The results in oygen isotopic composition on a 1300 μm section of the coral show variations up to 10 ‰ (figure 3).

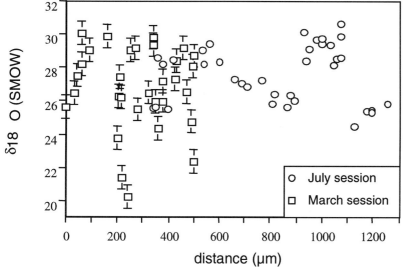

Figure 3 : $\delta^{18}O$ data obtained by SIMS measurements during two different sessions.

3. Conclusion
The variations in $\delta^{18}O$ in corals are explained either by changes in temperature or by changes in the oxygen isotopic composition of the seawater. A variation of 10 ‰ in $\delta^{18}O$ implies a variation in temperature of about 50 °C. So changes in temperature cannot explain our results. Variations in composition of the seawater is also rulled out as it is very stable with only little variation of salinity in this area (0.4 ‰). So it is impossible that this small scale variation reflects a short term variation in environmental parameters. Rather these variations are more likely due to a difference of incorporation of elements under biological control [10]. We can also propose an influence of the activity of the symbiotic algae (zooxanthellae). But because of the link of the $\delta^{18}O$ variations with the structure of the coral, variations in the extension seem more likely.

References

[1] D. W. Knutson, R. W. Buddemeier and R. V. Smith, Science 177 (1972) 270.
[2] R. G. Fairbanks and R. E. Dodge, Geochim. Cosmochim.Acta 43 (1979) 1009.
[3] J. J. Leder, P. K. Swart, A. M. Szmant and R. E. Dodge, Geochim. Cosmochim. Acta 60 (1996) 2857.
[4] S. De Villiers, G. T. Shen and B. K. Nelson, Geochim. Cosmochim. Acta 58 (1994) 197.
[5] M. T. McCulloch, M. K. Gagan, G. E. Mortimer, A. R. Chivas and P. J. Isdale, Geochim. Cosmochim. Acta 58 (1994) 2747.
[6] C.-C. Shen, T. Lee, C.-Y. Chen, C.-H. Wang, C.-F. Dal and L.-A. Li, Geochim. Cosmochim. Acta 60 (1996) 3849.
[7] T. Mitsuguchi, E. Matsumoto, O. Abe, T. Uchida and P. J. Isdale, Science 274 (1996) 961.
[8] G. R. Min, R. L. Edwards, F. W. Taylor, J. Recy, C. D. Gallup and J. W. Beck, Geochim. Cosmochim. Acta 59 (1995) 2025.
[9] T. McConnaughey, Geochim. Cosmochim. Acta 53 (1989) 151.
[10] L. S. Land, J. C. Lang and D. J. Barnes, Marine Biol. 33 (1975) 221.

A. Benninghoven, P. Bertrand, H.-N. Migeon and H.W. Werner (Editors).
Proceedings of the 12th International Conference on Secondary Ion Mass Spectrometry,
Brussels, Belgium, 5-11 September 1999
© 2000 Elsevier Science B.V. All rights reserved.

SIMS GOLD ANALYSES OF SEA FLOOR SULFIDE MINERALS

L.J. Cabri[a], G. McMahon[b], N.S. Bortnikov[c], I.V. Vikentiev[c] and Yu.A. Bogdanov[d]

[a]CANMET, MMSL, 555 Booth Street, Ottawa Canada K1A OG1
[b]CANMET, MTL, 568 Booth Street, Ottawa Canada K1A OG1
[c]IGEM, Russian Academy of Sciences, Staromonety 35, Moscow, Russia
[d]Shirshov Institute of Oceanology, Russian Academy of Sciences, Moscow, Russia

1. Introduction

The discovery that modern submarine deposits are enriched in gold [1] has focused study on the occurrence and distribution of gold with relation to the sulfide minerals (e.g. [2]. These mineral deposits are the analogue of ancient volcanogenic massive sulfide (VMS) ore deposits - important sources of base metals and gold.

Previous studies have shown that bulk gold contents usually range from 0.07 to 4.9 g/t [3], but significant gold enrichment was found in many samples. These results (using bulk analytical techniques) do not provide an understanding of the mode of occurrence and how the gold content varies within individual sulfide minerals and between mineral grains.

Modern sea floor massive sulfide ores are considered to be new potential metal resources, therefore the characterization of the mode of gold occurrence in the sulfide ores is important to efficient metallurgical processing. This requires quantification of the concentration, distribution, and nature of gold in sulfide minerals. To address this problem we have used Secondary Ion Mass Spectrometry (SIMS), that has a detection level of well below one part per million by weight (ppmw). The method also has depth-profiling capabilities permitting the detection of buried inclusions, and the possibility of imaging the specimen with any desired secondary ion to produce maps of element distribution [4].

In this paper we compare data on the gold content in sea floor sulfides obtained using SIMS from two fields located at Atlantic mid-ocean ridge and at a back-arc spreading zone in the South Pacific, where high gold concentrations in ore have been previously recorded.

2. Samples

The samples studied were collected during cruises of the Russian research vessel *Academic Mstislav Keldysh* by dives of the *Mir* submersible at two localities. The "Vienna wood" vent (sample 2555-2) occurs within the central graben of the Manus back arc spreading centre (3°9, 85' S, 150°16, 78' E) [5]. The sulfide edifices at this vent consist of basal crust surmounted by several pipe-like active and exiting chimneys. The main sulfide minerals found are sphalerite, pyrite, marcasite, and chalcopyrite, which are common, galena, wurtzite and unidentified Ag-Pb sulfosalts, which are rare [6]. Concentric zonation with respect to a fluid conduit was observed. Colloform and dentritic textures are common, but euhedral grains of sphalerite and pyrite are also found. Sample No 2255-2 represents the cap of a small chimney 25-cm high. Sphalerite and iron disulfides prevail in this sample (about 30%), silica comprises about 35%, chalcopyrite and galena - about 2%. It contains (wt %) Zn 18, Fe 14, Cu 0.6, Pb 1.5, Ag - 707 ppm. INNA analyses showed that the gold concentration is 0.3 ppm in copper ores and 6.6 to 12.5 ppm in zinc ores (Vikent'ev and Bortnikov, unpublished), and higher grades of 52.5 ppm have been reported [7].

The "Logachev field" contains a hydrothermal massive sulfide deposit, located on the eastern slope of the Mid-Atlantic Ridge (MAR), 14°45′N. A mound 5-10 m high, 200 m long, and 100 m wide is surmounted by numerous conical or antler-shaped constructions (10-15 cm high) and sulfide chimneys about 3 m high and 0.5 to 0.8 m in diameter. The mound consists of chalcopyrite, marcasite, pyrite and sphalerite, minor pyrrhotite, isocubanite, bornite, and digenite. Amorphous silica and gypsum were found. The bulk volume of the sulfide ore is estimated to be 205,000 m^3 [8]. Significant concentrations of gold (average 10.71 ppm, up to 42.52 ppm) were reported from some hand specimens [9].

3. Analytical methodology

Graphite-loaded polished sections of the samples were used for SIMS analyses, with a Cameca IMS 4f instrument using a Cs$^+$ beam. Quantitation of the analyses (± 12% to ± 29%) was done using Relative Sensitivity Factors (RSF), obtained by performing depth profiles on standards implanted with a known concentration of gold [10]. The minimum detection levels (MDL) were estimated by measurement of background counts on the implant standard's depth profiles done during the same analytical session corresponding to Au concentrations which ranged from 85 to 90 ppbw in pyrite and 16 to 77 ppbw in chalcopyrite. The chalcopyrite standard was also used for the chalcopyrite + isocubanite analyses. Ion images of 100 μm in diameter were acquired from the multichannel plate/fluorescent screen assembly using a Photometrics Series 200 CCD camera. All instrumental parameters remained similar to those used for the quantitative analyses with the exception of the contrast aperture, which was reduced to 100 μm to improve the spatial resolution of the images.

4. Results

Pyrite, pyrite-marcasite intergrowths, chalcopyrite, chalcopyrite-isocubanite intergrowths and sphalerite were analyzed for trace gold concentrations. Results are given in table 1.

Table 1 SIMS analyses of sea floor sulfide minerals

Sample	Mineral(s)	Range ppmw Au	Average	n
Manus 2255-2-B	pyrite	5.05-26.34	15.60	2
Manus 2255-2-B	chalcopyrite	0.04-0.25	0.09	7
Manus 2255-2-C	pyrite+marcasite	0.60-2.16	1.57	7
Manus 2255-2-C	chalcopyrite	<0.08-0.31	0.13	7
Manus 2255-2-D	pyrite+marcasite	4.61-31.58	11.28	13
MAR 3454-3	chalcopyrite	0.08-1.09	0.38	10
MAR 3454-4	chalcopyrite+isocubanite	0.13-2.21	0.66	10

Pyrite and pyrite + marcasite attain higher average Au contents than chalcopyrite or chalcopyrite + isocubanite. In the Manus basin sample gold was also detected in sphalerite (cubic ZnS, which usually contains x% Fe and 0.x wt% Cd) but could not be quantified. We have been unable to perform depth profiles on many other samples of sphalerite (with a wide range of Fe contents) from ancient VMS as well as modern sea floor deposits because of sample charging under the Cs beam. Investigation of this phenomenon by SEM and ion imaging has shown: (a) that the non-charging sphalerite contains abundant very fine inclusions of chalcopyrite, known as "chalcopyrite disease" (Figs. 1,2) and, (b) that the Au and Se appears to be only associated with areas of sphalerite containing abundant chalcopyrite inclusions (Fig. 3).

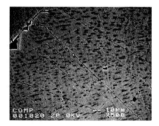

Fig. 1. SEM BSE image showing abundant micro-inclusions of chalcopyrite.

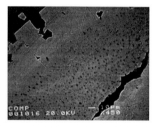

Fig. 2. SEM BSE image with a border zone (upper left) free of inclusions.

5. Discussion and conclusion

The gold content in sea floor sulfides from two fields located at Atlantic mid-ocean ridge (Logachev field at $14^{\circ}45'$ N) and at a back-arc spreading zone (the "Vienna wood" vent, $3^{\circ}9$, 85' S, $150^{\circ}16$, 78' E, Manus basin, in the South Pacific) was studied using SIMS. Fe disulfides and Cu-Fe sulfides were found to be the most important gold carriers in ores. Chalcopyrite ($CuFeS_2$) has a concentration in a range from <0.77-1.085 ppmw Au. Gold content in isocubanite (cubic $CuFe_2S_3$) containing chalcopyrite inclusions ranges from 0.130 to 2.206 ppmw. The Fe disulfides (pyrite and marcasite, both FeS_2) contain a significant concentration of gold (from 0.602 to 31.584 ppmw). Of particular interest in this study was the discovery of gold in sphalerite, estimated to be a few ppmw.

Gold concentrations for pyrite and pyrite + marcasite found in this study are much higher than previously reported by SIMS analyses of two sulfides from the TAG hydrothermal field on the MAR (MIR zone) [2]. From 0.8 to 2.0 ppm Au were reported in pyrite (n=3) and from <0.05 to 1.0 ppm Au in chalcopyrite (n=12), together the occurrence of native gold grains up to 4 μm in diameter [2]. Our results for chalcopyrite (n=10) and chalcopyrite + isocubanite (n=10) on a MAR sample from the Logachev field are similar. These authors also concluded that the gold in pyrite and marcasite represents only about 10% of the total gold for their samples. A strong correlation of bulk Zn to Au was reported from lower temperature white smokers from the MIR zone [3], whereas the Cu-rich samples from higher temperature black smokers are uniformly Au-poor by comparison. In this study, however, we show that the highest Au concentration actually occurs in pyrite/marcasite from a sphalerite-rich sample and, that Au associated with sphalerite is in the chalcopyrite that occurs as micro-inclusions in the sphalerite.

SIMS ion images of sphalerite area in Figure 1

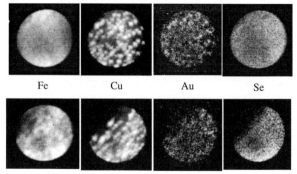

SIMS ion images of sphalerite area in Figure 2

Fig. 3. SIMS ion images of sphalerite (sample 2255-2). Diameter of images is 100 μm.

1022

Acknowledgements

NSB and IVV acknowledge support from the Russian Foundation for Basic Research (Projects 97-05-64804 and 98-05-65008). LJC is grateful to J.H.G. Laflamme for technical support.

References

[1]. M.D. Hannington, J.M. Peter and S.D. Scott, Econ. Geol., 81 (1986) 1867.

[2] M.D. Hannington, et al., Can. Mineral., 33 (1995) 1285.

[3] M.D. Hannington P.M. Herzig and Scott S.D. in R.P. Foster (ed) Gold Metallogeny and Exploration, Blackie, (1991) 249-282.

[4] L.J.Cabri and G. McMahon 1996 EPD Congress, Proc. (Ed. G.W. Warren), Warrendale, The Minerals, Metals & Materials Society (1996) 313.

[5] Bornikov and Lisitsin, A.P. In: Geology and Mineral Resources of the World Oceans, VNIIOceangeologiya, St-Petersburg, (1997) 158-173 (in Russian).

[6] T.N. Shadlun, N.S. Bortnikov and Yu.A. Bogdanov, Geol. Ore Dep., 34 (1992) 3.

[7] W. Tufar, Mitt. Osterr. Ges., 82, (1990)183.

[8] Bogdanov, Yu. A., N.S. Bortnikov, et al, Geol. Ore Dep. 39 (1997) 68.

[9] Mozgova N.N. Oral communication to NSB, (1997).

[10] L.J. Cabri and G. McMahon, Can. Mineral. 33 (1995) 349.

COMBINATION WITH OTHER TECHNIQUES

A. Benninghoven, P. Bertrand, H.-N. Migeon and H.W. Werner (Editors).
Proceedings of the 12th International Conference on Secondary Ion Mass Spectrometry,
Brussels, Belgium, 5-11 September 1999
© 2000 Elsevier Science B.V. All rights reserved.

A NEW TECHNOLOGY FOR UPPERMOST SURFACE ANALYSIS USING ESDMS - A COMPARISON WITH SIMS

S. Seki[1] and H. Tamura[2]

[1] Faculty of Engineering, Takushoku University, 815-1 Tatemachi, Hachioji, Tokyo 193-8585,
Japan, e-mail: sseki@la.takushoku-u.ac.jp
[2] Nippon Institute of Technology, Miyashirocho, Saitama 345-8501, Japan
e-mail: h.tamura@infotopia.or.jp

1. Introduction

Electron stimulated desorption mass spectrometry (ESDMS) is the method to do mass spectrometric analysis of ions desorbed by the electron beam impact. So far the ESD phenomenon has mostly been studied for the desorption of species adsorbed on the surface using low energy electrons below several hundred eV. However, we have studied the ESDMS using rather high energy electrons of keV order and have obtained various characteristics that have never been seen in other surface analysis techniques[1-4]. In SIMS, the collision cascade induced by the ion impact is formed along the ion path and the ions sputtered from the several layers of the surface are detected as the signals. Thus the information depth in SIMS is considered to be about 1 nm which corresponds to 3~4 atomic layers. Therefore, SIMS is intrinsically a destructive analysis and it is not appropriate to say that SIMS is very sensitive to the surface species. On the other hand, electron bombardment is less destructive or very mild for surface species. ESDMS has some unique features which have not been observed in other surface analysis techniques. We are now developing new equipment for the analysis and observation of the surface using an electron beam. In this report, we present the characteristic features of ESDMS and compare them with SIMS.

2. Experimental

The SIMS and ESDMS experiments were performed using the SIMS instruments, a Hitachi IMA 3000 equipped with a sector type mass spectrometer and a Ulvac-Phi 6650 equipped with a quadrupole mass spectrometer. In the present ESDMS experiment, the electron gun, which is normally used for charge compensation during the SIMS measurement of non-conductive samples, was used as the electron source. The electron beam energy for ESDMS was changed from 0.5 to 5 keV. The electron current desity was roughly estimated to be 1~10 µA/cm². In SIMS, the Cs+ and O2+ beams with an energy of 3 keV were used.

To clarify the characteristics of ESDMS and SIMS, various kinds of samples such as semiconductors, metal deposited films, metals, organic materials and Langmuir-Blodgett (LB) films were used in this study. As for LB films, Barium stearate LB films were prepared on silicon wafers by hydrophobic treatment.

3. Results and Discussion

The ESDMS measurements for adsorbates, semiconductors, metals and organic materials measurements have been performed. The ions such as 1H+, 12C+, 14N+, 16O+, 19F+, 23Na+, 35Cl+, 37Cl+ and 39K+ originating from the surface adsorbates were generally observed with good sensitivity in the ESDMS spectra. As for the organic compounds, the fragment ions which provide the information on the molecular structure were succesfully observed [1, 3]. In this study, to measure the monolayer sample, the barium stearate LB films were used. In the 2-layered barium stearate LB film, one monolayer of barium atoms is formed between the LB layers. Figures 1a) and 1b) show the SIMS spectrum and the time dependence of the signal intensities of 138Ba+ and 133Cs+, respectively. Fig. 1b) shows that the 138Ba+ signals decrease with time, which shows that Ba atoms in the barium monolayer gradually decrease during the sputtering. In case of ESDMS, unlike the case of SIMS, the 138Ba+ signals lasted for a long time without decreasing as shown in Fig. 2b). It has been generally observed in ESDMS that the signal intensities are almost constant for a long time, though the reason is not yet clear.

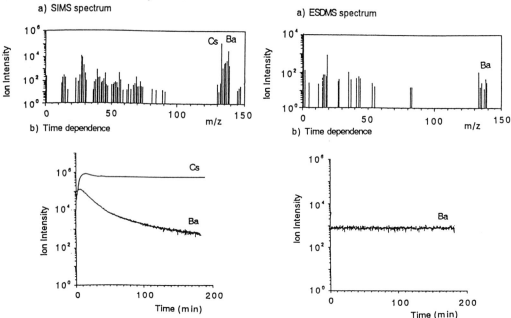

Fig. 1 a) SIMS spectrum and b) ion intensities as a function of time for a 2-layered barium stearate LB film.

Fig. 2 a) ESDMS spectrum and b) ion intensities as a function of time for a 2-layered barium stearate LB film.

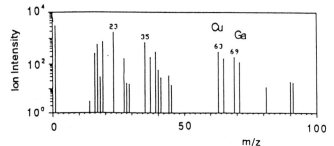

Fig. 3 ESDMS spectrum of copper surface deposited on GaAs wafer.

In ESDMS, the substrate ions from semiconductors and metals were also observed. Fig. 3 shows the ESDMS spectrum of the copper surface thinly deposited on a GaAs wafer. The substrate ions of 63Cu+, 65Cu+, 69Ga+ and 71Ga+ were observed besides the adsorbed species such as F, Na, Cl and those mentioned above. These substrate ions were also stably observed without decreasing. We measured the ESDMS spectra for the aluminum sheet and the silicon wafer with the electron energy of 0.5 keV, 1 keV, 1.5 keV, 2 keV, 3 keV, 4keV and 5 keV. The spectral patterns and ion intensities for the electron energy from 1keV to 5 keV were approximately similar to each other. Fig. 4a) shows a typical ESDMS spectrum of aluminum sheet for the 5 keV electron impact. However, when the electron energy is lowered to 0.5 keV the intensity decrease of the substrate ion of 27Al+ by an order of magnitude and the slight change in the spectral pattern were observed, as shown in Fig. 4b).

A similar electron energy dependence was observed for the silicon wafer.

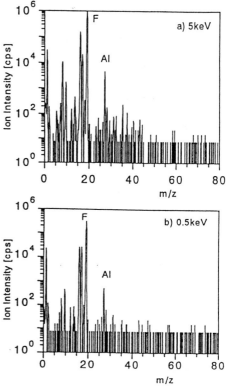

Fig. 4 ESDMS spectra of aluminum sheet at the electron energy of a) 5 keV and b) 0.5 keV.

Until now the work on ESD has been mostly done using low energy electrons and has been focused on adsorbates weakly bonded to the substrate [5, 6]. When the high energy electrons in the keV range are used, however, other phenomena that have not been observed under the low energy electron impact will occur. According to the Knotek-Feibelmann model for ESD, the initial excitation of a core level induced by the primary electron impact and the subsequent Auger decay create a two-hole repulsive final state which can lead to desorption [7, 8]. While the actual mechanism for our ESDMS has not yet been proven, the keV-order electrons are enough to excite the core electron. For this mechanism, more work is needed. We should also consider the lifetime of the desorbed ion, that is, the probability of the neutralization of positive ions by electron capture during the ejection, especially in case of metals.

4. Summary

The ESDMS has specific features that complement SIMS as follows: 1) It is very sensitive to the uppermost layers of the surface. 2) The substrate ions of semiconductors and metals are detected. 3) The atomic ions and the molecular informative ions originating from the adsorbate and organic material are detected. 4) The ESDMS signals last for a long time

1028

without decreasing even for a monolayer. 5) Furthermore, it will be possible to estimate whether the detected ions originate from the adsorbed layer or from the substrate by optimizing the electron beam conditions. These characteristics will lead to the development of a new surface analysis method using an electron beam as a highly sensitive tool for the uppermost surface.

References

[1] S. Seki, H. Sumiya and H. Tamura, J. Surf. Sci. Soc.Jpn., 13, 249 (1992).
[2] S. Seki, H. Sumiya, H. Tamura and H. Hirose, "Secondary Ion Mass Spectrometry, SIMS IX", Eds. A. Benninghoven, Y. Nihei, R. Shimizu and H. W. Werner (John Wiley, Chichester, 1994) p. 519.
[3] S. Seki, H. Sumiya and H. Tamura, J. Surf. Sci. Soc.Jpn., 16, 135 (1995).
[4] S. Seki, H. Sumiya, K. Muto and H. Tamura, Surf. Interface Anal., 25, 155 (1997).
[5] D. Menzel, Surface Sci. , 47, 370 (1975).
[6] T. E. Madey and J. T. Yates, Jr., J. Vac. Sci. Technol., 8, 525 (1971).
[7] M. L. Knotek and P. J. Feibelman, Phys. Rev. Lett., 40, 964 (1978).
[8] D. E. Ramaker, "Desorption Induced by Electroic Transitions, DIET I " Eds. N. H. Tolk, M. M. Traum, J. C. Tully and T. E. Madey (Springer-Verlag, Berlin, 1983) p. 70.

A. Benninghoven, P. Bertrand, H.-N. Migeon and H.W. Werner (Editors).
Proceedings of the 12th International Conference on Secondary Ion Mass Spectrometry,
Brussels, Belgium, 5-11 September 1999
© 2000 Elsevier Science B.V. All rights reserved.

MASS RESOLVED LOW-ENERGY ION SCATTERING SPECTROMETRY:DEVELOPMENT AND APPLICATIONS

A.Tolstogouzov*, S. Daolio and C. Pagura

Istituto di Polarografia ed Elettrochimica Preparativa (IPELP-CNR), Corso Stati
Uniti 4, 35127 Padova, Italy; e-mail: alexander@ipelp.pd.cnr.it
* Permanent address: Ryazan State Radio Engineering Academy, Gagarina str.
59/1, Ryazan 391000, Russia

1. Introduction

Low-energy (0.5-5 keV) ion scattering spectrometry (LEISS) has found wide applications in surface elemental and structure analysis [1-3]. LEISS, using inert gas primary ions, has a unique ability to analyze the most top layer of a solid owing to specific aspects of ion-neutralization phenomena and large scattering cross sections.

Most part of the LEISS work was carried out with light projectiles like $^3He^+$ and $^4He^+$ to study processes where only the surface is involved. In this field an appreciable progress was reached. Contrariwise, the amount of LEISS studies by using heavier ions (such as Ne^+ or Ar^+), generating the signal as well as producing controlled sputtering of the sample, is considerably less by the following reasons: (1) the analysis is limited to the situation in which the projectile has a mass somewhat lower than the sample atoms, (2) the mass resolution is generally little, and (3) the elemental sensitivity is poor, mainly for the considerable level of background signal.

An essential improvement can be reached by additional mass analysis of the scattering ions. The purpose of our work is to elaborate the mass resolved low-energy ion scattering spectrometry, labeled as MARISS by Wittmaack [4], as a powerful analytical tool for studying surface and subsurface compositions, and understanding particle-surface interaction phenomena. In this report some recent results of MARISS development and applications obtained in our laboratory are briefly presented.

2. Method and experimental

MARISS energy spectra were interpreted on the basis of a well-known binary elastic collision model [1]. The observed peak with an energy E is due to a single collision event in which a primary ion of mass M_0 and energy E_0 is scattered from a target atom of mass M_1, that was initially at rest. The following relation calculates the mass M_1:

$$M_1 = M_0 \cdot \frac{1 + E/E_0 - 2\sqrt{E/E_0} \cdot cos\theta}{1 - E/E_0} , \qquad (1)$$

where θ is the laboratory scattering angle (usually for composition analysis $\theta \geq 90°$) and the relative mass ratio $M_1/M_0 > 1$.

As compared with conventional low-energy ion scattering spectrometry, the MARISS technique: (1) avoids interference between scattered and sputtered ions, (2) suppresses the background related to doubly (or multiply) charged ions and (3) provides a useful opportunity to operate with a "mixed" primary ion beam containing different types of projectiles, for instance, He^+ and Ne^+.

MARISS data shown in Fig.1 emphasize the above-mentioned preferences. The energy distribution of $^{20}Ne^+$ ions scattered off the Al (Fig.1a) is masked entirely by the $^{27}Al^+$ secondary ions. By this reason, LEISS analysis of Al and other atoms with a target-to-projectile mass ratio of near unity using heavy primaries is practically impossible. Fig.1b exhibits the mass resolved ion scattering spectrum of a Cu sample. The backgrounds are relatively small and the dynamic range of the useful signal $^{20}Ne^+$-to-Cu is about 10^3. It follows that the ion intensity can be used for quantification directly, i.e. without any fitting and peak deconvolution, which are typical procedures for LEISS studies using He^+ ions [2].

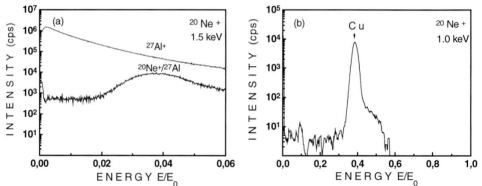

Fig.1. Mass resolved energy distributions of $^{20}Ne^+$ ions scattered off Al (a) and Cu (b) samples (scattering angle is $\theta = 120°$, specular reflection geometry). The energy spectrum of $^{27}Al^+$ secondary ions was obtained under identical experimental conditions.

All our experiments were performed using a custom-build instrumental set-up based on the EQS 1000 Mass Energy Analyser with MASsoft software, manufactured by Hiden Analytical (UK). Unlike the already cited MARISS apparatus, our instrument operated with the sample at fixed (ground) potential, without any electric fields between the sample and the analyser. In this way, all scattering parameters were kept constant during experiments. Details of our system are given elsewhere [5].

3. Results of MARISS applications

It is known [2] that low-energy scattering spectrometry does not exhibit the dramatic influence of "matrix effect" on the ion yields and superior depth resolution can be reached. Hereafter, MARISS applications for quantification and depth profiles are discussed.

Quantitative analysis. The ion scattering signal S due to the *i*-component in the surface of the sample can be written according to [2] as:

$$S_i = I \cdot P_i^+ \cdot N_i \cdot \sigma_i \cdot F, \qquad (2)$$

where I is the primary ion current at the target; P_i^+ is the fraction of the primary particles scattered as ions by i-component (the so-called ion-survival probability); N_i is the surface atom density, σ_i is the cross section per solid angle and F is an experimental factor including the roughness of the surface [2].

Recently, a dual-isotope surface composition (DISC) technique involving the use of ^{3}He$^+$ and ^{4}He$^+$ for determination of P_i^+ has been reported by Brongersma et al. [6]. Wittmaack [4] has proposed the multi-isotope approach for investigation of the ion-survival probability. Our way is based on using the two isotopes Ne$^+$ primary ion beam (90.5% ^{20}Ne$^+$ and 9.2% ^{22}Ne$^+$) for in situ determination of P_i^+. An application of this procedure for Ne$^+$ scattered from the pure Cu sample (Fig.1b) and from an Au-Cu-Ag alloy (with 30 at. % Cu concentration) is shown.

In the case of our experimental conditions, namely low ion velocities, large scattering angle and specular reflection geometry, the ion fraction is a consequence of Auger and resonance neutralization [2,3] and is given by

$$P^+ = exp(-\alpha/v), \qquad (3)$$

where $1/v = 1/v_{in} + 1/v_{out}$, with v_{in} and v_{out} being the normal components of velocities of the ion on the incoming and outgoing (final) parts of the trajectory, and α is the characteristic velocity which is dependent on the electronic energy levels of the ion and the surface atom. Therefore, α's for scattering of the two different Ne$^+$ isotopes are the same. This characteristic velocity is the only unknown that remains, since the velocities both for ^{20}Ne$^+$ and ^{22}Ne$^+$ can be calculated from experimental energy spectra. From Eq's (2) and (3) one finds that

$$\alpha = ln(\frac{^{20}S}{^{22}S} \cdot \frac{^{22}I}{^{20}I} \cdot \frac{^{22}\sigma}{^{20}\sigma}) \times (\frac{1}{^{22}v} - \frac{1}{^{20}v})^{-1}, \qquad (4)$$

where the upper index of all factors indicates the mass of Ne isotope ions.

For the scattering ion intensities, the areas under the experimental peaks were determined, the primary ion isotope current ratio was assumed equal to the natural isotope ratio, i.e. 0.102, and the cross section for scattering of Ne$^+$ isotopes was practically identical (for $\theta =$ const). So, the value of α was estimated as $(2.6 \pm 0.2) \times 10^4$ m/s for Ne$^+$ scattered off the pure Cu ($E_0 = 1$ keV, $\theta = 120°$). Practically the same result was obtained for Cu as a component of Au-Cu-Ag alloy. The order of magnitude of the characteristic velocity is comparable with that found by Wittmaack, i.e. $\alpha = 1.5 \times 10^4$ m/s for Kr$^+$-to-Nb ($E_0 = 10$ keV, $\theta = 124°$) [4].

It should be stressed here that our updated DISC procedure using the MARISS technique and two isotopes of Ne$^+$ (simultaneously) as primary ion beam has been done without any modification of experimental parameters such as primary energy and angle of scattering (or registration). Moreover, no precise primary ion current measurement was needed. In this way, a simple, rapid and rather correct MARISS data quantification without calibration samples is really possible.

4. *Depth profiling.* It is of great interest to utilize a combination of SIMS and MARISS for depth profiles and to summarize the advantages of these techniques in one instrument. Most of the previous studies were performed using a specially adjusted standard SIMS apparatus [7] with known limitations for low-energy ion scattering spectrometry. Our approach is based on the elimination of any methodological boundaries between mass and energy analysis of scattered/sputtered ions by using a special "devoted" SIMS-MARISS instrument [5].

The data of cobalt oxide film (10-20 nm), obtained by chemical vapour deposition on indium tin oxide substrate [8], demonstrate one possible application of this instrument for routine depth profiling analysis. To solve the problem of MARISS light surface atom moni-

toring, a mixed He^+-Ne^+ primary ion beam produced by a Leybold-Specs ion source (mod. IQE 12/38) was applied along with an accurate mass separation of scattered ions.

SIMS-MARISS depth profiles, i.e. intensities of corresponding secondary ion mass ($^{59}Co^+$ and $^{115}In^+$) and ion scattered energy ($^{20}Ne^+/Co$, $^{20}Ne^+/In$ and $^4He^+/O$) peaks versus sputtering time, are represented in Fig. 2. All measurements were performed almost simultaneously using the MASsoft program for system control and data acquisition. The dynamic range of the In-signal (the substrate ions) on the film-substrate boundary obtained by the MARISS technique is bigger than by SIMS, i.e. 2.3×10^3 versus 40, due to the smaller information depth of the scattered ions.

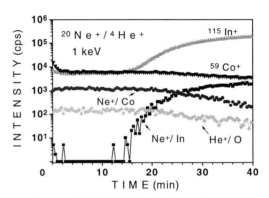

Fig. 2. SIMS-MARISS depth profiles of cobalt oxide film ($^{20}Ne^+/$ $^4He^+$, 1 keV/ 1 μA, 2×2 mm^2, 20% electronic gating, θ =118°). Peaks of interest: SIMS - $^{115}In^+$, $^{59}Co^+$; MARISS - $^{20}Ne^+/In$ (596 eV), $^{20}Ne^+/Co$ (352 eV), $^4He^+/O$ (474 eV),

A similar result was obtained for the Co-signal (the film ions), i.e. 8 for MARISS and 3 for SIMS. The decreasing of $^4He^+/O$ ion-scattered signal on the boundary also was registered. Our first experimental data demonstrate a high potentiality of the SIMS-MARISS depth profile combination with prevalent benefits of the second technique.

Acknowledgements

This work and A.Tolstogouzov are supported by the "Progetto Finalizzato MSTA II" of CNR Italy.

References
[1] D.P.Smith, J. Appl. Phys. 38 (1967) 340.
[2] H.Niehus, W.Heiland and E.Taglauer, Surf. Sci. Rep.17 (1993) 213.
[3] J.W.Rabalais, Surf. Sci. 299/300 (1994) 219.
[4] K.Wittmaack, Surf. Sci. 345 (1996) 110.
[5] A.Tolstogouzov, S.Daolio and C.Pagura, Surf. Sci. 441 (1999) 213.
[6] P.A.J.Ackermans, M.A.P.Creuwels, H.H.Brongersma and P.J.Scanlon, Surf.Sci. 227 (1990) 361.
[7] K.Wittmaack, in: Sputtering by Particle Bombardment III, Characteristics of Sputtered Particles, Technical Applications, ed. R.Behrisch and K. Wittmaack, Springer, Berlin, 1991, p.161.
[8] D.Barreca, V.Di Noto, M.Fabrizio, C.Massignan, C.Piccirillo and E.Tondello, in preparation.

A. Benninghoven, P. Bertrand, H.-N. Migeon and H.W. Werner (Editors).
Proceedings of the 12th International Conference on Secondary Ion Mass Spectrometry,
Brussels, Belgium, 5-11 September 1999

STATIC TOF-SIMS AND FOURIER TRANSFORM LASER MICROPROBE MASS SPECTROMETRY FOR MOLECULAR INFORMATION ON INORGANIC COATINGS ON ALUMINIUM

E. Cuynen[1] , L. Van Vaeck[2] and P. Van Espen
MiTAC, Department of Chemistry, University of Antwerp,
B-2610 Antwerp, Belgium, e-mail: cuynen@uia.ac.be

1. Introduction

Material research of thin coatings aims at the precise characterization of composition, thickness and structure in order to understand the chemical and/or physical interaction between the coating and its environment. These interactions occur between molecules rather than atoms so that direct molecular information is required. Traditional methods such as Electron Microscopy, Auger spectroscopy or X-Ray Fluorescence provide elemental ratios to estimate the global composition of the sample whereas techniques such as Infra-Red, XPS or Raman Spectroscopy detect the specific bonds in functional groups. Static SIMS (S-SIMS) and Fourier transform laser mass spectrometry (FT LMMS) emerge as potential tools for molecular information, because their signals directly refer to intact molecule.

The mechanical properties of Al are exploited in many applications including architecture, transport, aerospace and electronics, packaging of foodstuffs and beverages. Chemical conversion is an important (chemical) surface treatment to improve corrosion resistance and paint adhesion. The process involves the formation of insoluble inorganic compounds at the surface by immersion of the Al in an appropriate solution in the absence of an external electrical field. The molecular chemistry of this process is not yet fully understood.

The purpose of this paper is to assess the potential of S-SIMS and FT LMMS for molecular information in the case of chromium phosphate conversion coatings on Al. Special attention was paid to the relative importance of adducts, molecular and structural fragment ions at high m/z since they provide molecular information.

2. Experiment

Coatings were grown on cold rolled sheets (AA1050) which were electropolished, degreased and etched. The chemical conversion was carried out in a solution containing 0.71 g l[-1] HF, 64 g l[-1] H_3PO_4 and 10 g l[-1] CrO_3. More details can be found elsewhere [1].

In this work, a TOF SIMS instrument (Cameca Ion Tof IV, Münster, Germany) was used. The samples were bombarded with 25 keV Ga $^+$ bunches of 800 ps. The spot diameter was about 3–4 µm . The mass resolution (FWHM) was typically ~ 2000 at $m/z = 1$ and ~6500 at $m/z = 35$. Spectra were acquired by rastering the beam over 20 x 20 µm^2 for 60 s. The total

---

[1]Indebted to the Flemish Institute for the Promotion of Scientific-Technological Research in Industry (IWT).
[2]Indebted to the Flemish Fund for Scientific Research (FWO) as research director.

ion dose was kept under 10^{14} ions/cm^2. The vacuum in the sample chamber was $\sim 2 \times 10^{-8}$ mbar.

Laser mass spectra were obtained by a Spectrospin CMS-47X FTMS (Bruker Instruments Inc., Billerica, MA, USA) with external source, modified into a laser microprobe [2]. The instrument was equipped with an Infinity Cell™ [3] in a 4.7 Tesla magnet. A frequency quadrupled Nd:YAG laser (λ= 266 nm), with fill-in optics for a nearly Gaussian beam was focused to a spot of 5µm in the 45°reflection geometry. The power density can be varied between $10^6 - 10^{10}$ W/cm^2. The pressure in the source and cell were 10^{-6} Torr and 10^{-10} Torr, respectively. The mass resolution routinely exceeded 10^5 at m/z =1000. The relative mass accuracy was of the order of 1 ppm, allowing «unambiguous» identification of the ion's elemental composition. The combination of ionisation by extremely short pulses (4 ns), electrostatic fields for the ion transfer from source to cell and ion detection in an ion trap inherently limited the m/z range of panoramic registration [4] to a factor 2.5 (e.g. m/z 100-250).

3. Results and discussion

The negative TOF S-SIMS mass spectrum in Fig. 1(a) shows that most of the ion current is carried by the low m/z ions, O$^-$, PO$_2^-$ and PO$_3^-$. The peak at m/z 43 is assigned to AlO$^-$ which refers to the Al substrate. Signals due to organic surface contamination, e.g. C$^-$, CH$^-$ and CN$^-$ are rather low in this particular sample. The peaks at m/z 100, 147 and 163 are assigned to CrO$_3^-$, CrPO$_4^-$ and CrPO$_4$.O$^-$ respectively. The relative intensities of the main signals closely agree with those in the mass spectrum from a CrPO$_4$ standard.

The CrO$_3^-$ ions are considered as structural fragments (not recombination clusters) because oxysalts undergo in both S-SIMS and FT LMMS the characteristic decomposition or fragmentation into the corresponding oxide ions [2]. Strictly speaking, CrO$_3^-$ is a molecular ion and CrPO$_4$.O$^-$ refers to an adduct of the neutral analyte with a stable charged species detected as such (O$^-$). Together with PO$_2^-$ and PO$_3^-$, these signals are used for molecular identification. The latter peaks are at least 100 times less intense than the fragment ions PO$_x^-$. This significant intensity difference between low and high signals is a typical feature for oxides [5], binary [6] and oxysalts in S-SIMS.

Exp. m/z amu	Assignment	Error ppm
62.9641	PO$_2^-$	0.07
78.9590	PO$_3^-$	0.85
99.9258	CrO$_3^-$	0.19
146.894	CrPO$_4^-$	0.08
183.856	CrO$_3$.CrO$_2^-$	0.50
225.853	CrPO$_4$.PO$_3^-$	0.01
246.820	CrO$_3$.CrPO$_4^-$	0.23
262.815	CrO$_3$.CrO$_3$.PO$_2^-$	0.35
288.817	P$_2$O$_5$.CrPO$_4^-$	0.08
304.812	P$_2$O$_5$.CrO$_3$.PO$_3^-$	0.45

Table 1: Measurement and ion assignment of the major negative ions in the FT LMMS mass spectrum.

Fig 1(b) shows the FT LMMS data for the same sample. Ions shared with S-SIMS include structural fragments PO$_2^-$, PO$_3^-$ and the molecular ion CrPO$_4^-$, whereas numerous additional adducts occur. Table 1 summarizes the accurate m/z measurement and ion assignment. A typical feature of FT LMMS, is that the relative intensities of most molecule-specific signals among different spectra that cover a broad mass range, stay within a factor 100.

The spreading on the kinetic energy and the ion formation time causes that ions near the limits of the m/z window are still detected but their intensity becomes underestimated [7].

For instance, the PO_2^- ions represent a larger fraction of the initial ion population than observed in Fig. 1(b).

As to the sensitivity, the FT LMMS data were collected from an area of about 4000 μm² whereas the S-SIMS data were obtained from primary ion pulses on an area of 400 μm². However, one must bear in mind that the information depth of S-SIMS is a few monolayers while the ions in FT LMMS originate from a surface layer of 10–50 nm thick [4], depending on the material. Therefore, in our opinion, the gain in specificity from the higher mass resolution and mass accuracy vs. S-SIMS compensates for the larger area to be analysed at least for samples with sufficiently thick conversion layers.

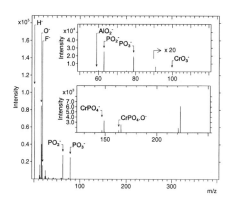 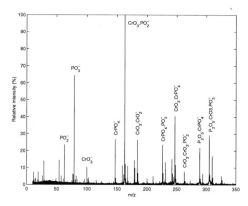

(a) S-SIMS ion mass spectrum obtained after 60 s rastering an area of 400 μm²

(b) FT LMMS ion mass spectrum obtained by analyzing an area of 4000 μm²

Figure 1: Negative ion mass spectra of a chromium-phosphate conversion coating on Al (600 s conversion time).

4. Conclusion

It was demonstrated in this particular test case that S-SIMS and FT LMMS both yield sufficient diagnostic signals to allow the molecular identification of the chromium phosphate coating. In addition to the main fragments and the molecular ions shared with S-SIMS, FT LMMS provides structurally relevant adducts, such as $CrPO_4.PO_3^-$, $CrO_3.CrPO_4^-$, $CrO_3.CrPO_4.O^-$. A general tendency is that the structural fragments (lower m/z ions) in S-SIMS are usually much more intense than adduct signals (higher m/z ions). The spectra typically cover a broad dynamic range (4 decades). In contrast, the most molecule-specific signals in FT LMMS remain within an intensity range of 100. If only S-SIMS spectra are available and in absence of a priori knowledge, the mass resolution and mass accuracy sometimes become insufficient to allow unambiguous identification. Because of the information depth, LMMS is less sensitive to surface contamination than S-SIMS. Together with the relatively poor ionisation efficiencies of high *m/z* adduct ions, this can prevent the identification of the analyte in applications of S-SIMS. In practice, the routinely achievable high mass accuracy and mass resolution in FT LMMS combined with the larger number of structural adducts within a limited intensity range make that FT LMMS provides a solid base for confirmation of S-SIMS signals. However, the latter method remains mandatory for surface coatings in the range of monolayer thickness. Summarizing, our results stress the benefits from the complementary use of FT LMMS and S-SIMS.

Reference

[1] E. Cuynen, P. Van Espen, G. Goeminne and H. Terryn. *J. Anal. At. Spectrom.*, 14:483–486, 1999.

[2] K. Poels, L. Van Vaeck and R. Gijbels. *Anal. Chem.*, 70:504–512, 1998.

[3] P. Caravatti, M. Alleman. *Org. Mass Spectrom.*, 26:514–518, 1991.

[4] L. Van Vaeck, W. Van Roy, H. Struyf, F. Adams and P. Caravatti. *Rapid Comm. Mass Spectrom.*, 7:323–331, 1993

[5] E. Cuynen, L. Van Vaeck and P. Van Espen. *Rapid Comm. Mass Spectrom.*, 13:2287–2301, 1999.

[6] R. Van Ham, A. Adriaens, L. Van Vaeck and F. Adams. *Nucl. Intrum. Meth. B.*, 1999. In press.

[7] H. Struyf, L. Van Vaeck and R. Van Grieken. *Rapid Comm. Mass Spectrom.*, 10:551–561, 1996.

A. Benninghoven, P. Bertrand, H.-N. Migeon and H.W. Werner (Editors).
Proceedings of the 12th International Conference on Secondary Ion Mass Spectrometry,
Brussels, Belgium, 5-11 September 1999

INTERMIXING STUDIES ON Al/Ge BILAYERS USING SIMS AND LOW ENERGY POSITRON BEAM

G.Raghavan, G. Venugopal Rao, G. Amarendra, A.K.Tyagi and B. Viswanathan

Indira Gandhi Centre for Atomic Research, Kalpakkam – 603102, INDIA.,e-mail : gr@igcar.ernet.in

1. Introduction

The intricate relationship between interdiffusion and defect formation in thin film couples is a problem of significant interest for both basic and applied research. The interface across diffusion couples is a region of high defect concentration whose evolution under heat treatment depends on the diffusion coefficients of the components. Thus, diffusion and defect evolution have to be concurrently investigated for a correct understanding of the underlying process. In this paper we report, for the first time, a detailed study of these aspects in Al-Ge thin film bilayers using concurrent measurements of secondary ion mass spectrometry (SIMS) and low energy positron beam (LEPB) spectroscopy. The Al/Ge binary alloy system is a simple eutectic with very poor solid solubilities of the components. The equilibrium phase diagram of this system does not allow for any crystalline phase of the alloy other than a mixture of pure Al and Ge. Hence, this is a fairly simple system for the intended study. While SIMS has high elemental sensitivity, depth resolved Doppler broadened line shape signals from LEPB have a high sensitivity for vacancy type defects [1]. Therefore, a combined study provides complementary information on the system. Since the defect sensitive line shape parameter used to analyze the positron data is also sensitive to changes in elemental composition of the material, we have used SIMS depth profiles in conjunction with LEPB data. Given these facts, combined investigations with LEPB and SIMS on the same sample is not only necessary but is also expected to provide interesting insights about the processes involved in thin film junctions. Preliminary results of this work have been presented earlier in a conference proceedings [2].

2. Experimental Details

Bilayer films of Al-Ge were grown from high purity materials (99.999%) by thermal evaporation. The films were grown on a Si(100) substrate in a vacuum of 10^{-6} torr. Samples were prepared with a nominal thickness of Al (125 nm) /Ge (80 nm) on 0.5 mm thick Si(100) substrate. Actual layer thicknesses were measured in-situ using a quartz thickness monitor, which had been calibrated for various substrate positions using a surface profilometer (DEKTAK 3030). The as grown Al layers were nanocrystalline with a typical grain size of 20-50 nm [3]. The as-grown Ge layers were found to be amorphous. The Sample was annealed at various temperatures between 300 – 670 K for 2 hours in a vacuum of 10^{-6} torr. LEPB and SIMS measurements were made on the specimens after each step of heat treatment. SIMS measurements have been carried out on the samples using a CAMECA IMS 4f machine, with a Cs^+ primary ion beam of energy 10 keV. The Cs beam was rastered over an area of 250 μm x 250 μm and the CsM^+ (M = Al, Ge) secondary ions were collected from the central 60 μm area to avoid crater wall effects. . It is well established in SIMS literature that the yield of CsM^+ complexes is relatively free of matrix effects. The quantified SIMS depth profiles are given in fig.1. The LEPB measurements were made at room temperature using a UHV compatible, magnetically guided facility described elsewhere [4]. The positron beam energy E_p was varied from 200 eV to 20 keV in small incremental steps so as to profile different sample depths. The Doppler broadening of the 511 keV annihilation gamma ray is monitored using a HPGe detector of 25% efficiency. A line shape S-parameter [1], which represents valence electron annihilation events, is defined as a ratio of the total counts in the central peak region to the total photo peak counts. It is known that S-parameter is very sensitivity to the presence of open-volume defects and is used in the present paper to monitor the evolution of defects.

3. Results and Discussion

Fig.1. shows the result of the SIMS measurements made on the same specimen in the as-grown condition and under heat treatment. In the as-grown film, the concentration profiles of Al and Ge are well separated indicating that there is no interdiffusion in the as-grown specimen. Even after annealing this specimen to 370 K, only a marginal interdiffusion is noticed. As the annealing temperature is increased beyond 370 K, substantial interdiffusion is seen to occur. A significant amount of Ge is observed to have preferentially diffused into the surface region of Al layers. As annealing temperature is further increased, most of the Ge segregates to the surface and the regions near the interface and below it become enriched in Al. For the presentation and discussion of the results, we have chosen specific two depth regions between 20-65 nm (Al region) and 110-150 nm (Al/Ge interface region). The ratio of Al/Ge concentrations and that of the S-parameter likewise are averaged over the above depth regions.

(a) Al-region

Fig. 2 (a) shows the variation of the normalized S-parameter as a function of annealing temperature. The S-parameter decreases till 370 K, exhibits a plateau between 370 and 570 K and then decreases again beyond 570 K. These observations may be explained as follows. From fig.1 and the Al/Ge ratio extracted from fig. 2(b) of SIMS data, it is seen that there is very little intermixing of the Al and Ge layers in this temperature interval. Hence, the fall in S is only due to the annealing of native defects and grain growth in the Al region. Between 370 K and 520 K, it may be seen from fig. 2(b) that the Al/Ge concentration ratio decreases significantly, indicating extensive ingress of Ge into the Al region. In this temperature range there are two competing processes: (1) annealing of defects and the ingress of Ge, which has a lower S-parameter value as compared with Al. Both these effects tend to decrease the S-parameter and (2) new defects are produced in the Al region due to the ingress of Ge, which increases the S-parameter, thereby producing the opposite effect. Thus, the competition between these effects results in the observed plateau in the S-parameter. Beyond 570 K, there is only a marginal change in the Al/Ge ratio, whereas there is a sharp fall in S. At this stage, imaging SIMS and TEM studies indicate a substantial precipitation of Ge occurring in this region [3]. It is quite conceivable that decoration of vacancies by Ge clusters at higher annealing temperatures provide nuclei for Ge precipitation. These precipitates grow with an incoherent interface between the matrix and the precipitates, leading to the production of misfit dislocations. Such a precipitation of Ge occurs at the surface and sub-surface regions. The preferential annihilation of positrons at precipitate/matrix is well established in positron literature and hence the steep fall in S is attributed to the preferential annihilation of positrons from the Ge rich sites. Furthermore, the vacancy mediated Ge precipitation in Al/Ge alloys has been observed even for very low Ge concentrations with similar variations in the defect parameter [5].

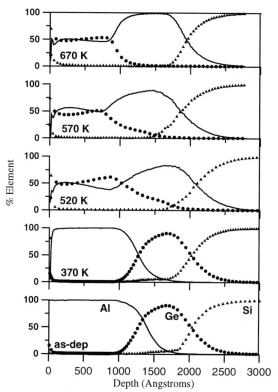

Fig. 1. SIMS concentration depth profiles
at various annealing temperatures

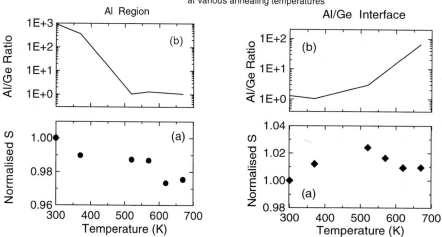

Fig. 2. (a) Normalised S-parameter and
(b) Al/Ge concentration ratio versus
annealing temperature

Fig. 3. (a) Normalised S-parameter and
(b) Al/Ge concentration ratio versus
annealing temperature

(b) Al-Ge interface region

From fig.3(a) it is seen that the S-parameter increases by nearly 25% in the annealing range up to 520 K. It is seen from fig.3(b) that the corresponding Al/Ge concentration ratio increases marginally. However, there is a substantial rise in the S-parameter, which is hence, ascribed to defect production at the interface. Strong vacancy production is expected to occur when one of the components, namely Ge has a much larger diffusion coefficient, as compared to the other component. This vacancy build-up explains the increase in the S-parameter up to 520 K. Beyond 520 K, the S-parameter tends to decrease and then level off, to value that is 10% higher than that for the as-grown interface. At this stage, the interface region gets substantially enriched in Al. This should, however, lead to a further increase of the S-parameter, which is not observed in the present case. This suggests that the defects in this region are getting annealed out substantially. However, it may be noted that the final S-parameter value is still higher than that of initial Al-layer, indicating the presence of higher defect concentration. The nature of the defects identified at various stages of annealing has been verified by independent positron lifetime measurements [6]. The interfacial vacancy structure is inferred to be a small vacancy cluster up to a tri-vacancy.

4. Summary

The evolution of Al-Ge bilayers under heat treatment has been investigated by a combined measurement and analysis of SIMS and LEPB data. The data from these two techniques are mutually consistent. SIMS measurements provide evidence of extensive intermixing upon heat treatment. Substantial amount of Ge segregates to the surface at the later stages of annealing. Analysis of the LEPB lineshape as a function of annealing temperature indicates a strong vacancy production at the Al/Ge interface brought about by the rapid diffusion of Ge in the Al regions. These defects are identified as tri-vacancies. At higher annealing temperatures, it is found that Ge precipitates in the near surface region of the sample.

References

[1] P.J. Schultz and K.G. Lynn, Rev. Mod. Phys. **60**, 701 (1988) ; *Positron Solid State Physics*, Eds. W. Brandt and A. Dupasquier (North Holland, Amsterdam, 1983).
[2] G. Venugopal Rao, G. Raghavan, G. Amarendra, A.K. Tyagi and B. Viswanathan, Mat. Sci. Forum **255**, 692 (1997)
[3] G. Raghavan, R. Divakar, S. Tripurasundari, D. Sundararaman and A.K. Tyagi, Scripta Materialia **38**, 50 (1998)
[4] G. Amarendra, B. Viswanathan, G. Venugopal Rao, J. Parimala and B. Purniah, Current Science **73**, 409 (1997)
[5] H. Murukami, I. Kanazawa, T. Kurihara, T. Shimizu and M. Doyama in *"Positron Annihilation"* Eds. P.G. Coleman, S.C. Sharma and L.M. Diana (1982), p. 263
[6] G. Raghavan and R. Rajaraman, to be published.

INDEX OF CHAIRPERSONS

INDEX OF REVIEWERS

Schueler	Bruno W.	Physical Electronics, Inc.
Schuhmacher	Michel	Cameca Instruments
Simons	David S.	NIST
Slodzian	Georges	University of Paris-Sud
Spool	Alan M.	IBM Corporation
Stevie	Fred A.	Lucent Technologies, MS DLab
Terhorst	Markus	University of Muenster
Tran Minh	Duc	Biophy Research S.A.
Van der Heide	Paul	University of Houston
Vanden Eynde	Xavier	Université Catholique de Louvain
Vandervorst	Wilfried	IMEC
Vickerman	John C.	UMIST
Von Criegern	Rolf	Siemens AG
Werner	H.W.	TU Vienna
Wiedmann	Lothar	University of Muenster
Williams	Peter	Arizona State University
Wittmaack	Klaus	GSF- FZ für Umwelt und Gesundheit
Wucher	Andreas	University of Essen
Zalm	Peer C.	Philips Research Lab

AUTHOR INDEX

SUBJECT INDEX

(The page given is the first page of the article in which the keyword appears)

1058